Handbook of
Protein Sequence Analysis

A Compilation of Amino Acid Sequences of Proteins
with an Introduction to the Methodology

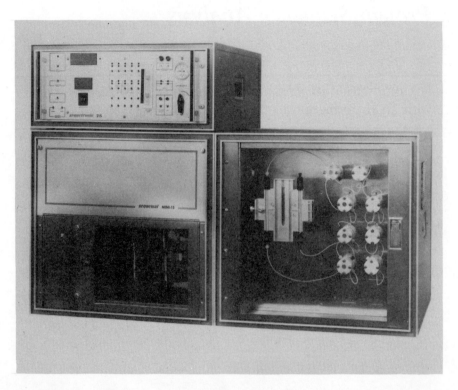

The Sequemat Mini-15 Solid Phase Sequencer. This instrument is able to determine a minimum of fifteen residues per day of a suitable derivatized peptide or protein. It possesses two columns so permitting the simultaneous sequence analysis of two samples. (Reproduced by courtesy of Sequemat Inc., Watertown, Massachusetts, USA.)

Handbook of
Protein Sequence Analysis

A Compilation of Amino Acid Sequences
of Proteins with an Introduction to the
Methodology

Second Edition

L. R. Croft
Lecturer in Biochemistry,
University of Salford

A Wiley–Interscience Publication

JOHN WILEY & SONS
Chichester · New York · Brisbane · Toronto

6440 –6362

CHEMISTRY

British Library Cataloguing in Publication Data

Croft, Laurence Raymond
    Handbook of protein sequence analysis. — 2nd ed.
    1. Proteins — Analysis   2. Amino acids
    I. Title   II. Handbook of protein sequences
    547'.75   QD431   79-41487

    ISBN 0 471 27703 7

Typeset by Preface Ltd, Salisbury, Wilts. and printed
by Page Bros. (Norwich) Ltd., Norwich

To
Jane Elizabeth

Contents

Preface to the First Edition

It has been the aim in preparing this work to collect together all the available complete protein and peptide amino acid sequence information, so that it may be put into a form that is readily to hand. Initially this was intended to be a personal collection, which I intended to use as a convenient source for comparing and detecting proteins with related sequences. Subsequently it was suggested to me that this collection could quickly be reproduced, and if made available in loose-leaf format, might be of assistance to other workers with similar aims. I hope that this expectation will be fulfilled.

Although the title of 'protein sequence' is used, it is applied in a very general sense as to include what normally would be called peptides. The peptides that have been included, are related to proteins either by their mode of biosynthesis or are directly derived from proteins. This collection does not therefore contain for example, those peptides of a cyclic nature or those containing D-amino acids.

In a work such as this great care has been taken to avoid errors; if there are any that have been missed I would be very grateful to be informed, so that they may be corrected. I would also be pleased to be informed about important omissions that I have made. These will be incorporated into the annual supplements that are hoped to be prepared.

May 1973   L. R. CROFT

Preface to the Second Edition

It is now five years since the publication of the *Handbook of Protein Sequences*, and since that time two additional supplements have appeared, Supplement A covering the period 1973 to July 1974, and Supplement B covering the period up to August 1975. It was apparent, from the size of these supplements that the field was developing so rapidly, that the continued production of biennial supplements would soon prove inadequate, and so it was decided to produce an entirely new edition. This new edition contains material published up to the end of 1978 and, although similar in appearance to the original *Handbook*, it nevertheless contains not only new sequences but also a complete reappraisal of the sequence data. Also the section on human haemoglobins has been revised and reorganized, and the section containing notes on individual proteins has been brought up-to-date to contain much new information.

I would like to acknowledge the encouragement and valuable comments I have received from people throughout the world and, in particular, I am very grateful to my publishers for their continual encouragement and patience, without whom this compilation would not have appeared.

Salford   L. R. CROFT

August 1979

Abbreviations

ALA	Alanine
ARG	Arginine
ASN	Asparagine
ASP	Aspartic acid
ASX	Aspartic acid or asparagine (undefined)
CYS	Cysteine
GLU	Glutamic acid
GLN	Glutamine
GLX	Glutamic acid or glutamine (undefined)
GLY	Glycine
HIS	Histidine
ILE	Isoleucine
LEU	Leucine
LYS	Lysine
MET	Methionine
PHE	Phenylalanine
PRO	Proline
SER	Serine
THR	Threonine
TRP	Tryptophan
TYR	Tyrosine
VAL	Valine
CMC	S-carboxymethylcysteine
MMA	ω-N-monomethylarginine
DMA	ω-NN'-dimethylarginine
MML	ε-N-methyl lysine
DML	ε-NN-dimethyl lysine
TML	ε-NNN-trimethyl lysine
ACL	ε-N acetyl lysine
PYG	Pyroglutamic acid
PSE	O-phosphoserine
OOO	Deletion, i.e. no amino acid residue in this position
<u>ASN</u>	Residue underlined indicates carbohydrate attachment site
MMH	N-τ-Methyl histidine

NMA	N-methyl alanine
NMM	N-methyl methionine
XXX	Unidentified amino acid related to arginine
GLA	γ-carboxy glutamic acid
HYP	Hydroxy proline

In sequences:

LEU ALA GLY ... indicates the established amino acid sequence.

(LEU, ALA, GLY) ... indicates that the amino acid sequence is unknown.

AC LEU ... indicates an N-terminal acetylated residue.

... LEU NH$_2$ indicates a C-terminal amidated residue.

Introduction

Knowledge of the complete amino acid sequence of a protein may be desirable for one or more reasons. If the protein is an enzyme, it may be in order to obtain an understanding of its mechanism of action, or it may be a means for studying the evolutionary history of life. It is now well established that proteins are useful tools with which to trace the thread of evolution and they are in a sense 'ultramicrofossils'. Such studies are now vigorously pursued on a world-wide scale (Table 1).

Further, the protein might be of immediate medical interest, and the sequence needed to form the basis for a synthetic programme, or an investigation as to its origin. The recent enkephalin 'bandwagon' is a good example of this. Agricultural archaeology is another area in which the importance of amino acid sequence information is now well established, and an understanding of early selective breeding has been derived from analytical studies of ancient protein material, particularly the collagens of bone, tendon, or skin, and the keratins of hair, which may be perfectly preserved through 20 000 years, and indeed much longer.

Table 1. The origin of sequence information published during 1977 and 1978

Country where the work was performed	% of the total
U.S.A.	29
Japan	13
W. Germany	12
South Africa	10
U.K.	8
France	6
Holland	6
Belgium	3
Australia	3
Sweden	3
U.S.S.R.	2
Italy	1
Taiwan	1
Canada	1
Switzerland	1

2

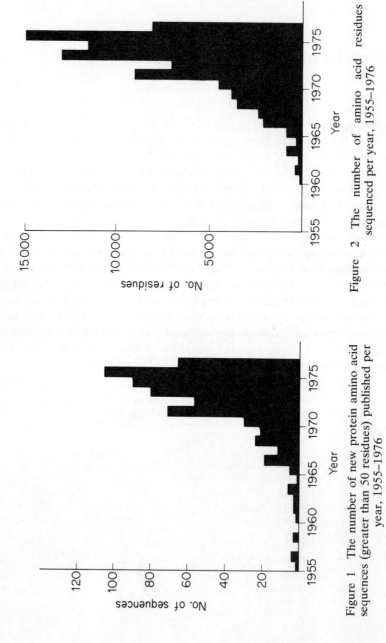

Figure 1 The number of new protein amino acid sequences (greater than 50 residues) published per year, 1955–1976

Figure 2 The number of amino acid residues sequenced per year, 1955–1976

It is only twenty-five years ago that the determination of an amino acid sequence of a protein was looked upon as an impossible task, yet during this period the methods of sequence determination have been developed to such a sophistication that today this task, to many, is considered routine. If we look at the number of sequences deduced per year over the last 25 years we can clearly see that this endeavour up to about 1973, was at an explosive stage of development, and that after this time the number of sequences deduced levelled off to an approximate doubling of information every two or three years (Figures 1 and 2). Yet as a whole the development of protein structure determination has been painfully slow if compared to other fields of scientific endeavour.

HISTORICAL PERSPECTIVES

It was about the turn of the century that the 'peptide hypothesis' of protein structure was put forward by Hofmeister and Fischer. Emil Fischer applied the methods of organic chemistry to the problem of protein structure, and obtained from the hydrolysates of various proteins many peptides in crystalline form, which were compared with synthetic samples. These early triumphs firmly established the basic concepts of protein structure, but in the years that followed, it was clear that the methods of classical organic chemistry were inadequate, and fifty years were to elapse before any further progress was made. By this time the techniques of paper chromatography and electrophoresis had been introduced as a means for checking homogeneity and confirming identity, and it was by using these methods that Sanger was able to determine the complete amino acid sequence of insulin in 1955. This was the culmination of a decade of work by Sanger; the choice of insulin, a small protein of 51 residues and readily available in large amounts, was indeed fortunate. If a larger protein had been chosen for sequence analysis, for example haemoglobin, the work could very well still be in progress, if not abandoned many years ago. Sanger's achievement must surely rank as one of the great landmarks in science this century, as it provided the proof that proteins indeed had unique structures and could be regarded as molecules and not vague colloids. The development of the genetic code was a direct consequence of Sanger's work and subsequently led to the advent of the new science of molecular biology. It can now be clearly seen that what Sanger did was to be courageous enough to apply new, and at the time controversial, methods to this particular area of natural product chemistry. Chromatographic and electrophoretic criteria were employed for confirmation of purity in place of the usual crystallization and melting point tests. It was subsequently shown by chemical synthesis, and X-ray crystallography, that this approach was valid, and comparable to other more classical methods of structure determination, and the way was then open for more people to enter and develop this field. And how the field has developed is illustrated in Tables 2 and 3; the first shows how techniques

Table 2. Amount and estimated time taken to sequence a hypothetical peptide having 50 amino acid residues, at four different times during the last 30 years

Year	Amount required	Time taken
1950	100 g	10 years
1960	10 g	3 years
1970	1 g	1 year
1980	1 mg	1 week

have improved in sensitivity and how the time taken to sequence a hypothetical 50-residue peptide has decreased during the last three decades.

The second (Table 3) lists some of the major landmarks in this field during the last three decades. Progress was enhanced by the introduction of two important developments, namely, the automatic amino acid analyser, which replaced the rather subjective visual quantification of amino acids that had previously been derived from paper chromatograms, and the ingenious stepwise degradation procedure devised by P. Edman. Both of these were catalysts for the rapid growth of this area of biochemistry. It is interesting to compare development in the United States with that of the United Kingdom. Although the initial work on sequencing took place in Britain, it can be clearly seen that the lead was quickly taken over by American workers who were more willing, and financially able to adopt automated procedures, such as the amino acid analyser. It is still true that in Britain it is much easier to raise funds for personnel than it is for the purchase of sophisticated equipment, and this is only too evident when one compares the number of automatic sequencers in university biochemistry departments in

Table 3. Landmarks in protein sequence determination in the last 25 years

Year	Protein Sequence	Number of residues
1955	Insulin	51
1961	Haemoglobin beta chain	145
1962	Haemoglobin alpha chain	141
1962	Cytochrome c	105
1963	Ribonuclease	124
1963	Lysozyme	129
1965	Myoglobin	153
1965	Virus coat protein	159
1966	Trypsinogen	216
1967	Glyceraldehyde 3-phosphate dehydrogenase	340
1969	Immunoglobin γ-chain	446
1973	Immunoglobulin μ-chain	537
1975	Serum albumin	585
1978	β-galactosidase	1021

the U.K., to that in the United States. However, there have been advantages with this situation, as scientists are much more ready to innovate when a particular piece of machinery is unavailable. A particular instance is the development of the dansyl-Edman procedure of Gray and Hartley. This without question is a major rival to the automatic sequencer, yet is so facile.

BASIC APPROACH TO PROTEIN SEQUENCING

Before work on the amino acid sequence can even be considered the protein under investigation must be established to be homogeneous. Discussion on the methods available for the purification of proteins is considered to be outside the scope of this small book; there are however many excellent reference books available to adequately cover this field, which has during the last decade altered very little. Some discussion, however, will be given concerning what criteria should be used to assess the purity of a protein preparation.

It is true to say that the only real proof that a protein is homogeneous is that it possesses a unique amino acid sequence, so at the commencement of a sequence investigation it is impossible to know that the protein is 100% pure. At best, therefore, one can only apply a number of tests, none in themselves being infallible, but when taken together, some confidence as to the protein's purity should be possible. The following tests should be included:

(1) The protein should be homogeneous in size. Molecular weight estimates may be obtained from ultracentrifuge studies, gel filtration measurements, or by DISC-gel electrophoresis in the presence of sodium dodecyl sulphate.

(2) The protein should be homogeneous in charge. This information may be readily derived from electrophoretic studies using a variety of media (cellogel, polyacrylamide gels, startch gels and agar gel) and over a pH range. The more sensitive technique of isoelectric focusing should also be employed.

(3) The protein should have a unique amino acid composition, that should not vary during any further attempt at purification.

(4) The protein should have unique amino- and carboxyl-terminal residues. Quantitative measurements of these residues should give an estimate of the molecular weight, which should agree with that previously determined.

(5) Any further attempt to purify the protein should not lead to an increase in its biological activity. Any decrease observed would probably indicate partial denaturation during the purification step.

(6) It should be possible to crystallize the protein.

During the author's investigations on lens proteins, one particular protein, γ_{IV}-crystallin, was found to fulfil all the above criteria, yet during subsequent sequence investigations it was found to consist of at least three homologous proteins. Such are the frustrations of sequence projects and it is well to begin any such work by a preliminary investigation as to the sequences around particular regions of the molecule, such as for example the cysteine residues. The results from such a study would give confidence to proceed further with the investigation.

Having taken reasonable steps to ensure that the protein under investigation is reasonably pure, it is then possible to embark on the actual sequence determination. This will entail the following stages:

(1) The amino acid composition of the protein is determined and an investigation as to whether there are any other substances covalently attached to the protein, such as carbohydrate, is carried out.

(2) The amino acid sequences at the amino- and carboxyl-termini are determined.

(3) The protein is treated with a specific endoprotease, or chemical reagent, to fragment it into a number of peptides. The actual one used will depend on the overall strategy. Two approaches are possible: first a large number of small fragments might result, with the consequent problems of separation and purification; secondly, a small number of large fragments might result, which usually present solubility problems, as large hydrophobic peptides are usually insoluble in aqueous media, unless one resorts to the messy and expensive use of 6 M urea solutions. Probably the most useful cleavage procedure is tryptic digestion.

(4) Each of the peptides produced from (3) are purified and their amino acid compositions determined. These should add up to the overall amino acid composition of the protein. Failure to do so would probably indicate missing peptides.

(5) The amino acid sequence of each of the purified peptides is determined. A comparison of the methods available is given in Table 4.

Table 4. Comparison of conventional methods for amino acid sequence determination

Method	Size of suitable peptide (residues)	Approximate amount needed (nmol)	Comments
Manual methods	10	50	Simple and cheap
Automatic:			
(a) soild phase	10–15	100 ⎫	requires costly
(b) liquid phase	20	250 ⎬	equipment, and
Mass spectroscopy	5–10	100 ⎭	specialized expertise

(6) Stages (3)–(5) are repeated using a reagent of different specificity in order to overlap the initial peptides. This might well be cyanogen bromide.

(7) It should be possible to assemble the complete sequence from the information gained in these experiments, however further reagents may be employed to elucidate the sequence at problematical regions.

In recent years the strategy has somewhat changed, with more emphasis on the use of automatic procedures, which work best on large peptide fragments. Thus the fragmentation of a protein into a small number of large peptides is normally the first step. For example, a protein of 160 amino acid residues could be fragmented into four peptides each of approximately 40 residues. Each of these could be completely sequenced in the sequencer, and when this information is combined with knowledge of the sequences of the terminal regions a complete sequence should be realized.

FUTURE PROSPECTS

Microsequencing

These developments have occurred to enable biochemists to investigate minute quantities of biologically active proteins, such as histocompatibility factors and prohormones. Several approaches have been proposed but they have in common the use of radioactively labelled protein to increase the sensitivity of established procedures. The protein is labelled either by chemical or biological means. In the case of biological incorporation of radioisotope, this may be achieved by allowing translation of the protein mRNA to occur in a reticulocyte lysate containing a mixture of radioactive amino acids. Alternatively radioactive amino acids may be incorporated by incubation of living cells synthesizing the protein of interest; however, the problem here is the difficulty of getting the non-essential amino acids labelled. The chemical approach has been to use ^{35}S-phenylisothiocyanate of high specific activity in a preliminary coupling step in the Edman degradation. The released thiazolines after conversion to their respective PTH-amino acids are mixed with unlabelled carrier PTH-amino acids, and separated by TLC and identified by autoradiography.

Microsequencing therefore promises to be generally applicable to the determination of the primary structure of trace quantities of biologically important proteins, and has in the order of 10 000 times the sensitivity of conventional methods.

Nucleic Acid Sequencing

Techniques for the sequence determination of nucleic acids have increased beyond all expectations during the last decade, and so too have the techniques for the isolation of specific mRNA molecules. Considering the relative ease by which the sequences of nucleotides may be determined in these products, it has been looked upon by some workers as an alternative procedure whereby protein sequence determination might be arrived at. This, however, is somewhat a controversial area at the present time of writing, and it does not seem feasible that this approach will replace the classical methods of protein sequencing within the near future.

ABBREVIATIONS AND CONVENTIONS

As information on the amino acid sequences of proteins has increased, methods have been devised to abbreviate and simplify this information. To begin with the term 'amino acid sequence' is synonymous with the 'primary structure' of a protein, these terms being completely interchangeable. However, the covalent structure of a protein refers to the location of all the covalent bonds present in a protein molecule, and may include location of disulphide bridges, and the position of prosthetic groups, and thus has not the same meaning as the former two terms.

The primary structure of a peptide is normally presented as a sequence of amino acid residues using the well-known three-letter code to represent these (see Abbreviations).
For example,

Ala–Gly–Ser

represents a tripeptide formed between the amino acids alanine, glycine and serine. It may also be written as

Ala.Gly.Ser

or simply,

Ala Gly Ser (also ALA GLY SER).

By convention the residue on the far left, namely alanine, is always the N-terminal residue, i.e. it possesses a free α-amino group, and the residue on the far right is the C-terminal residue, i.e. has a free α-carboxyl group, in this instance the amino acid serine. The peptide bond is represented by the hyphen, or period, or simply a space, whereas a comma indicates that the sequence of the amino acids is not known.

CHAPTER 1

Enzymic Cleavage of Proteins

The early studies on the amino acid sequences of proteins were performed using partial acid hydrolysis as a method of degradation, for there was a reluctance amongst biochemists to employ proteolytic enzymes for fear of transpeptidation. These misapprehensions were soon realized to be without substance, and the use of enzymes in this field became widely accepted. Nevertheless, in more recent times, as a consequence of the trend toward automatic sequencing and the need for large peptide fragments, biochemists have looked again at proteolytic enzymes to find ways of limiting their activity, or to seek new, more specific ones. Chemical methods, at one time quite ignored by the majority of workers, are once again in fashion. Thus at the present time this field is in a state of flux, and for the purpose of this section only the proteases that in the past have been most useful will be considered, together with a summary of the recently introduced enzymes.

GENERAL PROCEDURES FOR ENZYME HYDROLYSIS

In all enzyme reactions there are four main factors to consider, namely

- (1) pH,
- (2) temperature,
- (3) the enzyme: substrate ratio, and
- (4) the period of incubation.

The optimum conditions for a particular hydrolysis are best found by trial and error, following the progress of the reaction by peptide mapping.

Preparation of the Protein for Enzyme Digestion

Native proteins are not generally susceptible to enzymic hydrolysis. There are cases, however, where a susceptible bond might be accessible to the enzyme active site and be cleaved, possibly leading to several large fragments; such specific reactions are unusual, for what normally happens in these circumstances is a slow denaturation and hydrolysis of the protein substrate—which is unsatisfactory. The protein must therefore be denatured prior to enzymic digestion; this process, at one time a complete mystery to biochemists, is now thought to involve the unfolding and destruction of the

9

secondary and tertiary structures of the macromolecule, converting all conformations present to a random coil rigid structure. Such a configuration is readily amiable to enzymic hydrolysis.

Methods of Protein Denaturation

(i) Heating: boiling in a water bath for between 10–60 minutes; the protein usually precipitates under these conditions and is collected by centrifugation.

(ii) Treatment with strong acid: (e.g. trichloroacetic acid) the protein is precipitated from aqueous solution with 10% trichloroacetic acid, collected by centrifugation and washed several times with water.

(iii) Performic acid oxidation: the protein is treated with an excess of HCOOOH at 0°C for about 2 hours, after which it is precipitated from

Table I. Useful proteolytic enzymes

Enzyme	Source	Specificity: cleavage on the C-terminal side of	N-terminal side of	Optimal pH
Trypsin	Ox pancreas	Arg, Lys (except when Pro next residue)		8–9
Chymotrypsin	Ox pancreas	Trp, Tyr, Phe, Leu and to a lesser extent Met, Asn, Gln, His (except when Pro is the next residue)		8–9
Thermolysin	*Bacillus thermoproteolyticus*		All hydrophobic amino acids except e.g. -*x*-Leu-Pro- not cleaved	8
Pepsin	Ox pancreas	Similar but less specific than chymotrypsin, cleaving mainly on the N- and C- sides of aromatic amino acids and leucine		2

solution by 25% trichloroacetic acid, collected by centrifugation and washed thoroughly. This treatment oxidizes the cystine/cysteine residues to cysteic acids, the methionine to methionine sulphone, and the tryptophan is completely destroyed.

(iv) S-carboxymethylation: the protein in 6M-urea is treated with a reducing agent to convert the cystines to cysteine residues, and these are modified by either iodoacetic acid or iodoacetamide, at pH 6–8, in the dark, for about 1 hour. The protein is obtained after dialysis by lyophilization.

(1) TRYPSIN

Specificity

Trypsin has been the most useful of all the proteolytic enzymes, because of its high specificity, cleaving only on the C-terminal side of lysine and arginine residues. It has been used to study the number and nature of the subunits of many proteins, using the simple technique of peptide mapping, the number of peptides being equal to the sum of the lysine and arginine residues plus one (the C-terminal peptide), in the case of identical subunits. However, it should be borne in mind that repetitive sequences of either lysine or arginine are only cleaved slowly, resulting in an extra peptide, it is thought that this is due to the influence of the polar side chain on the cleavage of the bond to be cleaved. Kasper (1975) reports that the sequence Arg–CySO$_3$H is only partially cleaved; however, the present author has found the same sequence to be rapidly cleaved by trypsin, in the lens protein γ-crystallin, and it is clear that the local environment affects the susceptibility of a particular bond. Bonds involving the amino acid proline are not cleaved, but there are exceptions

'Contaminating' Chymotryptic Activity

Some commercial preparations of trypsin may contain small amounts of chymotryptic activity, which, during the course of a digestion, may produce unwanted peptides, as well as reducing the yield of the tryptic peptides. Thus, cleavage of the bond between Tyr[28]–Phe[29] in γ-crystallin was always observed (Croft 1972a, b), and a similar cleavage was found by Enfield *et al*. (1975) in their study of rabbit muscle parvalbumin: in this case the bond Phe[18]–Ala[19] was always cleaved. Chymotryptic activity can be reduced by treating the trypsin preparation with a chymotrypsin inhibitor such as L-(1-tosyl amido-2-phenyl) ethyl chloromethyl ketone (TPCK); however, Richardson *et al*. (1978), in their work on the sequence of the α-subunit of pea lectin, always found the Tyr[4]–Thr[5] bond to be cleaved, even after the trypsin had been treated with TPCK, and they had also, as an added precaution, treated the trypsin with 1 mM-HCl to further inactivate any residual chymotrypsin activity. It is interesting that a similar anomalous cleavage has been reported to occur during the tryptic digestion of lentil lectin, a protein homologous to the pea protein (Foriers *et al* 1978).

Aspecific Cleavage

The reports mentioned above clearly indicate the important role the substrate has on the course of the enzyme digestion, and this idea has been further substantiated by the finding of van Den Berg *et al.* (1977) that many aspecific cleavages were found in tryptic digests of guinea pig ribonuclease A, that were not found with guinea pig ribonuclease B, even though the same preparation of trypsin was used. One unusual cleavage was between Lys^{113}–Pro^{114}, and this was found also in digests of ox seminal ribonuclease. That trypsin can, in certain circumstances, hydrolyse the bond between Lys(or Arg) and Pro, is now well established. Bennett *et al.* (1978), in their study of dihydrofolate reductase, found that the bond between 52–53 was cleaved by trypsin: the sequence around the susceptible bond was –Gly^{51}–Arg^{52}–Pro^{53}–Leu^{54}–, and a similar hydrolysis was found by Croft (1972a, b), between residues 48 and 49 in the sequence –Gln^{47}–Arg^{48}–Pro^{49}–Asp^{50}–, of the lens protein γ-crystallin. Carnegie (1969) also found that trypsin was able to cleave the Arg–Pro bond, in the sequence –Gln–Arg–Pro–Gly–, during his investigations on the encephalitogenic protein from human myelin. This protein also contained the interesting methylated derivatives of arginine, namely ω-N-monomethyl Arg, and ω-N,N'-dimethyl Arg, which resisted tryptic hydrolysis (Dunkley and Carnegie 1974); however, some unusual amino acids in proteins do render the peptide bonds susceptible to cleavage by trypsin, for example S-aminoethyl cysteinyl bonds are cleaved by trypsin, though not as rapidly as its lysine analogue.

Limitation of Cleavage by Chemical Modification

As trypsin can cleave on the C-terminal sides of both lysine and arginine, it is clear that its usefulness could be enhanced if its activity could be limited to one or other of these residues. Many chemical procedures have been introduced to this end. Most have been directed toward the ε-amino group of lysine (being simpler to modify than the guanidinium group of arginine), and the most successful has been citraconic anhydride, introduced by Dixon and Perham (1968), having the added bonus that it is readily removed. This reagent has been used to identify and isolate the N-terminal peptide from

(N–citraconyl)Gly–(ε–N–citraconyl) Lys–Ile–Thr–Phe–Tyr–Glu–Asp–Arg
(Peptide *N*)

pH 2.0
20 hours

Gly–Lys–Ile–Thr–Phe–Tyr–Glu–Asp–Arg
(Peptide *N'*)

Trypsin

Gly–Lys
(Peptide *N'a*)

Ile–Thr–Phe–Tyr–Glu–Asp–Arg
(Peptide *N'b*)

Figure I   Isolation of the N-terminal peptide from γ-crystallin
using citraconic anhydride to limit the cleavage with trypsin to
arginyl peptide bonds

γ-crystallin (Croft 1972a). The citraconylated protein was digested with
trypsin and the very acidic peptide (*N*) isolated by paper electrophoresis.
The blocking groups were readily removed by incubation in dilute acetic
acid overnight, and the resulting peptide (*N'*) further treated with trypsin to
give peptides *N'a*, and *N'b* (Figure I).

A related procedure has been introduced for arginine residues by Patthy
and Smith (1975). Arginyl residues were found to be specifically blocked by
reaction with cyclohexane-1,2-dione in borate buffer (pH 8–9) to form N^7,
N^8 (1,2-dihydroxycyclohex-1,2-ylene) derivatives. These can be stabilized by

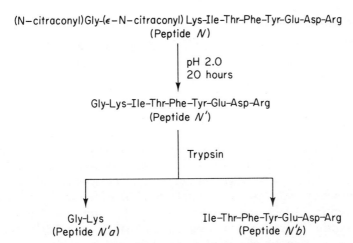

the presence of borate ions, the product being resistant to cleavage by
trypsin; however, the arginine is readily regenerated by mild treatment with
hydroxylamine.

General Reaction Conditions

The peptide or protein (200 nmol) is dissolved in 0.2 ml of 1% NH_4HCO_3. The enzyme (2 nmol, 0.05 mg) dissolved in 1 mM-HCl, is added and the mixture incubated for 3–4 hours at 37°C.

(2) CHYMOTRYPSIN

Chymotrypsinogen is the inactive precursor of chymotrypsin, and is a single-chain polypeptide of 245 amino acid residues, stabilized by five disulphide bridges. The zymogen has no proteolytic activity and is activated by trypsin, which hydrolyses the peptide bond between Arg^{15}–Ile^{16}, forming π-chymotrypsin, which acts upon itself to form the fully active α-chymotrypsin, liberating two peptides Ser^{14}–Arg^{15}, and Thr^{147}–Asn^{148} in the process. α-Chymotrypsin consists therefore of three chains A, B and C, containing 13, 130, and 96 amino acids respectively, joined together by two disulphide bridges. The specificity of this enzyme is not as high as that of trypsin, but nevertheless it has proved invaluable to the protein biochemist. In general the active enzyme cleaves preferentially the peptide bond on the C-terminal side of aromatic and bulky hydrophobic amino acids (Tyr, Trp, Phe, Met and Leu). However, cleavage may also occur on the C-terminal side of Gln, Asn, His and Thr. A high enzyme-to-substrate ratio may enhance these minor splits, and even bonds like Ala–Val are cleaved, as in Ferredoxin II from *Chlorobium limicola* (Tanaka *et al.* 1975). The rate of hydrolysis tends to be slowed down by the presence of polar groups—these may be terminal amino groups, or side-chain carboxylic acids—and it is wise to view the whole environment around a particular peptide bond when considering its susceptibility to this enzyme.

General Reaction Conditions

The peptide or protein (0.2 mol) is dissolved in 0.2 ml of 1% NH_4HCO_3, the enzyme (0.05 mg, 2 nmol) is added and the mixture incubated at 37°C for 3–4 hours.

(3) PEPSIN

The specificity of pepsin is similar to that of chymotrypsin but as its optimum pH is at pH 2, it has proved very valuable to the biochemist, particularly during investigations of the location of disulphide bridges, as in acid solution disulphide interchange reactions are minimal. It does, however, differ from chymotrypsin in its ability to cleave peptide bonds on both the N- and C-terminal sides of susceptible residues. In the main these are the aromatic amino acids and leucine; it does not hydrolyse bonds attached to proline residues.

General Reaction Conditions

The protein (100 nmol) is dissolved in 5% formic acid (0.1 ml) and to it is added pepsin (1μ1, of a solution prepared by adding 1 mg of pepsin to 1 ml of 0.5 M NaCl). The digestion is allowed to proceed at room temperature, for 1 hour.

(4) THERMOLYSIN

This is the least specific of the proteases so far discussed, and for that reason it has had only limited application in the fragmentation of proteins, the peptides produced being small and tedious to purify. It has, however, been of considerable use in the fragmentation of large peptides from a primary digest. Thermolysin is a metalloenzyme containing one Zn and three to four Ca atoms per molecule. The function of the Ca is to enhance the stability of the enzyme, and it is thus advisable to include a small amount of calcium ions in the reaction medium.

Thermolysin cleaves on the N-terminal side of hydrophobic amino acids, namely Ile, Leu, Val, Phe, Ala, Met and Tyr, however, if the carboxyl of the said amino acid is joined to the imino acid proline, hydrolysis does not occur. Needless to say, there are instances in the literature outside this category. Emmens *et al.* (1976) found the bond Thr[99]–Ser[100] in pike whale ribonuclease to be cleaved by thermolysin. The local environment plays an important role in these aspecific cleavages. Hydrolysis can occur on the N-terminal side of cysteic acid residues when the subsequent residue in the chain is lysine (Scheffer and Beintema 1974), and it is thought that the sulphonic acid side chain is shielded by the proximal ϵ-amino group of the lysine. And Matsubara *et al.* (1970) found thermolysin to cleave on the N-terminal side of glutamyl residues when it was adjacent to arginine.

General Reaction Conditions

The peptide (300 nmol) is dissolved in ammonium acetate buffer (0.5 ml, 0.2 M, pH 8.5, containing 5 mM CaCl$_2$) and the enzyme (0.1 mg) added in 100 μl of the same buffer. Reaction continues at 40°C for about 3 hours.

(5) RECENTLY INTRODUCED PROTEOLYTIC ENZYMES

There has been and still is a major search for highly specific proteolytic endopeptidases. Many have been described in the literature but few have been successfully used in amino acid sequence determination; Table II lists several new proteases that have been applied with some degree of success. These will not be considered here in detail, as they have not been used extensively enough to warrant a comprehensive evaluation, except the 'Glu' protease which in recent years has found widespread application. This

Table II. Recently introduced proteases

Enzyme	Source	Specificity: cleavage on the C-terminal side of	N-terminal side of	Reference
Clostripain	*Clostridium histolyticum*	Arg		Mitchell and Harrington (1968)
'Pro' protease	Lamb kidney	Pro		Fleer *et al.* (1978)
'Lys' protease	*Armillaria mellea*, Myxobacter		Lys	Gregory (1975); Jörnvall (1977)
'Glu' protease	*Staphylococcus aureus*	Glu		Houmard and Drapeau (1972)

enzyme cleaves on the carboxyl side of glutamyl residues and has proved very useful in the differentiation of Glu/Gln residues, and in providing the investigator with peptides possessing C-terminal glutamic acid, enabling facile attachment to resins for the solid-phase Edman degradation.

Staphylococcal Protease

This is one of the most interesting and useful of the many endopeptidases introduced in recent years. It was first isolated from *Staphylococcus aureus*, strain V_8, by Houmard and Drapeau (1972). These investigators found that this protease, with the remarkably low molecular weight of 12 000, could cleave on the C-terminal side of glutamyl and aspartyl residues when the hydrolysis is performed in phosphate buffer (pH 7.8). If, however, the buffer is changed to either NH_4HCO_3 (pH 7.8) or ammonium acetate (pH 4.0), cleavage only at glutamyl residues occurs. The nature of the amino acid attached to the carboxyl of the glutamyl residue, except proline, did not influence the rate of hydrolysis, and as glutaminyl residues were not cleaved at all it was concluded that the γ-carboxylic acid group was the essential feature necessary for reaction with the enzyme.

As the enzyme is now commercially available, more reports on its specificity toward different substrates have appeared in the literature and some of these are summarized in Table III.

In their original work, Houmard and Drapeau noted that under certain circumstances aspartyl bonds might be hydrolysed if the adjacent residue was of small molecular size and in fact they found that the –Asp–Gly– bond was slowly hydrolysed, with the explanation that such reaction was a consequence of the β-carboxyl of Asp becoming accessible to the enzyme-binding site; however, it is difficult on this basis to account for some of the cleavages reported in Table III.

Table III. Aspecific cleavages observed using the enzyme *Staphylococcus aureus* protease

Protein	Cleavages observed		Reference
α-subunit of	174–175	Asp-Ala	Ovchinnikov *et al.*
DNA-dependent	197–198	Asp-Leu	(1977)
RNA-polymerase	233–234	Asp-Leu	
	280–281	Asp-Leu	
	21–22	Ser-Thr	
	49–50	Ser-Ser	
	266–267	Ser-Ala	
	313–314	Ser-Leu	
Pike whale RNase	14–15	Asp-	Emmens *et al.* (1976)
	53–54	Asp-	
	83–84	Asp-	
	121–122	Asp-	
	45–46	Thr-Phe	
Kangaroo RNase	121–122	Asp-	
Horse pancreas	7–8	Ser-Met	Evenberg *et al.* (1977)
phospholipase A_2	107–108	Ser-Lys	
Ox phospholipase A_2	10–11	Lys-Cys	Fleer *et al.* (1978)
	43–44	Arg-Cys	
α-subunit of pea lectin		Asp-	Richardson *et al.* (1978)
		Asp-	

Sutton *et al.* (1977) confirmed the supposition that the –Glu–Pro– bond is not hydrolysed by this enzyme, and also found that N-terminal glutamyl residues were quantitatively released, contrary to the findings of Hitz *et al.* (1977). However, not all glutamyl bonds are susceptible to hydrolysis, strongly suggesting that the local environment has some importance. Vandekerckhove and van Montagu (1977), found that due to its hydrophobic character, the A-protein of Coliphage MS2 was not attacked at all by this enzyme even after prolonged incubation. Hitz *et al.* (1977) reported that glutamyl residues in the sequence –Glu–Glu– were not cleaved. However, other glutamyl residues may resist hydrolysis; Brosius and Arfsten (1978) found that the glutamyl residue at position 2 of the peptide Gln–Glu–Gln–Met–Lys–Gln–Asp–Val–Pro–Ser–Phe–Arg–Pro–Gly–Asp–Thr–Val–Glu, isolated from the ribosomal protein L19, was also not hydrolysed. Nevertheless, this enzyme, in the short time it has been available, has proved extremely valuable to protein chemists: van Dijk *et al.* (1976) in their work on the sequence of muskrat ribonuclease found it useful in the assignment of amide groups; the tryptic peptide isolated (Figure II) was hydrolysed to give two peptides which were purified and analysed clearly indicating where the amide group was located. This enzyme has also been used to help correct the amino acid sequence of the snake

18

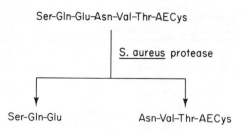

Ser–Gln–Glu–Asn–Val–Thr–AECys

S. aureus protease

Ser–Gln–Glu   Asn–Val–Thr–AECys

Figure II   Treatment of a tryptic peptide
from muskrat ribonuclease with *S. aureus*
protease

erabutoxins (Maeda and Tamiya 1977). A tryptic peptide was isolated from
these neurotoxins and its partial sequence –Gly–(Glu,Ser)–Ser– deduced;
further work using the subtractive Edman degradation led to the incorrect
formulation –Gly–Ser–Glu–Ser– due to contamination by Glu, arising from
incomplete reaction; however, the correct sequence –Gly–Glu–Ser–Ser– was
found after hydrolysis of the peptide with *S.aureus* protease.

A more recent application of this valuable new proteinase has been by
Begg *et al.* (1978) in their investigation of the location of disulphide bridges
in human β-thromboglobulin, and they conclude that as disulphide
interchange reactions are minimal at its optimal pH (4.0), this enzyme might
become a useful alternative to pepsin in such investigations.

CHAPTER 2

Chemical Methods of Cleavage

(1) CYANOGEN BROMIDE

The pseudo-halogen cyanogen bromide is the most useful of the many chemical methods of peptide chain cleavage that have been introduced. Its discovery by Gross and Witkop (1962) followed a detailed and systematic search for a reagent that would form a sulphonium salt with methionine sufficiently labile to undergo intramolecular displacement and decomposition under relatively mild conditions. This reagent has the unique specificity of breaking peptide bonds on the carboxyl side of methionine residues, and as these residues are relatively rare in proteins, the products formed are usually large peptides. These peptides in the past have been valuable in the ordering of the tryptic peptides obtained from a primary digest of a protein and at present are equally valuable in providing large fragments to subject to automated Edman degradation either in the liquid phase or solid phase sequencer. In the latter procedure they have the added advantage of ease of attachment to the supporting resin as a consequence of their terminal lactone structure.

Mechanism

The mechanism of the reaction of cyanogen bromide with a methionine residue in a peptide chain is illustrated in Figure III. Reaction takes place usually in strong acid solution, at room temperature, and under these conditions methylthiocyanate is formed, and the hydrogen bromide salt of the iminolactone, which subsequently spontaneously decomposes to homoserine lactone.

Specificity

(a) Reaction with Methionine residues

(i) methionine in the middle of a peptide chain

$$-Ala-Met-Phe- \xrightarrow[\text{CNBr}]{} -Ala-Homoserine\ lactone + NH_2Phe-$$

19

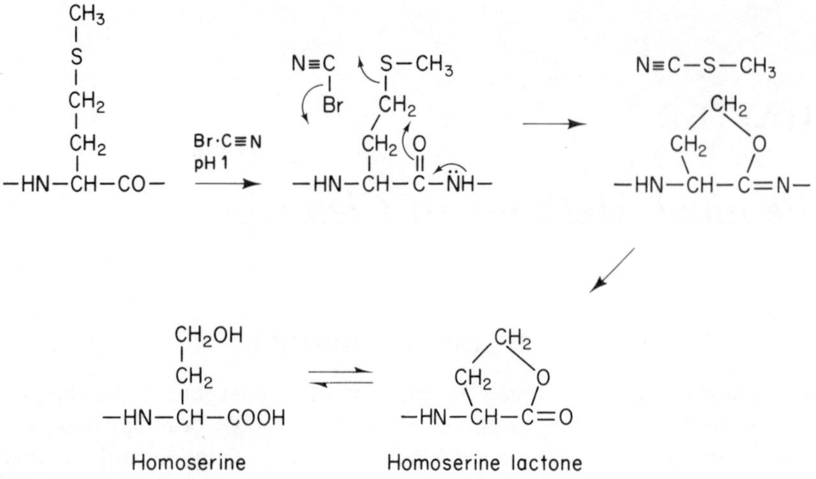

Figure III   Reaction of CNBr with methionine residues in a peptide chain

(ii) methionine N-terminal

$$NH_2Met–Ala– \xrightarrow{CNBr} \text{Homoserine lactone} + NH_2Ala–$$

(iii) multiple residues of methionine

$$–Phe–Met–Met–Ala– \xrightarrow{CNBr} –Phe–\text{Homoserine lactone} + \text{Homoserine–}$$

$$\text{lactone} + NH_2–Ala–$$

(iv) N-acetyl methionine residues

A feature not uncommon is the N-acetyl methionine residue at the N-terminal of a protein; this has been found to incompletely react with CNBr so that approximately 10% of the methionyl peptide bond remains uncleaved due to the formation of O-acetyl-homoserine (Carpenter and Shiigi 1974).

(b) Reaction with Cys, Met(SO) and Met(SO₂) residues

Cysteine is reported to undergo slow reaction with CNBr but peptide chain cleavage is not known to result (Gross and Witkop 1962). However, the reaction undergone does not appear to affect subsequent performic acid oxidation of the cysteine residues, for this is frequently a useful step to render the peptides soluble, particularly if they are large fragments. Methionine sulphone and methionine sulphoxide, occasional artefacts in proteins, do not react with cyanogen bromide and as the former is readily reduced back to methionine during the course of normal acid hydrolysis it could lead to the conclusion being made that incomplete cleavage had occurred; however, a method for the preliminary reduction of these artefacts using mercapto-ethanol under relatively mild conditions has been described recently (Naider and Bohak 1972).

Reaction Conditions

Approximately a 30–100-fold molar excess of CNBr over the methionine present is used*. The solvent most commonly used is 70% (v/v) formic acid and the reaction temperature is usually 25°C, for a period of 24 hours. Following reaction the mixture is diluted 10-fold with distilled water and the solution freeze-dried. Alternatively the reaction may be performed in 70% trifluoroacetic acid at 25°C for 12 hours (Ferrell et al. 1978), and is terminated by diluting with distilled water to 5% trifluoroacetic acid concentration. Unreacted protein is precipitated in this way and removed by centrifugation; the soluble peptides are then obtained by lyophilization of the solution.

Lactone/Peptide Conversion

Electrophoresis of freshly isolated cyanogen bromide peptides usually reveals multiple peptides due to the partial hydrolysis of the lactone ring and it is desirable for future handling of the peptides to get them completely either into the lactone or peptide form. Conversion to the lactone is readily accomplished by treating the peptide with trifluoroacetic acid for 1 hour at 25°C. Alternatively the peptide form can be obtained by treating the mixture with a solution of 0.1% NH_4OH for 15 min. However the lactone form is of great value if the peptide is to be subsequently sequenced using the solid phase sequencer, for it can readily be attached to the matrix resin.

Problems

(i) Aspecific cleavages

Some proteins have been found to be difficult to cleave with CNBr: fortunately these are few in number. Scheffer and Beintema (1974) have reported that extensive aspecific cleavage occurred during the CNBr digestion of horse ribonuclease, in particular cleavage on the carboxyl side of several tyrosine residues was found. Apparently this was accompanied by chemical modification of the phenolic groups, as no tyrosine residues could be subsequently identified by specific staining reagents. Further, Simon-Becam et al. (1978) found that CNBr digestion of cytochrome C

---

*Cyanogen bromide is highly toxic and as it is quite volatile (m.pt 52°, b.pt 61°) care must be exercised in its use. All handling must be carried out in a fume cupboard and all apparatus after use washed in strong hypochlorite solution, to destroy excess cyanide. Care must be also taken during subsequent freeze-drying to ensure that no volatile cyanides enter the oil pump; an appropriate cold trap should be employed to this end.

from *Schizosaccharomyces pombe* cleaved the peptide chain on the N-terminal side of cysteine residues. This was ascribed to the formation of a dehydroalanyl residue formed during the incomplete S-carboxymethylation of the apoprotein and subsequent cleavage occurring in the acid medium of the reaction, in general, this has been found to facilitate the cyclization of N-terminal glutamine residues forming pyroglutamyl residues.

(ii) Incomplete reaction

Cyanogen bromide digestion of human urogastrone, a potent inhibitor of gastric acid secretion, was found by the I.C.I. investigators to be incomplete (Gregory and Preston 1977); although amino acid analysis of the reaction product indicated complete conversion of the methionine residue to homoserine, no chain fission was found. The amino acid sequence around the particular methionine was –Cys–Met–Tyr–. A similar case was found in the coat protein of the alfalfa mosaic virus (van Beynum *et al.* 1977). Incomplete reaction was found to occur between residues 127–128 (Met–Gln) and 155–156 (Met–Glx) whereas Met–Val bonds in the protein were completely cleaved. These difficulties led to problems during subsequent attempts to purify the cyanogen bromide peptides. It is of interest to note that again the homoserine content of the products was that to be expected for complete conversion of the methionines, yet for some unknown reason the cleavage step had failed. Possibly it is the specific amino acids involved as there are many reports of the sequence Met–Thr presenting difficulties of cleavage. Enfield *et al.* (1975) treated rabbit muscle parvalbumin with CNBr to find that Met residue 2 in the sequence

Ac–Ala–Met–Thr–Glu . . .

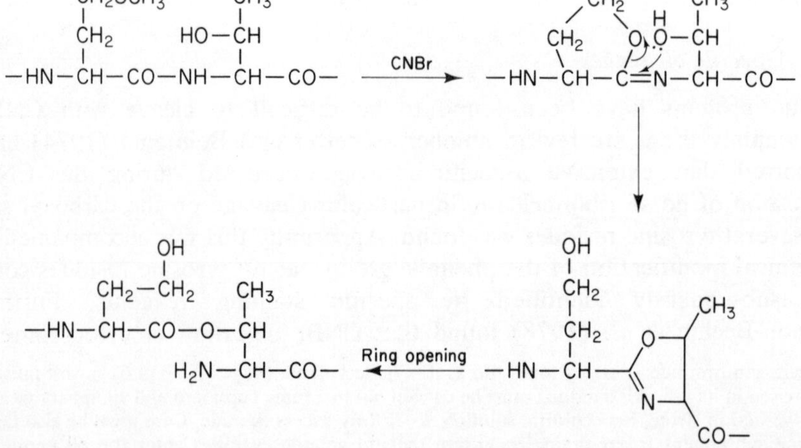

Figure IV   The reaction of the Met–Thr peptide bond with cyanogen bromide

failed to react. Stone and Phillips (1977) also found that a Met–Thr bond (residues 37–38) of dihydrofolate reductase failed to cleave, although conversion to the homoserine had occurred. Possibly this is due to the interaction of the neighbouring hydroxy group of threonine with the intermediate iminolactone to form a homoseryl-O-threonyl peptide as illustrated in Figure IV.

One possible way to circumvent these difficulties is to perform the reaction in 70% TFA rather than the conventional formic acid (Scheffer and Beintema 1974).

(2) HYDROXYLAMINE

Deselnicu *et al.* (1973) have shown, using the model compound Z–Asn–Gly–OEt, that NH_2OH reacts and cleaves specifically the peptide bond between asparagine and glycine amino acid residues. They have suggested that reaction proceeds through the intermediate formation of a succinimide ring and leads eventually to specific fission of the Asn–Gly bond. The reaction mechanism is illustrated in Figure V.

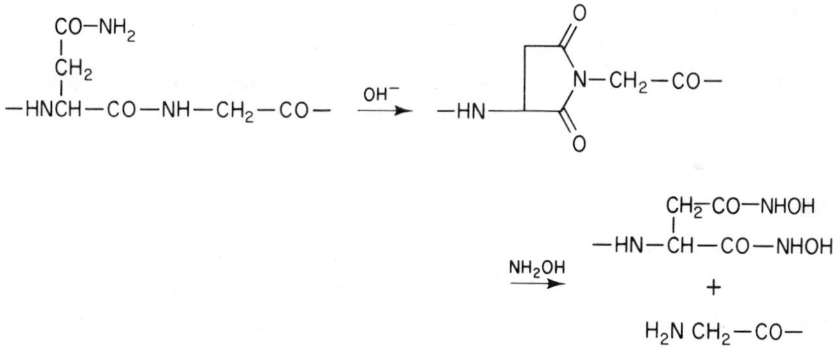

Figure V   The reaction of NH_2OH with the peptide bond between Asn–Gly

This reaction has been used by the Russian biochemists to cleave the single Asn–Gly peptide bond in the α-subunit of DNA-dependent RNA polymerase from *E. coli* (Ovchinnikov *et al.* 1977). Two peptides were obtained after chromatography on Sephadex G100, one from the N-terminal portion contained residues 1–208, and the other was from the C-terminal region and contained residues 209–329 (Figure VI).

This latter peptide had N-terminal glycine and was sequenced up to residue 234 in a Beckman 890C liquid phase sequencer. This information provided vital confirmation of the amino acid sequence of a difficult region of the protein.

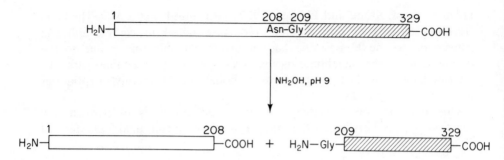

Figure VI   The cleavage of the α-subunit of DNA-dependent RNA-polymerase by NH₂OH

Reaction Conditions

In a typical reaction the protein is added to a solution of 6 M guanidine HCl containing about a hundredfold molar excess of NH$_2$OH.HCl, previously adjusted to pH 9.0 with 4.5 M LiOH. The reaction is allowed to proceed at 45°C for 4–5 hours, the pH being readjusted every 15 min by the addition of 5 μl portions of 4.5 M LiOH (Frank *et al.* 1978). Finally the reaction is terminated by lowering the pH to between 2 and 3 using 9% HCO$_2$H. The reaction mixture is desalted on a small column of Sephadex G25 and the resulting peptides further purified on a column of Sephadex G75.

Alignment of CNBr Peptides

The present trend on protein sequence determination studies is to produce a small number of large peptide fragments. This may be achieved in either of two ways: first the action of proteolytic enzymes might be reduced by a preliminary chemical modification of the protein under study; or secondly a chemical means for chain fragmentation may be used, which may have a greater specificity. In a study of the β-subunit of C-Phycocyanin from the cyanobacterium *Mastigocladus laminosus*, NH$_2$OH has been used to align the CNBr peptides (Frank *et al.* 1978). The β-subunit of the protein was treated with NH$_2$OH and the products separated on a column of Sephadex G75. Six peptides were obtained and following a detailed examination of one of these the alignment of the CNBr peptides could be achieved. A similar strategy was used by Hogg and Hermodson (1977), in their investigation of the structure of the L-arabinose-binding protein from *E. coli*. This protein was treated with NH$_2$OH and cleavage of the Asn–Gly peptide bond between residues 232–233 was achieved. The resulting peptides were fractionated on Sephadex G75 and from subsequent studies on these peptides it was possible to align two of the cyanogen bromide peptides, which was an essential step in the structure elucidation.

(3) BNPS-SKATOLE

BNPS-skatole* (2-(2-Nitrophenyl sulphenyl)-3-methyl-3'-bromoindolenine), is formed by the reaction of 2-(2-nitrophenyl sulphenyl)-3-methyl indole with one equivalent of N-bromosuccinimide in dilute acetic acid. It is an extremely mild source of positive bromine. Unlike N-bromosuccinimide, this

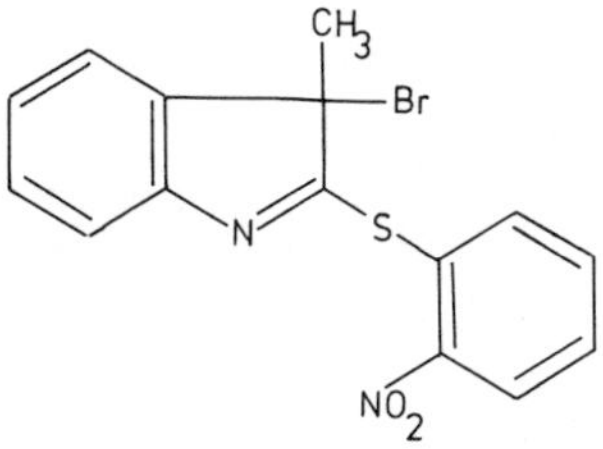

reagent under suitable conditions reacts specifically with tryptophan residues in proteins, and as tryptophan is a rare amino acid in all proteins, the use of this reagent in producing large peptide fragments has increased in favour over the last few years.

General Reaction Conditions

There have been various methods for its use described in the literature and it is obvious that reaction will depend to a great extent on the protein being investigated. In general it is best to do several trial experiments to find the most suitable conditions. A general outline of the procedure used is as follows.

The protein is dissolved in either aqueous acetic or formic acid (50–70%) and to this is added a 5–10-fold excess of BNPS-skatole. Reaction is allowed to proceed at room temperature, in the dark, for between 6 and 48 hours. Following reaction the mixture is diluted with water, and excess reagent/side products removed either by centrifugation or solvent extraction. The reaction mixture is then desalted in a small column of Sephadex G25 before final purification of the peptides is carried out.

Applications and Problems

Protein S_6 of the small ribosomal subunit of E. coli was found to contain a single tryptophan residue and BNPS-skatole was used to cleave at this position in an attempt to obtain large peptide fragments suitable for

---

*BNPS-skatole (mol.wt 363.17; m.pt 97–100°C) is unstable at room temperature and decomposes with the liberation of bromine, becoming dark brown in colour. However, if kept in the deep-freeze it is stable for several months. It is not very soluble in aqueous solutions.

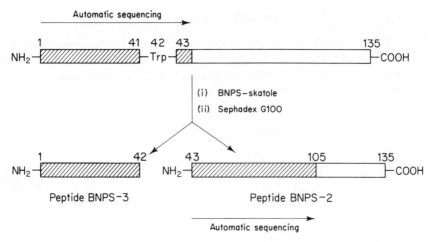

Figure VII   The reaction of BNPS-skatole with ribosomal protein S6

automatic sequencing (Hitz *et al.* 1977). The reaction course was monitored by polyacrylamide gel electrophoresis, which initially indicated that the extent of cleavage was about 16%. However, by carefully adding higher amounts of reagent and improving its solubilisation by adding 25% ethanol it was possible to increase the cleavage up to 50%. The two resulting peptide fragments were obtained by chromatography on Sephadex G100. The largest peptide (BNPS-2) contained 93 residues and the smaller one (BNPS-3) contained 42 amino acids (Figure VII). The amino acid sequence of the first 62 amino acids of peptide BNPS-2 was obtained by liquid phase automatic sequencing, and as the intact protein had been sequenced up to residue 44, by the same method, 82% of the whole sequence had been deduced as a result of this single specific fragmentation.

Cleavage of the single tryptophan residue of the α-subunit of DNA-dependent RNA polymerase was also obtained using this procedure (Ovchinnikov *et al.* 1977), enabling the C-terminal sequence of this protein to be elucidated. It is interesting to note that in this instance the peptide bond cleaved was Trp–Pro, indicating that the imino acid did not hinder the course of reaction. Nevertheless, if proper care is not exercised in this reaction, side reactions may occur leading to the production of a large number of peptide fragments, probably as a result of cleavage at modified tyrosine residues, as was found in the studies on the L-arabinose-binding protein from *E.coli* (Hogg and Hermodson 1977). In this study many more fragments were obtained than expected from the tryptophan content of the protein, and in fact bromotyrosine was subsequently found in some of the peptides studied. However, such side reactions can be reduced and eliminated if the procedure is carried out in the presence of a large excess of free tyrosine, which functions as a scavenger (Fontana 1972). This technique was used by Sepulveda *et al.* (1975), in their studies on pig pepsin. Alternatively, phenol has also been successfully employed to the same end by Frank *et al.* (1978) in studies on the structure of the α-subunit of C-Phycocyanin.

When reaction at tyrosine has been subdued in this way the only other amino acid residue that may undergo oxidation has been found to be methionine, which is converted to the suphoxide. However, this modification can be readily removed at the end of the reaction by the addition of either thioglycollic acid (Fontana 1972), or β-mercaptoethanol as used by Wang *et al.* (1977) in their studies on the amino acid sequence of apomyoglobin from the Pacific dolphin. Therefore, under rigorously controlled conditions only the amino acid tryptophan is modified by BNPS-skatole, and in fact the location of the single tryptophan, at position 128 of the α-subunit of C-Phycocyanin, was established on the basis of cleavage at that point with this reagent (Frank *et al.* 1978).

(4) N-BROMOSUCCINIMIDE (NBS)

This reagent[*] has been used to cleave peptide bonds on the carboxyl side of tyrosine and tryptophan amino acid residues in proteins and peptides. Its selectivity is, however, less than that of BNPS-skatole. It is a source of positive bromine and it is this reactive species that is responsible for polypeptide chain cleavage. The positive bromine ion reacts with the indole nucleus of tryptophan, oxidizing it and inducing peptide fission with the formation of a lactone structure at the C-terminal of the newly formed cleaved peptide. Oxidation sometimes occurs without peptide chain cleavage, depending upon the reaction conditions, which must be experimented with to maximum advantage.

General Procedure

The protein is dissolved in either a solution of 8 M urea adjusted to pH 4.0 with acetic acid, or an aqueous solution of 50% acetic acid. At least a

---

[*]N-bromosuccinimide (mol.wt 178; m.pt 173°C) is best purified before it is used for peptide chain cleavage by recrystallisation from ten times its weight of water (Fieser and Fieser 1967).

twofold molar excess of NBS is added in a small volume of the same buffer. Reaction is allowed to proceed for about one hour, at room temperature, in the dark. Immediately after reaction the mixture is fractionated on a column of Sephadex G50.

Applications and Problems

The method has been successfully applied to the elucidation of the structure of the coat protein of alfalfa mosaic virus (van Beynum *et al.* 1977). In this study a cyanogen bromide peptide CBII was treated with NBS and two peptides isolated by chromatography on Sephadex G50, CBII-BS1 with nine residues, and CBII-BS2 with 26 residues. Studies on the amino acid sequence of these peptides provided additional information for the correct alignment of the tryptic peptides of this cyanogen bromide peptide. However, there are problems associated with this method of cleavage, mainly because of its lack of specificity, as illustrated by the investigations on the structure of a cyanogen bromide peptide (CNBr VI) from the enzyme dihydrofolate reductase from a methotrexate-resistant mutant of *E.coli* (Bennett *et al.* 1978). The carboxymethylated peptide was treated with NBS for 30 min in 50% acetic acid and the products fractionated on Sephadex G50. It was clear from the number of peaks obtained that cleavage had occurred at both tryptophan and tyrosine residues. However, from the mixture only two peptides were isolated and studied, $N1$ (residues 93–133) and $N2$ (residues 134–159) (Figure VIII). Edman degradation of peptide $N2$ provided essential evidence for the sequence of this cyanogen bromide peptide.

Attempts have been made to limit the cleavage of proteins by NBS to just the tyrosine residues by prior chemical modification of the tryptophan. This

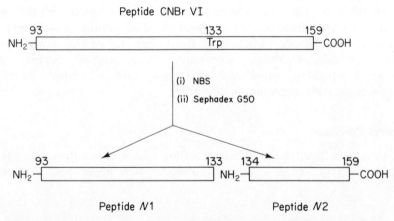

Figure VIII Cleavage at the single tryptophan residue of peptide CNBrVI by NBS (other peptides were also obtained, probably due to cleavage at tyrosine residues)

has been accomplished by ozonolysis of the indole nucleus to give N-formyl-kynurenine derivatives, which are unreactive towards NBS; this technique has been successfully applied to studies on the α-chain of human haemoglobin (Previero *et al.* 1967).

Recent studies, however, have shown that if N-chlorosuccinimide (NCS) is used in place of NBS, many of the problems are overcome and specific cleavage at tryptophanyl bonds in proteins is obtained (Shechter *et al.* 1976) and it would seem that this reagent is comparable to BNPS-skatole in its selectivity.

(5) PARTIAL ACID HYDROLYSIS

Partridge and Davis (1950) observed that partial acid hydrolysis of a protein with dilute (0.25 M) acetic acid, under reflux, led to the preferential release of aspartic acid. The reaction may be formulated as:

$$\ldots \text{X--Y--Asp--W--Z} \ldots \xrightarrow{\text{H}^+} \ldots \text{X--Y} + \text{Asp} + \text{W--Z} \ldots$$

where X, Y, W and Z represent any amino acid, other than Asp and Asn. Schultz *et al.* (1962) showed that if dilute mineral acid is used then the Asn is hydrolysed initially to Asp, and is subsequently released.

This method of selective cleavage at aspartic acid residues of a protein chain has been successfully exploited by Croft (1972a, b) in the elucidation of the amino acid sequence of the lens protein γ-crystallin. In this study a preliminary investigation of the release of aspartic acid from the protein by boiling 0.25 M acetic acid was made (Figure IX). The protein (25 mg) was then hydrolysed, in 20 ml of 0.25 M acetic acid at 100° in an evacuated

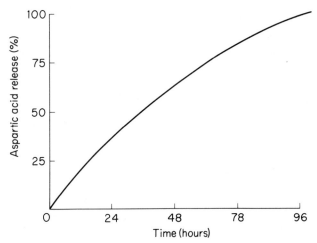

Figure IX   The release of aspartic acid from γ-crystallin
by hydrolysis with 0.25 M aspartic acid at 100°C

Carius tube, and after 86 hours the solution was freeze-dried. By using a combination of electrophoresis and paper chromatographic methods the peptide Ser–Ile–Arg–Val was isolated, which provided important information for the alignment of two tryptic peptides.

Other workers have also resorted to partial acid hydrolysis to provide them with essential overlapping information. Fowler and Zabin (1978), in their monumental studies of the amino acid sequence of β-galactosidase from *Escherichia coli*, used a novel method of partial acid hydrolysis. The carboxymethylated enzyme (0.5 g) was incubated at pH 2.5 in 7 M guanidine hydrochloride for 120 hours at 40°. Extensive cleavage throughout the 1021-residue molecule was observed and from the complex mixture of peptides was isolated peptide AS-1 which provided the key information for the alignment of two cyanogen bromide peptides.

(6) N → O ACYL REARRANGEMENT

In anhydrous acid the peptide bond of seryl (and to a lesser extent threonyl) is known to undergo intramolecular rearrangement to the adjacent hydroxyl group to form an ester link (Elliott 1952), thus:

$$-CHR\cdot CO\cdot NH\cdot CH\cdot CONH- \quad \underset{OH^-}{\overset{H^+}{\rightleftarrows}} \quad \overset{+}{H_3}N-CH\cdot CO\cdot NH-$$

with $HO\cdot CH_2$ on the left and $-CHR\cdot CO\cdot O\cdot CH_2$ on the right.

The ester bond formed is much more labile to nucleophilic attack than the original peptide bond and under mildly basic conditions may be selectively and completely cleaved. However, as under these mildly basic conditions the N → O acyl shift is reversible, the amino groups must first be blocked before selective cleavage is attempted.

This procedure has been successfully applied by Macleod *et al.* (1977) to histone H1 from trout testis. In this investigation the histone was incubated in concentrated H_2SO_4 for an extended period of time and before cleavage at the ester bonds was attempted, the exposed amino groups were blocked with a reversible acylating agent. The ester bonds were then cleaved with the powerful nucleophile hydroxylamine, thus:

$$-H\ N-CH\cdot CO\cdot NH- \quad \overset{NH_2OH}{\longrightarrow} \quad -HN\cdot CH\cdot CO\cdot NH-$$

with $-CHR\cdot CO\cdot O\cdot CH_2$ on the left and $HO\cdot CH_2$, $-CHR\cdot CO\cdot NH\ OH$ on the right.

and in this way three peptides were obtained, each containing N-terminal serine.

CHAPTER 3

The Purification of Peptides

One of the major problems in sequence analysis is the fractionation and purification of peptides. Unfortunately, during the last few years there has been little improvement in the techniques used. The strategy employed by the investigator may be the classical approach, that is the protein is fragmented into a large number of small peptides that have to be separated and purified; or the protein is split into a small number of large peptides. There are snags in both procedures: in the first case the fractionation is difficult because of the large number of fragments present and in the second instance the peptides, because of their size, are usually difficult to solubilize, and the use of disaggregating media, such as 6 M urea, may have to be employed, which is both messy and expensive.

The main procedures in current usage for the purification of peptides are:

(1) gel filtration;
(2) ion-exchange chromatography;
(3) preparative chromatography and electrophoresis.

(1) GEL FILTRATION
(gel chromatography, gel permeation chromatography etc.)

Gel filtration finds its main use in peptide purification either as a first step in the fractionation of an enzyme digest, or in the separation of a small number of peptides differing considerably in molecular weight, for example, after treatment of a protein with cyanogen bromide. The principles of gel filtration are very simple. If a sample consisting of substances differing in molecular size is applied to a column of gel filtration media and is eluted with a suitable buffer, the sample percolates through the bed. If the molecules are too large to penetrate the matrix they are eluted ahead of those that can, the latter being eluted in order of decreasing molecular weight. However, peptides of similar molecular weight may be separated, in the presence of detergents, such as dodecylamine, or dodecanoic acid, on the basis of charge differences (Strid 1973).

It is now generally appreciated that phenomena other than molecular sieving occur during gel chromatography of peptides. These include:

(*a*) interaction between acidic peptides and carboxyl groups on the gel resulting in their partial exclusion; this interaction may be reduced by using weak buffers;

(b) aromatic amino acids interact with the gel matrix and are retarded; this is sometimes dramatic with tryptophanyl peptides;

(c) hydrophobic peptides may participate in hydrophobic bonding with the gel matrix.

These interactions are never very significant except in the case of tryptophanyl peptides, when they can be used to advantage in their purification. Gel filtration therefore offers a simple, reproducible (with 100% recoveries) and quick method for peptide purification.

There are two main types of gel matrix employed in peptide purification, namely Sephadex and Bio Gel.

Sephadex

This is prepared by cross-linking dextran (poly(α-1,6-D-anhydrogluco-pyranose)) with epichlorohydrin. The extent of cross-linking is controlled by the dextran chain length and the percentage of epichlorohydrin. The types of gel available, together with their fractionation ranges, are given in Table IV. Sephadexes are insoluble in water yet stable in weakly acid or alkaline solution; however, above pH 12 and below pH 2 they are degraded, and as small amounts of soluble dextrans are to be found in the effluents of these gels it is inadvisable to use them in the purification of glycopeptides.

Table IV. Gel filtration media suitable for peptide purification

Type	Fractionation range (molecular weight)
(i) Sephadex	
G10	< 700
G15	<1500
G25	1000–5000
G50	1500–30 000
(2) Bio-gels	
P2	200–1800
P4	800–4000
P6	1000–6000
P10	1500–20 000

Bio-Gels

These are prepared by cross-linking acrylamide ($CH_2{=}CH.CONH_2$) with N,N′methylene bis acrylamide ($CH_2{=}CH.CONH.CH_2NH.CO.CH{=}CH_2$). These gels are stable in most commonly used buffers in the pH range 1–10; however, beyond pH 10 the amide groups of the matrix become labile and tend to hydrolyse.

Procedures

Equipment

The column used is best made of sturdy plastic or glass (not metal), with a bed support of the same diameter as the column, made of nylon cloth (400 mesh) and not of glass sinters which tend to get clogged, or glass wool which introduces an undesirable dead volume. The outlet tube should be of narrow bore and if possible the column should be enclosed in a constant-temperature water jacket. The length : diameter ratio of the column should be about 100 : 1; a greater length may be obtained by coupling several columns in series. Gregoire and Rochat (1977) obtained an excellent separation of peptides from the tryptic digest of a neurotoxin from the African cobra by using two 2 × 200 cm columns in series; and Bhown *et al.* (1977) achieved a good separation of the tryptic peptides from human J-chain by using an arrangement of three columns, 2 × 112 cm each in tandem (Figure X).

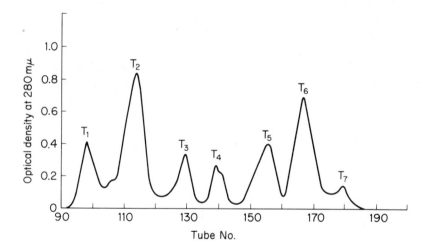

Figure X   Gel filtration of tryptic digest of citraconylated J-chain (160 mg) on two P-10 columns (Bio–Rad, 200–400 mesh, 2.0 × 112 cm) in 1% NH_4HCO_3 attached in tandem. (Reprinted with permission from *Bhown et al.* (1977), *Biochemistry*, **16**, 3501. Copyright by the American Chemical Society)

The sample to be applied to the column must be free of suspended matter and have a viscosity not greater than twice that of the eluant buffer. The sample volume should be about 1% of the bed volume. If a pump is employed the flow rate should not exceed 90% that obtainable by gravity flow. The resolution is best with a low flow rate and no advantage is gained by using ascending flow rather than the usual descending method.

Elution Solvents

The first criterion for a solvent is that it will dissolve adequately the peptides; second, that it will not interfere with the detection of the peptides; and third, it must be possible to remove it without contaminating the peptide with salts or other residues. The following have been successfully employed for the separation of peptides on gel chromatography:

(i) 0.1 M ammonium acetate, pH 8–9;
(ii) 1% NH_4HCO_3;
(iii) 1 M NH_4OH, or 1 M acetic acid;
(iv) 6 M guanidine hydrocholoride, or 6 M urea;
(v) 50% acetic acid, or formic acid.

The last two have been used to fractionate cyanogen bromide peptides and other large fragments. With 6 M urea the danger of carbamoylation is always present, particularly if old or heated solutions are used; these should be avoided; after fractionation the urea can be removed, provided the peptides are of high molecular weight by dialysis. The same applies for 6 M guanidinium chloride. Strong solutions of acetic and formic acid may be removed by high-vacuum distillation using a two-stage oil pump, protected with two liquid nitrogen traps and a third trap of sodium hydroxide pellets. Figure XI shows the successful separation of the cyanogen bromide peptides from dihydrofolate reductase by gel filtration on a column of Sephadex G50 eluting with 50% acetic acid (Bennett *et al*. 1978). As gel chromatography does not differentiate between the acid/lactone forms of the cyanogen

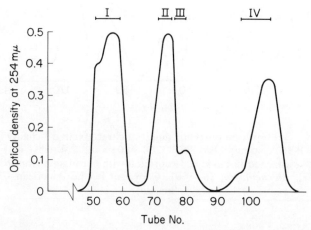

Figure XI   Gel filtration of peptides produced by CNBr digestion of dihydrofolate reductase. The column (0.9 × 100 cm) was eluted at the rate of 10 ml/h with 50% acetic acid. (Reprinted with permission from Bennett *et al*. (1978), *Biochemistry*, **17**, 1328. Copyright by the American Chemical Society)

bromide peptides, it has an inherent advantage over other forms of purification.

Detection of Peptides from Gel Filtration Columns

The usual method for detecting peptides in the eluent is by absorption in the UV at 280 mμ, 230 mμ, or 215 mμ; however, if the absorption of the elution buffer, or the lack of specific absorption in the peptide, makes this impracticable then peptides may be detected with ninhydrin, after alkaline hydrolysis of a small amount of each fraction. Alternatively, reaction with fluorescamine is more direct and readily performed (e.g. 10 μl of each tube is spotted on chromatography paper, previously sprayed with 0.4 M sodium borate, pH 9.3, and then dipped in 0.1% fluorescamine in acetone); this method has been used in many instances.

(2) ION-EXCHANGE CHROMATOGRAPHY

Soon after the introduction of ion-exchange chromatography for amino acid separations, attempts were made to use these systems for the separation of peptides from enzyme digests. Unfortunately, as inorganic salts were used in the construction of the pH gradients, great difficulty was experienced in the extrication of the small quantities of peptide material from the bulk of inorganic salts. Various ingenious methods were suggested to overcome these difficulties, none of them too successful, and it was not until volatile buffers were introduced by S. G. Waley and others, that the use of ion-exchange chromatography for the purification of peptides became a practicable proposition.

Table V. Ion exchange media for peptide fractionation

Type	Functional group	Properties
(a) CATION		
Dowex 50	$-SO_3^-\,Na^+$	strongly acidic
(equivalent BioRad		strong cation exchanger
Aminex 50W)		weak cation exchanger
(CM-Cellulose		
CM-Sephadex)	$-CH_2CO_2^-\,Na^+$	
P-Cellulose	$-O-\overset{\displaystyle O-}{\underset{\displaystyle O-}{P}}=O\;\;2Na^+$	intermediate strength cation exchanger
(b) ANION		
Dowex 1	$-\overset{+}{N}(CH_3)_3\,\overset{-}{Cl}$	strongly basic, strong anion exchanger
(DEAE-Cellulose		weak anion exchanger
DEAE-Sephadex)	$-CH_2CH_2\overset{+}{N}H(C_2H_5)_2\,\overset{-}{Cl}$	

Some of the ion-exchange resins in common use in peptide purification at the present time are listed in Table V.

Separation of Peptides on Bio-Rad Aminex 50W × 2

Only the minimum of details of the method will be given here, as excellent technical reviews are available (Schroeder 1972). Various column sizes may be used, and the ones illustrated (Table VI) are those in common use in the author's laboratory. Excellent separations are obtained using a linear gradient of buffers that gradually increase in concentration and pH (Table

Table VI. Particulars of columns and eluents suitable for peptide fractionation

Column dimensions (cm)	Weight of digest (mg)	Volume applied (ml)	Volume of eluents (ml)	
			pH 3.1	pH 5.0
55 × 0.9	90	1	200	200
90 × 0.9	200	2	500	500

VII) this being achieved by employing two vessels of matching diameter connected together (Figure XII).

The most useful and universal method for the fractionation of tryptic digests (and it has been these digests more than any other that have been studied in this way) is the strongly acidic sulphonated polystyrene resin, Dowex 50, or its equivalent Bio-Rad Aminex 50W. The degree of cross-linkage (which is usually expressed as × 2 etc.) represents the porosity of the resin to molecules, and has been usually 2% (i.e. × 2); however, satisfactory results can be obtained using the higher cross-linked resins up to × 8 (which is the resin normally employed in amino acid analysis). Consideration as to the mesh size should be given as this determines not only the flow rate but the resolution obtained (a satisfactory one is the 200–400 mesh size).

Before any attempt is made to fractionate a complex peptide mixture, it is essential to do a preliminary analysis to estimate the total number of

Table VII. Volatile buffers for ion-exchange chromatography (Schroeder, 1972)

Pyridine concentration (M)	pH	Pyridine	Glacial acetic acid
		(ml/2000 ml)	
0.2	3.1	32.3	557
2	5.0	322.5	286.5

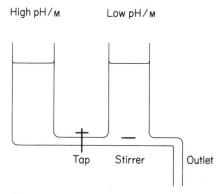

Figure XII Apparatus for linear
gradient elution

peptides in the digest. This is best achieved by peptide mapping, and as the peptides are eluted from the column they are checked off against the original composition of the mixture, so as to ensure that no peptides are lost. In particular, basic peptides may on occasions be irreversibly bound to the polystyrene resins, as was found by Ovchinnikov *et al.* (1977) who 'lost' two strongly basic peptides from a *S. aureus* protease digest of the α-subunit of RNA polymerase, when fractionated on the AG50 × 2 resin. This simple system of 'book-keeping' is an easy way of insuring against such a loss, that could have disastrous consequences when the protein sequence is reconstructed.

The resin to be used is packed into the water-jacketed column under gravity and equilibrated with starting buffer overnight. The tryptic digest is brought to pH 2 with 6 M HCl and any insoluble material removed by centrifugation. This material is known colloquially as the 'tryptic core' and must be preserved for subsequent examination. The clear supernatant is applied to the column under force of gravity and elution is commenced with the linear gradient from 0.2 M pyridine–acetate (pH 3.1) to 2 M pyridine–acetate (pH 5.0), the volumes employed depending on the column size. The temperature of elution is 40° and fractions of approximately 2 ml are collected every 20 min. Peptide material may be detected in the fractions after alkaline hydrolysis of a small portion and reaction with ninhydrin. Excellent results are almost always obtained: Figure XIII illustrates the separation of tryptic peptides from γ-crystallin fraction IV (Slingsby and Croft 1978). Peptides are readily recoverable from the main peptide peaks after removal of the volatile solvents by rotary evaporation and lyophilization. Occasionally some pyridine salts persist, with the result that streaking is observed on subsequent paper chromatography and the only recourse is to repeat the lyophilization process. Yields of about 70% recovery are normally obtained—not as high as from gel chromatography—however, the resolution obtained is far superior.

38

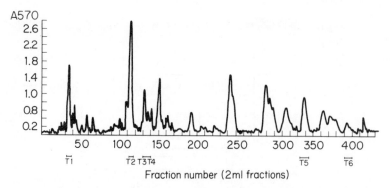

Figure XIII Fractionation of tryptic peptides from γ-crystallin on Bio–Rad Aminex 50 W × 2, column size 90 × 0.9 cm. Elution, at 40°C, was achieved with a gradient from 0.2 M pyridine/acetate buffer pH 3.1 to 2 M pyridine acetate buffer pH 5.0, 500 ml of each buffer being used. (Reproduced from Slingsby and Croft 1978)

Many workers have reported that occasionally the same peptide may be found in two separate parts of the resulting chromatogram. In some cases it is readily explained, if for example methionine was present in the peptide, the two forms probably represent different oxidation levels of the methionine sulphur. However, some instances are not so easily accounted for; thus Slingsby (1974) found the peptide

Ala–Val–Asp–Phe–Tyr

in two well-separated fractions during ion-exchange chromatography of a tryptic digest of γ-crystallin (fraction IV), and it can only be speculated that this peptide must exist in two distinct conformers that are resolved due to differ interactions with the polystyrene matrix. The presence of two adjacent aromatic residues could be a source of such conformational disparity.

The Use of Micro-Columns

One of the problems associated with polystyrene resins is that high losses of certain peptides may occasionally occur. In the main these are due to both ionic and non-ionic interactions, and may be reduced, although not altogether eliminated, by the use of micro-columns containing only a small quantity of ion-exchange resin. Such a novel column of dimensions 0.3 × 10 cm was used by Wittmann-Liebold and Marzinzig (1977) to resolve the tryptic peptides from the ribosomal protein L28, with Dowex M71 resin (equivalent to 50W × 7) and eluting with a pyridine–formate gradient at 55°C. An even smaller column (0.25 × 10 cm) was used by Chen (1977) to separate the tryptic peptides from 2 mg of the ribosomal protein S9. However, care must be taken when using these micro-columns that peptides are not lost by adherence to the glass surfaces, as was discovered by Chen et al. (1975) when a tryptic peptide of 14 amino acid residues was lost in this way from a tryptic digest of the ribosomal protein L27. The technique generally employed to detect peptides from these micro-columns is TLC. A small sample (40 μl) is removed from each fraction and spotted on a thin layer plate of cellulose and chromatography is performed in the solvent pyridine–n-butanol–acetic acid–water (50 : 75 : 15 : 60, v/v). The peptides are detected by staining with ninhydrin.

Other Ion-Exchange Media

Successful separations of peptides are not always achieved on polystyrene resins: Jackson *et al*. (1977) attempted to fractionate proteolytic digests of hen plasma low density lipoproteins on Dowex resins and after many unsuccessful attempts resorted to other methods of fractionation. A selection of useful alternative ion-exchange materials is given in Table VIII. In general the resolution obtained with these materials is inferior to that achieved with Dowex resins, but the loading capacity is greater (Chen 1977).

By a skilful combination of these various techniques the fractionation of the peptides of a tryptic digest is now readily achieved and this can be no better illustrated than by the work of Chen *et al*. (1975) on the structure of protein L27 which was successfully sequenced using a total of 24 mg of protein. Two tryptic digestions were performed, one on the citraconylated protein, a total of 10 mg of protein being used. The skilful way the peptides were fractionated is illustrated in Figure XIV.

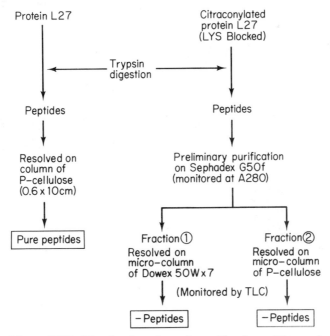

Figure XIV The fractionation of peptides from 10 mg of the ribosomal protein L27 by Chen *et al*. (1975)

Table VIII. Selected examples of the purification of peptides using different ion-exchange resins

Matrix	Type	Nature of protein digest	Elution	Method of detection	Reference
Polystyrene	Dowex 71 (Beckman resin M71 equivalent to Dowex 50W × 7)	Tryptic digest of ribosomal protein L28	Pyridine–formate gradient 0.1 M (pH 2.7)–1.0 M (pH 6.5) and 1.0 M (pH 6.5)–2.0 M (pH 6.5)	Not given	Wittmann-Liebold and Marzinzig (1977)
Cellulose	DEAE	Purification of selected tryptic peptides	Linear gradient 0.025 M–0.5 M NH_4HCO_3	Fluorescamine	Bhown et al. (1977)
	CM		Linear gradient 0.025 M–0.5 M ammonium acetate (pH 4.5)		
	Phospho-P11	Tryptic peptides from CNBr peptide of chick skin collagen	Linear salt gradient $0 \to 0.3$ M NaCl, in 0.04 M sodium acetate buffer (pH 3.8)	Absorption at 230 mμ	Dixit et al. (1977a,b)
Sephadex	DEAE–(A25)	Purification of tryptic peptides	Linear gradient 0.005–0.3 M NH_4HCO_3, pH 8.5	Not given	van Hoegaerden and Strosberg (1978)
	SP–	Separation of CNBr peptides	0.17 M pyridine acetate pH 4.7	Ninhydrin	Ferrell et al. (1978)

(3) PREPARATIVE PEPTIDE MAPPING

The purification of peptides by preparative peptide mapping is both rapid and sensitive. It is also an easy technique to master. In principle, the enzyme digest is subjected to a two-stage process involving a combination of electrophoresis and chromatography, one of these being performed in a direction at right angles to the other. It may be carried out on sheets of chromatography paper, or on thin layers. The former has been widely used in the past, but due to the increased demand for greater sensitivity, thin layer peptide mapping is now in vogue. This extremely simple two-step procedure, that can readily be performed within a 24-hour period, may resolve most of the components of an enzymic digest of a protein. However, to isolate the individual peptides they must be adequately detected, without loss of their chemical integrity, and this demands a mild and simple reagent. Ninhydrin has commonly been used for this purpose, but the new reagent fluorescamine is now considered to be preferable.

Peptide Mapping Using Paper Chromatography

Of the two chromatographic media available, paper is probably the easier to handle and is considerably cheaper than thin layers. Furthermore, advantage may be taken of the many grades of paper available (Table IX). No. 20 paper has been found to result in excellent peptide maps in the author's laboratory (Figure XV), and it is surprising that this paper has not found much use in other laboratories.

For the electrophoretic separation, either high voltage or low voltage may be used. The author has found that the latter results in superior separations, albeit taking longer to perform. Furthermore, high-voltage electrophoresis requires access to expensive equipment. Chromatography, which is usually performed following the electrophoretic separation, is normally carried out

Table IX. Comparison of different qualities of chromatography paper useful for preparative peptide mapping

Grade	Loading capacity (mg)	Resolution	General comments
3MM	5–8	Not very good	Solvent flow is fast in chromatography direction; easy to handle.
No. 1	<1	Better than 3MM	Difficult to handle
No. 20	<2	Excellent resolution	Solvent flow is slow in chromatography direction; easy to handle.

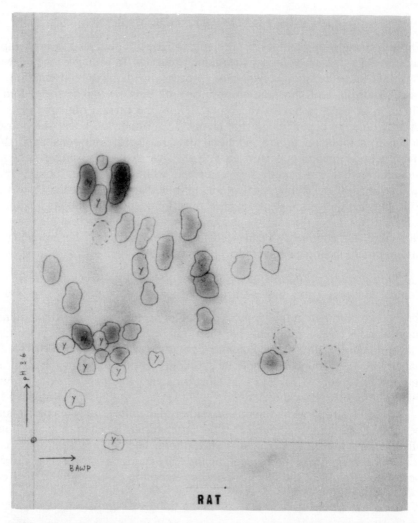

Figure XV Peptide map of a tryptic digest of rat γ-crystallin on Whatman
No. 20 paper. Electrophoresis was performed first at pH 3.6, followed by
chromatography at right angles in the solvent BAWP

in the descending mode. The actual practical aspects of these techniques are
beyond the scope of this review, and the reader is asked to refer to the many
excellent texts available in this field. However a selection of several of the
more useful electrophoresis buffers and chromatographic solvents are
included for completeness (Table X).

Improved peptide separations may be obtained if the chromatography
step is repeated (Hoerman and Kamel 1967).

Table X. Some useful buffers and solvents for peptide mapping on paper

Application	Components (v/v)	pH	Reference
Electrophoresis	pyridine : acetic acid : water; (25 : 1 : 474)	6.5	⎫
	pyridine : acetic acid : water; (1 : 10 : 989)	3.6	⎬ Sargent (1965)
	formic acid : acetic acid : water; (52 : 29 : 919)	1.9	⎭
	pyridine : acetic acid : water; (1 : 10 : 289)	3.5	Kondo et al. (1978)
	pyridine : acetic acid : water; (25 : 1 : 225)	6.5	Walker et al. (1977)
	pyridine : acetic acid : water; (3 : 20 : 780)	3.7	Closset et al. (1978)
Chromatography	butan-1-ol : pyridine : acetic acid : water; (15 : 10 : 3 : 12)		Waley and Watson (1953)
	butan-1-ol : acetic acid : water; (4 : 1 : 5) (upper phase only; lower in bottom of tank)		Evenberg et al. (1977)
	pyridine : isoamyl alcohol : 0.1N NH$_4$OH; (6 : 3 : 5)		Tanaka et al. (1977)
	butan-1-ol : pyridine : acetic acid : water; (15 : 10 : 1 : 12)		Walker et al. (1977)

Peptide Mapping Using Thin Layer Chromatography

The use of thin layers for peptide mapping offers the considerable advantages of increased speed and sensitivity. Thin layer plates are also more compact and easier to handle, requiring less bulky equipment. However, they are costly to purchase.

Suitable thin layers of approximately 0.1 mm in thickness may be of silica, polyamide, or cellulose. The latter are the most useful and are available commercially, on plastic, or aluminium foil backings. Chen *et al*. (1975) have recommended that before use the layers should be purified by elution with 5% pyridine, followed by 1.5% formic acid. Again, electrophoresis may be either at high voltage or low voltage, with chromatography, which is usually performed overnight, in the ascending mode. Typical buffers and solvents are shown in Table XI.

The usual load on thin layers is considerably less than on papers, a typical amount being about 0.2 mg. Usually more material is available and it is generally the procedure to run a number of plates simultaneously.

Table XI. Useful buffers and solvents for peptide mapping on thin layers of cellulose

Application	Components (v/v)	Reference
Electrophoresis	pyridine : acetic acid : acetone : water; (1 : 2 : 8 : 40) (pH 4.4)	Chen (1977)
Chromatography	butan-1-ol : pyridine : acetic acid : water; (15 : 10 : 3 : 12)	Chen *et al*. (1975)
	butan-1-ol : pyridine : acetic acid : water; (75 : 50 : 16 : 15)	Chen (1977)

Detection and Elution of Peptides from Paper and Thin Layer Chromatograms

The detection of peptides on maps may be accomplished either by dipping, or spraying, with an appropriate reagent, or by autoradiography, this latter technique being particularly suitable in micro-sequencing.

In the past, a dilute solution of ninhydrin (2 mg/ml in acetone) has been widely used to detect peptides; however, for preparative purposes, it has the drawback that there is considerable destruction of the N-terminal residue. Fluorescamine (shown here) is probably the best reagent at present available to detect peptides, which when employed at the appropriate concentration leads to no loss of the amino-terminal residue. This reagent, which is non-fluorescent, reacts at alkaline pH with amino groups to form a highly fluorescent product. In a typical example Fleer *et al*. (1978) used this reagent to detect the peptides on finger-prints of the protein phospholipase A_2. The paper was first sprayed with 10% (v/v) pyridine in acetone, followed by a solution of 2 mg of fluorescamine in 100 ml 1% (v/v) pyridine in acetone. After drying, the peptides appeared as fluorescent spots, which were cut out and eluted. Vandekerckhove and van Montagu (1974) estimate that this reagent is capable of detecting as little as 0.01 nmol of a peptide. It is also capable of locating peptides having N-terminal isoleucine, which are not always detectable with ninhydrin: however, it does not detect peptides having N-terminal proline residues, unless lysine is present in the peptide.

After detection the peptides may be eluted with any, or a combination of the solvents in Table XII. Beyreuther *et al.* (1975) recommend that this elution be performed at 4°C, so as to avoid any possible deamidation of the peptide.

Table XII. Useful solvents for the elution of peptides from peptide maps

Solvent	Reference
50% acetic acid	Chen (1977)
50% formic acid	Vandekerckhove and van Montagu (1974)
50% pyridine	Evenberg *et al.* (1977)
1% NH_4HCO_3 (pH 9.0)	Evenberg *et al.* (1977);
0.1 M NH_3	van Den Berg *et al.* (1977)
1 M acetic acid	Beyreuther *et al.* (1975)
electrophoresis buffer	van Hoegaerden and Strosberg (1978)

No exact formulation for the successful elution of a peptide can be given, for it depends to a great extent on the properties of the peptide that is to be eluted. Some investigators, for example Fleer *et al.* (1978), to ensure successful elution of the peptide, employ a succession of three solvents. Most peptides would be eluted under these conditions, but there is always the odd hydrophobic peptide that evades all elution attempts. These difficult peptides are not always large, for example the pentapeptide

Ala–Ile–Asp–Leu–Tyr

was found to resist all the usual elution solvents, presumably as a consequence of its hydrophobic character; it was eventually successfully eluted by the imaginative application of the chromatographic solvent (Slingsby 1974).

CHAPTER 4

The Sequenator

The sequenator is the product of the scientific genius of Pehr Edman (1916–1977). In 1950 he published his paper, which now must rank as one of the most important of recent times: *'A Method for the Determination of the Amino Acid Sequence in Peptides'* (Edman 1950). For the remainder of his life Edman was committed to the development of his concept of a fully automatic machine for the sequential degradation of proteins. This vision culminated in the publication, in the first issue of the *European Journal of Biochemistry*, of his article describing such an instrument, to which he gave the name 'sequenator' (Edman and Begg 1967) (see Figure XVI). The

Figure XVI Photograph of the original sequenator. (Reproduced from Edman and Begg (1967) by permission of *European Journal of Biochemistry*)

Table XIII. Some of the results obtained using commercial sequencers (excluding the Beckman Sequencer)

Sequencer model	Manufacturer	No. of residues sequenced	Protein/peptide, and the approximate weight used (if given)	Reference
JEOL JAS 47K	JEOLCO (Japan)	40	Ferredoxin (4 mg)	Hase et al. (1976)
		Not given	Cardiotoxin of Bungarus fasciatus venom	Lu and Lo (1978)
SOCOSI P110	SOCOSI (France)	16	Horse MSEL- neurophysin	Chauvet et al. (1977)
		45	Whale MSEL-neurophysin	Chauvet et al. (1978)
SOCOSI PS100	SOCOSI (France)	26	Toxin III from Anemonia sulcata (1 mg)	Martinez et al. (1977)
		46	Neurotoxin I of the snake Naja mossambica mossambica (2 mg)	Gregoire and Rochat (1977)
Illitron	Illinois Tool Works, Chicago (USA)	36	Soyabean leghaemoglobin C_2	Hurrell and Leach (1977)
			κ-chain of mouse myeloma	Smith (1978)
		40	Bence Jones protein Dil (5 mg)	Smithies et al. (1971)

Table XIV. Some results obtained using the Beckman Sequencer

Protein/Peptide	No. of residues sequenced	Approximate amount used (mg)	Average repetitive yield (%)	Reference
C-Phycocyanin (β-)	100	5	Not given	Frank et al. (1978)
C-Phycocyanin (α-)	85	5	Not given	Frank et al. (1978)
Thrombin (β-chain)	70	Not given	98	Butkowski et al. (1977)
β-Thromboglobulin	69	3	97	Begg et al. (1978)
Dihydrofolate reductase	60	7	Not given	Stone et al. (1977)
Dihydrofolate reductase	56	8	96	Bennett et al. (1978)
lac Repressor	54	4	96	Beyreuther et al. (1975)
Azotoflavin	53	6	95.4	Tanaka et al. (1977)
Phospholipase A_2 (peptide)	48	6	Not given	Evenberg et al. (1977)
Histone $H_2B_{(1)}$	47	7	Not given	Strickland et al. (1977)
Collagen peptide	45	9	95	Butler et al. (1977)
Phospholipase A_2	41	7	Not given	Evenberg et al. (1977)
Bungarotoxin	39	2	96.6	Kondo et al. (1978)
Flagellin	39	Not given	97	DeLange et al. (1976)
Uteroglobin	36	5	98	Ponstingl et al. (1978)
Rabbit antibody L-chain	35	Not given	95–98	van Hoegaerden and Strosberg (1978)
Histone H_2B	34	10	95	Kootstra and Bailey (1978)
Pea lectin (α-subunit)	30	6	93	Richardson et al. (1978)
Prethrombin	29	Not given	98	Butkowski et al. (1977)
Ribosomal protein L19	28	1	Not given	Brosius and Arfsten (1978)
Biotin carrier protein	24	1	Not given	Sutton et al. (1977)

machine is now commercially available and is in use in almost all protein chemistry laboratories throughout the world. The story of Edman's dedication and vision is a fascinating one and has recently been portrayed by one of his close associates (Niall 1977).

Table XIII gives several illustrative instances of the application of commercial sequencers to particular proteins, excluding the most widely used machine, the Beckman 890C sequencer, selected examples from which, taken from the recent literature, are contained in Table XIV. The basic design of all these machines is very similar: they are referred to as 'liquid-phase', or, 'spinning-cup' sequencers to distinguish them from the other available sequencer, the solid-phase modification. As the name 'spinning-cup' implies, these machines are constructed around a central rotating glass cup in which the protein is evenly spread around the walls by the centrifugal force of rotation. The principle is that the thin film of protein so induced provides a large surface area for reactions to occur in high yield—an essential criterion for success in any controlled, repetitive chemical degradation. A simple calculation indicates that the film formed is about 100 molecules thick, and it is this thin molecular layer that facilitates the reaction to occur in high yield.

It can reasonably be assumed that a sequence determination ceases to provide useful information when the over-all yield has fallen to 30%, as at this level the amino acid phenylthiohydantoins cannot be identified against the background, which is partially due to non-specific cleavages of the peptide chain and to incomplete reaction at each step. An indication of this latter factor is conveyed by the term the 'repetitive yield' which theoretically should be 100%, but never attains this in practice. The number of steps possible for any given repetitive yield can readily be calculated. Table XV illustrates the number of steps possible for repetitive yields of 99%, 95% and 90%.

Thus it would appear from this table that with a repetitive yield of 99% at least 100 residues could be sequenced, whereas with a yield of 90% this is drastically reduced to little more than 10 steps. Edman originally reported a repetitive yield of slightly greater than 98% and subsequent workers have little improved on this, although as can be seen from Table *XIV* Frank *et al.*

Table XV. Percentage over-all yield after *n* steps in the sequential degradation of a protein assuming different repetitive yields

	Repetitive yield		
n	99%	95%	90%
10	90	60	35
50	60	8	0.5
100	36	0.6	0.003

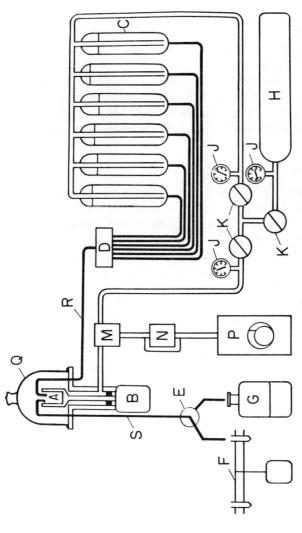

Figure XVII Design of the original sequenator. (A, spinning cup; B, motor; C, reservoirs; D, M, and N valves; E, outlet; F, fraction collector; P, pump; Q, bell jar) (Reproduced from Edman and Begg (1967), by permission of *European Journal of Biochemistry*)

(1978) must have achieved yields of 99% to accomplish a sequence of 100 residues using the Beckman 890C sequencer, but few other workers have attained this degree of success. On average, using the Beckman instrument, most operators obtain a repetitive yield of about 96% and sequence in the order of 40 residues.

INSTRUMENTATION

The general design of the sequenator of Edman and Begg is shown in Figure XVII. This instrument is only designed for the coupling and cleavage reactions of the Edman degradation. The conversion reaction, that is the transformation of the unstable 2-anilino-5-thiazolinone derivatives to the isomeric and more stable 3-phenyl-2-thiohydantoins is performed manually outside the machine. A recent modification, however, has been the addition of an automated conversion device (Wittmann-Liebold 1973).

Materials Used in its Construction

The corrosive nature of the reagents employed in the Edman degrada-tion has severely limited the range of materials useful in the construction of a sequenator (see Figure XVIII). Only borosilicate glass, PTFE (polytetrafluoroethylene). Kel-F (polytrifluorochloroethylene) and gold are used in direct contact with the reagents. Where contact is only with the reagent vapours the finest grade of stainless steel can be used. As the

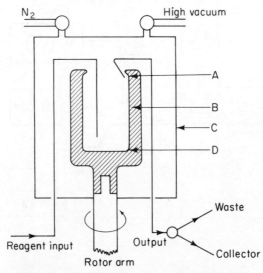

Figure XVIII   Simplified view of the reaction cup of the sequenator. A, undercut; B, precision-made glass spinning cup; C, sealed and thermostatically maintained reaction chamber; D, rounded corners

phenylthiocarbamyl group can easily be desulphurized by oxygen, bringing the degradation to an abrupt halt, the reaction is performed in an inert atmosphere, hence the surface area within the reaction cell of the synthetic polymers PTFE, Kel-F etc., and of the delivery system is kept to a minimum as these materials are slightly permeable to oxygen.

The highly inflammable nature of some of the reagents has also meant that all sparking electrical contacts must be excluded, or hermetically sealed: failure to observe these warnings, originally made by Edman, led to disastrous consequences for some of the early versions of the machine.

DESIGN FEATURES

Delivery System

In the original design the delivery system was based on a positive pressure of nitrogen—the reagents being pressurized from a nitrogen cylinder with the

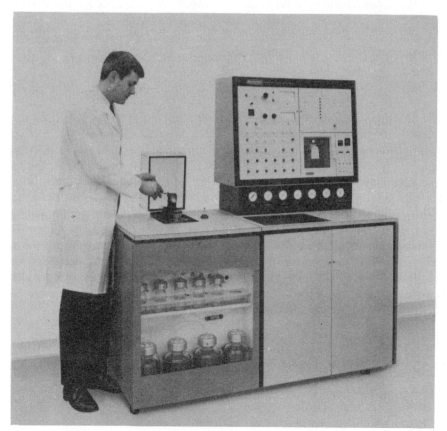

Figure XIX   The Beckman Sequencer 890C. (By courtesy of Beckman Instruments Inc.)

reaction cell kept at a lower pressure. This differential pressure is maintained, thus controlling the volume of reagent or solvent admitted to the cup by the time the appropriate valve is kept open. This principle is also employed in the Beckman sequencer, whereas the JEOL machine uses pumps. The reagents are kept in individual reservoirs each having four connections, one for the nitrogen supply, another for the exit of the chemical, a third for a gas vent and the fourth for refilling. The outlet lines from the reagent and solvent reservoir go to a delivery valve, of which there are four, one for each reagent–solvent pair. Each double port valve and delivery line may be used to deliver a solvent and a reagent, e.g. phenylisothiocynate and benzene; Quadrol and ethylacetate; heptafluorobutyric acid and butyl chloride. In this way the solvent washes out the reagent, thus ensuring that no lines become blocked, and as there is no general manifold there is virtually no chance of cross-contamination. All plastic delivery lines are kept as short as possible to minimize oxygen diffusion. In the Beckman machine there is a 'space reducer' (cf Figure XIX) that dips (on a hinged joint) into the reaction cup. This core through which the four reagent–solvent delivery lines are fed, reduces the vapour space in the reaction cup, thus reducing the loss of volatile solvents used in the reaction. It also holds the line through which reagents, solvents and the thiazoline amino acids are removed.

The Reaction Cup

The reaction cup is a precision-made Pyrex-glass container which in the original design had the dimensions 26 mm internal diameter and 31 mm high, however this has subsequently been enlarged to 51 mm internal diameter by 60 mm high (Begg et al. 1978). Attempts have been made to construct cups of PTFE, or other plastics, which have so far only been partially successful, for they have the disadvantage of difficulty in cleaning, and prevent the operator from having a clear view of the reactions taking place inside. The cup is carefully constructed so that the corners are gently rounded to facilitate cleaning. The surface is highly polished and there is a millimetre scale inscribed on the wall to assist calibration. Near the top of the vessel there is an undercut to assist in the scooping operation and to make the accuracy of the delivery of reagents and solvents less critical, as the film height is maintained constant throughout the various cycles.

The cup can be driven by a magnetic drive system as in the Beckman machine, or it might be mounted directly on the end of the motor shaft. In the Edman–Begg machine only one speed was possible (1400 rpm) whereas the Beckman instrument has a variable speed (1200 rpm and 1800 rpm); this has the advantage that as the cup spins faster the level of liquid rises higher. Thus the protein is introduced when the cup is spinning at 1200 rpm and the reagents at the higher speed, which ensures complete coverage of the protein film. The higher speeds are also useful in peptide degradations as the thinner solvent layer formed reduces the losses of slightly soluble peptides. Recently a larger cup, working at a faster speed (3000 rpm) has been introduced (Begg *et al.* 1978).

It is recommended that approximately every 3 months the cup is cleaned in *aqua regia* followed by repolishing the cup surface with cerium oxide.

Drive Mechanism

In the original design the cup was mounted directly on an extended stainless steel motor shaft. However, as it was subsequently found that the seals around where the shaft entered the reaction chamber developed leaks and required regular maintenance, later models of the sequencer employed a magnetic drive assembly. The use of volatile buffers in the sequencing of peptides tends to cause an accumulation of gummy deposits around the drive area and this may cause it to seize up.

Heating System

Two types of heating system have been employed. In the Edman–Begg design the bell jar and the reaction cup were both heated by means of a transparent metallic electroconductive heating layer on the glass surface, whereas in the Beckman machine the glass reaction chamber containing the reaction cup is completely enclosed within a second outer Perspex enclosure, the temperature of which is maintained by circulating hot air from a heater. In some recent models the cap of the reaction cup is heated to a slightly higher temperature than the cup itself, so reducing condensation.

Fraction Collector

The thiazolinones are collected in a refrigerated fraction collector maintained at about $2°C$, and in the Beckman machine the contents of the tubes can be taken to dryness by a jet of nitrogen and the compartment automatically evacuated to remove the resulting toxic and inflammable vapours.

REAGENTS AND SOLVENTS

Much emphasis has been laid on the purity of the reagents and solvents. It is vital to remove all traces of aldehydes that might block the sequential degradation by reacting with the terminal amino group. A summary of the purification steps, recommended by Edman and Begg, for the essential reagents and solvents is given in Table XVI. Batches of chemicals that have been pretested on the sequencer may be purchased from several manufacturers. These reagents are extremely expensive and may amount to approximately 10% of the purchase price of the machine per annum.

56

Table XVI. Recommended purification and storage procedures for reagents and solvents used in liquid phase sequencing

Reagent/Solvent	Purification	Storage
PITC (phenyl isothiocyanate)	Distillation *in vacuo* (1 mm Hg pressure); the fraction distilling at 55° is collected.	In general it is unstable on storage, therefore best to distil as required. It may be stored however, out of direct light, in an evacuated desiccator over P_2O_5.
'Quadrol' (N,N,N',N'tetrakis-2-hydroxypropyl-ethylene diamine)	Purified by passing through a column of amberlite IRA-500 (sulphite) followed by distillation at 120° (10^{-3} mm Hg).	The Quadrol-trifluoroacetic acid salt may be stored for up to a year in amber bottles in a freezer.
n-HFBA (n-heptafluorobutyric acid) TFA (trifluoroacetic acid)	First they are exhaustively oxidized with CrO_3 and then distilled and dried over anhydrous $CaSO_4$. Redistillation is then performed.	Stored in amber bottles in a cold room for up to 6 months. The H_2O content is maintained at 0.01% by careful addition of trifluoroacetic anhydride (Begg *et al.* 1978).
Benzene	Analytical grade is further purified by fractional freezing followed by a distillation (b.pt. 80–81°).	Stored in amber bottles in cold room for up to 6 months.
Butyl chloride (1-chlorobutane)	Purified by passage through a column of activated granular charcoal followed by distillation (b.pt. 78°).	Stored in amber bottles in cold room for up to 6 months.
Ethyl acetate	Passed through a column of activated Al_2O_3, redistilled and dried on a molecular sieve (Type 4A, Union Carbide).	Stored under nitrogen (<10 ppm of O_2) in amber bottles in cold room for up to 6 months.
Heptane	Treated overnight with an aqueous solution of $KMnO_4$, washed with H_2O, then dried over Na_2SO_4 and distilled.	Stored in cold room in amber bottles for up to 6 months.

PROCEDURES

The sequence analysis of large proteins and smaller peptides requires different tactics. Proteins are sequenced in non-volatile buffers and reagents, whereas peptides require volatile reagents. Each of the approaches will now be considered in detail.

(1) The Automatic Degradation of Proteins

Sample Preparation

The freeze-dried protein sample must be salt-free and may be in its native state, however, better results are obtained if it is completely denatured either by performic acid oxidation, or following reduction and alkylation of the cysteine residues. It is best if the protein is soluble in the reagents used, though successful sequences have been obtained on proteins insoluble in the reagents.

Programmes

There are two possible programmes that can be used when sequencing proteins: the single cleavage and the double cleavage programme. Essentially, the double cleavage programme, which was used successfully by Kondo *et al.* (1978) in their study of the sequence of the A and B chains of β-bungarotoxin, puts the protein through the acid cleavage reaction twice. This ensures complete removal of the N-terminal residue, but only one extraction with butyl chloride is collected as there is insufficient material in the second extraction to justify its collection, so this is diverted to waste. An outline of the seven steps in the double cleavage programme is contained in Figure XX.

Reagent Modifications

(i) THEED NNN′N′ Tetrakis (2-hydroxyethyl)ethylene diamine (THEED) has been used in place of Quadrol in the coupling reaction (Begg and Morgan 1976). It has the advantage that it may readily be prepared free of contaminating aldehydes that tend to reduce the repetitive yield when Quadrol buffers are employed, for example regular repetitive yields of 98% are obtained in contrast to the 94% when quadrol buffers are used. However there are problems associated with the use of THEED; impurities present in it may be extracted by the chlorobutane into the thiazolinone fraction and these interfere with the TLC identification of the PTH-amino acids. It is therefore suggested that when this buffer is employed, back hydrolysis of the PTH be used for the identification of the amino acid residue.

The preparation of THEED starting from ethylenediamine and ethylene oxide has been described (Begg *et al.* 1978).

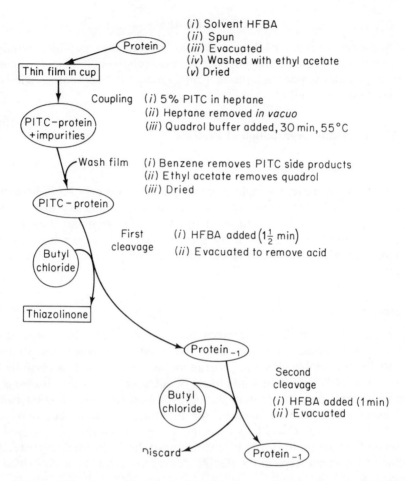

Figure XX   An outline of the 'double cleavage' programme in liquid
phase sequencing

(ii) Pentafluoropropionic Acid   Inglis and Burley (1977) in their study of
the sequence of Apovitellenin I from duck eggs found that heptafluorobutyric acid was not readily removed after the cleavage reaction
and consequently the residual acid caused a loss of hydrophobic peptides
during thiazolinone extraction. This problem was overcome by using the
more volatile pentafluoropropionic acid for cleavage and the mixture 1,2
dichloroethane–benzene (3 : 1) to extract the thiazolinone.

Programme Modifications

(i) Preconditioning   Kootstra and Bailey (1978) found that improved
yields could be obtained if the protein film in the spinning cup was subjected

to one complete degradation cycle in the absence of PITC to precondition the protein film.

(ii) Cleavage of Prolyl Residues   Where prolyl residues are known to occur from preliminary experiments the cleavage time is extended threefold to avoid incomplete cleavage (Begg *et al.* 1978).

(iii) Addition of PITC before the Coupling Buffer Thomsen *et al.* (1976) report that non-specific cleavage can be reduced if the usual order of addition of PITC and coupling buffer is reversed. They claim that these cleavages are due to acid-catalysed $N \rightarrow O$ acyl shifts involving seryl hydroxyl groups.

(iv) The Repetitive Yield and Length of Run   The repetitive yield obtained by Edman and Begg was slightly greater than 98% and allowed 60 residues of apomyoglobin to be determined. This performance has rarely been equalled by the many commercial instruments available (Table XIII). The reasons for this must be a combination of operator inefficiency and the use of inferior quality reagents.

That some of the commercial machines are capable of a greater efficiency has been shown by Frank *et al.* (1978), who sequenced 100 residues of a protein with the Beckman 890C sequencer. The repetitive yield in this case must have been almost 99%. Most operators, however, achieve yields of about 95% that make possible a run of about 40 residues; a typical example is shown in Figure XXI.

Sometimes even these sort of yields are not achieved, resulting in a gradual carry-over of amino acids that increase during the run, for example in the sequence determination of S-pyridylethyl (insulin-like) Growth Factor (Rinderknecht and Humbel 1978) the carry over was 14% at step 3 rising to 72% at step 25; however, this amount of carry-over did not prevent

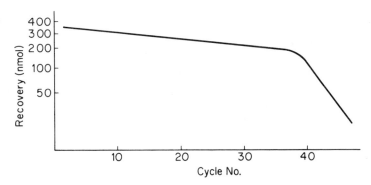

Figure XXI Automated Edman degradation of rabbit uteroglobin, showing the gradual decline in yield. (Adapted from Ponstingl *et al.* 1978)

identification up to residue 31. Nevertheless, better results ought to be possible, and in those few cases where the protein presents particular problems, duplication of the sequence run is essential ('Documentation of Results in The Determination of the Covalent Structure of Proteins'. *J. Biol. Chem.* (1976) **251**, 11–12).

(2) The Automatic Degradation of Peptides

The procedures used for the automatic sequence analysis of proteins cannot be applied to peptides. Peptides, particularly when they are hydrophobic in nature, tend to be lost in the extraction into the organic solvents. Several attempts have been made to modify the procedures to avoid these losses. Two factors must be taken into account: first, as a peptide is smaller than a protein there are therefore fewer non-specific cleavage points which results in a clearer background than that found for proteins; secondly, as there will be fewer polar groups present than in a protein, and taking into account its smaller size, the peptide will be lost to a greater extent during the extraction process into the organic solvent, than for a protein. The programme employed therefore should reduce the amount of solvent washes and, in the main, should involve only a single cleavage. It has been found that most of the losses occur during the extraction with butyl chloride following the acid cleavage, and to a lesser extent during the extraction with ethyl acetate. The peptides most likely to be lost by this 'washing out' will be those hydrophobic ones and those having several lysine residues, the ε-amino groups of which react with the PITC to form phenyl thiocarbamoyl derivatives, so becoming more soluble in the organic solvent. The following attempts have been made to prevent this 'washing out'.

(1) The Use of Volatile Buffers

The replacement of quadrol by a volatile buffer would remove the necessity of an ethyl acetate wash. Two such buffers have been used: NN-dimethylbenzylamine (DMBA) and NN-dimethylalkylamine (DMAA). Of these the DMAA buffer is the more volatile and causes problems in the coupling, as it tends to evaporate, leading to a reduction in the pH of the reaction medium. Deposits have also been found to form around the drive mechanism, which necessitates frequent cleaning of this area, and the oil in the vacuum pump requires frequent replacement when this buffer is used: however, it has been successfully used in a number of investigations. Macleod *et al.* (1977), in their study of trout-testis histone H1, employed DMAA buffer and found that improved repetitive yields could be obtained; Stone *et al.* (1977) also used this buffer for the sequencing of peptides from dihydrofolate reductase. The less volatile DMBA has also found considerable application, amongst others, in studies of the peptides from the neurotoxins of the African cobra (Gregoire and Rochat 1977): this work was achieved with a SOCOSI sequencer. Rochat *et al.* (1976) found that DMBA enabled as little as 20 nmol of a pentapeptide to be completely sequenced.

(2) Modification of Lysine Residues

(i) Reaction with 4-sulpho-phenylisothiocyanate converts the ε-amino group of lysine to a sulphophenylthiocarbamoyl derivative imparting

improved hydrophobicity to the peptide chain. With this modification it is possible to obtain high degradation yields using the regular PITC-quadrol buffer; this was the technique used by Mak and Jones (1976) in their study of wheat β-purothionin, and Stone *et al.* (1977) in studies on dihydrofolate reductase. Strickland *et al.* (1977) found that if peptides are 'anchored' into the cup by reacting the ε-amino groups with 4-sulpho-phenylisothiocyanate, yields of up to 90.3% were obtained making it possible to sequence up to 37 residues of a cyanogen bromide peptide isolated from the histone $H_2B_{(1)}$ from sea urchin sperm. van den Berg *et al.* (1976) used this reagent to sequence peptides from coypu RNase; the peptides after modification were desalted on a column of Sephadex G15 and then sequenced in a JEOL sequencer using the 'S4 programme' in which 10% of the residual peptide is withdrawn from the cup and the N-terminal identified by dansylation.

Dwulet and Gurd (1976) have recommended the use of the *meta*-isomer of SPITC viz. 3-sulpho-phenylisothiocyanate, which has several advantages over the 4-isomer, including a greater coupling efficiency, the repetitive yield increasing by 2–3%, and the fact that the sequencing product, namely ε(3-SPTC)-PTH-lysine can be converted to free lysine after back-hydrolysis more readily than from the derivative of 4-SPITC.

(ii) Braunitzer Reagents Braunitzer and co-workers have introduced a number of improved derivatives to modify the ε-amino groups of lysyl residues (as shown in the structures) (Braunitzer *et al.* 1971, 1973).

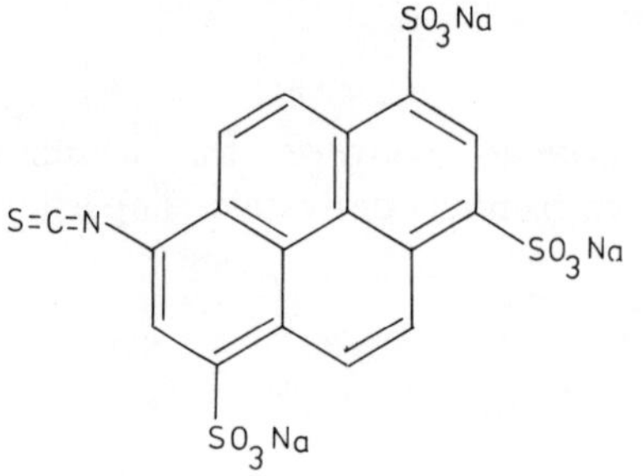

(i)

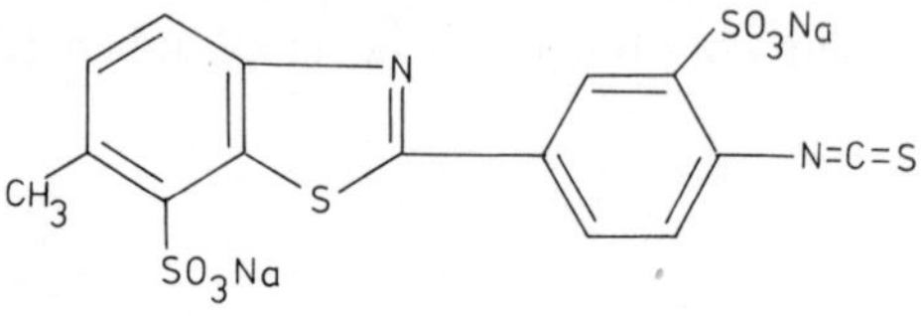

(ii)

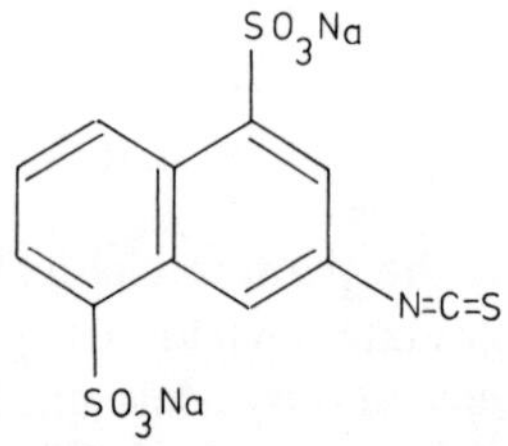

(iii)

Reagent (iii) permits high degradation yields with the normal quadrol buffer system, and the peptides derivatized have excellent film-forming characteristics that are important in automated sequencing.

(3) Modification of Acidic Peptides

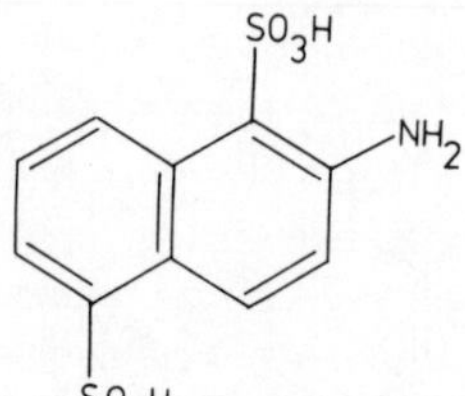

Acidic or neutral peptides lacking lysyl residues can be modified by reaction of the carboxyl groups with the reagent 2-amino-naphthalene 1,5-disulphonic acid. This renders the peptide more hydrophilic and less likely to be lost during extraction into the organic solvents during the sequencing. This reagent is coupled to the peptide by using a water-soluble carbodiimide (Foster *et al.* 1973), the most usual being N-ethyl, N′-(3-dimethyl aminopropyl) carbodiimide (Dixit *et al.* 1977a,b). (Care

$$CH_3CH_2-N=C=N-CH_2CH_2CH_2N\begin{smallmatrix}CH_3\\ \\CH_3\end{smallmatrix}$$

must be taken when handling these reagents, in particular they must not be allowed to come into contact with the skin or eyes). As with the SPITC reagents the modified amino acid residues cannot be identified as PTH derivatives during the automatic sequencing and therefore have to be identified by back hydrolysis.

(4) Modification of Cysteine-containing Peptides

Peptides containing cysteine residues may be modified by reaction with the sodium salt of 2-bromoethane sulphonic acid prior to sequencing; however, as cysteine is not a very common amino acid residue in proteins it is not as useful as other available methods (Niketic *et al.* 1974). Alternatively, cysteine may be converted to the polar cysteic acid after performic acid oxidation, but this has the disadvantage of destroying any tryptophan residues that might be present.

Modified Programmes for Use with Peptides

Hogg and Hermodson (1977) introduced a slightly modified 'peptide programme' that enabled the sequence of peptides to be determined to within several residues of the C-terminus. In principle this involved the introduction of steps designed to precipitate the peptide with the organic solvents. For example, benzene was allowed to fill the reaction cup and remain in it for an interval of 20 s, so as to complete the precipitation, and this was subsequently followed by a precipitation step with chlorobutane. Similar tactics were employed by O'Donnell and Inglis (1974) in their study of feather keratin, that enabled them to sequence 53 residues of a large peptide. They also found it advantageous to employ a prolonged drying period following the cleavage with acid; this was found to reduce the 'washing-out' of the peptide during the extraction of the thiazolinone.

An alternative strategy was used by Tanaka *et al.* (1975) in their study of *Spinulina maxima* ferredoxin. In this investigation, the repetitive yield by step 29 had so dramatically dropped that they imaginatively withdrew the peptide from the cup and performed a further 18 additional steps manually. This was the first time this had been done. Furthermore subsequent workers have combined the conventional dansyl method, and the automatic Edman procedure by taking 10% of the peptide material from the cup at each stage for N-terminal analysis. (van Den Berg *et al.*

1977). It would appear therefore that in the future automated and manual methods might be complementary to each other.

THE USE OF CARRIERS

The amount of peptide needed to form a stable film in the cup is between 1 and 2 mg. Thus for a peptide of 50 residues, about 200 nmol is required, and as it is essential to repeat the sequencing at least once then a total of about 400 nmol is needed, i.e. about 2 mg.

For smaller peptides this amount is far in excess of that needed for manual determination, so to overcome this problem the use of an inert 'carrier' has been introduced. The ideal properties of a carrier should be:

(1) stability, during the sequential degradation;
(2) polarity, so as to reduce loss during the solvent wash;
(3) ability to form a stable thin film that is both firm and even.

The two types of carrier that have so far been used are either synthetic polymers, or small proteins with blocked amino termini. Of this latter type, the French group at Marseille have employed hake parvalbumin in their SOCOSI sequencer with considerable success. Martinez *et al.* (1977) have sequenced up to residue 26 of a polypeptide toxin in the presence of 2 mg of parvalbumin. This technique made it possible to sequence as little as 20 nmol of peptide, thus enhancing the sensitivity of the automated method (Rochat *et al.* 1976).

The Use of Synthetic Polymers

(1) Polybrene

'Polybrene' is the trade name for the polymer 1,5-dimethyl-1,5-diazaundecamethylene polymethobromide. When as little as 3 mg of this polymer is added directly to the peptide solution it has been found to effectively retain small peptides in the spinning cup (Tarr *et al.* 1978). This has the advantage that no chemical modification of the peptide is necessary and enables a high repetitive yield to be obtained. Using this innovation Frank *et al.* (1978), were able to sequence small peptides right up to the C-terminal residue, in their study of the structure of C-Phycocyanin.

(2) Succinylated Poly-ornithine

The successful use of succinylated poly-L-ornithine as a 'carrier' in the automatic sequencer has been described (Silver and Hood 1974). The addition of this synthetic material to the peptide reduces the 'washing-out' of the peptide material and assists in the holding of small amounts of hydrophobic peptides in the cup. Inglis and Burley (1977), in their study of the sequence of egg apovitellenin, added 5 mg of this carrier to 500 nmol of a CNBr peptide and it enabled them to completely determine its sequence.

(3) (Norleu–Arg)$_{27}$

Niall et al. (1974) have suggested the use of the synthetic polymer (Norleu–Arg)$_{27}$ as a carrier. Using this substance, a linear rather than an exponential decrease in the yield was found with myoglobin as a trial protein. One problem, however, was the release of arginine from the carrier, which caused confusion when arginine was present in the sequential degradation. Attempts have been made to produce a carrier based on homoarginine.

(4) Chemically Modified Lysozyme

Frank et al (1978) have added a modified lysozyme (lysozyme reacted with sulphobenzoic acid anhydride to block its N-terminus) to approximately 300 nmol of peptide derived from C-Phycocyanin. It was found to successfully hold the peptide in the spinning cup during the sequential degradation.

CHAPTER 5

The Solid-phase Sequencer

The solid-phase sequencer was designed primarily for the automatic sequencing of peptides containing approximately 30 amino acids or less, i.e. those that would tend to be 'washed-out' in the spinning-cup sequenator. Laursen (1971) was the first person to design such a machine and his publication gave extensive details that have enabled other groups to construct their own machines (Wiman 1977). Also there are at least three commercially available versions of this instrument (Table XVII), and furthermore it is also possible to convert the liquid-phase sequenator into a solid-phase machine, this being easier to accomplish with the Jeol sequenator; nevertheless a permanent conversion would not be sensible from an economic point of view. This is because the principal attraction of the solid-phase sequencer is its low cost compared to the spinning-cup instrument, and this low capital cost reflects the overall simplicity of this machine. Although simple in construction, the solid-phase sequencer has not had the overall success the liquid-phase model has achieved. Possibly this reflects the smaller number of these instruments in operation, but more realistically it is a consequence of the involved chemical manipulations that are necessary in this method of automatic sequencing. Although not completely satisfactory in themselves, more development being needed in this area, the additional chemistry necessary has not attracted workers to adopt this method of sequencing. However, the relatively low cost of the solid-phase sequencer has in more recent years attracted interest, particularly from the individual worker who could not justify the massive capital cost of a spinning-cup sequencer.

It is clear that if the chemical steps necessary for solid-phase sequencing

Table XVII. Solid-phase sequencers and their manufacturers

Instrument	Manufacturer
SEQUEMAT (Models 10K and 12)	Sequemat Inc., Massachusetts, USA.
LKB (Model 4020) (see Figure XXII)	LKB Biochrom. Ltd, Cambridge Science Park, U.K.
SOCOSI (Model PS300)*	SOCOSI, France.

*Also sold in kit-form for self-assembly.

could be simplified, and improved in effectiveness, there could be a revival of interest in this method of sequencing.

GENERAL PRINCIPLE

The peptide must be covalently bound to an insoluble residue to be available for reaction with the Edman reagent. This and other reagents are pumped over the immobilized peptide and the appropriate fraction containing the anilinothiazolinone collected for identification. 'Washing-out' of the peptide by the reagents is thus completely avoided. This elegant method of sequencing was originally seen in primitive form in the 'paper-strip' procedure devised by Fraenkel-Conrat *et al.* (1955), which although a brilliant innovation, that was designed in an attempt to meet the expanding demand for sequence information, never 'caught-on' universally due to several minor difficulties.

INSTRUMENT DESIGN

The basic design of the solid-phase sequencer is shown in the simplified block diagram and the more detailed design of the original version of Laursen's is shown in Figure XXIII.

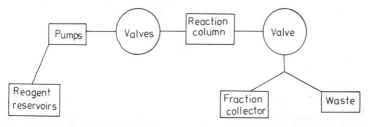

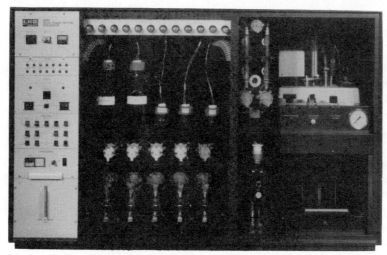

Figure XXII   The LKB solid phase sequencer (by courtesy of LKB Biochrom Ltd, Cambridge)

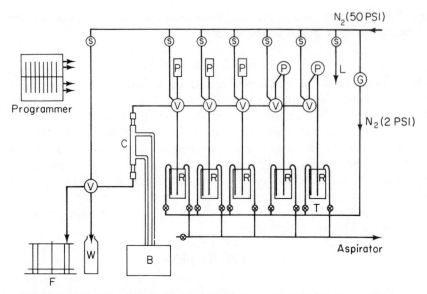

Figure XXIII   Diagram of the layout of the original solid phase sequencer. (B, water bath; C, column; F, fraction collector; G, gas cylinder; P, pump; R, reservoir; V, S, valves.) (Reproduced from Laursen (1972), by permission of Academic Press, Inc.)

Reaction Column

The reaction chamber in the LKB and Sequemat instruments is a jacketed glass microbore column in which is situated the immobilized peptide. Normally the bulk of the resin-bound peptide is small and it is usual to enhance this by the addition of inert glass beads; this also, in the case of polystyrene-based supports, reduces the effects of the resin swelling and shrinking in the reaction column. Two columns are usually employed, and in some cases these have different internal diameters that permit the accommodation of distinct supporting materials. To maintain the column at a constant temperature, which is normally 45°C, water is circulated through the surrounding jacket by an integral water bath.

The Shaking Reaction Chamber

The reaction chamber in the French SOCOSI (PS300) machine, instead of being a column, consists of a unique shaking chamber. This vessel, which is thermostatted at 45°C, is shaken vertically. It has an internal volume of approximately 3 ml and to ensure efficient shaking the reagent volume should be more than 1.5–2 ml. This clever design eliminates the necessity for high-pressure pumps that are needed in the column version, the reagents being stored and pushed through by pressurized nitrogen gas. The disadvantage of this design, apart from the low washing efficiency achieved,

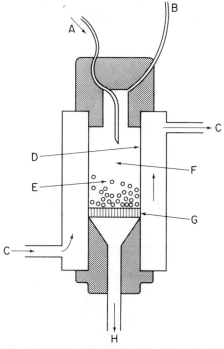

Figure XXIV Simplified drawing of the shaking reaction vessel of the SOCOSI sequencer. (A, inlet reagent tube; B decompression tube; C, circulating water bath; D, internal facings coated with Kel-F; E, resin particles; F, reaction chamber; G. sintered glass filter; H outlet)

is that reagents may become entrapped in the joints and glass filter of the reaction vessel.

MATERIALS AND REAGENTS

The materials used in the construction of the sequencer, like the spinning-cup sequenator, are governed by the high chemical reactivity of the reagents of the Edman degradation, therefore all components that come into direct contact with these reagents are constructed of Teflon, Tefzel, Delrin, Kel-F, glass or stainless steel. The pumps in the LKB version are made entirely of glass and PTFE, with pistons of sapphire.

The demand on reagent purity is not as great as that necessary with the spinning-cup machine, by virtue of the fact that impurities cannot accumulate but are continuously washed through. In fact Laursen (1971) found ordinary reagent grade materials satisfactory; nevertheless for extended sequencing it is desirable to have analytical grade reagents. Even

Table XVIII. Preparation and properties of supports used in solid-phase sequencing

Support	Preparation
Amino polystyrene	Polystyrene (400 mesh) $\xrightarrow[\text{1 h, 0°C}]{\text{HNO}_3\ (95\%)}$ Nitropolystyrene $\xrightarrow[\text{140°, 15 min}]{\text{SnCl}_2/\text{DMF}}$ Aminopolystyrene ($NO_2 \rightarrow NH_2$)
Triethylene tetramine polystyrene	Chloromethyl-polystyrene ($-CH_2Cl$) $\xrightarrow[\text{100°C, 90 min}]{\text{NH}_2(\text{CH}_2)_2\text{NH}(\text{CH}_2)_2\text{NH}(\text{CH}_2)_2\text{NH}_2}$ Triethylene tetraamine-polystyrene ($-[CH_2-NH(CH_2)_2-]_3 NH_2$)
3-Amino propylglass	Porous glass (400 mesh, 75 Å pore diam.) ($-OH$) + 3-Amino propyl tricthoxysilane in dry acetone ($EtO-Si(OEt)_2-(CH_2)_3NH_2$) $\xrightarrow{25°}$ 3-Amino propyl glass ($-O-Si(-O-)-(CH_2)_3NH_2$)
N(2-aminoethyl)-3-aminopropylglass	Porous glass (400 mesh, 75 Å pore diam.) ($-OH$) + N-(2-aminoethyl) 3-amino propyl trimethoxy silane (4% in acetone) ($MeO-Si(OMe)_2-(CH_2)_3NH(CH_2)_2NH_2$) $\xrightarrow{25°}$ ($-O-Si(-O-)(CH_2)_3NH(CH_2)_2NH_2$)

this entails a considerable saving on the expense of the high-purity reagents needed in the liquid-phase machine.

Types of Support

Much thought and ingenuity has been given in the search for an ideal type of support. Up to date no such material has yet been discovered and the ones that are available must be employed with discernment. In general, the requirements for a support are threefold:

(1) it must be inert to the wide range of chemicals employed;
(2) it must be stable to the mechanical stresses involved; and
(3) it must be permeable to both peptides and reagents.

A selection of supports that have been successfully employed are listed in Table XVIII, which also gives details of their preparation. The strategical problems involved in choosing a support must include a number of factors, in particular the size of the peptide must be taken into account, as well as the method of chemical attachment to be employed. Polystyrene-based supports, although adequately supplied with amino groups, do not swell in aqueous buffers, which limits their use to those peptide derivatives that are soluble in organic solvents. Whereas porous glass derivatives, on the other hand, cannot be highly substituted with amino groups and the coupling of

Colour	Storage conditions	General comments
Brown	Very stable and may be stored for long periods under refrigeration	Best used when the coupling reagent is p-phenylene diisothiocyanate. Suitable for peptides <35 residues.
White	Unstable and best prepared as needed; however it is stable for several months in deep freeze.	The best choice if coupling the peptide by its c-terminus. It is particularly effective for coupling homoserine lactone activated peptides. Suitable for peptides <70 residues.
Yellow	Stable at 4°C for at least 6 months.	Suitable for large peptides and small proteins, however the coupling procedure employed is less critical than for the polystyrene-based supports. They are not suitable for peptides <15 residues as these tend to absorb on to the glass surface.
Gold	Stable at 4°C for at least 6 months.	

the peptide is generally inefficient. The answer to these problems is a hydrophilic support that would swell in both aqueous and organic media. One such polymeric material is polyacrylamide, however this has the disadvantage that it is degraded in the presence of trifluoroacetic acid. To overcome these problems there has been some recent work on the modification of this polymer, with the introduction of the resins: β-alanyl-hexamethylene diamine polydimethyl acrylamide, and N-aminoethylpolyacrylamide (Atherton *et al.* 1976, Cavadore *et al.* 1976).

The Chemistry of the Coupling Procedures

There have been many attempts to devise a suitable means for the covalent coupling of the peptide, or protein, to the inert support. Much of this has been possible due to developments that have occurred in the field of solid state peptide synthesis. There are basically four approaches possible, for attaching the peptide to the inert support; these are:

(1) attachment through C-terminal homoserine lactone;
(2) attachment by activation of the C-terminal carboxyl group;
(3) attachment through side-chain amino groups; and
(4) attachment of the protein to the support *via* cysteine residues. Each of these will now be considered in detail.

(1) Attachment Through C-terminal Homoserine Lactone

Cyanogen bromide fragments, excepting the one derived from the C-terminal region of the protein, terminate in homoserine. By treatment with anhydrous trifluoroacetic acid the C-terminal homoserine residue is converted quantitatively into the lactone, viz.

terminal homoserine   terminal homoserine lactone

The lactone ring formed is activated sufficiently to undergo rapid aminolysis with a polymeric amine. In a typical experiment the peptide after treatment with TFA is dried down and coupled directly onto a triethylenetetramine derivative of polystyrene by simply stirring in dimethylformamide. Following coupling, excess amino sites on the resin are blocked with methyl isothiocyanate $(CH_3 N = C = S)$ and the peptide sequenced.

peptide with terminal homoserine lactone

coupled peptide

This is a very elegant and simple procedure. The product is formed in high yield and the method has the advantage that during sequencing of the coupled peptide no gaps are to be expected, in contrast to other procedures. However it is only applicable to cyanogen bromide peptides which does limit its usefulness.

(2) Attachment by Activation of the C-terminal Carboxyl Group

All the methods available for the attachment of a peptide to an insoluble support by means of its terminal carboxyl group present the problem that no matter what procedure is used, inevitably side-chain carboxyl groups will also be attached to the resin. One solution to this dilemma is to hydrolyse the protein into peptides that terminate in either glutamic acid or aspartic acid. This may be accomplished by using the staphylococcal, or 'Glu' protease. Another ingenious approach for tryptic peptides has been to react all the available carboxyl groups with glycinamide in the presence of a carbodiimide. The terminal carboxyl group may be specifically unmasked by reacting the peptide with trypsin (see Figure XXV).

The method, however, has the disadvantage that the modified internal residues of glutamic and aspartic acids cannot be directly identified as their PTH derivatives, and indirect methods such as back hydrolysis are adopted.

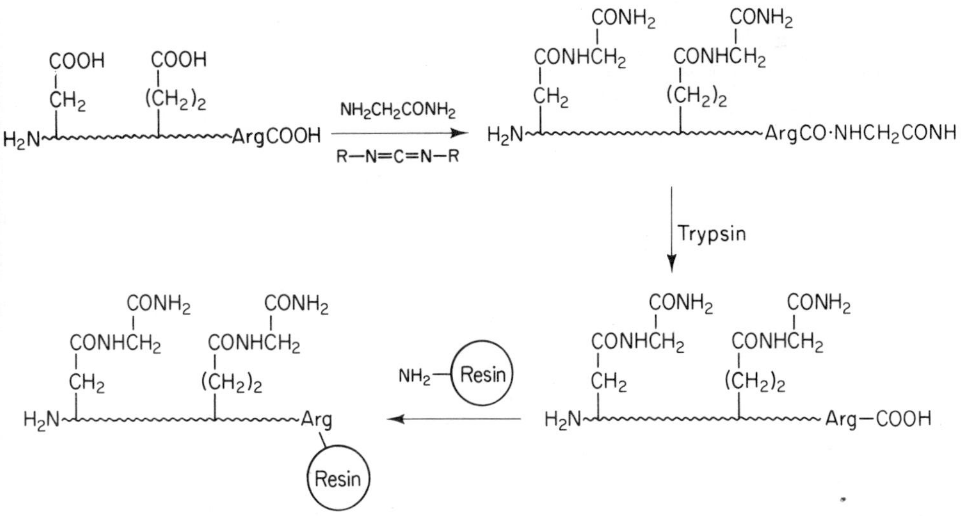

Figure XXV   Blocking side chain carboxyl groups with glycinamide

(i) Using N,N'carbonyldiimidazole   Historically this is an important method for coupling the peptide to the inert support as it was one of the first methods used (Laursen 1971). N,N'carbonyl-diimidazole (mol.wt 162.16, m.pt $116°–118°$) reacts readily with carboxylic acids forming imidazolides, that undergo rapid aminolysis with an amino polymer (see Figure XXVI). This method requires both protection of amino side chains in the peptide and the use of anhydrous solvents. The amino group is best protected by t-butyl azidoformate which is an excellent blocking group for it may be readily removed in the presence of trifluoroacetic acid.

Despite coupling efficiencies of greater than 80% (Laursen 1971) this method has received little attention. The use of carbonyldiimidazole

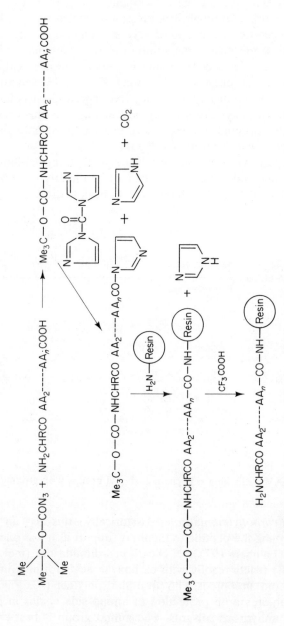

Figure XXVI Coupling peptides to insoluble membranes using N,N′carbonyl diimidazole

demands stringent anhydrous conditions, which are on the whole unsatisfactory with the majority of water-soluble peptides. A further problem is the additional work involved in the protection of the amino terminal residue. Nevertheless both these problems have been elegantly avoided by Beyreuther *et al*. (1978), who first subjected the peptide to reaction with phenylisothiocyanate followed by coupling under anhydrous conditions to 3-aminopropylglass. Finally, there is the problem that side chain carboxyls are modified when coupling with carbonyl diimidazole: the glutamyl residue is bound to the support which leads to gaps in the sequence; whereas aspartyl residues undergo cyclic imide formation, thereby bringing the sequencing procedure to a premature end.

(ii) Using carbodiimides Carbodiimides are useful reagents for the coupling of peptides to supporting media, under conditions that favour selective blocking of the side-chain carboxyl groups (Previero *et al*. 1973). As a preliminary step it is essential to block terminal amino groups with a reversible blocking group, such as t-butoxy-carbonylazide. The success of this method depends on the ability of the investigator to exclude all extraneous nucleophiles during the activation process, thereby reducing the number of side products. Previero *et al*. (1973) found that under certain conditions the carbodiimide could provide selective blocking of side-chain carboxyl groups.

For this purpose water-soluble carbodiimides are used, e.g. N-ethyl-N'(3-dimethyl aminopropyl)carbodiimide. It was found that this reagent reacts initially with side-chain carboxyls to give an O-acyl urea derivative which subsequently rearranges to give an inactive N-acyl urea, whereas the C-terminal carboxyl group reacts with the carbodiimide to form an oxazolinone which is still reactive to suitable nucleophiles, such as amino groups. In theory this is good, however in practice experience shows that side reactions may occur and the coupling efficiency obtained is quite variable (see Figure XXVII).

This technique was employed by Lindemann and Wittman-Liebold (1977) to couple tryptic peptides from the ribosomal protein S13, to aminopolystyrene and enabled peptides in the range 30–100 nmol to be successfully sequenced. Also, Beyreuther *et al*. (1977) in their studies of the structure of the phosphocarrier protein HBr of the phosphoenol-pyruvate-dependent phosphotransferase system of *Staphylococcus aureus*, used carbodiimide to couple peptides in the range 20–100 nmol to an inert support. These workers used the novel technique, that was subsequently employed by K. J. Dilley (Protein Chemistry Note 6, LKB Ltd) in sequencing chick histone H_5, of blocking the amino residue with phenylisothiocyanate. The phenylthiocarbamoyl peptide derivative was extracted into benzene and activated by carbodiimide in dimethylformamide before coupling to the support. This method eliminates the need for a subsequent unblocking step as the Edman degradation may proceed once coupling is complete.

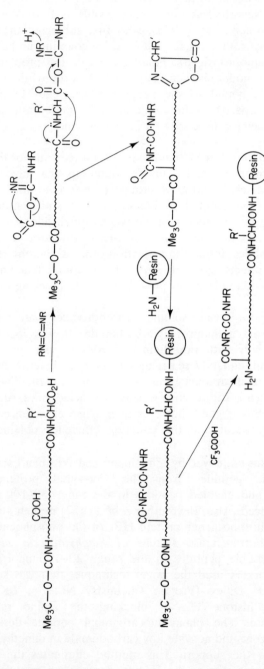

Figure XXVII Coupling peptides to insoluble membrane with carbodiimide

(3) Attachment by Side-chain Amino Groups

(1) Use of p-phenylene diisothiocyanate Peptides and proteins may be bound covalently to aminated supports using the bifunctional reagent p-phenylene diisothiocyanate (DITC). In the coupling process it is essential to use a large excess of reagent so as to prevent cross-linking, or even polymerisation of the peptide. Coupling yields of up to 100% have been reported (Laursen *et al.* 1972); however, this method is limited to those peptides containing lysine, or arginine.

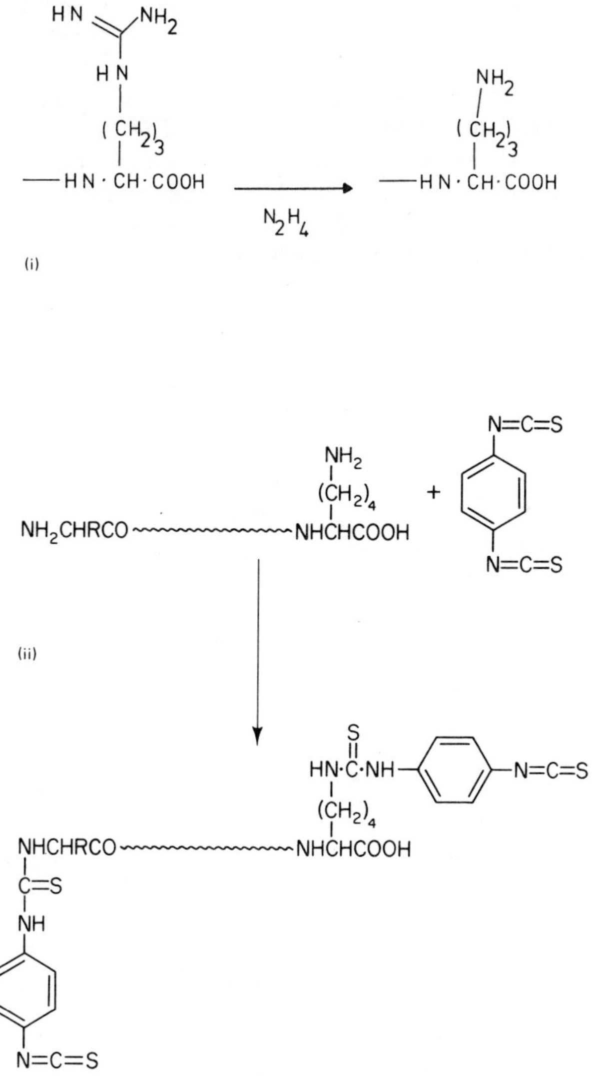

Figure XXVIII (i) Conversion of Arg→Orn. (ii) Activation of peptides with *p*-phenylene diisothiocyanate

The arginine must, prior to coupling, be converted to ornithine. This is usually performed with aqueous hydrazine (50%, at 70° for 15 min): however, the author has found these conditions to occasionally lead to chain cleavage and it is advisable to perform a preliminary small-scale experiment before commiting the whole of the sample to this treatment. Laursen *et al.* (1972) have also reported difficulties with the hydrazine treatment; in particular it is essential to remove all traces of the base before coupling as this will reduce the coupling efficiency.

Coupling is actually performed in two stages; first the peptide is activated by treatment with a 50–100-fold molar excess of p-phenylene diisothiocyanate which reacts with all available amino groups (as shown in Figure XXVIII).

In the second stage, coupling is performed by adding the aminated support to the activated peptide (see Figure XXIX).

Once the peptide is bound, excess amino groups on the support are blocked by treatment with methyl isothiocyanate. With this technique Chen *et al.* (1978) have reported coupling yields of up to 70%, involving tryptic peptides from human myeloma λ-chain protein to aminopolystyrene. One

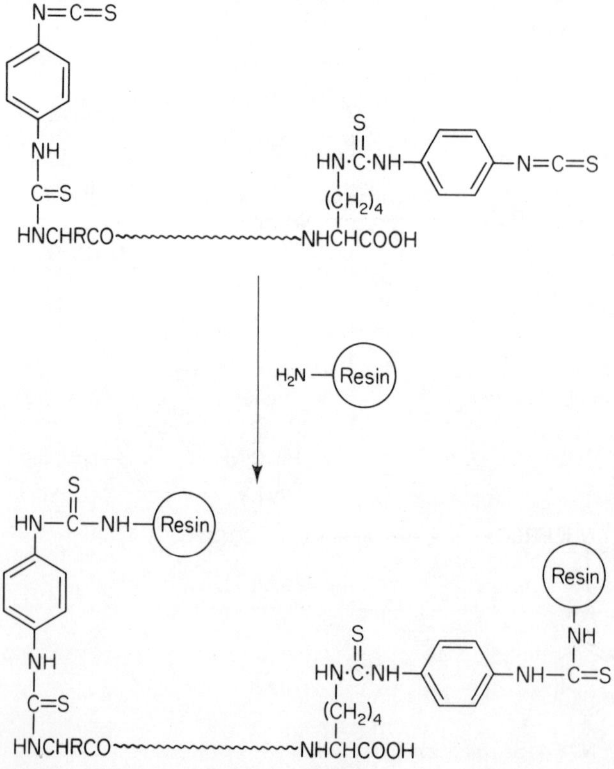

Figure **XXIX** Coupling of activated peptides to an aminated support

point that must be noted is that the lysyl/ornithyl, and amino terminal residues, are irrevocably bound to the resin and this results in gaps in the sequence. These drawbacks, however, did not prevent Hitz *et al.* (1977) sequencing the ribosomal protein S6 up to residue 34, after it had been attached to aminopolystyrene. It is interesting to note that, in comparision, they were able to sequence up to residue 44 with a Beckman liquid-phase sequencer, slightly more sample being required in this case.

(ii) Use of N(p-isothiocyanatobenzoyl) DL-*homoserine lactone* Herbrink (1976) introduced the bifunctional reagent N(p-isothiocyanatobenzoyl)

DL-homoserine lactone for the specific attachment of peptides to an aminated support (see Figure XXX). This reagent contained two functional groups differing in reactivity. Using this reagent, cross-linking of peptides, which is occasionally observed with bifunctional reagents bearing two identical reactive groups, is virtually eliminated. This reagent therefore combines the reactivity of the di-isothiocyanate method with the specificity of the homoserine lactone method. Herbrink successfully applied this procedure to a number of tryptic peptides from the β-Bp-chain of bovine β-crystallin.

(4) Attachment of Proteins to Inert Supports

(i) Use of p-phenylene diisothiocyanate A slightly different technique is employed than that with peptides. The support, rather than the peptide, is activated with the reagent (see Figure XXXI)

In a typical experiment p-phenylene diisothiocyanate is dissolved in dimethylformamide to give a 25–100-fold excess of reagent over the available amino groups on the aminated support. The aminopropyl glass is added in small portions under a nitrogen atmosphere over a period of one hour and the product is filtered and carefully washed. The activated support is then added to the protein dissolved in a small volume of aqueous pyridine containing N-methyl morpholine. After 10 min at room temperature the product is filitered off and washed.

(ii) Attachment of proteins to inert supports by their cysteine residues Chang *et al.* (1977) found it possible to attach proteins *via* their cysteine residues to an iodoacetamide derivative of porous glass beads (see

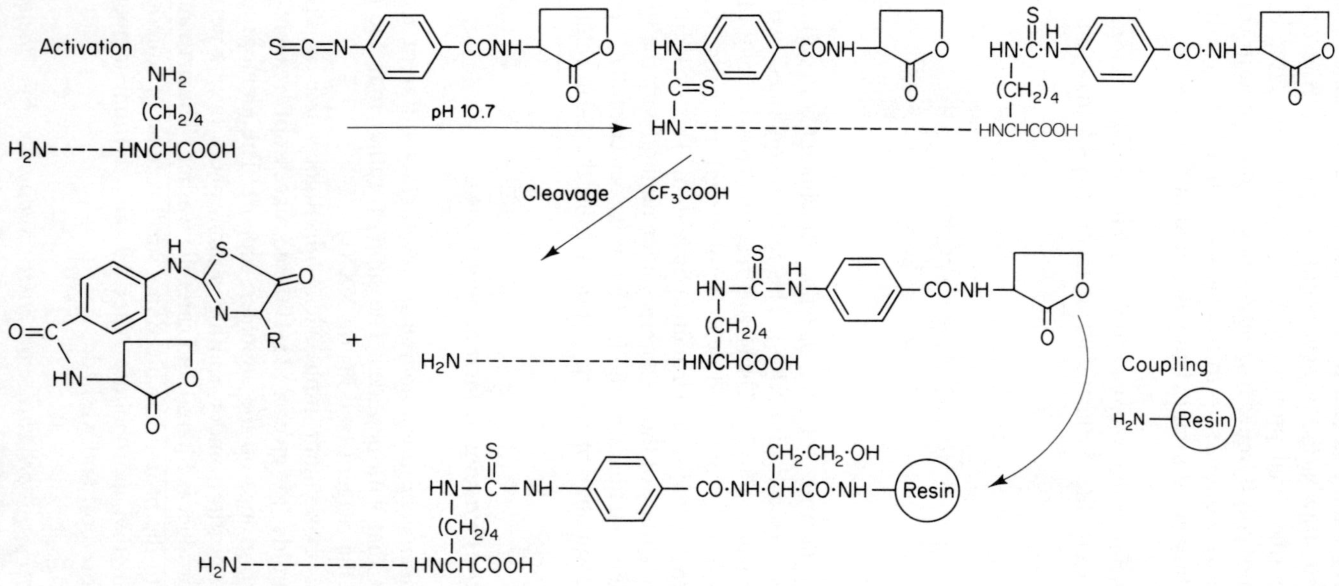

Figure XXX Activation and coupling of peptides to an aminated support using N(p-isothiocyanatobenzoyl) DL-homoserine lactone

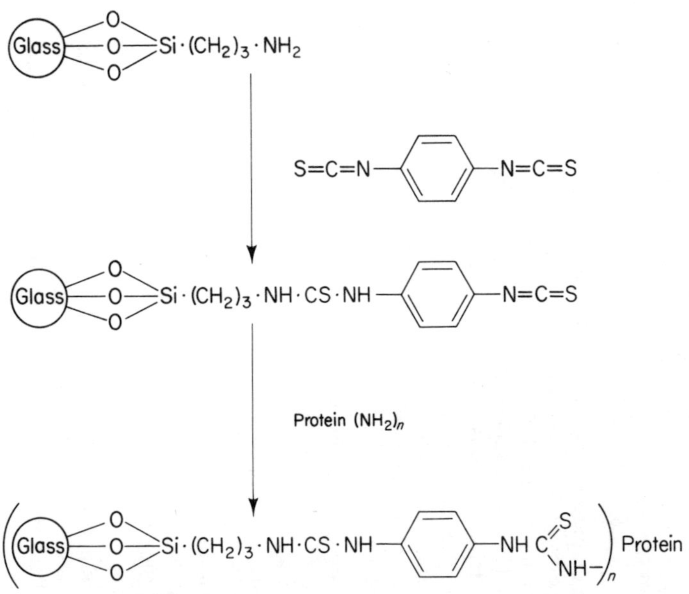

Figure XXXI   Coupling of proteins to a porous glass support previously activated with p-phenylene diisothiocyanate

Figure XXXII). The strategy in this case was again to activate the matrix rather than the ligand.

The activated glass support was prepared by suspending amino propyl-glass in a solution of ethylacetate containing iodoacetate and dicyclohexylcarbodiimide for approximately 2 hours. The protein was attached by simply stirring it in 8 M urea solution in the presence of derivatized glass. Finally, when attachment was complete, excess iodoacetamide glass was destroyed by adding mercaptoethanol.

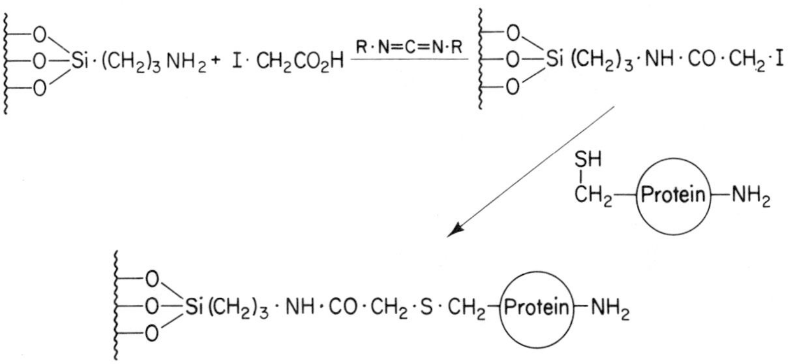

Figure XXXII   Attachment of proteins to 3-amino propyl glass previously activated by iodoacetate

Table XIX. Design features of three commercially available solid-phase sequencers

	Sequemat	LKB	Socosi
Reagent storage system	Reagent reservoirs consist of glass vessels with special adaptors that permit easy refilling. The reagents are maintained under nitrogen.	Reagents are contained in five amber coloured bottles and are maintained in an oxygen-free atmosphere.	There are five reservoir vessels under nitrogen pressure.
Pumping system	Milton-Roy mini pumps are used for dichloroethane and methanol. For TFA and PITC Harvard Apparatus infusion-withdrawal pumps are used fitted with 5 ml Hamilton gas-tight syringes.	Five pumps are employed, one for each reagent/solvent. The body of each pump is constructed of glass, with seals of PTFE and a sapphire plunger. The delivery rate is variable. They are mounted together with their motors on a pull-out tray that makes them accessible for easy maintenance.	Pumps are not employed. The reagents/solvents flow throughout the instrument under inducement of nitrogen pressure.
Reagent valves	Pneumatically actuated valves made of either Kel-F or Tefzel, or Delrin. (Delrin is not used near TFA which rapidly attacks it.)	Reagent valves are actuated by N_2 pressure set at 65 lb/sq. in and constructed of Kel-F, or Delrin/Kel-F. A pressure sensor in the N_2 line monitors the actuating pressure and in the event of a pressure drop the programme is stopped until the pressure returns to normal.	
Fraction collector	Constructed of stainless steel with two concentric rows each having a capacity for 24 tubes. This allows thiazolinones from two different peptides to be collected simultaneously. It is enclosed in a stainless steel box thus avoiding the possibility of corrosion by TFA vapours. It is not refrigerated.	This is capable of collecting up to 48 samples, i.e. two rows of 24 tubes permitting collection from each column. It is coated with an acid-resistant polymeric substance to ensure long life. It is maintained in an atmosphere of nitrogen.	The fraction collector is maintained in a nitrogen atmosphere and is refrigerated.

PERSPECTIVES

Initially the solid-phase sequencer may be seen as a cheap alternative to the costly liquid-phase machine, as it is approximately one-fifth of the capital cost. Furthermore, regardless of the initial outlay, when it is compared with the spinning-cup sequencer it is seen that it has the further advantage that the highly refined reagents which are vital for the success of this latter instrument are not neccessary. It is pertinent to point out that not only are the maintenance costs less, but that, theoretically, higher sequencing yields are possible with the solid-phase machine, since entirely organic solvents may be used throughout. The possibility of obtaining stepwise yields greater than 99%, leading to extended sequence runs, exist but has not yet been achieved. Possibly this reflects the reluctance of many investigators to adopt this method of sequencing on account of the involved chemistry of the coupling process. Although considerable research has been devoted to improving the coupling methods, the most expedient route has not yet been conceived and much more exploratory work has yet to be done. From publications of the period 1976–1978 the practical limit for length of sequence deduced by this method is around 25 residues. Employing a dual-column arrangement this could probably be achieved within a single working day, saving many man-hours over the manual alternative. Nevertheless, to justify the large capital cost of this machine, as with all costly instruments, it must be continuously operated, which demands a ready supply of pure peptides. This can only be realized by a group of workers, backed up by an efficient team of technicians, and such organizations are rarely seen in British institutions, at least. This situation probably accounts for the disappointing sales of these machines.

In conclusion, therefore, the solid-phase sequencer is at present limited by the difficult and complicated coupling process, yet it has the potential of being a more useful instrument than the spinning-cup sequencer. Overall it is a cheaper machine to purchase, run and maintain: however, these advantages cannot for the individual worker justify its purchase. This scientist must resist the temptation to elaborate his laboratory and continue to rely on the manual sequencing methods available.

CHAPTER 6

Identification of Amino Acid Phenylthiohydantoins

In general the chemical stability of the phenylthiohydantoin amino acids is very good, which makes them ideal derivatives of the amino acids for identification purposes. During the Edman degradation the thiazolinone is converted to the phenylthiohydantoin (PTH) of the amino acid by acid hydrolysis and is extracted by ethylacetate; however, not all the PTH-amino acids are soluble in the solvent, in particular PTH-Arg, PTH-His and PTH-CySO$_3$H remain in the aqueous phase.

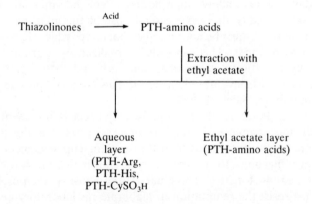

Scheme for extraction of PTH-amino acids.

With the exception of these three, most other PTH-amino acids have poor solubility in aqueous solutions.

All the PTH-amino acids have relatively high melting points and on the whole their thermal stability is good, with the exception of PTH-Ser, PTH-Thr and PTH-Cys. These three phenylthiohydantoins have the common feature of a good leaving group on the β-carbon atom of the side-chain viz. OH, or SH, with the consequence that β-elimination of this group readily occurs forming a dehydrophenylthiohydantoin. Thus dehydration of the PTH of Thr gives rise to 5-ethylidene-

84

3-phenyl-2-thiohydantoin:

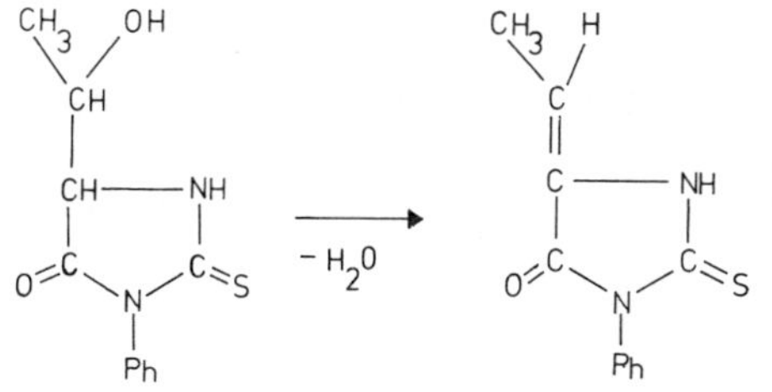

PTH–Thr
(λ_{max} 268 nm)

PTH–Δ Thr
(λ_{max} 325 nm)

This tendency for β-elimination is even stronger with PTH-Ser, the reaction being:

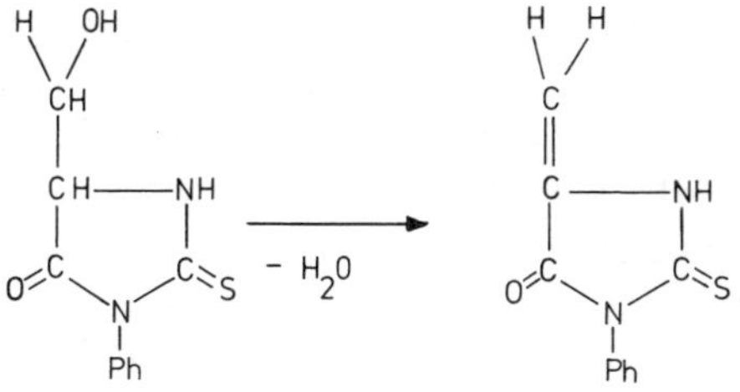

PTH–Ser

PTH–Δ Ser

The PTH dehydroserine formed is very unstable and tends to polymerize giving rise to pink polymers (Ingram 1953). This property has been used to positively identify seryl residues in proteins during Edman degradation with the automatic sequencer, the pink solution being taken as evidence for the presence of a Serine residue (Enfield et al. 1975).

As all PTH–amino acids tend to be light-sensitive, particularly PTH–Trp, it is advisable to keep standard PTH-solutions and those derived during stepwise degradation away from direct sunlight. However, after thin layer chromatography, PTH-Trp may be observed as a distinct yellow spot in visible light and this has been used to identify this phenylthiohydantoin after attempts to identify it by GLC had failed (Wunderer and Eulitz, 1978).

(1) THE IDENTIFICATION OF PTH-AMINO ACIDS BY THIN LAYER CHROMATOGRAPHY

This is by far the simplest method for the identification of PTH-amino acids. It is simple, cheap and rapid. It requires no specialist technical skills or equipment, and must be the method of choice for any newcomer to this field. Recent micro-analytical developments have made this method of analysing these amino acid derivatives almost as simple, and quick, as those that have been available for several years for the identification of dansyl-amino acids and it is likely that their impact will have a similar effect in the years to come. Apart from the advantages of speed, cheapness etc., this method has the important advantage of being able to directly identify the amides of glutamic and aspartic acid. This is not possible if the PTH-amino acid is hydrolysed back to the amino acid and subsequently analysed on an amino acid analyser.

In the main the recent advances in this area have been due to the introduction of high-quality manufactured thin layers, of either silica gel or polyamide, on plastic or aluminium foils, and the introduction of double-sided coated thin layers has been particularly beneficial.

Resolution of the PTH-amino Acids by One-dimensional TLC

There is a vast literature describing various solvent systems for the separation of PTH-amino acids and this has recently been reviewed (Rosmus and Deyl 1972). A selection only will be given here, including those methods which the author has found useful in his own research.

The method of Jeppsson and Sjöquist (1967) uses thin layers of silica gel plus a fluorescent indicator (Eastman) and chomatography is performed by the ascending technique in glass tanks lined with Whatman 3MM chromatography paper. The main solvent is system V comprising: heptane/propionic acid/ethylene chloride, (58 : 17 : 25, v/v) and with this system the separation illustrated in Figure XXXIIIa is obtained.

On the whole this is a satisfactory method for PTH-amino acid identification with an over-all sensitivity of about 5 nmol. There are some difficulties associated with the resolution of PTH-Pro, PTH-Phe and PTH-Met; PTH-Asp and PTH-Ser are also poorly resolved; however, this can be improved if the thin layer is rechromatographed in the same solvent. Also, to enhance the separation, particularly of those PTH-amino acids at the lower end of the thin layer, it is re-run in a further solvent, system IV, consisting of: heptane/n-butanol/formic acid, (50 : 30 : 9, v/v), the resulting separation is illustrated in Figure XXXIIIb. A further problem with this system is the separation of PTH-Arg and PTH-His. Jeppsson and Sjöquist suggested heating the thin layer whereupon the PTH of His turns yellow, thus distinguishing it from PTH-Arg. This is unsatisfactory and to overcome this difficulty specific spot tests for PTH-His and PTH-Arg have been applied after the thin layer chromatography. However, as contaminants from the Edman degradation may suppress the colour development of these tests rendering them ineffective and unreliable, this procedure also is not without its snags. To solve this problem Inagami (1973) introduced a method that gave a clear separation of these PTH amino acids, using the

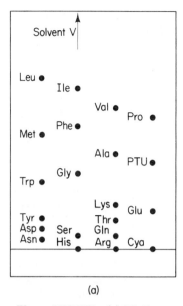 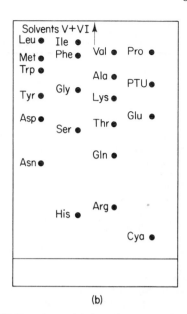

(a)   (b)

Figure XXXIII   (a) TLC separation of PTH-amino acids in solvent system V; (b) TLC separation of PTH-amino acids after chromatography in solvent system V, followed by solvent system IV (Jeppsson and Sjoquist 1967)

solvent system, xylene/95% ethanol/acetic acid, (50 : 50 : 0.5, v/v) (R_f(PTH-His) 0.64; R_f(PTH-Arg) 0.37), and positively identifying the PTH-His after spraying with the Pauly reagent and PTH-Arg with the phenanthraquinone fluorescent stain reagent. The sensitivity by this method for PTH-His is about 2 nmol and that for PTH-Arg 0.05 nmol, compared with the over-all sensitivity of the Jeppsson and Sjöquist method of about 5 nmol.

This procedure for PTH-amino acid identification takes about 2–3 hours before a positive result is obtained, but as the automatic sequencer is able to produce PTH-amino acids awaiting identification at the rate of about one per hour, it is clear that when using the sequencer to its full capacity a bottle-neck situation would soon result at the identification stage. To overcome this quandary Kulbe (1974) introduced a simple, effective and quick method for the simultaneous identification of 10 PTH-amino acids on a single thin layer plate. Kulbe proposed using four standard mixtures (A, B, C, and D) of PTH-amino acids prepared at the concentration of 2 nmol/ml in methanol (Table XX).

Micropolyamide layers, coated on both sides, are used, cut to the dimensions 5 × 5 cm, or 2.5 × 2.5 cm; detection of the PTH-amino acids is made possible by incorporating a fluorescent indicator in the first solvent system, giving a detection limit of between 0.2 and 0.05 nmol. On one side of the layer are placed the standard mixtures A, B and C together with four unknowns and on the reverse side are spotted six further unknowns together

Table XX. Composition of the standard mixtures of PTH-amino acids used
in the procedure of Kulbe

Mixture A	Mixture B	Mixture C	Mixture D
Asn	Ala	Asp	Arg
CMC	Ile	Glu	His
Gln	Leu	Gly	CySO$_3$H
Lys	Tyr	Phe	
Met, MetSO$_2$	*N,N-DPhe	Thr	
Pro	*N-Phe	Val	
Ser			
Trp			

*Abbreviations: N,N-DPhe (N,N,diphenylthiourea; N-Phe (N-phenyl-
thiourea).

with mixture A. Ascending chromatography is performed in solvent I, comprising toluene/n-pentane/acetic acid, (60 : 30 : 16, v/v) followed by solvent II (25% aqueous acetic acid). The PTH-amino acids poorly resolved in this process, namely PTH-Leu, PTH-Ile, PTH-Thr and PTH-Phe, may be differentiated by doing a further run in solvent III, consisting of 40% aqueous pyridine/acetic acid, (9 : 1, v/v). PTH-His and PTH-Arg may be distinguished by one run in solvent II, the R_f values being 0.89 and 0.83 respectively. This excellent technique makes it possible to identify up to 20 unknown PTHs per hour.

Resolution of the PTH-aminoacids by Two-dimensional TLC

Polyamide thin layer sheets (Cheng-Chin) have been used to identify PTH-amino acids down to a lower limit of 0.05 nmol by incorporating a fluorescent indicator into the thin layer (Summers *et al.* 1973). Double-sided coated thin layers are used, thus allowing the unknown to be run on one side and selected standards on the reverse. This is a rapid method and enables a complete two-dimensional separation of the PTH-amino acids to be obtained within 30 min. The dimensions of the sheet employed are 5 × 5 cm and the fluorescent indicator is butyl PBD (2-(4'-t-butylphenyl)-5-(4'-biphenyl) 1,3,4-oxdiazole, dissolved in the first solvent. Chromatography is routinely performed in 150 ml glass beakers sealed with a small amount of parafilm. The solvents used are:

solvent I: toluene/n-pentane/acetic acid, (60 : 30 : 35, v/v) containing 250 mg of butyl PBD/litre;
solvent II: 35% aqueous acetic acid.

Separation of 16 of the PTH-amino acids was possible by this method, as illustrated in Figure XXXIV, and this was achieved within 30 min.

This procedure has been slightly modified by Kulbe (1974), who used the

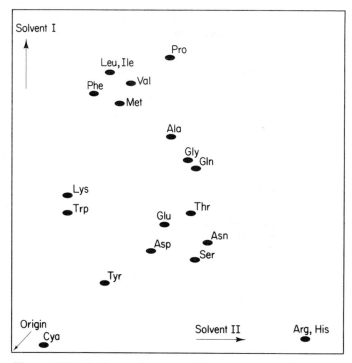

Figure XXXIV Separation of PTH-amino acids by two-dimensional TLC on polyamide layers (Summers *et al.* 1973)

solvents:

solvent I: toluene/n-pentane/acetic acid, (60 : 30 : 16, v/v) containing 250 mg/litre of fluorescent indicator;
solvent II: 25% aqueous acetic acid.

The moderately improved separation gives better resolutions of PTH-Glu and PTH-Gln, PTH-Asp and PTH-Asn; however the pairs PTH-His/PTH-Arg, PTH-Leu/PTH-Ile are still not completely separated and the use of a third solvent is necessary before a positive identification can be made.

Detection of PTH-amino Acids on Thin Layers

The simplest method of detecting PTH-amino acids involves the use of a fluorescent indicator incorporated into the thin layer. The plates may either be purchased with the fluorescent compound already in the layer, or it can, as in the method of Summers *et al.* (1973), be dissolved in the chromatography solvent. After development the PTH-amino acids may be identified by viewing the dry thin layer under a UV light, when they appear as dark areas on a bright fluorescent background.

Table XXI. Colours produced by PTH-amino acids after staining with ninhydrin–collidine reagent

PTH-amino acid	Colour produced
Glycine	Deep orange
Alanine	Red-violet
Serine	Red-violet
Threonine	Pale brown
Valine	No colour
Leucine	Faint grey
Isoleucine	Faint grey
Proline	Pale pink
Glutamic acid	Burnt umber
Aspartic acid	Pink
Glutamine	Brown
Asparagine	Lemon
Histidine	Pale yellow
Lysine	Faint pink
Arginine	Pale yellow
Phenylalanine	Faint yellow
Tyrosine	Lemon
Tryptophan	Yellow

However if there is any doubt as regards the identification, confirmation may be obtained after staining with the ninhydrin-collidine reagent Roseau and Pantel (1969), when the PTH-amino acids have characteristic colours (Table XXI); this innovation was very helpful in studies on the sequence of horse pancreatic ribonuclease (Scheffer and Beintema 1974).

Advantages of TLC

TLC identification of PTH-amino acids, particularly the innovations of Summers *et al.* (1973) and Kulbe (1974), is of major importance in amino acid sequencing. This has been made possible by the commercial availability of uniform and consistent thin layer sheets. Undoubtedly the principal attraction of this method is its low cost, particularly if the operation is scaled down to use the 2.5 × 2.5 cm layers, when amino acid residue identification is obtained for a fraction of a farthing. Its speed is another bonus and as the sequencer can produce about 20 PTH-amino acids per day, which of necessity must be identified as soon as possible, to avoid any decomposition caused by prolonged standing, it is the only means of keeping up with a machine working at full capacity. The method is also highly sensitive, having about 10 × the sensitivity of GLC, and it is very reliable, but above all its main advantage is in its simplicity—requiring no skilled technical assistance, or elaborate expensive equipment—it is clearly the method of choice.

(2) THE IDENTIFICATION OF PTH-AMINO ACIDS BY GAS LIQUID CHROMATOGRAPHY

The early attempts at separating the PTH-amino acids by GLC used essentially the same approach as that for other natural products (Pisano *et al.* 1962). The column packings used consisted of thin film coatings of very thermostable liquid phases, in conjunction with an argon ionization detection system. The initial results were satisfactory: however, difficulties were experienced with the phenylthiohydantoin derivatives of Ser, Thr, Asn, Gln, His and Arg. The phenylthiohydantoins of both Ser and Thr had undergone dehydration, and the derivatives of Gln and Asn had also been modified. It was also found that the PTH derivatives of the basic amino acids were not sufficiently volatile for analysis by this method. These initial stumbling-blocks were overcome by the introduction of new thermally stable and more polar polysiloxane liquid phases, together with the use of more powerful silylating reagents which were found to convert the relatively non-volatile and unstable PTH-amino acids to trimethylsilyl derivatives having satisfactory chromatographic properties. As yet, however, no satisfactory solution to the inherent involatility of PTH-Arg has been found, and this amino acid derivative cannot be identified by GLC analysis. Because of this, GLC analysis of PTH-amino acids cannot be considered as a complete method, in itself, and must always be used in conjunction with other analytical systems.

The procedure employed in most sequence laboratories is that originally described by Pisano *et al.* (1972). These workers considered the phenylthiohydantoin amino acids to fall into three categories, differing markedly in their volatilities and compatibilities with different liquid phases: namely, Groups I, II and III (Table XXII).

Group I includes the PTHs that are most volatile and in general give symmetrical peaks. Group II derivatives are the least volatile and are eluted long after those of Group I (with the exception of PTH-Trp) and tend to give unsymmetrical peaks due to interactions with the column packings. The

Table XXII. PTH-amino acids differing in gas chromatographic behaviour

Group I	Group II	Group III
PTH-Ala	PTH-Asn	PTH-Asp
PTH-Gly	PTH-Gln	PTH-CMC
PTH-Val	PTH-Tyr	PTH-CySO$_3$H
PTH-Leu	PTH-His	PTH-Glu
PTH-Ile	PTH-Trp	PTH-Lys
PTH-Met		PTH-Ser
PTH-Pro		PTH-Thr
PTH-Phe		

PTH-derivatives included in Group III must be modified by silylation before GLC analysis is attempted.

It is therefore clear that because of this spectrum in the properties of the PTH-amino acids it is not feasible to analyse for all possible ones in a single GLC analysis run, and in general it is necessary to analyse each residue derivative from the steps of the Edman degradation at least twice. Considering that one GLC run takes approximately 40 min, two runs would take about 2 hours taking into account any down-time. When working with the automatic sequencer about 20 residues per day are prepared for analysis and it is thus clear that a bottleneck of samples awaiting analysis would soon materialize if GLC was the only method of analysis employed. There are a few affluent laboratories that deploy two GLC machines to cope with this problem, one for analysis of the unmodified PTH-derivative, and the other for the silylated PTH-amino acid. An alternative less expensive approach has been to silylate all samples regardless of whether the amino acid derivative might be a member of Group I. However, as pointed out by Pisano et al. (1972) the identification of the majority of PTH-amino acids is not facilitated by silylation, for they found that although individually all PTHs would react quantitatively with the silylating agent, the rate of reaction and stability of the derivatives was highly variable, this being particularly true for phenythiohydantoins of Asn and Gln. Occasionally Pisano and co-workers observed no peaks after silylation, whereas before silylation reasonable responses had been observed. Silylation also has the disadvantage that many additional peaks are observed in the chromatogram that were not present in the unsilylated product; though fortunately none of these artefacts appear to coincide with the known retention times of any of the PTH-amino acids. Wunderer and Eulitz (1978) found that PTH-Ser on silylation gave two or three peaks and that this made quantitation impossible.

Tomita et al. (1978), in their studies on glycophorin A, one of the principal intrinsic transmembrane proteins of the human erythrocyte, adopted the compromise of identifying the PTH derivatives of Ala, Thr, Ser, Gly, Val, Pro, Leu and Ile by direct GLC analysis and a further eight PTH-amino acids (Met, Phe, Asp, Glu, Asn, Gln, Lys, Tyr) after silylation. The four remaining PTH amino acids, viz. PTH-Cys, PTH-Trp, PTH-His and PTH-Arg, were identified using other analytical procedures. Even with this approach difficulty was experienced in resolving PTH-Leu/Ile and in obtaining a satisfactory response from PTH-Asn and PTH-Gln. However, Bennett et al. (1978), in their studies on dihydrofolate reductase, found it possible to resolve PTH-Ile/Leu by using a column of 1.5% AN-600 instead of the usual 10% DC-560, and Closset et al. (1978) found they could obtain satisfactory resolution of this pair of phenylthiohydantoins by silylating the sample before analysis.

Reagents for Silylation

The usual reagent for the silylation of PTH-amino acids is either N,O-bis(trimethylsilyl) acetamide (BSA), or N,O-bis(trimethylsilyl) trifluoroacetamide (BSTFA).

$$
\begin{array}{cc}
Si(CH_3)_3 & Si(CH_3)_3 \\
| & | \\
O & O \\
| & | \\
CH_3-C=N-Si(CH_3)_3 & CF_3-C=N-Si(CH_3)_3 \\
\textit{BSA} & \textit{BSTFA}
\end{array}
$$

Both of these reagents are powerful trimethylsilyl donors and react to replace labile hydrogen in the amino acid derivatives with a $Si(CH_3)_3$ group. Thus the PTH-amino acids become N- and O-trimethylsilyl derivatives. The particular advantage of BSTFA over BSA is the greater volatility of its by-products monotrimethylsilyltrifluoroacetamide and trifluoroacetamide than that of the unfluorinated by-products of BSA. The by-products of BSTFA will usually elute well before any of the silylated amino acid derivatives.

A further silylating agent is N-methyl-N-trimethyl-silylhepta-fluorobutyramide, which has been used by Beyreuther *et al.* (1975) to

$$
CF_3CF_2CF_2-C{\overset{\displaystyle O}{\underset{\underset{\underset{CH_3}{|}}{N-Si(CH_3)_3}}{\diagdown}}}{\diagup}
$$

derivatize the PTHs of Glu, Asp, Ile and Tyr in their studies of the sequence of *lac* Repressor from *E. coli*.

Method of Silylation

Silylation of the PTH-amino acid may be carried out by mixing it in ethyl acetate with an equal volume of BSA in either a conical glass test tube, or equivalent plastic tube, of 0.5 ml capacity, sealed with a PTFE-lined rubber septum. The reaction vessel is heated in a water bath for 15 min at 50°C and the samples withdrawn directly through the septum with a 10 μl Hamilton syringe (Pisano *et al.* 1972).

However, the most successful method of silylation is the 'on-column' derivatization. This is usually performed by injecting the reagent with the sample into the column at an inlet temperature of about 250°C, the best results being obtained by filling the syringe first with the silylating agent and then the PTH-amino acid. The reverse sequence of operations has been

94

found to result in incomplete silylation, which shows up as double peaks for most of the PTH derivatives (Beyreuther *et al.* 1975).

General Procedure

The usual support is Chromosorb W (100–120 mesh) with a 10% stationary phase of either DC 560, or its equivalent SP 400; the former having been successfully used by amongst others, Tomita *et al.* (1978), and Butler *et al.* (1977), and the latter by Beyreuther *et al.* (1975), Bennett *et al.* (1978), and Butkowski *et al.* (1977). As metal columns cannot be used—they cause destruction of the PTH-amino acids—the usual column material is glass with dimensions of about 2 mm × 3 ft, and before use it is treated, together with the glass wool plug and the support, with dichlorodimethylsilane in toluene. This reduces the number of adsorptive sites, which tend to cause tailing of the samples. Before analysis is begun the column is conditioned at 300°C for 16 hours: however, analysis is performed with a column temperature somewhere between 165° and 300°C, the optimum temperature being determined by the investigator. Normally the carrier gas is nitrogen, at a flow rate of about 65 cm³/min. If helium is used instead, better resolution is obtained (Figure XXXV), at a small increase in cost.

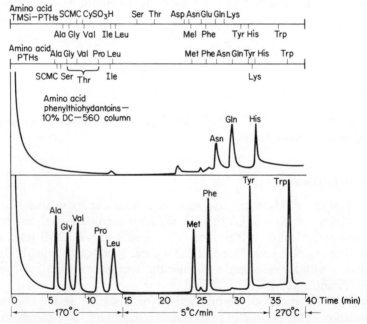

Figure XXXV   Separation of amino acid PTHs on a 4 ft × 2 mm, 10% DC-560 column. Sample sizes: 1 μg each PTH-Ala, Gly, Val, Pro, Leu, Met, Phe, and Tyr; 2 μg PTH-Trp, Asn, Gln, and His. Helium flow 65 ml/min. (From Pisano *et al.* (1972), reproduced by permission of Academic Press Inc.)

Advantages of GLC Analysis

The principal advantage of GLC analysis of PTH-amino acids is that it is quantitative, and repetitive yields may be calculated for most stages of the Edman stepwise degradation. Moreover interest is centred on this approach as it offers a possible means for the automated analysis of PTH-amino acids resulting from automated protein degradation. Automatic sample injectors are already on the commercial market and have given encouraging results with standards (Pisano *et al*. 1972). Samples may be analysed every 50 min and at this rate it seems possible that it could keep pace with the sequencer, even after including a silylation step. Nevertheless, there still remain several problems of derivatization to be solved before this costly aim is a reality.

Difficulties and Disadvantages of GLC Analysis

The major problems associated with this method of analysis are not related to the technology but to the chemistry of successful derivatisation. Although there are many reports in the literature of complete separations of most of the PTH-amino acids, when standards are used as samples, it is clear from the literature from sequence laboratories that GLC analysis, in the main, is used to analyse for at the most 16 of the 20 possible PTH derivatives. The four difficult samples are PTH-His, PTH-Arg, PTH-Cys and PTH-Trp. No successful method for the derivatisation of PTH-Arg has yet been devised and this surely deserves more attention than it has yet received. Some reports have indicated successful analysis of PTH-Cys, yet others report difficulties (Hogg and Hermodson 1977) and the same applies to PTH-Trp (Wunderer and Eulitz 1978). Even a stable derivative of cysteine, namely PTH-CMC, undergoes degradation during GLC analysis, giving rise to amongst other products PTH-dehydroserine which rapidly polymerises; however, PTH-pyridylethylated cysteine has been successfully analysed by GLC using an isothermal program at 220°C (Mak and Jones 1976).

Apart from these problems, which are of no mean significance, the other drawback to adopting this method for routine PTH-amino acid analysis is that it is beyond doubt a highly skilled technique requiring not only competent technical assistance but also expensive capital equipment. Also, it is not as quick as other available means of analysis and in a 8 hour working day it is not possible to identify all the PTH's derived from an automatic sequencer during the previous 24 hours. At present therefore, GLC analysis does not offer the many advantages that other methods of analysis have.

(3) IDENTIFICATION OF PTH-AMINO ACIDS BY HIGH-PRESSURE LIQUID CHROMATOGRAPHY (HPLC)

The relatively new technique of HPLC is now frequently being used to identify PTH-amino acids. It is a very sensitive and rapid method of analysis, but it does require expensive equipment and technical assistance. Nevertheless, it has been applied in recent years to several proteins, including: human prethrombin 2 (Butkowski *et al.* 1977); brain S-100 protein (Isobe *et al.* 1977a); bacteriophage T_4 internal protein I (Isobe *et al.* 1977b); dihydrofolate reductase from mouse sarcoma and an *E. coli* mutant (Rodkey and Bennett 1976, Bennett *et al.* 1978); and chick skin collagen (Dixit *et al.* 1977).

Although the resolution obtained is not as good as that obtained with GLC, HPLC has the following advantages:

(1) it is not necessary to prepare volatile derivatives;
(2) short analysis time—in some cases as little as 6 min;
(3) it is very sensitive and can go down to 50 pmol if a suitable gradient system is used;
(4) using this method it is possible to differentiate between PTH-Leu/Ile;
(5) it has the potential for automation.

Several different instruments have been employed for the analysis of PTH-amino acids, e.g. the Du Pont Model 830 liquid chromatograph, the Waters Associates ALC/GPC 202 high-pressure chromatograph etc. Each of these instruments has the essential features of a column, a reliable pump, a gradient maker capable of giving reproducible results, and a UV detection monitor coupled to a recording device.

Various stainless steel columns have been employed with diameters between 2 mm and 4 mm and lengths 15 cm to 500 cm, and may be purchased pre-packed with support, or may be packed dry with stationary phase in the laboratory. Supports that have been used include Partisil 5, or 10 (Reeve Angel), and μ Bondapak C_{18} (Waters Associates), with eluting solvents of diethylmethane containing 0.32–0.33% methanol, and acetonitrile–sodium acetate (pH 4.0) respectively. The PTH-amino acids are detected by their UV absorbance using a flow-through cell and UV monitor connected to a recording device. The PTH's are characterized by their retention times.

In general the PTH-amino acids fall into three separate groups depending upon their individual polarity:

Non-polar	*Relatively non-polar*	*Highly polar*
PTH-Pro	PTH-Trp	PTH-Cya
PTH-Leu	PTH-Gly	PTH-Glu
PTH-Ile	PTH-Lys	PTH-Asp
PTH-Val	PTH-Tyr	PTH-His
PTH-Phe	PTH-Thr	PTH-Arg
PTH-Met	PTH-Ser	
PTH-Ala	PTH-Asn	
	PTH-Gln	

Isobe and Okuyama (1978) were able to separate and identify all the PTH-amino acids except PTH-Arg, PTH-His and PTH-Cya by using two columns, one for the apolar and the other for the polar PTH's, in their studies on the S-100 protein from brain tissue.

The analysis of PTH-amino acids by HPLC is not without its difficulties, namely:

(1) obtaining reproducible retention times;
(2) the interference caused by UV-absorbing impurities resulting from the Edman degradation.

However, regardless of these minor difficulties this technique has an assured position in the armoury of methods for PTH-amino acid analysis. Firstly because it is the most likely candidate to be fully automated and linked to a sequencer, and secondly it is extremely useful in 'microsequencing'. In this technique the radioactive PTH-amino acid from the sequencer is mixed with non-radioactive PTH-amino acid standards and the mixture fractionated by HPLC. The effluent after passing through the UV detecting system is mixed with scintillation fluid and passed through a scintillation flow-cell. The output from the counter can then be displayed directly on the HPLC trace giving immediate identification of the radioactive amino acid.

(4) THE IDENTIFICATION OF PTH-AMINO ACIDS BY THEIR CONVERSION BACK TO AMINO ACIDS

This is probably the simplest procedure for the identification of PTH-amino acids and may also be applied to the precursor amino acid anilino-thiazolinones with a consequent saving in time. As both the equipment and expertise are readily available in all laboratories involved in amino acid sequencing it is clear that this approach has considerable advantages over other methods, and with the advent of rapid and highly sensitive analysers the capacity to maintain pace with the automatic sequencer. It is also conceivable that the thiazolinones from the sequencer could with the appropriate technical innovations be fed through a hydolysis coil to an automatic amino acid analyser, so perfecting the automatic sequencing of proteins. It is unfortunate that so little work has been done to improve the hydrolytic conditions that at present prevent this concept becoming a feasible and successful proposition.

The first serious study of the conditions necessary for the hydrolysis of PTH-amino acids was by van Orden and Carpenter (1964). They studied the hydrolysis of PTH's using either 0.1 N NaOH or 6 N HCl, and gave details of the conditions necessary for both of these reagents to back-hydrolyse most of the PTH-amino acids in reasonable yields. Several years elapsed before Smithies et al. (1971) made a detailed study of this problem and introduced two new reagents, viz. 57% HI and NaOH–dithionite. These investigators applied the new reagents to quantitate the steps in the automatic Edmon

Table XXIII. Methods for the hydrolysis of PTH-amino acids

Method	Details	Reference
Acid hydrolysis	(1) 6 N HCl, 150°C, 24 hours	van Orden and Carpenter (1964)
	(2) 57% HI, 127°C, 20 hours	Smithies et al. (1971)
	(3) 4 M CH_3SO_3H, 150°C, 4 hours	Mendez and Lai (1975)
	(4) 5.7 M HCl (+0.1% w/w $SnCl_2$) 150°C, 4 hours	Mendez and Lai (1975)
	(5) 55% HI, 130°C, 18 hours	Tomita et al. (1978)
Alkaline hydrolysis	(1) 0.1 N NaOH, 120°C, 12 hours	van Orden and Carpenter (1964)
	(2) 0.1 M $Na_2S_2O_4$ in 0.2 M NaOH, 127°C, 3.5 hours	Smithies et al. (1971)

Table XXIV. Percentage recoveries of amino acids after hydrolysis of their PTH-derivatives

Amino acid	57% HI (1)[i]	47% HI (3)	6 N HCl (2)	5.7 M HCl (3)[h]	4 M CH_3SO_3H (3)	0.2 N NaOH (1)[j]	0.1 N NaOH (2)	0.01 N NaOH (3)[k]
Asp	80	100	88	97	103	80	89	78
Thr	90[b]	89[b]	—	90[b]	18[b]	1	67[c]	20
Ser	50	1	—	68[d]	9	5[d]	—	1
Glu	80	100	81	97	100	50	66	23
Pro	70	78	88	94	91	70	96	94
Gly	80	95	104	99	99	80	96	118
Ala	90	100	78	99	100	80	86	102
Cys	60[e]	ND	ND	ND	ND	5[e]	ND	ND
Val	70	72	88	61	69	13	98	96
Met	—	—	67	92	75	90	84	76
Ile[f]	70	65	90	60	68	100	100	87
Leu	90	82	59	82	81	90	71	83
Tyr	60	80	76	67	70	100	97	92
Phe	80	72	86	70	72	100	95	88
His	20	100	ND	99	93	20	70	48
Trp	60[a]	ND	ND	97[a]	ND	40	ND	ND
Lys	70	100	ND	92	84	30	72	30
Arg	30	81	ND	99	85	5[g]	53[g]	44

References: (1) Smithies, O., Gibson, D., Fanning, E. M., Goodfliesh, R. M., Gilman, J. G., and Ballantyne, D. L. (1971) *Biochemistry* **10** 4912–4921. (2) van Orden, H. O. and Carpenter, F. H. (1964) *Biochem. Biophys. Res. Commun.* **14** 399–403.
(3) Mendez, E. and Lai, C. Y. (1975) *Anal. Biochem.* **68** 47–53.
Footnotes: ND, not determined; a, Trp was determined as Gly + Ala; b, Thr was determined as α-aminobutyric acid; c, Thr was determined as Gly; d, Ser was determined as Ala; e, Cys was determined as Ala; f, Ile includes the value for alloisoleucine; g, Arg was determined as ornithine; h, Contains 0.1% w/w of $SnCl_2$; i, the minimum recovery only is quoted; j, containing $Na_2S_2O_4$; k, containing 0.1% β-mercaptoethanol.

degradation. More recently, Mendez and Lai (1975) have introduced several new hydrolytic reagents and conditions, in particular describing the finding that 6 N HCl in the presence of $SnCl_2$ gives much improved recoveries than the acid alone. To date all these methods have been used in various sequence studies and the individual conditions are given in Table XXIII. The recoveries obtained from the different methods are summarized in Table XXIV.

All of the available methods have been found to give good yields of the following amino acids: Asp, Glu, Pro, Gly, Ala, Val, Leu, Tyr and Phe. The PTH's of Asn/Gln are always converted to the respective acids and this is one unsatisfactory aspect of this method; the location of the amides must then depend upon another method of identification. Isoleucine is always recovered as a mixture of the diastereoisomers Ile/allo-Ile; the latter isomer, having different chemical properties, is found to elute on ion-exchange chromatographic analysis in a different position than Ile, in fact allo-Ile is eluted slightly before Ile. Although no detailed study has been made on this isomerization it is thought to involve the dehydro intermediate:

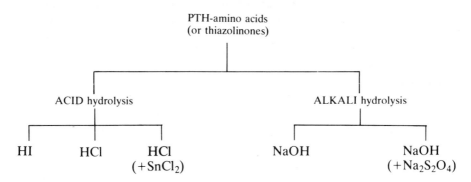

The derivatives of Trp and Cys are always destroyed, nevertheless attempts have been made to identify them by the artefacts formed on back-hydrolysis, namely Gly and Ala, from Trp, and Ala from Cys. The PTH of serine also in general gives poor recoveries and the corresponding derivative of Thr also gives rise to the artefact α-aminobutyric acid, or glycine, which may be used for its identification and quantitation.

Methods for the Back-hydrolysis of PTH-amino Acids

PTH-amino acids
(or thiazolinones)

ACID hydrolysis   ALKALI hydrolysis

HI   HCl   HCl   NaOH   NaOH
              $(+SnCl_2)$ $(+Na_2S_2O_4)$

(1) 6N HCl

In many instances this method is used to complement another method of identification, for example if TLC was the main method of identification, back-hydrolysis using 6 N HCl has been used to differentiate between PTH–Leu and PTH-Ile (Begg *et al.* 1978). The amino acids destroyed by this method are Thr, Ser, Cys, and Trp. Methionine is recovered in satisfactory yield. Mendez and Lai (1975) found that the yields may be increased by the incorporation of $SnCl_2$ in the hydrolysis solution, also this innovation enabled Thr to be quantitated as α-amino-butyric acid and serine as alanine. This approach has been used by Beyreuther *et al.* (1978) in their study of citrate-lyase acyl carrier protein.

(2) 57% HI

This has probably been the most widely used method, various concentrations of HI being employed in the range 44–57%, without any significant differences. The following modifications are observed with this procedure.

PTH — Asn/Gln ⟶ Asp/Glu

PTH — CMC ⎫
              ⎬ ⟶ Ala
PTH — Ser ⎭

PTH — Trp ⟶ Gly and Ala

PTH — Thr ⟶ α-aminobutyric acid.

If these artefacts are determined, the only amino acids not identified by this method will be Met and Cys, and in their study of the structure of Glycophorin A, Tomita *et al.* (1978) took the absence of any identifiable amino acid, at any step of the sequence degradation, after hydrolysis of the PTH-amino acid with HI, to be indicative of glycosylation.

Although PTH-Pro is hydrolysed in good yield to proline, some side reactions do occur giving rise to small amounts of artefactual material eluting on amino acid analysis near to histidine.

In general the approach is to use either the thiazolinone solution, or to combine both the ethylacetate and aqueous phases if conversion has been performed, and hydrolyse in sealed evacuated hydrolysis tubes or in open test tubes (50×10 mm) placed in a small desiccator (10 cm diameter). Each tube contains 0.1 ml of 57% HI, and an additional 25 ml of HI is placed into the bottom of the desiccator which is evacuated (0.01 Torr), fixed with a clamping ring and heated in a normal hydrolysis oven at 130°C for 20 hour. After this time the tubes are dried over NaOH pellets and P_2O_5

under high vacuum at 65°C. The residues are then ready for amino acid analysis. To quantitise each sample 50 nmol of PTH-norleucine is added prior to hydrolysis.

One of the problems associated with this method is that Ala may result from the degradation of at least three different precursors, namely PTH-Ala, PTH-CMC and PTH-Ser. To ensure positive identification the approach must be supplemented by another method. Closset *et al.* (1978), in their study of the sequence of the β-subunit of porcine follitropin, distinguished these three derivatives by the following criteria: the alanine derivative was determined by gas chromatography and by a high yield of free alanine after back hydrolysis and amino acid analysis. The CMC derivative was identified by its intrinsic radioactivity introduced by the use of ^{3}H-labelled iodoacetate for the alkylation of the cysteine residues in the protein. Finally CMC and the seryl derivative were also characterized by a low yield of free alanine on the amino acid analyser after back-hydrolysis.

(3) NaOH–dithionite

This method enables Met and Trp to be recovered unaltered, Met in yields close to the theoretical and Trp in about 50% yield. Alanine is recovered, but Ser and Cysteine (or CMC) are destroyed. Threonine is almost completely destroyed but gives a little α-aminobutyric acid. Arginine is also destroyed but a small amount of ornithine is recovered. Hydrolysis is performed in tubes placed in a desiccator with extra NaOH–dithionite solution placed at the bottom—this prevents the samples drying out. To each sample tube is added 0.2 ml of 0.1 M solution of $Na_2S_2O_4$ (sodium dithionite) in 0.2 M NaOH. The desiccator is sealed and heated in an autoclave at 127° at 21 lb/sq. in pressure. Following hydrolysis the samples are acidified by adding 20 μl of 3 M HCl containing 10% thiodiglycol (TDG), however it has been found that following this procedure (Glu/Gln) and (Asp/Asn) give other ninhydrin–reacting species that appear on the analyser near to the positions of Val and Pro respectively. If the samples are acidified in the presence of dithiothreitol (10%) instead of TDG more satisfactory results are obtained (Jabusch *et al.* 1978).

The combined use of both acid and alkaline hydrolysis is a satisfactory approach and was used by Stone *et al.* (1977) in their studies of the sequence of dihydrofolate reductase. Back-hydrolysis was routinely performed using 57% HI followed by hydrolysis with 0.1 M $Na_2S_2O_4$ in 0.2 M NaOH in those cases where the hydriodic procedure failed to give an unequivocal identification.

CHAPTER 7

Manual Methods of Amino Acid Sequencing

DETERMINATION OF N-TERMINAL RESIDUES AND SEQUENCES

The determination of amino terminal residues in both peptides and proteins is usually one of the first tasks performed in any sequence study. The finding of a unique amino terminal residue is good confirmation that the peptide/protein is as pure as hoped for. Two chemical approaches, that were devised during the period 1945–1950, are the main means of tackling this problem. The first involves labelling the amino terminal residue covalently with a suitable group that is stable to subsequent acid hydrolysis. The group is chosen for its ability to be detected by either colour, fluorescence, or radioactivity, and identification is made after comparing the product, after acid hydrolysis, with standard amino acid derivatives. This approach was first used by Sanger (1945), who employed 2,4-dinitrofluorobenzene for this purpose. This was the technique he later used in his classic work on the structure of insulin. The use of dinitrofluorobenzene was a brilliant piece of intuitive chemical innovation that was to initiate the subsequent rapid development in protein structure determination. However, at the present time this reagent is not used as it has been replaced by superior reagents (see Figure XXXVI).

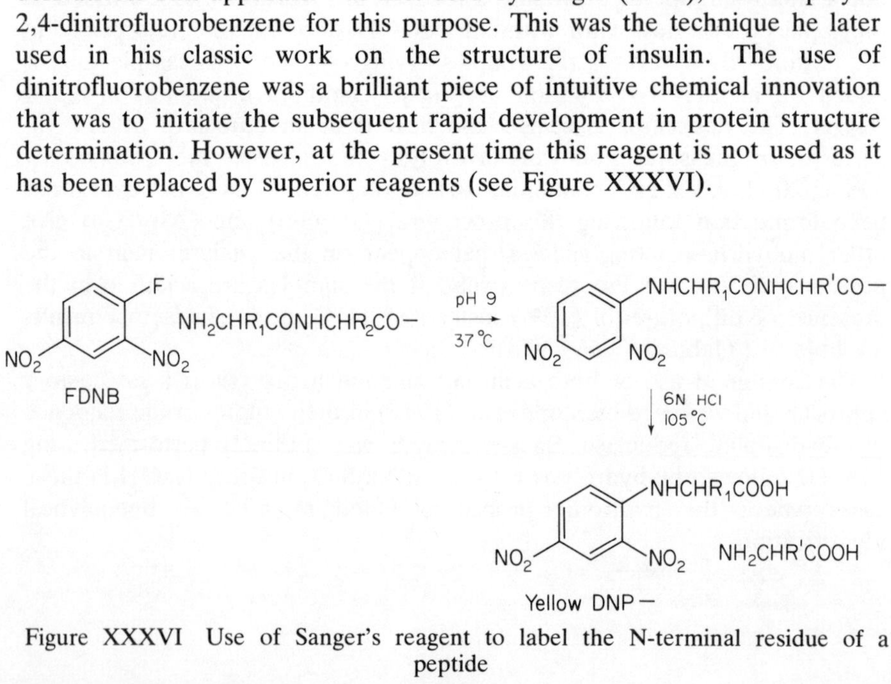

Figure XXXVI Use of Sanger's reagent to label the N-terminal residue of a peptide

102

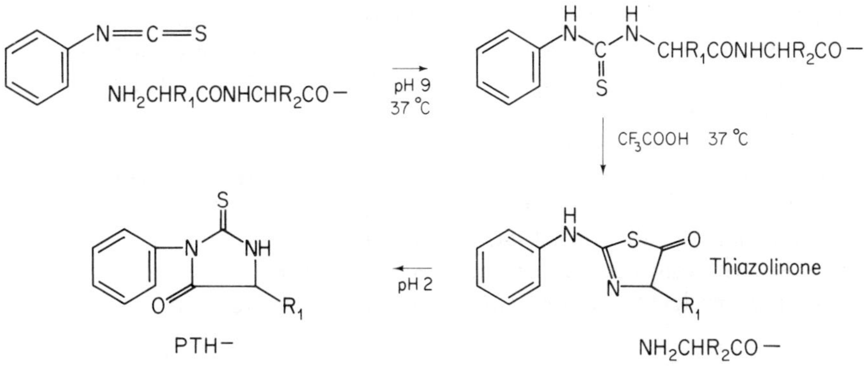

Figure XXXVII The Edman degradation reaction

The second approach was that devised by Edman in 1950, the procedure now bearing his name. The reagent used is phenylisothiocyanate, and this reacts at alkaline pH with the amino group of the N-terminal residue. The resulting N-phenylthiocarbamoyl derivative is cyclized in the presence of acid to give the thiazolinone corresponding to the N-terminal residue, and a peptide having one residue less than the original (Figure XXXVII). The thiazolinone is unstable and cannot be identified as such, however it is readily converted to the more stable phenylthiohydantoin in the presence of acid.

These two procedures are the mainspring from which all of the presently available manual sequencing methods have been derived. These methods will now be considered in detail.

(1) The Edman Method of Sequence Determination

(i) The Edman Degradation

There have been many modifications of the simple reaction sequence originally proposed by Edman. One of the most successful variations has been that devised by Peterson et al. (1972) and this is outlined below.

Stage 1 (coupling: the peptide (100 nmol) is dissolved in 0.2 ml of 0.4 M dimethyl-allylamine-trifluoroacetic acid buffer, pH 9.5, in 1-propanol–water (3 : 2 v/v). Phenylisothiocyanate (10 μl) is added under N_2 and the solution mixed. It is then incubated at 55°C for 20 min.

Stage 2 (washing): to the reaction mixture is added 1 ml of benzene, the solution mixed and centrifuged. The upper benzene layer is discarded, and the aqueous solution, after drying, is extracted with ethyl acetate (0.5 ml) under nitrogen. The ethyl acetate layer is discarded and the aqueous solution reduced to dryness.

Stage 3: cleavage is performed on the addition of 100 μl of trifluoroacetic

104

acid to the phenylthiocarbamoylated peptide and incubation at 55°C for 8 min. The trifluoroacetic acid is then removed in a stream of nitrogen.

Stage 4: the dried residue is extracted with anhydrous ether containing 10^{-4} M dithiothreitol (1.0 ml). The ether layer is collected and to it is added a small quantity of PTH-norleucine as an internal standard.

Stage 5 (conversion): the ether solution is reduced to dryness and conversion to the PTH-derivative is performed by the addition of 0.2 ml of 1 N HCl and incubation at 80°C for 10 min. This reaction mixture is extracted with ethyl acetate and both layers taken for analysis.

A single cycle of this procedure takes approximately 50 min, and the

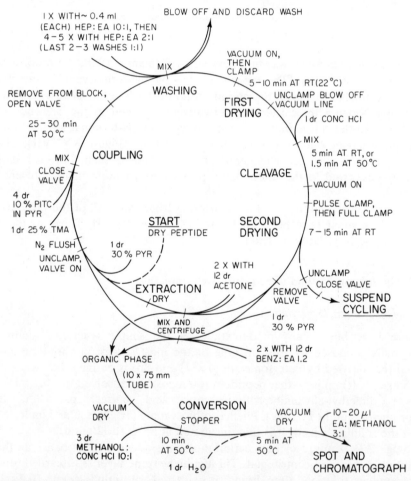

Figure XXXVIII The Edman cycle as proposed by Tarr (1975). Abbreviations: dr, drop; TMA, trimethylamine; PITC, phenylisothiocyanate; HEP, heptane; EA, ethyl acetate; RT, room temperature; BENZ, benzene.
(Reproduced by permission of Academic Press Inc.)

amino acid sequence of up to 20 residues may be routinely determined using less than 100 nmol of peptide. van Eerd and Takahashi (1976) introduced an important modification of this reaction: they added water directly to the residue after removal of the trifluoroacetic acid whereupon they extracted the thiazolinone with ethyl acetate. This was found to reduce mechanical losses of the peptide at each step of the Edman.

Walker et al. (1977) introduced the technique of 'double coupling', in which a further 10 μl of phenylisothiocyanate was added after 30 min of the coupling step. This procedure was used with peptides having a high proline content, as it is known that proline residues couple with some difficulty in the Edman procedure.

With hydrophobic peptides solubility problems can be overcome by the use of Braunitzer reagents, as is carried out in automatic liquid-phase sequencing. van Eerd and Takahashi (1976) used Braunitzer reagent 1 (4-sulphophenyl isothiocyanate) in place of phenylisothiocyanate in studies of tryptic peptides from ox cardiac troponin C. These authors report excellent accomplishments with the manual Edman degradation that enabled them to sequence the whole of this protein using only 60 mg. This efficient degradation enabled them to sequence up to 36 residues of one tryptic peptide. These results are certainly encouraging for those laboratories that lack the presence of an automatic sequencer.

Tarr (1975) has also introduced important modifications of the Edman degradation that enables up to 40 residues of a peptide to be sequenced manually using between 5 and 50 nmol of peptide. Tarr considered that the primary defect of the classical Edman degradation was due to desulphurization of the peptide by atmospheric oxygen and to this end he included ethanethiol in the coupling buffers to ensure reducing conditions. His reaction cycle is illustrated in Figure XXXVIII. Other modifications were the use of a micro-reaction vessel that enable the introduction and removal of reagents under a continuous nitrogen barrier. Also after coupling the washing procedure was improved by the use of heptane:ethyl acetate mixtures instead of benzene, and in particular cleavage was performed using concentrated HCl since Tarr considered that it is the trifluoroacetic acid that leads to the formation of accumulated 'oil' in the conventional Edman reaction. He was able to sequence manually 39 residues of a 44-residue peptide using this improved procedure, and pointedly commented that the actual length of sequence determination achieved was solely limited by the 'patience of the investigator'. Other successes with the manual Edman sequence degradation are summarized in Table XXV.

(ii) The 'Subtractive' Edman Method

The 'subtractive' Edman is only applicable to small peptides, as it depends on the difference in analysis before and after each step of the degradation.

Table XXV. Some achievements at determining long sequences using manual methods

Sample	Amount used (nmol)	No. of residues sequenced	Method used	Reference
Peptide	<50	39	Modified Edman	Tarr (1975)
Peptide	100	20	Edman method as modified by Peterson et al. (1972)	Tomita et al. (1978)
Peptide	100–250	21	Edman	Tanaka et al. (1977)
Ferredoxin, Chlorobium thiosulphatophilum	110	22	Edman	Hase et al. (1978)
IgG (heavy chain)	600	20	Dansyl–Edman	Percy and Buchwald (1972)
Peptide	250	20	Dansyl–Edman (modified)	Meagher (1975)
Lysozyme	10	19	Using dabsyl isothiocyanate	Chang (1977)
Ferredoxin, Chromatium vinosum	—	19	Edman	Hase et al. (1977)

It may, in certain circumstances, be used to determine the N-terminal sequence of large peptides, particularly if the residues in this region present difficulties of identification. In essence, after each step of the degradation a small sample of the remaining peptide is withdrawn and its amino acid composition determined. The difference between this and the analysis at the previous step is an indication of which amino acid was removed. An example of the use of this method to the peptide

Cya–His–Thr–Ala–Tyr–Gly–Lys

is given in Table XXVI.

Table XXVI. Subtractive Edman degradation: an example of its application to the heptapeptide Cya–His–Thr–Ala–Tyr–Gly–Lys

Amino acid*	Cya	Thr	Gly	Ala	Tyr	His	Lys
Step 0	1.0	0.8	1.1	1.0	0.9	0.8	1.0
Step 1	0.1	0.8	1.2	1.0	1.0	0.9	1.0
Step 2	—	0.9	1.2	1.0	1.0	0.1	1.0
Step 3	—	0.0	1.1	1.0	1.0	—	1.0
Step 4	—	—	1.0	0.0	1.0	—	1.0
Step 5	—	—	1.0	—	0.1	—	1.0
Step 6	—	—	0.2	—	—	—	1.0

*The composition of the peptide was determined at each step of the Edman degradation by amino acid analysis. The results are expressed as mols of amino acid residue per mol of lysine.

(2) N-Terminal Determination with Dansyl Chloride

The use of 'Dansyl' (5-dimethylamino naphthalene-1-sulphonyl) chloride as a labelling reagent was discovered by accident, by B. S. Hartley, during studies on chymotrypsin. It was found to react specifically with amino groups in this protein, forming derivatives that were stable to subsequent acid hydrolysis, and Hartley considered it would make a suitable N-terminal reagent, as its sensitivity was at least a hundred-fold greater than Sanger's reagent (2,4-dinitrofluorobenzene) (Hartley 1970). The mechanism of the reaction of this reagent with polypeptides is illustrated in Figure XXXIX.

High-voltage electrophoresis was originally used to separate the dansyl amino acids formed after hydrolysis of a dansylated peptide, however the usefulness of this reagent was vastly enhanced by the introduction of thin layer chromatography on polyamide layers for the separation of these

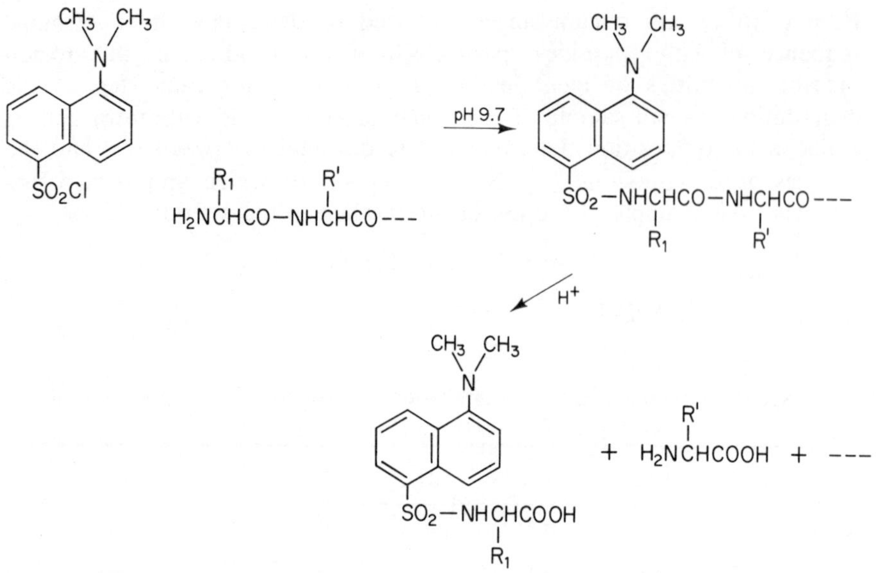

Figure XXXIX   Labelling the N-terminal residue of a peptide with dansyl chloride

derivatives. The most useful system is that introduced by Woods and Wang (1967): this is a two-dimensional thin layer chromatography on polyamide layers (Figure XL). Not all the normal dansyl amino acid derivatives are resolved by two chromatographic runs, so a third solvent, run in the same direction as the second, may be employed to resolve the dansyl derivatives of histidine, arginine and cysteic acid. Further, this step improves the separation between Thr/Ser, and Asp/Glu. The replacement of benzene with toluene in the second solvent system, resulting in virtually the same separation, has been suggested, on health considerations (Croft 1972).

The dansylation reaction, followed by subsequent separation of the dansyl-amino acids on polyamide, is an excellent method of N-terminal analysis: however, care has to be exercised to ensure that the dansylated peptide, or protein, has been completely hydrolysed, as this can lead to misinterpretation of the products when identified from polyamide thin layer plates; van Beynum et al. (1977) discovered such a mistake in the sequence of alfalfa mosaic virus coat protein. Initially the N-terminal of a tryptic peptide was identified as tyrosine, but it was in fact Ile-Leu. This was because the slowly hydrolysed dipeptide DNS-Ile-Leu appeared on polyamide layers in a similar position to DNS-Tyr. A similar finding was made by Dunkley and Carnegie (1974) in their work on rat myelin basic protein, during which they found that the related dansylated dipeptide DNS-Ile-Val was only slowly hydrolysed by acid. A compromise approach has to be reached, as too long a hydrolysis period is likely to destroy any DNS-Pro, if present.

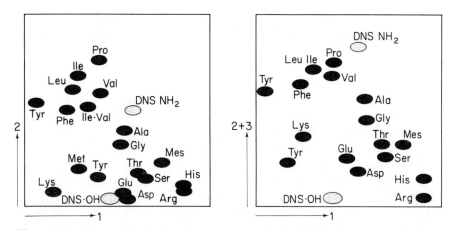

Figure XL Separation of dansyl amino acids on thin layers of polyamide according
to the method of Woods and Wang (1967)

The actual dansylation procedure for peptides is extremely simple: to approximately 100 pmol of peptide is added 100 µl of 0.2 M NaHCO$_3$ followed by 100 µl of 0.25% dansyl chloride in acetone. Reaction takes place at 37°C for 30 min, whereupon the reaction mixture is reduced to dryness. Hydrochloric acid (6 N, 200 µl) is added to the residue and the sample hydrolysed. The lower limit of detection is about 10 pmol. Proteins may be dansylated in 0.2 M NaHCO$_3$ containing 0.1% sodium dodecyl sulphate, after which they are precipitated with acetone, and washed with the same solvent before hydrolysis (Bennett *et al.* 1978). Alternatively proteins may be dansylated in solutions containing 6 M urea, from which they are precipitated with trichloroacetic acid (Mosesson *et al.* 1973).

Sequence Determination by the Dansyl–Edman Method

The straightforward manual Edman degradation is not without its difficulties. One problem is the partial extraction, and consequent loss, of hydrophobic phenylthiocarbamoyl peptides in the washing after cleavage to remove excess phenylisothiocyanate. Gray and Hartley (1963) introduced the procedure that instead of this extraction process, the reaction mixture is dried down and directly treated with acid. Following cleavage all unwanted products, including the thiazolinone, are extracted with n-butyl acetate and discarded. The N-terminal residue at each step of the degradation is identified by dansylation and hydrolysis of a small sample. This procedure also had the added advantage that the DNS-amino acids were more readily identifiable than the PTH-derivatives. This ingenious innovation has been largely responsible for the great upsurge in sequence information that emerged from the world's protein sequence laboratories during the decade 1964–1974. It has tremendous advantages over other methods, in particular it is an extremely simple procedure to implement, so was therefore available to even the smallest laboratory. The author has found that even the most junior technician can readily master this procedure, and with little experience, achieve about four residues per day.

A micro-version of the procedure has been introduced, by which it is possible to sequence as little as 1 nmol of a peptide, and this has been used to sequence part of Met-tRNA synthetase (Bruton and Hartley 1970). The reaction is carried out in micro-tubes (0.2 cm × 8 cm) and after reaction the DNS-amino acids are identified on small sheets of polyamide (7.5 × 7.5 cm). The procedure can also be applied to intact proteins: Weiner *et al.* (1972) have applied the method to proteins eluted from SDS-gels, determining up to 10 residues using only a few nmol of protein, and Percy and Buchwald (1972) have determined 20 residues of the N-terminal sequence of the heavy chain of IgG Sac.

For small peptides, of which the protein chemist might at some stage be encumbered with a large number, a procedure has been devised for rapid sequence determination (Gray and Smith 1970). Essentially, the peptide solution is divided into a number of portions and each one subjected to a successively greater number of cycles. No extraction is performed until the required number of cycles is complete, and all the samples are extracted simultaneously, saving considerable time. Dansylation is then performed, which should clearly indicate the sequence, e.g.

No. of cycles	Peptide resulting	N-terminal residue identified by DNS-Cl
0	Gly–Ala–Ser–Try	DNS-Gly
1	Ala–Ser–Tyr	DNS-Ala
2	Ser–Tyr	DNS-Ser
3	Tyr	DNS-Tyr

One of the most interesting and potentially useful modifications of the Dansyl-Edman degradation has been the enclosed nitrogen chamber version devised by Meagher (1975). This chamber (Figure XLI) is easily constructed in the laboratory and has been found to eliminate problems associated with the oxidation of phenylthiocarbamoyl peptides, and to reduce the loss of protein caused by hydrolysis, as a consequence of moisture in the trifluoroacetic acid used in the cleavage stage. Coupling is performed in aqueous 50% pyridine solution, containing 10^{-5} M dithiothreitol, with the addition of sodium dodecyl sulphate if the protein failed to dissolve well. The method was found to be capable of sequencing up to 12 samples simultaneously and with a speed approaching that of the automatic sequencer.

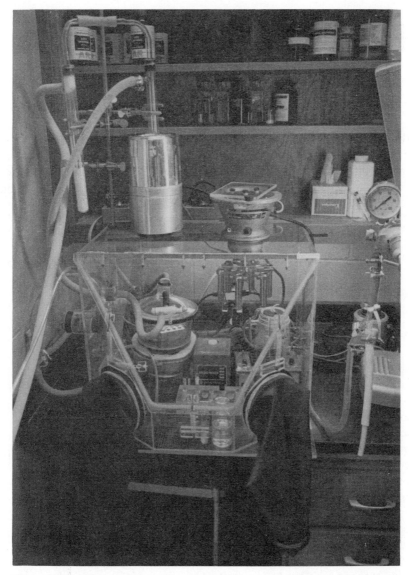

Figure XLI Photograph of the nitrogen chamber used by Meagher to sequence multiple samples of peptides. (Reproduced by courtesy of Dr R. B. Meagher)

(3) Other Useful N-terminal Reagents

Innumerable reagents for N-terminal determination have been proposed, but few have been chosen for practical application to proteins, and only a small number of the most useful will be covered here.

(i) Dabsyl Chloride

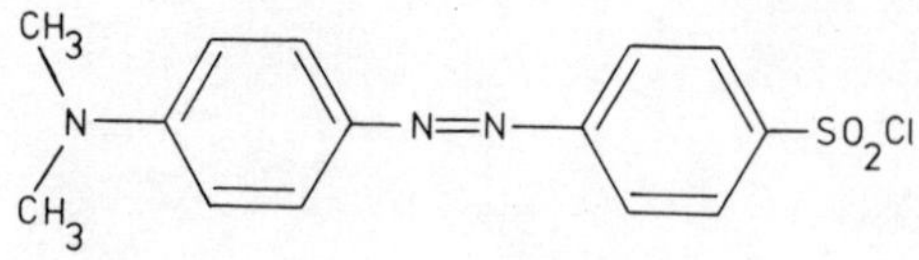

Dabsyl chloride (4-dimethyl aminoazobenzene-4′-sulphonyl chloride) was introduced as a chromophoric label for N-terminal residue determination of peptides and proteins, by Lin and Chang (1975). It has been found to be extensively sensitive, detectable in the 10^{-10} mole range by its intense colour.

(ii) Dabsyl Isothiocyanate

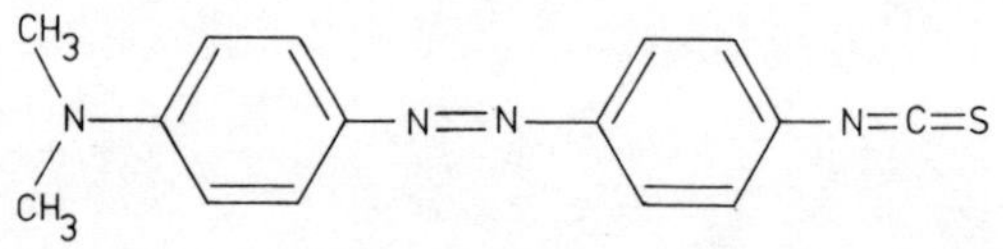

Dabsyl isothiocyanate (4,N,N-dimethyl aminoazobenzene 4′isothiocyanate) was introduced by Chang (1977) as an alternative to phenylisothiocyanate. It has the advantage that the thiazolinones formed on conversion to their thiohydantoin derivatives are readily visualized on polyamide thin layers, after chromatography, due to their intense colour. It was found possible to sequence a hexapeptide completely using only 2 nmol, and it was further used to sequence the first 12 residues of lysozyme employing 10 nmol of protein. It has however, the slight drawback of not reacting as readily with α-amino groups as does phenylisothiocyanate and rather drastic conditions are needed to affect reaction. Chang (1978) has made the interesting observation that this reagent reacts with N-terminal N-monomethyl amino acids directly to form the thiohydantoin ring and he has suggested that this might be the basis of a slightly new degradation procedure.

This reagent has also been attached to porous glass beads and used in a manual solid phase sequencing procedure (Chang *et al.* 1977). With this method it was possible to sequence up to 19 residues using less than 2 nmol of a protein; it was estimated that <0.1 nmol was needed at each step for identification.

(4) Use of Enzymes for N-terminal Determination

The aminopeptidases are a group of intracellular enzymes that hydrolyse amino terminal residues of peptides and proteins. Swine kidney is the major source of these enzymes, the two principal ones being leucine aminopeptidase (LAP) isolated from the supernatant fraction and aminopeptidase M from the microsomal fraction. These two enzymes have many properties in common but differ in their divalent cation requirements and in their specificities. In general they both show a broad specificity, with amino acids having hydrophobic side chains most easily hydrolysed: however, sequences of the type X–Pro are not cleaved by aminopeptidase M (van Beynum et al. 1977), e.g.

$$\overrightarrow{\text{Ile}}\text{—}\overrightarrow{\text{Ala}}\text{—}\overrightarrow{\text{Leu}}\text{—Gln—Pro} \ldots \ldots$$

LAP before use requires activation with Mg^{++} and assays are usually performed in tris buffers (0.1 M) at pH 8.6, whereas aminopeptidase M requires no activation and digests are performed in sodium phosphate buffers at pH 7.0. In general, after addition of the enzyme to the substrate, the release of amino acids from the N-terminus is measured kinetically and this gives some indication of the sequence in this region of the protein.

(5) The Determination of Blocked N-terminal Residues

(i) N-terminal Acetyl Groups

Interest in proteins having N-terminal acetyl groups has grown rapidly since Narita (1958) first demonstrated the presence of an N-terminal acetyl group in tobacco mosaic virus protein. Since that time many proteins have been found to have acetylated termini: some of these are tabulated in Table XXVII.

The N-terminal acetyl residue cannot be determined directly on the intact protein. The most precise approach is to isolate the blocked, ninhydrin-negative peptide from an enzymic digest of the protein and to elucidate its structure using mass spectrometry as described in chapter 8. However, chemical methods are quite satisfactory and in general involve digesting the protein with a proteinase of broad specificity, such as pronase from *Streptomyces griseus*. The acetyl-peptide may readily be isolated from the resulting mixture after chromatography on a column of Dowex 50(H^+) (Mok and Waley 1968).

(ii) Pyroglutamyl Residues

Pyrrolidone carboxylic acid (pyroglutamic acid) was found by Wilkinson *et al.* (1966) to be the N-terminal amino acid of the heavy chain of rabbit IgG. Subsequently it has been found to be present in many other proteins and peptides (see Table XXVIII). It is thought that it is formed when the peptide, or protein, is exposed to a slightly acidic environment, by

Table XXVII. Some proteins containing N-acetyl groups

Ac-Gly	Ac-Ser	Ac-Ala	Ac-Thr	Ac-Met	Ac-Trp	Ac-Val
Cytochrome c from: elephant, seal, bonito, horse, carp, dogfish, snapping turtle, kangaroo, zebra, hog, man, camel, ox, chicken, rabbit, *Euglena gracilis*.	Tobacco mosaic virus ribosomal protein, horse liver alcohol dehydrogenase, glyceraldehyde 3-PO_4 dehydrogenase, haemoglobin α-chain of *Catostomus clarkii*, ovine luteinizing hormone, melanocyte stimulating hormone, ox ferritin, histone f_{2a}.	Wool keratin, myelin basic protein, carp myogen, cytochrome c from: tomato, leek, spinach, cotton, maidenhair tree, castor, sesame, sunflower, mung bean, rape, buckwheat, cauliflower, pumpkin, wheat germ.	Ox fibrinogen.	α-crystallin.	$β_s$-crystallin.	Chick haemoglobin A1$β$

Table XXVIII. Proteins/peptides having N-terminal pyroglutamic acid

---

Carboxypeptidase inhibitor from potatoes
Cytochrome c' from Alcaligenes
Cytochrome c2 from *Rhodopseudomonas viridis*
Caerulein
Eledoisin
Alytesin
Bombesin
Uperolein
Xenopsin
Ameletin
Neurotensin
Gastrin (pig, man, ovine, ox, cat)
LH- and FSH-releasing hormone
Locust adipokinetic hormone
Blanching hormone
Bovine para kappa casein
Bovine kappa beta 1 casein
Alpha acid glycoprotein from human plasma
Human apolipoprotein Apolp GLN
Human apolipoprotein AII Rhesus monkey

Note: This list excludes the immunoglobulin chains.

cyclization of a precursor glutaminyl residue thus:

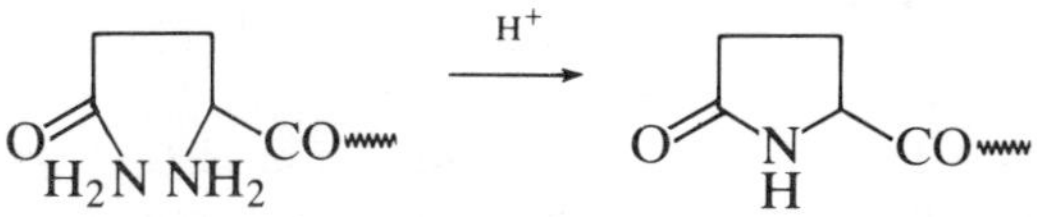

It is unlikely that a glutamyl residue would cyclize under these conditions, as has been proposed by certain workers.

This cyclic structure has posed considerable difficulties during sequence studies, notably in the Edman degradation which is dependent upon an available α-amino group. van Beynum *et al.* (1977) found that they could reduce the extent of cyclization of glutamine residues during the manual Edman degradation by performing the cleavage reaction of the previous residue, with trifluoroacetic acid, at $0°C$ for 10 min, instead of the usual $40°C$ and 30 min. O'Donnell and Inglis (1974) have found that the tendency of glutamine to cyclize is enhanced if it is followed in the sequence by a prolyl residue.

There have been many attempts to devise a procedure to chemically open the pyrrolidone ring. The most successful is methanolysis, whereby the peptide is treated at room temperature, with conc. HCl/methanol (1 : 11, v/v) for 2 days. Under these conditions the pyrrolidone ring is opened to give the γ-methyl ester of a glutamyl residue. This procedure was used by van Beynum *et al.* (1977) during an investigation of the structure of Alfalfa mosaic virus coat protein. However, side reactions, particularly hydrolysis of the peptide chain, occur if there are traces of water present (Kawasaki and Itano 1972).

Doolittle (1972) has been successful in isolating an enzyme from certain strains of *Pseudomonas* and *Bacillus subtilis*, that cleave pyroglutamyl residues from polypeptide chains. However, the isolation of these enzymes has posed considerable problems, and Podell and Abraham (1978) have developed a procedure for the release of pyroglutamyl residues from peptides using commercially available pyroglutamate aminopeptidase, isolated from calf liver.

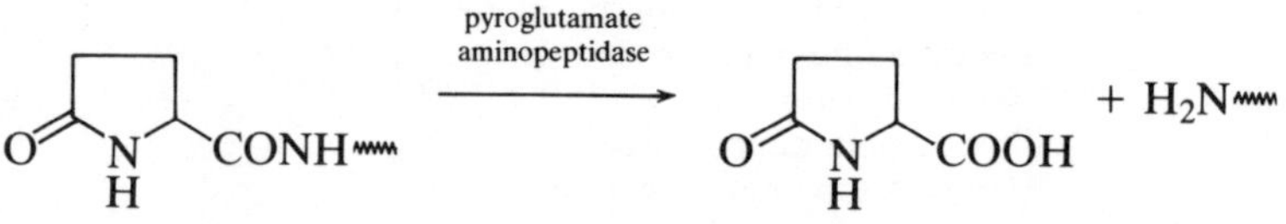

A related cyclization reaction has been found with N-terminal carboxamido-methyl cysteine residues (Gregory and Preston 1977), which condense to form a six-membered lactam ring thus:

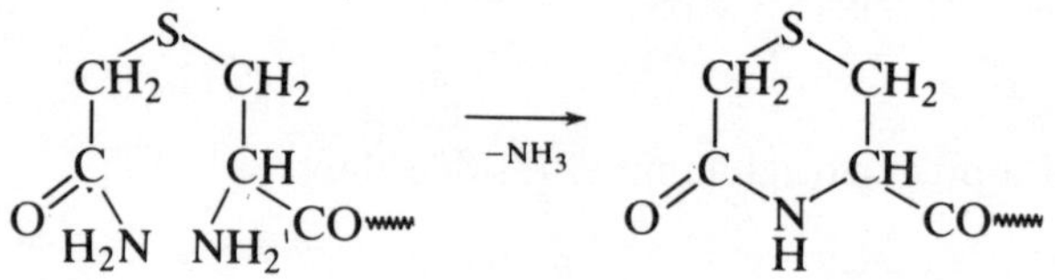

In related studies, Closset *et al.* (1978) have found that during automatic sequencing a very low yield was observed when carboxy-methyl cysteine was the N-terminal residue, and they suggest an analogous cyclization as above.

THE DETERMINATION OF C-TERMINAL RESIDUES AND SEQUENCES

(1) Hydrazinolysis

Hydrazinolysis was introduced by Akabori *et al.* (1952) for the determination of carboxyl-terminal residues in peptides and proteins. The general procedure is to treat the peptide, or protein, with the anhydrous reagent, in a sealed tube, at 100°C, for a period of time between 12 and 24 hours. Hydrazine sulphate is occasionally employed as a catalyst, enabling the reaction to be performed at a lower temperature, although the advantages gained in its use are in doubt. After reaction the excess hydrazine is removed by volatilization *in vacuo*. The reaction is summarized thus:

$$NH_2CHR_1CO \ldots\ldots\ldots NHCHR_nCONH.CHR_{n+1}COOH$$

$$\downarrow |N_2H_4$$

$$NH_2CHR_1CONHNH_2, \ldots\ldots NH_2CHR_nCONHNH_2, + NH_2CHR_{n+1}COOH$$

The hydrazine converts all the amino acid residues, except the C-terminal one, into their respective hydrazides. The C-terminal amino acid is then identified by chromatography, after it has been separated from the bulk of the hydrazides. In practice, this is not so easy to accomplish, since the reaction demands anhydrous hydrazine, which is difficult to prepare and dangerous to handle. However in certain circumstances this is an extremely useful procedure. Unfortunatley it is not applicable to C-terminal arginine, asparagine, or glutamine.

(2) Reaction with Carboxypeptidases

The most useful method for the determination of C-terminal residues is undoubtedly the enzymatic procedure. Carboxypeptidase reacts with peptides and proteins to release amino acids that have a free α-carboxyl group. At least four carboxypeptidases have been isolated and described namely, carboxypeptidases A, B, C and Y (Table XXIX). Generally the C-terminal sequence is determined by studying the kinetic release of amino acids from the peptide after the addition of the enzyme. Carboxypeptidase A, which is the best characterised, has been used most.

Table XXIX. Properties of carboxypeptidases (CBPs)

Enzyme	Source	Specificity	Optimum pH
CBP(A)	Pancreas	Removes all amino acids except lysine, arginine and proline	8.0
CBP(B)	Pancreas	Removes only lysine and arginine	8.0
CBP(C)	Citrus leaves	Liberates acidic, basic and neutral amino acids including proline	3.5
CBP(Y)	Baker's yeast	Liberates all C-terminal amino acids including proline	6.0

Usually carboxypeptidases do not react with native proteins, but there are exceptions, for example carboxypeptidase A was found to cause rapid release of C-terminal tyrosine from the lens protein γ-crystallin (Croft 1971; see Figure XLII). No further amino acids were liberated, until the protein had been denatured by performic acid oxidation, whereupon the amino acids released clearly indicated the C-terminal sequence of this protein to be (Figure XLII):

$$\text{www–Val–Met–Asp–Phe–Tyr–COOH}$$

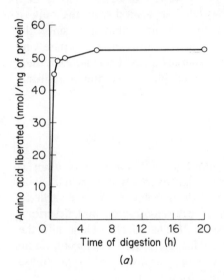

(a)

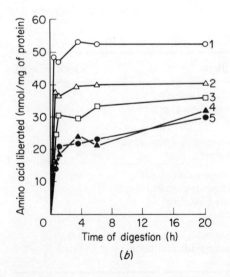

(b)

Figure XLII (a) Release of tyrosine from γ-crystallin by carboxypeptidase A (b) Release of amino acids from citraconylated, oxidized γ-crystallin by carboxypeptidase A. Curve 1, tyrosine; curve 2, phenylalanine; curve 3, aspartic acid; curve 4, valine; curve 5, methionine sulphone

Carboxypeptidase C was originally isolated from the peel of citrus fruits by Zuber (1964), who found that it was capable of releasing C-terminal proline, as well as other amino acids. Subsequently it has been prepared from germinated wheat and this preparation has been used in sequence studies on β-purothionin (Mak and Jones 1976). It is interesting that in this study the enzyme reacted with the protein in its native conformation, for as mentioned above this is untypical of the other carboxypeptidases. In related studies, Gregory and Preston (1977) found that whereas carboxypeptidases A and B failed to release amino acids from the C-terminus of urogastrone, the enzyme carboxypeptidase C released them in the expected order. This could possibly be due to partial denaturation of the native substrate in the acidic reaction medium of the carboxypeptidase C digestion.

The enzyme carboxypeptidase Y is isolated from baker's yeast and is sometimes referred to as 'phaseolain'. This carboxypeptidase exhibits a broad specificity towards most C-terminal amino acids, including proline, and may successfully be used in solutions of 6 M urea, as shown by Ponsting1 et al (1978) in their studies of the protein uteroglobin. Lee and Riordan (1978) report that most preparations are contaminated by a specific endopeptidase; however, this activity may be selectively inhibited by the addition of pepstatin A.

(3) C-Terminal Selective Tritium Labelling

Matsuo et al. (1966) introduced an extremely useful and specific method for the C-terminal determination of peptides and proteins. This method has been successfully used by Croft (1968) to determine the C-terminal residues of peptides isolated from the peptide antibiotic viomycin. The reaction may be summarized in the following steps:

(1) the peptide is treated with acetic anhydride to form a C-terminal oxazolone;
(2) base-catalyzed racemization is induced at the C_4 position of the oxazolone ring by pyridine; this is carried out in the presence of T_2O and tritium is therefore incorporated into the oxazolone ring;
(3) the oxazolone ring is opened to regenerate the C-terminal amino acid, that now contains the tritium in the α-position of this residue;
(4) any exchangeable isotope is removed by successive additions of water followed by evaporations;
(5) the peptide is finally hydrolysed and the amino acids separated by chromatography; the radioactive one is identified readily, as the C-terminal residue.

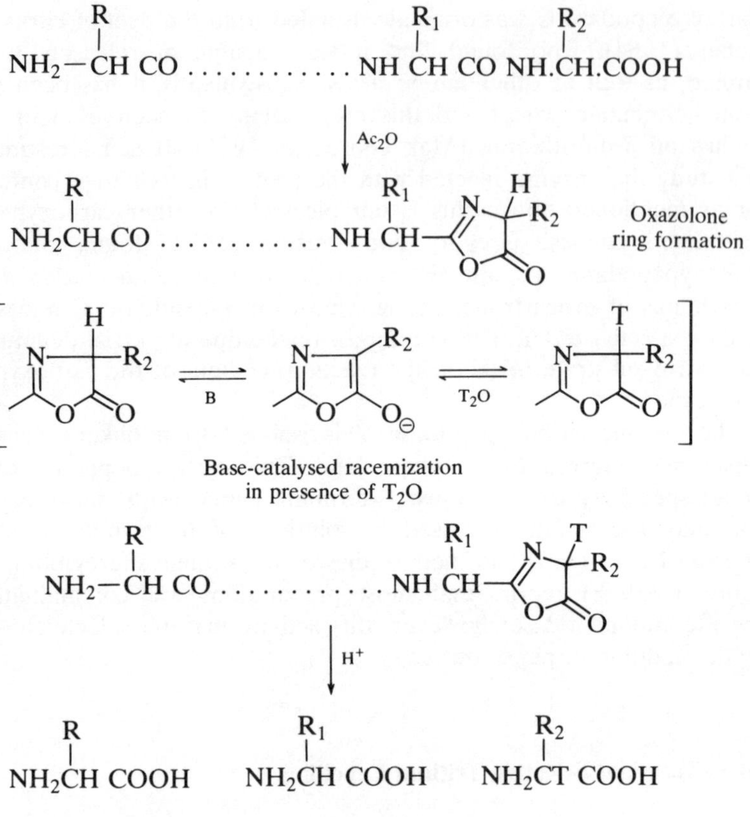

$$\underset{NH_2-\overset{\displaystyle R}{\underset{|}{C}H}\ CO}{} \ldots\ldots\ldots \underset{NH\ \overset{\displaystyle R_1}{\underset{|}{C}H}\ CO}{} NH.\underset{\overset{\displaystyle R_2}{\underset{|}{C}H}}{}.COOH$$

$\Big\downarrow Ac_2O$

$$\underset{NH_2\overset{\displaystyle R}{\underset{|}{C}H}\ CO}{} \ldots\ldots\ldots NH\ \overset{\displaystyle R_1}{\underset{|}{C}H}-$$ oxazolone ring formation

Base-catalysed racemization
in presence of T_2O

$$NH_2-\overset{\displaystyle R}{\underset{|}{C}H}\ CO \ldots\ldots\ldots NH\ \overset{\displaystyle R_1}{\underset{|}{C}H}-$$

$\Big\downarrow H^+$

$$\underset{NH_2\overset{\displaystyle R}{\underset{|}{C}H}\ COOH}{} \qquad \underset{NH_2\overset{\displaystyle R_1}{\underset{|}{C}H}\ COOH}{} \qquad \underset{NH_2\overset{\displaystyle R_2}{\underset{|}{C}T}\ COOH}{}$$

(4) 'Subtractive' C-terminal Determination

This method, recently introduced by Parham and Loudon (1978), is in principle similar to the old Dakin–West degradation of peptides. The peptide, which is immobilized via its amino terminus to porous glass beads, is treated with di-*p*-nitrophenylphosphoryl azide to convert all carboxylic acid groups to their corresponding acylazides, in one step, thus:

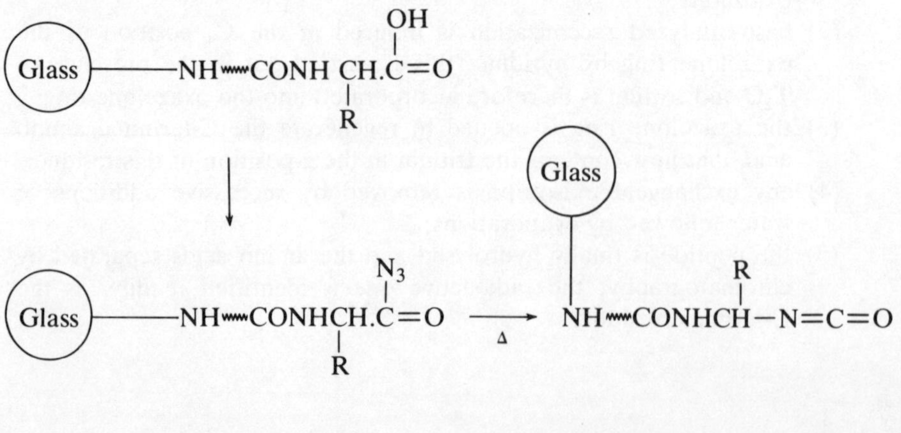

Glass——NH⌇CONH $\overset{OH}{\underset{R}{\underset{|}{C}H.\overset{|}{C}}}$=O

$\downarrow$

Glass——NH⌇CONH$\underset{R}{\underset{|}{C}H}.\overset{N_3}{\overset{|}{C}}$=O $\underset{\Delta}{\longrightarrow}$ NH⌇CONH$\underset{R}{\underset{|}{C}H}$—N=C=O (Glass)

Subsequent thermolysis of the acyl azide converts it into an isocyanate. Acid hydrolysis of this product leads to destruction of the C-terminal residue, which may readily be ascertained by the difference in amino acid content before and after reaction. In this respect, it is similar to the subtractive Edman degradation. However, this method is only suitable for small simple peptides, and with peptides of this type Parham and Loudon found that they lost their C-terminal residue in yields greater than 90%.

CHAPTER 8

Applications of Mass Spectrometry to the Sequence Analysis of Peptides and Proteins

In an attempt to devise an automated procedure for the sequence analysis of peptides and proteins, the attention and hope of many chemists, during the last two decades, has been focused on mass spectrometry. Yet despite the early promise of mass spectrometry, that was generated in the early days with studies on small synthetic peptides, peptide antibiotics, and the like, it has not become, contrary to general expectation, the panacea of the protein biochemist. At present the most successful procedure for peptide sequencing by mass spectrometry involves considerable initial chemical modification, including acetylation and permethylation of the peptide, which itself must not have more than, at the most, twelve residues. This derivation is necessary so as to enhance the volatility of the peptide and may further involve other chemical modification reactions. Fragmentation of the modified peptide in the mass spectrometer occurs in a stepwise manner with the loss of a derivatized amino acid residue, one by one, from the C-terminal end of the peptide chain. What occurs is virtually a simultaneous sequential degradation of the peptide from the C-terminus, in contrast to the Edman degradation which begins at the N-terminus of the polypeptide chain and is intermittent. As each amino acid residue derivative is of unique mass (except leucine/isoleucine, see Table XXX) the mass differences of the principal peaks in the resulting spectrum is an indication of the sequence of the peptide. The technique is very sensitive, requiring a similar amount of material as needed by the sequenator, and is reliable. Above all it is a very rapid technique, as up to 10 residues may be determined in one step. Furthermore, it offers the advantage of determining the sequence of peptides that might possess a blocked amino terminus, this being tedious by other means. Mass spectrometry is also capable of accurately analysing and resolving peptide mixtures, so avoiding the time-consuming and wasteful process of peptide isolation and purification.

Table XXX. Integral mass numbers corresponding to derivatives of the amino acids

Amino acid	Structure of derivative	A N-terminal mass	B Mass of residue	C C-terminal mass
Glycine	$\begin{array}{c} CH_3 \\ | \\ -N-CH_2-CO- \end{array}$	114	71	102
Alanine	$\begin{array}{c} CH_3 \\ | \\ -N-CH-CO- \\ | \\ CH_3 \end{array}$	128	85	116
Valine	$\begin{array}{c} CH_3 \\ | \\ -N-CH-CO- \\ | \\ CH(CH_3)_2 \end{array}$	156	113	144
Leucine†	$\begin{array}{c} CH_3 \\ | \\ -N-CH-CO- \\ | \\ CH_2 \\ | \\ CH(CH_3)_2 \end{array}$	170	127	158
Serine	$\begin{array}{c} CH_3 \\ | \\ -N-CH-CO- \\ | \\ CH_2 \\ | \\ O-CH_3 \end{array}$	158	115	146
Threonine	$\begin{array}{c} CH_3 \\ | \\ -N-CH-CO- \\ | \\ CH-O-CH_3 \\ | \\ CH_3 \end{array}$	172	129	160
Aspartic acid	$\begin{array}{c} CH_3 \\ | \\ -N-CH-CO- \\ | \\ CH_2 \\ | \\ CO-OCH_3 \end{array}$	186	143	174
Glutamic acid	$\begin{array}{c} CH_3 \\ | \\ -N-CH-CO- \\ | \\ CH_2 \\ | \\ CH_2 \\ | \\ CO-O-CH_3 \end{array}$	200	157	188

Table **XXX**. (*continued*)

Amino acid	Structure of derivative	A N-terminal mass	B Mass of residue	C C-terminal mass
Asparagine		199	156	187
Glutamine		213	170	201
Phenyl alanine		204	161	192
Tyrosine		234	191	222
Tryptophan		257	214	245
Lysine		241	198	229

Table XXX. (*continued*)

Amino acid	Structure of derivative	A N-terminal mass	B Mass of residue	C C-terminal mass
Histidine	CH₃ —N—CH—CO— CH₂ Imidazole—CH₃	208	165	196
Ornithine‡	CH₃ —N—CH—CO— (CH₂)₃ N(CH₃) CO—CH₃	227	184	215
Proline	H₂ C CH₂ CH₂ —N—CH—CO—	140	97	128

†Not differentiated from isoleucine.
‡Result of hydrazinolysis of arginine.

HISTORICAL DEVELOPMENT OF THE MASS SPECTROMETRIC METHOD OF PROTEIN/PEPTIDE SEQUENCING

The mass spectrometer has only during the last two decades become a major weapon in the armoury of the natural product chemist. And the technique has belatedly been applied to proteins and peptides derived thereof. The somewhat slow appreciation of the potential of mass spectrometry in peptide sequencing is undoubtedly due to the well-known reputation that peptides had of being involatile, as well as lacking many of the other aesthetic properties generally possessed by organic substances. However, during investigations on the mass spectrometry of peptide antibiotics and related naturally occurring peptides, the possibilities of this method were first realized.

Early attempts were directed at increasing the volatility of the peptide. Bieman and Vetter (1960) reduced the peptide with LiAlH₄ to give a polyaminoalcohol of enhanced volatility, that gave a relatively simple mass spectrum.

$$\text{H(NH CHCO)}_n\text{OH} \xrightarrow{\text{LiAlH}_4} \text{H(NH CH.CH}_2)_n\text{OH}$$

with R below each (on the CH carbon):

$$\underset{\displaystyle R}{\text{H(NH CHCO)}_n\text{OH}} \xrightarrow[\text{LiAlH}_4]{} \underset{\displaystyle R}{\text{H(NH CH.CH}_2)_n\text{OH}}$$

Electron impact of these derivatives gave principal ions that corresponded to the stepwise loss of amino acid units from the C-terminal end of the molecule and enabled simple peptide sequences to be deduced. However with amino acids with reactive side chains further chemical modification was necessary and the problems encountered led to the abandonment of this approach.

An alternative approach to obtain sufficiently volatile peptide derivatives was to employ the N-acyl peptide ester. Andersson (1958) attempted to do this using the trifluoroacetyl peptide ester, and these studies were extended by Stenhagen (1961). The cleavage patterns obtained with these derivatives were further studied by Prox and Weygand (1967). However, the most successful investigation of these early attempts was by the Russian group, led by Professor M. M. Shemyakin (Shemyakin *et al.* 1966). These investigations showed that it was possible to determine the sequences of peptides containing most of the common amino acids. The volatility of the peptide was enhanced by preparing the tert-butyl esters of the dodecyl peptide derivative. They found that the sequence of the peptide was readily observed from an analysis of the fragmentation pattern, which normally involved rupture of the peptide ester, followed by subsequent loss of each of the amino acid residues thus:

$$\text{R}-\text{CO}\dashv\text{NH}-\underset{\displaystyle R_1}{\text{CH}}\ \text{CO}\dashv\text{NH}\ \underset{\displaystyle R_2}{\text{CH}}\ \text{CO}\dashv\text{NH}\ \underset{\displaystyle R_3}{\text{CH}}-\text{CO}\dashv\text{OR}$$

This technique was found to work on a wide selection of peptides up to a nonapeptide, although this was not seen to be a limiting case.

Although these valiant efforts were seen to offer some hope to the protein chemist, they nevertheless did not bring the technique any nearer to becoming a practical possibility, and it was evident that a completely new approach to the problem was necessary. Fortunately this was on the horizon, and the breakthrough began with the structural work carried out on the peptidolipid fortuitine, isolated from *Mycobacterium fortuitum*. Preliminary chemical investigations on this substance indicated it to be essentially an N-acyl-oligopeptide methyl ester, but a total structure for the molecule could not be proposed. Fortunately, at that moment, M. Barber at the A.E.I. factory in Manchester was looking for high molecular weight compounds to test the performance of his new MS9 mass spectrometer, and it was to him that Professor E. Lederer forwarded a few mg of fortuitine. A mass spectrum was obtained showing two parent peaks at 1331 and 1359, corresponding to $C_{70}H_{125}N_9O_{15}$ and $C_{72}H_{129}N_9O_{15}$ respectively, due to its being a mixture of two homologues containing a C_{20} or a C_{22} fatty acid. Furthermore, it was possible to interpret the spectrum obtained, and the following structure for the peptidolipid was proposed (Barber *et al.* 1965):

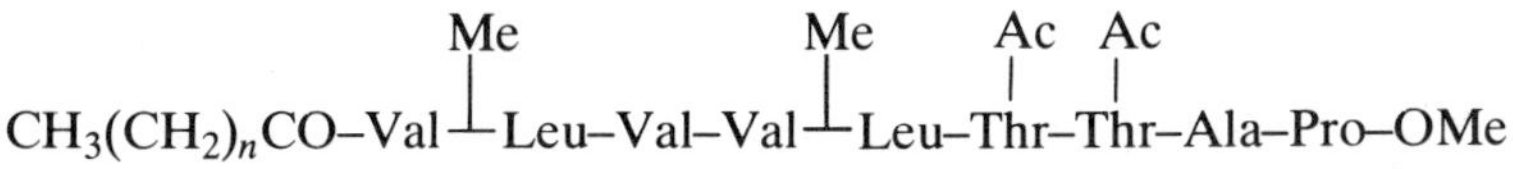

$$\begin{array}{ccccc} & \text{Me} & & \text{Me} & \text{Ac} \quad \text{Ac} \\ & | & & | & | \quad | \\ CH_3(CH_2)_nCO-Val-\!\!&\!\!Leu-Val-Val-\!\!&\!\!Leu-Thr-Thr-Ala-Pro-OMe \end{array}$$

$$(n = 18, 20)$$

Consideration of the success with fortuitine led workers to suspect that the major limiting factor in the volatility of oligopeptides was the inter-chain hydrogen bonding between the –CO–NH– groups, for fortuitine possessed three tertiary amide bonds. Simultaneous work on the peptide antibiotics reinforced these impressions, as many peptide antibiotics in common with fortuitine contained N-methyl amino acids. These unusual amino acids, as in the peptides enniatin and etamycin, rendered the peptides soluble in organic solvents and enhanced their volatility, so much so that mass spectrometry was feasible. It was therefore reasoned that this increase in volatility was due to a reduction in the hydrogen bonding between the peptide chains, and it was this fact that spurred Das and his colleagues to modify peptides by N-methylation (Das *et al.* 1967). The results were more than encouraging. In addition to giving excellent spectra there was the added bonus that the sequence ions were significantly more intense, making these derivatives suitable for low resolution work. Yet although the N-methylation procedure greatly extended the potential usefulness of mass spectrometry in amino acid sequencing, nevertheless it was not without significant difficulties. In the original procedure the acyl peptide ester was treated with methyl iodide in dimethylformamide and silver oxide.

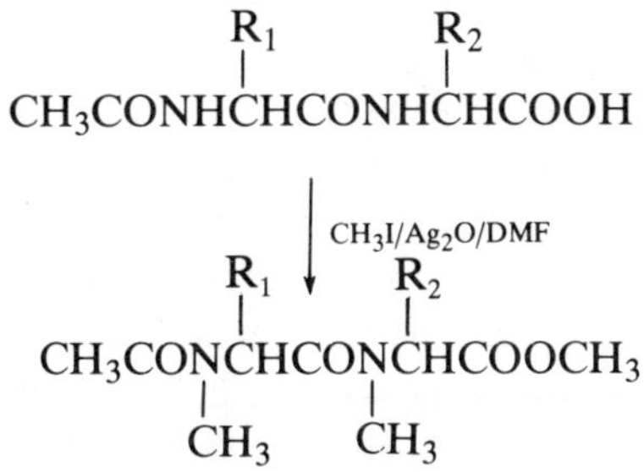

$$\begin{array}{cc} R_1 & R_2 \\ | & | \\ CH_3CONHCHCONHCHCOOH \end{array}$$

$$\bigg\downarrow \; CH_3I/Ag_2O/DMF$$

$$\begin{array}{cc} R_1 & R_2 \\ | & | \\ CH_3CONCHCONCHCOOCH_3 \\ | \quad\;\; | \\ CH_3 \quad CH_3 \end{array}$$

This treatment resulted in quantitative methylation of the peptide nitrogen atoms and side-chain functionalities, yielding permethyl derivatives of enhanced volatility. Agarwal *et al.* (1969) applied this procedure to gastrin and related peptides and discovered that the permethylation was not straightforward, in particular when the residues were methionine, glutamic acid and aspartic acid. Chain cleavage was found to occur with glutamyl

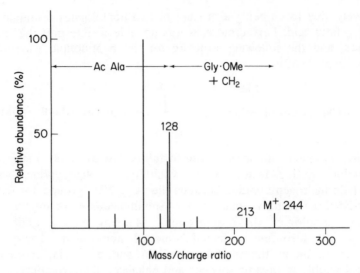

Figure XLIII   The mass spectrum of acetylated and permethylated
Ala–Gly showing C-methylation. M⁺, molecular ion

and methionyl residues, and in the case of aspartyl residues even more
complex reactions occurred. At this stage, Thomas (1969) proposed using
the Coggins and Benoiton method, previously employed in the O-per-
methylation of carbohydrates, as a means of permethylating peptides.
This involved treating the peptide in dimethyl formamide with sodium
hydride followed by methyl iodide. However, side reactions were found to
occur. One problem was extensive C-methylation, in particular glycine
residues were prone to this, as may be observed in the mass spectrum of
Ac–Ala–Gly–OH after permethylation using this method (Figure XLIII).

An alternative methylation procedure using methyl iodide and 'dimsyl'
sodium (methyl sulphinyl sodium), as originally described for
carbohydrates by Hakomori (1964), was used by Vilkas and Lederer
(1968). And this procedure was subsequently improved by reducing the
reaction time and limiting the formation of undesirable by-products of
peptides containing the troublesome amino acids, in particular aspartic
acid, glutamic acid and tryptophan (Thomas 1968). It is this method that
has become the basis of the most successful current procedure.

Although most of the usual amino acids were found to give permethyl
derivatives that resulted in successful spectra, the method until recently
was not applicable to several of the common amino acids, including
arginine, histidine, cysteine or its derivatives, and methionine. An attempt
to solve the problem for the sulphur-containing amino acids was made by
Thomas et al. (1968), who recommended desulphurization with Raney
nickel whereby the methionine residue was converted to a residue of
α-amino butyric acid. And in related studies quaternary salt formation of

DERIVATIZATION OF PEPTIDES

$$\underset{\text{Peptide}}{NH_2-\overset{\overset{\textstyle R_1}{|}}{C}H-CON-\underset{\underset{\textstyle H}{|}}{\overset{\overset{\textstyle R_2}{|}}{C}H}-COOH} + \quad \underset{CH_3CO}{\overset{CH_3CO}{\diagdown}}O$$

Acetic anhydride/dry MeOH
(1:4 v/v)

$$\underset{\text{N-acetyl peptide}}{CH_3CO-NH\;\overset{\overset{\textstyle R_1}{|}}{C}H-CO-NH-\overset{\overset{\textstyle R_2}{|}}{C}H-COOH}$$

'Dimsyl' sodium ← Dimethyl sulphoxide + Na⁺ H⁻ Sodium hydride

$$\left[CH_3CO-\underset{\underset{\textstyle \ominus}{|}}{\overset{\overset{\textstyle R_1}{|}}{N}}-CH-CO-\underset{\underset{\textstyle \ominus}{|}}{N}-\overset{\overset{\textstyle R_2}{|}}{C}H-CO-O^\ominus \right]$$

CH_3I

$$CH_3CO-\underset{\underset{\textstyle CH_3}{|}}{\overset{\overset{\textstyle R_1}{|}}{N}}-CH-CO-\underset{\underset{\textstyle CH_3}{|}}{N}-\overset{\overset{\textstyle R_2}{|}}{C}H-CO-O-CH_3$$

Permethylated acetyl peptide methyl ester

methionine was avoided by its temporary conversion to the sulphoxide, followed by permethylation under normal conditions and reduction back to N-methyl methionine (Roepstorff et al. 1970). A more successful approach to the problem was made by Polan et al. (1970) who carefully balanced the amount of base used in the deprotonation step of the permethylation procedure with the amount of methyl iodide added. More recently, Jones

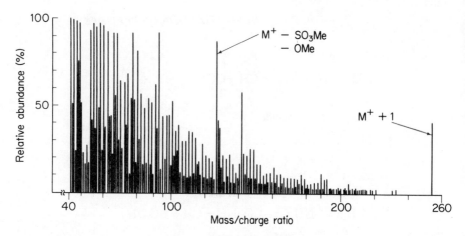

Figure XLIV   The mass spectrum of permethylated and acetylated cysteic acid (by courtesy of Dr G. M. Jones)

(1976) has found that successful mass spectra may be obtained from the fully oxidized derivative of the sulphur-containing amino acid, and Figure XLIV shows the mass spectrum of permethylated cysteic acid, which shows a clear and distinct molecular ion.

Arginine is another problematical amino acid and various strategies have been proposed. Vetter-Diechtl *et al.* (1968) recommended converting the guanidinyl group to a pyrimidyl derivative by condensation with a 1,3-diketone. Alternatively arginine-containing peptides have been derivatized after the arginyl residue had been modified by hydrazinolysis to an ornithyl residue thus:

A different approach to the derivatization of problematical amino acids was made by Morris (1972), who made a study of the rate of permethylation using the Hakomori procedure. It was found that using a shortened reaction time during the permethylation step, quaternization on histidine residues was appreciably slower than the rate of methylation. The success of this method was subsequently extended to include the sulphur-containing amino acids and arginine (Morris *et al.* 1973). This 'short' permethylation procedure is probably the best that is currently available and has been found to give good spectra with most peptides so far encountered. However, recently, Mahajan and Desiderio (1978) have described a new procedure whereby the permethylated peptides are reduced with borane–tetrahydrofuran and the products so formed have been found to be more volatile than the permethylated ones. The sensitivity was also increased, as little as 10 nmol of peptide being sufficient for sequence analysis.

To summarize this section, the following advantages are gained on permethylation of peptides:

(1) there is a decrease in zwitterionic character;
(2) there is an increase in volatility of the peptide due to an inhibition of interchain hydrogen bonding; and
(3) it stabilizes the particular fragmentation pathway, thereby giving maximum sequence information.

OUTLINE OF THE TECHNIQUE

Permethylation is carried out by adding the carbanion solution to the peptide dissolved in dimethyl sulphoxide. Methyl iodide is then carefully added under nitrogen and the reaction allowed to proceed for between 2 and 30 min. The reaction is terminated by the addition of excess distilled H_2O and the permethylated peptide extracted into chloroform. The sample is reduced to dryness and dissolved in a small volume of $CHCl_3$ (approximately 20 μl). By means of a fine capillary tube it is transferred and slowly dried on the quartz tip of the direct insertion probe. The probe is then introduced into the ion source of the mass spectrometer by use of the standard vacuum lock system, and to obtain the spectrum a steady temperature gradient is effected by fractional movement of the probe tip into the ion source. As it moves nearer the electron beam the temperature is slowly increased and the spectrum is continuously monitored until the peptide is seen to volatilize. At this point the temperature gradient is increased rapidly and the spectrum recorded.

Fragmentation of Peptides

Derivatized peptides when subjected to electron impact rupture principally at the amide bonds in two main modes (Shemyakin *et al.* 1966). The principal cleavage is that of the CO–N bond giving rise to the acylium ion, which can then lose the next amino acid residue by loss of carbon monoxide and a neutral imine fragment thus:

$$\underset{\substack{| \\ CH_3}}{\overset{\substack{R_1 \\ |}}{wwwCO-N-CH-CO}} \overset{b}{\vdots}\ \underset{\substack{| \\ CH_3}}{\overset{\substack{R_2 \\ |}}{N-CH-CO}} \overset{a}{\vdots}\ O-CH_3$$

Fission at a $(-OCH_3)$

$$\underset{\substack{| \\ CH_3}}{\overset{\substack{R_1 \\ |}}{wwwCO-N-CH-CO}}-\underset{\substack{| \\ CH_3}}{\overset{\substack{R_2 \\ |}}{N-CH-CO^+}}\ \text{Acylium ion}$$

Fission at b $\begin{pmatrix} -CO, \\ -N=CHR_2 \\ | \\ CH_3 \end{pmatrix}$

$$\underset{\substack{| \\ CH_3}}{\overset{\substack{R_1 \\ |}}{-CO-N-CH-CO^+}}$$

Methylation of the amide nitrogen is seen to promote cleavage at each amide linkage with charge retention on the acyl moiety; the resulting 'sequence ions' permit ready assignment of the primary structure of the peptide.

In addition to the peaks corresponding to peptide bond cleavage, the mass spectra of peptides always has additional peaks that correspond to side-chain fragmentation. With leucine, isoleucine and valine, loss of the side chain occurs *via* a McLafferty rearrangement and peaks corresponding to loss of olefinic fragments may be taken as diagnostic of these amino acids (Bricas *et al.* 1965):

$$\underset{\substack{| \\ C \\ CH_3\ CH_3}}{\overset{\substack{Me \\ | \\ N- \\ | \\ Ox}}{-N-CH-C}} \longrightarrow \underset{\substack{| \\ OH}}{\overset{\substack{Me \\ |}}{-N-CH=C}}\overset{Me}{\underset{|}{-N-}}$$

$$+ \quad CH_2=CMe_2$$

Serine residues undergo what is thought to be a thermal reaction with the elimination of CH_3OH by a β-elimination reaction thus:

$$\underset{\overset{|}{\underset{\overset{|}{OCH_3}}{CH_2}}}{-N-CH-CO-} \quad \xrightarrow[-CH_3OH]{\Delta} \quad \underset{\overset{|}{\underset{}{CH_2}}}{-N-C-CO-}$$

(with CH_3 on nitrogen in both structures, and the product showing $\overset{||}{CH_2}$)

High or Low Resolution Mass Spectrometry?

Morris *et al.* (1974a) have pointed out that the choice of instrument resolving power is important. Some groups have operated the instrument in the high resolution mode as this may give valuable information as to the chemical composition of the ions in the spectrum. However these authors point out and further demonstrate in their study of the enzyme ribitol dehydrogenase that high resolution mass spectrometry is not essential in the analysis of peptides (Morris *et al.* 1974b).

Examples of Its Application to Peptides

The mass spectrum of glutathione is illustrated in Figure XLV. This tripeptide (γ-Glu–Cys–Gly), which contains cysteine, was derivatized by a 'short' permethylation reaction. The spectrum shows the molecular ion at m/e 433 (0.3%), the loss of CH_3O (m/e 31) from the M^+ to m/e 402 (0.4%), loss of the glycyl residue minus H at m/e 330 (1.2%), loss of CO

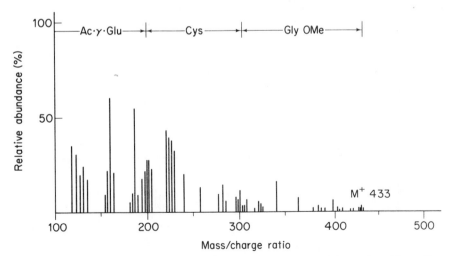

Figure XLV The mass spectrum of acetylated and permethylate glutathione (by courtesy by Dr G. M. Jones)

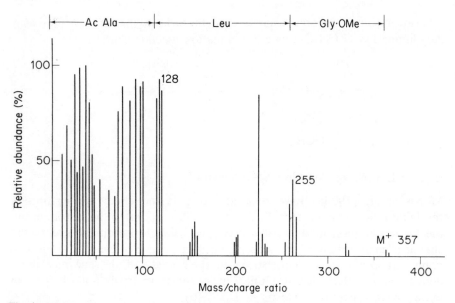

Figure XLVI   The mass spectrum of permethylated Ac–Ala–Leu–Gly (by courtesy
of Dr G. M. Jones)

(m/e 28) to m/e 302 (0.8%), and loss of the cysteinyl residue to m/e 200
(18%), which is the mass of the N-terminal residue. A further example is
of the tripeptide Ala–Leu-Gly (Figure XLVI).

One of the most important advantages of mass spectrometric analysis is
that of mixture analysis, as this may reduce the laborious and tedious

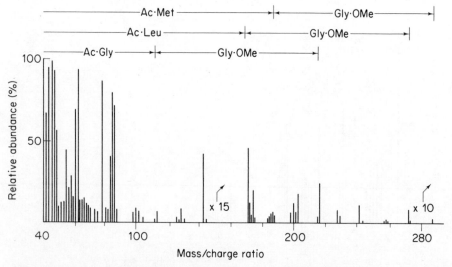

Figure XLVII   The mass spectra of a mixture of three dipeptides after acetylation
and permethylation (by courtesy of Dr G. M. Jones)

isolation procedures, that have so far been the rate-determining step. Mixture analysis may be accomplished by fractionation, within the mass spectrometer itself, by using a sample temperature gradient. The mass spectrum of a mixture of three simple dipeptides, namely Met–Gly, Leu–Gly, and Gly–Gly, is shown in Figure XLVII, to illustrate the technique.

Application to Proteins

The first published results of the application of mass spectrometry to peptides isolated from proteins was by Geddes *et al*. (1969), who determined the amino acid sequence of a peptide derived from silk fibroin, and shortly after this Agarwal *et al*. (1969) determined the structure of the peptide hormone gastrin. However, a more convincing demonstration of the potential of the mass spectrometric method was the analysis of a mixture of two octadecapeptides from swine immunoglobulin λ-chains (Franek *et al*. 1969). In this study it was possible to determine the sequence of the first 10 residues of the peptides as well as being able to locate the position of microheterogeneity. This early work on peptide mixtures was advanced by the studies of Morris *et al*. (1971), who modified the existing methods to be applicable to micro-quantities of peptide material. Furthermore Morris *et al*. (1974a) argued that high resolution mass spectrometry, involving the determination of the elemental composition of the significant ions in the spectrum, was unnecessary, and that low resolution mass spectrometry could cope adequately with complex peptide mixtures.

Some of the proteins that have been sequenced partially, or completely, by mass spectrometry are given in Table XXXI.

Table XXXI. Some applications of mass spectrometry to proteins

Protein/peptide	Reference
Silk fibroin	Geddes *et al*. (1969)
Feline gastrin	Agarwal *et al*. (1969)
Scotophobin	Desidero *et al*. (1971)
α-Lactalbumin	Bacon and Graham (1972)
Aspartate aminotransferase	Ovchinnikov *et al*. (1973)
Triose phosphate isomerase	Priddle and Offord (1974)
Ostrich cytochrome c	Howard *et al*. (1974)
Dihydrofolate reductase	Morris *et al*. (1974a)
Ribitol dehydrogenase	Morris *et al*. (1974b)
Rabbit myosin (alkali lightchain)	Frank and Weeds (1974)
Tobacco mosaic virus protein	Rees *et al*. (1974)
Prothrombin	Morris (1975)
Concanavalin A	Jones (1976)
Stellacyanin	Bergman *et al*. (1977)
Antifreeze glycoprotein	Morris *et al*. (1978)

Other workers have put forward the opinion that the methods described above are not entirely satisfactory for the resolution of peptides in the complex mixtures derived from the enzymic hydrolysis of proteins, and that alternative methods are needed to prepare peptide derivatives of greater volatility that possibly could be separated by gas chromatography followed by the 'on-line' mass spectrometric characterization of the mixture in a single step. The first attempt to solve the many technical problems was made by Calam (1972). Subsequently work involved the use of the N-trifluoroacetyl, and pentafluoropropionyl peptide methyl esters, but Nau (1974) reported that the O-trimethylsilylpolyamino alcohol obtained by LiAlD$_4$ reduction and trimethylsilylation of the N-acetyl oligopeptide methyl ester was more volatile, with an easily interpretable mass spectrum. Even more volatile derivatives were made by the LiAlD$_4$ reduction and O-trimethylsilylation of the corresponding perfluoroacylated oligopeptide methyl ester and it was found that all the amino acid residues including Arg, His, Trp, Gln and Asn could be derivatized by this technique without modification. In a further study the sequence of a 39 residue peptide was entirely deduced (Nau and Bieman 1976) by mass spectrometry. The peptide, a carboxypeptidase inhibitor from potatoes, was fragmented and the peptides esterified, trifluoroacetylated, deuteroalkylated by reduction with LiAlD$_4$ and O-trimethylsilyated. The resulting mixture was separated by GLC and analysed on a mass spectrometer linked up to a computer.

Glycoproteins

The mass spectrometric method has recently been applied to the antifreeze glycoproteins from the blood of the Antarctic fish *Trematomus borchgrevinki* (Morris *et al.* 1978); and the Cu-containing glycoprotein stellacyanin from the Lacquer tree (Bergman *et al.* 1977). In this former study it was found that during the permethylation reaction the 'dimsyl' carbanion abstracts the proton from the α-carbon atom, leading to β-elimination of the carbohydrate moiety thus:

Proteins with Blocked N-terminal Residues

The mass spectra methods differs from the classical approach of sequence determination in the very important fact that it does not demand that the

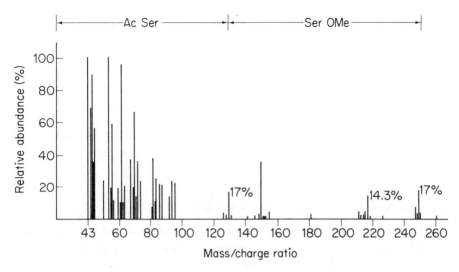

Figure XLVIII   The mass spectrum of permethylated Ac–Ser–Ser isolated from the N-terminus of ox ferritin (by courtesy of Dr I. Al-Hassan)

amino terminus be free. The N-terminus of ox ferritin was shown to be N-acetyl serine by permethylation of a blocked tryptic peptide (Al-Hassan 1976) (see Figure XLVIII), and a similar approach was made by Joassin and Gerday (1977) who deduced that the N-terminus of the major parvalbumin of whiting (*Gadus Merlangus*) was N-acetyl alanine. The strength of the information obtained by mass spectrometric analysis is far greater than that if a chemical method such as hydrazinolysis were employed, though the amount needed for each analysis is about comparable. Auffret *et al.* (1978) showed that the N-terminus of alcohol dehydrogenase from *Drosophila melanogaster* N-11 was N-acetyl serine using 50 nmol of peptide, which was considered to be near the practical limit of the technique.

Recently Pettigrew and Smith (1977) have found that certain proteins have N-terminal α-N-methyl amino acids. The biological significance of these findings is as yet unknown, but these workers have postulated that other proteins might also contain this type of modification. Almost simultaneously it was discovered that the N-terminus of the protein initiation factor IF-3 from *E. coli* was N-methyl methionine (Braver and Wittmann-Liebold 1977). This was determined by mass spectrometric analysis of the N-terminal PTH-derivative after one step of the Edman degradation.

Unusual Amino Acid Residues

Convincing evidence of the power and potential usefulness of the mass spectrometer in sequence analysis has come from studies on the vitamin

K-dependent part of prothrombin. Peptides from this protein were found to possess abnormal electrophoretic mobilities, yet using conventional chemical procedures no clue as to the nature of the 'prosthetic group', which must be acidic in nature, could be found. Amino acid analysis in particular did not indicate the presence of any unusual amino acid. Eventually the nature of this anomaly was solved independently by two groups of workers both employing mass spectrometry. Stenflo *et al.* (1974) studied pure peptides, whereas Magnusson *et al.* (1974) worked on peptide mixtures, however both groups identified the unusual amino acid γ-carboxyglutamic acid in the anomalous peptides.

Mass Spectrometry in Conjunction with Chemical Methods

Burgus *et al.* (1973) have identified some of the residues of ovine hypothalamic luteinizing-hormone-releasing factor by a combination of GLC and mass spectrometry of the PTH-derivatives. Moreover, if methyl isothiocyanate is used in place of the phenyl derivative the thiourea that results when the peptide is reacted has been found to rearrange and cleave to the thiohydantoin in the mass spectrometer ion source (Fairwell *et al.* 1973), and this has been proposed as the basis of a mass spectrometric–Edman method. Alternatively the PTH-amino acid obtained from the automatic sequenator may be identified directly by mass spectrometry. This may also permit the quantitation of these derivatives by concurrent analysis of deuterated analogues (Tschesche *et al.* 1972).

THE USE OF NEW IONIZATION TECHNIQUES

In recent years new ionization techniques have been developed that have prompted workers to investigate their applicability to the sequence analysis of peptides.

(i) Chemical Ionization

Generally chemical ionization gives rise to more complex spectra than does electron impact, however the spectra usually exhibit highly abundant molecular-weight-determining ions, as is to be expected from the 'milder' ionization processes involved. Usually methane reagent gas is employed, though Morris *et al.* (1978) have recently employed ammonia reagent gas in a study of the structure of the glycoproteins of antarctic fish.

Krutzsch and Kindt (1979) have studied the chemical ionization spectra of 40 dipeptides as their trimethylsilylated derivatives and have reported this technique to be at least ten times as sensitive as electron ionization methods. Two intense ions were found in each spectrum, namely $[M + 1]^+$ and $[M - 15]^+$ that allowed unambiguous assignments of the dipeptide molecular weights, and the principal ion in each spectrum was that derived from the N-terminal fragment $[Me_3Si\text{-}NH = CHR_1]^+$, formed by β-cleavage of the central CH–CO bond. Further it was suggested that this method could be used for the identification of dipeptides obtained from a protein after digestion with the enzyme dipeptidyl amino peptidase.

Chemical ionization therefore is a suitable method to supplement, rather than replace, electron ionization methods. However, at present this method has had little application to peptides, which probably reflects the lack of availability of suitable instruments to biochemists.

(ii) Photoionization

The technique of photoionization, as applied to peptides, has been compared to that of electron impact by Orlov et al. (1972). In this study it was found that photoionization gave rise to a simpler spectrum, the number of peaks observed, particularly at $m/e < 250$, being considerably reduced. Peptides were observed to fragment in a similar manner to that of electron ionization, however the lack of some sequence ions tended to result in ambiguities and an inability to sequence some regions of the peptide chain.

(iii) Field Desorption

Winkler and Beckley (1972) have applied field desorption mass spectrometry to a few small peptides and the results have been very encouraging in that strong molecular ions have been observed on underivatized peptides, some containing arginine, which would not have been volatile under normal conditions. The fact that no prior treatment of the peptide is needed to increase its volatility enabled smaller quantities of peptide to be used, and the sensitivity of the method is estimated to be approximately 10^{-8} g. However, field desorption studies provide little sequence information for underivatized peptides and the principal use of this technique is in providing a criterion of purity and molecular weight of a peptide. Morris et al. (1978) used this technique to determine the nominal mass of an acetyl permethyl derivative of a glycopeptide from the blood of an Antarctic fish. Approximate mass measurement was made on the major ion present which was found to be 1324, which corresponded to a peptide containing 14 amino acid residues.

PROSPECTS

The unique usefulness of mass spectrometry has been clearly shown in work on the identification of unusual amino acids in peptides. The technique is entirely suited to this, as in most instances only minute amounts of material are available and it is difficult to envisage these problems being successfully solved in any other way. The discovery of the amino acid γ-carboxyglutamic acid is such an example. It is clear that with the technique of mass spectrometry, as applied to proteins, so well developed, more of these unusual amino acids will be found probably having been overlooked in previous investigations.

It is clear that mass spectrometry is a valuable tool for the protein biochemist. It is nevertheless an expensive instrument, both to purchase and to maintain, and is obviously not going to be available to most investigators. The best that one may hope for, is to have some form of limited access to a mass spectrometer, though this itself is beset with difficulties. In particular such machines are usually in great demand by chemists, and any particular machine might routinely process 2000–3000 samples per year. For the organic chemist who can usually boost the abundance of high molecular weight ions in the spectrum by increasing the sample size over residual background, this offers no problem—however, this is not possible for the protein biochemist, who usually has only a very small sample available. The upshot is that under these circumstances the detection sensitivity and thus the length of peptide from which sequence information may be determined is about 6–7 residues. Considering that the amount of material required is around 10–30 nmol the technique offers little when compared to established 'wet' chemical methods such as the dansyl–Edman procedure. In conclusion therefore, if a suitable mass spectrometer is not available largely for peptide work, the classical methods are to be preferred, unless the presence of an unusual amino acid is suspected.

References

Agarwal, K. L., Kenner, G. W., and Sheppard, R. C. (1969) Feline gastrin. An example of peptide sequence analysis by mass spectrometry. *J. Amer. Chem. Soc.*, **91**, 3096–3097.

Akabori, S., Ohno, K., and Narita, K. (1952) On the hydrazinolysis of proteins and peptides: A method for the characterization of carboxyl-terminal amino acids in proteins. *Bull. Chem. Soc. Japan*, **25**, 214–218.

Al-Hassan, I. A. A. (1976) Studies on bovine spleen ferritin. *Ph.D. Thesis*, University of Salford.

Andersson, C. O. (1958) Mass spectrometric studies on amino acid and peptide derivatives. *Acta Chem. Scand.*, **12**, 1353.

Atherton, E., Bridgen, J., and Sheppard, R. C. (1976) A polyamide support for solid-phase sequencing. *FEBS Letters*, **64**, 173–175.

Auffret, A. D., Williams, D. H., and Thatcher, D. R. (1978) Identification of the blocked N-terminus of an alcohol dehydrogenase from *Drosophila melanogaster* M-11. *FEBS Letters*, **90**, 324–326.

Bacon, J. R. and Graham, G. N. (1972) Sequence studies on the milk protein α-lactalbumin by using mass spectrometry. *Biochem. J.*, **127**, 76P–77P.

Barber, M., Jolles, P., Vilkas, E., and Lederer, E. (1965) Determination of amino acid sequences in oligopeptides by mass spectrometry. I. The structure of fortuitine, an acyl-nonapeptide methyl ester. *Biochem. Biophys. Res. Commun.*, **18**, 469–473.

Begg, G. S. and Morgan, F. J. (1976) A non-volatile buffer with improved performance in automated protein sequencing. *FEBS Letter*, **66**, 243–245.

Begg, G. S., Pepper, D. S., Chesterman, C. N., and Morgan, F. J. (1978) Complete covalent structure of human β-thromboglobulin. *Biochemistry*, **17**, 1739–1744.

Bennett, C. D., Rodkey, J. A., Sondey, J. M. and Hirschmann, R. (1978) Dihydrofolate reductase: the amino acid sequence of the enzyme from a methotrexate-resistant mutant of *Escherichia coli*. *Biochemistry*, **17**, 1328–1337.

Berg, A. van Den, van Den Hende-Timmer, L., and Beintema, J. J. (1976) Isolation, properties and primary structure of coypu and chinchilla pancreatic ribonuclease. *Biochim. Biophys. Acta*, **453**, 400–409.

Berg, A. van Den, van Den Hende-Timmer, L., Hofsteenge, J., Gaastra, W., and Beintema, J. J. (1977) Guinea-pig pancreatic ribonucleases. Isolation, properties, primary structure and glycosidation. *Eur. J. Biochem.*, **75**, 91–100.

Bergman, C., Gandvik, E., Nyman, P. O., and Strid, L. (1977) The amino acid sequence of stellacyanin from the Lacquer tree. *Biochem. Biophys. Res. Commun.*, **77**, 1052–1059.

Beynum, G. M. A. van, DeGraaf, J. M., Castel, A., Kraal, B., and Bosch, L. (1977) Structural studies on the coat protein of Alfalfa mosaic virus—the complete primary structure. *Eur. J. Biochem.*, **72**, 63–78.

Beyreuther, K., Adler, K., Fanning, E., Murray, C., Klemm, A., and Geisler, N. (1975) Amino acid Sequence of *lac* repressor from *Escherichia coli*. *Eur. J. Biochem.*, **59**, 491–509.

Beyreuther, K., Bohmer, H., and Dimroth, P. (1978) Amino acid sequence of citrate-lyase acyl-carrier protein from *Klebsiella aerogenes*. *Eur. J. Biochem.*, **87**, 101–110.

Beyreuther, K., Raufuss, H., Schrecker, O., and Hengstenberg, W. (1977) The phosphoenolpyruvate-dependent phosphotransferase system of *Staphylococcus aureus*. *Eur. J. Biochem.*, **75**, 275–286.

Bhown, A. S., Mole, J. E., and Bennett, J. C. (1977) Primary structure of human J chain: isolation and characterization of tryptic and chymotryptic peptides of human J chain. *Biochemistry*, **16**, 3501–3507.

Biemann, K. and Vetter, W. (1960) Separation of peptide derivatives by gas chromatography combined with the mass spectrometric determination of the amino acid sequence. *Biochem. Biophys. Res. Commun.*, **3**, 578–584.

Braunitzer, G., Schrank, B., Petersen, S., and Petersen U. (1973) Automatic sequencing of insulin. *Hoppe-Seyler's Z. Physiol. Chem.*, **354**, 1563–1566.

Braunitzer, G., Schrank, B., and Ruhfus, A. (1971) On the complete automatic sequence analysis of peptides using quadrol. *Hoppe-Seyler's Z. Physiol. Chem.*, **352**, 1730–1732.

Braver, D. and Wittmann-Liebold, B. (1977) The primary structure of the initiation factor IF-3 from *E. coli*. *FEBS Letters*, **79**, 269–275.

Bricas, E., Van-Heijenoort, J., Barber, M., Wolstenholme, W. A., Das, B. C., and Lederer, E. (1965) Determination of amino acid sequences in oligopeptides by mass spectrometry. IV. Synthetic N-acyl oligopeptide methyl esters. *Biochemistry*, **4**, 2254–2260.

Brosius, J. and Arfsten, U. (1978) Primary structure of protein L19 from the large subunit of *Escherichia coli* ribosomes. *Biochemistry*, **17**, 508–516.

Bruton, C. J. and Hartley, B. S. (1970) Chemical studies on methionyl-tRNA synthetase from *Escherichia coli*. *J. Mol. Biol.*, **52**, 165–178.

Burgus, R., Ling, N., Butcher, M., and Guillemin, R. (1973) Primary structure of somatostatin, a hypothalamic peptide that inhibits the secretion of pituitary growth hormone. *Proc. Natn. Acad. Sci. U.S.A.*, **70**, 684–688.

Butkowski, R. J., Elion, J., Downing, M. R., and Mann, K. G. (1977) Primary structure of human prethrombin 2 and α-thrombin *J. Biol. Chem.*, **252**, 4942–4957.

Butler, W. T., Finch, J. E., and Miller, E. J. (1977) Covalent structure of cartilage collagen. Amino acid sequence of residues 363–551 of bovine α1(II) chains. *Biochemistry*, **16**, 4981–4990.

Calam, D. H. (1972) Gas chromatography of permethylated peptides. *J. Chrom.*, **70**, 146–150.

Carnegie, P. R. (1969) Digestion of an Arg–Pro bond by trypsin in the encephalitogenic basic protein of human myelin. *Nature*, **223**, 958–959.

Carpenter, F. H. and Shiigi, S. M. (1974) Cyanogen bromide treatment of N-acetylmethionyl residues without cleavage. *Biochemistry*, **13**, 5159–5164.

Cavadore, J.-C., Derancourt, J., and Previero, A. (1976) N-aminoethyl poly-acrylamide as support for solid-phase sequencing of proteins. *FEBS Letters*, **66**, 155–157.

Chang, J. Y. (1977) High-sensitivity sequence analysis of peptides and proteins by 4-NN-dimethylaminoazobenzene-4′-isothiocyanate. *Biochem. J.*, **163**, 517–520.

Chang, J. Y. (1978) A novel Edman-type degradation: direct formation of the thiohydantoin ring in alkaline solution by reaction of Edman-type reagents with N-monomethyl amino acids. *FEBS Letters*, **91**, 63–68.

Chang, J. Y., Creaser, E. H., and Hughes, G. J. (1977) A new approach for the solid phase sequence determination of proteins. *FEBS Letters*, **78**, 147–150.

Chauvet, M. T., Codogno, P., Chauvet, J., and Acher, R. (1977) Phylogeny of the neurophysins: complete amino acid sequence of horse MSEL-neurophysin. *FEBS Letters*, **80**, 374–376.

Chauvet, M. T., Codogno, P., Chauvet, J., and Acher, R. (1978) Phylogeny of neurophysins — complete amino acid sequence of whale (*Balaenoptera physalus*) MSEL-neurophysin. *FEBS Letters*, **88**, 91–93.

Chen, B. L., Chiu, Y. H., Humphrey, R. L., and Poljak, R. J. (1978) Amino acid sequence of the human myeloma lambda chain WIN. *Biochim. Biophys. Acta.*, **537**, 9–21.

Chen, R. (1977) Sequence determination of protein S9 from the *Escherichia coli* ribosome. *Hoppe-Seyler's Z. Physiol. Chem.*, **358**, 1415–1430.

Chen, R., Mende, L., and Arfsten, U. (1975) The primary structure of protein L27 from the peptidyl-tRNA binding site of *Escherichia coli* ribosomes. *FEBS Letters*, **59**, 96–99.

Closset, J., Maghuin-Rogister, G., Hennen, G., and Strosberg, A. D. (1978) Porcine follitropin—the amino acid sequence of the β-subunit. *Eur. J. Biochem.*, **86**, 115–120.

Croft, L. R. (1968) The structure of viomycin. *Ph.D. Thesis*, University of Nottingham.

Croft, L. R. (1971) C-terminal amino acid sequence of bovine γ-Crystallin. *Biochem. J.*, **121**, 557–559.

Croft, L. R. (1972a) The amino acid sequence of γ-Crystallin from calf lens. *Chem. Commun.*, **1972**, 437–438.

Croft, L. R. (1972b) The amino acid sequence of γ-Crystallin (fraction II) from calf lens. *Biochem J.*, **128**, 961–970.

Das, B. C., Gero, S. D., and Lederer, E. (1967) N-methylation of N-acyl oligopeptides. *Biochem. Biophys. Res. Commun.*, **29**, 211–215.

DeLange, R. J., Chang, J. Y., Shaper, J. H., and Glazer, A. N. (1976) Amino acid sequence of flagellin of *Bacillus subtilis* 168. *J. Biol. Chem.*, **251**, 705–711.

Deselnicu, M., Lange, P. M., and Heidemann, E. (1973) Studies on the cleavage of the $\alpha 2$ chain of collagen with hydroxylamine. *Hoppe-Seyler's Z. Physiol. Chem.*, **354**, 105–116.

Desidero, D. M., Ungar, G. and White, P. A. (1971) The use of mass spectrometry in the structural elucidation of Scotophobin — a specific behaviour-inducing brain peptide. *Chem. Commun.*, 432–433.

Dijk, H. van, Sloots, B., van den Berg, A., Gaastra, W., and Beintema, J. J. (1976) The primary structure of muskrat pancreatic ribonuclease. *Int. J. Peptide Protein Res.*, **8**, 305–316.

Dixit, S. N., Seyer, J. M., and Kang, A. H. (1977a) Covalent structure of collagen: amino acid sequence of chymotryptic peptides from the carboxyl-terminal region of $\alpha 2$-CB3 of chick-skin collagen. *Eur. J. Biochem.*, **81**, 599–607.

Dixit, S. N., Seyer, J. M., and Kang, A. H. (1977b) Covalent structure of collagen: isolation of chymotryptic peptides and amino acid sequence of the amino-terminal region of $\alpha 2$-CB3 from chick-skin collagen. *Eur. J. Biochem.*, **73**, 213–221.

Dixon, H. B. F. and Perham, R. N. (1968) Reversible blocking of amino groups with citraconic anhydride. *Biochem. J.*, **109**, 312–314.

Doolittle, R. F. (1972) Terminal pyrrolidone carboxylic acid: cleavage with enzymes, in *Methods in Enzymology*, Vol. **XXVB**, 231–244, Eds C. H. W. Hirs and S. N. Timasheff (Academic Press, London).

Dunkley, P. R. and Carnegie, P. R. (1974) Amino acid sequence of the smaller basic protein from rat brain myelin. *Biochem. J.*, **141**, 243–255.

Dwulet, F. E. and Gurd, F. R. N. (1976) A comparison of sulfonated phenylisothiocyanates for reducing losses of lysine-containing peptides during automated sequencing. *Anal. Biochem.*, **76**, 530–538.

Edman, P. (1950) Method for the determination of the amino acid sequence in peptides. *Acta Chem. Scand.*, **4**, 283–293.

Edman, P. and Begg, G. (1967) A protein sequenator. *Eur. J. Biochem.*, **1**, 80–91.

Eerd, J. P. van and Takahashi, K. (1976) Determination of the complete amino acid sequence of bovine cardiac troponin-C. *Biochemistry*, **15**, 1171–1180.

Elliott, D. F. (1952) A search for specific chemical methods for fission of peptide bonds I. *Biochem. J.*, **50**, 542–550.

Emmens, M., Welling, G. W., and Beintema, J. J. (1976) The amino acid sequence of pike-whale (Lesser Rorqual) pancreatic ribonuclease. *Biochem. J.*, **157**, 317–323.

Enfield, D. L., Ericsson, L. H., Blum, H. E., Fischer, E. H., and Neurath, H. (1975) Amino acid sequence of parvalbumin from rabbit skeletal muscle. *Proc. Natn. Acad. Sci. U.S.A.*, **72**, 1309–1313.

Evenberg, A., Meyer, H., Gaastra, W., Verheij, H. M., and deHaas, G. H. (1977) Amino acid sequence of phospholipase A_2 from horse pancreas. *J. Biol. Chem.*, **252**, 1189–1196.

Fairwell, T., Ellis, S., and Lovins, R. E. (1973) Quantitative protein sequencing using mass spectrometry: thermally induced formation of thiohydantoin amino acid derivatives from N-methyl- and N-phenylthiourea amino acids and peptides in the mass spectrometer. *Anal. Biochem.*, **53**, 115–123.

Ferrell, R. E., Stroup, S. K., Tanis, R. J., and Tashian, R. E. (1978) Amino acid sequence of rabbit carbonic anhydrase II. *Biochim. Biophys. Acta*, **533**, 1–11.

Fieser, L. F. and Fieser, M. (1967) *Reagents for Organic Synthesis* (John Wiley and Sons Ltd, New York).

Fleer, E. A. M., Verheij, H. M., and deHaas, G. H. (1978) The primary structure of bovine pancreatic phospholipase A_2. *Eur. J. Biochem.*, **82**, 261–269.

Fontana, A. (1972) Modification of tryptophan with BNPS-skatole (2-(2-nitrophenylsulfenyl)-3-methyl-3-bromoindolenine) in *Methods in Enzymology*, Vol. **XXV**, 419–423 Eds C. H. W. Hirs and S. N. Timasheff (Academic Press, London).

Foriers, A., DeNeve, R., Kanarek, L., and Strosberg, A. D. (1978) Common ancestor for concanavalin A and lectin from lentil? *Proc. Natn. Acad. Sci. U.S.A.*, **75**, 1136–1139.

Foster, J. A., Bruenger, E., Hu, C. L., Albertson, K., and Franzblau, C. (1973) A new technique for automated sequencing of non-polar peptides. *Biochem. Biophys. Res. Commun.*, **53**, 70–74

Fowler, A. V. and Zabin, I. (1978) Amino acid sequence of β-galactosidase XI. Peptide ordering procedures and the complete sequence. *J. Biol. Chem.*, **253**, 5521–5525.

Fraenkel-Conrat, H., Harris, J. I., and Levy, A. L. (1955) Recent developments in techniques for terminal and sequence studies in peptides and proteins. *Methods Biochem. Anal.*, **2**, 393–425.

Franek, F., Keil, B., Thomas, D. W., and Lederer, E. (1969) Chemical and mass spectral sequence of a peptide from the variable part of normal immunoglobulin lambda chains. *FEBS Letters*, **2**, 309–312.

Frank, G., Sidler, W., Widmer, H., and Zuber, H. (1978) The complete amino acid sequence of both subunits of C-phycocyanin from the Cyanobacterium *Mastigocladus laminosus*. *Hoppe-Seyler's Z. Physiol. Chem.*, **359**, 1491–1507.

Frank, G. and Weeds, A. G. (1974) The amino acid sequence of the alkali light chains of rabbit skeletal muscle myosin. *Eur. J. Biochem.*, **44**, 317–334.

Geddes, A. J., Graham, G. N., Morris, H. R., Lucas, F., Barber, M., and Wolstenholme, W. A. (1969) Mass-spectrometric determination of the amino acid sequences in peptides isolated from the protein silk fibroin of *Bombyx mori*. *Biochem J.*, **114**, 695–702.

Gray, W. R. and Hartley, B. S. (1963) A fluorescent end-group reagent for proteins and peptides. *Biochem. J.*, **89**, 59P.

Gray, W. R. and Smith, J. F. (1970) Rapid sequence analysis of small peptides. *Anal. Biochem.*, **33**, 36–42.

Gregoire, J. and Rochat, H. (1977) Amino acid sequences of Neurotoxins I and III of the Elapidae snake *Naja mossambica mossambica*. *Eur. J. Biochem.*, **80**, 283–293.

Gregory, H. (1975) The preparation of deslysylalanyl porcine and bovine insulins. *FEBS Letters*, **51**, 201–205.

Gregory, H. and Preston, B. M. (1977) The primary structure of human urogastrone. *Int. J. Peptide Protein Res.*, **9**, 107–118.

Gross, E. and Witkop, B. (1962) Nonenzymatic cleavage of peptide bonds: the methionine residues in bovine pancreatic ribonuclease. *J. Biol. Chem.*, **237**, 1856–1860.

Hakomori, S. I. (1964) A rapid permethylation of glycolipid and polysaccharide catalyzed by methyl sulfonyl carbanion in dimethyl sulfoxide. *J. Biochem.*, **55**, 205–208.

Hartley, B. S. (1970) Strategy and tactics in protein chemistry. *Biochem J.*, **119**, 805–822.

Hase, T., Matsubara, H., and Evans, M. C. W. (1977) The amino acid sequence of *Chromatium vinosum* ferredoxin: revisions. *J. Biochem.*, **81**, 1745–1749.

Hase, T., Wada, K., Ohmiya, M., and Matsubata, H. (1976) Amino acid sequence of a major component of *Nostoc muscorum* ferredoxin. *J. Biochem.*, **80**, 993–999.

Hase, T., Wakabayashi, S., Matsubara, H., Evans, M. C. W., and Jennings, J. V. (1978) Amino acid sequence of a ferredoxin from *Chlorobium thiosulfatophilum* strain Tassajara, photosynthetic green sulfur bacterium. *J. Biochem.*, **83**, 1321–1325.

Henderson, L. E., Henriksson, D., and Nyman, P. O. (1976) Primary structure of human carbonic anhydrase C. *J. Biol. Chem.*, **251**, 5457–5463.

Herbrink, P. (1976) The polypeptide chain composition of β-crystallin. *Ph.D. Thesis*, University of Nijmegen.

Hitz, H., Schafer, D., and Wittmann-Liebold, B. (1977) Determination of the complete amino acid sequence of protein S6 from the wild-type and a mutant of *Escherichia coli*. *Eur. J. Biochem.*, **75**, 497–512.

Hoegaerden, M. van and Strosberg, A. D. (1978) Sequence of a rabbit anti-*Micrococcus lysodeikticus* antibody light chain. *Biochemistry*, **17**, 4311–4317.

Hoerman, K. C. and Kamel, K. (1967) Recycled chromatograms for better peptide mapping. *Anal. Biochem.*, **21**, 107–10.

Hogg, R. W. and Hermodson, M. A. (1977) Amino acid sequence of the L-arabinose-binding protein from *Escherichia coli* B/r. *J. Biol. Chem.*, **252**, 5135–5141.

Houmard, J. and Drapeau, G. R. (1972) Staphylococcal protease: a proteolytic enzyme specific for glutamoyl bonds. *Proc. Natn. Acad. Sci. U.S.A.*, **69**, 3506–3509.

Howard, N. L., Joubert, F. J., and Strydom, D. J. (1974) The amino acid sequence of ostrich (*Struthio camelus*) cytochrome c. *Comp. Biochem. Physiol.* **48B**, 75–85.

Hurrell, J. G. R. and Leach, S. L. (1977) The amino acid sequence of soybean leghaemoglobin c_2. *FEBS Letters*, **80**, 23–26.

Inagami, T. (1973) Simultaneous identification of PTH derivatives of histidine and arginine by thin-layer chromatography. *Anal. Biochem.*, **52**, 318–321.

Inglis, A. S. and Burley, R. W. (1977) Determination of the amino acid sequence of Apovitellenin I from duck's egg yolk using an improved sequenator procedure: a comparison with other avian species. *FEBS Letters*, **73**, 33–37.

146

Ingram, V. M. (1953) Phenylthiohyantoins from serine and threonine. *J. Chem. Soc.*, **1953**, 3717–3718.

Isobe, T., Black, L. W., and Tsugita, A. (1977b) Complete amino acid sequence of bacteriophage T_4 internal protein I and its cleavage site on virus maturation. *J. Mol. Biol.*, **110**, 165–177.

Isobe, T., Nakajima, T., and Okuyama, T. (1977a) Reinvestigation of extremely acidic peptides in bovine brain. *Biochim. Biophys. Acta*, **494**, 222–232.

Isobe, T. and Okuyama, T. (1978) The amino acid sequence of S-100 protein (PAP I-b Protein) and its relation to the calcium binding proteins. *Eur. J. Biochem.*, **89**, 379–388.

Jabusch, J. R., Parmelee, D. C., and Deutsch, H. F. (1978) The effect of thiodiglycol and dithiothreitol on the alkaline hydrolysis products of certain amino acid phenylthiohydantoins. *Anal. Biochem.*, **91**, 532–542.

Jackson, R. L., Lin, H.-Y., Chan, L., and Means, A. R. (1977) Amino acid sequence of a major apoprotein from hen plasma very low density lipoprotein. *J. Biol. Chem.*, **252**, 250–253.

Jeppsson, J. and Sjöquist, J. (1967) Thin-layer chromatography of PTH amino acids. *Anal. Biochem.*, **18**, 264–269.

Joassin, L. and Gerday, C. (1977) The amino acid sequence of the major parvalbumin of the whiting (*Gadus merlangus*). *Comp. Biochem. Physiol.* **57B**, 159–161.

Jones, M. G. (1976) Structure and biological activity of peptides. *Ph.D. Thesis*, University of Salford.

Jörnvall, H. (1977) The primary structure of yeast alcohol dehydrogenase. *Eur. J. Biochem.*, **72**, 425–442.

Kasper, C. B. (1975) Fragmentation of proteins for sequence studies and separation of peptide mixtures, in *Protein Sequence Determination*, Ed. S. B. Needleman (Springer-Verlag, Berlin and New York), pp 114–161.

Kawasaki, I. and Itano, H. A. (1972) Methanolysis of the pyrrolidone ring of amino-terminal pyroglutamic acid in model peptides. *Anal. Biochem.*, **48**, 546–556.

Kondo, K., Narita, K., and Lee, C. (1978) Amino acid sequences of the two polypeptide chains in Bungarotoxin from the venom of *Bungarus multicinctus*. *J. Biochem.*, **83**, 101–115.

Kootstra, A. and Bailey, G. S. (1978) Primary structure of histone H2B from Trout (*Salmo trutta*) testes. *Biochemistry*, **17**, 2504–2509.

Krutzsch, H. C. and Kindt, T. J. (1979) The identification of trimethylsilylated dipeptides with chemical ionization mass spectrometry. *Anal. Biochem.*, **92**, 525–531.

Kulbe, K. D. (1974) Micropolyamide thin-layer chromatography of phenylthiohydantoin amino acids (PTH) at subnanomolar level. A rapid micro technique for simultaneous multisample identification after automated Edman degradations. *Anal. Biochem.*, **59**, 564–573.

Laursen, R. A. (1971) Solid-phase Edman degradation: an automatic peptide sequencer. *Eur. J. Biochem.*, **20**, 89–102.

Laursen, R. A. (1972) Automatic solid-phase Edman degradation, in *Methods in Enzymology*, Vol. **XXVB**, 344–359, Eds C. H. W. Hirs and S. N. Timasheff, (Academic Press, London).

Laursen, R. A., Horn, M. J., and Bonner, A. G. (1972) Solid-phase Edman degradation. The use of p-phenyl diisothiocyanate to attach lysine and arginine-containing peptides to insoluble resins. *FEBS Letters*, **21**, 67–71.

Lee, H. and Riordan, J. F. (1978) Does carboxypeptidase Y have intrinsic endopeptidase activity? *Biochem. Biophys. Res. Commun.*, **85**, 1135–1142.

Lin, J. K. and Chang, J. Y. (1975) Chromophoric labeling of amino acids with 4-dimethylaminobenzene-4'-sulfonyl chloride. *Anal. Chem.*, **47**, 1634–1638.

Lindemann, H. and Wittmann-Liebold, B. (1977) Primary structure of protein S13 from the small subunit of *E. coli* ribosomes. *Hoppe-Seyler's Z. Physiol. Chem.*, **358**, 843–863.

Lu, H. and Lo, T. (1978) Complete amino acid sequence of a new type of cardiotoxin of *Bungarus fasciatus* venom. *Int. J. Peptide Protein Res.*, **12**, 181–183.

Macleod, A. R., Wong, N. C. W., and Dixon, G. H. (1977) The amino acid sequence of Trout-testis histone H1. *Eur. J. Biochem.*, **78**, 281–291.

Maeda, N. and Tamiya, N. (1977) Correction of the partial amino acid sequence of Erabutoxins. *Biochem. J.*, **167**, 289–291.

Magnusson, S., Sottrup-Jensen, L., Petersen, T. E., Morris, H. R., and Dell, A. (1974) Primary Structure of the vitamin K-dependent part of prothrombin. *FEBS Letters*, **44**, 189–193.

Mahajan, V. K. and Desiderio, D. M. (1978) Mass spectrometry of acetylated, permethylated and reduced oligopeptides. *Biochem. Biophys. Res. Commun.*, **82**, 1104–1110.

Mak, A. S. and Jones, B. L. (1976) The amino acid sequence of wheat β-purothionin. *Can. J. Biochem.*, **22**, 835–842.

Martinez, G., Kopeyan, C., Schweitz, H., and Lazdunski, M. (1977) Toxin III from *Anemoniasulcata*: primary structure. *FEBS Letters*, **84**, 247–252.

Matsubara, H., Sasaki, R. K., Tsuchiya, D. K., and Evans, M. C. W. (1970) The amino acid sequence of *Chromatium Ferredoxin*. *J. Biol. Chem.*, **245**, 2121–2131.

Matsuo, H., Fujimoto, Y., and Tatsuno, T. (1966) A novel method for the determination of C-terminal amino acids in polypeptides by selective tritium labelling. *Biochem. Biophys. Res. Comm.*, **22**, 69–74.

Meagher, R. B. (1975) Rapid manual sequencing of multiple peptide samples in a nitrogen chamber. *Anal. Biochem.*, **67**, 404–412.

Mendez, E. and Lai, C. Y. (1975) Regeneration of amino acids from thiazolinones formed in the Edman degradation. *Anal. Biochem.*, **68**, 47–53.

Mitchell, W. M. and Harrington, W. F. (1968) Purification and properties of Clostridiopeptidase B (clostripain). *J. Biol. Chem.*, **243**, 4683–4692.

Mok, C. C. and Waley, S. G. (1968) N-terminal groups in lens proteins. *Exp. Eye Res.*, **7**, 148–153.

Morris, H. R. (1972) Studies towards the complete sequence determination of proteins by mass spectrometry: a rapid procedure for the successful permethylation of histidine-containing peptides. *FEBS Letters*, **22**, 257–260.

Morris, H. R. (1975) Protein sequence analysis and the discovery of a new amino acid in prothrombin. *Biochem. Soc. Trans.*, **3**, 465–467.

Morris, H. R., Batley, K. E., and Harding, N. G. L. (1974a) Dihydrofolate reductase: low resolution mass-spectrometric analysis of an elastase digest as a sequencing tool. *Biochem. J.*, **137**, 409–411.

Morris, H. R., Dickinson, R. J. and Williams, D. H. (1973) Studies towards the complete sequence determination of proteins by mass spectrometry; derivatisation of methionine, cysteine and arginine containing peptides. *Biochem. Biophys. Res. Commun.*, **51**, 247–255.

Morris, H. R., Thompson, M. R., Osuga, D. T., Ahmed, A. I., Chan, S. M., Vandenheede, J. R., and Feeney, R. E. (1978) Antifreeze glycoproteins from blood of an antarctic fish. *J. Biol. Chem.*, **253**, 5155–5162.

Morris, H. R., Williams, D. H., and Ambler, R. P. (1971) Determination of the sequence of protein-derived peptides and peptide mixtures by mass spectrometry. *Biochem. J.*, **125**, 189–201.

Morris, H. R., Williams, D. H., Midwinter, G. G., and Hartley, B. S. (1974b) A mass-spectrometric sequence study of the enzyme ribitol dehydrogenase from *Klebsiella aerogenes*. *Biochem. J.*, **141**, 701–713.

Mosesson, M. W., Finlayson, J. S., and Galanakis, D. K. (1973) The essential covalent structure of human fibrinogen evinced by analysis of derivatives formed during plasmic hydrolysis. *J. Biol. Chem.*, **248**, 7913–7929.

Naider, F. and Bohak, Z. (1972) Regeneration of methionyl residues from their sulfonium salts in peptides and proteins. *Biochemistry*, **11**, 3208–3211.

Narita, K. (1958) Isolation of an acetyl peptide from enzymic digests of TMV-protein. *Biochim. Biophys. Acta*, **28**, 184–191.

Nau, H. (1974) New dideutero-perfluoroalkylated oligopeptide derivatives for protein sequencing by gas chromatography–mass spectrometry. *Biochem. Biophys. Res. Commun.* **59**, 1088–1096.

Nau, H. and Bieman, K. (1976) Amino acid sequencing by gas chromatography–mass spectrometry using trifluoro-deuteroalkylated peptide derivatives. *Anal. Biochem.*, **73**, 175–186.

Niall, H. D. (1977) Pehr Edman—Obituary. *Nature*, **268**, 279–280.

Niall, H. D., Jacobs, J. W., van Rietschoten, J., and Tregear G. W. (1974) Protected Edman degradation: a new approach to microsequence analysis of proteins. *FEBS Letters*, **41**, 62–64.

Niketic, V., Thomsen, J., and Kristiansen, K., (1974) Modification of cysteine residues with sodium 2-bromoethane sulphonate. *Eur. J. Biochem.*, **46**, 547–551.

O'Donnell, I. J. and Inglis, A. S. (1974) Amino acid sequence of a feather keratin from Silver Gull (*Larus novae-hollandiae*) and comparison with one from Emu (*Dromaius novae-hollandiae*). *Aust. J. Biol. Sci.*, **27**, 369–382.

Orden, H. O. van and Carpenter, F. H. (1964) Hydrolysis of phenylthiohydantoins of amino acids. *Biochem. Biophys. Res. Commun.*, **14**, 399–403.

Orlov, V. M., Varshavsky, Y. M., and Kiryushkin, A. A. (1972) Comparative studies on photo-ionization and electron-impact ionization of peptide derivatives. *Organic Mass Spectrometry*, **6**, 9–20.

Ovchinnikov, Yu. A., Egorov, C. A., Aldanova, N. A., Feigina, M. Yu., Lipkin, V. M., Abdulaev, N. G., Grishin, E. V., Kiselev, A. P., Modyanov, N. N., Braunstein, A. E., Polyanovsky, O. L., and Nosikov, V. V. (1973) The complete amino acid sequence of cytoplasmic aspartate aminotransferase from pig heart. *FEBS Letters*, **29**, 31–34.

Ovchinnikov, Yu. A., Lipkin, V. M., Modyanov, N. N., Chertov, O. Yu., and Smirnov, Yu. V. (1977) Primary structure of α-subunit of DNA-dependent RNA polymerase from *Escherichia coli*. *FEBS Letters*, **76**, 108–111.

Parham, M. E. and Loudon, G. M. (1978) A new method of determination of the carboxyl-terminal residue of peptides. *Biochem. Biophys Res. Commun.*, **80**, 7–13.

Partridge, S. M. and Davis, H. F. (1950) Preferential release of aspartic acid during the hydrolysis of proteins. *Nature*, **165**, 62–63.

Patthy, L. and Smith, E. L. (1975) Identification of functional arginine residues in ribonuclease A and lysozyme. *J. Biol. Chem.*, **250**, 565–569.

Percy, M. E. and Buchwald, B. M. (1972) A manual method sequential Edman degradation followed by dansylation for the determination of protein sequences. *Anal. Biochem.*, **45**, 60–67.

Peterson, J. D., Nehrlich, S., Oyer, P. E., and Steiner, D. F. (1972) Determination of the amino acid sequence of the monkey, sheep and dog proinsulin C-peptides by a semi-micro Edman degradation procedure. *J. Biol. Chem.*, **247**, 4866–4871.

Pettigrew, G. W. and Smith, G. M. (1977) Novel N-terminal protein blocking group identified as dimethylproline. *Nature*, **265**, 661–662.

Pisano, J. J., Bronzert, T. J., and Brewer, H. B. (1972) Advances in the gas chromatographic analysis of amino acid phenyl- and methylthiohydantoins. *Anal. Biochem.*, **45**, 43–59.

Pisano, J. J., van den Heuvel, W. J. A., and Horning, E. C. (1962) Gas chromatography of phenylthiohydrantoin and dinitrophenyl derivatives of amino acids. *Biochem. Biophys. Res. Commun.*, **7**, 82–86.

Podell, D. N. and Abraham, G. N. (1978) A technique for the removal of pyroglutamic acid from the amino terminus of proteins using calf liver pyroglutamate amino peptidase. *Biochem. Biophys. Res. Commun.*, **81**, 176–185.

Polan, M. L., McMurray, W. J., Lipsky, S. R., and Lande, S. (1970) Mass spectrometry of cysteine-containing peptides. *Biochem. Biophys. Res. Commun.*, **38**, 1127–1133.

Ponstingl, H., Nieto, A., and Beato, M. (1978) Amino acid sequence of progesterone-induced rabbit uteroglobin. *Biochemistry*, **17**, 3908–3912.

Previero, A., Coletti-Previero, M. A., and Axelrud-Cavadore, C. (1967) Prevention of cleavage next to tryptophan residues during the oxidative splitting by N-bromosuccinimide of tyrosyl peptide bonds in proteins. *Arch. Biochem. Biophys.*, **122**, 434–438.

Previero, A., Derancourt, J., Coletti-Previero, M. A., and Laursen, R. A. (1973) Solid phase sequential analysis: specific linking of acidic peptides by their carboxyl ends to insoluble resins. *FEBS Letters*, **33**, 135–138.

Priddle, J. D. and Offord, R. E. (1974) The active centre of triose phosphate isomerase from chicken breast muscle. *FEBS Letters*, **39**, 349–352.

Prox, A. and Weygand, F. (1967) Sequenzanalyse von Peptiden durch Kombination von Gaschromatographie und Massenspektrometrie, in *Peptides* ed. H. C. Beyerman, A. van de Linde, and W. M. van den Brink (North-Holland Publishing Co., Amsterdam) pp 158–172.

Rees, M. W., Short, M. N., Self, R., and Eagles, J. (1974) The amino acid sequences of the tryptic peptides of the cowpea strain of tobacco mosaic virus protein. *Biomed. Mass Spectrom.*, **1**, 237–251.

Richardson, C., Behnke, W. D., Freisheim, J. H., and Blumenthal, K. M. (1978) The complete amino acid sequence of the α-subunit of pea lectin. *Biochim. Biophys. Acta*, **537**, 310–319.

Rinderknecht, E. and Humbel, R. E. (1978) The amino acid sequence of human insulin-like growth factor I and its structural homology with proinsulin. *J. Biol. Chem.*, **253**, 2769–2776.

Rochat, H., Bechis, G., Kopeyan, C., Gregoire, J., and van Rietschoten, J. (1976) Use of parvalbumin as a protecting protein in the sequenator: An easy and efficient way for sequencing small amounts of peptides. *FEBS Letters*, **64**, 404–408.

Rodkey, J. A. and Bennett, C. D. (1976) Micro Edman degradation: the use of high-pressure chromatography and gas chromatography in the amino terminal sequence determination of 8 nanomoles of dihydrofolate reductase from a mouse sarcoma. *Biochem. Biophys. Res. Commun.*, **72**, 1407–1413.

Roepstorff, P., Norris, K., Severinsen, S., and Brunfeldt, K. (1970) Mass spectrometry of peptide derivatives. Temporary protection of methionine as sulfoxide during permethylation. *FEBS Letters*, **9**, 235–238.

Roseau, G. and Pantel, P. (1969) Revelation coloree des spots de phenylthio hydantoin d'acides amines. *J. Chrom.*, **44**, 392–395.

Rosmus, J. and Deyl, Z. (1972) Chromatography of N-terminal amino acids and derivatives. *J. Chrom.*, **70**, 221–339.

Sanger, F. (1945) The free amino groups of insulin. *Biochem. J.*, **39**, 507–515.

Sargent, J. R. (1965) *Methods in Zone Electrophoresis* (B. D. H. Chemicals Ltd, Poole, Dorset).

Scheffer, A. J. and Beintema, J. J. (1974) Horse pancreatic ribonuclease. *Eur. J. Biochem.*, **46**, 221–233.

Schroeder, W. A. (1972) Separation of peptides by chromatography on columns of Dowex 50 with volatile developers, in *Methods in Enzymology*, Vol. **XXVB**, 203–213, Eds C. H. W. Hirs and S. N. Timasheff (Academic Press, London).

Schultz, J., Allison, H., and Grice, M. (1962) Specificity of the cleavage of proteins by dilute acid. *Biochemistry*, **1**, 694–698.

Sepulveda, P., Marciniszyn, J., Liu, D., and Tang, J. (1975) Primary structure of porcine pepsin III. *J. Biol. Chem.*, **250**, 5082–5088.

Shechter, Y., Patchornik, A., and Burstein, Y. (1976) Selective chemical cleavage of tryptophanyl peptide bonds by oxidative chlorination with N-chlorosuccinimide. *Biochemistry*, **15**, 5071–5075.

Shemyakin, M. M., Ovchinnikov, Yu. A., Kiryushkin, A. A., Vinogradova, E. I., Miroshnikov, A. I., Alakhov, Yu. B., Lipkin, V. M., Shvetsov, Yu. B., Wulfson, N. S., Rosinov, B. V., Bochkarev, V. N., and Burikov, V. M. (1966) Mass spectrometric determination of the amino acid sequence of peptides. *Nature*, **211**, 361–366.

Silver, J. and Hood, L. E. (1974) Automated microsequence analysis in the presence of a synthetic carrier. *Analyt. Biochem.*, **60**, 285–292.

Simon-Becam. A., Claisse, M., and Lederer, F. (1978) Cytochrome c from *Schizosaccharomyces pombe. Eur. J. Biochem.*, **86**, 407–416.

Slingsby, C. (1974) Structural studies on γ-Crystallin fraction IV. *D. Phil. Thesis*, University of Oxford.

Slingsby, C. and Croft, L. R. (1978) Structural studies on calf lens γ-Crystallin fraction IV: A comparison of the cysteine-containing tryptic peptides with the corresponding amino acid sequence of γ-Crystallin fraction II. *Exp. Eye Res.*, **26**, 291–304.

Smith, G. P. S. (1978) Sequence of the full length immunoglobulin κ-chain of mouse myeloma MPC11. *Biochem. J.*, **171**, 337–347.

Smithies, O., Gibson, D., Fanning, E. M., Goodfliesh, R. M., Gilman, J. G., and Ballantyne, D. L. (1971) Quantitative procedures for use with the Edman–Begg sequenator. Partial sequences of two unusual immunoglobulin light chains, Rzf and Sac. *Biochemistry*, **10**, 4912–4921.

Stenflo, J., Fernlund, P., Egan, W., and Roepstorff, P. (1974) Vitamin K-dependent modifications of glutamic acid residues in prothrombin. *Proc. Natn. Acad. Sci. U.S.A.* **71**, 2730–2733.

Stenhagen, E. (1961) Massenspektrometrie als Hilfsmittel bei der Strukturbestimmung organischer Verbindungen, besonders bei Lipiden und Peptiden. *Z. Analyt. Chem.*, **181**, 462–480.

Stone, D. and Phillips, A. W. (1977) The amino acid sequence of dehydrofolate reductase from L1210 cells. *FEBS Letters*, **74**, 85–87.

Stone, D., Phillips, A. W., and Burchall, J. J. (1977) The amino acid sequence of the dihydrofolate reductase of a Trimethoprim-resistant strain of *Escherichia coli. Eur. J. Biochem.*, **72**, 613–624.

Strickland, M., Strickland, W. N., Brandt, W. F., and von Holt, C. (1977) The complete amino acid sequence of histone $H_2B_{(1)}$ from sperm of the Sea Urchin *Parechinus angulosus. Eur. J. Biochem.*, **77**, 263–275.

Strid, L. (1973) Separation of peptides according to charge by gel filtration in presence of ionized detergents. *FEBS Letters*, **33**, 192–196.

Strydom, D. J. (1977) Snake venom toxins. The amino acid sequence of a short-neurotoxin homologue from *Dendroaspis polylepis polylepis* (Black Mamba) venom. *Eur. J. Biochem.*, **76**, 99–106.

Summers, M. R., Smythers, G. W., and Oroszlan, S. (1973) Thin-layer chromatography of sub-nanomole amounts of phenylthiohydantoin (PTH) amino acids on polyamide sheets. *Anal. Biochem.*, **53**, 624–628.

Sutton, M. R., Fall, R. R., Nervi, A. M., Alberts, A. W., Vagelos, P. R., and Bradshaw, R. A. (1977). Amino acid sequence of *Escherichia coli* biotin carboxyl carrier protein (9100). *J. Biol. Chem.*, **252**, 3934–3940.

Tanaka, M., Haniu, M., Yasunobu, K. T., Evans, M. C. W., and Rao, K. K. (1975) The amino acid sequenie of ferredoxin II from *Chlorobium limicola*, a photosynthetic green bacterium. *Biochemistry*, **14**, 1938–1943.

Tanaka, M., Haniu, M., Yasunobu, K. T., and Norton, T. R. (1977) Amino acid sequence of the *Anthopleura xanthogrammica* heart stimulant Anthopleurin A. *Biochemistry*, **16**, 204–208.

Tanaka, M., Haniu, M., Yasunobu, K. T., and Yoch, D. C. (1977) Complete amino acid sequence of Azotoflavin, a flavodoxin from *Azotobacter vinelandii*. *Biochemistry*, **16**, 3525–3537.

Tarr, G. E. (1975) A general procedure for the manual sequencing of small quantities of peptides. *Anal. Biochem.*, **63**, 361–370.

Tarr, G. E., Beecher, J. F., Bell, M., and McKean, D. J. (1978) Polyquarternary amines prevent peptide loss from sequenators. *Anal. Biochem.*, **84**, 622–627.

Thomas, D. W. (1968) Mass spectrometry of permethylated peptide derivatives: extension of the technique to peptides containing aspartic acid, glutamic acid or tryptophane. *Biochem. Biophys. Res. Commun.*, **33**, 483–486.

Thomas, D. W. (1969) Mass spectrometry of N-permethylated peptide derivatives: artifacts produced by C-methylation. *FEBS Letters*, **5**, 53–56.

Thomas, D. W., Das, B. C., Gero, S. D., and Lederer, E. (1968) Mass spectrometry of permethylated peptide derivatives: extension of the technique to peptides containing arginine or methionine. *Biochem. Biophys. Res. Commun.*, **32**, 519–525.

Thomsen, J., Bucher, D., Brunfeldt, K., Nexp, E., and Olsen, H. (1976) An improved procedure for automated Edman degradation used for determination of the N-terminal amino acid sequence of human transcobalamin I and human intrinsic factor. *Eur. J. Biochem.*, **69**, 87–96.

Tomita, M., Furthmayr, H., and Marchesi, V. T. (1978) Primary structure of human erythrocyte glycophorin A. Isolation and characterization of peptides and complete amino acid sequence. *Biochemistry*, **17**, 4756–4770.

Tschesche, H., Schneider, M., and Wachter, E. (1972) Mass spectral identification and quantification of phenylthiohydantoin derivatives from Edman degradation of proteins. *FEBS Letters*, **23**, 367–370.

Vandekerckhove, J. and van Montagu, M. (1974) Sequence analysis of fluorescamine-stained peptides and proteins purified on a nanomole scale. *Eur. J. Biochem.*, **44**, 279–288.

Vandekerckhove, J. S. and van Montagu, M. C. (1977) sequence of the A-protein of coliphage MS2. *J. Biol. Chem.*, **252**, 7773–7782.

Vetter-Diechtl, H., Vetter, W., Richter, W., and Bieman, K. (1968) Ein fur Massenspektrometrie und Gaschromatographie geeignetes Argininderivat. *Experientia*, **24**, 340–341.

Vilkas, E. and Lederer, E. (1968) N-methylation des peptides par la methode de Hakomori: structure du mycoside C_{b1}. *Tetrahedron Letters*, **1968**, 3089–3092.

Waley, S. G. and Watson, J. (1953) The action of trypsin on polylysine. *Biochem. J.*, **55**, 328–337.

Walker, J. M., Hastings, J. R. B., and Johns, E. W. (1977) The primary structure of a non-histone chromosomal protein. *Eur. J. Biochem.*, **76**, 461–468.

Wang, C., Avila, R., Jones, B. N., and Gurd, F. R. N. (1977) Complete primary structure of the major component myoglobin of Pacific Common Dolphin (*Delphinus delphis*). *Biochemistry*, **16**, 4978–4981.

Weiner, A. M., Platt, T., and Weber, K. (1972) Amino-terminal sequence analysis of proteins purified on a nanamole scale by gel electrophoresis. *J. Biol. Chem.*, **247**, 3242–3251.

Wilkinson, J. M. and Grand, R. J. A. (1978) The amino acid sequence of chicken fast-skeletal-muscle Troponin I. *Eur. J. Biochem.*, **82**, 493–501.

Wilkinson, J. M., Press, E. M., and Porter, R. R. (1966). The N-terminal sequence of the heavy chain of rabbit immunoglobulin IgG. *Biochemical J.*, **100**, 303–308.

152

Wiman, B. (1977) Primary structure of the B-chain of human plasmin. *Eur. J. Biochem.*, **76**, 129–137.

Winkler, H. D. and Beckley, H. D. (1972) Field desorption mass spectrometry of peptides. *Biochem. Biophys. Res. Commun.*, **46**, 391–398.

Wittmann-Liebold, B. (1973) Amino acid sequence studies on ten ribosomal proteins of *Escherichia coli* with an improved sequenator equipped with an automatic conversion device. *Hoppe-Seyler's Z. Physiol. Chem.*, **354**, 1415–1431.

Wittmann-Liebold, B. and Marzinzig, E. (1977) Primary structure of protein L28 from the large subunit of *Escherichia coli*. *FEBS Letters* **81**, 214–217.

Woods, K. R. and Wang, K. T. (1967) Separation of dansyl-amino acids on polyamide layer chromatography. *Biochim. Biophys. Acta*, **133**, 369–370.

Wunderer, G. and Eulitz, M. (1978) Amino acid sequence of toxin I from *Anemonia sulcata*. *Eur. J. Biochem.*, **89**, 11–17.

Zuber, H. (1964) Purification and properties of a new carboxypeptidase from citrus fruit. *Nature*, **201**, 613.

Protein Sequences

BOVINE GLUTAMATE DEHYDROGENASE

	1				5					10					15	
1	ALA	ASP	ARG	GLU	ASP	ASP	PRO	ASN	PHE	PHE	LYS	MET	VAL	GLU	GLY	15
16	PHE	PHE	ASP	ARG	GLY	ALA	SER	ILE	VAL	GLU	ASP	LYS	LEU	VAL	GLU	30
31	ASP	LEU	LYS	THR	ARG	GLN	THR	GLN	GLU	GLN	LYS	ARG	ASN	ARG	VAL	45
46	ARG	GLY	ILE	LEU	ARG	ILE	ILE	LYS	PRO	CYS	ASN	HIS	VAL	LEU	SER	60
61	LEU	SER	PHE	PRO	ILE	ARG	ARG	ASP	ASP	GLY	SER	TRP	GLU	VAL	ILE	75
76	GLU	GLY	TYR	ARG	ALA	GLN	HIS	SER	HIS	GLN	ARG	THR	PRO	CYS	LYS	90
91	GLY	GLY	ILE	ARG	TYR	SER	THR	ASP	VAL	SER	VAL	ASP	GLU	VAL	LYS	105
106	ALA	LEU	ALA	SER	LEU	MET	THR	TYR	LYS	CYS	ALA	VAL	VAL	ASP	VAL	120
121	PRO	PHE	GLY	GLY	ALA	LYS	ALA	GLY	VAL	LYS	ILE	ASN	PRO	LYS	ASN	135
136	TYR	THR	ASP	GLU	ASP	LEU	GLU	LYS	ILE	THR	ARG	ARG	PHE	THR	MET	150
151	GLU	LEU	ALA	LYS	LYS	GLY	PHE	ILE	GLY	PRO	GLY	VAL	ASP	VAL	PRO	165
166	ALA	PRO	ASN	MET	SER	THR	GLY	GLU	ARG	GLU	MET	SER	TRP	ILE	ALA	180
181	ASP	THR	TYR	ALA	SER	THR	ILE	GLY	HIS	TYR	ASP	ILE	ASN	ALA	HIS	195
196	ALA	CYS	VAL	THR	LYS	PRO	GLY	ILE	SER	GLN	GLY	GLY	ILE	HIS	GLY	210
211	ARG	ILE	SER	ALA	THR	GLY	ARG	GLY	VAL	PHE	GLY	HIS	ILE	GLU	ASN	225
226	PHE	ILE	GLU	ASN	ALA	SER	TYR	MET	SER	ILE	LEU	GLY	MET	THR	PRO	240
241	GLY	PHE	GLY	ASP	LYS	THR	PHE	ALA	VAL	GLN	GLY	PHE	GLY	ASN	VAL	255
256	GLY	LEU	HIS	SER	MET	ARG	TYR	LEU	HIS	ARG	PHE	GLY	ALA	LYS	CYS	270
271	VAL	ALA	VAL	GLY	GLU	SER	ASP	GLY	SER	ILE	TRP	ASN	PRO	ASP	GLY	285
286	ILE	ASP	PRO	LYS	GLU	LEU	GLU	ASP	PHE	LYS	LEU	GLN	HIS	GLY	THR	300
301	ILE	LEU	GLY	PHE	PRO	LYS	ALA	LYS	ILE	TYR	GLU	GLY	SER	ILE	LEU	315
316	GLU	VAL	ASP	CYS	ASP	ILE	LEU	ILE	PRO	ALA	ALA	SER	GLU	LYS	GLN	330
331	LEU	THR	LYS	SER	ASN	ALA	PRO	ARG	VAL	LYS	ALA	LYS	ILE	ILE	ALA	345
346	GLU	GLY	ALA	ASN	GLY	PRO	THR	THR	PRO	GLN	ALA	ASP	LYS	ILE	PHE	360
361	LEU	GLU	ARG	ASN	ILE	MET	VAL	ILE	PRO	ASP	LEU	TYR	LEU	ASN	ALA	375
376	GLY	GLY	VAL	THR	VAL	SER	TYR	PHE	GLX	LEU	LYS	ASN	LEU	ASN	HIS	390
391	VAL	SER	TYR	GLY	ARG	LEU	THR	PHE	LYS	TYR	GLU	ARG	ASP	SER	ASN	405
406	TYR	HIS	LEU	LEU	MET	SER	VAL	GLN	GLU	SER	LEU	GLU	ARG	LYS	PHE	420
421	GLY	LYS	HIS	GLY	GLY	THR	ILE	PRO	ILE	VAL	PRO	THR	ALA	GLU	PHE	435
436	GLN	ASP	ARG	ILE	SER	GLY	ALA	SER	GLU	LYS	ASP	ILE	VAL	HIS	SER	450
451	GLY	LEU	ALA	TYR	THR	MET	GLU	ARG	SER	ALA	ARG	GLN	ILE	MET	ARG	465
466	THR	ALA	MET	LYS	TYR	ASN	LEU	GLY	LEU	ASP	LEU	ARG	THR	ALA	ALA	480
481	TYR	VAL	ASN	ALA	ILE	GLU	LYS	VAL	PHE	ARG	VAL	TYR	ASN	GLU	ALA	495
496	GLY	VAL	THR	PHE	THR											510

Sequence of bovine liver glutamate dehydrogenase. VIII. Peptides produced by specific chemical cleavages; the complete sequence of the protein.
K. Moon and E. L. Smith.
J. Biol. Chem., **248**, 3082–3088 (1973).

ENZYMES

NEUROSPORA GLUTAMATE DEHYDROGENASE

```
        1               5                   10                      15
  1   AC  SER ASN LEU PRO SER GLU PRO GLU PHE GLU GLN ALA TYR LYS    15
 16   GLU LEU ALA TYR THR LEU GLU ASN SER SER LEU PHE GLN LYS HIS    30
 31   PRO GLU TYR ARG THR ALA LEU THR VAL ALA SER ILE PRO GLU ARG    45
 46   VAL ILE GLN PHE ARG VAL VAL TRP GLU ASP ASP ASP GLY ASN VAL    60
 61   GLN VAL ASN ARG GLY TYR ARG VAL GLN PHE ASN SER ALA LEU GLY    75
 76   PRO TYR LYS GLY GLY LEU ARG LEU HIS PRO SER VAL ASN LEU SER    90
 91   ILE LEU LYS PHE LEU GLY PHE GLU GLN ILE PHE LYS ASN ALA LEU   105
106   THR GLY LEU SER MET GLY GLY GLY LYS GLY GLY ALA ASP PHE ASP   120
121   PRO LYS GLY LYS SER ASP ALA GLU ILE ARG ARG PHE CYS CYS ALA   135
136   PHE MET ALA GLU LEU HIS LYS HIS ILE GLY ALA ASP THR ASP VAL   150
151   PRO ALA GLY ASP ILE GLY VAL GLY GLY ARG GLU ILE GLY TYR MET   165
166   PHE GLY ALA TYR ARG LYS ALA ALA ASN ARG PHE GLU GLY VAL LEU   180
181   THR GLY LYS GLY LEU SER TRP GLY GLY SER LEU ILE ARG PRO GLU   195
196   ALA THR GLY TYR GLY LEU VAL TYR TYR VAL GLY HIS MET LEU GLU   210
211   TYR SER GLY ALA GLY SER TYR ALA GLY LYS ARG VAL ALA LEU SER   225
226   GLY SER GLY ASN VAL ALA GLN TYR ALA ALA LEU LYS LEU ILE GLU   240
241   LEU GLY ALA THR VAL VAL SER LEU SER ASP SER LYS GLY ALA LEU   255
256   VAL ALA THR GLY GLU SER GLY ILE THR VAL GLU ASP ILE ASN ALA   270
271   VAL MET ALA ILE LYS GLU ALA ARG GLN SER LEU THR SER PHE GLN   285
286   HIS ALA GLY HIS LEU LYS TRP ILE GLU GLY ALA ARG PRO TRP LEU   300
301   HIS VAL GLY LYS VAL ASP ILE ALA LEU PRO CYS ALA THR GLU ASP   315
316   GLU VAL SER LYS GLU GLU ALA GLU GLY LEU LEU ALA ALA GLY CYS   330
331   LYS PHE VAL ALA GLU GLY SER ASN MET GLY CYS THR LEU GLU ALA   345
346   ILE GLU VAL PHE GLU ASN ASN ARG LYS GLU LYS LYS GLY GLU ALA   360
361   VAL TRP TYR ALA PRO GLY LYS ALA ALA ASN CYS GLY GLY VAL ALA   375
376   VAL SER GLY LEU GLU MET ALA GLN ASN SER GLN ARG LEU ASN TRP   390
391   THR GLN ALA GLU VAL ASP GLU LYS LEU LYS ASP ILE MET LYS ASN   405
406   ALA PHE PHE ASN GLY LEU ASN THR ALA LYS THR TYR VAL GLU ALA   420
421   ALA GLU GLY GLU LEU PRO SER LEU VAL ALA GLY SER ASN ILE ALA   435
436   GLY PHE VAL LYS VAL ALA GLN ALA MET HIS ASP GLN GLY ASP TRP   450
451   SER LYS ASN                                                   465
```

The amino acid sequence of Neurospora NADP-specific glutamate dehydrogenase. The tryptic peptides.
J. C. Wootton, J. G. Taylor, A. A. Jackson, G. K. Chambers, and J. R. S. Fincham.
Biochem. J., **149**, 739–748 (1975).
Peptides from digestion with a staphylococcal proteinase.
J. C. Wootton, A. J. Baron, and J. R. S. Fincham.
Biochem. J., **149**, 749–755 (1975).
Peptic and chymotryptic peptides and the complete sequence.
A. A. Holder, J. C. Wootton, A. J. Baron, G. K. Chambers, and J. R. S. Fincham.
Biochem. J., **149**, 757–773 (1975).

HORSE LIVER ALCOHOL DEHYDROGENASE

	1				5					10					15		
1	AC	SER	THR	ALA	GLY	LYS	VAL	ILE	LYS	CYS	LYS	ALA	ALA	VAL	LEU		15
16	TRP	GLU	GLU	LYS	LYS	PRO	PHE	SER	ILE	GLU	GLU	VAL	GLU	VAL	ALA		30
31	PRO	PRO	LYS	ALA	HIS	GLU	VAL	ARG	ILE	LYS	MET	VAL	ALA	THR	GLY		45
46	ILE	CYS	ARG	SER	ASP	ASP	HIS	VAL	VAL	SER	GLY	THR	LEU	VAL	THR		60
61	PRO	LEU	PRO	VAL	ILE	ALA	GLY	HIS	GLU	ALA	ALA	GLY	ILE	VAL	GLU		75
76	SER	ILE	GLY	GLU	GLY	VAL	THR	THR	VAL	ARG	PRO	GLY	ASP	LYS	VAL		90
91	ILE	PRO	LEU	PHE	THR	PRO	GLN	CYS	GLY	LYS	CYS	ARG	VAL	CYS	LYS		105
106	HIS	PRO	GLU	GLY	ASN	PHE	CYS	LEU	LYS	ASN	ASP	LEU	SER	MET	PRO		120
121	ARG	GLY	THR	MET	GLN	ASP	GLY	THR	SER	ARG	PHE	THR	CYS	ARG	GLY		135
136	LYS	PRO	ILE	HIS	HIS	PHE	LEU	GLY	THR	SER	THR	PHE	SER	GLN	TYR		150
151	THR	VAL	VAL	ASP	GLU	ILE	SER	VAL	ALA	LYS	ILE	ASP	ALA	ALA	SER		165
166	PRO	LEU	GLU	LYS	VAL	CYS	LEU	ILE	GLY	CYS	GLY	PHE	SER	THR	GLY		180
181	TYR	GLY	SER	ALA	VAL	LYS	VAL	ALA	LYS	VAL	THR	GLN	GLY	SER	THR		195
196	CYS	ALA	VAL	PHE	GLY	LEU	GLY	GLY	VAL	GLY	LEU	SER	VAL	ILE	MET		210
211	GLY	CYS	LYS	ALA	ALA	GLY	ALA	ALA	ARG	ILE	ILE	GLY	VAL	ASP	ILE		225
226	ASN	LYS	ASP	LYS	PHE	ALA	LYS	ALA	LYS	GLU	VAL	GLY	ALA	THR	GLU		240
241	CYS	VAL	ASN	PRO	GLN	ASP	TYR	LYS	LYS	PRO	ILE	GLN	GLU	VAL	LEU		255
256	THR	GLU	MET	SER	ASN	GLY	GLY	VAL	ASP	PHE	SER	PHE	GLU	VAL	ILE		270
271	GLY	ARG	LEU	ASP	THR	MET	VAL	THR	ALA	LEU	SER	CYS	CYS	GLN	GLU		285
286	ALA	TYR	GLY	VAL	SER	VAL	ILE	VAL	GLY	VAL	PRO	PRO	ASP	SER	GLN		300
301	ASN	LEU	SER	MET	ASN	PRO	MET	LEU	LEU	LEU	SER	GLY	ARG	THR	TRP		315
316	LYS	GLY	ALA	ILE	PHE	GLY	GLY	PHE	LYS	SER	LYS	ASP	SER	VAL	PRO		330
331	LYS	LEU	VAL	ALA	ASP	PHE	MET	ALA	LYS	LYS	PHE	ALA	LEU	ASP	PRO		345
346	LEU	ILE	THR	HIS	VAL	LEU	PRO	PHE	GLU	LYS	ILE	ASN	GLU	GLY	PHE		350
351	ASP	LEU	LEU	ARG	SER	GLY	GLU	SER	ILE	ARG	THR	ILE	LEU	THR	PHE		365

Note: This is the sequence for the E-chain.
Horse Liver Alcohol Dehydrogenase. The Primary Structure of the Protein Chain of the Ethanol-Active Isoenzyme.
H. Jörnvall.
Eur. J. Biochem., **16**, 25–40 (1970).
Note: The S-chain differs from the above at positions 17, 94, 101, 110, 366, the residues in these positions are GLN. ILE, SER, LEU, LYS respectively. Residue 115 also differs but the substitution has not been firmly established.
Horse Liver Alcohol Dehydrogenase. On the Primary Structures of the Isoenzymes.
H. Jörnvall.
Eur. J. Biochem., **16**, 41–49 (1970).

ENZYMES

GLYCERALDEHYDE 3-PHOSPHATE DEHYDROGENASE FROM PIG MUSCLE

	1				5					10					15	
1	VAL	LYS	VAL	GLY	VAL	ASP	GLY	PHE	GLY	ARG	ILE	GLY	ARG	LEU	VAL	15
16	THR	ARG	ALA	ALA	PHE	ASN	SER	GLY	LYS	VAL	ASP	ILE	VAL	ALA	ILE	30
31	ASN	ASP	PRO	PHE	ILE	ASP	LEU	HIS	TYR	MET	VAL	TYR	MET	PHE	GLU	45
46	TYR	ASP	SER	THR	HIS	GLY	LYS	PHE	HIS	GLY	THR	VAL	LYS	ALA	GLU	60
61	ASP	GLY	LYS	LEU	VAL	ILE	ASP	GLY	LYS	ALA	ILE	THR	ILE	PHE	GLN	75
76	GLU	ARG	ASP	PRO	ALA	ASN	ILE	LYS	TRP	GLY	ASP	ALA	GLY	THR	ALA	90
91	TYR	VAL	VAL	GLU	SER	THR	GLY	VAL	PHE	THR	THR	MET	GLU	LYS	ALA	105
106	GLY	ALA	HIS	LEU	LYS	GLY	GLY	ALA	LYS	ARG	VAL	ILE	ILE	SER	ALA	120
121	PRO	SER	ALA	ASP	ALA	PRO	MET	PHE	VAL	MET	GLY	VAL	ASN	HIS	GLU	135
136	LYS	TYR	ASP	ASN	SER	LEU	LYS	ILE	VAL	SER	ASN	ALA	SER	CYS	THR	150
151	THR	ASN	CYS	LEU	ALA	PRO	LEU	ALA	LYS	VAL	ILE	HIS	ASP	HIS	PHE	165
166	GLY	ILE	VAL	GLU	GLY	LEU	MET	THR	THR	VAL	HIS	ALA	ILE	THR	ALA	180
181	THR	GLN	LYS	THR	VAL	ASP	GLY	PRO	SER	GLY	LYS	LEU	TRP	ARG	ASP	195
196	GLY	ARG	GLY	ALA	ALA	GLN	ASN	ILE	ILE	PRO	ALA	SER	THR	GLY	ALA	210
211	ALA	LYS	ALA	VAL	GLY	LYS	VAL	ILE	PRO	GLU	LEU	ASP	GLY	LYS	LEU	225
226	THR	GLY	MET	ALA	PHE	ARG	VAL	PRO	THR	PRO	ASN	VAL	SER	VAL	VAL	240
241	ASP	LEU	THR	CYS	ARG	LEU	GLU	LYS	PRO	ALA	LYS	TYR	ASP	ASP	ILE	255
256	LYS	LYS	VAL	VAL	LYS	GLN	ALA	SER	GLU	GLY	PRO	LEU	LYS	GLY	ILE	270
271	LEU	GLY	TYR	THR	GLU	ASP	GLN	VAL	VAL	SER	CYS	ASP	PHE	ASN	ASP	285
286	SER	THR	HIS	SER	SER	THR	PHE	ASP	ALA	GLY	ALA	GLY	ILE	ALA	LEU	300
301	ASN	ASP	HIS	PHE	VAL	LYS	LEU	ILE	SER	TRP	TYR	ASP	ASN	GLU	PHE	315
316	GLY	TYR	SER	ASN	ARG	VAL	VAL	ASP	LEU	MET	VAL	HIS	MET	ALA	SER	330
331	LYS	GLU														345

Glyceraldehyde 3-Phosphate Dehydrogenase from Pig Muscle.
J. I. Harris and R. N. Perham.
Nature, **219**, 1025–1028 (1968).

GLYCERALDEHYDE 3-PHOSPHATE DEHYDROGENASE FROM LOBSTER MUSCLE

	1				5					10					15	
1	AC	SER	LYS	ILE	GLY	ILE	ASP	GLY	PHE	GLY	ARG	ILE	GLY	ARG	LEU	15
16	VAL	LEU	ARG	ALA	ALA	LEU	SER	CYS	GLY	ALA	GLN	VAL	VAL	ALA	VAL	30
31	ASN	ASP	PRO	PHE	ILE	ALA	LEU	GLU	TYR	MET	VAL	TYR	MET	PHE	LYS	45
46	TYR	ASP	SER	THR	HIS	GLY	VAL	PHE	LYS	GLY	GLU	VAL	LYS	MET	GLU	60
61	ASP	GLY	ALA	LEU	VAL	VAL	ASP	GLY	LYS	LYS	ILE	THR	VAL	PHE	ASN	75
76	GLU	MET	LYS	PRO	GLU	ASN	ILE	PRO	TRP	SER	LYS	ALA	GLY	ALA	GLU	90
91	TYR	ILE	VAL	GLU	SER	THR	GLY	VAL	PHE	THR	THR	ILE	GLU	LYS	ALA	105
106	SER	ALA	HIS	PHE	LYS	GLY	GLY	ALA	LYS	LYS	VAL	VAL	ILE	SER	ALA	120
121	PRO	SER	ALA	ASP	ALA	PRO	MET	PHE	VAL	CYS	GLY	VAL	ASN	LEU	GLU	135
136	LYS	TYR	SER	LYS	ASP	MET	THR	VAL	VAL	SER	ASN	ALA	SER	CYS	THR	150
151	THR	ASN	CYS	LEU	ALA	PRO	VAL	ALA	LYS	VAL	LEU	HIS	GLU	ASN	PHE	165
166	GLU	ILE	VAL	GLU	GLY	LEU	MET	THR	THR	VAL	HIS	ALA	VAL	THR	ALA	180
181	THR	GLN	LYS	THR	VAL	ASP	GLY	PRO	SER	ALA	LYS	ASP	TRP	ARG	GLY	195
196	GLY	ARG	GLY	ALA	ALA	GLN	ASN	ILE	ILE	PRO	SER	SER	THR	GLY	ALA	210
211	ALA	LYS	ALA	VAL	GLY	LYS	VAL	ILE	PRO	GLU	LEU	ASP	GLY	LYS	LEU	225
226	THR	GLY	MET	ALA	PHE	ARG	VAL	PRO	THR	PRO	ASP	VAL	SER	VAL	VAL	240
241	ASP	LEU	THR	VAL	ARG	LEU	GLY	LYS	GLU	CYS	SER	TYR	ASP	ASP	ILE	255
256	LYS	ALA	ALA	MET	LYS	THR	ALA	SER	GLU	GLY	PRO	LEU	GLN	GLY	PHE	270
271	LEU	GLY	TYR	THR	GLU	ASP	ASP	VAL	VAL	SER	SER	ASP	PHE	ILE	GLY	285
286	ASP	ASN	ARG	SER	SER	ILE	PHE	ASP	ALA	LYS	ALA	GLY	ILE	GLN	LEU	300
301	SER	LYS	THR	PHE	VAL	LYS	VAL	VAL	SER	TRP	TYR	ASP	ASN	GLU	PHE	315
316	GLY	TYR	SER	GLN	ARG	VAL	ILE	ASP	LEU	LEU	LYS	HIS	MET	GLN	LYS	330
331	VAL	ASP	SER	ALA												345

Amino acid Sequence of Glyceraldehyde 3-Phosphate Dehydrogenase from Lobster Muscle.
B. E. Davidson, M. Sajgò, H. F. Noller, and J. I. Harris.
Nature, **216**, 1181–1185 (1967).

ENZYMES

GLYCERALDEHYDE 3-PHOSPHATE DEHYDROGENASE (B. STEAROTHERMOPHILUS)

	1			5					10					15		
1	ALA	VAL	LYS	VAL	GLY	ILE	ASN	GLY	PHE	GLY	ARG	ILE	GLY	ARG	ASN	15
16	VAL	PHE	ARG	ALA	ALA	LEU	LYS	ASN	PRO	ASP	ILE	GLU	VAL	VAL	ALA	30
31	VAL	ASN	ASP	LEU	THR	ASN	ALA	ASP	GLY	LEU	ALA	HIS	LEU	LEU	LYS	45
46	TYR	ASP	SER	VAL	HIS	GLY	ARG	LEU	ASP	ALA	GLU	VAL	VAL	VAL	ASN	60
61	ASP	GLY	ASP	VAL	SER	VAL	ASN	GLY	LYS	GLU	ILE	ILE	VAL	LYS	ALA	75
76	GLU	ARG	ASN	PRO	GLU	ASN	LEU	ALA	TRP	GLY	GLU	ILE	GLY	VAL	ASP	90
91	ILE	VAL	VAL	GLU	SER	THR	GLY	ARG	PHE	THR	LYS	ARG	GLU	ASP	ALA	105
106	ALA	LYS	HIS	LEU	GLU	ALA	GLY	ALA	LYS	LYS	VAL	ILE	ILE	SER	ALA	120
121	PRO	ALA	LYS	VAL	GLU	ASN	ILE	THR	VAL	VAL	MET	GLY	VAL	ASN	GLN	135
136	ASP	LYS	TYR	ASP	PRO	LYS	ALA	HIS	HIS	VAL	ILE	SER	ASN	ALA	SER	150
151	CYS	THR	THR	ASN	CYS	LEU	ALA	PRO	PHE	ALA	LYS	VAL	LEU	HIS	GLN	165
166	GLU	PHE	GLY	ILE	VAL	ARG	GLY	MET	MET	THR	THR	VAL	HIS	SER	TYR	180
181	THR	ASN	ASN	GLN	ARG	ILE	LEU	ASP	LEU	PRO	HIS	LYS	ASP	LEU	ARG	195
196	GLY	ALA	ARG	ALA	ALA	ALA	GLU	SER	ILE	ILE	PRO	THR	THR	THR	GLY	210
211	ALA	ALA	LYS	ALA	VAL	ALA	LEU	VAL	LEU	PRO	GLU	LEU	LYS	GLY	LYS	225
226	LEU	ASN	GLY	MET	ALA	MET	ARG	VAL	PRO	THR	PRO	ASN	VAL	SER	VAL	240
241	VAL	ASP	LEU	VAL	ALA	GLU	LEU	GLU	LYS	GLU	VAL	THR	VAL	GLU	GLU	255
256	VAL	ASN	ALA	ALA	LEU	LYS	ALA	ALA	ALA	GLU	GLY	GLU	LEU	LYS	GLY	270
271	ILE	LEU	ALA	TYR	SER	GLU	GLU	PRO	LEU	VAL	SER	ARG	ASN	TYR	ASN	285
286	GLY	SER	THR	VAL	SER	SER	THR	ILE	ASP	ALA	LEU	SER	THR	MET	VAL	300
301	ILE	ASP	GLY	LYS	MET	VAL	LYS	VAL	VAL	SER	TRP	TYR	ASP	ASN	GLU	315
316	THR	GLY	TYR	SER	HIS	ARG	VAL	VAL	ASP	LEU	ALA	ALA	TYR	ILE	ASN	330
331	ALA	LYS	GLY	LEU												345

Sequence and structure of D-glyceraldehyde 3-phosphate dehydrogenase from *Bacillus stearothermophilus*.
G. Biesecker, J. I. Harris, J. C. Thierry, J. E. Walker, and A. J. Wonacott.
Nature, **266**, 328–333 (1977).

LACTATE DEHYDROGENASE—DOGFISH

	1				5					10					15	
1	AC	ALA	THR	LEU	LYS	ASP	LYS	LEU	ILE	GLY	HIS	LEU	ALA	THR	SER	15
16	GLN	GLU	PRO	ARG	SER	TYR	ASN	LYS	ILE	THR	VAL	VAL	GLY	VAL	GLY	30
31	ALA	VAL	GLY	MET	ALA	CYS	ALA	ILE	SER	ILE	LEU	MET	LYS	ASP	LEU	45
46	ALA	ASP	GLU	VAL	ALA	LEU	VAL	ASP	VAL	MET	GLU	ASP	LYS	LEU	LYS	60
61	GLY	GLU	MET	MET	ASP	LEU	GLN	HIS	GLY	SER	LEU	PHE	LEU	HIS	THR	75
76	ALA	LYS	ILE	VAL	SER	GLY	LYS	ASP	TYR	SER	VAL	SER	ALA	GLY	SER	90
91	LYS	LEU	VAL	VAL	ILE	THR	ALA	GLY	ALA	ARG	GLN	GLN	GLU	GLY	GLU	105
106	SER	ARG	LEU	ASN	LEU	VAL	GLN	ARG	ASN	VAL	ASN	ILE	PHE	LYS	PHE	120
121	ILE	ILE	PRO	ASN	ILE	VAL	LYS	HIS	SER	PRO	ASP	CYS	ILE	ILE	LEU	135
136	VAL	VAL	SER	ASN	PRO	VAL	ASP	VAL	LEU	THR	TYR	VAL	ALA	TRP	LYS	150
151	LEU	SER	GLY	LEU	PRO	MET	HIS	ARG	ILE	ILE	GLY	SER	GLY	CYS	ASN	165
166	LEU	ASP	SER	ALA	ARG	PHE	ARG	TYR	LEU	MET	GLY	GLU	ARG	LEU	GLY	180
181	VAL	HIS	SER	CYS	SER	CYS	HIS	GLY	TRP	VAL	ILE	GLY	GLU	HIS	GLY	195
196	ASP	SER	VAL	PRO	SER	VAL	TRP	SER	GLY	MET	TRP	ASN	ALA	LEU	LYS	210
211	GLU	LEU	HIS	PRO	GLU	LEU	GLY	THR	ASN	LYS	ASP	LYS	GLN	ASP	TRP	225
226	LYS	LYS	LEU	HIS	LYS	ASP	VAL	VAL	ASP	SER	ALA	TYR	GLU	VAL	ILE	240
241	LYS	LEU	LYS	GLY	TYR	THR	SER	TRP	ALA	ILE	GLY	LEU	SER	VAL	ALA	255
256	ASP	LEU	ALA	GLU	THR	ILE	MET	LYS	ASN	LEU	CYS	ARG	VAL	HIS	PRO	270
271	VAL	SER	THR	MET	VAL	LYS	ASP	PHE	TYR	GLY	ILE	LYS	ASP	ASN	VAL	285
286	PHE	LEU	SER	LEU	PRO	CYS	VAL	LEU	ASN	ASP	HIS	GLY	ILE	SER	ASN	300
301	ILE	VAL	LYS	MET	LYS	LEU	LYS	PRO	ASP	GLU	GLU	GLN	GLN	LEU	GLN	315
316	LYS	SER	ALA	THR	THR	LEU	TRP	ASP	ILE	GLN	LYS	ASP	LEU	LYS	PHE	330

Amino acid sequence of Dogfish Muscle Lactate Dehydrogenase.
S. S. Taylor.
J. Biol. Chem., **252**, 1799–1806 (1977).

ENZYMES

TRIOSE PHOSPHATE ISOMERASE FROM RABBIT MUSCLE

	1			5					10					15		
1	ALA	PRO	SER	ARG	LYS	PHE	PHE	VAL	GLY	GLY	ASN	TRP	LYS	MET	ASN	15
16	GLY	ARG	LYS	LYS	ASN	LEU	GLY	GLU	LEU	ILE	THR	THR	LEU	ASN	ALA	30
31	ALA	LYS	VAL	PRO	ALA	ASP	THR	GLU	VAL	VAL	CYS	ALA	PRO	PRO	THR	45
46	ALA	TYR	ILE	ASP	PHE	ALA	ARG	GLN	LYS	LEU	ASP	PRO	LYS	ILE	ALA	60
61	VAL	ALA	ALA	GLN	ASN	CYS	TYR	LYS	VAL	THR	ASN	GLY	ALA	PHE	THR	75
76	GLY	GLU	ILE	SER	PRO	GLY	MET	ILE	LYS	ASP	CYS	GLY	ALA	THR	TRP	90
91	VAL	VAL	LEU	GLY	HIS	SER	GLU	ARG	ARG	HIS	VAL	PHE	GLY	GLU	SER	105
106	ASP	GLU	LEU	ILE	GLY	GLN	LYS	VAL	ALA	HIS	ALA	LEU	SER	GLU	GLY	120
121	LEU	GLY	VAL	ILE	ALA	CYS	ILE	GLY	GLU	LYS	LEU	ASP	GLU	ARG	GLU	135
136	ALA	GLY	ILE	THR	GLU	LYS	VAL	VAL	PHE	GLU	GLN	THR	LYS	VAL	ILE	150
151	ALA	ASP	ASN	VAL	LYS	ASP	TRP	SER	LYS	VAL	VAL	LEU	ALA	TYR	GLU	165
166	PRO	VAL	TRP	ALA	ILE	GLY	THR	GLY	LYS	THR	ALA	THR	PRO	GLN	GLN	180
181	ALA	GLN	GLU	VAL	HIS	GLU	LYS	LEU	ARG	GLY	TRP	LEU	LYS	SER	ASN	195
196	VAL	SER	ASP	ALA	VAL	ALA	GLN	SER	THR	ARG	ILE	ILE	TYR	GLY	GLY	210
211	SER	VAL	THR	GLY	ALA	THR	CYS	LYS	GLU	LEU	ALA	SER	GLN	PRO	ASP	225
226	VAL	ASP	GLY	PHE	LEU	VAL	GLY	GLY	ALA	SER	LEU	LYS	PRO	GLU	PHE	240
241	VAL	ASP	ILE	ILE	ASN	ALA	LYS	GLN								255

The Amino Acid Sequence of Rabbit Muscle Triose Phosphate Isomerase.
P. H. Corran and S. G. Waley.
FEBS Letters, **30**, 97–99 (1973).
The tryptic peptides of rabbit muscle triose phosphate isomerase.
P. H. Corran and S. G. Waley.
Biochem. J., **139**, 1–10 (1974).
The amino acid sequence of rabbit muscle triose phosphate isomerase.
P. H. Corran and S. G. Waley.
Biochem. J., **145**, 335–344 (1975).

ENZYMES

TRIOSE PHOSPHATE ISOMERASE FROM CHICKEN MUSCLE

	1				5					10					15	
1	ALA	PRO	OOO	ARG	LYS	PHE	PHE	VAL	GLY	GLY	ASN	TRP	LYS	MET	ASN	15
16	GLY	LYS	ARG	LYS	LYS	SER	LEU	GLY	GLU	LEU	ILE	HIS	THR	LEU	ASP	30
31	GLY	ALA	LYS	LEU	SER	ALA	ASP	THR	GLU	VAL	VAL	CYS	GLY	ALA	PRO	45
46	SER	ILE	TYR	LEU	ASP	PHE	ALA	ARG	GLN	LYS	LEU	ASP	ALA	LYS	ILE	60
61	GLY	VAL	ALA	ALA	GLN	(ASN, CYS)	TYR	LYS	VAL	PRO	LYS	GLY	ALA	PHE		75
76	THR	GLY	GLU	ILE	SER	PRO	ALA	MET	ILE	LYS	ASP	ILE	GLY	ALA	ALA	90
91	TRP	VAL	ILE	LEU	GLY	HIS	SER	GLU	ARG	ARG	HIS	VAL	PHE	GLY	GLU	105
106	SER	ASP	GLU	LEU	ILE	GLY	GLN	LYS	VAL	ALA	HIS	ALA	LEU	ALA	GLU	120
121	GLY	LEU	GLY	VAL	ILE	ALA	CYS	ILE	GLY	GLU	LYS	LEU	ASP	GLU	ARG	135
136	GLU	ALA	GLY	ILE	THR	GLU	LYS	VAL	VAL	PHE	GLN	GLU	THR	LYS	ALA	150
151	ILE	ALA	ASP	ASN	VAL	LYS	ASP	TRP	SER	LYS	VAL	VAL	LEU	ALA	TYR	165
166	GLU	PRO	VAL	TRP	ALA	ILE	GLY	THR	GLY	LYS	THR	ALA	THR	PRO	GLN	180
181	GLN	ALA	GLN	GLU	VAL	HIS	GLU	LYS	LEU	ARG	GLY	TRP	LEU	LYS	THR	195
196	HIS	VAL	SER	ASP	ALA	VAL	ALA	VAL	GLN	SER	ARG	ILE	ILE	TYR	GLY	210
211	GLY	SER	VAL	THR	GLY	GLY	(ASN, CYS)	LYS	GLU	LEU	ALA	SER	GLN	HIS		225
226	ASP	VAL	ASP	GLY	PHE	LEU	VAL	GLY	GLY	ALA	SER	LEU	LYS	PRO	GLU	240
241	PHE	VAL	ASP	ILE	ILE	ASN	ALA	LYS	HIS							255

Note: Residue 3 is shown as a deletion to maximize homology with the enzyme from rabbit muscle.

Studies on the subunit structure and amino acid sequence of triose phosphate isomerase from chicken breast muscle.

A. J. Furth, J. D. Milman, J. D. Priddle, and R. E. Offord.

Biochem. J., **139**, 11–25 (1974).

Structure of chicken muscle triose phosphate isomerase determined crystallographically at 2.5 Å resolution, using amino acid sequence data.

D. W. Banner, A. C. Bloomer, G. A. Petsko, D. C. Phillips, C. I. Pogson, I. A. Wilson, P. H. Corran, A. J. Furth, J. D. Milman, R. E. Offord, J. D. Priddle, and S. G. Waley.

Nature, **255**, 609–614 (1975).

ENZYMES

TRIOSE PHOSPHATE ISOMERASE FROM COELACANTH MUSCLE

	1				5					10					15	
1	ALA	PRO	OOO	ARG	LYS	PHE	PHE	VAL	GLY	GLY	ASN	TRP	LYS	MET	ASN	15
16	GLY	ASP	LYS	LYS	SER	LEU	GLY	GLU	LEU	ILE	GLN	THR	LEU	ASN	ALA	30
31	ALA	LYS	VAL	PRO	PHE	THR	GLY	GLU	ILE	VAL	CYS	ALA	PRO	PRO	GLU	45
46	ALA	TYR	LEU	ASP	PHE	ALA	ARG	LEU	LYS	VAL	ASP	PRO	LYS	PHE	GLY	60
61	VAL	ALA	ALA	GLN	ASN	CYS	TYR	LYS	VAL	SER	LYS	GLY	ALA	PHE	THR	75
76	GLY	GLU	ILE	SER	PRO	ALA	MET	ILE	LYS	ASP	CYS	GLY	VAL	THR	TRP	90
91	VAL	ILE	LEU	GLY	HIS	SER	GLU	ARG	ARG	HIS	VAL	PHE	GLY	GLU	SER	105
106	ASP	GLU	LEU	ILE	GLY	GLN	LYS	VAL	SER	HIS	ALA	LEU	SER	GLU	GLY	120
121	LEU	GLY	VAL	VAL	ALA	CYS	ILE	GLY	GLU	LYS	LEU	ASP	GLU	ARG	GLU	135
136	ALA	GLY	ILE	THR	GLU	GLY	VAL	VAL	PHE	GLU	VAL	THR	GLU	VAL	ILE	150
151	ALA	ASP	ASP	VAL	LYS	ASP	TRP	SER	LYS	VAL	VAL	LEU	ALA	TYR	GLU	165
166	PRO	VAL	TRP	ALA	ILE	GLY	THR	GLY	LYS	THR	ALA	SER	PRO	GLN	GLN	180
181	SER	GLN	GLU	LEU	HIS	GLY	LYS	LEU	ARG	LYS	TRP	LEU	LYS	GLU	ASN	195
196	VAL	SER	GLU	THR	VAL	ALA	ASP	SER	VAL	ARG	ILE	ILE	TYR	GLY	GLY	210
211	SER	VAL	THR	GLY	ALA	THR	CYS	LYS	GLU	LEU	ALA	SER	GLU	PRO	ASP	225
226	VAL	ASP	GLY	PHE	LEU	VAL	GLY	GLY	ALA	SER	LEU	LYS	PRO	GLU	PHE	240
241	VAL	GLU	TYR	LYS	ASP	VAL	ARG	GLN								255

Note: Residue 3 is shown as a deletion so as to maximize homology with the enzyme from rabbit muscle.

Triose Phosphate Isomerase from the Coelacanth—An approach to the rapid determination of an amino acid sequence with small amounts of material.
E. Kolb, J. I. Harris, and J. Bridgen.
Biochem. J., **137**, 185–197 (1974).

*A typographical error in the above paper resulted in two non-identical sequences (Figures 5 and 6) being presented. I thank Dr. J. Bridgen (University of Cambridge) for confirming that the sequence shown above (taken from Figure 6) is the correct one.

RABBIT MUSCLE ALDOLASE

	1			5					10					15		
1	PRO	HIS	SER	HIS	PRO	ALA	LEU	THR	PRO	GLU	GLN	LYS	LYS	GLU	LEU	15
16	SER	ASP	ILE	ALA	HIS	ARG	ILE	VAL	ALA	PRO	GLY	LYS	GLY	ILE	LEU	30
31	ALA	ALA	ASP	GLN	SER	THR	GLY	SER	ILE	ALA	LYS	ARG	LEU	GLN	SER	45
46	ILE	GLY	THR	GLU	ASN	THR	GLU	GLU	ASN	ARG	ARG	PHE	TYR	ARG	GLN	60
61	LEU	LEU	LEU	THR	ALA	ASP	ASP	ARG	VAL	ASN	PRO	CYS	ILE	GLY	GLY	75
76	VAL	ILE	LEU	PHE	HIS	GLU	THR	LEU	TYR	GLN	LYS	ALA	ASP	ASP	GLY	90
91	ARG	PRO	PHE	PRO	GLN	VAL	ILE	LYS	SER	LYS	GLY	GLY	VAL	VAL	GLY	105
106	ILE	LYS	VAL	ASP	LYS	GLY	VAL	VAL	PRO	LEU	ALA	GLY	THR	ASP	GLY	120
121	GLU	THR	THR	THR	GLN	GLY	LEU	ASP	GLY	LEU	SER	GLU	ARG	CYS	ALA	135
136	GLN	TYR	LYS	LYS	ASP	GLY	ALA	ASP	PHE	ALA	LYS	TRP	ARG	CYS	VAL	150
151	LEU	LYS	ILE	GLY	GLN	HIS	THR	PRO	SER	ALA	LEU	ALA	ILE	MET	GLU	165
166	ASN	ALA	ASN	VAL	LEU	ALA	ARG	TYR	ALA	SER	ILE	CYS	GLN	GLN	ASN	180
181	GLY	PRO	ILE	GLU	VAL	PRO	GLU	ILE	LEU	PRO	ASP	GLY	ASP	HIS	ASP	195
196	LEU	LYS	ARG	CYS	GLN	TYR	VAL	THR	GLN	LYS	VAL	LEU	ALA	ALA	VAL	210
211	TYR	LYS	ALA	LEU	SER	ASN	HIS	HIS	ILE	TYR	LEU	GLN	GLY	THR	LEU	225
226	LEU	LYS	PRO	ASN	MET	VAL	THR	PRO	GLY	HIS	ALA	CYS	THR	GLN	LYS	240
241	TYR	SER	HIS	GLN	GLN	ILE	ALA	MET	ALA	THR	VAL	THR	ALA	LEU	ARG	255
256	ARG	THR	VAL	PRO	PRO	ALA	VAL	THR	GLY	VAL	THR	PHE	LEU	SER	GLY	270
271	SER	GLU	GLU	GLU	GLU	GLY	ALA	SER	ILE	ASN	LEU	ASN	ALA	ILE	ASN	285
286	LYS	CYS	PRO	LEU	LEU	TRP	PRO	LYS	ALA	LEU	THR	PHE	SER	TYR	GLY	300
301	ARG	ALA	LEU	GLN	ALA	SER	ALA	LEU	LYS	ALA	TRP	GLY	GLY	LYS	LYS	315
316	GLU	ASN	LEU	LYS	ALA	ALA	GLN	GLU	GLU	TYR	VAL	LYS	ARG	ALA	LEU	330
331	ALA	ASN	SER	LEU	ALA	CYS	GLN	GLY	LYS	TYR	THR	PRO	SER	GLY	GLN	345
346	ALA	GLY	ALA	ALA	ALA	SER	GLU	SER	LEU	PHE	ILE	SER	ASN	HIS	ALA	360
361	TYR															375

Note: The above sequence is that of the beta-subunit. The alpha subunit is different in that residue 358 is ASP.

Amino acid sequence of rabbit muscle aldolase and the structure of the active center.
C. Y. Lai, N. Nakai, and D. Chang.
Science, **183**, 1204–1206 (1974).
Studies on the structure of rabbit muscle aldolase. Determination of the primary structure of the COOH-terminal BrCN peptide: the complete sequence of the subunit polypeptide chain.
C. Y. Lai.
Arch. Biochem. Biophys., **166**, 358–368 (1975).

ENZYMES

RABBIT MUSCLE ALDOLASE

	1			5					10					15		
1	PRO	HIS	SER	HIS	PRO	ALA	LEU	THR	PRO	GLU	GLN	LYS	LYS	GLU	LEU	15
16	ASP	SER	ILE	ALA	HIS	ARG	ILE	VAL	ALA	PRO	GLY	LYS	GLY	ILE	LEU	30
31	ALA	ALA	ASP	GLU	SER	THR	GLY	SER	ILE	ALA	LYS	LYS	LEU	GLN	SER	45
46	ILE	GLY	GLX	THR	ASX	THR	GLX	GLX	ASX	ARG	ARG	PHE	TYR	ARG	ALA	60
61	PHE	PRO	GLU	ASP	ASN	GLY	ARG	PRO	VAL	ILE	LYS	GLN	LEU	LEU	LEU	75
76	THR	ALA	ASP	ASP	ARG	VAL	ASN	PRO	CYS	ILE	GLY	GLY	VAL	ILE	LEU	90
91	PHE	HIS	GLU	THR	TYR	GLN	LEU	LYS	GLY	GLY	VAL	VAL	GLY	ILE	LYS	105
106	VAL	ASP	LYS	GLY	VAL	PRO	LEU	ALA	GLY	GLU	THR	THR	THR	ASX	GLX	120
121	GLY	LEU	ASP	GLY	LEU	SER	GLU	ARG	CYS	ALA	GLN	TYR	LYS	LYS	ASN	135
136	GLY	ALA	ASP	PHE	ALA	LYS	TRP	ARG	CYS	VAL	LEU	LYS	ILE	GLY	GLU	150
151	HIS	THR	PRO	SER	ALA	LEU	ALA	MET	GLU	ASN	ALA	ASN	VAL	LEU	ALA	165
166	ARG	TYR	ALA	SER	ILE	CYS	GLN	GLU	ASN	GLY	PRO	ILE	GLU	VAL	PRO	180
181	GLU	ILE	LEU	PRO	ASN	GLY	ASN	HIS	ASP	LEU	LYS	ARG	CYS	GLN	TYR	195
196	VAL	THR	GLU	LYS	VAL	LEU	ALA	ALA	VAL	TYR	LYS	ALA	LEU	SER	ASN	210
211	HIS	HIS	ILE	TYR	LEU	GLN	GLY	THR	LEU	LEU	LYS	PRO	ASN	MET	VAL	225
226	THR	PRO	GLY	HIS	ALA	CYS	THR	GLN	LYS	TYR	SER	HIS	GLU	GLN	ILE	240
241	ALA	MET	ALA	THR	VAL	THR	ALA	LEU	ARG	GLY	ARG	THR	VAL	PRO	PRO	255
256	ALA	VAL	THR	GLY	VAL	THR	PHE	LEU	LEU	SER	GLY	GLU	SER	GLX	GLX	270
271	GLX	GLX	GLY	ALA	SER	SER	VAL	THR	PRO	ASX	ILE	ILE	ASN	LEU	ASN	285
286	ALA	ILE	ASN	LYS	CYS	PRO	LEU	LEU	LYS	PRO	TRP	ALA	LEU	THR	PHE	300
301	GLY	SER	TYR	GLY	ARG	ALA	LEU	GLN	ALA	SER	ALA	LEU	LYS	ALA	TRP	315
316	GLY	GLY	LYS	LYS	GLU	ASN	LEU	LYS	ALA	ALA	GLN	GLU	GLU	TYR	VAL	330
331	LYS	ARG	ALA	LEU	ALA	ASN	SER	LEU	ALA	CYS	GLN	GLY	LYS	TYR	THR	345
346	PRO	GLY	ALA	SER	GLU	SER	GLY	ALA	ALA	ALA	GLN	LEU	PHE	ILE	SER	360
361	ASN	HIS	ALA	TYR												375

The amino acid sequence of rabbit muscle aldolase.
M. Sajgó and G. Hajós.
Acta Biochim. Biophys. Acad. Sci. Hung., **9**, 239–241 (1974).

ASPARTATE AMINOTRANSFERASE FROM PIG HEART

	1				5					10					15	
1	ALA	PRO	PRO	SER	VAL	PHE	ALA	GLU	VAL	PRO	GLN	ALA	GLN	PRO	VAL	15
16	LEU	VAL	PHE	LYS	LEU	ILE	ALA	ASP	PHE	ARG	GLU	ASP	PRO	ASP	PRO	30
31	ARG	LYS	VAL	ASN	LEU	GLY	VAL	GLY	ALA	TYR	ARG	THR	ASP	ASP	CYS	45
46	GLN	PRO	TRP	VAL	LEU	PRO	VAL	VAL	ARG	LYS	VAL	GLU	GLN	ARG	ILE	60
61	ALA	ASN	ASP	SER	SER	LEU	ASN	HIS	GLU	TYR	LEU	PRO	ILE	LEU	GLY	75
76	LEU	ALA	GLU	PHE	ARG	THR	CYS	ALA	SER	ARG	LEU	ALA	LEU	GLY	ASP	90
91	ASP	SER	PRO	ALA	LEU	GLN	GLU	LYS	ARG	VAL	GLY	GLY	VAL	GLN	SER	105
106	LEU	GLY	GLY	THR	GLY	ALA	LEU	ARG	ILE	GLY	ALA	GLU	PHE	LEU	ALA	120
121	ARG	TRP	TYR	ASN	GLY	THR	ASN	ASN	LYS	ASP	THR	PRO	VAL	TYR	VAL	135
136	SER	SER	PRO	THR	TRP	GLU	ASN	HIS	ASP	GLY	VAL	PHE	THR	THR	ALA	150
151	GLY	PHE	LYS	ASP	ILE	ARG	SER	TYR	ARG	TYR	TRP	ASP	THR	GLU	LYS	165
166	ARG	GLY	LEU	ASP	LEU	GLN	GLY	PHE	LEU	SER	ASP	LEU	GLU	ASN	ALA	180
181	PRO	GLU	PHE	SER	ILE	PHE	VAL	LEU	HIS	ALA	CYS	ALA	HIS	ASN	PRO	195
196	THR	GLY	THR	ASP	PRO	THR	PRO	GLU	GLN	TRP	LYS	GLN	ILE	ALA	SER	210
211	VAL	MET	LYS	ARG	ARG	PHE	LEU	PHE	PRO	PHE	PHE	ASP	SER	ALA	TYR	225
226	GLN	GLY	PHE	ALA	SER	GLY	ASN	LEU	GLU	LYS	ASP	ALA	TRP	ALA	ILE	240
241	ARG	TYR	PHE	VAL	SER	GLU	GLY	PHE	GLU	LEU	PHE	CYS	ALA	GLN	SER	255
256	PHE	SER	LYS	ASN	PHE	GLY	LEU	TYR	ASN	GLU	ARG	VAL	GLY	ASN	LEU	270
271	THR	VAL	VAL	ALA	LYS	GLU	PRO	ASP	SER	ILE	LEU	ARG	VAL	LEU	SER	285
286	GLN	MET	GLU	LYS	ILE	VAL	ARG	VAL	THR	TRP	SER	ASN	PRO	PRO	ALA	300
301	GLN	GLY	ALA	ARG	ILE	VAL	ALA	ARG	THR	LEU	SER	ASP	PRO	GLU	LEU	315
316	PHE	HIS	GLU	TRP	THR	GLY	ASN	VAL	LYS	THR	MET	ALA	ASP	ARG	ILE	330
331	LEU	SER	MET	ARG	SER	GLU	LEU	ARG	ALA	ARG	LEU	GLU	ALA	LEU	LYS	345
346	THR	PRO	GLY	THR	TRP	ASN	HIS	ILE	THR	ASP	GLN	ILE	GLY	MET	PHE	360
361	SER	PHE	THR	GLY	LEU	ASN	PRO	LYS	GLN	VAL	GLU	TYR	LEU	ILE	ASN	375
376	GLU	LYS	HIS	ILE	TYR	LEU	LEU	PRO	SER	GLY	ARG	ILE	ASN	MET	CYS	390
391	GLY	LEU	THR	THR	LYS	ASN	LEU	ASP	TYR	VAL	ALA	THR	SER	ILE	HIS	405
406	GLU	ALA	VAL	THR	LYS	ILE	GLN									420

The Complete Amino Acid Sequence of Cytoplasmic Aspartate Aminotransferase from Pig Heart.
Yu. A. Ovchinnikov, C. A. Egorov, N. A. Aldanova, M. Yu. Feigina, V. M. Lipkin, N. G. Abdulaev, E. V. Grishin, A. P. Kiselev, N. N. Modyanov, A. E. Braunstein, O. L. Polyanovsky, and V. V. Nosikov.
FEBS Letters, **29**, 31–34 (1973).
Dispute:
The primary structure of aspartate aminotransferase from pig heart muscle determined in part using a protease with specificity for lysine.
S. Doonan, H. J. Doonan, R. Hanford, C. A. Vernon, J. M. Walker, F. Bossa, D. Barra, M. Carloni, P. Fasella, F. Riva, and P. L. Walton.
FEBS Letters, **38**, 229–233 (1974).
The differences reported are:

Residue	Reported sequence	This paper
63	ASP	ASN
288	GLU	GLN

ENZYMES

ASPARAGINASE FROM E. COLI

	1				5					10					15	
1	LEU	PRO	ASN	ILE	THR	ILE	LEU	ALA	THR	GLY	GLY	THR	ILE	ALA	GLY	15
16	GLY	GLY	ASP	SER	ALA	THR	LYS	SER	ASN	TYR	THR	ALA	GLY	LYS	VAL	30
31	GLY	VAL	GLU	ASN	LEU	VAL	ASN	ALA	VAL	PRO	GLN	LEU	LYS	ASP	ILE	45
46	ALA	ASN	VAL	LYS	GLY	GLU	GLN	VAL	VAL	ASN	ILE	GLY	SER	GLN	ASP	60
61	MET	ASN	ASP	ASP	VAL	TRP	LEU	THR	LEU	ALA	LYS	LYS	ILE	ASN	THR	75
76	ASP	CYS	ASP	LYS	THR	ASP	GLY	PHE	VAL	ILE	THR	HIS	GLY	THR	ASP	90
91	THR	MET	GLU	GLU	THR	ALA	TYR	PHE	LEU	ASP	LEU	THR	VAL	LYS	CYS	105
106	ASP	LYS	PRO	VAL	MET	VAL	GLY	ALA	MET	ARG	PRO	SER	THR	SER	MET	120
121	SER	ALA	ASP	GLY	PRO	PHE	ASN	LEU	TYR	ASN	ALA	VAL	THR	ALA	ALA	135
136	ASP	LYS	ALA	SER	ALA	ASN	ARG	GLY	VAL	LEU	VAL	MET	ASN	ASP	THR	150
151	VAL	LEU	ASP	GLY	ARG	ASP	VAL	THR	LYS	THR	ASN	THR	THR	ASP	VAL	165
166	ALA	THR	PHE	LYS	SER	VAL	ASN	TYR	GLY	PRO	LEU	GLY	TYR	ILE	HIS	180
181	ASP	GLY	LYS	ILE	ASP	TYR	GLN	ARG	THR	PRO	ALA	ARG	LYS	HIS	THR	195
196	SER	ASP	THR	PRO	PHE	ASP	VAL	SER	LYS	LEU	ASN	GLU	LEU	PRO	LYS	210
211	VAL	GLY	ILE	VAL	TYR	ASN	TYR	ALA	ASN	ALA	SER	ASP	LEU	PRO	ALA	225
226	LYS	ALA	LEU	VAL	ASP	ALA	GLY	TYR	ASP	GLY	ILE	VAL	SER	ALA	GLY	240
241	VAL	GLY	ASP	GLY	ASN	LEU	TYR	LYS	THR	VAL	PHE	ASP	THR	LEU	ALA	255
256	THR	ALA	ALA	LYS	ASP	GLY	THR	ALA	VAL	ARG	SER	SER	ARG	VAL	PRO	270
271	THR	GLY	ALA	THR	THR	GLN	ASP	ALA	GLU	VAL	ASP	ASP	ALA	LYS	TYR	285
286	GLY	PHE	VAL	ALA	SER	GLY	THR	LEU	ASN	PRO	GLN	LYS	ALA	ARG	VAL	300
301	LEU	LEU	GLN	ALA	LEU	THR	GLN	THR	LYS	ASP	PRO	GLN	GLN	ILE	GLN	315
316	GLN	ILE	PHE	ASN	GLN	TYR										330

Amino acid sequence of L-asparaginase from *Escherichia coli*.
T. Maita, K. Morokuma, and G. Matsuda.
J. Biochem., **76**, 1351–1354 (1974).

ACYL CARRIER PROTEIN FROM E. COLI

	1			5					10					15		
1	SER	THR	ILE	GLU	GLU	ARG	VAL	LYS	LYS	ILE	ILE	GLY	GLU	GLN	LEU	15
16	GLY	VAL	LYS	GLN	GLU	GLU	VAL	THR	ASP	ASN	ALA	SER	PHE	VAL	GLU	30
31	ASP	LEU	GLY	ALA	ASP	SER	LEU	ASP	THR	VAL	GLU	LEU	VAL	MET	ALA	45
46	LEU	GLU	GLU	GLU	PHE	ASP	THR	GLU	ILE	PRO	ASP	GLU	GLU	ALA	GLU	60
61	LYS	ILE	THR	THR	VAL	GLN	ALA	ALA	ILE	ASP	TYR	ILE	ASN	GLY	HIS	75
76	GLN	ALA														90

The Complete Amino Acid Sequence of the Acyl Carrier Protein of *Escherichia coli*.
T. C. Vanaman, S. J. Wakil, and R. L. Hill.
J. Biol. Chem., **243**, 6420–6431 (1968).

ASPARTATE TRANSCARBAMYLASE FROM E. COLI

	1			5					10					15		
1	MET	THR	HIS	ASN	ASP	LYS	LEU	GLN	VAL	ALA	GLU	ILE	LYS	ARG	GLY	15
16	THR	VAL	ILE	ASN	HIS	ILE	PRO	ALA	GLU	ILE	GLY	PHE	LYS	LEU	LEU	30
31	SER	LEU	PHE	LYS	LEU	THR	GLU	THR	GLN	ASP	ARG	ILE	THR	ILE	GLY	45
46	LEU	ASN	LEU	PRO	SER	GLY	GLU	MET	GLY	ARG	LYS	ASP	LEU	ILE	LYS	60
61	ILE	GLU	ASN	THR	PHE	LEU	SER	GLU	ASX	GLX	VAL	ASX	GLX	LEU	ALA	75
76	LEU	TYR	ALA	PRO	GLN	ALA	THR	VAL	ASN	ARG	ILE	ASN	ASP	TYR	GLU	90
91	VAL	VAL	GLY	LYS	SER	ARG	PRO	SER	LEU	PRO	GLU	ARG	ASN	ILE	ASP	105
106	VAL	LEU	VAL	CYS	PRO	ASP	SER	ASN	CYS	ILE	SER	HIS	ALA	GLU	PRO	120
121	VAL	SER	SER	SER	PHE	ALA	VAL	ARG	ARG	ALA	ASX	ASX	ILE	ALA	LEU	135
136	LYS	CYS	LYS	TYR	CYS	GLU	LYS	GLU	PHE	SER	HIS	ASN	VAL	VAL	LEU	150
151	ALA	ASN														165

New Structural Model of *E. Coli* Aspartate Transcarbamylase and the Amino Acid Sequence
of the regulatory polypeptide chain.
K. Weber.
Nature, **218**, 1116–1119 (1968).

ENZYMES

*TRYPTOPHAN SYNTHETASE α-CHAIN—*E. COLI

	1				5					10					15	
1	MET	GLN	ARG	TYR	GLU	SER	LEU	PHE	ALA	GLN	LEU	LYS	GLU	ARG	LYS	15
16	GLU	GLY	ALA	PHE	VAL	PRO	PHE	VAL	THR	LEU	GLY	ASP	PRO	GLY	ILE	30
31	GLU	GLN	SER	LEU	LYS	ILE	ASP	THR	LEU	ILE	GLU	ALA	GLY	ALA	ASP	45
46	ALA	LEU	GLU	LEU	GLY	ILE	PRO	PHE	SER	ASP	PRO	LEU	ALA	ASP	GLY	60
61	PRO	THR	ILE	GLN	ASN	ALA	THR	LEU	ARG	ALA	PHE	ALA	ALA	GLY	VAL	75
76	THR	PRO	ALA	GLN	CYS	PHE	GLU	MET	LEU	ALA	LEU	ILE	ARG	GLN	LYS	90
91	HIS	PRO	THR	ILE	PRO	ILE	GLY	LEU	LEU	MET	TYR	ALA	ASN	LEU	VAL	105
106	PHE	ASN	LYS	GLY	ILE	ASP	GLU	PHE	TYR	ALA	GLN	CYS	GLU	LYS	VAL	120
121	GLY	VAL	ASP	SER	VAL	LEU	VAL	ALA	ASP	VAL	PRO	VAL	GLN	GLU	SER	135
136	ALA	PRO	PHE	ARG	GLN	ALA	ALA	LEU	ARG	HIS	ASN	VAL	ALA	PRO	ILE	150
151	PHE	ILE	CYS	PRO	PRO	ASN	ALA	ASP	ASP	ASP	LEU	LEU	ARG	GLN	ILE	165
166	ALA	SER	TYR	GLY	ARG	GLY	TYR	THR	TYR	LEU	LEU	SER	ARG	ALA	GLY	180
181	VAL	THR	GLY	ALA	GLU	ASN	ARG	ALA	ALA	LEU	PRO	LEU	ASN	HIS	LEU	195
196	VAL	ALA	LYS	LEU	LYS	GLU	TYR	ASN	ALA	ALA	PRO	PRO	LEU	GLN	GLY	210
211	PHE	GLY	ILE	SER	ALA	PRO	ASP	GLN	VAL	LYS	ALA	ALA	ILE	ASP	ALA	225
226	GLY	ALA	ALA	GLY	ALA	ILE	SER	GLY	SER	ALA	ILE	VAL	LYS	ILE	ILE	240
241	GLU	GLN	HIS	ASN	ILE	GLU	PRO	GLU	LYS	MET	LEU	ALA	ALA	LEU	LYS	255
256	VAL	PHE	VAL	GLN	PRO	MET	LYS	ALA	ALA	THR	ARG	SER				270

The Amino Acid Sequence of the A protein (α-subunit) of the Tryptophan synthetase of *Escherichia coli*.
J. R. Guest, G. R. Drapeau, B. C. Carlton, and C. Yanofsky.
J. Biol. Chem., **242**, 5442–5446 (1967).

TRYPTOPHAN SYNTHETASE OF A. AEROGENES, α-CHAIN

	1				5					10					15	
1	MET	GLN	ARG	TYR	GLU	THR	LEU	PHE	ALA	GLN	LEU	LYS	LYS	ARG	ARG	15
16	GLU	GLY	ALA	PHE	VAL	PRO	PHE	VAL	ILE	LEU	GLY	ASP	PRO	GLY	THR	30
31	GLU	GLN	SER	LEU	LYS	ILE	ILE	ASP	ALA	LEU	ILE	GLU	GLY	GLY	ALA	45
46	ASP	ALA	LEU	GLU	LEU	GLY	ILE	PRO	PHE	SER	ASN	PRO	LEU	ALA	ASP	60
61	GLY	PRO	THR	ILE	GLY	ASN	ALA	ALA	LEU	ARG	ALA	PHE	ALA	ALA	GLY	75
76	VAL	THR	PRO	ALA	GLN	CYS	PHE	GLU	MET	LEU	ALA	LEU	ILE	ARG	GLN	90
91	ASN	HIS	PRO	THR	ILE	PRO	ILE	GLY	LEU	LEU	MET	TYR	ALA	LYS	LEU	105
106	VAL	PHE	SER	PRO	GLY	ILE	ASP	ALA	PHE	TYR	ALA	GLN	CYS	ALA	ARG	120
121	VAL	GLY	VAL	ASP	SER	VAL	LEU	VAL	ALA	ASP	VAL	PRO	VAL	GLU	GLU	135
136	SER	ALA	PRO	PHE	ARG	GLN	ALA	ALA	MET	ARG	HIS	ASN	ILE	ALA	PRO	150
151	ILE	PHE	ILE	CYS	PRO	PRO	ASN	ALA	ASP	ASP	ASP	LEU	LEU	ARG	GLN	165
166	ILE	ALA	SER	TYR	GLY	ARG	GLY	TYR	THR	TYR	LEU	LEU	SER	ARG	ALA	180
181	GLY	VAL	THR	GLY	ALA	GLU	ASN	ARG	ALA	ALA	LEU	PRO	LEU	HIS	HIS	195
196	LEU	VAL	GLU	LYS	LEU	ALA	GLU	TYR	HIS	ALA	ALA	PRO	PRO	LEU	GLN	210
211	GLY	PHE	GLY	ILE	SER	ALA	PRO	GLU	GLN	VAL	SER	ALA	ALA	ILE	ASP	225
226	ALA	GLY	ALA	ALA	GLY	ALA	ILE	SER	GLY	SER	ALA	ILE	VAL	LYS	ILE	240
241	ILE	GLU	ARG	HIS	LEU	ASP	GLU	PRO	GLN	THR	MET	LEU	ASP	GLU	LEU	255
256	LYS	ALA	PHE	VAL	GLN	SER	LEU	LYS	ALA	ALA	THR	LYS	THR	ALA		270

Amino acid sequence studies with the tryptophan synthetase α-chain of *Aerobacter aerogenes*.
S.-L. Li and C. Yanofsky.
J. Biol. Chem., **248**, 1837–1843 (1973).

ENZYMES

TRYPTOPHAN SYNTHETASE OF S. TYPHIMURIUM, *α-CHAIN*

	1				5					10					15	
1	MET	GLU	ARG	TYR	GLU	ASN	LEU	PHE	ALA	GLN	LEU	ASN	ASP	ARG	ARG	15
16	GLU	GLY	ALA	PHE	VAL	PRO	PHE	VAL	THR	LEU	GLY	ASP	PRO	GLY	ILE	30
31	GLU	GLN	SER	LEU	LYS	ILE	ILE	ASP	THR	LEU	ILE	ASP	ALA	GLY	ALA	45
46	ASP	ALA	LEU	GLU	LEU	GLY	VAL	PRO	PHE	SER	ASN	PRO	LEU	ALA	ASP	60
61	GLY	PRO	THR	ILE	GLN	ASN	ALA	ASN	LEU	ARG	ALA	PHE	ALA	ALA	GLY	75
76	VAL	THR	PRO	ALA	GLN	CYS	PHE	GLU	MET	LEU	ALA	LEU	ILE	ARG	GLN	90
91	ASN	HIS	PRO	THR	ILE	PRO	VAL	GLY	LEU	LEU	MET	TYR	ALA	LYS	LEU	105
106	VAL	PHE	SER	PRO	GLY	ILE	ASP	GLU	LEU	TYR	ALA	ARG	CYS	GLU	GLN	120
121	VAL	GLY	VAL	ASP	SER	VAL	LEU	VAL	ALA	ASP	VAL	PRO	VAL	GLN	GLU	135
136	SER	ALA	PRO	PHE	ARG	GLN	ALA	ALA	LEU	ARG	HIS	ASN	ILE	ALA	PRO	150
151	ILE	PHE	ILE	CYS	PRO	PRO	ASN	ALA	ASP	ASP	ASP	LEU	LEU	ARG	GLN	165
166	VAL	ALA	SER	TYR	GLY	ARG	GLY	TYR	THR	TYR	LEU	LEU	SER	ARG	SER	180
181	GLY	VAL	THR	GLY	ALA	GLU	ASN	ARG	GLY	ALA	LEU	PRO	LEU	HIS	HIS	195
196	LEU	ILE	GLU	LYS	LEU	LYS	GLU	TYR	HIS	ALA	ALA	PRO	ALA	LEU	GLN	210
211	GLY	PHE	GLY	ILE	SER	SER	PRO	GLU	GLN	VAL	VAL	ALA	ALA	ILE	ARG	225
226	ALA	GLY	ALA	ALA	GLY	ALA	ILE	SER	GLY	SER	ALA	ILE	VAL	LYS	ILE	240
241	ILE	GLU	LYS	ASN	LEU	ALA	SER	PRO	LYS	GLN	MET	LEU	ALA	GLU	LEU	255
256	ARG	SER	PHE	VAL	SER	ALA	MET	LYS	ALA	ALA	SER	ARG	ALA			270

Amino acid sequence studies with the tryptophan synthetase α-chain of *Salmonella typhimurium*.
S.-L. Li and C. Yanofsky.
J. Biol. Chem., **248**, 1830–1836 (1973).

DIHYDROFOLATE REDUCTASE FROM S. FAECIUM

	1			5					10					15	
1	MET	PHE	ILE	SER	MET	TRP	ALA	GLN	ASP	LYS	ASN	GLY	LEU	ILE	GLY	15
16	LYS	ASP	GLY	LEU	LEU	PRO	TRP	ARG	LEU	PRO	ASN	ASP	MET	ARG	PHE	30
31	PHE	ARG	GLU	HIS	THR	MET	ASP	LYS	ILE	LEU	VAL	MET	GLY	ARG	LYS	45
46	THR	TYR	GLU	GLY	MET	GLY	LYS	LEU	SER	LEU	PRO	TYR	ARG	HIS	ILE	60
61	ILE	VAL	LEU	THR	THR	GLN	LYS	ASP	PHE	LYS	VAL	GLU	LYS	ASN	ALA	75
76	GLU	VAL	LEU	HIS	SER	ILE	ASP	GLU	LEU	LEU	ALA	TYR	ALA	LYS	ASP	90
91	ILE	PRO	GLU	ASP	ILE	TYR	VAL	SER	GLY	GLY	SER	ARG	ILE	PHE	GLN	105
106	ALA	LEU	LEU	PRO	GLU	THR	LYS	ILE	ILE	TRP	ARG	THR	LEU	ILE	ASP	120
121	ALA	GLU	PHE	GLU	GLY	ASP	THR	PHE	ILE	GLY	GLU	ILE	ASP	PHE	THR	135
136	SER	PHE	GLU	LEU	VAL	GLU	GLU	HIS	GLU	GLY	ILE	VAL	ASN	GLN	GLU	150
151	ASN	GLN	TYR	PRO	HIS	ARG	PHE	GLN	LYS	TRP	GLN	LYS	MET	SER	LYS	165
166	VAL	VAL														180

The structure of the mutant dihydrofolate reductase from *Streptococcus faecium*. Amino acid sequence of peptide CNBr 7 and complete sequence of the protein.
D. L. Peterson, J. M. Gleisner and R. L. Blakley.
J. Biol. Chem., **250**, 4945–4954 (1975).

DIHYDROFOLATE REDUCTASE—E. COLI MUTANT

	1			5					10					15	
1	MET	ILE	SER	LEU	ILE	ALA	ALA	LEU	ALA	VAL	ASP	ARG	VAL	ILE	GLY	15
16	MET	GLU	ASN	ALA	MET	PRO	TRP	ASN	LEU	PRO	ALA	ASP	LEU	ALA	TRP	30
31	PHE	LYS	ARG	ASN	THR	LEU	ASP	LYS	PRO	VAL	ILE	MET	GLY	ARG	HIS	45
46	THR	TRP	GLU	SER	ILE	GLY	ARG	PRO	LEU	PRO	GLY	ARG	LYS	ASN	ILE	60
61	ILE	LEU	SER	SER	GLN	PRO	GLY	THR	ASP	ASP	ARG	VAL	THR	TRP	VAL	75
76	LYS	SER	VAL	ASP	GLU	ALA	ILE	ALA	ALA	CYS	GLY	ASN	VAL	PRO	GLU	90
91	ILE	MET	VAL	ILE	GLY	GLY	GLY	ARG	VAL	TYR	GLU	GLN	PHE	LEU	PRO	105
106	LYS	ALA	GLN	LYS	LEU	TYR	LEU	THR	HIS	ILE	ASP	ALA	GLU	VAL	GLU	120
121	GLY	ASP	THR	HIS	PHE	PRO	ASP	TYR	GLU	PRO	ASP	ASP	TRP	GLU	SER	135
136	VAL	PHE	SER	GLU	PHE	HIS	ASN	ALA	ASP	ALA	GLN	ASN	SER	HIS	SER	150
151	TYR	CYS	PHE	LYS	ILE	LEU	GLU	ARG	ARG							165

Dihydrofolate reductase: The amino acid sequence of the enzyme from a methotrexate-resistant mutant of *Escherichia coli*.
C. D. Bennett, J. A. Rodkey, J. M. Sondey, and R. Hirschmann.
Biochemistry, **17**, 1328–1336 (1978).

ENZYMES

DIHYDROFOLATE REDUCTASE—E. COLI

		1			5					10					15	
1	MET	ILE	SER	LEU	ILE	ALA	ALA	LEU	ALA	VAL	ASP	ARG	VAL	ILE	GLY	15
16	MET	GLU	ASN	ALA	MET	PRO	TRP	ASN	LEU	PRO	ALA	ASP	LEU	ALA	TRP	30
31	PHE	LYS	ARG	ASN	THR	LEU	ASP	LYS	PRO	VAL	ILE	MET	GLY	ARG	HIS	45
46	THR	TRP	GLU	SER	ILE	GLY	ARG	PRO	LEU	PRO	GLY	ARG	LYS	ASN	ILE	60
61	ILE	LEU	SER	SER	GLN	PRO	GLY	THR	ASP	ASP	ARG	VAL	THR	TRP	VAL	75
76	LYS	SER	VAL	ASP	GLU	ALA	ILE	ALA	ALA	CYS	GLY	ASN	VAL	PRO	GLU	90
91	ILE	MET	VAL	ILE	GLY	GLY	GLY	ARG	VAL	TYR	GLU	GLN	PHE	LEU	PRO	105
106	LYS	ALA	GLN	LYS	LEU	TYR	LEU	THR	HIS	ILE	ASP	ALA	GLN	VAL	GLU	120
121	GLY	ASP	THR	HIS	PHE	PRO	ASP	TYR	GLU	PRO	ASP	ASP	TRP	GLU	SER	135
136	VAL	PHE	SER	GLU	PHE	HIS	ASP	ALA	ASP	ALA	GLN	ASN	SER	HIS	SER	150
151	TYR	CYS	PHE	GLU	ILE	LEU	GLU	ARG	ARG							165

The amino acid sequence of the dihydrofolate reductase of a trimethoprim-resistant strain of *Escherichia coli*.
D. Stone, A. W. Phillips, and J. J. Burchall.
Eur. J. Biochem., **72**, 613–624 (1977).

DIHYDROFOLATE REDUCTASE—MOUSE

		1			5					10					15	
1	VAL	ARG	PRO	LEU	ASN	CYS	ILE	VAL	ALA	VAL	SER	GLN	ASN	MET	GLY	15
16	ILE	GLY	LYS	ASN	GLY	ASP	LEU	PRO	TRP	PRO	PRO	LEU	ARG	ASP	GLN	30
31	PHE	LYS	TYR	PHE	GLN	ARG	MET	THR	THR	THR	SER	SER	VAL	GLN	GLY	45
46	LYS	GLN	ASN	LEU	VAL	ILE	MET	GLY	ARG	LYS	THR	TRP	PHE	SER	ILE	60
61	PRO	GLU	LYS	ASN	ARG	PRO	LEU	LYS	ASP	ARG	ILE	ASN	ILE	VAL	LEU	75
76	SER	ARG	GLU	LEU	LYS	GLU	PRO	PRO	ARG	GLY	ALA	HIS	PHE	LEU	ALA	90
91	LYS	SER	LEU	ASP	ASP	ALA	LEU	ARG	LEU	ILE	GLN	GLU	PRO	GLU	LEU	105
106	ALA	SER	LYS	VAL	ASP	MET	VAL	TRP	ILE	VAL	GLY	GLY	SER	SER	VAL	120
121	TYR	GLU	GLN	ALA	MET	ASN	GLU	PRO	GLY	HIS	LEU	ARG	LEU	PHE	VAL	135
136	THR	ARG	ILE	MET	GLN	GLU	PHE	GLU	SER	ASP	THR	PHE	PHE	PRO	GLU	150
151	ILE	ASP	LEU	GLY	LYS	TYR	LYS	LEU	LEU	PRO	GLU	TYR	PRO	GLY	VAL	165
166	LEU	SER	GLU	VAL	GLN	GLU	GLU	ASP	GLY	ILE	LYS	TYR	LYS	PHE	GLU	180
181	VAL	TYR	GLU	LYS	LYS	ASP										195

The amino acid sequence of dihydrofolate reductase from L 1210 cells.
D. Stone and A. W. Phillips.
FEBS Letters, **74**, 85–87 (1977).

CARBONIC ANHYDRASE B

	1		5				10						15			
1	AC	ALA	SER	PRO	ASP	TRP	GLY	TYR	ASP	ASP	LYS	ASN	GLY	GLN	PRO	15
16	GLU	TRP	SER	LYS	LEU	TYR	PRO	ILE	ALA	ASN	GLY	ASN	ASN	GLN	SER	30
31	PRO	VAL	ASP	ILE	LYS	THR	SER	GLU	THR	LYS	HIS	ASP	THR	SER	LEU	45
46	LYS	PRO	ILE	SER	VAL	SER	TYR	ASN	PRO	ALA	THR	ALA	LYS	GLU	ILE	60
61	ILE	ASN	VAL	GLY	HIS	SER	PHE	HIS	VAL	ASN	PHE	GLU	ASP	ASN	ASN	75
76	ASP	ARG	SER	VAL	LEU	LYS	GLY	GLY	PRO	PHE	SER	ASP	SER	TYR	ARG	90
91	LEU	PHE	GLN	PHE	HIS	PHE	HIS	TRP	GLY	SER	THR	ASN	GLU	HIS	GLY	105
106	SER	GLU	HIS	THR	VAL	ASP	GLY	VAL	LYS	TYR	SER	ALA	GLU	LEU	HIS	120
121	VAL	ALA	HIS	TRP	ASN	SER	ALA	LYS	TYR	SER	SER	LEU	ALA	GLU	ALA	135
136	ALA	SER	LYS	ALA	ASP	GLY	LEU	ALA	VAL	ILE	GLY	VAL	LEU	MET	LYS	150
151	VAL	GLY	GLU	ALA	ASN	PRO	LYS	LEU	GLN	LYS	VAL	LEU	ASP	ALA	LEU	165
166	GLN	ALA	ILE	LYS	THR	LYS	GLY	LYS	ARG	ALA	PRO	PHE	THR	ASN	PHE	180
181	ASP	PRO	SER	THR	LEU	LEU	PRO	SER	SER	LEU	ASP	PHE	TRP	THR	TYR	195
196	PRO	GLY	SER	LEU	THR	HIS	PRO	PRO	LEU	TYR	GLU	SER	VAL	THR	TRP	210
211	ILE	ILE	CYS	LYS	GLU	SER	ILE	SER	VAL	SER	SER	GLU	GLN	LEU	ALA	225
226	GLN	PHE	ARG	SER	LEU	LEU	SER	ASN	VAL	GLU	GLY	ASP	ASN	ALA	VAL	240
241	PRO	MET	GLN	HIS	ASN	ASN	ARG	PRO	THR	GLN	PRO	LEU	LYS	GLY	ARG	255
256	THR	VAL	ARG	ALA	SER	PHE										270

Amino acid sequence of human erythrocyte carbonic anhydrase B.
B. Anderson, P. O. Nyman, and L. Strid.
Biochem. Biophys. Res. Commun., **48**, 670–677 (1972).
Note: A sequence for the enzyme and very similar to that above has also been published and subsequently revised:
Human Carbonic Anhydrase. The complete structure of carbonic anhydrase B.
K.-T. D. Lin and H. F. Deutsch.
J. Biol. Chem., **248**, 1885–1893 (1973); and *J. Biol. Chem.*, **249**, 2329–2337 (1974).

ENZYMES

CARBONIC ANHYDRASE C

	1				5					10					15	
1	AC	SER	HIS	HIS	TRP	GLY	TYR	GLY	LYS	HIS	ASN	GLY	PRO	GLU	HIS	15
16	TRP	HIS	LYS	ASP	PHE	PRO	ILE	ALA	LYS	GLY	GLU	ARG	GLN	SER	PRO	30
31	VAL	ASP	ILE	ASP	THR	HIS	THR	ALA	LYS	TYR	ASP	PRO	SER	LEU	LYS	45
46	PRO	LEU	SER	VAL	SER	TYR	ASP	GLN	ALA	THR	SER	LEU	ARG	ILE	LEU	60
61	ASN	ASN	GLY	HIS	ALA	PHE	ASN	VAL	GLU	PHE	ASP	ASP	SER	GLN	ASP	75
76	LYS	ALA	VAL	LEU	LYS	GLY	GLY	PRO	LEU	ASP	GLY	THR	TYR	ARG	LEU	90
91	ILE	GLN	PHE	HIS	PHE	HIS	TRP	GLY	SER	LEU	ASP	GLY	GLN	GLY	SER	105
106	GLU	HIS	THR	VAL	ASP	LYS	LYS	LYS	TYR	ALA	ALA	GLU	LEU	HIS	LEU	120
121	VAL	HIS	TRP	ASN	THR	LYS	TYR	GLY	ASP	PHE	GLY	LYS	ALA	VAL	GLN	135
136	GLN	PRO	ASP	GLY	LEU	ALA	VAL	LEU	GLY	ILE	PHE	LEU	LYS	VAL	GLY	150
151	SER	ALA	LYS	PRO	GLY	LEU	GLN	LYS	VAL	VAL	ASP	VAL	LEU	ASP	SER	165
166	ILE	LYS	THR	LYS	GLY	LYS	SER	ALA	ASP	PHE	THR	ASN	PHE	ASP	PRO	180
181	ARG	GLY	LEU	LEU	PRO	GLU	SER	LEU	ASP	TYR	TRP	THR	TYR	PRO	GLY	195
196	SER	LEU	THR	THR	PRO	PRO	LEU	LEU	GLU	CYS	VAL	THR	TRP	ILE	VAL	210
211	LEU	LYS	GLU	PRO	ILE	SER	VAL	SER	SER	GLU	GLN	VAL	LEU	LYS	PHE	225
226	ARG	LYS	LEU	ASN	PHE	ASN	GLY	GLU	GLY	GLU	PRO	GLU	GLU	LEU	MET	240
241	VAL	ASP	ASN	TRP	ARG	PRO	ALA	GLN	PRO	LEU	LYS	ASN	ARG	GLN	ILE	255
256	LYS	ALA	SER	PHE	LYS											270

Primary structure of Human carbonic anhydrase C.
L. E. Henderson, D. Henriksson, and P. O. Nyman.
J. Biol. Chem., **251**, 5457–5463 (1976).

CARBONIC ANHYDRASE C

	1				5					10					15	
1	AC	SER	HIS	HIS	TRP	GLY	TYR	GLY	LYS	HIS	ASN	GLY	PRO	GLU	HIS	15
16	TRP	HIS	LYS	ASP	PHE	PRO	ILE	ALA	LYS	GLY	GLU	ARG	GLN	SER	PRO	30
31	VAL	ASP	ILE	ASP	THR	HIS	THR	ALA	LYS	TYR	ASP	PRO	SER	LEU	LYS	45
46	PRO	LEU	SER	VAL	SER	TYR	ASP	GLN	ALA	THR	SER	LEU	ARG	ILE	LEU	60
61	ASN	ASN	GLY	HIS	ALA	PHE	ASN	VAL	GLU	PHE	ASP	ASP	SER	GLU	ASP	75
76	LYS	ALA	VAL	LEU	LYS	GLY	GLY	PRO	LEU	ASP	GLY	THR	TYR	ARG	LEU	90
91	ILE	GLN	PHE	HIS	PHE	HIS	TRP	GLY	SER	LEU	ASN	GLY	GLN	GLY	SER	105
106	GLU	HIS	THR	VAL	ASP	LYS	LYS	LYS	TYR	ALA	ALA	GLU	LEU	HIS	LEU	120
121	VAL	HIS	TRP	ASN	THR	LYS	TYR	GLY	ASP	PHE	GLY	LYS	ALA	VAL	GLN	135
136	GLU	PRO	ASP	GLY	LEU	ALA	VAL	LEU	GLY	ILE	PHE	LEU	LYS	VAL	GLY	150
151	SER	ALA	PRO	LYS	GLY	LEU	GLN	LYS	VAL	VAL	ASP	VAL	LEU	ASP	SER	165
166	ILE	LYS	THR	LYS	GLY	LYS	SER	ALA	ASP	PHE	THR	ASN	PHE	ASP	PRO	180
181	ARG	GLY	LEU	LEU	PRO	GLU	SER	LEU	ASP	TYR	TRP	THR	TYR	PRO	GLY	195
196	SER	LEU	THR	THR	PRO	PRO	LEU	LEU	GLN	CYS	VAL	THR	TRP	ILE	VAL	210
211	LEU	LYS	GLU	PRO	ILE	SER	VAL	SER	SER	GLU	GLN	VAL	LEU	LYS	PHE	225
226	ARG	LYS	LEU	ASN	PHE	ASN	GLY	GLU	GLY	GLU	PRO	GLU	GLU	LEU	MET	240
241	VAL	ASP	ASN	TRP	ARG	PRO	ALA	GLN	PRO	LEU	LYS	ASN	ARG	GLN	ILE	255
256	LYS	ALA	SER	PHE	LYS											270

Human Carbonic Anhydrases. The complete primary structure of the C. isozyme.
K.-T. D. Lin and H. F. Deutsch.
J. Biol. Chem., **249**, 2329–2337 (1974).

ENZYMES

CARBONIC ANHYDRASE C—SHEEP

```
         1              5                   10                  15
  1  AC  SER HIS HIS TRP GLY TYR GLY GLU HIS ASN GLY PRO GLU HIS   15
 16  TRP HIS LYS ASP PHE PRO ILE ALA ASP GLY GLU ARG GLN SER PRO   30
 31  VAL ASP ILE ASP THR LYS ALA VAL VAL PRO ASP PRO ALA LEU LYS   45
 46  PRO LEU ALA LEU LEU TYR GLU GLN ALA ALA SER ARG ARG MET VAL   60
 61  ASN ASN GLY HIS SER PHE ASN VAL GLU PHE ASP ASP SER GLN ASP   75
 76  LYS ALA VAL LEU LYS ASP GLY PRO LEU THR GLY THR TYR ARG LEU   90
 91  VAL GLN PHE HIS PHE HIS TRP GLY SER SER ASP ASP GLN GLY SER  105
106  GLU HIS THR VAL ASP ARG LYS LYS TYR ALA ALA GLU LEU HIS LEU  120
121  VAL HIS TRP ASN THR LYS TYR GLY ASP PHE GLY THR ALA ALA GLN  135
136  GLN PRO ASP GLY LEU ALA VAL VAL GLY VAL PHE LEU LYS VAL GLY  150
151  ASP ALA ASN PRO ALA LEU GLN LYS VAL LEU ASP VAL LEU ASP SER  165
166  ILE LYS THR LYS GLY LYS SER ALA ASP PHE PRO ASN PHE ASP PRO  180
181  SER SER LEU LEU LYS ARG ALA LEU ASN TYR TRP THR TYR PRO GLY  195
196  SER LEU THR ASN PRO PRO LEU LEU GLU SER VAL THR TRP VAL VAL  210
211  LEU LYS GLU PRO THR SER VAL SER SER GLN GLN MET LEU LYS PHE  225
226  ARG SER LEU ASN PHE ASN ALA GLU GLY GLU PRO GLU LEU LEU MET  240
241  LEU ALA ASN TRP ARG PRO ALA GLN PRO LEU LYS ASN ARG GLN VAL  255
256  ARG VAL PHE PRO LYS                                          270
```

Amino acid sequence of sheep carbonic anhydrase C.
R. J. Tanis, R. E. Ferrell, and R. E. Tashian.
Biochim. Biophys. Acta, **371**, 534–548 (1974).

CARBONIC ANHYDRASE II—RABBIT

	1	5	10	15	
1	AC SER HIS HIS	TRP GLY TYR GLY LYS	HIS ASN GLY PRO GLU HIS		15
16	TRP HIS LYS ASP	PHE PRO ILE ALA ASP	GLY GLU ARG GLN SER PRO		30
31	ILE ASP ILE ASP	THR ASP ALA ALA LYS	HIS ASP PRO SER LEU LYS		45
46	PRO LEU ARG VAL	SER TYR GLU HIS PRO	ILE SER ARG ARG ILE ILE		60
61	ASN ASN GLY HIS	SER PHE ASN VAL GLU	PHE ASP ASP SER HIS ASP		75
76	LYS SER VAL LEU	LYS GLU GLY PRO LEU	GLU GLY THR TYR ARG LEU		90
91	ILE GLN PHE HIS	PHE HIS TRP GLY SER	SER ASP GLY GLU GLY SER		105
106	GLU HIS THR VAL	ASN LYS LYS LYS TYR	ALA ALA GLU LEU HIS LEU		120
121	VAL HIS TRP ASN	THR LYS TYR GLY ASP	PHE GLY LYS ALA VAL LYS		135
136	HIS PRO ASP GLY	LEU ALA VAL LEU GLY	ILE PHE LEU LYS ILE GLY		150
151	SER ALA THR PRO	GLY LEU GLN LYS VAL	VAL ASP THR LEU SER SER		165
166	ILE LYS THR LYS	GLY LYS SER VAL ASP	PHE THR ASN PHE ASP PRO		180
181	ARG GLY LEU LEU	PRO GLU SER LEU ASP	TYR TRP THR TYR PRO GLY		195
196	SER LEU THR THR	PRO PRO LEU LEU GLN	CYS VAL THR TRP ILE VAL		210
211	LEU LYS GLU PRO	ILE THR VAL SER SER	GLU GLN MET LEU LYS PHE		225
226	ARG ASN LEU ASN	PHE ASN LYS GLU ALA	GLU PRO GLU GLU PRO MET		240
241	VAL ASP ASN TRP	ARG PRO THR GLN PRO	LEU LYS GLY ARG GLN VAL		255
256	LYS ALA SER PHE	VAL			270

Amino acid sequence of rabbit carbonic anhydrase II.
R. E. Ferrell, S. K. Stroup, R. J. Tanis, and R. E. Tashian.
Biochim. Biophys. Acta, **533**, 1–11 (1978).

180

ENZYMES

λ *PHAGE ENDOLYSIN*

	1		5					10						15	
1	MET	VAL	GLU	ILE	ASN	ASN	GLN	ARG	LYS	ALA	PHE	LEU	ASP	MET	LEU	15
16	ALA	TRP	SER	GLU	GLY	THR	(ASX,	ASX,	GLY)	ARG	GLX	LYS	THR	ARG	ASN	30
31	HIS	GLY	TYR	ASP	VAL	ILE	VAL	GLY	GLY	GLU	LEU	PHE	THR	ASP	TYR	45
46	SER	ASP	(HIS, | PRO)	ARG	LYS	LEU	VAL	THR	LEU	ASN	PRO	LYS	LEU	LYS	60
61	SER	THR	GLY	ALA	GLY	ARG	TYR	GLN	LEU	LEU	SER	ARG	TRP	ASP	ALA	75
76	TYR	ARG	LYS	GLN	LEU	GLY	LEU	LYS	ASP	PHE	SER	PRO	LYS	SER	GLN	90
91	ASP	ALA	VAL	ALA	LEU	GLN	GLN	ILE	LYS	GLU	ARG	GLY	ALA	LEU	PRO	105
106	MET	ILE	ASP	ARG	GLY	ASP	ILE	ARG	GLN	ALA	ILE	ASP	ARG	CYS	SER	120
121	ASN	ILE	TRP	ALA	SER	LEU	PRO	GLY	ALA	GLY	TYR	GLY	GLN	PHE	GLU	135
136	HIS	LYS	ALA	ASP	SER	LEU	ILE	ALA	LYS	PHE	LYS	GLU	ALA	GLY	GLY	150
151	THR	VAL	ARG	GLU	ILE	ASP	VAL									165

Amino acid Sequence of λ Phage Endolysin.
M. Imada and A. Tsugita.
Nature (New Biol.), **233**, 230–231 (1971).

Δ⁵-3-KETOSTEROID ISOMERASE

	1		5					10						15	
1	MET	ASN	THR	PRO	GLU	HIS	MET	THR	ALA	VAL	VAL	GLN	ARG	TYR	VAL	15
16	ALA	ALA	LEU	ASN	ALA	GLY	ASN	LEU	ASN	GLY	ILE	VAL	ALA	LEU	PHE	30
31	ALA	ASP	ASN	ALA	THR	VAL	GLU	ASN	PRO	VAL	GLY	SER	GLU	PRO	ARG	45
46	SER	GLY	THR	ALA	ALA	ILE	ARG	GLU	PHE	TYR	ALA	ASN	SER	LEU	LYS	60
61	LEU	PRO	LEU	ALA	VAL	GLU	LEU	THR	GLN	GLU	VAL	ARG	ALA	VAL	ALA	75
76	ASN	GLN	ALA	ALA	PHE	ALA	PHE	THR	VAL	SER	PHE	GLU	TYR	GLN	GLY	90
91	ARG	LYS	THR	VAL	VAL	ALA	PRO	ILE	ASP	HIS	PHE	ARG	PHE	ASN	GLY	105
106	ALA	GLY	LYS	VAL	VAL	SER	MET	ARG	ALA	LEU	PHE	GLY	GLU	LYS	ASN	120
121	ILE	HIS	ALA	GLY	ALA											135

The Amino Acid Sequence of Δ⁵-3-ketosteroid Isomerase of *Pseudomonas testosteroni*.
A. M. Benson, R. Jarabak, and P. Talalay.
J. Biol. Chem., **246**, 7514–7525 (1971).

PENICILLINASE FROM S. AUREUS

	1				5					10					15	
1	LYS	GLU	LEU	ASN	ASP	LEU	GLU	LYS	LYS	TYR	ASN	ALA	HIS	ILE	GLY	15
16	VAL	TYR	ALA	LEU	ASP	THR	LYS	SER	GLY	LYS	GLU	VAL	LYS	PHE	ASN	30
31	SER	ASP	LYS	ARG	PHE	ALA	TYR	ALA	SER	THR	SER	LYS	ALA	ILE	ASN	45
46	SER	ALA	ILE	LEU	LEU	GLU	GLN	VAL	PRO	TYR	ASN	LYS	LEU	ASN	LYS	60
61	LYS	VAL	HIS	ILE	ASN	LYS	ASP	ASP	ILE	VAL	ALA	TYR	SER	PRO	ILE	75
76	LEU	GLU	LYS	TYR	VAL	GLY	LYS	ASP	ILE	THR	LEU	LYS	ALA	LEU	ILE	90
91	GLU	ALA	SER	MET	THR	TYR	SER	ASP	ASN	THR	ALA	ASN	ASN	LYS	ILE	105
106	ILE	LYS	GLU	ILE	GLY	GLY	ILE	LYS	LYS	VAL	LYS	GLN	ARG	LEU	LYS	120
121	GLU	LEU	GLY	ASP	LYS	VAL	THR	ASN	PRO	VAL	ARG	TYR	GLU	ILE	GLU	135
136	LEU	ASN	TYR	TYR	SER	PRO	LYS	SER	LYS	LYS	ASP	THR	SER	THR	PRO	150
151	ALA	ALA	PHE	GLY	LYS	THR	LEU	ASN	LYS	LEU	ILE	ALA	ASN	GLY	LYS	165
166	LEU	SER	LYS	GLU	ASN	LYS	LYS	PHE	LEU	LEU	ASP	LEU	MET	LEU	ASN	180
181	ASN	LYS	SER	GLY	ASP	THR	LEU	ILE	LYS	ASP	GLY	VAL	PRO	LYS	ASP	195
196	TYR	LYS	VAL	ALA	ASP	LYS	SER	GLY	GLN	ALA	ILE	THR	TYR	ALA	SER	210
211	ARG	ASN	ASP	VAL	ALA	PHE	VAL	TYR	PRO	LYS	GLY	GLN	SER	GLU	PRO	225
226	ILE	VAL	LEU	VAL	ILE	PHE	THR	ASN	LYS	ASP	ASN	LYS	SER	ASP	LYS	240
241	PRO	ASN	ASP	LYS	LEU	ILE	SER	GLU	THR	ALA	LYS	SER	VAL	MET	LYS	255
256	GLU	PHE														270

The amino acid sequence of *Staphylococcus aureus* Penicillinase.
R. P. Ambler.
Biochem. J., **151**, 197–218 (1975).

ENZYMES

PENICILLINASE FROM B. LICHENIFORMIS

	1				5					10					15	
1	LYS	THR	GLU	MET	LYS	ASP	ASP	PHE	ALA	LYS	LEU	GLU	GLU	GLN	PHE	15
16	ASP	ALA	LYS	LEU	GLY	ILE	PHE	ALA	LEU	ASP	THR	GLY	THR	ASN	ARG	30
31	THR	VAL	ALA	TYR	ARG	PRO	ASP	GLU	ARG	PHE	ALA	PHE	ALA	SER	THR	45
46	ILE	LYS	ALA	LEU	THR	VAL	GLY	VAL	LEU	LEU	GLN	GLN	LYS	SER	ILE	60
61	GLU	ASP	LEU	ASN	GLN	ARG	ILE	THR	TYR	THR	ARG	ASP	ASP	LEU	VAL	75
76	ASN	TYR	ASN	PRO	ILE	THR	GLU	LYS	HIS	VAL	ASP	THR	GLY	MET	THR	90
91	LEU	LYS	GLU	LEU	ALA	ASP	ALA	SER	LEU	ARG	TYR	SER	ASP	ASN	ALA	105
106	ALA	GLN	ASN	LEU	ILE	LEU	LYS	GLN	ILE	GLY	GLY	PRO	GLU	SER	LEU	120
121	LYS	LYS	GLU	LEU	ARG	LYS	ILE	GLY	ASP	GLU	VAL	THR	ASN	PRO	GLU	135
136	ARG	PHE	GLU	PRO	GLU	LEU	ASN	GLU	VAL	ASN	PRO	GLY	GLU	THR	GLN	150
151	ASP	THR	SER	THR	ALA	ARG	ALA	LEU	VAL	THR	SER	LEU	ARG	ALA	PHE	165
166	ALA	LEU	GLU	ASP	LYS	LEU	PRO	SER	GLU	LYS	ARG	GLU	LEU	LEU	ILE	180
181	ASP	TRP	MET	LYS	ARG	ASN	THR	THR	GLY	ASP	ALA	LEU	ILE	ARG	ALA	195
196	GLY	VAL	PRO	ASP	GLY	TRP	GLU	VAL	ALA	ASP	LYS	THR	GLY	ALA	ALA	210
211	SER	TYR	GLY	THR	ARG	ASN	ASP	ILE	ALA	ILE	ILE	TRP	PRO	PRO	LYS	225
226	GLY	ASP	PRO	VAL	VAL	LEU	ALA	VAL	LEU	SER	SER	ARG	ASP	LYS	LYS	240
241	ASP	ALA	LYS	TYR	ASP	ASP	LYS	LEU	ILE	ALA	GLU	ALA	THR	LYS	VAL	255
256	VAL	MET	LYS	ALA	LEU	ASN	MET	ASN	GLY	LYS						270

The amino acid sequence of Penicillinase of *Bacillus licheniformis*.
R. J. Meadway.
Biochem. J., **115**, 12P–13P (1969).

HUMAN ADENYLATE KINASE

	1				5					10					15	
1	AC	MET	GLU	GLU	LYS	LEU	LYS	LYS	THR	LYS	ILE	ILE	PHE	VAL	VAL	15
16	GLY	GLY	PRO	GLY	SER	GLY	LYS	GLY	THR	GLN	CYS	GLU	LYS	ILE	VAL	30
31	GLN	LYS	TYR	GLY	TYR	THR	HIS	LEU	SER	THR	GLY	ASP	LEU	LEU	ARG	45
46	SER	GLU	VAL	SER	SER	GLY	SER	ALA	ARG	GLY	LYS	LYS	LEU	SER	GLU	60
61	ILE	MET	GLU	LYS	GLY	GLN	LEU	VAL	PRO	LEU	GLU	THR	VAL	LEU	ASP	75
76	MET	LEU	ARG	ASP	ALA	MET	VAL	ALA	LYS	VAL	ASN	THR	SER	LYS	GLY	90
91	PHE	LEU	ILE	ASP	GLY	TYR	PRO	ARG	GLU	VAL	GLN	GLN	GLY	GLU	GLU	105
106	PHE	GLU	ARG	ARG	ILE	GLY	GLN	PRO	THR	LEU	LEU	LEU	TYR	VAL	ASP	120
121	ALA	GLY	PRO	GLU	THR	MET	THR	ARG	ARG	LEU	LEU	LYS	ARG	GLY	GLU	135
136	THR	SER	GLY	ARG	VAL	ASP	ASP	ASN	GLU	GLU	THR	ILE	LYS	LYS	ARG	150
151	LEU	GLU	THR	TYR	TYR	LYS	ALA	THR	GLU	PRO	VAL	ILE	ALA	PHE	TYR	165
166	GLU	LYS	ARG	GLY	ILE	VAL	ARG	LYS	VAL	ASN	ALA	GLU	GLY	SER	VAL	180
181	ASP	GLU	VAL	PHE	SER	GLN	VAL	CYS	THR	HIS	LEU	ASP	ALA	LEU	LYS	195

Primary and tertiary structure of the principal human adenylate kinase.
I. von Zabern, B. Wittmann-Liebold, R. Untucht-Grau, R. H. Schirmer, and E. F. Pai.
Eur. J. Biochem., **68**, 281–290 (1976).

PORCINE ADENYLATE KINASE

	1			5					10					15		
1	AC	MET	GLU	GLU	LYS	LEU	LYS	LYS	SER	LYS	ILE	ILE	PHE	VAL	VAL	15
16	GLY	GLY	PRO	GLY	SER	GLY	LYS	GLY	THR	GLN	CYS	GLU	LYS	ILE	VAL	30
31	GLN	LYS	TYR	GLY	TYR	THR	HIS	LEU	SER	THR	GLY	ASP	LEU	LEU	ARG	45
46	ALA	GLU	VAL	SER	SER	GLY	SER	ALA	ARG	GLY	LYS	MET	LEU	SER	GLU	60
61	ILE	MET	GLU	LYS	GLY	GLN	LEU	VAL	PRO	LEU	GLU	THR	VAL	LEU	ASP	75
76	MET	LEU	ARG	ASP	ALA	MET	VAL	ALA	LYS	VAL	ASP	THR	SER	LYS	GLY	90
91	PHE	LEU	ILE	ASP	GLY	TYR	PRO	ARG	GLU	VAL	LYS	GLN	GLY	GLU	GLU	105
106	PHE	GLU	ARG	LYS	ILE	GLY	GLN	PRO	THR	LEU	LEU	LEU	TYR	VAL	ASP	120
121	ALA	GLY	PRO	GLU	THR	MET	THR	LYS	ARG	LEU	LEU	LYS	ARG	GLY	GLU	135
136	THR	SER	GLY	ARG	VAL	ASP	ASP	ASN	GLU	GLU	THR	ILE	LYS	LYS	ARG	150
151	LEU	GLU	THR	TYR	TYR	LYS	ALA	THR	GLU	PRO	VAL	ILE	ALA	PHE	TYR	165
166	GLU	LYS	ARG	GLY	ILE	VAL	ARG	LYS	VAL	ASN	ALA	GLU	GLY	SER	VAL	180
181	ASP	ASP	VAL	PHE	SER	GLN	VAL	CYS	THR	HIS	LEU	ASP	THR	LEU	LYS	195

The amino acid sequence of porcine adenylate kinase from skeletal muscle.
A. Heil, G. Müller, L. Noda, T. Pinder, H. Schirmer, I. Schirmer, and I. von Zabern.
Eur. J. Biochem., **43**, 131–144 (1974).

RIBITOL DEHYDROGENASE FROM KLEBSIELLA AEROGENES

	1			5					10					15		
1	MET	LYS	HIS	SER	VAL	SER	SER	MET	ASN	THR	SER	LEU	SER	GLY	LYS	15
16	VAL	ALA	ALA	ILE	THR	GLY	ALA	ALA	SER	GLY	ILE	GLY	LEU	GLU	CYS	30
31	ALA	ARG	THR	LEU	LEU	GLY	ALA	GLY	ALA	LYS	VAL	VAL	LEU	ILE	ASP	45
46	ARG	GLU	GLY	GLU	LYS	LEU	ASN	LYS	LEU	VAL	ALA	GLU	LEU	GLY	GLN	60
61	ASN	ALA	PHE	ALA	LEU	GLN	VAL	ASP	LEU	MET	GLN	ALA	ASP	GLN	VAL	75
76	ASP	ASN	LEU	LEU	GLN	GLY	ILE	LEU	GLN	LEU	THR	GLY	ARG	LEU	ASP	90
91	ILE	PHE	HIS	ALA	ASN	ALA	GLY	ALA	TYR	ILE	GLY	GLY	PRO	VAL	ALA	105
106	GLU	GLY	ASP	PRO	ASP	VAL	TRP	ASP	ARG	VAL	LEU	HIS	LEU	ASN	ILE	120
121	ASN	ALA	ALA	PHE	ARG	CYS	VAL	ARG	SER	VAL	LEU	PRO	HIS	LEU	LEU	135
136	ALA	GLN	LYS	SER	GLY	ASP	ILE	ILE	PHE	THR	ALA	VAL	ILE	ALA	GLY	150
151	VAL	VAL	ILE	PRO	GLU	TRP	GLU	PRO	VAL	TYR	THR	ALA	SER	LYS	PHE	165
166	ALA	VAL	GLN	ALA	PHE	VAL	HIS	THR	THR	ARG	ARG	GLN	VAL	ALA	GLN	180
181	TYR	GLY	VAL	ARG	VAL	GLY	ALA	VAL	LEU	PRO	GLY	PRO	VAL	VAL	THR	195
196	ALA	LEU	LEU	ASP	ASP	TRP	PRO	LYS	ALA	LYS	MET	ASP	GLU	ALA	LEU	210
211	ALA	ASP	GLY	SER	LEU	MET	GLN	PRO	ILE	GLU	VAL	ALA	GLU	SER	VAL	225
226	LEU	PHE	MET	VAL	THR	ARG	SER	LYS	ASN	VAL	THR	VAL	ARG	ASP	ILE	240
241	VAL	ILE	LEU	PRO	ASN	SER	VAL	ASP	LEU							255

A mass-spectrometric sequence study of the enzyme ribitol dehydrogenase from *Klebsiella aerogenes*.
H. R. Morris, D. H. Williams, G. G. Midwinter, and B. S. Hartley.
Biochem. J., **141**, 701–713 (1974).

ENZYMES

BOVINE ERYTHROCYTE SUPEROXIDE DISMUTASE

	1				5					10					15	
1	AC	ALA	THR	LYS	ALA	VAL	CYS	VAL	LEU	LYS	GLY	ASP	GLY	PRO	VAL	15
16	GLN	GLY	THR	ILE	HIS	PHE	GLU	ALA	LYS	GLY	ASP	THR	VAL	VAL	VAL	30
31	THR	GLY	SER	ILE	THR	GLY	LEU	THR	GLU	GLY	ASP	HIS	GLY	PHE	HIS	45
46	VAL	HIS	GLN	PHE	GLY	ASP	ASN	THR	GLN	GLY	CYS	THR	SER	ALA	GLY	60
61	PRO	HIS	PHE	ASN	PRO	LEU	SER	LYS	LYS	HIS	GLY	GLY	PRO	LYS	ASP	75
76	GLU	GLU	ARG	HIS	VAL	GLY	ASP	LEU	GLY	ASN	VAL	THR	ALA	ASP	LYS	90
91	ASN	GLY	VAL	ALA	ILE	VAL	ASP	ILE	VAL	ASP	PRO	LEU	ILE	SER	LEU	105
106	SER	GLY	GLU	TYR	SER	ILE	ILE	GLY	ARG	THR	MET	VAL	VAL	HIS	GLU	120
121	LYS	PRO	ASP	ASP	LEU	GLY	ARG	GLY	GLY	ASN	GLU	GLU	SER	THR	LYS	135
136	THR	GLY	ASN	ALA	GLY	SER	ARG	LEU	ALA	CYS	GLY	VAL	ILE	GLY	ILE	150
151	ALA	LYS														165

Bovine erythrocyte superoxide dismutase, complete amino acid sequence.
H. M. Steinman, V. R. Naik, J. L. Abernethy, and R. L. Hill.
J. Biol. Chem., **249**, 7326–7338 (1974).

PHOSPHOLIPASE-A FROM BEE VENOM

	1				5					10					15	
1	ILE	ILE	TYR	PRO	GLY	THR	LEU	TRP	CYS	GLY	HIS	GLY	ASN	LYS	SER	15
16	SER	GLY	PRO	ASN	GLU	LEU	GLY	ARG	PHE	LYS	HIS	THR	ASP	ALA	CYS	30
31	CYS	ARG	THR	HIS	ASP	MET	CYS	PRO	ASN	VAL	MET	SER	ALA	GLY	GLU	45
46	SER	LYS	HIS	GLY	LEU	THR	ASP	THR	ALA	SER	ARG	LEU	SER	CYS	ASN	60
61	ASP	ASN	ASP	LEU	PHE	TYR	LYS	ASP	SER	ALA	ASP	THR	ILE	SER	SER	75
76	TYR	PHE	VAL	GLY	LYS	MET	TYR	PHE	ASN	LEU	ILE	ASN	THR	LYS	CYS	90
91	TYR	LYS	LEU	GLU	HIS	PRO	VAL	THR	GLY	CYS	GLY	GLU	ARG	THR	GLU	105
106	GLY	ARG	CYS	LEU	HIS	TYR	THR	VAL	ASP	LYS	SER	LYS	PRO	LYS	VAL	120
121	TYR	GLN	TRP	PHE	ASP	LEU	ARG	LYS	TYR							135

Note: This enzyme contains covalently bound carbohydrate.
The Primary Structure of Phospholipase-A from Bee Venom.
R. A. Shipolini, G. L. Callewaert, R. C. Cottrell, and C. A. Vernon.
FEBS Letters, **17**, 39–40 (1971).

PHOSPHOLIPASE A FROM PIG PANCREAS

	1				5					10					15	
1	GLX	GLU	GLY	ILE	SER	SER	ARG	ALA	LEU	TRP	GLN	PHE	ARG	SER	MET	15
16	ILE	LYS	CYS	ALA	ILE	PRO	GLY	SER	HIS	PRO	LEU	MET	ASP	PHE	ASN	30
31	ASN	TYR	GLY	CYS	TYR	CYS	GLY	LEU	GLY	GLY	SER	GLY	THR	PRO	VAL	45
46	ASN	GLU	LEU	ASN	ARG	CYS	GLU	HIS	THR	ASP	ASN	CYS	TYR	ARG	ASP	60
61	ALA	LYS	ASN	LEU	ASN	ASP	SER	CYS	LYS	PHE	LEU	VAL	ASP	ASN	PRO	75
76	TYR	THR	GLU	SER	TYR	SER	TYR	CYS	SER	SER	ASN	THR	GLU	ILE	THR	90
91	CYS	ASN	SER	LYS	ASN	ASN	ALA	CYS	GLU	ALA	PHE	ILE	CYS	ASN	ASP	105
106	ARG	ASN	ALA	ALA	ILE	CYS	PHE	SER	LYS	ALA	PRO	TYR	ASN	LYS	GLU	120
121	HIS	LYS	ASN	LEU	ASN	THR	LYS	LYS	TYR	CYS						135

Note: (i) This enzyme occurs as its zymogen (sequence shown above); the active enzyme results after enzymic removal of residues 1–7. (ii) Disulphide bridges are between CYS 18 and 83; CYS 34 and 130; CYS 36 and 51; CYS 57 and 111; CYS 68 and 98; CYS 91 and 103.

Studies on Phospholipase A and its Zymogen from porcine pancreas. II. The assignment of position of the six disulphide bridges.
G. H. DeHaas, A. J. Slotboom, P. P. M. Bonsen, W. Nieuwenhuizen, L. L. M. van Deenen, S. Maroux, V. Dlouha, and P. Desnuelle.
Biochim. Biophys. Acta, **221**, 54–61 (1970).
Studies on Phospholipase A and its Zymogen from porcine pancreas. I. The complete amino acid sequence.
G. H. DeHaas, A. J. Slotboom, P. P. M. Bonsen, L. L. M. van Deenen, S. Maroux, A. Puigserver, and P. Desnuelle.
Biochim. Biophys.' Acta, **221**, 31–53 (1970).

PHOSPHOLIPASE A (FRACTION DE-I)—RINGHALS

	1				5					10					15	
1	ASN	LEU	TYR	GLN	PHE	LYS	ASN	MET	ILE	LYS	CYS	THR	VAL	PRO	SER	15
16	ARG	SER	TRP	TRP	HIS	PHE	ALA	ASN	TYR	GLY	CYS	TYR	CYS	GLY	ARG	30
31	GLY	GLY	SER	GLY	THR	PRO	VAL	ASP	ASP	LEU	ASP	ARG	CYS	CYS	GLN	45
46	THR	HIS	ASP	ASN	CYS	TYR	SER	ASP	ALA	GLU	LYS	ILE	SER	GLY	CYS	60
61	ARG	PRO	TYR	PHE	LYS	THR	TYR	SER	TYR	ASP	CYS	THR	LYS	GLY	LYS	75
76	LEU	THR	CYS	LYS	GLU	GLY	ASN	ASN	GLU	CYS	ALA	ALA	PHE	VAL	CYS	90
91	LYS	CYS	ASP	ARG	LEU	ALA	ALA	ILE	CYS	PHE	ALA	GLY	ALA	HIS	TYR	105
106	ASN	ASP	ASN	ASN	ASN	TYR	ILE	ASP	LEU	ALA	ARG	HIS	CYS	GLN		120

Hemachatus haemachatus (Ringhals) venom. Purification, some properties and amino acid sequence of phospholipase A (Fraction DE-I).
F. J. Joubert.
Eur. J. Biochem., **52**, 539–554 (1975).

ENZYMES

PHOSPHOLIPASE A (FRACTION DE-I)—FOREST COBRA

```
       1            5                    10                   15
  1  ASN LEU TYR GLN PHE LYS ASN MET ILE HIS CYS THR VAL PRO ASN   15
 16  ARG PRO TRP TRP HIS PHE ALA ASN TYR GLY CYS TYR CYS GLY ARG   30
 31  GLY GLY LYS GLY THR PRO VAL ASP ASP LEU ASP ARG CYS CYS GLN   45
 46  ILE HIS ASP LYS CYS TYR ASP GLU ALA GLU LYS ILE SER GLY CYS   60
 61  TRP PRO TYR ILE LYS THR TYR THR TYR GLU SER CYS GLN GLY THR   75
 76  LEU THR CYS LYS ASP GLY GLY LYS CYS ALA ALA SER VAL CYS ASP   90
 91  CYS ASP ARG VAL ALA ALA ASN CYS PHE ALA ARG ALA THR TYR ASN  105
106  ASP LYS ASN TYR ASN ILE ASP PHE ASN ALA ARG CYS GLN          120
```

PHOSPHOLIPASE A (FRACTION DE-II)—FOREST COBRA

```
       1            5                    10                   15
  1  ASN LEU TYR GLU PHE LYS ASN MET ILE GLN CYS THR VAL PRO ASN   15
 16  ARG SER TRP TRP HIS PHE ALA ASN TYR GLY CYS TYR CYS GLY ARG   30
 31  GLY GLY SER GLY THR PRO VAL ASP ASP LEU ASP ARG CYS CYS GLN   45
 46  ILE HIS ASP ASN CYS TYR GLY GLU ALA GLU LYS ILE SER GLY CYS   60
 61  TRP PRO TYR ILE LYS THR TYR THR TYR GLN SER CYS GLN GLY THR   75
 76  LEU THR SER CYS GLY ALA ASN ASN LYS CYS ALA ALA SER VAL CYS   90
 91  ASP CYS ASP ARG VAL ALA ALA ASN CYS PHE ALA ARG ALA THR TYR  105
106  ASN ASP LYS ASN TYR ASN ILE ASP PHE ASN ALA ARG CYS GLN      120
```

Note: Another fraction DE-IIA was found to have identical sequence to that of fraction DE-II except that residues 104 and 106 are PRO and ILE respectively.
Naja melanoleuca (Forest cobra) venom. The amino acid sequence of phospholipase A, fractions DE-I and DE-II.
F. J. Joubert.
Biochim. Biophys. Acta, **379**, 345–359 (1975).

PHOSPHOLIPASE A (FRACTION DE-III)—FOREST COBRA

	1				5					10					15	
1	ASN	LEU	TYR	GLN	PHE	LYS	ASN	MET	ILE	HIS	CYS	THR	VAL	PRO	ASN	15
16	ARG	SER	TRP	TRP	HIS	PHE	ALA	ASN	TYR	GLY	CYS	TYR	CYS	GLY	ARG	30
31	GLY	GLY	SER	GLY	THR	PRO	VAL	ASP	ASP	LEU	ASP	ARG	CYS	CYS	GLN	45
46	ILE	HIS	ASP	ASN	CYS	TYR	GLY	GLU	ALA	GLU	LYS	ILE	SER	GLY	CYS	60
61	TRP	PRO	TYR	ILE	LYS	THR	TYR	THR	TYR	ASP	SER	CYS	GLN	GLY	THR	75
76	LEU	THR	SER	CYS	GLY	ALA	ALA	ASN	ASN	CYS	ALA	ALA	SER	VAL	CYS	90
91	ASP	CYS	ASP	ARG	VAL	ALA	ALA	ASN	CYS	PHE	ALA	ARG	ALA	PRO	TYR	105
106	ILE	ASP	LYS	ASN	TYR	ASN	ILE	ASP	PHE	ASN	ALA	ARG	CYS	GLN		120

Note: Another fraction DE-IIIA was found to have identical sequence to that of fraction DE-III except that residues 104 and 106 are THR and ASN respectively.
Naja melanoleuca (Forest cobra) venom. The amino acid sequence of phospholipase A, fraction DE-III.
F. J. Joubert.
Biochim. Biophys. Acta, **379**, 329–344 (1975).

PHOSPHOLIPASE A—FROM BITIS GABONICA *VENOM*

	1				5					10					15	
1	ASP	LEU	THR	GLN	PHE	GLY	ASN	MET	ILE	ASN	LYS	MET	GLY	GLN	SER	15
16	VAL	PHE	ASP	TYR	ILE	TYR	TYR	GLY	CYS	TYR	CYS	GLY	TRP	GLY	GLY	30
31	LYS	GLY	LYS	PRO	ILE	ASP	ALA	THR	ASP	ARG	CYS	CYS	PHE	VAL	HIS	45
46	ASP	CYS	CYS	TYR	GLY	LYS	MET	GLY	THR	TYR	ASP	THR	LYS	TRP	THR	60
61	SER	TYR	ASN	TYR	GLU	ILE	GLN	ASN	GLY	GLY	ILE	ASP	CYS	ASP	GLU	75
76	ASP	PRO	GLN	LYS	LYS	GLU	LEU	CYS	GLU	CYS	ASP	ARG	VAL	ALA	ALA	90
91	ILE	CYS	PHE	ALA	ASN	ASN	ARG	ASN	THR	TYR	ASN	SER	ASN	TYR	PHE	105
106	GLY	HIS	SER	SER	SER	LYS	CYS	THR	GLY	THR	GLU	GLN	CYS			120

Bitis gabonica venom. The amino acid sequence of phospholipase A.
D. P. Botes and C. C. Viljoen.
J. Biol. Chem., **249**, 3827–3835 (1974).

188

ENZYMES

PHOSPHOLIPASE A₂—BOVINE

	1				5					10					15	
1	ALA	LEU	TRP	GLN	PHE	ASN	GLY	MET	ILE	LYS	CYS	LYS	ILE	PRO	SER	15
16	SER	GLU	PRO	LEU	LEU	ASP	PHE	ASN	ASN	TYR	GLY	CYS	TYR	CYS	GLY	30
31	LEU	GLY	GLY	SER	GLY	THR	PRO	VAL	ASP	ASP	LEU	ASP	ARG	CYS	CYS	45
46	GLN	THR	HIS	ASP	ASN	CYS	TYR	LYS	GLN	ALA	LYS	LYS	LEU	ASP	SER	60
61	CYS	LYS	VAL	LEU	VAL	ASP	ASN	PRO	TYR	THR	ASN	ASN	TYR	SER	TYR	75
76	SER	CYS	SER	ASN	ASN	GLU	ILE	THR	CYS	SER	SER	GLU	ASN	ASN	ALA	90
91	CYS	GLU	ALA	PHE	ILE	CYS	ASN	CYS	ASP	ARG	ASN	ALA	ALA	ILE	CYS	105
106	PHE	SER	LYS	VAL	PRO	TYR	ASN	LYS	GLU	HIS	LYS	ASN	LEU	ASP	LYS	120
121	LYS	ASN	CYS													135

The primary structure of bovine pancreatic phospholipase A₂.
E. A. M. Fleer, H. M. Verheij, and G. H. de Haas.
Eur. J. Biochem., **82**, 261–269 (1978).

PHOSPHOLIPASE A₂—HORSE

	1				5					10					15	
1	ALA	VAL	TRP	GLN	PHE	ARG	SER	MET	ILE	GLN	CYS	THR	ILE	PRO	ASN	15
16	SER	LYS	PRO	TYR	LEU	GLU	PHE	ASN	ASP	TYR	GLY	CYS	TYR	CYS	GLY	30
31	LEU	GLY	GLY	SER	GLY	THR	PRO	VAL	ASP	GLU	LEU	ASP	ALA	CYS	CYS	45
46	GLN	VAL	HIS	ASP	ASN	CYS	TYR	THR	GLN	ALA	LYS	GLU	LEU	SER	SER	60
61	CYS	ARG	PHE	LEU	VAL	ASP	ASN	PRO	TYR	THR	GLU	SER	TYR	LYS	PHE	75
76	SER	CYS	SER	GLY	THR	GLU	VAL	THR	CYS	SER	ASP	LYS	ASN	ASN	ALA	90
91	CYS	GLU	ALA	PHE	ILE	CYS	ASN	CYS	ASP	ARG	ASN	ALA	ALA	ILE	CYS	105
106	PHE	SER	LYS	ALA	PRO	TYR	ASN	PRO	GLU	ASN	LYS	ASN	LEU	ASP	SER	120
121	LYS	ARG	LYS	ALA	CYS											135

Amino acid sequence of Phospholipase A₂ from horse pancreas.
A. Evenberg, H. Meyer, W. Gaastra, H. M. Verheij, and G. H. de Haas.
J. Biol. Chem., **252**, 1189–1196 (1977).

ENZYMES

BOVINE TRYPSINOGEN

	1			5			10				15					
1	VAL	ASP	ASP	ASP	ASP	LYS	ILE	VAL	GLY	GLY	TYR	THR	CYS	GLY	ALA	15
16	ASN	THR	VAL	PRO	TYR	GLN	VAL	SER	LEU	ASN	SER	GLY	TYR	HIS	PHE	30
31	CYS	GLY	GLY	SER	LEU	ILE	ASN	SER	GLN	TRP	VAL	VAL	SER	ALA	ALA	45
46	HIS	CYS	TYR	LYS	SER	GLY	ILE	GLN	VAL	ARG	LEU	GLY	GLN	ASP	ASN	60
61	ILE	ASN	VAL	VAL	GLU	GLY	ASN	GLN	GLN	PHE	ILE	SER	ALA	SER	LYS	75
76	SER	ILE	VAL	HIS	PRO	SER	TYR	ASN	SER	ASN	THR	LEU	ASN	ASN	ASP	90
91	ILE	MET	LEU	ILE	LYS	LEU	LYS	SER	ALA	ALA	SER	LEU	ASN	SER	ARG	105
106	VAL	ALA	SER	ILE	SER	LEU	PRO	THR	SER	CYS	ALA	SER	ALA	GLY	THR	120
121	GLN	CYS	LEU	ILE	SER	GLY	TRP	GLY	ASN	THR	LYS	SER	SER	GLY	THR	135
136	SER	TYR	PRO	ASP	VAL	LEU	LYS	CYS	LEU	LYS	ALA	PRO	ILE	LEU	SER	150
151	ASN	SER	SER	CYS	LYS	SER	ALA	TYR	PRO	GLY	GLN	ILE	THR	SER	ASN	165
166	MET	PHE	CYS	ALA	GLY	TYR	LEU	GLU	GLY	GLY	LYS	ASP	SER	CYS	GLN	180
181	GLY	ASP	SER	GLY	GLY	PRO	VAL	VAL	CYS	SER	GLY	LYS	LEU	GLN	GLY	195
196	ILE	VAL	SER	TRP	GLY	SER	GLY	CYS	ALA	GLN	LYS	ASN	LYS	PRO	GLY	210
211	VAL	TYR	THR	LYS	VAL	CYS	ASN	TYR	VAL	SER	TRP	ILE	LYS	GLN	THR	225
226	ILE	ALA	SER	ASN												240

Note: Disulphide bridges between CYS 13 and 143; CYS 31 and 47; CYS 115 and 216; CYS 122 and 189; CYS 154 and 168; CYS 179 and 203.
Covalent Structure of Bovine Trypsinogen, the position of the remaining amides.
O. Mikeš, V. Holeyšovský, V. Tomášek, and F. Šorm.
Biochem. Biophys. Res. Commun., **24**, 346–352 (1966).
Correction. Position 177 assigned ASP, in place of ASN. Homologies in Serine Proteinases.
B. S. Hartley.
Phil. Trans. Roy. Soc. London, B **257**, 77–87 (1970).

ENZYMES

PORCINE TRYPSIN

	1				5					10					15	
1					ILE	VAL	GLY	GLY	TYR	THR	CYS	ALA	ALA			15
16	ASN	SER	VAL/ILE	PRO	TYR	GLN	VAL	SER	LEU	ASN	SER	GLY	SER	HIS	PHE	30
31	CYS	GLY	GLY	SER	LEU	ILE	ASN	SER	GLN	TRP	VAL	VAL	SER	ALA	ALA	45
46	HIS	CYS	TYR	LYS	SER	ARG	ILE	GLN	VAL	ARG	LEU	GLY	GLU	HIS	ASN	60
61	ILE	ASP	VAL	LEU	GLU	GLY	ASN	GLU	GLN	PHE	ILE	ASN	ALA	ALA	LYS	75
76	ILE	ILE	THR	HIS	PRO	ASN	PHE	ASN	GLY	ASN	THR	LEU	ASP	ASN	ASP	90
91	ILE	MET	LEU	ILE	LYS	LEU	SER	SER	PRO	ALA	THR	LEU	ASN	SER	ARG	105
106	VAL	ALA	THR	VAL	SER	LEU	PRO	ARG	SER	CYS	ALA	ALA	ALA	GLY	THR	120
121	GLU	CYS	LEU	ILE	SER	GLY	TRP	GLY	ASN	THR	LYS	SER	SER	GLY	SER	135
136	SER	TYR	PRO	SER	LEU	LEU	GLN	CYS	LEU	LYS	ALA	PRO	VAL	LEU	SER	150
151	ASP	SER	SER	CYS	LYS	SER	SER	TYR	PRO	GLY	GLN	ILE	THR	GLY	ASN	165
166	MET	ILE	CYS	VAL	GLY	PHE	LEU	GLU	GLY	GLY	LYS	ASP	SER	CYS	GLN	180
181	GLY	ASP	SER	GLY	GLY	PRO	VAL	VAL	CYS	ASN	GLY	GLN	LEU	GLN	GLY	195
196	ILE	VAL	SER	TRP	GLY	TYR	GLY	CYS	ALA	GLN	LYS	ASN	LYS	PRO	GLY	210
211	VAL	TYR	THR	LYS	VAL	CYS	ASN	TYR	VAL	ASN	TRP	ILE	GLN	GLN	THR	225
226	ILE	ALA	(ALA,	ASN)												240

Notes: (i) The residues above are placed, i.e. starting with residue 7, so as to correspond with bovine trypsin. (ii) Charles *et al.* (1963) describes the activation peptide of porcine trypsinogen and the C-terminal sequence. These are:

    Activation peptide
    PHE PRO THR ASP ASP ASP ASP LYS,
    C-terminal sequence
    ALA ASN.

Sur le trypsinogene et la trypsine de porc.
M. Charles, M. Rovery, A. Guidoni, and P. Desnuelle.
Biochim. Biophys. Acta, **69**, 115–129 (1963).
Determination of the amino acid sequence of porcine trypsin by sequenator analysis.
M. A. Hermodson, L. H. Ericsson, H. Neurath, and K. A. Walsh.
Biochemistry, **12**, 3146–3153 (1973).

DOGFISH TRYPSIN

	1				5					10					15		
1	ILE	VAL	GLY	GLY	TYR	GLU	CYS	PRO	LYS	HIS	ALA	ALA	PRO	TRP	THR		15
16	VAL	SER	LEU	ASN	VAL	GLY	TYR	HIS	PHE	CYS	GLY	GLY	SER	LEU	ILE		30
31	ALA	PRO	GLY	TRP	VAL	VAL	SER	ALA	ALA	HIS	CYS	TYR	GLN	ARG	ARG		45
46	ILE	GLN	VAL	ARG	LEU	GLY	GLU	HIS	ASP	ILE	SER	ALA	ASN	GLU	GLY		60
61	ASP	GLU	THR	TYR	ILE	ASP	SER	SER	MET	VAL	ILE	ARG	HIS	PRO	ASN		75
76	TYR	SER	GLY	TYR	ASP	LEU	ASP	ASN	ASP	ILE	MET	LEU	ILE	LYS	LEU		90
91	SER	LYS	PRO	ALA	ALA	LEU	ASN	ARG	ASN	VAL	ASP	LEU/PRO	ILE	SER	LEU		105
106	PRO	THR	GLY	CYS	ALA	TYR	ALA	GLY	GLU	MET	CYS	LEU	ILE	SER	GLY		120
121	TRP	GLY	ASN	THR	MET	ASP	GLY	ALA	VAL	SER	GLY	ASP	GLN	LEU	GLN		135
136	CYS	LEU	ASP	ALA	PRO	VAL	LEU	SER	ASP	ALA	GLU	CYS	LYS	GLY	ALA		150
151	TYR	PRO	GLY	MET	ILE	THR	ASN	ASN	MET	MET	CYS	VAL	GLY	TYR	MET		165
166	GLU	GLY	GLY	LYS	ASP	SER	CYS	GLN	GLY	ASP	SER	GLY	GLY	PRO	VAL		180
181	VAL	CYS	ASN	GLY	MET	LEU	GLN	GLY	ILE	VAL	SER	TRP	GLY	TYR	GLY		195
196	CYS	ALA	GLU	ARG	ASP	HIS	PRO	GLY	VAL	TYR	THR	ARG	VAL	CYS	HIS		210
211	TYR	VAL	SER	TRP	ILE	HIS	GLU	THR	ILE	ALA	SER	VAL					225

Amino acid sequence of dogfish trypsin.
K. Titani, L. H. Ericsson, H. Neurath, and K. A. Walsh.
Biochemistry, **14**, 1358–1366 (1975).

192

ENZYMES

TRYPSIN FROM STREPTOMYCES GRISEUS

	1				5					10					15	
1	VAL	VAL	GLY	GLY	THR	ARG	ALA	ALA	GLN	GLY	GLU	PHE	PRO	PHE	MET	15
16	VAL	ARG	LEU	SER	MET	GLY	CYS	GLY	GLY	ALA	LEU	TYR	ALA	GLN	ASP	30
31	ILE	VAL	LEU	THR	ALA	ALA	HIS	CYS	VAL	SER	GLY	SER	GLY	ASN	ASN	45
46	THR	SER	ILE	THR	ALA	THR	GLY	GLY	VAL	VAL	ASP	LEU	GLN	SER	ALA	60
61	VAL	LYS	VAL	ARG	SER	THR	LYS	VAL	LEU	GLN	ALA	PRO	GLY	TYR	ASN	75
76	GLY	THR	GLY	LYS	ASP	TRP	ALA	LEU	ILE	LYS	LEU	ALA	GLN	PRO	ILE	90
91	ASN	GLN	PRO	THR	LEU	LYS	ILE	ALA	THR	THR	THR	ALA	TYR	ASN	GLN	105
106	GLY	THR	PHE	THR	VAL	ALA	GLY	TRP	GLY	ALA	ASN	ARG	GLU	GLY	GLY	120
121	SER	GLN	GLN	ARG	TYR	LEU	LEU	LYS	ALA	ASN	VAL	PRO	PHE	VAL	SER	135
136	ASP	ALA	ALA	CYS	ARG	SER	ALA	TYR	GLY	ASN	GLU	LEU	VAL	ALA	ASN	150
151	GLU	GLU	ILE	CYS	ALA	GLY	TYR	PRO	ASP	THR	GLY	GLY	VAL	ASP	THR	165
166	CYS	GLN	GLY	ASP	SER	GLY	GLY	PRO	MET	PHE	ARG	LYS	ASP	ASN	ALA	180
181	ASP	GLU	TRP	ILE	GLN	VAL	GLY	ILE	VAL	SER	TRP	GLY	TYR	GLY	CYS	195
196	ALA	ARG	PRO	GLY	TYR	PRO	GLY	VAL	TYR	THR	GLU	VAL	SER	THR	PHE	210
211	ALA	SER	ALA	ILE	ALA	SER	ALA	ALA	ARG	THR	LEU					225

Note: Disulphide bridges are between residues CYS 22 and 38; CYS 139 and 154; CYS 166 and 195.
Amino acid sequence of *Streptomyces griseus* trypsin.
R. W. Olafson, L. Jurášek, M. R. Carpenter, and L. B. Smillie.
Biochemistry, **14**, 1168–1177 (1975).

BOVINE CHYMOTRYPSINOGEN A

	1				5					10					15	
1	CYS	GLY	VAL	PRO	ALA	ILE	GLN	PRO	VAL	LEU	SER	GLY	LEU	SER	ARG	15
16	ILE	VAL	ASN	GLY	GLU	GLU	ALA	VAL	PRO	GLY	SER	TRP	PRO	TRP	GLN	30
31	VAL	SER	LEU	GLN	ASP	LYS	THR	GLY	PHE	HIS	PHE	CYS	GLY	GLY	SER	45
46	LEU	ILE	ASN	GLU	ASN	TRP	VAL	VAL	THR	ALA	ALA	HIS	CYS	GLY	VAL	60
61	THR	THR	SER	ASP	VAL	VAL	VAL	ALA	GLY	GLU	PHE	ASP	GLN	GLY	SER	75
76	SER	SER	GLU	LYS	ILE	GLN	LYS	LEU	LYS	ILE	ALA	LYS	VAL	PHE	LYS	90
91	ASN	SER	LYS	TYR	ASN	SER	LEU	THR	ILE	ASN	ASN	ASP	ILE	THR	LEU	105
106	LEU	LYS	LEU	SER	THR	ALA	ALA	SER	PHE	SER	GLN	THR	VAL	SER	ALA	120
121	VAL	CYS	LEU	PRO	SER	ALA	SER	ASP	ASP	PHE	ALA	ALA	GLY	THR	THR	135
136	CYS	VAL	THR	THR	GLY	TRP	GLY	LEU	THR	ARG	TYR	THR	ASN	ALA	ASN	150
151	THR	PRO	ASP	ARG	LEU	GLN	GLN	ALA	SER	LEU	PRO	LEU	LEU	SER	ASN	165
166	THR	ASN	CYS	LYS	LYS	TYR	TRP	GLY	THR	LYS	ILE	LYS	ASP	ALA	MET	180
181	ILE	CYS	ALA	GLY	ALA	SER	GLY	VAL	SER	SER	CYS	MET	GLY	ASP	SER	195
196	GLY	GLY	PRO	LEU	VAL	CYS	LYS	LYS	ASN	GLY	ALA	TRP	THR	LEU	VAL	210
211	GLY	ILE	VAL	SER	TRP	GLY	SER	SER	THR	CYS	SER	THR	SER	THR	PRO	225
226	GLY	VAL	TYR	ALA	ARG	VAL	THR	ALA	LEU	VAL	ASN	TRP	VAL	GLN	GLN	240
241	THR	LEU	ALA	ALA	ASN											255

Note: Disulphide bridges are between CYS 1 and 122; CYS 42 and 58; CYS 136 and 201; CYS 168 and 182; CYS 191 and 220.
Amino acid Sequence of Bovine Chymotrypsinogen A.
B. S. Hartley.
Nature, **201**, 1284–1287 (1964).
Location of Disulphide bridges by diagonal paper electrophoresis. The disulphide bridges of bovine chymotrypsinogen A.
J. R. Brown and B. S. Hartley.
Biochem. J., **101**, 214–228 (1966).
Corrections to the Amino Acid sequence of Bovine Chymotrypsinogen A.
B. S. Hartley and D. K. Kauffman.
Biochem. J., **101**, 229–231 (1966).
Role of a Buried Acid Group in the Mechanism of Action of Chymotrypsin.
D. M. Blow, J. J. Birktoft, and B. S. Hartley.
Nature, **221**, 337–340 (1969).

ENZYMES

BOVINE CHYMOTRYPSINOGEN B

	1				5					10					15	
1	CYS	GLY	VAL	PRO	ALA	ILE	GLN	PRO	VAL	LEU	SER	GLY	LEU	ALA	ARG	15
16	ILE	VAL	ASN	GLY	GLU	ASP	ALA	VAL	PRO	GLY	SER	TRP	PRO	TRP	GLN	30
31	VAL	SER	LEU	GLN	ASP	SER	THR	GLY	PHE	HIS	PHE	CYS	GLY	GLY	SER	45
46	LEU	ILE	SER	GLU	ASP	TRP	VAL	VAL	THR	ALA	ALA	HIS	CYS	GLY	VAL	60
61	THR	THR	SER	ASP	VAL	VAL	VAL	ALA	GLY	GLU	PHE	ASP	GLN	GLY	LEU	75
76	GLU	THR	GLU	ASP	THR	GLN	VAL	LEU	LYS	ILE	GLY	LYS	VAL	PHE	LYS	90
91	ASN	PRO	LYS	PHE	SER	ILE	LEU	THR	VAL	ARG	ASN	ASP	ILE	THR	LEU	105
106	LEU	LYS	LEU	ALA	THR	PRO	ALA	GLN	PHE	SER	GLU	THR	VAL	SER	ALA	120
121	VAL	CYS	LEU	PRO	SER	ALA	ASP	GLU	ASP	PHE	PRO	ALA	GLY	MET	LEU	135
136	CYS	ALA	THR	THR	GLY	TRP	GLY	LYS	THR	LYS	TYR	ASN	ALA	LEU	LYS	150
151	THR	PRO	ASP	LYS	LEU	GLN	GLN	ALA	THR	LEU	PRO	ILE	VAL	SER	ASN	165
166	THR	ASP	CYS	ARG	LYS	TYR	TRP	GLY	SER	ARG	VAL	THR	ASP	VAL	MET	180
181	ILE	CYS	ALA	GLY	ALA	SER	GLY	VAL	SER	SER	CYS	MET	GLY	ASP	SER	195
196	GLY	GLY	PRO	LEU	VAL	CYS	GLN	LYS	ASN	GLY	ALA	TRP	THR	LEU	ALA	210
211	GLY	ILE	VAL	SER	TRP	GLY	SER	SER	THR	CYS	SER	THR	SER	THR	PRO	225
226	ALA	VAL	TYR	ALA	ARG	VAL	THR	ALA	LEU	MET	PRO	TRP	VAL	GLN	GLU	240
241	THR	LEU	ALA	ALA	ASN											255

Structure of Chymotrypsinogen B compared with Chymotrypsinogen A and with Trypsinogen. L. B. Smillie, A. Furka, N. Nagabhushan, K. J. Stevenson, and C. O. Parkes. *Nature*, **218**, 343–346 (1968).

THERMOLYSIN

	1			5					10					15		
1	ILE	THR	GLY	THR	SER	THR	VAL	GLY	VAL	GLY	ARG	GLY	VAL	LEU	GLY	15
16	ASP	GLN	LYS	ASN	ILE	ASN	THR	THR	TYR	SER	THR	TYR	TYR	TYR	LEU	30
31	GLN	ASP	ASN	THR	ARG	GLY	ASP	GLY	ILE	PHE	THR	TYR	ASP	ALA	LYS	45
46	TYR	ARG	THR	THR	LEU	PRO	GLY	SER	LEU	TRP	ALA	ASP	ALA	ASP	ASN	60
61	GLN	PHE	PHE	ALA	SER	TYR	ASP	ALA	PRO	ALA	VAL	ASP	ALA	HIS	TYR	75
76	TYR	ALA	GLY	VAL	THR	TYR	ASP	TYR	TYR	LYS	ASN	VAL	HIS	ASN	ARG	90
91	LEU	SER	TYR	ASP	GLY	ASN	ASN	ALA	ALA	ILE	ARG	SER	SER	VAL	HIS	105
106	TYR	SER	GLN	GLY	TYR	ASN	ASN	ALA	PHE	TRP	ASN	GLY	SER	GLU	MET	120
121	VAL	TYR	GLY	ASP	GLY	ASP	GLY	GLN	THR	PHE	ILE	PRO	LEU	SER	GLY	135
136	GLY	ILE	ASP	VAL	VAL	ALA	HIS	GLU	LEU	THR	HIS	ALA	VAL	THR	ASP	150
151	TYR	THR	ALA	GLY	LEU	ILE	TYR	GLN	ASN	GLU	SER	GLY	ALA	ILE	ASN	165
166	GLU	ALA	ILE	SER	ASP	ILE	PHE	GLY	THR	LEU	VAL	GLU	PHE	TYR	ALA	180
181	ASN	LYS	ASN	PRO	ASP	TRP	GLU	ILE	GLY	GLU	ASP	VAL	TYR	THR	PRO	195
196	GLY	ILE	SER	GLY	ASP	SER	LEU	ARG	SER	MET	SER	ASP	PRO	ALA	LYS	210
211	TYR	GLY	ASP	PRO	ASP	HIS	TYR	SER	LYS	ARG	TYR	THR	GLY	THR	GLN	225
226	ASP	ASN	GLY	GLY	VAL	HIS	ILE	ASN	SER	GLY	ILE	ILE	ASN	LYS	ALA	240
241	ALA	TYR	LEU	ILE	SER	GLN	GLY	GLY	THR	HIS	TYR	GLY	VAL	SER	VAL	255
256	VAL	GLY	ILE	GLY	ARG	ASP	LYS	LEU	GLY	LYS	ILE	PHE	TYR	ARG	ALA	270
271	LEU	THR	GLN	TYR	LEU	THR	PRO	THR	SER	ASN	PHE	SER	GLN	LEU	ARG	285
286	ALA	ALA	ALA	VAL	GLN	SER	ALA	THR	ASP	LEU	TYR	GLY	SER	THR	SER	300
301	GLX	GLX	VAL	ALA	SER	VAL	LYS	GLN	ALA	PHE	ASP	ALA	VAL	GLY	VAL	315
316	LYS															330

The Amino Acid Sequence of Thermolysin.
K. Titani, M. A. Hermodson, L. H. Ericsson, K. A. Walsh, and H. Neurath.
Nature (New Biol.), **238**, 35–37 (1972).

ENZYMES

PORCINE PEPSIN

	1				5					10					15	
1	ILE	GLY	ASP	GLU	PRO	LEU	GLU	ASN	TYR	LEU	ASP	THR	GLU	TYR	PHE	15
16	GLY	THR	ILE	GLY	ILE	GLY	THR	PRO	ALA	GLN	ASP	PHE	THR	VAL	ILE	30
31	PHE	ASP	THR	GLY	SER	SER	ASN	LEU	TRP	VAL	PRO	SER	VAL	TYR	CYS	45
46	SER	SER	LEU	ALA	CYS	SER	ASP	HIS	ASN	GLN	PHE	ASN	PRO	ASP	SER	60
61	ASP	SER	THR	PHE	GLU	ALA	THR	PSE	GLN	GLU	LEU	SER	ILE	THR	TYR	75
76	GLY	THR	GLY	SER	MET	THR	GLY	ILE	LEU	GLY	TYR	ASP	THR	VAL	GLN	90
91	VAL	GLY	GLY	ILE	SER	ASP	THR	ASN	GLN	ILE	PHE	GLY	LEU	SER	GLU	105
106	THR	GLU	PRO	GLY	SER	PHE	LEU	TYR	TYR	ALA	PRO	PHE	ASP	GLY	ILE	120
121	LEU	GLY	LEU	ALA	TYR	PRO	SER	ILE	SER	ALA	SER	GLY	ALA	THR	PRO	135
136	VAL	PHE	ASP	ASN	LEU	TRP	ASP	GLN	GLY	LEU	VAL	SER	GLN	ASP	LEU	150
151	PHE	SER	VAL	TYR	LEU	SER	SER	ASN	ASP	ASP	SER	GLY	SER	VAL	VAL	165
166	LEU	LEU	GLY	GLY	ILE	ASP	SER	SER	TYR	TYR	THR	GLY	SER	LEU	ASN	180
181	TRP	VAL	PRO	VAL	SER	VAL	GLU	GLY	TYR	TRP	GLN	ILE	THR	LEU	ASP	195
196	SER	ILE	THR	MET	ASP	GLY	GLU	THR	ILE	ALA	CYS	SER	GLY	GLY	CYS	210
211	GLN	ALA	ILE	VAL	ASP	THR	GLY	THR	SER	LEU	LEU	THR	GLY	PRO	THR	225
226	SER	ALA	ILE	ALA	ILE OOO	ASN	ILE	GLN	SER	ASP	ILE	GLY	ALA	SER	GLU	240
241	ASN	SER	ASP	GLY	GLU	MET	VAL	ILE	SER	CYS	SER	SER	ILE	ASP	SER	255
256	LEU	PRO	ASP	ILE	VAL	PHE	THR	ILE	ASP	GLY	VAL	GLN	TYR	PRO	LEU	270
271	SER	PRO	SER	ALA	TYR	ILE	LEU	GLN	ASP	ASP	ASP	SER	CYS	THR	SER	285
286	GLY	PHE	GLU	GLY	MET	ASP	VAL	PRO	THR	SER	SER	GLY	GLU	LEU	TRP	300
301	ILE	LEU	GLY	ASP	VAL	PHE	ILE	ARG	GLN	TYR	TYR	THR	VAL	PHE	ASP	315
316	ARG	ALA	ASN	ASN	LYS	VAL	GLY	LEU	ALA	PRO	VAL	ALA				330

Notes: (i) Disulphide bridges are between CYS 45 and 50; CYS 206 and 210; and CYS 250 and 283. (ii) Residue 230 (ILE) is absent in some preparations. (iii) A minor component of commercial pepsin has two extra amino acids at the N-terminus, ALA LEU.
Primary structure of porcine pepsin. III. Amino acid sequence of a cyanogen bromide fragment CB2A, and the complete structure of porcine pepsin.
P. Sepulveda, J. Marciniszyn, D. Liu, and J. Tang.
J. Biol. Chem., **250**, 5082–5088 (1975).
A slightly different and incomplete sequence for porcine pepsin has also been published:
Tentative amino acid sequence of hog pepsin.
L. Morávek and V. Kostka.
FEBS Letters, **35**, 276–278 (1973).

PAPAIN

	1				5					10					15		
1	ILE	PRO	GLU	TYR	VAL	ASP	TRP	ARG	GLN	LYS	GLY	ALA	VAL	THR	PRO	15
16	VAL	LYS	ASN	GLN	GLY	SER	CYS	GLY	SER	CYS	TRP	ALA	PHE	SER	ALA	30
31	VAL	VAL	THR	ILE	GLU	GLY	ILE	ILE	LYS	ILE	ARG	THR	GLY	ASN	LEU	45
46	ASN	GLN	TYR	SER	GLU	GLN	GLU	LEU	LEU	ASP	CYS	ASP	ARG	ARG	SER	60
61	TYR	GLY	CYS	ASN	GLY	GLY	TYR	PRO	TRP	SER	ALA	LEU	GLN	LEU	VAL	75
76	ALA	GLN	TYR	GLY	ILE	HIS	TYR	ARG	ASN	THR	PRO	TYR	TYR	GLU	GLY	90
91	VAL	GLN	ARG	TYR	CYS	ARG	SER	ARG	GLU	LYS	GLY	PRO	TYR	ALA	ALA	105
106	LYS	THR	ASP	GLY	VAL	ARG	GLN	VAL	GLN	PRO	TYR	ASN	GLN	GLY	ALA	120
121	LEU	LEU	TYR	SER	ILE	ALA	ASN	GLN	PRO	VAL	SER	VAL	VAL	LEU	GLN	135
136	ALA	ALA	GLY	LYS	ASP	PHE	GLN	LEU	TYR	ARG	GLY	GLY	ILE	PHE	VAL	150
151	GLY	PRO	CYS	GLY	ASN	LYS	VAL	ASP	HIS	ALA	VAL	ALA	ALA	VAL	GLY	165
166	TYR	ASN	PRO	GLY	TYR	ILE	LEU	ILE	LYS	ASN	SER	TRP	GLY	THR	GLY	180
181	TRP	GLY	GLU	ASN	GLY	TYR	ILE	ARG	ILE	LYS	ARG	GLY	THR	GLY	ASN	195
196	SER	TYR	GLY	VAL	CYS	GLY	LEU	TYR	THR	SER	SER	PHE	TYR	PRO	VAL	210
211	LYS	ASN														225

Note: Disulphide bridges are between residues CYS 22 and 63; CYS 56 and 95; and CYS 153 and 200.

The Complete Amino Acid Sequence of Papain.

R. E. J. Mitchel, I. M. Chaiken, and E. L. Smith.

J. Biol. Chem., **245**, 3485–3492 (1970).

Correction: Residue 64 is ASN, not ASP.

A reinvestigation of residues 64–68 and 175 in papain.

S. S. Husain and G. Lowe.

Biochem. J., **116**, 689–692 (1970).

ENZYMES

SUBTILISIN BPN′

	1				5					10					15	
1	ALA	GLN	SER	VAL	PRO	TYR	GLY	VAL	SER	GLN	ILE	LYS	ALA	PRO	ALA	15
16	LEU	HIS	SER	GLN	GLY	TYR	THR	GLY	SER	ASN	VAL	LYS	VAL	ALA	VAL	30
31	ILE	ASP	SER	GLY	ILE	ASP	SER	SER	HIS	PRO	ASP	LEU	LYS	VAL	ALA	45
46	GLY	GLY	ALA	SER	MET	VAL	PRO	SER	GLU	THR	PRO	ASN	PHE	GLN	ASP	60
61	ASP	ASN	SER	HIS	GLY	THR	HIS	VAL	ALA	GLY	THR	VAL	ALA	ALA	LEU	75
76	ASN	ASN	SER	ILE	GLY	VAL	LEU	GLY	VAL	ALA	PRO	SER	SER	ALA	LEU	90
91	TYR	ALA	VAL	LYS	VAL	LEU	GLY	ASP	ALA	GLY	SER	GLY	GLN	TYR	SER	105
106	TRP	ILE	ILE	ASN	GLY	ILE	GLU	TRP	ALA	ILE	ALA	ASN	ASN	MET	ASP	120
121	VAL	ILE	ASN	MET	SER	LEU	GLY	GLY	PRO	SER	GLY	SER	ALA	ALA	LEU	135
136	LYS	ALA	ALA	VAL	ASP	LYS	ALA	VAL	ALA	SER	GLY	VAL	VAL	VAL	VAL	150
151	ALA	ALA	ALA	GLY	ASN	GLU	GLY	SER	THR	GLY	SER	SER	SER	THR	VAL	165
166	GLY	TYR	PRO	GLY	LYS	TYR	PRO	SER	VAL	ILE	ALA	VAL	GLY	ALA	VAL	180
181	ASP	SER	SER	ASN	GLN	ARG	ALA	SER	PHE	SER	SER	VAL	GLY	PRO	GLU	195
196	LEU	ASP	VAL	MET	ALA	PRO	GLY	VAL	SER	ILE	GLN	SER	THR	LEU	PRO	210
211	GLY	ASN	LYS	TYR	GLY	ALA	TYR	ASN	GLY	THR	SER	MET	ALA	SER	PRO	225
226	HIS	VAL	ALA	GLY	ALA	ALA	ALA	LEU	ILE	LEU	SER	LYS	HIS	PRO	ASN	240
241	TRP	THR	ASN	THR	GLN	VAL	ARG	SER	SER	LEU	GLN	ASN	THR	THR	THR	255
256	LYS	LEU	GLY	ASP	SER	PHE	TYR	TYR	GLY	LYS	GLY	LEU	ILE	ASN	VAL	270
271	GLN	ALA	ALA	ALA	GLN											285

Subtilisin BPN′. 7. Isolation of cyanogen bromide peptides and the complete amino acid sequence.
F. S. Markland and E. L. Smith.
J. Biol. Chem., **242**, 5198–5211 (1967).

SUBTILISIN CARLSBERG

	1				5					10					15	
1	ALA	GLN	THR	VAL	PRO	TYR	GLY	ILE	PRO	LEU	ILE	LYS	ALA	ASP	LYS	15
16	VAL	GLN	ALA	GLN	GLY	PHE	LYS	GLY	ALA	ASN	VAL	LYS	VAL	ALA	VAL	30
31	LEU	ASP	THR	GLY	ILE	GLN	ALA	SER	HIS	PRO	ASP	LEU	ASN	VAL	VAL	45
46	GLY	GLY	ALA	SER	PHE	VAL	ALA	GLY	GLU	ALA	TYR	ASN	THR	ASP	GLY	60
61	ASN	GLY	HIS	GLY	THR	HIS	VAL	ALA	GLY	THR	VAL	ALA	ALA	LEU	ASP	75
76	ASN	THR	THR	GLY	VAL	LEU	GLY	VAL	ALA	PRO	SER	VAL	SER	LEU	TYR	90
91	ALA	VAL	LYS	VAL	LEU	ASN	SER	SER	GLY	SER	GLY	SER	TYR	SER	GLY	105
106	ILE	VAL	SER	GLY	ILE	GLU	TRP	ALA	THR	THR	ASN	GLY	MET	ASP	VAL	120
121	ILE	ASN	MET	SER	LEU	GLY	GLY	ALA	SER	GLY	SER	THR	ALA	MET	LYS	135
136	GLN	ALA	VAL	ASP	ASN	ALA	TYR	ALA	ARG	GLY	VAL	VAL	VAL	VAL	ALA	150
151	ALA	ALA	GLY	ASN	SER	GLY	ASN	SER	GLY	SER	THR	ASN	THR	ILE	GLY	165
166	TYR	PRO	ALA	LYS	TYR	ASP	SER	VAL	ILE	ALA	VAL	GLY	ALA	VAL	ASP	180
181	SER	ASN	SER	ASN	ARG	ALA	SER	PHE	SER	SER	VAL	GLY	ALA	GLU	LEU	195
196	GLU	VAL	MET	ALA	PRO	GLY	ALA	GLY	VAL	TYR	SER	THR	TYR	PRO	THR	210
211	ASN	THR	TYR	ALA	THR	LEU	ASN	GLY	THR	SER	MET	ALA	SER	PRO	HIS	225
226	VAL	ALA	GLY	ALA	ALA	ALA	LEU	ILE	LEU	SER	LYS	HIS	PRO	ASN	LEU	240
241	SER	ALA	SER	GLN	VAL	ARG	ASN	ARG	LEU	SER	SER	THR	ALA	THR	TYR	255
256	LEU	GLY	SER	SER	PHE	TYR	TYR	GLY	LYS	GLY	LEU	ILE	ASN	VAL	GLU	270
271	ALA	ALA	ALA	GLN												285

Subtilisin Carlsberg. The Complete Sequence; Comparison with BPN′, Evolutionary Relationships.
E. L. Smith, R. J. DeLange, W. H. Evans, M. Landon, and F. S. Markland.
J. Biol. Chem., **243**, 2184–2191 (1968).

ENZYMES

SUBTILISIN AMYLOSACCHARITICUS

	1				5					10					15		
1	ALA	GLN	SER	VAL	PRO	TYR	GLY	ILE	SER	GLN	ILE	LYS	ALA	PRO	ALA		15
16	LEU	HIS	SER	GLN	GLY	TYR	THR	GLY	SER	ASN	VAL	LYS	VAL	ALA	VAL		30
31	ILE	ASP	SER	GLY	ILE	ASP	SER	SER	HIS	PRO	ASP	LEU	ASN	VAL	ARG		45
46	GLY	GLY	ALA	SER	PHE	VAL	PRO	SER	GLU	THR	PRO	ASN	TYR	GLN	ASP		60
61	GLY	SER	SER	HIS	GLY	THR	HIS	VAL	ALA	GLY	THR	ILE	ALA	ALA	LEU		75
76	ASN	ASN	SER	ILE	GLY	VAL	LEU	GLY	VAL	ALA	PRO	SER	SER	ALA	LEU		90
91	TYR	ALA	VAL	LYS	VAL	LEU	ASP	SER	THR	GLY	SER	GLY	GLN	TYR	SER		105
106	TRP	ILE	ILE	ASN	GLY	ILE	GLU	TRP	ALA	ILE	SER	ASN	ASN	MET	ASP		120
121	VAL	ILE	ASN	MET	SER	LEU	GLY	GLY	PRO	SER	GLY	SER	THR	ALA	LEU		135
136	LYS	THR	VAL	VAL	ASP	LYS	ALA	VAL	SER	SER	GLY	ILE	VAL	VAL	ALA		150
151	ALA	ALA	ALA	GLY	ASN	GLU	GLY	SER	SER	GLY	SER	SER	SER	THR	VAL		165
166	GLY	TYR	PRO	ALA	LYS	TYR	PRO	SER	THR	ILE	ALA	VAL	GLY	ALA	VAL		180
181	ASN	SER	SER	ASN	GLN	ARG	ALA	SER	PHE	SER	SER	ALA	GLY	SER	GLU		195
196	LEU	ASP	VAL	MET	ALA	PRO	GLY	VAL	SER	ILE	GLN	SER	THR	LEU	PRO		210
211	GLY	GLY	THR	TYR	GLY	ALA	TYR	ASN	GLY	THR	SER	MET	ALA	THR	PRO		225
226	HIS	VAL	ALA	GLY	ALA	ALA	ALA	LEU	ILE	LEU	SER	LYS	HIS	PRO	THR		240
241	TRP	THR	ASN	ALA	GLN	VAL	ARG	ASP	ARG	LEU	GLU	SER	THR	ALA	THR		255
256	TYR	LEU	GLY	ASP	SER	PHE	TYR	TYR	GLY	LYS	GLY	LEU	ILE	ASN	VAL		270
271	GLN	ALA	ALA	ALA	GLN												285

Subtilisin Amylosacchariticus III. Isolation and sequence of the chymotryptic peptides and the complete amino acid sequence.
M. Kurihara, F. S. Markland, and E. L. Smith.
J. Biol. Chem., **247**, 5619–5631 (1972).

PORCINE ELASTASE

	1				5					10					15	
1	VAL	VAL	GLY	GLY	THR	GLU	ALA	GLN	ARG	ASN	SER	TRP	PRO	SER	GLN	15
16	ILE	SER	LEU	GLN	TYR	ARG	SER	GLY	SER	SER	TRP	ALA	HIS	THR	CYS	30
31	GLY	GLY	THR	LEU	ILE	ARG	GLN	ASN	TRP	VAL	MET	THR	ALA	ALA	HIS	45
46	CYS	VAL	ASP	ARG	GLU	LEU	THR	PHE	ARG	VAL	VAL	VAL	GLY	GLU	HIS	60
61	ASN	LEU	ASN	GLN	ASN	ASN	GLY	THR	GLU	GLN	TYR	VAL	GLY	VAL	GLN	75
76	LYS	ILE	VAL	VAL	HIS	PRO	TYR	TRP	ASN	THR	ASP	ASP	VAL	ALA	ALA	90
91	GLY	TYR	ASP	ILE	ALA	LEU	LEU	ARG	LEU	ALA	GLN	SER	VAL	THR	LEU	105
106	ASN	SER	TYR	VAL	GLN	LEU	GLY	VAL	LEU	PRO	ARG	ALA	GLY	THR	ILE	120
121	LEU	ALA	ASN	ASN	SER	PRO	CYS	TYR	ILE	THR	GLY	TRP	GLY	LEU	THR	135
136	ARG	THR	ASN	GLY	GLN	LEU	ALA	GLN	THR	LEU	GLN	GLN	ALA	TYR	LEU	150
151	PRO	THR	VAL	ASP	TYR	ALA	ILE	CYS	SER	SER	SER	SER	TYR	TRP	GLY	165
166	SER	THR	VAL	LYS	ASN	SER	MET	VAL	CYS	ALA	GLY	GLY	ASN	GLY	VAL	180
181	ARG	SER	GLY	CYS	GLN	GLY	ASP	SER	GLY	GLY	PRO	LEU	HIS	CYS	LEU	195
196	VAL	ASN	GLY	GLN	TYR	ALA	VAL	HIS	GLY	VAL	THR	SER	PHE	VAL	SER	210
211	ARG	LEU	GLY	CYS	ASN	VAL	THR	ARG	LYS	PRO	THR	VAL	PHE	THR	ARG	225
226	VAL	SER	ALA	TYR	ILE	SER	TRP	ILE	ASN	ASN	VAL	ILE	ALA	SER	ASN	240

Evidence for the amino acid sequence of porcine pancreatic elastase.
D. M. Shotton and B. S. Hartley.
Biochem. J., **131**, 643–675 (1973).

α-LYTIC PROTEASE

	1				5					10					15	
1	ALA	ASN	ILE	VAL	GLY	GLY	ILE	GLU	TYR	SER	ILE	ASN	ASN	ALA	SER	15
16	LEU	CYS	SER	VAL	GLY	PHE	SER	VAL	THR	ARG	GLY	ALA	THR	LYS	GLY	30
31	PHE	VAL	THR	ALA	GLY	HIS	CYS	GLY	THR	VAL	ASN	ALA	THR	ALA	ARG	45
46	ILE	GLY	GLY	ALA	VAL	VAL	GLY	THR	PHE	ALA	ALA	ARG	VAL	PHE	PRO	60
61	GLY	ASN	ASP	ARG	ALA	TRP	VAL	SER	LEU	THR	SER	ALA	GLN	THR	LEU	75
76	LEU	PRO	ARG	VAL	ALA	ASN	GLY	SER	SER	PHE	VAL	THR	VAL	ARG	GLY	90
91	SER	THR	GLU	ALA	ALA	VAL	GLY	ALA	ALA	VAL	CYS	ARG	SER	GLY	ARG	105
106	THR	THR	GLY	TYR	GLN	CYS	GLY	THR	ILE	THR	ALA	LYS	ASN	VAL	THR	120
121	ALA	ASN	TYR	ALA	GLU	GLY	ALA	VAL	ARG	GLY	LEU	THR	GLN	GLY	ASN	135
136	ALA	CYS	MET	GLY	ARG	GLY	ASP	SER	GLY	GLY	SER	TRP	ILE	THR	SER	150
151	ALA	GLY	GLN	ALA	GLN	GLY	VAL	MET	SER	GLY	GLY	ASN	VAL	GLN	SER	165
166	ASN	GLY	ASN	ASN	CYS	GLY	ILE	PRO	ALA	SER	GLN	ARG	SER	SER	LEU	180
181	PHE	GLU	ARG	LEU	GLN	PRO	ILE	LEU	SER	GLN	TYR	GLY	LEU	SER	LEU	195
196	VAL	THR	GLY													210

Note: Disulphide bridges are between CYS 17 and 37; CYS 101 and 111; CYS 137 and 170. Primary Structure of α-lytic protease: a Bacterial homologue of the pancreatic serine proteases.
M. O. J. Olson, N. Nagabhushan, M. Dzwiniel, L. B. Smillie, and D. R. Whitaker.
Nature, **228**, 438–442 (1970).

ENZYMES

PRETHROMBIN 2 AND α-THROMBIN—HUMAN

```
        1                   5                   10                      15
  1   THR ALA THR SER  GLU TYR GLN THR PHE  PHE ASN PRO ARG THR PHE    15
 16   GLY SER GLY GLU  ALA ASN CYS GLY LEU  ARG PRO LEU PHE GLU LYS    30
 31   LYS SER LEU GLU  ASN LYS THR GLU ARG  GLU LEU LEU GLU SER TYR    45
 46   ILE ASP GLY ARG ILE  VAL GLU GLY SER  ASN ALA GLU ILE  GLY MET   60
 61   SER PRO TRP GLN  VAL MET LEU PHE ARG  LYS SER PRO GLN GLU LEU    75
 76   LEU CYS GLY ALA SER  LEU ILE  SER ASN ARG TRP  VAL LEU THR ALA   90
 91   ALA HIS CYS LEU LEU  TYR PRO PRO TRP  ASN LYS ASN PHE THR GLU   105
106   ASN ASP LEU LEU  VAL ARG ILE  GLY LYS HIS  SER ARG THR ARG TYR  120
121   GLU ARG ASN ILE  GLU LYS ILE  SER MET LEU GLU LYS ILE  TYR ILE  135
136   HIS PRO ARG TYR  ASN TRP ARG GLU ASN  LEU ASP ARG ASP ILE  ALA  150
151   LEU MET LYS LEU LYS  LYS PRO VAL ALA  PHE SER ASP TYR ILE  HIS  165
166   PRO VAL CYS LEU PRO  ASN ARG GLU THR  ALA ALA SER LEU LEU GLY   180
181   ALA GLY TYR LYS  GLY ARG VAL THR GLY  TYR GLY ASN LEU LYS SER   195
196   THR VAL THR ALA ASP  VAL GLY LYS GLY  GLN PRO SER VAL LEU GLN   210
211   VAL VAL ASN LEU ALA  LEU VAL GLN ARG  PRO VAL CYS LYS ASP SER   225
226   THR ARG ILE  ARG ILE  THR ASP ASN MET PHE CYS ALA GLY TYR LYS   240
241   PRO ASP GLU GLY LYS  ARG GLY ASP ALA  CYS GLU GLY ASP SER GLY   255
256   GLY PRO PHE VAL MET  LYS SER PRO PHE  ASN ASN ARG TRP TYR GLN   270
271   MET GLY ILE  VAL SER TRP GLY GLU GLY  CYS ASP ARG ASP GLY LYS   285
286   TYR GLY PHE TYR THR HIS  VAL PHE ARG  LEU LYS LYS TRP ILE  GLN  300
301   LYS VAL ILE  ASP GLN PHE GLY GLU                                315
```

Note: α-Thrombin is a two-chain molecule generated from prethrombin 2 by Factor Xa cleavage of an ARG–ILE bond (residues 49–50). The action of thrombin on human prethrombin 2 gives rise to a molecule of prethrombin $2_{(des\ 1–13)}$.
Primary Structure of Human Prethrombin 2 and α-Thrombin.
R. J. Butkowski, J. Elion, M. R. Downing, and K. G. Mann.
J. Biol. Chem., **252**, 4942–4957 (1977).

ENZYMES

STREPTOCOCCAL PROTEINASE

	1				5					10					15		
1	GLN	PRO	VAL	VAL	LYS	SER	LEU	LEU	ASP	SER	LYS	GLY	ILE	HIS	TYR	15
16	ASN	GLN	GLY	ASN	PRO	TYR	ASN	LEU	LEU	THR	PRO	VAL	ILE	GLU	LYS	30
31	VAL	LYS	PRO	GLY	GLU	GLN	SER	PHE	VAL	GLY	GLN	ALA	ALA	THR	GLY	45
46	HIS	CYS	VAL	ALA	THR	ALA	THR	ALA	GLN	ILE	MET	LYS	TYR	HIS	ASN	60
61	TYR	PRO	ASP	LYS	GLY	LEU	LYS	ASN	TYR	THR	TYR	THR	LEU	SER	SER	75
76	ASN	PRO	ASP	TYR	PHE	ASP	HIS	PRO	LYS	ASN	LEU	PHE	ALA	ALA	ILE	90
91	SER	THR	ARG	GLN	TYR	ASP	TRP	ASN	ASN	ILE	LEU	PRO	THR	TYR	SER	105
106	GLY	ARG	GLN	SER	GLN	ASN	VAL	LYS	MET	ALA	ILE	SER	GLU	LEU	MET	120
121	ALA	ASP	VAL	GLY	ILE	SER	VAL	ASP	MET	ASP	TYR	GLY	PRO	SER	SER	135
136	GLY	SER	ALA	GLY	SER	SER	ARG	VAL	GLN	ARG	ALA	LEU	LYS	GLU	ASN	150
151	PHE	GLY	TYR	ASN	GLN	SER	VAL	HIS	GLN	ILE	ASP	ARG	GLY	ASP	PHE	165
166	SER	LYS	GLN	ASP	TRP	GLU	ALA	GLN	ILE	ASP	LYS	GLU	LEU	SER	GLN	180
181	ASN	GLN	PRO	VAL	TYR	TYR	GLU	GLY	VAL	GLY	LYS	VAL	GLY	GLY	HIS	195
196	ALA	PHE	VAL	ILE	ASP	ASP	GLY	ALA	GLY	ARG	ASN	PHE	TYR	HIS	VAL	210
211	ASP	TRP	GLY	TRP	GLY	GLY	VAL	SER	ASP	GLY	PHE	PHE	ARG	LEU	ASP	225
226	ALA	LEU	ASN	PRO	SER	ALA	LEU	GLY	THR	GLY	GLY	GLY	ALA	GLY	GLY	240
241	PHE	ASN	GLY	TYR	GLU	SER	ALA	VAL	VAL	GLY	ILE	LYS	PRO			255

Primary structure of streptococcal proteinase. III. Isolation of cyanogen bromide peptides: complete structure of the polypeptide chain.
J. Y. Tai, A. A. Kortt, T.-Y. Liu, and S. D. Elliott.
J. Biol. Chem., **251**, 1955–1959 (1976).

ENZYMES

PROTEASE A FROM STREPTOMYCES GRISEUS

```
         1              5                    10                    15
  1  ILE ALA GLY GLY GLU ALA ILE  THR THR GLY GLY SER ARG CYS SER   15
 16  LEU GLY PHE ASN VAL SER VAL ASN GLY VAL ALA HIS ALA LEU THR     30
 31  ALA GLY HIS CYS THR SER ASN ILE  SER ALA SER TRP SER ILE  GLY   45
 46  THR ARG THR GLY THR SER PHE PRO ASN ASN ASP TYR GLY ILE  ILE   60
 61  ARG HIS SER ASN PRO ALA ALA ALA ASN GLY ARG VAL TYR LEU TYR    75
 76  ASN GLY SER TYR GLN ASP ILE  THR THR ALA GLY ASN ALA PHE VAL   90
 91  GLY GLN ALA VAL GLN ARG SER GLY SER THR THR GLY LEU ARG SER   105
106  GLY SER VAL THR GLY LEU ASN ALA THR VAL ASN TYR GLY SER SER   120
121  GLY ILE  VAL TYR GLY MET ILE  GLN THR ASN VAL CYS ALA GLN PRO 135
136  GLY ASP SER GLY GLY SER LEU PHE ALA GLY SER THR ALA LEU GLY   150
151  LEU THR SER GLY GLY SER GLY ASN CYS ARG THR GLY GLY THR THR   165
166  PHE TYR GLN PRO VAL THR GLU ALA LEU SER ALA TYR GLY ALA THR   180
181  VAL LEU                                                        195
```

Note: Disulphide bridges are between residues CYS 14 and 34; CYS 132 and 159.
The amino acid sequence and predicted structure of *Streptomyces griseus* protease A.
P. Johnson and L. B. Smillie.
FEBS Letters, **47**, 1–6 (1974).

PROTEASE B FROM STREPTOMYCES GRISEUS

```
         1              5                    10                    15
  1  ILE SER GLY GLY ASP ALA ILE  TYR SER SER THR GLY ARG CYS SER   15
 16  LEU GLY PHE ASN VAL ARG SER GLY SER THR TYR TYR PHE LEU THR     30
 31  ALA GLY HIS CYS THR ASP GLY ALA THR GLY(THR, TRP) ALA ASN SER   45
 46  ALA ARG THR THR VAL LEU GLY THR THR SER GLY SER SER PHE PRO     60
 61  ASN ASN ASP TYR GLY ILE  VAL ARG TYR THR ASN THR THR ILE  PRO  75
 76  LYS ASP GLY THR VAL GLY GLY GLN ASP ILE  THR SER ALA ALA ASX   90
 91  ALA THR VAL GLY MET ALA VAL THR ARG ARG GLY SER THR THR GLY   105
106  THR HIS (SER, GLY, SER) VAL THR ALA LEU ASN ALA THR VAL ASN TYR 120
121  (GLY GLY GLY ASP VAL TYR) GLY MET ILE  ARG THR ASN VAL CYS ALA 135
136  GLU PRO GLY ASP SER GLY GLY PRO LEU TYR SER GLY THR ARG ALA   150
151  ILE  GLY LEU THR SER GLY GLY SER GLY(ASN, CYS) SER SER GLY GLY 165
166  THR THR (PHE, PHE, GLN, PRO, VAL, THR) GLU ALA LEU SER (VAL, TYR, GLY) 180
181  ALA SER VAL TYR                                                195
```

Note: Disulphide bridges are between residues CYS 14 and 34; CYS 134 and 161.
Amino acid sequence of *Streptomyces griseus* protease B, a major component of pronase.
L. Jurášek, M. R. Carpenter, L. B. Smillie, A. Gertler, S. Levy, and L. H. Ericsson.
Biochem. Biophys. Res. Commun., **61**, 1095–1100 (1974).

CARBOXYPEPTIDASE A

	1				5					10					15		
1	ALA	ARG	SER	THR	ASN	THR	PHE	ASN	TYR	ALA	THR	TYR	HIS	THR	LEU	15
16	ASP	GLU	ILE	TYR	ASP	PHE	MET	ASP	LEU	LEU	VAL	ALA	GLN	HIS	PRO	30
31	GLU	LEU	VAL	SER	LYS	LEU	GLN	ILE	GLY	ARG	SER	TYR	GLU	GLY	ARG	45
46	PRO	ILE	TYR	VAL	LEU	LYS	PHE	SER	THR	GLY	GLY	SER	ASN	ARG	PRO	60
61	ALA	ILE	TRP	ILE	ASP	LEU	GLY	ILE	HIS	SER	ARG	GLU	TRP	ILE	THR	75
76	GLN	ALA	THR	GLY	VAL	TRP	PHE	ALA	LYS	LYS	PHE	THR	GLU	ASN	TYR	90
91	GLY	GLN	ASN	PRO	SER	PHE	THR	ALA	ILE	LEU	ASP	SER	MET	ASP	ILE	105
106	PHE	LEU	GLU	ILE	VAL	THR	ASN	PRO	ASN	GLY	PHE	ALA	PHE	THR	HIS	120
121	SER	GLU	ASN	ARG	LEU	TRP	ARG	LYS	THR	ARG	SER	VAL	THR	SER	SER	135
136	SER	LEU	CYS	VAL	GLY	VAL	ASP	ALA	ASN	ARG	ASN	TRP	ASP	ALA	GLY	150
151	PHE	GLY	LYS	ALA	GLY	ALA	SER	SER	SER	PRO	CYS	SER	GLU	THR	TYR	165

166	HIS	GLY	LYS	TYR	ALA	ASN	SER	GLU	VAL	GLU	VAL	LYS	SER	ILE/VAL	VAL	180

181	ASP	PHE	VAL	LYS	ASN	HIS	GLY	ASN	PHE	LYS	ALA	PHE	LEU	SER	ILE	195
196	HIS	SER	TYR	SER	GLN	LEU	LEU	LEU	TYR	PRO	TYR	GLY	TYR	THR	THR	210
211	GLN	SER	ILE	PRO	ASP	LYS	THR	GLU	LEU	ASN	GLN	VAL	ALA	LYS	SER	225

226	ALA	VAL	ALA/GLU	ALA	LEU	LYS	SER	LEU	TYR	GLY	THR	SER	TYR	LYS	TYR	240

241	GLY	SER	ILE	ILE	THR	THR	ILE	TYR	GLN	ALA	SER	GLY	GLY	SER	ILE	255
256	ASP	TRP	SER	TYR	ASN	GLN	GLY	ILE	LYS	TYR	SER	PHE	THR	PHE	GLU	270
271	LEU	ARG	ASP	THR	GLY	ARG	TYR	GLY	PHE	LEU	LEU	PRO	ALA	SER	GLN	285
286	ILE	ILE	PRO	THR	ALA	GLN	GLU	THR	TRP	LEU	GLY	VAL	LEU	THR	ILE	300

301	MET	GLU	HIS	THR	VAL/LEU	ASN	ASN									315

Note: This is the alpha form.
The Amino Acid Sequence of Bovine Carboxypeptidase A.
R. A. Bradshaw, L. H. Ericsson, K. A. Walsh, and H. Neurath.
Proc. Natn. Acad. Sci. U.S.A., **63**, 1389–1394 (1969).

ENZYMES

BOVINE CARBOXYPEPTIDASE B

	1				5					10					15	
1	THR	THR	GLY	HIS	SER	TYR	GLU	LYS	TYR	ASN	ASN	TRP	GLU	THR	ILE	15
16	GLU	ALA	TRP	THR	GLU	GLN	VAL	ALA	SER	GLU	ASN	PRO	ASP	LEU	ILE	30
31	SER	ARG	SER	ALA	ILE	GLY	THR	THR	PHE	LEU	GLY	ASN	THR	ILE	TYR	45
46	LEU	LEU	LYS	VAL	GLY	LYS	PRO	GLY	SER	ASN	LYS	PRO	ALA	VAL	PHE	60
61	MET	ASP	CYS	GLY	PHE	HIS	ALA	ARG	GLU	TRP	ILE	SER	PRO	ALA	PHE	75
76	CYS	GLN	TRP	PHE	VAL	ARG	GLU	ALA	VAL	ARG	THR	TYR	GLY	ARG	GLU	90
91	ILE	HIS	MET	THR	GLU	PHE	LEU	ASP	LYS	LEU	ASP	PHE	TYR	VAL	LEU	105
106	PRO	VAL	VAL	ASN	ILE	ASP	GLY	TYR	ILE	TYR	THR	TRP	THR	THR	ASN	120
121	ARG	MET	TRP	ARG	LYS	THR	ARG	SER	THR	ARG	ALA	GLY	SER	SER	CYS	135
136	THR	GLY	THR	ASP	LEU	ASN	ARG	ASN	PHE	ASP	ALA	GLY	TRP	CYS	SER	150
151	ILE	GLY	ALA	SER	ASN	ASN	PRO	CYS	SER	GLU	THR	TYR	CYS	GLY	SER	165
166	ALA	ALA	GLU	SER	GLU	LYS	GLU	SER	LYS	ALA	VAL	ALA	ASP	PHE	ILE	180
181	ARG	ASN	HIS	LEU	SER	SER	ILE	LYS	ALA	TYR	LEU	THR	ILE	HIS	SER	195
196	TYR	SER	GLN	MET	MET	LEU	TYR	PRO	TYR	SER	TYR	ASP	TYR	LYS	LEU	210
211	PRO	LYS	ASN	ASN	VAL	GLU	LEU	ASN	THR	LEU	ALA	LYS	GLY	ALA	VAL	225
226	LYS	LYS	LEU	ALA	SER	LEU	HIS	GLY	THR	THR	TYR	SER	TYR	GLY	PRO	240
241	GLY	ALA	THR	THR	ILE	TYR	PRO	ALA	SER	GLY	GLY	SER	ASP	ASP	TRP	255
256	ALA	TYR	ASP	GLN	GLY	ILE	LYS	TYR	SER	PHE	THR	PHE	GLU	LEU	ARG	270
271	ASP	LYS	GLY	ARG	TYR	GLY	PHE	VAL	LEU	PRO	GLU	SER	GLN	ILE	GLN	285
286	PRO	THR	CYS	GLU	GLU	THR	MET	LEU	ALA	ILE	LYS	TYR	VAL	THR	SER	300
301	TYR	VAL	LEU	GLU	HIS	LEU										315

Note: Disulphide bridges have been placed between residues CYS 63 and 76; CYS 135 and 158; CYS 149 and 163.
Amino acid sequence of bovine carboxypeptidase B.
K. Titani, L. H. Ericsson, K. A. Walsh and H. Neurath.
Proc. Natn. Acad. Sci. U.S.A., **72**, 1666–1670 (1975).

DNA-DEPENDENT RNA POLYMERASE (α-SUBUNIT)—E. COLI

	1				5					10					15	
1	MET	GLN	GLY	SER	VAL	THR	GLU	PHE	LEU	LYS	PRO	ARG	LEU	VAL	ASP	15
16	ILE	GLU	GLN	VAL	SER	SER	THR	HIS	ALA	LYS	VAL	THR	LEU	GLU	PRO	30
31	LEU	GLU	ARG	GLY	PHE	GLY	HIS	THR	LEU	GLY	ASN	ALA	LEU	ARG	ARG	45
46	ILE	LEU	LEU	SER	SER	MET	PRO	GLY	CYS	ALA	VAL	THR	GLU	VAL	GLU	60
61	ILE	ASP	GLY	VAL	LEU	HIS	GLU	TYR	SER	THR	LYS	GLU	GLY	VAL	GLN	75
76	GLU	ASP	ILE	LEU	GLU	ILE	LEU	LEU	ASN	LEU	LYS	GLY	LEU	ALA	VAL	90
91	ARG	VAL	GLN	GLY	LYS	ASP	GLU	VAL	ILE	LEU	THR	LEU	ASN	LYS	SER	105
106	GLY	ILE	GLY	PRO	VAL	THR	ALA	ALA	ASP	ILE	THR	HIS	ASP	GLY	ASP	120
121	VAL	GLU	ILE	VAL	LYS	PRO	GLN	HIS	VAL	ILE	CYS	HIS	LEU	THR	ASP	135
136	GLU	ASN	ALA	SER	ILE	SER	MET	ARG	ILE	LYS	VAL	GLN	ARG	GLY	ARG	150
151	GLY	TYR	VAL	PRO	ALA	SER	THR	ARG	ILE	HIS	SER	GLU	GLU	ASP	GLU	165
166	ARG	PRO	ILE	GLY	ARG	LEU	LEU	VAL	ASP	ALA	CYS	TYR	SER	PRO	VAL	180
181	GLU	ARG	ILE	ALA	TYR	ASN	VAL	GLU	ALA	ALA	ARG	VAL	GLU	GLN	ARG	195
196	THR	ASP	LEU	ASP	LYS	LEU	VAL	ILE	GLU	MET	GLU	THR	ASN	GLY	THR	210
211	ILE	ASP	PRO	GLU	GLU	ALA	ILE	ARG	ARG	ALA	ALA	THR	ILE	LEU	ALA	225
226	GLU	GLN	LEU	GLU	ALA	PHE	VAL	ASP	LEU	ARG	ASP	VAL	ARG	GLN	PRO	240
241	GLU	VAL	LYS	GLU	GLU	LYS	PRO	GLU	PHE	ASP	PRO	ILE	LEU	LEU	ARG	255
256	PRO	VAL	ASP	ASP	LEU	GLU	LEU	THR	VAL	ARG	SER	ALA	ASN	CYS	LEU	270
271	LYS	ALA	GLU	ALA	ILE	HIS	TYR	ILE	GLY	ASP	LEU	VAL	GLN	ARG	THR	285
286	GLU	VAL	GLU	LEU	LEU	LYS	THR	PRO	ASN	LEU	GLY	LYS	LYS	SER	LEU	300
301	THR	GLU	ILE	LYS	ASP	VAL	LEU	ALA	SER	ARG	GLY	LEU	SER	LEU	GLY	315
316	MET	ARG	LEU	GLU	ASN	TRP	PRO	PRO	ALA	SER	ILE	ALA	ASP	GLU		330

Primary structure of α-subunit of DNA-dependent RNA polymerase from *Escherichia coli*. Yu. A. Ovchinnikov, V. M. Lipkin, N. N. Modyanov, O. Yu. Chertov, and Yu. V. Smirnov. *FEBS Letters*, **76**, 108–111 (1977).

ENZYMES

RHODANESE—BOVINE LIVER

	1				5					10					15	
1	VAL	HIS	GLN	VAL	LEU	TYR	ARG	ALA	LEU	VAL	SER	THR	LYS	TRP	LEU	15
16	ALA	GLU	SER	VAL	ARG	ALA	GLY	LYS	VAL	GLY	PRO	GLY	LEU	ARG	VAL	30
31	LEU	ASP	ALA	SER	TRP	TYR	SER	PRO	GLY	THR	ARG	GLU	ALA	ARG	LYS	45
46	GLU	TYR	LEU	GLU	ARG	HIS	VAL	PRO	GLY	ALA	SER	PHE	PHE	ASP	ILE	60
61	GLU	GLU	CYS	ARG	ASP	LYS	ALA	SER	PRO	TYR	GLU	VAL	MET	LEU	PRO	75
76	SER	GLU	ALA	GLY	PHE	ALA	ASP	TYR	VAL	GLY	SER	LEU	GLY	ILE	SER	90
91	ASN	ASP	THR	HIS	VAL	VAL	VAL	TYR	ASN	GLY	ASP	ASP	LEU	GLY	SER	105
106	PHE	TYR	ALA	PRO	ARG	VAL	TRP	TRP	MET	PHE	ARG	VAL	PHE	GLY	HIS	120
121	ARG	THR	VAL	SER	VAL	LEU	ASN	GLY	GLY	PHE	ARG	ASN	TRP	LEU	LYS	135
136	GLU	GLY	HIS	PRO	VAL	THR	SER	GLU	PRO	SER	ARG	PRO	GLU	PRO	ALA	150
151	ILE	PHE	LYS	ALA	THR	LEU	ASN	ARG	SER	LEU	LEU	LYS	THR	TYR	GLU	165
166	GLN	VAL	LEU	GLU	ASN	LEU	GLU	SER	LYS	ARG	PHE	GLN	LEU	VAL	ASP	180
181	SER	ARG	ALA	GLN	GLY	ARG	TYR	LEU	GLY	THR	GLN	PRO	GLU	PRO	ASP	195
196	ALA	VAL	GLY	LEU	ASP	SER	GLY	HIS	ILE	ARG	GLY	SER	VAL	ASN	MET	210
211	PRO	PHE	MET	ASP	PHE	LEU	THR	GLU	ASN	GLY	PHE	GLU	LYS	SER	PRO	225
226	GLU	GLU	LEU	ARG	ALA	MET	PHE	GLU	ALA	LYS	LYS	VAL	ASP	LEU	THR	240
241	LYS	PRO	LEU	ILE	ALA	THR	CYS	ARG	LYS	GLY	VAL	THR	ALA	CYS	HIS	255
256	ILE	ALA	LEU	ALA	ALA	TYR	LEU	CYS	GLY	LYS	PRO	ASP	VAL	ALA	ILE	270
271	TYR	ASP	GLY	SER	TRP	PHE	GLU	TRP	PHE	HIS	ARG	ALA	PRO	PRO	GLU	285
286	THR	TRP	VAL	SER	GLN	GLY	LYS	GLY								300

The Covalent Structure of Bovine Liver Rhodanese.
J. Russell, L. Weng, P. S. Keim, and R. L. Heinrikson.
J. Biol. Chem., **253**, 8102–8108 (1978).

BOVINE RIBONUCLEASE

	1			5					10				15			
1	LYS	GLU	THR	ALA	ALA	ALA	LYS	PHE	GLU	ARG	GLN	HIS	MET	ASP	SER	15
16	SER	THR	SER	ALA	ALA	SER	SER	SER	ASN	TYR	CYS	ASN	GLN	MET	MET	30
31	LYS	SER	ARG	ASN	LEU	THR	LYS	ASP	ARG	CYS	LYS	PRO	VAL	ASN	THR	45
46	PHE	VAL	HIS	GLU	SER	LEU	ALA	ASP	VAL	GLN	ALA	VAL	CYS	SER	GLN	60
61	LYS	ASN	VAL	ALA	CYS	LYS	ASN	GLY	GLN	THR	ASN	CYS	TYR	GLN	SER	75
76	TYR	SER	THR	MET	SER	ILE	THR	ASP	CYS	ARG	GLU	THR	GLY	SER	SER	90
91	LYS	TYR	PRO	ASN	CYS	ALA	TYR	LYS	THR	THR	GLN	ALA	ASN	LYS	HIS	105
106	ILE	ILE	VAL	ALA	CYS	GLU	GLY	ASN	PRO	TYR	VAL	PRO	VAL	HIS	PHE	120
121	ASP	ALA	SER	VAL												135

Sequence of the Amino Acid Residues in Bovine Pancreatic Ribonuclease: Revisions and Confirmations.
D. G. Smyth, W. H. Stein, and S. Moore.
J. Biol. Chem., **238**, 227–234 (1963).
Note: Disulphide bonds are between CYS 26 and 84; CYS 40 and 95; CYS 58 and 110; CYS 65 and 72.

PORCINE RIBONUCLEASE

	1			5					10				15			
1	LYS	GLU	SER	PRO	ALA	LYS	LYS	PHE	GLN	ARG	GLN	HIS	MET	ASP	PRO	15
16	ASP	SER	SER	SER	SER	ASN	SER	SER	ASN	TYR	CYS	ASN	LEU	MET	MET	30
31	SER	ARG	ARG	ASN	MET	THR	GLN	GLY	ARG	CYS	LYS	PRO	VAL	ASN	THR	45
46	PHE	VAL	HIS	GLU	SER	LEU	ALA	ASP	VAL	GLN	ALA	VAL	CYS	SER	GLN	60
61	ILE	ASN	VAL	ASN	CYS	LYS	ASN	GLY	GLN	THR	ASN	CYS	TYR	GLN	SER	75
76	ASN	SER	THR	MET	HIS	ILE	THR	ASP	CYS	ARG	GLN	THR	GLY	SER	SER	90
91	LYS	TYR	PRO	ASN	CYS	ALA	TYR	LYS	THR	THR	GLN	ALA	ASN	LYS	HIS	105
106	ILE	ILE	VAL	ALA	CYS	GLU	GLY	ASN	PRO	PRO	VAL	PRO	VAL	HIS	PHE	120
121	ASP	ALA	SER	VAL												120

The Primary Structure of Porcine Pancreatic Ribonuclease. 2. The Amino Acid Sequence of the reduced S-aminoethylated protein.
R. L. Jackson and C. H. W. Hirs.
J. Biol. Chem., **245**, 637–653 (1970).
And
Affinity chromatography of porcine pancreatic ribonuclease and reinvestigation of the N-terminal amino acid sequence.
R. K. Wierenga, J. D. Huizinga, W. Gaastra, G. W. Welling, and J. J. Beintema.
FEBS Letters, **31**, 181–185 (1973).

ENZYMES

HORSE RIBONUCLEASE

	1				5					10					15		
1	LYS	GLU	SER	PRO	ALA	MET	LYS	PHE	GLU	ARG	GLN	HIS	MET	ASP	SER	15
16	GLY	SER	THR	SER	SER	ASN	PRO	THR	ASN	TYR	CYS	ASN	GLN	MET	MET	30
31	LYS	ARG	ARG	ASN	MET	THR	GLN	GLY	CYS	LYS	PRO	VAL	ASN	THR	PHE	45
46	VAL	HIS	GLU	PRO	LEU	ALA	ASP	VAL	GLN	ALA	ILE	CYS	LEU	GLN	LYS	60
61	ASN	ILE	THR	CYS	LYS	ASN	GLY	GLN	SER	ASN	CYS	TYR	GLN	SER	SER	75
76	SER	SER	MET	HIS	ILE	THR	ASP	CYS	ARG	LEU	THR	SER	GLY	SER	LYS	90
91	TYR	PRO	ASN	CYS	ALA	TYR	GLN	THR	SER	GLN	LYS	GLU	ARG	HIS	ILE	105
106	ILE	VAL	ALA	CYS	GLU	GLY	ASN	PRO	TYR	VAL	PRO	VAL	HIS	PHE	ASP	120
121	ALA	SER	VAL	GLN	THR											135

Horse pancreatic ribonuclease.
A. J. Scheffer and J. J. Beintema.
Eur. J. Biochem., **46**, 221–233 (1974).

OVINE RIBONUCLEASE

	1				5					10					15		
1	LYS	GLU	SER	ALA	ALA	ALA	LYS	PHE	GLU	ARG	GLN	HIS	MET	ASP	SER	15
16	SER	THR	SER	SER	ALA	SER	SER	SER	ASN	TYR	CYS	ASN	GLN	MET	MET	30
31	LYS	SER	ARG	ASN	LEU	THR	GLN	ASP	ARG	CYS	LYS	PRO	VAL	ASN	THR	45
46	PHE	VAL	HIS	GLN	SER	LEU	ALA	ASP	VAL	GLN	ALA	VAL	CYS	SER	GLN	60
61	LYS	ASN	VAL	ALA	CYS	LYS	ASN	GLY	GLN	THR	ASN	CYS	TYR	GLN	SER	75
76	TYR	SER	THR	MET	SER	ILE	THR	ASP	CYS	ARG	GLU	THR	GLY	GLY SER	SER	90
91	LYS	TYR	PRO	ASN	CYS	ALA	TYR	LYS	THR	THR	GLN	ALA	GLN	LYS	HIS	105
106	ILE	ILE	VAL	ALA	CYS	GLU	GLY	ASN	PRO	TYR	VAL	PRO	VAL	HIS	PHE	120
121	ASP	ALA	SER	VAL												135

The amino acid sequence of ovine pancreatic ribonuclease A.
R. Kobayashi, C. H. W. Hirs, and M. Hagenhuber.
J. Biol. Chem., **248**, 7833–7837 (1973).
And
The primary structure of goat and sheep pancreatic ribonucleases.
G. W. Welling, A. J. Scheffer, and J. J. Beintema.
FEBS Letters, **41**, 58–61 (1974).
Note: This paper confirms the above sequence except for residue 103, which was found to be GLU, and that at position 89 only SER was indicated.

GOAT RIBONUCLEASE

	1				5					10					15		
1	LYS	GLU	SER	ALA	ALA	ALA	LYS	PHE	GLU	ARG	GLN	HIS	MET	ASP	SER		15
16	SER	THR	SER	SER	ALA	SER	SER	SER	ASN	TYR	CYS	ASX	GLX	MET	MET		30
31	LYS	SER	ARG	ASN	LEU	THR	GLN	ASP	ARG	CYS	LYS	PRO	VAL	ASN	THR		45
46	PHE	VAL	HIS	GLU	SER	LEU	ALA	ASP	VAL	GLX	ALA	VAL	CYS	SER	GLX		60
61	LYS	ASN	VAL	ALA	CYS	LYS	ASN	GLY	GLX	THR	ASX	CYS	TYR	GLN	SER		75
76	TYR	SER	THR	MET	SER	ILE	THR	ASX	CYS	ARG	GLX	THR	GLY	SER	SER		90
91	LYS	TYR	PRO	ASN	CYS	ALA	TYR	LYS	THR	THR	GLN	ALA	GLU	LYS	HIS		105
106	ILE	ILE	VAL	ALA	CYS	GLX	GLY	ASX	PRO	TYR	VAL	PRO	VAL	HIS	PHE		120
121	ASP	ALA	SER	VAL													135

The primary structure of goat and sheep pancreatic ribonucleases.
G. W. Welling, A. J. Scheffer, and J. J. Beintema.
FEBS Letters, **41**, 58–61 (1974).

RAT RIBONUCLEASE

	1				5					10					15		
1	GLY	GLU	SER	ARG	GLU	SER	SER	ALA	ASP	LYS	PHE	LYS	ARG	GLN	HIS		15
16	MET	ASP	THR	GLU	GLY	PRO	SER	LYS	SER	SER	PRO	THR	TYR	CYS	ASN		30
31	GLN	MET	MET	LYS	ARG	GLN	GLY	MET	THR	LYS	GLY	SER	CYS	LYS	PRO		45
46	VAL	ASN	THR	PHE	VAL	HIS	GLU	PRO	LEU	GLU	ASP	VAL	GLN	ALA	ILE		60
61	CYS	SER	GLN	GLY	GLN	VAL	THR	CYS	LYS	ASN	GLY	ARG	ASP	ASN	CYS		75
76	HIS	LYS	SER	SER	SER	THR	LEU	ARG	ILE	THR	ASP	CYS	ARG	LEU	LYS		90
91	GLY	SER	SER	LYS	TYR	PRO	ASN	CYS	THR	TYR	ASN	THR	THR	ASN	SER		105
106	GLU	LYS	HIS	ILE	ILE	ILE	ALA	CYS	ASP	GLY	ASN	PRO	TYR	VAL	PRO		120
121	VAL	HIS	PHE	ASP	ALA	SER	VAL										135

Amino acid sequence in rat pancreatic ribonuclease.
J. J. Beintema and M. Gruber.
Biochim. Biophys. Acta, **147**, 612–614 (1967).
And
Rat pancreatic ribonuclease. II. Amino acid sequence.
J. J. Beintema and M. Gruber.
Biochim. Biophys. Acta, **310**, 161–173 (1973).

ENZYMES

MUSKRAT RIBONUCLEASE

	1			5						10					15		
1	LYS	GLU	THR	SER	ALA	GLN	LYS	PHE	GLU	ARG	GLN	HIS	MET	ASP	SER		15
16	THR	GLY	SER	SER	SER	SER	SER	(PRO,	THR,	TYR)	CYS	ASN	GLN	MET	MET		30
31	LYS	ARG	ARG	GLU	MET	THR	GLN	GLY	TYR	CYS	LYS	PRO	VAL	ASN	THR		45
46	PHE	VAL	HIS	GLU	PRO	LEU	ALA	ASP	VAL	GLN	ALA	VAL	CYS	SER	GLN		60
61	GLU	ASN	VAL	THR	CYS	LYS	ASN	GLY	ASN	SER	ASN	CYS	TYR	LYS	SER		75
76	ARG	SER	ALA	LEU	HIS	ILE	THR	ASP	CYS	ARG	LEU	LYS	GLY	ASN	SER		90
91	LYS	TYR	PRO	ASN	CYS	ASP	TYR	GLN	(THR,	SER,	GLN,	LEU)	GLN	LYS	GLN		105
106	VAL	ILE	VAL	ALA	CYS	GLU	GLY	SER	PRO	PHE	VAL	PRO	VAL	HIS	PHE		120
121	ASP	ALA	SER	VAL													135

The primary structure of muskrat pancreatic ribonuclease.
H. van Dijk, B. Sloots, A. van den Berg, W. Gaastra, and J. J. Beintema.
Int. J. Peptide Protein Res., **8**, 305–316 (1976).

CHINCHILLA RIBONUCLEASE

	1			5						10					15		
1	LYS	GLU	SER	SER	ALA	MET	LYS	PHE	GLN	ARG	GLN	HIS	MET	ASP	SER		15
16	SER	GLY	SER	PRO	SER	THR	ASN	ALA	ASN	TYR	CYS	ASN	GLU	MET	MET		30
31	LYS	GLY/ASP	ARG	ASN	MET	THR	GLN	GLY	TYR	CYS	LYS	PRO	VAL	ASN	THR		45
46	PHE	VAL	HIS	GLU	PRO	LEU	ALA	ASP	VAL	GLN	ALA	VAL	CYS	PHE	GLN		60
61	LYS	ASN	VAL	PRO	CYS	LYS	ASN	GLY	GLN	SER	ASN	CYS	TYR	GLN	SER		75
76	ASN	SER	ASN	MET	HIS	ILE	THR	ASP	CYS	ARG	LEU	THR	SER	ASN	SER		90
91	LYS	TYR	PRO	ASN	CYS	SER	TYR	ARG	THR	SER	ARG	GLU	ASN	LYS	GLY		105
106	ILE	ILE	VAL	ALA	CYS	GLU	GLY	ASN	PRO	TYR	VAL	PRO	VAL	HIS	PHE		120
121	ASP	ALA	SER	VAL													135

GUINEA PIG RIBONUCLEASE A

	1			5						10					15		
1	ALA	GLU	SER	SER	ALA	MET	LYS	PHE	GLU	ARG	GLN	HIS	VAL	ASP	SER		15
16	GLY	GLY	SER	SER	SER	SER	ASN	ALA	ASN	TYR	CYS	ASN	GLU	MET	MET		30
31	LYS	LYS	ARG	GLU	MET	THR	LYS	ASP	ARG	CYS	LYS	PRO	VAL	ASN	THR		45
46	PHE	VAL	HIS	GLU	PRO	LEU	ALA	GLU	VAL	GLN	ALA	VAL	CYS	SER	GLN		60
61	ARG	ASN	VAL	SER	CYS	LYS	ASN	GLY	GLN	THR	ASN	CYS	TYR	GLN	SER		75
76	TYR	SER	SER	MET	HIS	ILE	THR	GLU	CYS	ARG	LEU	THR	SER	GLY	SER		90
91	LYS	PHE	PRO	ASN	CYS	SER	TYR	ARG	THR	SER	GLN	ALA	GLN	LYS	SER		105
106	ILE	ILE	VAL	ALA	CYS	GLU	GLY	LYS	PRO	TYR	VAL	PRO	VAL	HIS	PHE		120
121	ASP	ASN	SER	VAL													135

GUINEA PIG RIBONUCLEASE B

	1	5				10					15				
1	ALA	GLU	SER	SER	ALA	MET	LYS	PHE	GLN	ARG	GLN	HIS	MET	ASP	PRO	15
16	GLU	GLY	SER	PRO	SER	ASN	SER	SER	ASN	TYR	CYS	ASN	VAL	MET	MET	30
31	ILE	ARG	ARG	ASN	MET	THR	GLN	GLY	ARG	CYS	LYS	PRO	VAL	ASN	THR	45
46	PHE	VAL	HIS	GLU	SER	LEU	ALA	ASP	VAL	GLN	ALA	VAL	CYS	PHE	GLN	60
61	LYS	ASN	VAL	PRO LEU	CYS	LYS	ASN	GLY	GLN	THR	ASN	CYS	TYR	GLN	SER	75
76	TYR	SER	ARG	MET	ARG	ILE	THR	ASP	CYS	ARG	VAL	THR	SER	SER	SER	90
91	LYS	PHE	PRO	ASN	CYS	SER	TYR	ARG	MET	SER	GLN	ALA	GLN	LYS	SER	105
106	ILE	ILE	VAL	ALA	CYS	GLU	GLY	ASP	PRO	TYR	VAL	PRO	VAL	HIS	PHE	120
121	ASP	ALA	SER	VAL	GLU	PRO	SER	THR								135

Note: Guinea pig ribonuclease B is a glycoprotein.
Non-constant evolution rates in amino acid sequences of guinea pig, chinchilla and coypu pancreatic ribonucleases.
A. van den Berg and J. J. Beintema.
Nature, **253**, 207–210 (1975).
And
Isolation, properties and primary structure of coypu and chinchilla pancreatic ribonuclease.
A. van den Berg, L. van den Hende-Timmer, and J. J. Beintema.
Biochim. Biophys. Acta, **453**, 400–409 (1976).

GIRAFFE RIBONUCLEASE

	1	5				10					15				
1	LYS	GLU	SER	ALA	ALA	ALA	LYS	PHE	GLU	ARG	GLN	HIS	ILE	ASP	SER	15
16	SER	THR	SER	SER	VAL	SER	SER	SER	ASN	TYR	CYS	ASN	GLN	MET	MET	30
31	THR	SER	ARG	ASN	LEU	THR	GLN	ASP	ARG	CYS	LYS	PRO	VAL	ASN	THR	45
46	PHE	VAL	HIS	GLU	SER	LEU	ALA	ASP	VAL	GLN	ALA	VAL	CYS	SER	GLN	60
61	LYS	ASN	VAL	ALA	CYS	LYS	ASN	GLY	GLN	THR	ASN	CYS	TYR	GLN	SER	75
76	TYR	SER	ALA	MET	SER	ILE	THR	ASP	CYS	ARG	GLU	THR	GLY	ASN	SER	90
91	LYS	TYR	PRO	ASN	CYS	ALA	TYR	GLN	THR	THR	GLN	ALA	GLU	LYS	HIS	105
106	ILE	ILE	VAL	ALA	CYS	GLU	GLY	ASN	PRO	TYR	VAL	PRO	VAL	HIS	TYR	120
121	ASP	ALA	SER	VAL												135

The primary structure of giraffe pancreatic ribonuclease.
W. Gaastra, G. Groen, G. W. Welling, and J. J. Beintema.
FEBS Letters, **41**, 227–232 (1974).

ENZYMES

RED-DEER RIBONUCLEASE

		1			5				10				15		
1	LYS	GLU	SER	ALA	ALA	ALA	LYS	PHE	GLU	ARG	GLN	HIS	MET	ASX	SER	15
16	THR	SER	SER	ALA	SER	SER	SER	(PRO,	ASX,	TYR)	CYS	ASN	GLN	MET	MET	30
31	GLN	SER	ARG	LYS	MET	THR	GLN	ASP	ARG	CYS	LYS	PRO	VAL	ASN	THR	45
46	PHE	VAL	HIS	GLU	SER	LEU	ALA	ASX	VAL	GLX	ALA	VAL	CYS	PHE	GLN	60
61	LYS	ASN	VAL	ALA	CYS	LYS	ASN	GLY	GLN	SER	ASN	CYS	TYR	GLX	SER	75
76	ASN	SER	ALA	MET	HIS	ILE	THR	ASX	CYS	ARG	GLX	SER	GLY	ASX	SER	90
91	LYS	TYR	PRO	ASN	CYS	VAL	TYR	LYS	ALA	THR	GLX	ALA	GLX	LYS	HIS	105
106	ILE	ILE	VAL	ALA	CYS	GLX	GLY	ASX	PRO	TYR	VAL	PRO	VAL	HIS	PHE	120
121	ASP	ALA	SER	VAL												135

ROE-DEER RIBONUCLEASE

		1			5				10				15		
1	LYS	GLU	SER	ALA	ALA	ALA	LYS	PHE	GLU	ARG	GLN	HIS	MET	ASX	SER	15
16	THR	SER	SER	ALA	SER	SER	SER	(PRO,	ASX,	TYR)	CYS	ASN	GLN	MET	MET	30
31	GLN	SER	ARG	ASN	LEU	THR	GLN	ASP	ARG	CYS	LYS	PRO	VAL	ASN	THR	45
46	PHE	VAL	HIS	GLU	SER	LEU	ALA	ASX	VAL	GLX	ALA	VAL	CYS	PHE	GLN	60
61	LYS	ASN	VAL	ALA/ILE	CYS	LYS	ASN	GLY	GLN	SER	ASN	CYS	TYR	GLX	SER	75
76	ASN	SER	ALA	MET	HIS	ILE	THR	ASX	CYS	ARG	GLX	SER	GLY	ASX	SER	90
91	LYS	TYR	PRO	ASN	CYS	VAL	TYR	LYS	ALA	THR	GLX	ALA	GLX	LYS	HIS	105
106	ILE	ILE	VAL	ALA	CYS	GLX	GLY	ASX	PRO	TYR	VAL	PRO	VAL	HIS	PHE	120
121	ASP	ALA	SER	VAL												135

Note: The Roe-deer enzyme exists as both a carbohydrate-free form and as a glycosidated form.

Amino acid sequences of red-deer and roe-deer pancreatic ribonucleases.

H. Zwiers, A. J. Scheffer, and J. J. Beintema.
Eur. J. Biochem., **36**, 569–574 (1973).

REINDEER RIBONUCLEASE

	1	5				10				15					
1	LYS	GLU	SER	ALA	ALA	ALA	LYS	PHE	GLU	ARG	GLN	HIS	MET	ASP	PRO	15
16	SER	PRO	SER	SER	ALA	SER	SER	SER	ASN	TYR	CYS	ASN	GLN	MET	MET	30
31	GLN	SER	ARG	ASP	LEU	THR	GLN	ASP	ARG	CYS	LYS	PRO	VAL	ASN	THR	45
46	PHE	VAL	HIS	GLU	SER	LEU	ALA	ASP	VAL	GLN	ALA	VAL	CYS	PHE	GLN	60
61	LYS	ASN	VAL	ALA	CYS	LYS	ASN	GLY	GLN	SER	ASN	CYS	TYR	GLN	SER	75
76	ASN	SER	ALA	MET	HIS	ILE	THR	ASP	CYS	ARG	GLU	THR	GLY	SER	SER	90
91	LYS	TYR	PRO	ASN	CYS	VAL	TYR	LYS	THR	THR	GLN	ALA	GLU	LYS	HIS	105
106	ILE	ILE	VAL	ALA	CYS	GLU	GLY	ASN	PRO	TYR	VAL	PRO	VAL	HIS	PHE	120
121	ASP	ALA	SER	VAL												135

MOOSE RIBONUCLEASE

	1	5				10				15					
1	LYS	GLU	SER	ALA	ALA	ALA	LYS	PHE	GLU	ARG	GLN	HIS	MET	ASP	PRO	15
16	SER	ALA	SER	SER	ILE	SER	SER	SER	ASN	TYR	CYS	ASN	GLN	MET	MET	30
31	GLN	SER	ARG	<u>ASN</u>	LEU	THR	GLN	ASP	ARG	CYS	LYS	PRO	VAL	ASN	THR	45
46	PHE	VAL	HIS	GLU	SER	LEU	ALA	ASP	VAL	GLN	ALA	VAL	CYS	PHE	GLN	60
61	LYS	ASN	VAL	ALA	CYS	LYS	ASN	GLY	GLN	SER	ASN	CYS	TYR	GLN	SER	75
76	ASN	SER	ALA	MET	HIS	ILE	THR	ASP	CYS	ARG	GLU	SER	GLY	ASN	SER	90
91	ASP	TYR	PRO	ASN	CYS	VAL	TYR	LYS	THR	THR	GLN	ALA	GLU	LYS	HIS	105
106	ILE	ILE	VAL	ALA	CYS	GLU	GLY	ASN	PRO	TYR	VAL	PRO	VAL	HIS	PHE	120
121	ASP	ALA	SER	VAL												135

Note: Moose ribonuclease is a glycoprotein.

ENZYMES

FALLOW DEER RIBONUCLEASE

	1				5					10					15	
1	LYS	GLU	SER	ALA	ALA	ALA	LYS	PHE	GLU	ARG	GLN	HIS	MET	ASP	PRO	15
16	SER	MET	SER	SER	ALA	SER	SER	SER	ASN	TYR	CYS	ASN	GLN	MET	MET	30
31	GLN	SER	ARG	LYS	MET	THR	GLN	ASP	ARG	CYS	LYS	PRO	VAL	ASN	THR	45
46	PHE	VAL	HIS	GLU	SER	LEU	ALA	ASP	VAL	GLN	ALA	VAL	CYS	PHE	GLN	60
61	LYS	ASN	VAL	ALA	CYS	LYS	ASN	GLY	GLN	SER	ASN	CYS	TYR	GLN	SER	75
76	ASN	SER	ALA	MET	HIS	ILE	THR	ASP	CYS	ARG	GLU	SER	GLY	ASN	SER	90
91	LYS	TYR	PRO	ASN	CYS	VAL	TYR	LYS	ALA	THR	GLN	ALA	GLU	LYS	HIS	105
106	ILE	ILE	VAL	ALA	CYS	GLU	GLY	ASN	PRO	TYR	VAL	PRO	VAL	HIS	PHE	120
121	ASP	ALA	SER	VAL												135

The amino acid sequences of reindeer, moose and fallow deer pancreatic ribonucleases.
G. Leijenaar-van den Berg and J. J. Beintema.
FEBS Letters, **56**, 101–107 (1975).

DROMEDARY RIBONUCLEASE

	1				5					10					15	
1	SER	GLU	THR	ALA	ALA	GLU	LYS	PHE	GLU	ARG	GLN	HIS	MET	ASP	SER	15
16	TYR	SER	SER	SER	SER	SER	ASN	SER	ASN	TYR	CYS	ASN	GLN	MET	MET	30
31	LYS	ARG	ARG	GLU	MET	THR	ASN	GLY	CYS	LYS	PRO	VAL	ASN	THR	PHE	45
46	ILE	HIS	GLU	SER	LEU	GLU	ASP	VAL	GLN	ALA	VAL	CYS	SER	GLN	LYS	60
61	SER	VAL	THR	CYS	LYS	ASN	GLY	GLN	THR	ASN	CYS	HIS	GLN	SER	SER	75
76	THR	SER	MET	HIS	ILE	THR	ASP	CYS	ARG	GLU	THR	GLY	SER	SER	LYS	90
91	TYR	PRO	ASN	CYS	ALA	TYR	LYS	ALA	SER	ASN	LEU	GLN / LYS	LYS	HIS	ILE	105
106	ILE	ILE	ALA	CYS	GLU	GLY	ASN	PRO	TYR	VAL	PRO	VAL	HIS	PHE	ASP	120
121	ALA	SER	VAL													135

The amino acid sequence of dromedary pancreatic ribonuclease.
G. W. Welling, G. Groen, and J. J. Beintema.
Biochem. J., **147**, 505–511 (1975).

COYPU RIBONUCLEASE

	1				5					10					15	
1	SER	GLU	SER	SER	ALA	LYS	LYS	PHE	GLU	ARG	GLN	HIS	MET	ASP	SER	15
16	ARG	GLY	SER	PRO	SER	THR	ASN	PRO	ASN	TYR	CYS	ASN	GLU	MET	MET	30
31	LYS	SER	ARG	ASN	MET	THR	GLN	GLY	ARG	CYS	LYS	PRO	VAL	ASN	THR	45
46	PHE	VAL	HIS	GLU	PRO	LEU	ALA	ASP	VAL	GLN	ALA	VAL	CYS	PHE	GLN	60
61	LYS	ASN	VAL	LEU	CYS	LYS	ASN	GLY	GLN	THR	ASN	CYS	TYR	GLN	SER	75
76	ASN	SER	ASN	MET	HIS	ILE	THR	ASP	CYS	ARG	VAL	THR	SER	ASN	SER	90
91	ASP	TYR	PRO	ASN	CYS	SER	TYR	ARG	THR	SER	GLN	GLU	GLU	LYS	SER	105
106	ILE	VAL	VAL	ALA	CYS	GLU	GLY	ASN	PRO	TYR	VAL	PRO	VAL	HIS	PHE	120
121	ASP	ALA	SER	VAL	ALA	ALA	SER	ALA								135

Non-constant evolution rates in amino acid sequences of guinea pig, chinchilla and coypu pancreatic ribonucleases.
A. van den Berg and J. J. Beintema.
Nature, **253**, 207–210 (1975).

ELAND RIBONUCLEASE

	1				5					10					15	
1	LYS	GLU	THR	ALA	ALA	ALA	LYS	PHE	GLU	ARG	GLN	HIS	MET	ASP	SER	15
16	SER	THR	SER	SER	ALA	SER	SER	SER	ASN	TYR	CYS	ASN	GLN	MET	MET	30
31	LYS	SER	ARG	ASP	MET	THR	LYS	ASP	ARG	CYS	LYS	PRO	VAL	ASN	THR	45
46	PHE	VAL	HIS	GLX	SER	LEU	ALA	ASX	VAL	GLX	ALA	VAL	CYS	SER	GLX	60
61	LYS	ASX	VAL	ALA	CYS	LYS	ASX	GLY	GLX	THR	ASX	CYS	TYR	GLX	SER	75
76	TYR	SER	THR	MET	SER	ILE	THR	ASX	CYS	ARG	GLX	THR	GLY	SER	SER	90
91	LYS	TYR	PRO	ASX	CYS	ALA	TYR	LYS	THR	THR	GLX	ALA	GLX	LYS	HIS	105
106	ILE	ILE	VAL	ALA	CYS	GLX	GLY	ASX	PRO	TYR	VAL	PRO	VAL	HIS	PHE	120
121	ASX	ALA	SER	VAL												135

Studies on the covalent structure of eland pancreatic ribonuclease.
F. Russchen, G. de Vrieze, W. Gaastra, and J. J. Beintema.
Biochim. Biophys. Acta, **427**, 719–726 (1976).

ENZYMES

GNU RIBONUCLEASE

	1			5					10					15		
1	LYS	GLU	SER	ALA	ALA	ALA	LYS	PHE	GLU	ARG	GLN	HIS	MET	ASP	SER	15
16	SER	THR	SER	SER	ALA	SER	SER	SER	ASN	TYR	CYS	ASN	GLN	MET	MET	30
31	LYS	SER	ARG	ASN	LEU	THR	GLN	ASP	ARG	CYS	LYS	PRO	VAL	ASN	THR	45
46	PHE	VAL	HIS	GLU	PRO	LEU	ALA	ASP	VAL	GLN	ALA	VAL	CYS	SER	GLN	60
61	LYS	ASN	VAL	ALA	CYS	LYS	ASN	GLY	GLN	THR	ASN	CYS	TYR	GLN	SER	75
76	TYR	SER	THR	MET	SER	ILE	THR	ASP	CYS	ARG	GLU	THR	GLY	SER	SER	90
91	LYS	TYR	PRO	ASN	CYS	ALA	TYR	LYS	ALA	THR	GLN	ALA	LYS	LYS	HIS	105
106	ILE	ILE	VAL	ALA	CYS	GLU	GLY	ASN	PRO	TYR	VAL	PRO	VAL	HIS	PHE	120
121	ASP	ALA	SER	VAL												135

The amino acid sequence of gnu pancreatic ribonuclease.
G. Groen, G. W. Welling, and J. J. Beintema.
FEBS Letters, **60**, 300–304 (1975).

TOPI RIBONUCLEASE

	1			5					10					15		
1	LYS	GLU	SER	ALA	ALA	ALA	LYS	PHE	GLX	ARG	GLX	HIS	MET	ASX	SER	15
16	SER	THR	SER	SER	ALA	SER	SER	SER	ASX	TYR	CYS	ASX	GLX	MET	MET	30
31	LYS	SER	ARG	ASN	LEU	THR	GLN	ASP	ARG	CYS	LYS	PRO	VAL	ASX	THR	45
46	PHE	VAL	HIS	GLX	SER	LEU	ALA	ASX	VAL	GLX	ALA	VAL	CYS	SER	GLX	60
61	LYS	ASX	VAL	ALA	CYS	LYS	ASX	GLY	GLX	THR	ASX	CYS	TYR	GLX	SER	75
76	TYR	SER	THR	MET	SER	ILE	THR	ASX	CYS	ARG	GLX	THR	GLY	SER	SER	90
91	LYS	TYR	PRO	ASX	CYS	ALA	TYR	LYS	THR	THR	GLN	ALA	LYS	LYS	HIS	105
106	ILE	ILE	VAL	ALA	CYS	GLX	GLY	ASX	PRO	TYR	VAL	PRO	VAL	HIS	PHE	120
121	ASX	ALA	SER	VAL												135

The amino acid sequence of topi pancreatic ribonuclease.
H. Kuper and J. J. Beintema.
Biochim. Biophys. Acta, **446**, 337–344 (1976).

PIKE-WHALE RIBONUCLEASE

	1				5					10					15	
1	ARG	GLU	SER	PRO	ALA	MET	LYS	PHE	GLN	ARG	GLN	HIS	MET	ASP	SER	15
16	GLY	ASN	SER	PRO	GLY	ASN	ASN	PRO	ASN	TYR	CYS	ASN	GLN	MET	MET	30
31	MET	ARG	ARG	LYS	MET	THR	GLN	GLY	ARG	CYS	LYS	PRO	VAL	ASN	THR	45
46	PHE	VAL	HIS	GLU	SER	LEU	GLU	ASP	VAL	LYS	ALA	VAL	CYS	SER	GLN	60
61	LYS	ASN	VAL	LEU	CYS	LYS	ASN	GLY	ARG	THR	ASN	CYS	TYR	GLU	SER	75
76	ASN	SER	THR	MET	HIS	ILE	THR	ASP	CYS	ARG	GLN	THR	GLY	SER	SER	90
91	LYS	TYR	PRO	ASN	CYS	ALA	TYR	LYS	THR	SER	GLN	LYS	GLU	LYS	HIS	105
106	ILE	ILE	VAL	ALA	CYS	GLU	GLY	ASN	PRO	TYR	VAL	PRO	VAL	HIS	PHE	120
121	ASP	ASN	SER	VAL												135

The amino acid sequence of pike-whale (Lesser Rorqual) pancreatic ribonuclease.
M. Emmens, G. W. Welling, and J. J. Beintema.
Biochem. J., **157**, 317–323 (1976).

RIBONUCLEASE OF BACILLUS AMYLOLIQUEFACIENS

	1				5					10					15	
1	ALA	GLN	VAL	ILE	ASN	THR	PHE	ASP	GLY	VAL	ALA	ASP	TYR	LEU	GLN	15
16	THR	TYR	HIS	LYS	LEU	PRO	ASN	ASP	TYR	ILE	THR	LYS	SER	GLU	ALA	30
31	GLN	ALA	LEU	GLY	TRP	VAL	ALA	SER	LYS	GLY	ASN	LEU	ALA	ASP	VAL	45
46	ALA	PRO	GLY	LYS	SER	ILE	GLY	GLY	ASP	ILE	PHE	SER	ASN	ARG	GLU	60
61	GLY	LYS	LEU	PRO	GLY	LYS	SER	GLY	ARG	THR	TRP	ARG	GLU	ALA	ASP	75
76	ILE	ASN	TYR	THR	SER	GLY	PHE	ARG	ASN	SER	ASP	ARG	ILE	LEU	TYR	90
91	SER	SER	ASP	TRP	LEU	ILE	TYR	LYS	THR	THR	ASP	HIS	TYR	GLN	THR	105
106	PHE	THR	LYS	ILE	ARG											120

Amino acid Sequence of Extracellular Ribonuclease (Barnase) of *Bacillus amyloliquefaciens*.
R. W. Hartley and E. A. Barker.
Nature (New Biol.), **235**, 15–16 (1972).

220

ENZYMES

RIBONUCLEASE T1

	1				5					10					10	
1	ALA	CYS	ASP	TYR	THR	CYS	GLY	SER	ASN	CYS	TYR	SER	SER	SER	ASP	15
16	VAL	SER	THR	ALA	GLN	ALA	ALA	GLY	TYR	GLN	LEU	HIS	GLU	ASP	GLY	30
31	GLU	THR	VAL	GLY	SER	ASN	SER	TYR	PRO	HIS	LYS	TYR	ASN	ASN	TYR	45
46	GLU	GLY	PHE	ASP	PHE	SER	VAL	SER	SER	PRO	TYR	TYR	GLU	TRP	PRO	60
61	ILE	LEU	SER	SER	GLY	ASP	VAL	TYR	SER	GLY	PRO	GLY	SER	GLY	ALA	75
76	ASP	ARG	VAL	VAL	PHE	ASN	GLU	ASN	ASN	GLN	LEU	ALA	GLY	VAL	ILE	90
91	THR	HIS	THR	GLY	ALA	SER	GLY	ASN	ASN	PHE	VAL	GLU	CYS	THR		105

The Structure and Function of Ribonuclease T1.15. The complete Amino Acid Sequence of Ribonuclease T1.
K. Takahashi.
J. Biochem., **70**, 617–634 (1971).

RIBONUCLEASE St

	1				5					10					15	
1	GLU	ALA	PRO	CYS	GLY	ASP	THR	SER	GLY	PHE	GLU	GLN	VAL	ARG	LEU	15
16	ALA	ASP	LEU	PRO	PRO	GLU	ALA	THR	ASP	THR	GLY	TYR	GLU	LEU	ILE	30
31	GLU	LYS	GLY	GLY	PRO	TYR	PRO	TYR	PRO	GLU	ASP	GLY	THR	VAL	PHE	45
46	GLU	ASN	ARG	GLU	GLY	ILE	LEU	PRO	ASP	CYS	ALA	GLU	GLY	TYR	TYR	60
61	HIS	GLU	TYR	THR	VAL	LYS	THR	PRO	SER	GLY	ASP	ASP	ARG	GLY	ALA	75
76	ARG	ARG	PHE	VAL	VAL	GLY	ASP	GLY	GLY	GLU	TYR	PHE	TYR	THR	GLU	90
91	ASP	HIS	TYR	GLU	SER	PHE	ARG	LEU	THR	ILE	VAL	ASN				105

Note: A disulphide bond joins residue CYS 4 to CYS 55.
The amino acid sequence of ribonuclease St.
N. Yoshida, A. Sasaki, M. A. Rashid, and H. Otsuka.
FEBS Letters, **64**, 122–125 (1976).

RIBONUCLEASE U2

	1				5					10					15	
1	CYS	ASN	ILE	PRO	GLU	SER	THR	ASN	CYS	GLY	GLY	ASN	VAL	TYR	SER	15
16	ASN	ASP	ASP	ILE	ASN	THR	ALA	ILE	GLN	GLY	ALA	LEU	ASP	ASP	VAL	30
31	ALA	ARG	PRO	ASP	GLY	ASP	ASN	TYR	PRO	HIS	GLN	TYR	TYR	ASP	GLU	45
46	ALA	SER	ASP	GLN	ILE	THR	LEU	CYS	CYS	GLY	PRO	GLY	SER	TRP	SER	60
61	GLU	PHE	PRO	LEU	VAL	TYR	ASN	GLY	PRO	TYR	TYR	SER	SER	ARG	ASP	75
76	ASN	TYR	VAL	SER	PRO	GLY	PRO	ASP	ARG	VAL	ILE	TYR	GLN	THR	ASN	90
91	THR	GLY	GLU	PHE	CYS	ALA	THR	VAL	THR	HIS	THR	GLY	ALA	ALA	SER	105
106	TYR	ASP	GLY	PHE	THR	GLN	CYS	SER								120

The amino acid sequence of ribonuclease U2 from *Ustilago sphaerogena*.
S. Sato and T. Uchida.
Biochem. J., **145**, 353–360 (1975).

STAPHYLOCOCCAL NUCLEASE STRAIN V8

	1				5					10					15	
1	ALA	THR	SER	THR	LYS	LYS	LEU	HIS	LYS	GLU	PRO	ALA	THR	LEU	ILE	15
16	LYS	ALA	ILE	ASP	GLY	ASP	THR	VAL	LYS	LEU	MET	TYR	LYS	GLY	GLN	30
31	PRO	MET	THR	PHE	ARG	LEU	LEU	LEU	VAL	ASP	THR	PRO	GLN	THR	LYS	45
46	HIS	PRO	LYS	LYS	GLY	VAL	GLU	LYS	TYR	GLY	PRO	GLU	ALA	SER	ALA	60
61	PHE	THR	LYS	LYS	MET	VAL	GLU	ASN	ALA	LYS	LYS	ILE	GLU	VAL	GLU	75
76	PHE	ASN	LYS	GLY	GLN	ARG	THR	ASP	LYS	TYR	GLY	ARG	GLY	LEU	ALA	90
91	TYR	ILE	TYR	ALA	ASP	GLY	LYS	MET	VAL	ASN	GLU	ALA	LEU	VAL	ARG	105
106	GLN	GLY	LEU	ALA	LYS	VAL	ALA	TYR	VAL	TYR	LYS	PRO	ASN	ASN	THR	120
121	HIS	GLU	GLN	LEU	LEU	ARG	LYS	SER	GLU	ALA	GLN	ALA	LYS	LYS	GLU	135
136	LYS	LEU	ASN	ILE	TRP	SER	GLU	ASN	ASP	ALA	ASP	SER	GLY	GLN		150

The Amino Acid Sequence of an Extracellular Nuclease of *Staphylococcus . aureus*. 3. Complete Amino Acid Sequence.
H. Taniuchi, C. B. Anfinsen, and A. Sodja.
J. Biol. Chem., **242**, 4752–4758 (1967).
In corrected form.
H. Taniuchi, C. L. Cusumano, C. B. Anfinsen, and J. L. Cone.
J. Biol. Chem., **243**, 4775–4777 (1968).

ENZYMES

STAPHYLOCOCCAL NUCLEASE FOGGI STRAIN

	1				5					10					15	
1	ALA	THR	SER	THR	LYS	LYS	LEU	HIS	LYS	GLU	PRO	ALA	THR	LEU	ILE	15
16	LYS	ALA	ILE	ASP	GLY	ASP	THR	VAL	LYS	LEU	MET	TYR	LYS	GLY	GLN	30
31	PRO	MET	THR	PHE	ARG	LEU	LEU	LEU	VAL	ASP	THR	PRO	GLU	THR	LYS	45
46	HIS	PRO	LYS	LYS	GLY	VAL	GLU	LYS	TYR	GLY	PRO	GLU	ALA	SER	ALA	60
61	PHE	THR	LYS	LYS	MET	VAL	GLU	ASN	ALA	LYS	LYS	ILE	GLX	VAL	GLX	75
76	PHE	ASX	LYS	GLY	GLN	ARG	THR	ASX	LYS	TYR	GLY	ARG	GLY	LEU	ALA	90
91	TYR	ILE	TYR	ALA	ASP	GLY	LYS	MET	VAL	ASN	GLU	ALA	LEU	VAL	ARG	105
106	GLN	GLY	LEU	ALA	LYS	VAL	ALA	TYR	VAL	TYR	LYS	PRO	ASN	ASN	THR	120
121	HIS	GLU	GLN	HIS	LEU	ARG	LYS	SER	GLX	ALA	GLX	ALA	LYS	LYS	GLU	135
136	LYS	LEU	ASX	ILE	TRP	SER	GLU	ASX	ASX	ALA	ASX	SER	GLY	GLN		150

Staphylococcal Nuclease (Foggi Strain). 2. The Amino Acid Sequence.
J. L. Cone, C. L. Cusumano, H. Taniuchi, and C. B. Anfinsen.
J. Biol. Chem., **246**, 3103–3110 (1971).

BOVINE PANCREATIC DEOXYRIBONUCLEASE A

	1				5					10					15	
1	LEU	LYS	ILE	ALA	ALA	PHE	ASN	ILE	ARG	THR	PHE	GLY	GLU	THR	LYS	15
16	MET	SER	ASN	ALA	THR	LEU	ALA	SER	TYR	ILE	VAL	ARG	ARG	TYR	ASP	30
31	ILE	VAL	LEU	ILE	GLU	GLN	VAL	ARG	ASP	SER	HIS	LEU	VAL	ALA	VAL	45
46	GLY	LYS	LEU	LEU	ASP	TYR	LEU	ASN	GLN	ASP	ASP	PRO	ASN	THR	TYR	60
61	HIS	TYR	VAL	VAL	SER	GLU	PRO	LEU	GLY	ARG	ASN	SER	TYR	LYS	GLU	75
76	ARG	TYR	LEU	PHE	LEU	PHE	ARG	PRO	ASN	LYS	VAL	SER	VAL	LEU	ASP	90
91	THR	TYR	GLN	TYR	ASP	ASP	GLY	CYS	GLU	SER	CYS	GLY	ASN	ASP	SER	105
106	PHE	SER	ARG	GLU	PRO	ALA	VAL	VAL	LYS	PHE	SER	SER	HIS	SER	THR	120
121	LYS	VAL	LYS	GLU	PHE	ALA	ILE	VAL	ALA	LEU	HIS	SER	ALA	PRO	SER	135
136	ASP	ALA	VAL	ALA	GLU	ILE	ASN	SER	LEU	TYR	ASP	VAL	TYR	LEU	ASP	150
151	VAL	GLN	GLN	LYS	TRP	HIS	LEU	ASN	ASP	VAL	MET	LEU	MET	GLY	ASP	165
166	PHE	ASN	ALA	ASP	CYS	SER	TYR	VAL	THR	SER	SER	GLN	TRP	SER	SER	180
181	ILE	ARG	LEU	ARG	THR	SER	SER	THR	PHE	GLN	TRP	LEU	ILE	PRO	ASP	195
196	SER	ALA	ASP	THR	THR	ALA	THR	SER	THR	ASN	CYS	ALA	TYR	ASP	ARG	210
211	ILE	VAL	VAL	ALA	GLY	SER	LEU	LEU	GLN	SER	SER	VAL	VAL	GLY	PRO	225
226	SER	ALA	ALA	PRO	PHE	ASP	PHE	GLN	ALA	ALA	TYR	GLY	LEU	SER	ASN	240
241	GLU	MET	ALA	LEU	ALA	ILE	SER	ASP	HIS	TYR	PRO	VAL	GLU	VAL	THR	255
256	LEU	THR														270

Note: Disulphide bridges link residues CYS 98 and 101; CYS 170 and 206.
Bovine Pancreatic Deoxyribonuclease A. Isolation of cyanogen bromide peptides; complete covalent structure of the polypeptide chain.
T.-H. Liao, J. Salnikow, S. Moore, and W. H. Stein.
J. Biol. Chem., **248**, 1489–1495 (1973).

HUMAN LEUKAEMIA LYSOZYME

	1				5					10					15		
1	LYS	VAL	PHE	GLU	ARG	CYS	GLU	LEU	ALA	ARG	THR	LEU	LYS	ARG	LEU		15
16	GLY	MET	ASP	GLY	TYR	ARG	GLY	ILE	SER	LEU	ALA	ASN	TRP	MET	CYS		30
31	LEU	ALA	LYS	TRP	GLU	SER	GLY	TYR	ASN	THR	ARG	ALA	THR	ASN	TYR		45
46	ASN	ALA	GLY	ASP	ARG	SER	THR	ASP	TYR	GLY	ILE	PHE	GLN	ILE	ASN		60
61	SER	ARG	TYR	TRP	CYS	ASN	ASP	GLY	LYS	THR	PRO	GLY	ALA	VAL	ASN		75
76	ALA	CYS	HIS	LEU	SER	CYS	SER	ALA	LEU	LEU	GLN	ASP	ASN	ILE	ALA		90
91	ASP	ALA	VAL	ALA	CYS	ALA	LYS	ARG	VAL	ARG	ASP	PRO	GLN	GLY	ILE	105
106	ARG	ALA	TRP	VAL	ALA	TRP	ARG	ASN	ARG	CYS	GLN	ASN	ARG	ASP	VAL	120
121	ARG	GLN	TYR	VAL	GLN	GLY	CYS	GLY	VAL							135

Note: Disulphide bridges identical to Hen egg lysozyme.
Primary Structure of Lysozyme from Man and Goose.
R. E. Canfield, S. Kammerman, J. H. Sobel, and F. J. Morgan.
Nature (New Biol.), **232**, 16–17 (1971).

HUMAN MILK LYSOZYME

	1				5					10					15		
1	LYS	VAL	PHE	GLU	ARG	CYS	GLU	LEU	ALA	ARG	THR	LEU	LYS	ARG	LEU		15
16	GLY	MET	ASP	GLY	TYR	ARG	GLY	ILE	SER	LEU	ALA	ASN	TRP	MET	CYS		30
31	LEU	ALA	LYS	TRP	GLU	SER	GLY	TYR	ASN	THR	ARG	ALA	THR	ASN	TYR		45
46	ASN	ALA	GLY	ASP	ARG	SER	THR	ASP	TYR	GLY	ILE	PHE	GLN	ILE	ASN		60
61	SER	ARG	TYR	TRP	CYS	ASN	ASP	GLY	LYS	THR	PRO	GLY	ALA	VAL	ASN		75
76	ALA	CYS	HIS	LEU	SER	CYS	SER	ALA	LEU	LEU	GLN	ASP	ASN	ILE	ALA		90
91	ASP	ALA	VAL	ALA	CYS	ALA	LYS	ARG	VAL	VAL	ARG	ASP	PRO	GLN	GLY	105
106	ILE	ARG	ALA	TRP	VAL	ALA	TRP	ARG	ASN	ARG	CYS	GLN	ASN	ARG	ASP	120
121	VAL	ARG	GLN	TYR	VAL	GLN	GLY	CYS	GLY	VAL						135

Comparison between Human and Bird Lysozymes: Note concerning the previously observed deletion.
J. Jollès and P. Jollès.
FEBS Letters, **22**, 31–33 (1972).

ENZYMES

LYSOZYME FROM BABOON MILK

	1			5					10					15		
1	LYS	ILE	PHE	GLU	ARG	CYS	GLU	LEU	ALA	ARG	THR	LEU	LYS	ARG	LEU	15
16	GLY	LEU	ASP	GLY	TYR	ARG	GLY	ILE	SER	LEU	ALA	ASN	TRP	VAL	CYS	30
31	LEU	ALA	LYS	TRP	GLU	SER	ASP	TYR	ASN	THR	GLN	ALA	THR	ASN	TYR	45
46	ASN	PRO	GLY	ASP	GLN	SER	THR	ASP	TYR	GLY	ILE	PHE	GLN	ILE	ASN	60
61	SER	HIS	TYR	TRP	CYS	ASN	ASP	GLY	LYS	THR	PRO	GLY	ALA	VAL	ASN	75
76	ALA	CYS	HIS	ILE	SER	CYS	ASN	ALA	LEU	LEU	GLN	ASP	ASN	ILE	THR	90
91	ASP	ALA	VAL	ALA	CYS	ALA	LYS	ARG	VAL	VAL	SER	ASP	PRO	GLN	GLY	105
106	ILE	ARG	ALA	TRP	VAL	ALA	TRP	ARG	ASN	HIS	CYS	GLN	ASN	ARG	ASP	120
121	VAL	SER	GLN	TYR	VAL	GLN	GLY	CYS	GLY	VAL						135

Amino acid sequence of lysozyme from baboon milk.
J. Hermann, J. Jollès, D. H. Buss, and P. Jollès.
J. Mol. Biol., **79**, 587–595 (1973).

HEN EGG LYSOZYME

	1			5					10					15		
1	LYS	VAL	PHE	GLY	ARG	CYS	GLU	LEU	ALA	ALA	ALA	MET	LYS	ARG	HIS	15
16	GLY	LEU	ASP	ASN	TYR	ARG	GLY	TYR	SER	LEU	GLY	ASN	TRP	VAL	CYS	30
31	ALA	ALA	LYS	PHE	GLU	SER	ASN	PHE	ASN	THR	GLN	ALA	THR	ASN	ARG	45
46	ASN	THR	ASP	GLY	SER	THR	ASP	TYR	GLY	ILE	LEU	GLN	ILE	ASN	SER	60
61	ARG	TRP	TRP	CYS	ASP	ASN	GLY	ARG	THR	PRO	GLY	SER	ARG	ASN	LEU	75
76	CYS	ASN	ILE	PRO	CYS	SER	ALA	LEU	LEU	SER	SER	ASP	ILE	THR	ALA	90
91	SER	VAL	ASN	CYS	ALA	LYS	LYS	ILE	VAL	SER	ASP	GLY	ASP	GLY	MET	105
106	ASN	ALA	TRP	VAL	ALA	TRP	ARG	ASN	ARG	CYS	LYS	GLY	THR	ASP	VAL	120
121	GLN	ALA	TRP	ILE	ARG	GLY	CYS	ARG	LEU							135

Note: Disulphide bridges are between CYS 6 and 127; CYS 30 and 115; CYS 64 and 80; CYS 76 and 94.
The Amino Acid Sequence of Egg White Lysozyme.
R. E. Canfield.
J. Biol. Chem., **238**, 2698–2707 (1963); and **240**, 1997–2002 (1965).

GUINEA-HEN EGG LYSOZYME

	1			5					10					15		
1	LYS	VAL	PHE	GLY	ARG	CYS	GLU	LEU	ALA	ALA	ALA	MET	LYS	ARG	HIS	15
16	GLY	LEU	ASP	ASN	TYR	ARG	GLY	TYR	SER	LEU	GLY	ASN	TRP	VAL	CYS	30
31	ALA	ALA	LYS	PHE	GLU	SER	ASN	PHE	ASN	SER	GLN	ALA	THR	ASN	ARG	45
46	ASN	THR	ASP	GLY	SER	THR	ASP	TYR	GLY	VAL	LEU	GLN	ILE	ASN	SER	60
61	ARG	TRP	TRP	CYS	ASN	ASP	GLY	ARG	THR	PRO	GLY	SER	ARG	ASN	LEU	75
76	CYS	ASN	ILE	PRO	CYS	SER	ALA	LEU	GLN	SER	SER	ASP	ILE	THR	ALA	90
91	THR	ALA	ASN	CYS	ALA	LYS	LYS	ILE	VAL	SER	ASP	GLY	ASP	GLY	MET	105
106	ASN	ALA	TRP	VAL	ALA	TRP	ARG	LYS	HIS	CYS	LYS	GLY	THR	ASP	VAL	120
121	ARG	VAL	TRP	ILE	LYS	GLY	CYS	ARG	LEU							135

Amino Acid Sequence of Guinea-Hen Egg-White Lysozyme.
J. Jollès, E. van Leemputten, A. Mouton, and P. Jollès.
Biochim. Biophys. Acta, **257**, 497–510 (1972).

DUCK EGG LYSOZYME II

	1			5					10					15		
1	LYS	VAL	TYR	SER	ARG	CYS	GLU	LEU	ALA	ALA	ALA	MET	LYS	ARG	LEU	15
16	GLY	LEU	ASP	ASN	TYR	ARG	GLY	TYR	SER	LEU	GLY	ASN	TRP	VAL	CYS	30
31	ALA	ALA	ASN	TYR	GLU	SER	SER	PHE	ASN	THR	GLN	ALA	THR	ASN	ARG	45
46	ASN	THR	ASP	GLY	SER	THR	ASP	TYR	GLY	ILE	LEU	GLU	ILE	ASN	SER	60
61	ARG	TRP	TRP	CYS	ASP	ASN	GLY	LYS	THR	PRO	GLY	SER	LYS	ASN	ALA	75
76	CYS	GLY	ILE	PRO	CYS	SER	VAL	LEU	LEU	ARG	SER	ASP	ILE	THR	GLU	90
91	ALA	VAL	ARG	CYS	ALA	LYS	ARG	ILE	VAL	SER	ASP	GLY	ASP	GLY	MET	105
106	ASN	ALA	TRP	VAL	ALA	TRP	ARG	ASN	ARG	CYS	ARG	GLY	THR	ASP	VAL	120
121	SER	LYS	TRP	ILE	ARG	GLY	CYS	ARG	LEU							135

226

ENZYMES

DUCK EGG LYSOZYME III

	1			5						10					15		
1	LYS	VAL	TYR	GLU	ARG	CYS	GLU	LEU	ALA	ALA	ALA	MET	LYS	ARG	LEU		15
16	GLY	LEU	ASP	ASN	TYR	ARG	GLY	TYR	SER	LEU	GLY	ASN	TRP	VAL	CYS		30
31	ALA	ALA	ASN	TYR	GLU	SER/GLY	SER	PHE	ASN	THR	GLN	ALA	THR	ASN	ARG		45
46	ASN	THR	ASP	GLY	SER	THR	ASP	TYR	GLY	ILE	LEU	GLU	ILE	ASN	SER		60
61	ARG	TRP	TRP	CYS	ASP	ASN	GLY	LYS	THR	PRO	ARG	ALA	LYS	ASN	ALA		75
76	CYS	GLY	ILE	PRO	CYS	SER	VAL	LEU	LEU	ARG	SER	ASP	ILE	THR	GLU		90
91	ALA	VAL	LYS	CYS	ALA	LYS	ARG	ILE	VAL	SER	ASP	GLY	ASP	GLY	MET		105
106	ASN	ALA	TRP	VAL	ALA	TRP	ARG	ASN	ARG	CYS	LYS	GLY	THR	ASP	VAL		120
121	SER	ARG	TRP	ILE	ARG	GLY	CYS	ARG	LEU								135

Multiple forms of Duck-Egg White Lysozyme. Primary Structure of Two Duck Lysozymes.
J. Hermann, J. Jollès and P. Jollès.
Eur. J. Biochem., **24**, 12–17 (1971).

T4 PHAGE LYSOZYME

	1			5						10					15		
1	MET	ASN	ILE	PHE	GLU	MET	LEU	ARG	ILE	ASP	GLU	GLY	LEU	ARG	LEU		15
16	LYS	ILE	TYR	LYS	ASP	THR	GLU	GLY	TYR	TYR	THR	ILE	GLY	ILE	GLY		30
31	HIS	LEU	LEU	THR	LYS	SER	PRO	SER	LEU	ASN	ALA	ALA	LYS	SER	GLU		45
46	LEU	ASP	LYS	ALA	ILE	GLY	ARG	ASN	CYS	ASN	GLY	VAL	ILE	THR	LYS		60
61	ASP	GLU	ALA	GLU	LYS	LEU	PHE	ASN	GLN	ASP	VAL	ASP	ALA	ALA	VAL		75
76	ARG	GLY	ILE	LEU	ARG	ASN	ALA	LYS	LEU	LYS	PRO	VAL	TYR	ASP	SER		90
91	LEU	ASP	ALA	VAL	ARG	ARG	CYS	ALA	LEU	ILE	ASN	MET	VAL	PHE	GLN		105
106	MET	GLY	GLU	THR	GLY	VAL	ALA	GLY	PHE	THR	ASN	SER	LEU	ARG	MET		120
121	LEU	GLN	GLN	LYS	ARG	TRP	ASP	GLU	ALA	ALA	VAL	ASN	LEU	ALA	LYS		135
136	SER	ARG	TRP	TYR	ASN	GLN	THR	PRO	ASN	ARG	ALA	LYS	ARG	VAL	ILE		150
151	THR	THR	PHE	ARG	THR	GLY	THR	TRP	ASP	ALA	TYR	LYS	ASN	LEU			165

The Amino Acid Sequence of T4 Phage Lysozyme.
M. Inouye, M. J. Lorena, and A. Tsugita.
J. Biol. Chem., **245**, 3467–3478 (1970); and **246**, 4100–4101 (1971).

LYSOZYME OF CHALAROPSIS

	1				5					10					15	
1	THR	VAL	GLN	GLY	PHE	ASP	ILE	SER	SER	TYR	GLN	PRO	SER	VAL	ASN	15
16	PHE	ALA	GLY	ALA	TYR	SER	ALA	GLY	ALA	ARG	PHE	VAL	ILE	ILE	LYS	30
31	ALA	THR	GLU	GLY	THR	SER	TYR	THR	ASN	PRO	SER	PHE	SER	SER	GLN	45
46	TYR	ASN	GLY	ALA	THR	THR	ALA	THR	GLY	ASN	TYR	PHE	ILE	ARG	GLY	60
61	GLY	TYR	HIS	PHE	ALA	HIS	PRO	GLY	GLU	THR	THR	GLY	ALA	ALA	GLN	75
76	ALA	ASP	TYR	PHE	ILE	ALA	HIS	GLY	GLY	GLY	TRP	SER	GLY	ASP	GLY	90
91	ILE	THR	LEU	PRO	GLY	MET	LEU	ASP	LEU	GLU	SER	GLU	GLY	SER	ASN	105
106	PRO	ALA	CYS	TRP	GLY	LEU	SER	ALA	ALA	SER	MET	VAL	ALA	TRP	ILE	120
121	LYS	ALA	PHE	SER	ASP	ARG	TYR	HIS	ALA	VAL	THR	GLY	ARG	TYR	PRO	135
136	MET	LEU	TYR	THR	ASN	PRO	SER	TRP	TRP	SER	SER	CYS	THR	GLY	ASN	150
151	SER	ASN	ALA	PHE	VAL	ASN	THR	ASN	PRO	LEU	VAL	LEU	ALA	ASN	ARG	165
166	TYR	ALA	SER	ALA	PRO	GLY	THR	ILE	PRO	GLY	GLY	TRP	PRO	TYR	GLN	180
181	THR	ILE	TRP	GLN	ASN	SER	ASP	ALA	TYR	ALA	TYR	GLY	GLY	SER	ASN	195
196	ASN	PHE	ILE	ASN	GLY	SER	ILE	ASP	ASN	LEU	LYS	LYS	LEU	ALA	THR	210
211	GLY															225

Note: There is a single disulphide bond between residues CYS 108 and 147.
The N,O-diacetylmuramidase of *Chalaropsis* species.
J. W. Felch, T. Inagami, and J. H. Hash.
J. Biol. Chem., **250**, 3713–3720 (1975).

HUMAN α-LACTALBUMIN

	1				5					10					15	
1	LYS	GLN	PHE	THR	LYS	CYS	GLU	LEU	SER	GLN	LEU	LEU	LYS	ASP	ILE	15
16	ASP	GLY	TYR	GLY	GLY	ILE	ALA	LEU	PRO	GLU	LEU	ILE	CYS	THR	MET	30
31	PHE	HIS	THR	SER	GLY	TYR	ASP	THR	GLN	ALA	ILE	VAL	GLU	ASN	ASP	45
46	GLN	SER	THR	GLU	TYR	GLY	LEU	PHE	GLN	ILE	SER	ASN	LYS	LEU	TRP	60
61	CYS	LYS	SER	SER	GLN	VAL	PRO	GLN	SER	ARG	ASN	ILE	CYS	ASP	ILE	75
76	SER	CYS	ASP	LYS	PHE	LEU	ASN	ASP	ASN	ILE	THR	ASN	ASN	ILE	MET	90
91	CYS	ALA	LYS	LYS	ILE	LEU	ASP	ILE	LYS	GLY	ILE	ASN	TYR	TRP	LEU	105
106	ALA	HIS	LYS	ALA	LEU	CYS	THR	GLU	LYS	LEU	GLU	GLN	TRP	LEU	CYS	120
121	GLU	LYS	LEU													135

The Complete Amino Acid Sequence of Human α-Lactalbumin.
J. B. C. Findlay and K. Brew.
Eur. J. Biochem., **27**, 65–86 (1972).

ENZYMES

GUINEA-PIG α-LACTALBUMIN

	1				5					10					15	
1	LYS	GLN	LEU	THR	LYS	CYS	ALA	LEU	SER	HIS	GLU	LEU	ASN	ASP	LEU	15
16	ALA	GLY	TYR	ARG	ASP	ILE	THR	LEU	PRO	GLU	TRP	LEU	CYS	ILE	ILE	30
31	PHE	HIS	ILE	SER	GLY	TYR	ASP	THR	GLN	ALA	ILE	VAL	LYS	ASN	SER	45
46	ASN	HIS	LYS	GLU	TYR	GLY	LEU	PHE	GLN	ILE	ASN	ASN	LYS	ASP	PHE	60
61	CYS	GLU	SER	SER	THR	THR	VAL	GLN	SER	ARG	ASP	ILE	CYS	ASP	ILE	75
76	SER	CYS	ASP	LYS	LEU	LEU	ASN	ASP	ASN	LEU	THR	ASN	ASN	ILE	MET	90
91	CYS	VAL	LYS	LYS	ILE	LEU	ASP	ILE	LYS	GLY	ILE	ASN	TYR	TRP	LEU	105
106	ALA	HIS	LYS	PRO	LEU	CYS	SER	ASP	LYS	LEU	GLU	GLN	TRP	TYR	CYS	120
121	GLU	ALA	GLN													135

The Complete Amino Acid Sequence of Guinea-Pig α-Lactalbumin.
K. Brew.
Eur. J. Biochem., **27**, 341–353 (1972).

BOVINE α-LACTALBUMIN

	1				5					10					15	
1	GLU	GLN	LEU	THR	LYS	CYS	GLU	VAL	PHE	ARG	GLU	LEU	LYS	ASP	LEU	15
16	LYS	GLY	TYR	GLY	GLY	VAL	SÉR	LEU	PRO	GLU	TRP	VAL	CYS	THR	THR	30
31	PHE	HIS	THR	SER	GLY	TYR	ASP	THR	GLU	ALA	ILE	VAL	GLU	ASN	ASN	45
46	GLN	SER	THR	ASP	TYR	GLY	LEU	PHE	GLN	ILE	ASN	ASN	LYS	ILE	TRP	60
61	CYS	LYS	ASN	ASP	GLN	ASP	PRO	HIS	SER	SER	ASN	ILE	CYS	ASN	ILE	75
76	SER	CYS	ASP	LYS	PHE	LEU	ASN	ASN	ASP	LEU	THR	ASN	ASN	ILE	MET	90
91	CYS	VAL	LYS	LYS	ILE	LEU	ASP	LYS	VAL	GLY	ILE	ASN	TYR	TRP	LEU	105
106	ALA	HIS	LYS	ALA	LEU	CYS	SER	GLU	LYS	LEU	ASP	GLN	TRP	LEU	CYS	120
121	GLU	LYS	LEU													135

The Complete Amino Acid Sequence of Bovine α-Lactalbumin.
K. Brew, F. J. Castellino, T. C. Vanaman, and R. L. Hill.
J. Biol. Chem., **245**, 4570–4582 (1970).

INHIBITORS

KAZAL'S INHIBITOR

	1				5					10					15		
1	ASN	ILE	LEU	GLY	ARG	GLU	ALA	LYS	CYS	THR	ASN	GLU	VAL	ASN	GLY		15
16	CYS	PRO	ARG	ILE	TYR	ASN	PRO	VAL	CYS	GLY	THR	ASP	GLY	VAL	THR		30
31	TYR	SER	ASN	GLU	CYS	LEU	LEU	CYS	MET	GLU	ASN	LYS	GLU	ARG	GLN		45
46	THR	PRO	VAL	LEU	ILE	GLN	LYS	SER	GLY	PRO	CYS						60

The Structure of the Bovine Pancreatic Secretory Trypsin Inhibitor—Kazal's Inhibitor. II. The order of the tryptic peptides.
L. J. Greene and D. C. Bartelt.
J. Biol. Chem., **244**, 2646–2657 (1969).

COW COLOSTRUM TRYPSIN INHIBITOR (COMPONENT B2)

	1				5					10					15		
1	PHE	GLN	THR	PRO	PRO	ASP	LEU	CYS	GLN	LEU	PRO	GLN	ALA	ARG	GLY		15
16	PRO	CYS	LYS	ALA	ALA	LEU	LEU	ARG	TYR	PHE	TYR	ASX	SER	THR	SER		30
31	ASN	ALA	CYS	GLU	PRO	PHE	THR	TYR	GLY	GLY	CYS	GLN	GLY	ASN	ASN		45
46	ASX	ASN	PHE	GLU	THR	THR	GLU	MET	CYS	LEU	ARG	ILE	CYS	GLU	PRO		60
61	PRO	GLN	GLN	THR	ASP	LYS	SER										75

Primary Structure of Trypsin Inhibitor from cow Colostrum (component B2).
D. Čechová, V. Jonáková and F. Šorm.
Coll. Czech. Chem. Comm., **36**, 3342–3357 (1971).

KALLIKREIN INACTIVATOR (TRASYLOL)

	1				5					10					15		
1	ARG	PRO	ASP	PHE	CYS	LEU	GLU	PRO	PRO	TYR	THR	GLY	PRO	CYS·	LYS		15
16	ALA	ARG	ILE	ILE	ARG	TYR	PHE	TYR	ASN	ALA	LYS	ALA	GLY	LEU	CYS		30
31	GLN	THR	PHE	VAL	TYR	GLY	GLY	CYS	ARG	ALA	LYS	ARG	ASN	ASN	PHE		45
46	LYS	SER	ALA	GLU	ASN	CYS	MET	ARG	THR	CYS	GLY	GLY	ALA				60

Note: Disulphide bridges join residues CYS 5 and 55; CYS 14 and 38; and CYS 30 and 51. The disulphide linkages in kallikrein inactivator of bovine lung.
F. A. Anderer and S. Hörnle.
J. Biol. Chem., **241**, 1568–1572 (1966).

INHIBITORS

TRYPSIN INHIBITOR II FROM PORCINE PANCREAS

	1				5					10					15	
1	ARG	GLU	ALA	THR	CYS	THR	SER	GLU	VAL	SER	GLY	CYS	PRO	LYS	ILE	15
16	TYR	ASN	PRO	VAL	CYS	GLY	THR	ASP	GLY	ILE	THR	TYR	SER	ASN	GLU	30
31	CYS	VAL	LEU	CYS	SER	GLU	ASN	LYS	LYS	ARG	GLN	THR	PRO	VAL	LEU	45
46	ILE	GLN	LYS	SER	GLY	PRO	CYS									60

On Trypsin Inhibitors 7. The Primary Structure of the specific trypsin inhibitor II (KAZAL-type) from porcine pancreas.
H. Tschesche and E. Wachter.
Hoppe-Seyler's Z. Physiol. Chem., **351**, 1449–1459 (1970).

TRYPSIN INHIBITOR I FROM PORCINE PANCREAS

	1				5					10					15	
1	THR	SER	PRO	GLN	ARG	GLU	ALA	THR	CYS	THR	SER	GLU	VAL	SER	GLY	15
16	CYS	PRO	LYS	ILE	TYR	ASN	PRO	VAL	CYS	GLY	THR	ASP	GLY	ILE	THR	30
31	TYR	SER	ASN	GLU	CYS	VAL	LEU	CYS	SER	GLU	ASN	LYS	LYS	ARG	GLN	45
46	THR	PRO	VAL	LEU	ILE	GLN	LYS	SER	GLY	PRO	CYS					60

The Primary Structure of the Porcine Pancreatic Secretory Trypsin Inhibitor I.
D. C. Bartelt and L. J. Greene.
J. Biol. Chem., **246**, 2218–2229 (1971).

PROTEINASE INHIBITOR FROM CANINE SUBMANDIBULAR GLANDS

	1				5					10					15	
1	GLY	PRO	PRO	PRO	ALA	ILE	GLY	ARG	GLX	VAL	ASX	CYS	SER	ASX	TYR	15
16	LYS	GLY	LYS	GLY	SER	GLU	ILE	ALA	CYS	PRO	ARG	LEU	HIS	GLX	PRO	30
31	ILE	CYS	GLY	THR	ASP	HIS	LYS	THR	TYR	SER	ASN	GLX	CYS	MET	LEU	45
46	CYS	ALA	PHE	THR	LEU	ASP	LYS	LYS	PHE	GLX	VAL	ARG	LYS	LEU	GLN	60
61	ASP	THR	ALA	CYS	ASP	ILE	GLU	CYS	THR	GLU	TYR	SER	ASP	MET	CYS	75
76	THR	MET	ASP	TYR	ASX	ARG	PRO	LEU	TYR	CYS	GLY	SER	ASP	GLY	LYS	90
91	ASN	TYR	SER	ASN	LYS	CYS	SER	PHE	CYS	ASN	ALA	VAL	LYS	SER	ARG	105
106	GLY	THR	ILE	PHE	TRP	LEU	ALA	LYS	HIS	GLY	GLU	CYS				120

Note: The above sequence is of Inhibitor I; the other inhibitor found in the submandibular glands was Inhibitor 3: this differed from the above sequence by the exchange of LYS for GLX at position 9.
The Amino acid sequence of the double-headed proteinase inhibitor from submandibular glands III.
K. Hochstraber, G. Bretzel, E. Wachter, and S. Heindl.
Hoppe-Seyler's Z. Physiol. Chem., **356**, 1865–1877 (1975).

INHIBITORS

STREPTOMYCES SUBTILISIN INHIBITOR

	1				5					10					15	
1	ASP	ALA	PRO	SER	ALA	LEU	TYR	ALA	PRO	SER	ALA	LEU	VAL	LEU	THR	15
16	VAL	GLY	LYS	GLY	VAL	SER	ALA	THR	THR	ALA	ALA	PRO	GLU	ARG	ALA	30
31	VAL	THR	LEU	THR	CYS	ALA	PRO	GLY	PRO	SER	GLY	THR	HIS	PRO	ALA	45
46	ALA	GLY	SER	ALA	CYS	ALA	ASP	LEU	ALA	ALA	VAL	GLY	GLY	ASP	LEU	60
61	ASN	ALA	LEU	THR	ARG	GLY	GLU	ASP	VAL	MET	CYS	PRO	MET	VAL	TYR	75
76	ASP	PRO	VAL	LEU	LEU	THR	VAL	ASP	GLY	VAL	TRP	GLN	GLY	LYS	ARG	90
91	VAL	SER	TYR	GLU	ARG	VAL	PHE	SER	ASN	GLU	CYS	GLU	MET	ASN	ALA	105
106	HIS	GLY	SER	SER	VAL	ALA	PHE	PHE								120

Note: Disulphide bridges join residues CYS 35 and 50; CYS 71 and 101.
Amino acid sequence of an alkaline proteinase inhibitor (*Streptomyces* Subtilisin inhibitor) from *Streptomyces albogriseolus* S-3253.
T. Ikenaka, S. Odani, M. Sakai, Y. Nabeshima, S. Sato, and S. Murao.
J. Biochem., **76**, 1191–1209 (1974).

ISOINHIBITOR K FROM SNAIL

	1				5					10					15	
1	GLU	GLY	ARG	PRO	SER	PHE	CYS	ASN	LEU	PRO	ALA	GLU	THR	GLY	PRO	15
16	CYS	LYS	ALA	SER	PHE	ARG	GLN	TYR	TYR	TYR	ASN	SER	LYS	SER	GLY	30
31	GLY	CYS	GLN	GLN	PHE	ILE	TYR	GLY	GLY	CYS	ARG	GLY	ASN	GLN	ASN	45
46	ARG	PHE	ASP	THR	THR	GLN	GLN	CYS	GLN	GLY	VAL	CYS	VAL			60

The amino acid sequence of isoinhibitor K from snails (*Helix pomatia*). A sequence determination by automated Edman degradation and mass-spectral identification of the phenylthiohydantoins.
H. Tschesche and T. Dietl.
Eur. J. Biochem., **58**, 439–451 (1975).

INHIBITOR II FROM RUSSELL'S VIPER VENOM

	1				5					10					15	
1	HIS	ASP	ARG	PRO	THR	PHE	CYS	ASN	LEU	ALA	PRO	GLU	SER	GLY	ARG	15
16	CYS	ARG	GLY	HIS	LEU	ARG	ARG	ILE	TYR	TYR	ASN	LEU	GLU	SER	ASN	30
31	LYS	CYS	LYS	VAL	PHE	PHE	TYR	GLY	GLY	CYS	GLY	GLY	ASN	ALA	ASN	45
46	ASN	PHE	GLU	THR	ARG	ASP	GLU	CYS	ARG	GLU	THR	CYS	GLY	GLY	LYS	60

Note: Disulphide bridges link residues CYS 7 and 57; CYS 16 and 40; CYS 32 and 53.
Primary structure of proteinase inhibitor II isolated from the venom of Russell's viper (*Vipera russelli*).
H. Takahashi, S. Iwanaga, Y. Hokama, T. Suzuki, and T. Kitagawa.
FEBS Letters, **38**, 217–221 (1974); and *J. Biochem.*, **76**, 721–733 (1974).

INHIBITORS

PROTEINASE INHIBITOR II—RINGHAL'S COBRA

	1				5					10					15	
1	ARG	PRO	ASP	PHE	CYS	GLU	LEU	PRO	ALA	GLU	THR	GLY	LEU	CYS	LYS	15
16	ALA	TYR	ILE	ARG	SER	PHE	HIS	TYR	ASN	LEU	ALA	ALA	GLN	GLN	CYS	30
31	LEU	GLN	PHE	ILE	TYR	GLY	GLY	CYS	GLY	GLY	ASN	ALA	ASN	ARG	PHE	45
46	LYS	THR	ILE	ASP	GLU	CYS	ARG	ARG	THR	CYS	VAL	GLY				60

PROTEINASE INHIBITOR II—NAJA NIVEA

	1				5					10					15	
1	ARG	PRO	ARG	PHE	CYS	GLU	LEU	PRO	ALA	GLU	THR	GLY	LEU	CYS	LYS	15
16	ALA	ARG	ILE	ARG	SER	PHE	HIS	TYR	ASN	ARG	ALA	ALA	GLN	GLN	CYS	30
31	LEU	GLU	PHE	ILE	TYR	GLY	GLY	CYS	GLY	GLY	ASN	ALA	ASN	ARG	PHE	45
46	LYS	THR	ILE	ASP	GLU	CYS	HIS	ARG	THR	CYS	VAL	GLY				60

Snake venom proteinase inhibitors. III. Isolation of five polypeptide inhibitors from the venoms of *Hemachatus haemachatus* (Ringhal's cobra) and *Naja nivea* (Cape cobra) and the complete amino acid sequences of two of them.
Y. Hokama, S. Iwanaga, T. Tatsuki, and T. Suzuki.
J. Biochem., **79**, 559–578 (1976).

CHYMOTRYPTIC INHIBITOR I FROM POTATOES

	1				5					10					15	
1	LYS	GLU	PHE	GLU	CYS	ASP	GLY	LYS	LEU	SER	TRP	PRO	GLU	LEU	ILE	15
16	GLY	VAL	PRO	THR	LYS	LEU	ALA	LYS	GLU	ILE	ILE	GLU	LYS	GLN	ASN	30
31	SER	LEU	ILE	SER	ASN	VAL	HIS	ILE	LEU	LEU	ASN	GLY	SER	PRO	VAL	45
46	THR	LEU	ASP	TYR	ARG	CYS	ASN	ARG	VAL	ARG	LEU	PHE	ASP	ASP	ILE	60
61	LEU	GLY	SER	VAL	VAL	ASP	LEU	PRO	ARG	VAL	ALA					75

Notes: (i) Some subunits may have residue 1 (LYS) deleted. (ii) Extensive microheterogeneity has been detected in the subunits of this protein, as summarized below:

Residue no.	Additional amino acids identified	Residue no.	Additional amino acids identified
6	ASN, LYS	59	ASN
10	GLN	63	TYR, ASN
24	GLY	66	GLN
34	THR	67	ILE
37	GLN	69	VAL
40	LYS	70	LEU
47	MET	71	GLY
49	PHE, LEU		

Chymotryptic inhibitor I from potatoes: the amino acid sequences of subunits B, C and D. M. Richardson and L. Cossins.
FEBS Letters, **45**, 11–13 (1974); and *FEBS Letters*, **52**, 161 (1975).

INHIBITORS

CHYMOTRYPTIC INHIBITOR I FROM POTATOES (SUBUNIT A)

	1				5					10					15	
1	GLU	PHE	GLU	CYS	ASP	GLY	LYS	LEU	GLN	TRP	PRO	GLU	LEU	ILE	GLY	15
16	VAL	PRO	THR	LYS	LEU	ALA	LYS	GLU	ILE	ILE	GLU	LYS	GLN	ASN	SER	30
31	LEU	ILE	SER	ASN	VAL	HIS	ILE	LEU	LEU	ASN	GLY	SER	PRO	VAL	THR	45
46	LEU	ASP	ILE	LEU	GLY	ASP	VAL	VAL	GLN	LEU	PRO	VAL	VAL	GLY	MET	60
61	ASP	PHE	ARG	CYS	ASP	ARG	VAL	ARG	LEU	PHE	ASP	ASP	ILE	LEU	GLY	75
76	SER	VAL	VAL	GLN	ILE	PRO	ARG	VAL	ALA							90

Chymotryptic Inhibitor I from potatoes. The amino acid sequence of Subunit A.
M. Richardson.
Biochem. J., **137**, 101–112 (1974).

ACTIVE FRAGMENT OF POTATO PROTEINASE INHIBITOR IIA

	1				5					10					15	
1	SER	GLU	GLY	SER	PRO	GLU	ASN	ARG	ILE	CYS	THR	ASN	ASN	CYS	ALA	15
16	GLY	TYR	LYS	GLY	CYS	ASN	TYR	ASN	CYS	ASP	THR	ASN	ILE	ALA	SER	30
31	TYR	LYS	SER	VAL	CYS	GLU	GLY	GLU	PHE	ASP	PRO	LYS	CYS	LEU	ARG	45

Note: Disulphide bridges join residues CYS 10 and 24; CYS 14 and 35; CYS 43 and 20.
Amino acid sequence of an active fragment of potato proteinase inhibitor IIa.
T. Iwasaki, T. Kiyohara, and M. Yoshikawa.
J. Biochem., **79**, 381–391 (1976).

CARBOXYPEPTIDASE INHIBITOR FROM POTATOES

	1				5					10					15	
1	PYG GLN OOO	HIS	ALA	ASP	PRO	ILE	CYS	ASN	LYS	PRO	CYS	LYS	THR	HIS		15
16	ASP	ASP	CYS	SER	GLY	ALA	TRP	PHE	CYS	GLN	ALA	CYS	TRP	ASN	SER	30
31	ALA	ARG	THR	CYS	GLY	PRO	TYR	VAL	GLY							45

The amino acid sequence of a carboxypeptidase inhibitor from potatoes.
G. M. Hass, H. Nau, K. Biemann, D. T. Grahn, L. H. Ericsson, and H. Neurath.
Biochemistry, **14**, 1334–1342 (1975).

INHIBITORS

SOYABEAN PROTEINASE INHIBITOR C-II

	1				5					10					15	
1	SER	ASP	HIS	SER	SER	SER	ASP	ASP	GLU	SER	SER	LYS	PRO	CYS	CYS	15
16	ASP	LEU	CYS	MET	CYS	THR	ALA	SER	MET	PRO	PRO	GLN	CYS	HIS	CYS	30
31	ALA	ASP	ILE	ARG	LEU	ASN	SER	CYS	HIS	SER	ALA	CYS	ASP	ARG	CYS	45
46	ALA	CYS	THR	ARG	SER	MET	PRO	GLY	GLN	CYS	ARG	CYS	LEU	ASP	THR	60
61	THR	ASP	PHE	CYS	TYR	LYS	PRO	CYS	LYS	SER	GLU	SER	ASP	ASP	ASP	75
76	ASP															90

SOYABEAN PROTEINASE INHIBITOR D-II

	1				5					10					15	
1	SER	ASP	GLN	SER	SER	SER	TYR	ASP	ASP	ASP	GLU	TYR	SER	LYS	PRO	15
16	CYS	CYS	ASP	LEU	CYS	MET	CYS	THR	ARG	SER	MET	PRO	PRO	GLN	CYS	30
31	SER	CYS	GLU	ASP	ILE	ARG	LEU	ASN	SER	CYS	HIS	SER	ASP	CYS	LYS	45
46	SER	CYS	MET	CYS	THR	ARG	SER	GLN	PRO	GLY	GLN	CYS	ARG	CYS	LEU	60
61	ASP	THR	ASN	ASP	PHE	CYS	TYR	LYS	PRO	CYS	LYS	SER	ARG	ASP	ASP	75

The amino acid sequences of two soyabean double headed proteinase inhibitors and evolutionary consideration of the legume proteinase inhibitors.
S. Odani and T. Ikenaka.
J. Biochem., **80**, 641–643 (1976).

INHIBITORS

SOYABEAN TRYPSIN INHIBITOR (KUNITZ)

	1				5					10					15	
1	ASP	PHE	VAL	LEU	ASP	ASN	GLU	GLY	ASN	PRO	LEU	GLU	ASN	GLY	GLY	15
16	THR	TYR	TYR	ILE	LEU	SER	ASP	ILE	THR	ALA	PHE	GLY	GLY	ILE	ARG	30
31	ALA	ALA	PRO	THR	GLY	ASN	GLU	ARG	CYS	PRO	LEU	THR	VAL	VAL	GLN	45
46	SER	ARG	ASN	GLU	LEU	ASP	LYS	GLY	ILE	GLY	THR	ILE	ILE	SER	PRO	60
61	SER	TYR	ARG	ILE	ARG	PHE	ILE	ALA	GLU	GLY	HIS	PRO	LEU	SER	LEU	75
76	LYS	PHE	ASP	SER	PHE	ALA	VAL	ILE	MET	LEU	CYS	VAL	GLY	ILE	PRO	90
91	THR	GLU	TRP	SER	VAL	VAL	GLU	ASP	LEU	PRO	GLU	GLY	PRO	ALA	VAL	105
106	LYS	ILE	GLY	GLU	ASN	LYS	ASP	ALA	MET	ASP	GLY	TRP	PHE	ARG	LEU	120
121	GLU	ARG	VAL	SER	ASP	ASP	GLU	PHE	ASN	ASN	TYR	LYS	LEU	VAL	PHE	135
136	CYS	PRO	GLN	GLN	ALA	GLU	ASP	ASP	LYS	CYS	GLY	ASP	ILE	GLY	ILE	150
151	SER	ILE	ASP	ASP	ASP	GLY	HIS	THR	ARG	ARG	LEU	VAL	VAL	SER	LYS	165
166	ASN	LYS	PRO	LEU	VAL	VAL	GLN	PHE	GLN	LYS	LEU	ASP	LYS	GLU	SER	180
181	LEU															195

Note: Disulphide bridges are between CYS 39 and 86; CYS 136 and 145.
Studies on soyabean trypsin inhibitors. 3. Amino acid sequences of the carboxyl-terminal region and the complete amino acid sequence of soyabean trypsin inhibitor (Kunitz).
T. Koide and T. Ikenaka.
Eur. J. Biochem., **32**, 417–431 (1973).

TRYPSIN INHIBITOR D-II—SOYABEAN

	1				5					10					15	
1	SER	ASP	GLN	SER	SER	SER	TYR	ASP	ASP	ASP	GLU	TYR	SER	LYS	PRO	15
16	CYS	CYS	ASP	LEU	CYS	MET	CYS	THR	ARG	SER	MET	PRO	PRO	GLN	CYS	30
31	SER	CYS	GLU	ASP	ILE	ARG	LEU	ASN	SER	CYS	HIS	SER	ASP	CYS	LYS	45
46	SER	CYS	MET	CYS	THR	ARG	SER	GLN	PRO	GLY	GLN	CYS	ARG	CYS	LEU	60
61	ASP	THR	ASN	ASP	PHE	CYS	TYR	LYS	PRO	CYS	LYS	SER	ARG	ASP	ASP	75

Studies on Soyabean Trypsin Inhibitors. XII Linear sequences of two soyabean double-headed trypsin inhibitors, D-II and E-I.
S. Odani and T. Ikenaka.
J. Biochem., **83**, 737–745 (1978).

INHIBITORS

BOWMAN–BIRK SOYABEAN TRYPSIN INHIBITOR

	1			5					10					15		
1	ASP	ASP	GLU	SER	SER	LYS	PRO	CYS	CYS	ASP	GLN	CYS	ALA	CYS	THR	15
16	LYS	SER	ASN	PRO	PRO	GLN	CYS	ARG	CYS	SER	ASP	MET	ARG	LEU	ASN	30
31	SER	CYS	HIS	SER	ALA	CYS	LYS	SER	CYS	ILE	CYS	ALA	LEU	SER	TYR	45
46	PRO	ALA	GLN	CYS	PHE	CYS	VAL	ASP	ILE	THR	ASP	PHE	CYS	TYR	GLU	60
61	PRO	CYS	LYS	PRO	SER	GLU	ASP	ASP	LYS	GLU	ASN					75

Studies on Soyabean Trypsin Inhibitors. 4. Complete Amino Acid Sequence and
anti-proteinase sites of Bowman–Birk Soyabean Proteinase Inhibitor.
S. Odani and T. Ikenaka.
J. Biochem., **71**, 839–848 (1972).

ARACHIS HYPOGAEA *TRYPSIN INHIBITOR*

	1			5					10					15		
1	CYS	THR	ASX	LYS	THR	GLX	GLY	ARG	CYS	PRO	VAL	THR	GLX	CYS	ARG	15
16	SER	ASX	PRO	PRO	GLX	CYS	ARG	ALA	PRO	PRO	TYR	PHE	GLX	CYS	VAL	30
31	CYS	VAL	ASX	THR	PHE	ASX	HIS	CYS	PRO	ALA	SER	CYS	ASX	SER	CYS	45
46	CYS	THR	ARG													60

Plant protease inhibitors 8. The amino acid sequence of the trypsin inhibitor from the seeds of
Arachis hypogaea.
K. Hochstrasser, K. Illchmann, and E. Werle.
Hoppe-Seyler's Z. Physiol. Chem., **351**, 1503–1512 (1970).

LIMA BEAN PROTEASE INHIBITOR COMPONENT IV

	1			5					10					15		
1	SER	GLY	HIS	HIS	GLU	HIS	SER	THR	ASP	GLX	PRO	SER	GLX	SER	SER	15
16	CYS	LYS	PRO	CYS	ASN	HIS	CYS	CYS	CYS	LEU	SER/ALA	THR	LYS	SER	ILE	30
31	PRO	PRO	GLX	CYS	ARG	CYS	THR/SER	ASP	LEU/PHE	ARG	LEU	ASP	SER	CYS	HIS	45
46	SER	CYS	ALA	LYS	CYS	CYS	ILE	SER	THR	LEU	SER	ILE	PRO	ALA	GLN	60
61	CYS	VAL	THR	(ILE,	ASP)	ASX	ASP	PHE	CYS	TYR	GLU	CYS	PRO	LYS	SER	75
76	SER	HIS	SER	ASP	ASP	ASP	ASN	ASN	ASN							90

Amino Acid Sequence of Lima Bean Protease Inhibitor Component IV.
C. G. L. Tan and F. C. Stevens.
Eur. J. Biochem., **18**, 515–523 (1971).

INHIBITORS

TRYPSIN INHIBITOR II' FROM GARDEN BEAN

	1				5					10					15	
1	GLX	PRO	SER	GLX	SER	SER	PRO	PRO	CYS	CYS	ASX	ILE	CYS	VAL	CYS	15
16	THR	ALA	SER	ILE	PRO	PRO	GLN	CYS	(ILE,	CYS,	THR,	ASX,	VAL)	ARG	LEU	30
31	ASX	SER	CYS	HIS	SER	ALA	CYS	LYS	SER	CYS	MET	CYS	THR	ARG	SER	45
46	MET	PRO	GLY	LYS	CYS	ARG	CYS	LEU	ASX	THR	THR	ASX	TYR	CYS	TYR	60
61	LYS	SER	CYS	LYS	SER	ASX	SER	GLY	GLX	ASX	ASX					75

Note: The above sequence is of inhibitor II': inhibitor II differs from the above by having an extra eight amino acids at the N-terminus; the sequence of these extra residues is as yet undetermined.

The partial amino acid sequence of trypsin inhibitor II from garden bean, *Phaseolus vulgaris*, with location of the trypsin and elastase-reactive sites.

K. A. Wilson and M. Laskowski, Sr.

J. Biol. Chem., **250**, 4261–4267 (1975).

PROTEASE INHIBITORS FROM PINEAPPLE STEM

A-CHAIN

	1			5					10					15	
1	(1)	GLU	TYR	LYS	CYS	TYR	CYS	(8)	ASP	THR	TYR	SER	ASP	CYS	PRO	15
16	GLY	PHE	CYS	LYS	LYS	CYS	LYS	ALA	GLU	PHE	GLY	LYS	TYR	ILE	CYS	30
31	LEU	ASP	LEU	ILE	SER	PRO	ASN	ASP	CYS	VAL	LYS					45

B-CHAIN

	1			5					10			15	
1	(1)	ALA	CYS	SER	GLU	CYS	VAL	CYS	PRO	LEU	(11)		15

Notes: (i) There is a group of related inhibitors; each consists of an A-chain joined by disulphide bridges to a B-chain. In all there are three A-chains and four B-chains; they differ because of microheterogeneity at positions (1) and (8) of the A-chain, and (1) and (11) of the B-chain. (ii) Differences between the chains are:

Chain	(1)	(8)	Chain	(1)	(11)
A1	ASP	ALA	B1	THR	ARG
A2	PYG	THR	B2	THR	GLN
A3	GLU	THR	B3	OOO	ARG
			B4	OOO	GLN

Primary structural analysis of sulphydryl protease inhibitors from pineapple stem.

M. N. Reddy, P. S. Keim, R. L. Heinrikson, and F. J. Kézdy.

J. Biol. Chem., **250**, 1741–1750 (1975).

SOMATOMEDIN B

	1			5						10					15		
1	ASP	GLN	GLU	SER	CYS	LYS	GLY	ARG	CYS	THR	GLU	GLY	PHE	ASN	VAL		15
16	ASP	LYS	LYS	CYS	GLN	CYS	ASP	GLU	LEU	CYS	SER	TYR	TYR	GLN	SER		30
31	ASN	CYS	THR	CYS	TYR	THR	ALA	GLU	CYS	LYS	PRO	GLN	VAL	THR			45

Primary structure of somatomedin B. A growth hormone-dependent serum factor with protease inhibiting activity.
L. Fryklund and H. Sievertsson.
FEBS Letters, **87**, 55–60 (1978).

240

GLOBINS

HUMAN HAEMOGLOBIN α-CHAIN

	1				5					10					15	
1	VAL	LEU	SER	PRO	ALA	ASP	LYS	THR	ASN	VAL	LYS	ALA	ALA	TRP	GLY	15
16	LYS	VAL	GLY	ALA	HIS	ALA	GLY	GLU	TYR	GLY	ALA	GLU	ALA	LEU	GLU	30
31	ARG	MET	PHE	LEU	SER	PHE	PRO	THR	THR	LYS	THR	TYR	PHE	PRO	HIS	45
46	PHE	ASP	LEU	SER	HIS	GLY	SER	ALA	GLN	VAL	LYS	GLY	HIS	GLY	LYS	60
61	LYS	VAL	ALA	ASP	ALA	LEU	THR	ASN	ALA	VAL	ALA	HIS	VAL	ASP	ASP	75
76	MET	PRO	ASN	ALA	LEU	SER	ALA	LEU	SER	ASP	LEU	HIS	ALA	HIS	LYS	90
91	LEU	ARG	VAL	ASP	PRO	VAL	ASN	PHE	LYS	LEU	LEU	SER	HIS	CYS	LEU	105
106	LEU	VAL	THR	LEU	ALA	ALA	HIS	LEU	PRO	ALA	GLU	PHE	THR	PRO	ALA	120
121	VAL	HIS	ALA	SER	LEU	ASP	LYS	PHE	LEU	ALA	SER	VAL	SER	THR	VAL	135
136	LEU	THR	SER	LYS	TYR	ARG										150

The Structure of Human Hemoglobin.
W. Konigsberg and R. J. Hill.
J. Biol. Chem., **237**, 3157–3162 (1962).

MONKEY HAEMOGLOBIN α-CHAIN

	1				5					10					15	
1	VAL	LEU	SER	PRO	ALA	ASP	LYS	SER	ASN	VAL	LYS	ALA	ALA	TRP	GLY	15
16	LYS	VAL	GLY	GLY	HIS	ALA	GLY	GLU	TYR	GLY	ALA	GLU	ALA	LEU	GLU	30
31	ARG	MET	PHE	LEU	SER	PHE	PRO	THR	THR	LYS	THR	TYR	PHE	PRO	HIS	45
46	PHE	ASP	LEU	SER	HIS	GLY	SER	ALA	GLN	VAL	LYS	GLY	HIS	GLY	LYS	60
61	LYS	VAL	ALA	ASP	ALA	LEU	THR	LEU	ALA	VAL	GLY	HIS	VAL	ASP	ASP	75
76	MET	PRO	ASN	ALA	LEU	SER	ALA	LEU	SER	ASP	LEU	HIS	ALA	HIS	LYS	90
91	LEU	ARG	VAL	ASP	PRO	VAL	ASN	PHE	LYS	LEU	LEU	SER	HIS	CYS	LEU	105
106	LEU	VAL	THR	LEU	ALA	ALA	HIS	LEU	PRO	ALA	GLU	PHE	THR	PRO	ALA	120
121	VAL	HIS	ALA	SER	LEU	ASP	LYS	PHE	LEU	ALA	SER	VAL	SER	THR	VAL	135
136	LEU	THR	SER	LYS	TYR	ARG										150

The Primary Structure of Adult Hemoglobin from *Macaca mulatta* Monkey.
G. Matsuda, T. Maita, H. Takei, H. Ota, M. Yamaguchi, T. Miyauchi, and M. Migita.
J. Biochem., **64**, 279–282 (1968).

GLOBINS

HAEMOGLOBIN α-CHAIN—CAPUCHIN MONKEY

	1				5					10					15	
1	VAL	LEU	SER	PRO	ALA	ASP	LYS	THR	ASN	VAL	LYS	THR	ALA	TRP	GLY	15
16	LYS	VAL	GLY	GLY	HIS	ALA	GLY	ASP	TYR	GLY	ALA	GLU	ALA	LEU	GLU	30
31	ARG	MET	PHE	LEU	SER	PHE	PRO	THR	THR	LYS	THR	TYR	PHE	PRO	HIS	45
46	PHE	ASP	LEU	SER	HIS	GLY	SER	ALA	GLN	VAL	LYS	GLY	HIS	GLY	LYS	60
61	LYS	VAL	ALA	ASP	ALA	LEU	SER	ASN	ALA	VAL	ALA	HIS	VAL	ASP	ASP	75
76	MET	PRO	ASN	ALA	LEU	SER	ALA	LEU	SER	ASP	LEU	HIS	ALA	HIS	LYS	90
91	LEU	ARG	VAL	ASP	PRO	VAL	ASN	PHE	LYS	LEU	LEU	SER	HIS	CYS	LEU	105
106	LEU	VAL	THR	LEU	ALA	ALA	HIS	HIS	PRO	ALA	ASP	PHE	THR	PRO	ALA	120
121	VAL	HIS	ALA	SER	LEU	ASP	LYS	PHE	LEU	ALA	SER	VAL	SER	THR	VAL	135
136	LEU	THR	SER	LYS	TYR	ARG										150

The amino acid sequences of the α and β polypeptide chains of adult hemoglobin of the Capuchin Monkey (*Cebus apella*).
G. Matsuda, T. Maita, B. Watanabe, A. Araya, K. Morokuma, Y. Ota, M. Goodman, J. Barnabas, and W. Prychodko.
Hoppe-Seyler's Z. Physiol. Chem., **354**, 1513–1516 (1973).

HAEMOGLOBIN α-CHAIN—SAVANNAH MONKEY

	1				5					10					15	
1	VAL	LEU	SER	PRO	ALA	ASP	LYS	SER	ASN	VAL	LYS	ALA	ALA	TRP	GLY	15
16	LYS	VAL	GLY	GLY	HIS	ALA	GLY	GLU	TYR	GLY	ALA	GLU	ALA	LEU	GLU	30
31	ARG	MET	PHE	LEU	SER	PHE	PRO	THR	THR	LYS	THR	TYR	PHE	PRO	HIS	45
46	PHE	ASP	LEU	SER	HIS	GLY	SER	ALA	GLN	VAL	LYS	GLY	HIS	GLY	LYS	60
61	LYS	VAL	ALA	ASP	ALA	LEU	THR	LEU	ALA	VAL	GLY	HIS	VAL	ASP	ASP	75
76	MET	PRO	HIS	ALA	LEU	SER	ALA	LEU	SER	ASP	LEU	HIS	ALA	HIS	LYS	90
91	LEU	ARG	VAL	ASP	PRO	VAL	ASN	PHE	LYS	LEU	LEU	SER	HIS	CYS	LEU	105
106	LEU	VAL	THR	LEU	ALA	ALA	HIS	LEU	PRO	ALA	GLU	PHE	THR	PRO	ALA	120
121	VAL	HIS	ALA	SER	LEU	ASP	LYS	PHE	LEU	ALA	SER	VAL	SER	THR ·VAL		135
136	LEU	THR	SER	LYS	TYR	ARG										150

The amino acid sequences of the α and β polypeptide chains of adult hemoglobin of the Savannah Monkey (*Cercopithecus aethiops*).
G. Matsuda, T. Maita, B. Watanabe, A. Araya, K. Morokuma, M. Goodman, and W. Prychodko.
Hoppe-Seyler's Z. Physiol. Chem., **354**, 1153–1155 (1973).

GLOBINS

HAEMOGLOBIN α-CHAIN—JAPANESE MONKEY

```
        1           5                    10                      15
  1  VAL LEU SER PRO ALA ASP LYS SER ASN VAL LYS ALA ALA TRP GLY   15
 16  LYS VAL GLY GLY HIS ALA GLY GLU TYR GLY ALA GLU ALA LEU GLU   30
 31  ARG MET PHE LEU SER PHE PRO THR THR LYS THR TYR PHE PRO HIS   45
 46  PHE ASP LEU SER HIS GLY SER ALA GLN VAL LYS GLY HIS GLY LYS   60
 61  LYS VAL ALA ASP ALA LEU THR LEU ALA VAL GLY HIS VAL ASP ASP   75
 76  MET PRO ASN ALA LEU SER ALA LEU SER ASP LEU HIS ALA HIS LYS   90
 91  LEU ARG VAL ASP PRO VAL ASN PHE LYS LEU LEU SER HIS CYS LEU  105
106  LEU VAL THR LEU ALA ALA HIS LEU PRO ALA GLU PHE THR PRO ALA  120
121  VAL HIS ALA SER LEU ASP LYS PHE LEU ALA SER VAL SER THR VAL  135
136  LEU THR SER LYS TYR ARG                                      150
```

The primary structures of α and β chains of adult hemoglobin of the Japanese monkey (*Macata fuscata fuscata*).

G. Matsuda, T. Maita, H. Ota, A. Araya, Y. Nakashima, U. Ishii, and M. Nakashima. *Int. J. Peptide Protein Res.*, **5**, 405–418 (1973).

HAEMOGLOBIN α-CHAIN—HANUMAN LANGUR

```
        1           5                    10                      15
  1  VAL LEU SER PRO ALA ASP LYS THR ASN VAL LYS ALA ALA TRP GLY   15
 16  LYS VAL GLY GLY HIS GLY GLY GLU TYR GLY ALA GLU ALA LEU GLU   30
 31  ARG MET PHE LEU SER PHE PRO THR THR LYS THR TYR PHE PRO HIS   45
 46  PHE ASP LEU SER HIS GLY SER ALA GLN VAL LYS GLY HIS GLY LYS   60
 61  LYS VAL ALA ASP ALA LEU THR ASN ALA VAL ALA HIS VAL ASP ASP   75
 76  MET PRO HIS ALA LEU SER ALA LEU SER ASP LEU HIS ALA HIS LYS   90
 91  LEU ARG VAL ASP PRO VAL ASN PHE LYS LEU LEU SER HIS CYS LEU  105
106  LEU VAL THR LEU ALA ALA HIS LEU PRO ALA GLU PHE THR PRO ALA  120
121  VAL HIS ALA SER LEU ASP LYS PHE LEU ALA SER VAL SER THR VAL  135
136  LEU THR SER LYS TYR ARG                                      150
```

The primary structures of the α and β polypeptide chains of adult hemoglobin of the Hanuman langur (*Presbytis entellus*).

G. Matsuda, T. Maita, Y. Nakashima, J. Barnabas, P. K. Ranjekar, and N. S. Gandhi. *Int. J. Peptide Protein Res.*, **5**, 423–425 (1973).

HAEMOGLOBIN α-CHAIN—ORANGUTAN

	1				5					10					15	
1	VAL	LEU	SER	PRO	ALA	ASP	LYS	THR	ASN	VAL	LYS	THR	ALA	TRP	GLY	15
16	LYS	VAL	GLY	ALA	HIS	ALA	GLY	ASP	TYR	GLY	ALA	GLU	ALA	LEU	GLU	30
31	ARG	MET	PHE	LEU	SER	PHE	PRO	THR	THR	LYS	THR	TYR	PHE	PRO	HIS	45
46	PHE	ASP	LEU	SER	HIS	GLY	SER	ALA	GLN	VAL	LYS	ASP	HIS	GLY	LYS	60
61	LYS	VAL	ALA	ASP	ALA	LEU	THR	ASN	ALA	VAL	ALA	HIS	VAL	ASP	ASP	75
76	MET	PRO	ASN	ALA	LEU	SER	ALA	LEU	SER	ASP	LEU	HIS	ALA	HIS	LYS	90
91	LEU	ARG	VAL	ASP	PRO	VAL	ASN	PHE	LYS	LEU	LEU	SER	HIS	CYS	LEU	105
106	LEU	VAL	THR	LEU	ALA	ALA	HIS	LEU	PRO	ALA	GLU	PHE	THR	PRO	ALA	120
121	VAL	HIS	ALA	SER	LEU	ASP	LYS	PHE	LEU	ALA	SER	VAL	SER	THR	VAL	135
136	LEU	THR	SER	LYS	TYR	ARG										150

Note: The above sequence is that of the α-I chain. The α-II chain differs in that residue 57 is GLY.
The amino acid sequences of the two main components of adult hemoglobin from orangutan (*Pongo pygmaeus*).
T. Maita, A. Araya, M. Goodman, and G. Matsuda.
Hoppe-Seyler's Z. Physiol. Chem., **359**, 129–132 (1978).

HAEMOGLOBIN α-CHAIN—SLENDER LORIS

	1				5					10					15	
1	VAL	LEU	SER	PRO	ALA	ASP	LYS	THR	ASN	VAL	LYS	GLY	ALA	TRP	GLU	15
16	LYS	VAL	GLY	GLY	HIS	ALA	GLY	GLU	TYR	GLY	ALA	GLU	ALA	LEU	GLU	30
31	ARG	MET	PHE	LEU	SER	PHE	PRO	THR	THR	LYS	THR	TYR	PHE	PRO	HIS	45
46	PHE	ASP	LEU	SER	HIS	GLY	SER	ALA	GLN	VAL	LYS	ALA	HIS	GLY	LYS	60
61	LYS	VAL	ALA	ASP	ALA	LEU	THR	THR	ALA	VAL	SER	HIS	VAL	ASP	ASP	75
76	MET	PRO	SER	ALA	LEU	SER	ALA	LEU	SER	ASP	LEU	HIS	ALA	HIS	LYS	90
91	LEU	ARG	VAL	ASP	PRO	VAL	ASN	PHE	LYS	LEU	LEU	SER	HIS	CYS	LEU	105
106	LEU	VAL	THR	LEU	ALA	CYS	HIS	HIS	PRO	ALA	ASP	PHE	THR	PRO	ALA	120
121	VAL	HIS	ALA	SER	LEU	ASP	LYS	PHE	LEU	ALA	SER	VAL	SER	THR	VAL	135
136	LEU	THR	SER	LYS	TYR	ARG										150

Amino acid sequences of the α and β chains of adult hemoglobin of the Slender Loris, *Loris tardigradus*.
T. Maita, M. Goodman, and G. Matsuda.
J. Biochem., **84**, 377–383 (1978).

GLOBINS

HAEMOGLOBIN α-CHAIN—SLOW LORIS

	1				5					10					15	
1	VAL	LEU	SER	PRO	ALA	ASP	LYS	THR	ASN	VAL	LYS	ALA	ALA	TRP	GLU	15
16	LYS	VAL	GLY	SER	HIS	ALA	GLY	ASP	TYR	GLY	ALA	GLU	ALA	LEU	GLU	30
31	ARG	MET	PHE	LEU	SER	PHE	PRO	THR	THR	LYS	THR	TYR	PHE	PRO	HIS	45
46	PHE	ASP	LEU	SER	HIS	GLY	SER	ALA	GLN	VAL	LYS	ALA	HIS	GLY	LYS	60
61	LYS	VAL	ALA	ASP	ALA	LEU	THR	ASN	ALA	VAL	SER	HIS	VAL	ASP	ASP	75
76	MET	PRO	SER	ALA	LEU	SER	ALA	LEU	SER	ASP	LEU	HIS	ALA	HIS	LYS	90
91	LEU	ARG	VAL	ASP	PRO	VAL	ASN	PHE	LYS	LEU	LEU	SER	HIS	CYS	LEU	105
106	LEU	VAL	THR	LEU	ALA	CYS	HIS	HIS	PRO	ALA	ASP	PHE	THR	PRO	ALA	120
121	VAL	HIS	ALA	SER	LEU	ASP	LYS	PHE	LEU	ALA	SER	VAL	SER	THR	VAL	135
136	LEU	THR	SER	LYS	TYR	ARG										150

The primary structures of the α and β polypeptide chains of adult hemoglobin of the slow loris (*Nycticebus coucang*).
G. Matsuda, T. Maita, B. Watanabe, H. Ota, A. Araya, M. Goodman, and W. Prychodko.
Int. J. Peptide Protein Res., **5**, 419–421 (1973).

HORSE HAEMOGLOBIN α-CHAIN

	1				5					10					15	
1	VAL	LEU	SER	ALA	ALA	ASP	LYS	THR	ASN	VAL	LYS	ALA	ALA	TRP	SER	15
16	LYS	VAL	GLY	GLY	HIS	ALA	GLY	GLU	TYR	GLY	ALA	GLU	ALA	LEU	GLU	30
31	ARG	MET	PHE	LEU	GLY	PHE	PRO	THR	THR	LYS	THR	TYR	PHE	PRO	HIS	45
46	PHE	ASP	LEU	SER	HIS	GLY	SER	ALA	GLN	VAL	LYS	ALA	HIS	GLY	LYS	60
61	LYS	VAL	ALA	ASP	GLY	LEU	THR	LEU	ALA	VAL	GLY	HIS	LEU	ASP	ASP	75
76	LEU	PRO	GLY	ALA	LEU	SER	ASN	LEU	SER	ASP	LEU	HIS	ALA	HIS	LYS	90
91	LEU	ARG	VAL	ASP	PRO	VAL	ASN	PHE	LYS	LEU	LEU	SER	HIS	CYS	LEU	105
106	LEU	SER	THR	LEU	ALA	VAL	HIS	LEU	PRO	ASN	ASP	PHE	THR	PRO	ALA	120
121	VAL	HIS	ALA	SER	LEU	ASP	LYS	PHE	LEU	SER	SER	VAL	SER	THR	VAL	135
136	LEU	THR	SER	LYS	TYR	ARG										150

Primary Structure of the α-chain of Horse Hemoglobin.
G. Braunitzer and G. Matsuda.
J. Biochem., **53**, 262–263 (1963).

GLOBINS

KANGAROO HAEMOGLOBIN α-CHAIN

	1			5					10					15		
1	VAL	LEU	SER	ALA	ALA	ASP	LYS	GLY	HIS	VAL	LYS	ALA	ILE	TRP	GLY	15
16	LYS	VAL	GLY	GLY	HIS	ALA	GLY	GLU	TYR	ALA	ALA	GLU	GLY	LEU	GLU	30
31	ARG	THR	PHE	HIS	SER	PHE	PRO	THR	THR	LYS	THR	TYR	PHE	PRO	HIS	45
46	PHE	ASP	LEU	SER	HIS	GLY	SER	ALA	GLN	ILE	GLN	ALA	HIS	GLY	LYS	60
61	LYS	ILE	ALA	ASP	ALA	LEU	GLY	GLN	ALA	VAL	GLU	HIS	ILE	ASP	ASP	75
76	LEU	PRO	GLY	THR	LEU	SER	LYS	LEU	SER	ASP	LEU	HIS	ALA	HIS	LYS	90
91	LEU	ARG	VAL	ASP	PRO	VAL	ASN	PHE	LYS	LEU	LEU	SER	HIS	CYS	LEU	105
106	LEU	VAL	THR	PHE	ALA	ALA	HIS	LEU	GLY	ASP	ALA	PHE	THR	PRO	GLU	120
121	VAL	HIS	ALA	SER	LEU	ASP	LYS	PHE	LEU	ALA	ALA	VAL	SER	THR	VAL	135
136	LEU	THR	SER	LYS	TYR	ARG										150

Amino acid sequence of the α-chain of Haemoglobin from the Grey Kangaroo, *Macropus giganteus*.
J. M. Beard and E. O. P. Thompson.
Aust. J. Biol. Sci., **24**, 765–786 (1971).

HAEMOGLOBIN α-CHAIN—ECHIDNA (MAJOR HAEMOGLOBIN HB-IB)

	1			5					10					15		
1	VAL	LEU	THR	ASP	ALA	GLU	LYS	LYS	GLU	VAL	THR	SER	LEU	TRP	GLY	15
16	LYS	ALA	SER	GLY	HIS	ALA	GLU	GLU	TYR	GLY	ALA	GLU	ALA	LEU	GLU	30
31	ARG	LEU	PHE	LEU	SER	PHE	PRO	THR	THR	LYS	THR	TYR	PHE	SER	HIS	45
46	MET	ASP	LEU	SER	LYS	GLY	SER	ALA	GLN	VAL	LYS	ALA	HIS	GLY	LYS	60
61	ARG	VAL	ALA	ASP	ALA	LEU	THR	THR	ALA	ALA	GLY	HIS	PHE	ASN	ASP	75
76	MET	ASP	SER	ALA	LEU	SER	ALA	LEU	SER	ASP	LEU	HIS	ALA	HIS	LYS	90
91	LEU	ARG	VAL	ASP	PRO	VAL	ASN	PHE	LYS	LEU	LEU	ALA	HIS	CYS	PHE	105
106	LEU	VAL	VAL	LEU	ALA	ARG	HIS	HIS	PRO	ALA	GLU	PHE	THR	PRO	SER	120
121	ALA	HIS	ALA	ALA	MET	ASP	LYS	PHE	LEU	SER	ARG	VAL	ALA	THR	VAL	135
136	LEU	THR	SER	LYS	TYR	ARG										150

Studies on monotreme proteins. II. Amino acid sequence of the α-chain in haemoglobin from the echidna, *Tachyglossus aculeatus aculeatus*.
R. G. Whittaker, W. K. Fisher, and E. O. P. Thompson.
Aust. J. Biol. Sci., **26**, 877–888 (1973).

246

GLOBINS

HAEMOGLOBIN α-CHAIN—ECHIDNA (MAJOR HAEMOGLOBIN HB-IA)

	1				5					10					15	
1	VAL	LEU	THR	ASP	ALA	GLU	LYS	LYS	GLU	VAL	THR	GLY	LEU	TRP	GLY	15
16	LYS	ALA	SER	GLY	HIS	ALA	GLU	GLU	TYR	GLY	ALA	GLU	ALA	LEU	GLU	30
31	ARG	LEU	PHE	LEU	SER	PHE	PRO	THR	THR	LYS	THR	TYR	PHE	SER	HIS	45
46	MET	ASP	LEU	SER	LYS	GLY	SER	ALA	GLN	VAL	LYS	ALA	HIS	GLY	LYS	60
61	ARG	VAL	ALA	ASP	ALA	LEU	THR	THR	ALA	ALA	GLY	HIS	PHE	ASN	ASP	75
76	MET	ASP	ASN	ALA	LEU	SER	ALA	LEU	SER	ASP	LEU	HIS	ALA	HIS	LYS	90
91	LEU	ARG	VAL	ASP	PRO	VAL	ASN	PHE	LYS	LEU	LEU	SER	HIS	CYS	PHE	105
106	LEU	VAL	VAL	LEU	ALA	ARG	HIS	HIS	PRO	GLU	GLU	PHE	THR	PRO	SER	120
121	ALA	HIS	ALA	ALA	MET	ASP	LYS	PHE	LEU	SER	ARG	VAL	ALA	THR	VAL	135
136	LEU	THR	SER	LYS	TYR	ARG										150

Studies on monotreme proteins IV. Amino acid sequence of haemoglobin IA of the echidna; a comparison of major haemoglobins from two geographical groups of echidnas.
S. J. Dodgson, W. K. Fisher, and E. O. P. Thompson.
Aust. J. Biol. Sci., **27**, 111–115 (1974).

HAEMOGLOBIN α-CHAIN—ECHIDNA (MINOR HAEMOGLOBIN HB-IIA)

	1				5					10					15	
1	VAL	LEU	THR	ASP	ALA	GLU	ARG	LYS	GLU	VAL	THR	SER	LEU	TRP	GLY	15
16	LYS	ALA	SER	GLY	HIS	ALA	GLU	ASP	TYR	GLY	ALA	GLU	ALA	LEU	GLU	30
31	ARG	LEU	PHE	LEU	SER	PHE	PRO	THR	THR	LYS	THR	TYR	PHE	SER	HIS	45
46	MET	ASP	LEU	SER	LYS	GLY	SER	ALA	HIS	VAL	ARG	ALA	HIS	GLY	LYS	60
61	LYS	VAL	ALA	ASP	ALA	LEU	THR	THR	ALA	VAL	GLY	HIS	PHE	ASN	ASP	75
76	MET	ASP	GLY	ALA	LEU	SER	ASP	LEU	SER	ASP	LEU	HIS	ALA	HIS	LYS	90
91	LEU	ARG	VAL	ASP	PRO	VAL	ASN	PHE	LYS	LEU	LEU	ALA	HIS	CYS	PHE	105
106	LEU	VAL	VAL	LEU	ALA	ARG	HIS	HIS	PRO	GLU	GLU	PHE	THR	PRO	SER	120
121	ALA	HIS	ALA	ALA	MET	ASP	LYS	PHE	LEU	SER	ARG	VAL	ALA	THR	VAL	135
136	LEU	THR	SER	LYS	TYR	ARG										150

Studies on monotreme proteins. III. Amino acid sequence of the α- and β-globin chains of the minor haemoglobin from the echidna *Tachyglossus aculeatus aculeatus*.
E. O. P. Thompson, W. K. Fisher, and R. G. Whittaker.
Aust. J. Biol. Sci., **26**, 1327–1335 (1973).

HAEMOGLOBIN α-CHAIN—OPOSSUM

	1				5					10					15		
1	VAL	LEU	SER	ALA	ASN	ASP	LYS	THR	ASN	VAL	LYS	GLY	ALA	TRP	SER		15
16	LYS	VAL	GLY	GLY	ASN	SER	GLY	ALA	TYR	MET	GLY	GLU	ALA	LEU	TYR		30
31	ARG	THR	PHE	LEU	SER	PHE	PRO	THR	THR	LYS	THR	TYR	PHE	PRO	ASN		45
46	TYR	ASP	PHE	SER	ALA	GLY	SER	ALA	GLN	ILE	LYS	THR	GLN	GLY	GLN		60
61	LYS	ILE	ALA	ASP	ALA	VAL	GLY	LEU	ALA	VAL	ALA	HIS	LEU	ASP	ASP		75
76	MET	PRO	THR	ALA	LEU	SER	SER	LEU	SER	ASP	LEU	HIS	ALA	HIS	GLU		90
91	LEU	LYS	VAL	ASP	PRO	VAL	ASN	PHE	LYS	PHE	LEU	CYS	HIS	ASN	VAL		105
106	LEU	VAL	THR	MET	ALA	ALA	HIS	LEU	GLY	LYS	ASP	PHE	THR	PRO	GLU		120
121	ILE	HIS	ALA	SER	MET	ASP	LYS	PHE	LEU	ALA	SER	VAL	SER	THR	VAL		135
136	LEU	THR	SER	LYS	TYR	ARG											150

Opossum Hb chain sequence and neutral mutation theory.
P. Stenzel.
Nature, **252**, 62–63 (1974).

RABBIT HAEMOGLOBIN α-CHAIN

	1				5					10					15		
1	VAL	LEU	SER	PRO	ALA	ASP	LYS	THR	ASN	ILE	LYS	THR	ALA	TRP	GLU		15
16	LYS	ILE	GLY	SER	HIS	GLY	GLY	GLU	TYR	GLY	ALA	GLU	ALA	VAL	GLU		30
31	ARG	MET	PHE	LEU	GLY	PHE	PRO	THR	THR	LYS	THR	TYR	PHE	PRO	HIS		45
46	PHE	ASP	LEU SER / PHE THR		HIS	GLY	SER	GLX	(GLN	ILE	LYS)	ALA	HIS	GLY	LYS		60
61	LYS	VAL	SER	GLU	ALA	LEU	THR	LYS	ALA	VAL	GLY	HIS	LEU	ASP	ASP		75
76	LEU	PRO	GLY	ALA	LEU	SER	THR	LEU	SER	ASP	LEU	HIS	ALA	HIS	LYS		90
91	LEU	ARG	VAL	ASP	PRO	VAL	ASN	PHE	LYS	LEU	LEU	SER	HIS	CYS	LEU		105
106	LEU	VAL	THR	LEU	ALA	ASN	HIS	HIS	PRO	SER	GLU	PHE	THR	PRO	ALA		120
121	VAL	HIS	ALA	SER	LEU	ASP	LYS	PHE	LEU	ALA	ASN	VAL	SER	THR	VAL		135
136	LEU	THR	SER	LYS	TYR	ARG											150

Haemoglobin 19. The primary structure of the α-chain of rabbit haemoglobin.
U. Flamm, J. S. Best, and G. Braunitzer.
Hoppe-Seyler's Z. Physiol. Chem., **352**, 885–895 (1971).

GLOBINS

HAEMOGLOBIN α-CHAIN—PIG

	1			5					10					15		
1	VAL	LEU	SER	ALA	ALA	ASP	LYS	ALA	ASN	VAL	LYS	ALA	ALA	TRP	GLY	15
16	LYS	VAL	GLY	GLY	GLN	ALA	GLY	ALA	HIS	GLY	ALA	GLU	ALA	LEU	GLU	30
31	ARG	MET	PHE	LEU	GLY	PHE	PRO	THR	THR	LYS	THR	TYR	PHE	PRO	HIS	45
46	PHE	ASN	LEU	SER	HIS	GLY	SER	ASP	GLN	VAL	LYS	ALA	HIS	GLY	GLN	60
61	LYS	VAL	ALA	ASP	ALA	LEU	THR	LYS	ALA	VAL	GLY	HIS	LEU	ASP	ASP	75
76	LEU	PRO	GLY	ALA	LEU	SER	ALA	LEU	SER	ASP	LEU	HIS	ALA	HIS	LYS	90
91	LEU	ARG	VAL	ASP	PRO	VAL	ASN	PHE	LYS	LEU	LEU	SER	HIS	CYS	LEU	105
106	LEU	VAL	THR	LEU	ALA	ALA	HIS	HIS	PRO	ASP	ASP	PHE	ASN	PRO	SER	120
121	VAL	HIS	ALA	SER	LEU	ASP	LYS	PHE	LEU	ALA	ASN	VAL	SER	THR	VAL	135
136	LEU	THR	SER	LYS	TYR	ARG										150

Hemoglobins, XXI: Sequence analysis of Porcine hemoglobin.
G. Braunitzer, B. Schrank, A. Stangl, and U. Scheithauer.
Hoppe-Seyler's Z. Physiol. Chem., **359**, 137–146 (1978).

HAEMOGLOBIN α-CHAIN—BADGER

	1			5					10					15		
1	VAL	LEU	SER	PRO	ALA	ASP	LYS	ALA	ASN	ILE	LYS	ALA	THR	TRP	ASP	15
16	LYS	ILE	GLY	GLY	HIS	ALA	GLY	GLU	TYR	GLY	GLY	GLU	ALA	LEU	GLU	30
31	ARG	THR	PHE	ALA	SER	PHE	PRO	THR	THR	LYS	THR	TYR	PHE	PRO	HIS	45
46	PHE	ASP	LEU	SER	HIS	GLY	SER	ALA	GLN	VAL	LYS	GLY	HIS	GLY	LYS	60
61	LYS	VAL	ALA	ASP	ALA	LEU	THR	ASN	ALA	VAL	ALA	HIS	LEU	ASP	ASP	75
76	LEU	PRO	GLY	ALA	LEU	SER	ALA	LEU	SER	ASP	LEU	HIS	ALA	TYR	LYS	90
91	LEU	ARG	VAL	ASP	PRO	VAL	ASN	PHE	LYS	LEU	LEU	SER	HIS	CYS	LEU	105
106	LEU	VAL	THR	LEU	ALA	CYS	HIS	HIS	PRO	ALA	GLU	PHE	THR	PRO	ALA	120
121	VAL	HIS	ALA	SER	LEU	ASP	LYS	PHE	LEU	SER	SER	VAL	SER	THR	VAL	135
136	LEU	THR	SER	LYS	TYR	ARG										150

The amino acid sequence of the α-chain of Badger (*Meles meles*) Haemoglobin.
I. Hombrados, E. Neuzil, B. Debuire, and K. Han.
Biochim. Biophys. Acta, **535**, 1–10 (1978).

GLOBINS

HAEMOGLOBIN α-CHAIN—RAT

	1				5					10					15	
1	VAL	LEU	SER	ALA	ASP	ASP	LYS	THR	ASN	ILE	LYS	ASN	CYS	TRP	GLY	15
16	LYS	ILE	GLY	GLY	HIS	GLY	GLY	GLU	TYR	GLY	GLU	GLU	ALA	LEU	GLN	30
31	ARG	MET	PHE	ALA	ALA	PHE	PRO	THR	THR	LYS	THR	TYR	PHE	SER	HIS	45
46	ILE	ASP	VAL	SER	PRO	GLY	SER	ALA	GLN	VAL	LYS	ALA	HIS	GLY	LYS	60
61	LYS	VAL	ALA	ASP	ALA	LEU	ALA	LYS	ALA	GLY	ALA	HIS	LEU	ASX	ASX	75
76	(GLX,	PRO,	VAL,	ALA)	LEU	SER	THR	LEU	SER	ASP	LEU	HIS	ALA	HIS	LYS	90
91	LEU	ARG	VAL	ASP	PRO	VAL	ASN	PHE	LYS	PHE	LEU	SER	HIS	CYS	LEU	105
106	LEU	VAL	THR	LEU	ALA	CYS	HIS	HIS	PRO	GLY	ASP	PHE	THR	PRO	ALA	120
121	MET	HIS	ALA	SER	LEU	ASP	LYS	PHE	LEU	GLY	ASN	MET	SER	ALA	(VAL,	135
136	LEU)	THR	SER	LYS	TYR	ARG										150

The amino acid sequence of the α-chain of the major haemoglobin of the rat (*Rattus norvegicus*).
C. G. Chua, R. W. Carrell, and B. H. Howard.
Biochem. J., **149**, 259–269 (1975).

HAEMOGLOBIN α-CHAIN—VIPER

	1				5					10					15	
1	VAL	LEU	SER	GLU	ASP	ASP	LYS	ASN	ARG	VAL	ARG	THR	SER	VAL	GLY	15
16	LYS	ASN	PRO	GLU	LEU	PRO	GLY	GLU	TYR	GLY	SER	GLU	THR	LEU	THR	30
31	ARG	MET	PHE	ALA	ALA	HIS	PRO	THR	THR	LYS	THR	TYR	PHE	PRO	HIS	45
46	PHE	ASP	LEU	SER	SER	GLY	SER	PRO	ASN	LEU	LYS	ALA	HIS	GLY	LYS	60
61	LYS	VAL	ILE	ASP	ALA	LEU	ASP	ASN	ALA	VAL	GLU	GLY	LEU	ASP	ASP	75
76	ALA	VAL	ALA	THR	LEU	SER	LYS	LEU	SER	ASP	LEU	HIS	ALA	GLN	LYS	90
91	LEU	ARG	VAL	ASP	PRO	ALA	ASN	PHE	LYS	ILE	LEU	SER	GLN	CYS ·	LEU	105
106	LEU	SER	THR	LEU	ALA	ASN	HIS	ARG	ASN	PRO	GLU	PHE	GLY	PRO	ALA	120
121	VAL	LEU	ALA	SER	VAL	ASP	LYS	PHE	LEU	CYS	ASN	VAL	SER	GLU	VAL	135
136	LEU	GLU	SER	LYS	TYR	ARG										150

Phylogeny of hemoglobins: the complete amino acid sequence of an α-chain of viper (*Vipera aspis*) hemoglobin.
M. Duguet, J.-P. Chauvet, and R. Acher.
FEBS Letters, **47**, 333–337 (1974).

GLOBINS

CHICKEN HAEMOGLOBIN α-CHAIN

	1		5				10					15			
1	VAL	LEU	SER	ASN	ALA	ASP	LYS	ASN	ASN	VAL	LYS	GLY	ILE	PHE	THR	15
16	LYS	ILE	ALA	GLY	HIS	ALA	GLU	GLU	TYR	GLY	ALA	GLU	THR	LEU	GLU	30
31	ARG	MET	PHE	ILE	GLY	PHE	PRO	THR	THR	LYS	THR	TYR	PHE	PRO	HIS	45
46	PHE	ASP	LEU	SER	HIS	GLY	SER	ALA	GLN	ILE	LYS	GLY	HIS	GLY	LYS	60
61	LYS	VAL	ALA	LEU	ALA	ILE	THR	ASN	ALA	ILE	GLU	HIS	ALA	ASP	ASP	75
76	ILE	SER	GLY	ALA	LEU	SER	LYS	LEU	SER	ASP	LEU	HIS	ALA	HIS	LYS	90
91	LEU	ARG	VAL	ASP	PRO	VAL	ASN	PHE	LYS	LEU	LEU	GLY	GLN	CYS	PHE	105
106	LEU	VAL	VAL	LEU	VAL	ALA	HIS	LEU	PRO	ALA	GLU	LEU	ALA	PRO	LYS	120
121	VAL	HIS	ALA	SER	LEU	ASP	LYS	PHE	LEU	CYS	ALA	VAL	GLY	THR	VAL	135
136	LEU	THR	ALA	LYS	TYR	ARG										150

The Primary Structure of α-Polypeptide Chain of A_{II} Component of Adult Chicken Hemoglobin.
G. Matsuda, H. Takei, K. C. Wu and T. Shiozawa.
Int. J. Prot. Res., **3**, 173–174 (1971).

HAEMOGLOBIN α-CHAIN—CHICKEN AI

	1		5				10					15			
1	MET	LEU	THR	ALA	GLU	ASP	LYS	LYS	LEU	ILE	GLN	GLN	ALA	TRP	GLU	15
16	LYS	ALA	ALA	SER	HIS	GLN	GLN	GLU	PHE	GLY	ALA	GLU	ALA	LEU	THR	30
31	ARG	MET	PHE	THR	THR	TYR	PRO	GLU	THR	LYS	THR	TYR	PHE	PRO	HIS	45
46	PHE	ASP	LEU	SER	PRO	GLY	SER	ASN	GLU	VAL	ARG	GLY	HIS	GLY	LYS	60
61	LYS	VAL	LEU	GLY	ALA	LEU	GLY	ASN	ALA	VAL	LYS	ASN	VAL	ASP	ASN	75
76	LEU	SER	GLN	ALA	MET	ALA	GLU	LEU	SER	ASN	LEU	HIS	ALA	TYR	ASN	90
91	LEU	ARG	VAL	ASP	PRO	VAL	ASN	PHE	LYS	LEU	LEU	SER	GLN	CYS	ILE	105
106	GLN	GLN	VAL	LEU	ALA	VAL	HIS	MET	GLY	LYS	ASP	TYR	THR	PRO	GLU	120
121	VAL	HIS	ALA	ALA	PHE	ASP	LYS	PHE	LEU	SER	ALA	VAL	SER	ALA	VAL	135
136	LEU	ALA	GLU	LYS	TYR	ARG										150

Amino acid sequence of the α-chain of chicken AI hemoglobin.
H. Takei, Y. Ota, K. C. Wu, T. Kiyohara, and G. Matsuda.
J. Biochem., **77**, 1345–1347 (1975).

CATOSTOMUS CLARKII *HAEMOGLOBIN α-CHAIN*

	1				5					10					15	
1	AC	SER	LEU	SER	ASP	LYS	ASP	LYS	ALA	ASP	VAL	LYS	ILE	ALA	TRP	15
16	ALA	LYS	ILE	SER	PRO	ARG	ALA	ASP	GLU	ILE	GLY	ALA	GLU	ALA	LEU	30
31	GLY	ARG	MET	LEU	THR	VAL	TYR	PRO	GLN	THR	LYS	THR	TYR	PHE	ALA	45
46	HIS	TRP	ALA	ASP	LEU	SER	PRO	GLY	SER	GLY	PRO	VAL	LYS	HIS	GLY	60
61	LYS	LYS	VAL	ILE	MET	GLY	ALA	ILE	GLY	ASP	ALA	VAL	THR	LYS	PHE	75
76	ASP	ASP	LEU	LEU	GLY	GLY	LEU	ALA	SER	LEU	SER	GLU	LEU	HIS	ALA	90
91	SER	LYS	LEU	ARG	VAL	ASP	PRO	SER	ASN	PHE	LYS	ILE	LEU	ALA	ASN	105
106	CYS	ILE	THR	VAL	VAL	ILE	MET	PHE	TYR	LEU	PRO	GLY	ASP	PHE	PRO	120
121	PRO	GLU	VAL	HIS	ALA	SER	VAL	ASP	LYS	PHE	PHE	GLN	ASN	LEU	ALA	135
136	LEU	ALA	LEU	GLY	GLN	LYS	TYR	ARG								150

Multiple Hemoglobins of Catostomid Fish. 2. The Amino Acid Sequence of the major α-chain
from *Catostomus Clarkii* Hemoglobins.
D. A. Powers and A. B. Edmundson.
J. Biol. Chem., **247**, 6694–6707 (1972).

CARP HAEMOGLOBIN α-CHAIN

	1				5					10					15	
1	AC	SER	LEU	SER	ASP	LYS	ASP	LYS	ALA	ALA	VAL	LYS	ILE	ALA	TRP	15
16	ALA	LYS	ILE	SER	PRO	LYS	ALA	ASP	ASP	ILE	GLY	ALA	GLU	ALA	LEU	30
31	GLY	ARG	MET	LEU	THR	VAL	THR	PRO	GLN	THR	LYS	THR	TYR	PHE	ALA	45
46	HIS	TRP	ALA	ASP	LEU	SER	PRO	GLY	SER	GLY	PRO	VAL	LYS	HIS	GLY	60
61	LYS	LYS	VAL	ILE	MET	GLY	ALA	VAL	GLY	ASP	ALA	VAL	SER	LYS	ILE	75
76	ASP	ASP	LEU	VAL	GLY	GLY	LEU	ALA	SER	LEU	SER	GLU	LEU	HIS	ALA	90
91	SER	LYS	LEU	ARG	VAL	ASP	PRO	ALA	ASN	PHE	LYS	ILE	LEU	ALA	ASN	105
106	HIS	ILE	VAL	VAL	GLY	ILE	MET	PHE	TYR	LEU	PRO	GLY	ASP	PHE	PRO	120
121	PRO	GLU	VAL	HIS	MET	SER	VAL	ASP	LYS	PHE	PHE	GLN	ASN	LEU	ALA	135
136	LEU	ALA	LEU	SER	GLU	LYS	TYR	ARG								150

The amino acid sequence of the α-chain of carp haemoglobin.
K. Hilse and G. Braunitzer.
Hoppe-Seyler's Z. Physiol. Chem., **349**, 433–450 (1968).

GLOBINS

HAEMOGLOBIN α-CHAIN—TROUT

	1				5					10					15	
1	SER	LEU	THR	ALA	LYS	ASP	LYS	SER	VAL	VAL	LYS	ALA	PHE	TRP	GLY	15
16	LYS	ILE	SER	GLY	LYS	ALA	ASP	VAL	VAL	GLY	ALA	GLU	ALA	LEU	GLY	30
31	ARG	ASP	LYS	MET	LEU	THR	ALA	TYR	PRO	GLN	THR	LYS	THR	TYR	PHE	45
46	SER	HIS	TRP	ALA	ASP	LEU	SER	PRO	GLY	SER	GLY	PRO	VAL	LYS	LYS	60
61	HIS	GLY	GLY	ILE	ILE	MET	GLY	ALA	ILE	GLY	LYS	ALA	VAL	GLY	LEU	75
76	MET	ASP	ASP	LEU	VAL	GLY	GLY	MET	SER	ALA	LEU	SER	ASP	LEU	HIS	90
91	ALA	PHE	LYS	LEU	ARG	VAL	ASP	PRO	GLY	ASN	PHE	LYS	ILE	LEU	SER	105
106	HIS	ASN	ILE	LEU	VAL	THR	LEU	ALA	ILE	HIS	PHE	PRO	SER	ASP	PHE	120
121	THR	PRO	GLU	VAL	HIS	ILE	ALA	VAL	ASP	LYS	PHE	LEU	ALA	ALA	VAL	135
136	SER	ALA	ALA	LEU	ALA	ASP	LYS	TYR	ARG							150

Note: This protein has an acetylated N-terminal residue.
Primary structure of hemoglobin from trout (*Salmo irideus*). Amino acid sequence of α-chain of Hb Trout I.
F. Bossa, D. Barra, R. Petruzelli, F. Martini, and M. Brunori.
Biochim. Biophys. Acta, **536**, 298–305 (1978).

HUMAN HAEMOGLOBIN β-CHAIN

	1				5					10					15	
1	VAL	HIS	LEU	THR	PRO	GLU	GLU	LYS	SER	ALA	VAL	THR	ALA	LEU	TRP	15
16	GLY	LYS	VAL	ASN	VAL	ASP	GLU	VAL	GLY	GLY	GLU	ALA	LEU	GLY	ARG	30
31	LEU	LEU	VAL	VAL	TYR	PRO	TRP	THR	GLN	ARG	PHE	PHE	GLU	SER	PHE	45
46	GLY	ASP	LEU	SER	THR	PRO	ASP	ALA	VAL	MET	GLY	ASN	PRO	LYS	VAL	60
61	LYS	ALA	HIS	GLY	LYS	LYS	VAL	LEU	GLY	ALA	PHE	SER	ASP	GLY	LEU	75
76	ALA	HIS	LEU	ASP	ASN	LEU	LYS	GLY	THR	PHE	ALA	THR	LEU	SER	GLU	90
91	LEU	HIS	CYS	ASP	LYS	LEU	HIS	VAL	ASP	PRO	GLU	ASN	PHE	ARG	LEU	105
106	LEU	GLY	ASN	VAL	LEU	VAL	CYS	VAL	LEU	ALA	HIS	HIS	PHE	GLY	LYS	120
121	GLU	PHE	THR	PRO	PRO	VAL	GLN	ALA	ALA	TYR	GLN	LYS	VAL	VAL	ALA	135
136	GLY	VAL	ALA	ASN	ALA	LEU	ALA	HIS	LYS	TYR	HIS					150

The constitution of normal adult haemoglobin.
G. Braunitzer, R. Gehring-Müller, N. Hilschmann, K. Hilse, G. Hobom, V. Rudloff, and B. Wittmann-Liebold.
Hoppe-Seyler's Z. Physiol. Chem., **325**, 283–286 (1961).

MONKEY HAEMOGLOBIN β-CHAIN

	1				5					10					15	
1	VAL	HIS	LEU	THR	PRO	GLU	GLU	LYS	ASN	ALA	VAL	THR	THR	LEU	TRP	15
16	GLY	LYS	VAL	ASN	VAL	ASP	GLU	VAL	GLY	GLY	GLU	ALA	LEU	GLY	ARG	30
31	LEU	LEU	LEU	VAL	TYR	PRO	TRP	THR	GLN	ARG	PHE	PHE	GLU	SER	PHE	45
46	GLY	ASP	LEU	SER	SER	PRO	ASP	ALA	VAL	MET	GLY	ASN	PRO	LYS	VAL	60
61	LYS	ALA	HIS	GLY	LYS	LYS	VAL	LEU	GLY	ALA	PHE	SER	ASP	GLY	LEU	75
76	ASN	HIS	LEU	ASP	ASN	LEU	LYS	GLY	THR	PHE	ALA	GLN	LEU	SER	GLU	90
91	LEU	HIS	CYS	ASP	LYS	LEU	HIS	VAL	ASP	PRO	GLU	ASN	PHE	LYS	LEU	106
106	LEU	GLY	ASN	VAL	LEU	VAL	CYS	VAL	LEU	ALA	HIS	HIS	PHE	GLY	LYS	120
121	GLU	PHE	THR	PRO	GLN	VAL	GLN	ALA	ALA	TYR	GLN	LYS	VAL	VAL	ALA	135
136	GLY	VAL	ALA	ASN	ALA	LEU	ALA	HIS	LYS	TYR	HIS					150

The Primary Structure of Adult Hemoglobin from *Macaca mulatta* Monkey.
G. Matsuda, T. Maita, H. Takei, H. Ota, M. Yamaguchi, T. Miyauchi, and M. Migita.
J. Biochem., **64**, 279–282 (1968).

HAEMOGLOBIN β-CHAIN—CAPUCHIN MONKEY

	1				5					10					15	
1	VAL	HIS	LEU	THR	ALA	GLU	GLU	LYS	SER	ALA	VAL	THR	THR	LEU	TRP	15
16	GLY	LYS	VAL	ASN	VAL	ASP	GLU	VAL	GLY	GLY	GLU	ALA	LEU	GLY	ARG	30
31	LEU	LEU	VAL	VAL	TYR	PRO	TRP	THR	GLN	ARG	PHE	PHE	ASP	SER	PHE	45
46	GLY	ASP	LEU	SER	THR	PRO	ASP	ALA	VAL	MET	ASN	ASN	PRO	LYS	VAL	60
61	LYS	ALA	HIS	GLY	LYS	LYS	VAL	LEU	GLY	ALA	PHE	SER	ASP	GLY	LEU	75
76	THR	HIS	LEU	ASP	ASN	LEU	LYS	GLY	THR	PHE	ALA	GLN	LEU	SER	GLU	90
91	LEU	HIS	CYS	ASP	LYS	LEU	HIS	VAL	ASP	PRO	GLU	ASN	PHE	ARG	LEU	105
106	LEU	GLY	ASN	VAL	LEU	VAL	CYS	VAL	LEU	ALA	HIS	HIS	PHE	GLY	LYS	120
121	GLU	PHE	THR	PRO	GLN	VAL	GLN	ALA	ALA	TYR	GLN	LYS	VAL	VAL	ALA	135
136	GLY	VAL	ALA	THR	ALA	LEU	ALA	HIS	LYS	TYR	HIS					150

The amino acid sequence of the α and β polypeptide chains of adult hemoglobin of the Capuchin monkey (*Cebus apella*).
G. Matsuda, T. Maiti, B. Watanabe, A. Araya, K. Morokuma, Y. Ota, M. Goodman, J. Barnabas, and W. Prychodko.
Hoppe-Seyler's Z. Physiol. Chem., **354**, 1513–1516 (1973).

254

GLOBINS

HAEMOGLOBIN β-CHAIN—SAVANNAH MONKEY

	1				5					10					15	
1	VAL	HIS	LEU	THR	PRO	GLU	GLU	LYS	THR	ALA	VAL	THR	THR	LEU	TRP	15
16	GLY	LYS	VAL	ASN	VAL	ASP	GLU	VAL	GLY	GLY	GLU	ALA	LEU	GLY	ARG	30
31	LEU	LEU	VAL	VAL	TYR	PRO	TRP	THR	GLN	ARG	PHE	PHE	GLU	SER	PHE	45
46	GLY	ASP	LEU	SER	SER	PRO	ASP	ALA	VAL	MET	GLY	ASN	PRO	LYS	VAL	60
61	LYS	ALA	HIS	GLY	LYS	LYS	VAL	LEU	GLY	ALA	PHE	SER	ASP	GLY	LEU	75
76	ALA	HIS	LEU	ASP	ASN	LEU	LYS	GLY	THR	PHE	ALA	GLN	LEU	SER	GLU	90
91	LEU	HIS	CYS	ASP	LYS	LEU	HIS	VAL	ASP	PRO	GLU	ASN	PHE	LYS	LEU	105
106	LEU	GLY	ASN	VAL	LEU	VAL	CYS	VAL	LEU	ALA	HIS	HIS	PHE	GLY	LYS	120
121	GLU	PHE	THR	PRO	GLN	VAL	GLN	ALA	ALA	TYR	GLN	LYS	VAL	VAL	ALA	135
136	GLY	VAL	ALA	ASN	ALA	LEU	ALA	HIS	LYS	TYR	HIS					150

The amino acid sequence of the α and β polypeptide chains of adult hemoglobin of the Savannah monkey (*Cercopithecus aethiops*).
G. Matsuda, T. Maita, B. Watanabe, A. Araya, K. Morokuma, M. Goodman, and W. Prychodko.
Hoppe-Seyler's Z. Physiol. Chem., **354**, 1153–1155 (1973).

HAEMOGLOBIN β-CHAIN—JAPANESE MONKEY

	1				5					10					15	
1	VAL	HIS	LEU	THR	PRO	GLU	GLU	LYS	ASN	ALA	VAL	THR	THR	LEU	TRP	15
16	GLY	LYS	VAL	ASN	VAL	ASP	GLU	VAL	GLY	GLY	GLU	ALA	LEU	GLY	ARG	30
31	LEU	LEU	VAL	VAL	TYR	PRO	TRP	THR	GLN	ARG	PHE	PHE	GLU	SER	PHE	45
46	GLY	ASP	LEU	SER	SER	PRO	ASP	ALA	VAL	MET	GLY	ASN	PRO	LYS	VAL	60
61	LYS	ALA	HIS	GLY	LYS	LYS	VAL	LEU	GLY	ALA	PHE	SER	ASP	GLY	LEU	75
76	ASN	HIS	LEU	ASP	ASN	LEU	LYS	GLY	THR	PHE	ALA	GLN	LEU	SER	GLU	90
91	LEU	HIS	CYS	ASP	LYS	LEU	HIS	VAL	ASP	PRO	GLU	ASN	PHE	LYS	LEU	105
106	LEU	GLY	ASN	VAL	LEU	VAL	CYS	VAL	LEU	ALA	HIS	HIS	PHE	GLY	LYS	120
121	GLU	PHE	THR	PRO	GLN	VAL	GLN	ALA	ALA	TYR	GLN	LYS	VAL	VAL	ALA	135
136	GLY	VAL	ALA	ASN	ALA	LEU	ALA	HIS	LYS	TYR	HIS					150

The Primary Structure of the β-polypeptide chain of adult Hemoglobin of the Japanese Monkey (*Macaca fuscata fuscata*).
G. Matsuda, T. Maita, Y. Tanaka, H. Ota, I. Tachikawa, A. Araya, and Y. Nakashima.
Int. J. Peptide Protein Res., **3**, 53–55 (1971).

HAEMOGLOBIN β-CHAIN—SLOW LORIS

	1				5					10					15		
1	VAL	HIS	LEU	THR	GLY	GLU	GLU	LYS	SER	ALA	VAL	THR	ALA	LEU	TRP		15
16	GLY	LYS	VAL	ASN	VAL	ASP	ASP	VAL	GLY	GLY	GLU	ALA	LEU	GLY	ARG		30
31	LEU	LEU	VAL	VAL	TYR	PRO	TRP	THR	GLN	ARG	PHE	PHE	GLU	SER	PHE		45
46	GLY	ASP	LEU	SER	SER	PRO	SER	ALA	VAL	MET	GLY	ASN	PRO	LYS	VAL		60
61	LYS	ALA	HIS	GLY	LYS	LYS	VAL	LEU	SER	ALA	PHE	SER	ASP	GLY	LEU		75
76	ASN	HIS	LEU	ASP	ASN	LEU	LYS	GLY	THR	PHE	ALA	LYS	LEU	SER	GLU		90
91	LEU	HIS	CYS	ASP	LYS	LEU	HIS	VAL	ASP	PRO	GLU	ASN	PHE	ARG	LEU	105
106	LEU	GLY	ASN	VAL	LEU	VAL	VAL	VAL	LEU	ALA	HIS	HIS	PHE	GLY	LYS	120
121	ASP	PHE	THR	PRO	GLN	VAL	GLN	SER	ALA	TYR	GLN	LYS	VAL	VAL	ALA	135
136	GLY	VAL	ALA	ASN	ALA	LEU	ALA	HIS	LYS	TYR	HIS					150

The primary structures of the α and β polypeptide chains of adult hemoglobin of the slow loris (*Nycticebus coucang*).
G. Matsuda, T. Maita, B. Watanabe, H. Ota, A. Araya, M. Goodman, and W. Prychodko. *Int. J. Peptide Protein Res.*, **5**, 419–421 (1973).

HAEMOGLOBIN β-CHAIN—SLENDER LORIS

	1				5					10					15		
1	VAL	HIS	LEU	THR	GLY	GLU	GLU	LYS	SER	ALA	VAL	THR	GLY	LEU	TRP		15
16	GLY	LYS	VAL	ASN	VAL	GLU	ASP	VAL	GLY	GLY	GLU	ALA	LEU	GLY	ARG		30
31	LEU	LEU	VAL	VAL	TYR	PRO	TRP	THR	GLN	ARG	PHE	PHE	GLU	SER	PHE		45
46	GLY	ASP	LEU	SER	SER	PRO	SER	ALA	VAL	MET	GLY	ASP	PRO	LYS	VAL		60
61	LYS	ALA	HIS	GLY	LYS	LYS	VAL	LEU	SER	ALA	PHE	SER	ASP	GLY	LEU		75
76	ASN	HIS	LEU	ASP	ASN	LEU	LYS	GLY	THR	PHE	ALA	LYS	LEU	SER	GLU		90
91	LEU	HIS	CYS	ASP	LYS	LEU	HIS	VAL	ASP	PRO	GLU	ASN	PHE	ARG	LEU	105
106	LEU	GLY	ASN	VAL	LEU	VAL	VAL	VAL	LEU	ALA	HIS	HIS	PHE	GLY	LYS	120
121	ASP	PHE	THR	PRO	GLN	VAL	GLN	SER	ALA	TYR	GLN	LYS	VAL	VAL´ALA		135
136	GLY	VAL	ALA	ASN	ALA	LEU	ALA	HIS	LYS	TYR	HIS					150

Amino acid sequences of the α and β chains of adult hemoglobin of the Slender Loris, *Loris tardigradus*.
T. Maita, M. Goodman, and G. Matsuda. *J. Biochem.*, **84**, 377–383 (1978).

GLOBINS

HAEMOGLOBIN β-CHAIN—ORANGUTAN

	1				5					10					15	
1	VAL	HIS	LEU	THR	PRO	GLU	GLU	LYS	SER	ALA	VAL	THR	ALA	LEU	TRP	15
16	GLY	LYS	VAL	ASN	VAL	ASP	GLU	VAL	GLY	GLY	GLU	ALA	LEU	GLY	ARG	30
31	LEU	LEU	VAL	VAL	TYR	PRO	TRP	THR	GLN	ARG	PHE	PHE	GLU	SER	PHE	45
46	GLY	ASP	LEU	SER	THR	PRO	ASP	ALA	VAL	MET	GLY	ASN	PRO	LYS	VAL	60
61	LYS	ALA	HIS	GLY	LYS	LYS	VAL	LEU	GLY	ALA	PHE	SER	ASP	GLY	LEU	75
76	ALA	HIS	LEU	ASP	ASN	LEU	LYS	GLY	THR	PHE	ALA	LYS	LEU	SER	GLU	90
91	LEU	HIS	CYS	ASP	LYS	LEU	HIS	VAL	ASP	PRO	GLU	ASN	PHE	ARG	LEU	105
106	LEU	GLY	ASN	VAL	LEU	VAL	CYS	VAL	LEU	ALA	HIS	HIS	PHE	GLY	LYS	120
121	GLU	PHE	THR	PRO	GLN	VAL	GLN	ALA	ALA	TYR	GLN	LYS	VAL	VAL	ALA	135
136	GLY	VAL	ALA	ASN	ALA	LEU	ALA	HIS	LYS	TYR	HIS					150

The amino acid sequences of the two main components of adult hemoglobin from orangutan (*Pongo pygmaeus*).
T. Maita, A. Araya, M. Goodman, and G. Matsuda.
Hoppe-Seyler's Z. Physiol. Chem., **359**, 129–132 (1978).

HAEMOGLOBIN β-CHAIN—HANUMAN LANGUR

	1				5					10					15	
1	VAL	HIS	LEU	THR	PRO	GLU	GLU	LYS	ALA	ALA	VAL	THR	ALA	LEU	TRP	15
16	GLY	LYS	VAL	ASN	VAL	ASP	GLU	VAL	GLY	GLY	GLU	ALA	LEU	GLY	ARG	30
31	LEU	LEU	VAL	VAL	TYR	PRO	TRP	THR	GLN	ARG	PHE	PHE	GLU	SER	PHE	45
46	GLY	ASP	LEU	SER	SER	PRO	ASP	ALA	VAL	MET	GLY	ASN	PRO	LYS	VAL	60
61	LYS	ALA	HIS	GLY	LYS	LYS	VAL	LEU	GLY	ALA	PHE	SER	ASP	GLY	LEU	75
76	ALA	HIS	LEU	ASP	ASN	LEU	LYS	GLY	THR	PHE	ALA	GLN	LEU	SER	GLU	90
91	LEU	HIS	CYS	ASP	LYS	LEU	HIS	VAL	ASP	PRO	GLU	ASN	PHE	ARG	LEU	105
106	LEU	GLY	ASN	VAL	LEU	VAL	CYS	VAL	LEU	ALA	HIS	HIS	PHE	GLY	LYS	120
121	GLU	PHE	THR	PRO	GLN	VAL	GLN	ALA	ALA	TYR	GLN	LYS	VAL	VAL	ALA	135
136	GLY	VAL	ALA	ASN	ALA	LEU	ALA	HIS	LYS	TYR	HIS					150

The primary structures of the α and β polypeptide chains of adult hemoglobin of the hanuman Langur (*Presbytis entellus*).
G. Matsuda, T. Maita, Y. Nakashima, J. Barnabas, P. K. Ranjekar, and N. S. Gandhi.
Int. J. Peptide Protein Res., **5**, 423–425 (1973).

GLOBINS

HAEMOGLOBIN β-CHAIN OF MOUSE (STRAIN C57BL)

	1				5					10					15	
1	VAL	HIS	LEU	THR	ASP	ALA	GLU	LYS	ALA	ALA	VAL	SER	GLY	LEU	TRP	15
16	GLY	LYS	VAL	ASN	ALA	ASP	GLY	VAL	GLY	GLY	GLU	ALA	LEU	GLY	ARG	30
31	LEU	LEU	VAL	VAL	TYR	PRO	TRP	THR	GLN	ARG	TYR	PHE	ASP	SER	PHE	45
46	GLY	ASP	LEU	SER	SER	ALA	SER	ALA	ILE	MET	GLY	ASN	ALA	LYS	VAL	60
61	LYS	ALA	HIS	GLY	LYS	LYS	VAL	ILE	THR	ALA	PHE	SER	ASP	GLY	LEU	75
76	ASN	HIS	LEU	ASP	ASN	LEU	LYS	GLY	THR	PHE	ALA	SER	LEU	SER	GLU	90
91	LEU	(HIS,	CYS,	ASP)	LYS	LEU	(HIS,	VAL,	ASP,	PRO,	GLU,	ASN,	PHE)	ARG	LEU	105
106	LEU	(GLY,	ASN,	MET,	ILE,	VAL,	ILE,	VAL)	LEU	GLY	(HIS,	HIS,	LEU)	GLY	LYS	120
121	ASP	PHE	THR	PRO	ALA	(ALA,	GLN,	ALA)	ALA	PHE	GLN	LYS	VAL	VAL	ALA	135
136	GLY	VAL	ALA	ALA	ALA	LEU	ALA	HIS	LYS	TYR	HIS					150

Note: The sequence of the polypeptide chain from mouse strains SWR and NB have identical sequence except that residues 72 and 73 are ASP, SER.
Sequence of amino acids in the β chain of single hemoglobin from C57BL, SWR and NB mice.
R. A. Popp.
Biochim. Biophys. Acta, **303**, 52–60 (1973).

HAEMOGLOBIN β-CHAIN—BADGER

	1				5					10					15	
1	VAL	HIS	LEU	THR	ALA	GLU	GLU	LYS	SER	ALA	VAL	THR	SER	LEU	TRP	15
16	GLY	LYS	VAL	ASN	VAL	ASP	GLU	VAL	GLY	GLY	GLU	ALA	LEU	GLY	ARG	30
31	LEU	LEU	VAL	VAL	TYR	PRO	TRP	THR	GLN	ARG	TYR	PHE	ASP	SER	PHE	45
46	GLY	ASP	LEU	SER	THR	PRO	ASP	ALA	VAL	MET	GLY	ASN	PRO	LYS	VAL	60
61	LYS	ALA	HIS	GLY	LYS	LYS	VAL	LEU	ASN	SER	PHE	SER	GLU	GLY	LEU	75
76	LYS	ASN	LEU	ASP	ASN	LEU	LYS	GLY	THR	PHE	ALA	LYS	LEU	SER	GLU	90
91	LEU	HIS	CYS	ASP	LYS	LEU	HIS	VAL	ASP	PRO	GLU	ASN	PHE	LYS	LEU	105
106	LEU	GLY	ASN	VAL	LEU	VAL	CYS	VAL	LEU	ALA	HIS	HIS	PHE	GLY	LYS	120
121	GLU	PHE	THR	PRO	GLN	VAL	GLN	ALA	ALA	TYR	GLN	LYS	VAL	VAL	ALA	135
136	GLY	VAL	ALA	ASN	ALA	LEU	ALA	HIS	LYS	TYR	HIS					150

Primary sequence of the β-chain of badger haemoglobin.
I. Hombrados, S. Ducastaing, A. Iron, E. Neuzil, B. Debuire, and K. Han.
Biochim. Biophys. Acta, **427**, 107–118 (1976).

GLOBINS

RABBIT HAEMOGLOBIN β-CHAIN

	1				5					10					15	
1	VAL	HIS	LEU	SER	SER	GLU	GLU	LYS	SER	ALA	VAL	THR	ALA	LEU	TRP	15
16	GLY	LYS	VAL	ASN	VAL	GLU	GLU	VAL	GLY	GLY	GLU	ALA	LEU	GLY	ARG	30
31	LEU	LEU	VAL	VAL	TYR	PRO	TRP	THR	GLN	ARG	PHE	PHE	GLU	SER	PHE	45
46	GLY	ASP	LEU	SER	SER	ALA	ASN	ALA	VAL	MET	ASN	ASN	PRO	LYS	VAL	60
61	LYS	ALA	HIS	GLY	LYS	LYS	VAL	LEU	ALA	ALA	PHE	SER	GLU	GLY	LEU	75
76	SER	HIS	LEU	ASP	ASN	LEU	LYS	GLY	THR	PHE	ALA	LYS	LEU	SER	GLU	90
91	LEU	HIS	CYS	ASP	LYS	LEU	HIS	VAL	ASP	PRO	GLU	ASP	PHE	ARG	LEU	105
106	LEU	GLY	ASN	VAL	LEU	VAL	ILE	VAL	LEU	SER	HIS	HIS	PHE	GLY	LYS	120
121	GLU	PHE	THR	PRO	GLN	(VAL, GLU)	ALA	ALA	TYR	GLN	LYS	VAL	VAL	ALA		135
136	GLY	VAL	ALA	ASN	ALA	LEU	ALA	HIS	LYS	TYR	HIS					150

The phylogeny of Haemoglobins. Primary structure of Rabbit Haemoglobin.
G. Braunitzer, J. S. Best, U. Flamm, and B. Schrank.
Hoppe-Seyler's Z. Physiol. Chem., **347**, 207–211 (1966).
An isoleucine–valine substitution in the β-chain of rabbit haemoglobin.
J. Bricker and M. D. Garrick.
Biochim. Biophys. Acta, **351**, 437–441 (1974).
This paper reports the variant β 112 ILE–VAL in rabbit haemoglobin.

HAEMOGLOBIN β-CHAIN—PIG

	1				5					10					15	
1	VAL	HIS	LEU	SER	ALA	GLU	GLU	LYS	GLU	ALA	VAL	LEU	GLY	LEU	TRP	15
16	GLY	LYS	VAL	ASN	VAL	ASP	GLU	VAL	GLY	GLY	GLU	ALA	LEU	GLY	ARG	30
31	LEU	LEU	VAL	VAL	TYR	PRO	TRP	THR	GLN	ARG	PHE	PHE	GLU	SER	PHE	45
46	GLY	ASP	LEU	SER	ASN	ALA	ASP	ALA	VAL	MET	GLY	ASN	PRO	LYS	VAL	60
61	LYS	ALA	HIS	GLY	LYS	LYS	VAL	LEU	GLN	SER	PHE	SER	ASP	GLY	LEU	75
76	LYS	HIS	LEU	ASP	ASN	LEU	LYS	GLY	THR	PHE	ALA	LYS	LEU	SER	GLU	90
91	LEU	HIS	CYS	ASP	GLN	LEU	HIS	VAL	ASP	PRO	GLU	ASN	PHE	ARG	LEU	105
106	LEU	GLY	ASN	VAL	ILE	VAL	VAL	VAL	LEU	ALA	ARG	ARG	LEU	GLY	HIS	120
121	ASP	PHE	ASN	PRO	ASP	VAL	GLN	ALA	ALA	PHE	GLN	LYS	VAL	VAL	ALA	135
136	GLY	VAL	ALA	ASN	ALA	LEU	ALA	HIS	LYS	TYR	HIS					150

Hemoglobins, XXI: Sequence analysis of porcine hemoglobin.
G. Braunitzer, B. Schrank, A. Stangl, and U. Scheithauer.
Hoppe-Seyler's Z. Physiol. Chem., **359**, 137–146 (1978).

KANGAROO HAEMOGLOBIN β-CHAIN

	1			5					10					15		
1	VAL	HIS	LEU	THR	ALA	GLU	GLU	LYS	ASN	ALA	ILE	THR	SER	LEU	TRP	15
16	GLY	LYS	VAL	ALA	ILE	GLU	GLN	THR	GLY	GLY	GLU	ALA	LEU	GLY	ARG	30
31	LEU	LEU	ILE	VAL	TYR	PRO	TRP	THR	SER	ARG	PHE	PHE	ASP	HIS	PHE	45
46	GLY	ASP	LEU	SER	ASN	ALA	LYS	ALA	VAL	MET	ALA	ASN	PRO	LYS	VAL	60
61	LEU	ALA	HIS	GLY	ALA	LYS	VAL	LEU	VAL	ALA	PHE	GLY	ASP	ALA	ILE	75
76	LYS	ASN	LEU	ASP	ASN	LEU	LYS	GLY	THR	PHE	ALA	LYS	LEU	SER	GLU	90
91	LEU	HIS	CYS	ASP	LYS	LEU	HIS	VAL	ASP	PRO	GLU	ASN	PHE	LYS	LEU	105
106	LEU	GLY	ASN	ILE	ILE	VAL	ILE	CYS	LEU	ALA	GLU	HIS	PHE	GLY	LYS	120
121	GLU	PHE	THR	ILE	ASP	SER	GLN	VAL	ALA	THR	GLN	LYS	LEU	VAL	ALA	135
136	GLY	VAL	ALA	ASN	ALA	LEU	ALA	HIS	LYS	TYR	HIS					150

Studies on Marsupial proteins. II. Amino acid sequence of the β-chain of haemoglobin from the grey kangaroo, *Macropus giganteus*.
G. M. Air and E. O. P. Thompson.
Aust. J. Biol. Sci., **22**, 1437–1454 (1969).

POTOROO β-GLOBIN

	1			5					10					15		
1	VAL	HIS	LEU	SER	SER	GLU	GLU	LYS	GLY	LEU	ILE	THR	SER	LEU	TRP	15
16	GLY	LYS	ILE	ASP	ILE	GLU	GLN	THR	GLY	GLY	GLU	ALA	LEU	GLY	ARG	30
31	LEU	LEU	ILE	VAL	TYR	PRO	TRP	THR	SER	ARG	PHE	PHE	ASP	HIS	PHE	45
46	GLY	ASP	LEU	SER	SER	ALA	LYS	ALA	VAL	LEU	GLY	ASN	ALA	LYS	VAL	60
61	LEU	ALA	HIS	GLY	ALA	LYS	VAL	LEU	VAL	SER	PHE	GLY	ASP	ALA	ILE	75
76	LYS	ASN	LEU	ASP	ASN	LEU	LYS	GLY	THR	PHE	ALA	LYS	LEU	SER	GLU	90
91	LEU	HIS	CYS	ASP	LYS	LEU	HIS	VAL	ASP	PRO	GLU	ASN	PHE	LYS	LEU	105
106	LEU	GLY	ASN	VAL	LEU	VAL	ILE	CYS	LEU	ALA	GLU	HIS	PHE	GLY	LYS	120
121	ASP	PHE	THR	ILE	ASP	ALA	GLN	VAL	ALA	TRP	GLN	LYS	LEU	VAL.	ALA	135
136	GLY	VAL	ALA	ASN	ALA	LEU	ALA	HIS	LYS	TYR	HIS					150

Studies on Marsupial Proteins. VI. Evolutionary changes in β-Globins of macropodidae and the amino acid sequence of β-globin from *Potorous Tridactylus*.
E. O. P. Thompson and G. M. Air.
Aust. J. Biol. Sci., **24**, 1199–1217 (1971).

GLOBINS

HAEMOGLOBIN β-CHAIN OF CHICK (COMPONENT AII)

	1				5					10					15	
1	VAL	HIS	TRP	THR	ALA	GLU	GLU	LYS	GLN	LEU	ILE	THR	GLY	LEU	TRP	15
16	GLY	LYS	VAL	ASN	VAL	ALA	GLU	CYS	GLY	ALA	GLU	ALA	LEU	ALA	ARG	30
31	LEU	LEU	ILE	VAL	TYR	PRO	TRP	THR	GLN	ARG	PHE	PHE	ALA	SER	PHE	45
46	GLY	ASN	LEU	SER	SER	PRO	THR	ALA	ILE	LEU	GLY	ASN	PRO	MET	VAL	60
61	ARG	ALA	HIS	GLY	LYS	LYS	VAL	LEU	THR	SER	PHE	GLY	ASP	ALA	VAL	75
76	LYS	ASN	LEU	ASP	ASN	ILE	LYS	ASN	THR	PHE	SER	GLN	LEU	SER	GLU	90
91	LEU	HIS	CYS	ASP	LYS	LEU	HIS	VAL	ASP	PRO	GLU	ASN	PHE	ARG	LEU	105
106	LEU	GLY	ASP	ILE	LEU	ILE	ILE	VAL	LEU	ALA	ALA	HIS	PHE	SER	LYS	120
121	ASP	PHE	THR	PRO	GLU	CYS	GLN	ALA	ALA	TRP	GLN	LYS	LEU	VAL	ARG	135
136	VAL	VAL	ALA	HIS	ALA	LEU	ALA	ARG	LYS	TYR	HIS					150

Amino acid sequence of a β-chain of AII component of adult chicken haemoglobin.
G. Matsuda, T. Maita, K. Mizuno, and H. Ota.
Nature (New Biol.), **244**, 244 (1973).

FROG HAEMOGLOBIN β-CHAIN

	1				5					10					15	
1	GLY	SER	ASP	LEU	VAL	SER	GLY	PHE	TRP	GLY	LYS	VAL	ASP	ALA	HIS	15
16	LYS	ILE	GLY	GLY	GLU	ALA	LEU	ALA	ARG	LEU	LEU	VAL	VAL	TYR	PRO	30
31	TRP	THR	GLN	ARG	TYR	PHE	THR	THR	PHE	GLY	ASN	LEU	GLY	SER	ALA	45
46	ASP	ALA	ILE	CYS	HIS	ASN	ALA	LYS	VAL	LEU	ALA	HIS	GLY	GLU	LYS	60
61	VAL	LEU	ALA	ALA	ILE	GLY	GLU	GLY	LEU	LYS	HIS	PRO	GLU	ASN	LEU	75
76	LYS	ALA	HIS	TYR	ALA	LYS	LEU	SER	GLU	TYR	HIS	SER	ASN	LYS	LEU	90
91	HIS	VAL	ASP	PRO	ALA	ASN	PHE	ARG	LEU	LEU	GLY	ASN	VAL	PHE	ILE	105
106	THR	VAL	LEU	ALA	ARG	HIS	PHE	GLN	HIS	GLU	PHE	THR	PRO	GLU	LEU	120
121	GLN	HIS	ALA	LEU	GLU	ALA	HIS	PHE	CYS	ALA	VAL	GLY	ASP	ALA	LEU	135
136	ALA	LYS	ALA	TYR	HIS											150

Phylogeny of Hemoglobins. β-Chain of Frog (*Rana esculenta*) Hemoglobin.
J.-P. Chauvet and R. Acher.
Biochemistry, **11**, 916–927 (1972).

GLOBINS

HUMAN FETAL HAEMOGLOBIN γ-CHAIN

	1				5					10					15	
1	GLY	HIS	PHE	THR	GLU	GLU	ASP	LYS	ALA	THR	ILE	THR	SER	LEU	TRP	15
16	GLY	LYS	VAL	ASN	VAL	GLU	ASP	ALA	GLY	GLY	GLU	THR	LEU	GLY	ARG	30
31	LEU	LEU	VAL	VAL	TYR	PRO	TRP	THR	GLN	ARG	PHE	PHE	ASP	SER	PHE	45
46	GLY	ASN	LEU	SER	SER	ALA	SER	ALA	ILE	MET	GLY	ASN	PRO	LYS	VAL	60
61	LYS	ALA	HIS	GLY	LYS	LYS	VAL	LEU	THR	SER	LEU	GLY	ASP	ALA	ILE	75
76	LYS	HIS	LEU	ASP	ASP	LEU	LYS	GLY	THR	PHE	ALA	GLN	LEU	SER	GLU	90
91	LEU	HIS	CYS	ASP	LYS	LEU	HIS	VAL	ASP	PRO	GLU	ASN	PHE	LYS	LEU	105
106	LEU	GLY	ASN	VAL	LEU	VAL	THR	VAL	LEU	ALA	ILE	HIS	PHE	GLY	LYS	120
121	GLU	PHE	THR	PRO	GLU	VAL	GLN	ALA	SER	TRP	GLN	LYS	MET	VAL	THR	135
136	GLY	VAL	ALA	SER	ALA	LEU	SER	SER	ARG	TYR	HIS					150

The Amino Acid Sequence of the γ-Chain of Human Fetal Hemoglobin.
W. A. Schroeder, J. R. Shelton, J. B. Shelton, J. Cormick, and R. T. Jones.
Biochemistry, **2**, 992–1008 (1963).

BOVINE FETAL HAEMOGLOBIN γ-CHAIN

	1				5					10					15	
1	MET	LEU	SER	ALA	GLU	GLU	LYS	ALA	ALA	VAL	THR	SER	LEU	PHE	ALA	15
16	LYS	VAL	LYS	VAL	ASP	GLU	VAL	GLY	GLY	GLU	ALA	LEU	GLY	ARG	LEU	30
31	LEU	VAL	VAL	TYR	PRO	TRP	THR	GLN	ARG	PHE	PHE	GLU	SER	PHE	GLY	45
46	ASP	LEU	SER	SER	ALA	ASP	ALA	ILE	LEU	GLY	ASN	PRO	LYS	VAL	LYS	60
61	ALA	HIS	GLY	LYS	LYS	VAL	LEU	ASP	SER	PHE	CYS	GLU	GLY	LEU	LYS	75
76	GLN	LEU	ASP	ASP	LEU	LYS	GLY	ALA	PHE	ALA	SER	LEU	SER	GLU	LEU	90
91	HIS	CYS	ASP	LYS	LEU	HIS	VAL	ASP	PRO	GLU	ASN	PHE	ARG	LEU	LEU	105
106	GLY	ASN	VAL	LEU	VAL	VAL	VAL	LEU	ALA	ARG	ARG	PHE	GLY	SER	GLU	120
121	PHE	SER	PRO	GLU	LEU	GLN	ALA	SER	PHE	GLN	LYS	VAL	VAL	THR	GLY	135
136	VAL	ALA	ASN	ALA	LEU	ALA	HIS	ARG	TYR	HIS						150

The Amino Acid Sequence of the γ-Chain of Bovine Fetal Hemoglobin.
D. R. Babin, W. A. Schroeder, J. R. Shelton, J. B. Shelton, and B. Robberson.
Biochemistry, **5**, 1297–1310 (1966).

GLOBINS

HAEMOGLOBIN δ-CHAIN—HUMAN

	1				5					10					15	
1	VAL	HIS	LEU	THR	PRO	GLU	GLU	LYS	THR	ALA	VAL	ASN	ALA	LEU	TRP	15
16	GLY	LYS	VAL	ASN	VAL	ASP	ALA	VAL	GLY	GLY	GLU	ALA	LEU	GLY	ARG	30
31	LEU	LEU	VAL	VAL	TYR	PRO	TRP	THR	GLN	ARG	PHE	PHE	GLU	SER	PHE	45
46	GLY	ASP	LEU	SER	SER	PRO	ASP	ALA	VAL	MET	GLY	ASN	PRO	LYS	VAL	60
61	LYS	ALA	HIS	GLY	LYS	LYS	VAL	LEU	GLY	ALA	PHE	SER	ASP	GLY	LEU	75
76	ALA	HIS	LEU	ASP	ASN	LEU	LYS	GLY	THR	PHE	SER	GLN	LEU	SER	GLU	90
91	LEU	HIS	CYS	ASP	LYS	LEU	HIS	VAL	ASP	PRO	GLU	ASN	PHE	ARG	LEU	105
106	LEU	GLY	ASN	VAL	LEU	VAL	CYS	VAL	LEU	ALA	ARG	ASN	PHE	GLY	LYS	120
121	GLU	PHE	THR	PRO	GLN	MET	GLN	ALA	ALA	TYR	GLN	LYS	VAL	VAL	ALA	135
136	GLY	VAL	ALA	ASN	ALA	LEU	ALA	HIS	LYS	TYR	HIS					150

Hemoglobin XXIII: Note on the sequence of the δ-chains of human hemoglobin.
G. Braunitzer, B. Schrank, A. Stangl, and M. Grillemeier.
Hoppe-Seyler's Z. Physiol. Chem., **359**, 777–783 (1978).

HUMAN HAEMOGLOBIN—ζ-CHAIN

	1				5					10					15	
1	GLY	LEU	SER	ILE	ALA	ASP	LYS	THR	SER	LEU	LYS	ASN	ALA	TRP	GLY	15
16	LYS	ILE	SER	THR	ASP	THR	THR	GLU	ILE	GLY	THR	GLU	ALA	LEU	GLU	30
31	ARG	LEU	HIS	LEU	SER	PHE	PRO	THR	GLN	LYS						45
46		PHE	LEU	SER	HIS	GLY	LEU	ALA	HIS	VAL	LYS	ALA	HIS	GLY	SER	60
61	LYS	VAL	ALA	GLY	ALA	LEU	THR	SER	ILE	LEU	GLY	PRO	VAL	ASP	SER	75
76	PHE	LYS	ASN	ALA	VAL	GLY	ALA	LEU	SER	GLU	VAL	HIS	ALA	LYS	ILE	90
91	LEU	ARG	VAL	ASP	PRO	VAL	ASN	PHE	ARG	ALA	LEU	SER	HIS	CYS	LEU	105
106	GLY	LYS	SER	LEU	GLX	ALA	HIS	LEU	TYR	ALA	GLX	PHE	THR	ILE	GLY	120
121	VAL	ASX	ALA	SER	LEU	ASP	LYS	PHE	LEU	ALA	SER	VAL	SER	THR	VAL	135
136	LEU	GLX	SER	LYS	TYR	ARG										150

Notes: (i) The above sequence is tentative. (ii) Residues 41–46 have not yet been identified. (iii) The N-terminus of the protein is blocked.
Human embryonic haemoglobins including a comparison by homology of the human zeta and alpha chains.
H. Kamuzora and H. Lehmann.
Nature, **256**, 511–513 (1975).

GLOBINS

LAMPREY HAEMOGLOBIN

	1				5					10					15		
1	PRO	ILE	VAL	ASP	THR	GLY	SER	VAL	ALA	PRO	LEU	SER	ALA	ALA	GLU		15
16	LYS	THR	LYS	ILE	ARG	SER	ALA	TRP	ALA	PRO	VAL	TYR	SER	THR ASN	TYR		30
31	GLU	THR	SER	GLY	VAL	ASP	ILE	LEU	VAL	LYS	PHE	PHE	THR	SER	THR		45
46	PRO	ALA	ALA	(GLN, GLU)	PHE	PHE	PRO	LYS	PHE	LYS	GLY	LEU	THR	THR			60
61	ALA	ASP	GLN	LEU	LYS	LYS	SER	ALA	ASP	VAL	ARG	TRP	HIS	ALA	GLU		75
76	ARG	ILE	ILE	ASN	ALA	VAL	ASN	ASP	ALA	VAL	ALA	SER	MET	ASP	ASP		90
91	THR	GLU	LYS	MET	SER	MET	LYS	ASN	LEU	SER	GLY	LYS	HIS	ALA	LYS		105
106	SER	PHE	GLN	VAL	ASP	PRO	GLN	TYR	PHE	LYS	VAL	LEU	ALA	ALA	VAL		120
121	ILE	ALA	ASP	THR	VAL	ALA	ALA	GLY	ASP	ALA	GLY	PHE	GLU	LYS	LEU		135
136	ARG	MET	ILE	CYS	ILE	LEU	LEU	ARG	SER	ALA	TYR						150

The Amino Acid Sequence of Haemoglobin V from the Lamprey, *Petromyzon marinus*.
S. L. Li and A. Riggs.
J. Biol. Chem., **245**, 6149–6169 (1970).

BLOODWORM HAEMOGLOBIN

	1				5					10					15		
1	GLY	LEU	SER	ALA	ALA	GLN	ARG	GLN	VAL	ILE	ALA	ALA	THR	TRP	LYS		15
16	ASP	ILE	ALA	GLY	ASN	ASP	ASN	GLY	ALA	GLY	VAL	GLY	LYS	ASP	CYS		30
31	LEU	ILE	LYS	HIS	LEU	SER	ALA	HIS	PRO	GLN	MET	ALA	ALA	VAL	PHE		45
46	GLY	PHE	SER	GLY	ALA	SER	ASP	PRO	ALA	VAL	ALA	ASP	LEU	GLY	ALA		60
61	LYS	VAL	LEU	ALA	GLX	ILE	GLY	VAL	ALA	VAL	SER	HIS	LEU	GLY	ASP		75
76	GLX	GLY	LYS	MET	VAL	ALA	GLN	MET	LYS	ALA	VAL	GLY	VAL	ARG	HIS		90
91	LYS	GLY	TYR	GLY	ASN	LYS	HIS	ILE	LYS	GLY	GLN	TYR	PHE	GLU	PRO		105
106	LEU	GLY	ALA	SER	LEU	LEU	SER	ALA	MET	GLU	HIS	ARG	ILE	GLY	GLY		120
121	LYS	MET	ASN	ALA	ALA	ALA	LYS	ASP	ALA	TRP	ALA	ALA	ALA	TYR	ALA		135
136	ASP	ILE	SER	GLY	ALA	LEU	ILE	SER	GLY	LEU	GLN	SER					150

The Amino Acid Sequence of the monomeric haemoglobin component from the bloodworm,
Glycera dibranchiata.
T. Imamura, T. O. Baldwin, and A. Riggs.
J. Biol. Chem., **247**, 2785–2797 (1972).

264

GLOBINS

HUMAN MYOGLOBIN

```
        1               5                      10                      15
  1  GLY LEU SER ASP GLY GLU TRP GLN LEU VAL LEU ASN VAL TRP GLY   15
 16  LYS VAL GLU ALA ASP ILE PRO GLY HIS GLY GLN GLU VAL LEU ILE   30
 31  ARG LEU PHE LYS GLY HIS PRO GLU THR LEU GLU LYS PHE ASP LYS   45
 46  PHE LYS HIS LEU LYS SER GLU ASP GLU MET LYS ALA SER GLU ASP   60
 61  LEU LYS LYS HIS GLY ALA THR VAL LEU THR ALA LEU GLY GLY ILE   75
 76  LEU LYS LYS LYS GLY HIS HIS GLU ALA GLU ILE LYS PRO LEU ALA   90
 91  GLN SER HIS ALA THR LYS HIS LYS VAL PRO ILE LYS TYR LEU GLU  105
106  PHE ILE SER GLU CYS ILE ILE GLN VAL LEU GLN SER LYS HIS PRO  120
121  GLY ASP PHE GLY ALA ASP ALA GLN GLY ALA MET ASN LYS ALA LEU  135
136  GLU LEU PHE ARG LYS ASP MET ALA SER ASN TYR LYS GLU LEU GLY  150
151  PHE GLN GLY                                                  165
```

Human Myoglobin. Primary Structure.
A. E. R. Herrera and H. Lehmann.
Nature (New Biol.), **232**, 149–152 (1971).
In corrected form:
The myoglobin of primates. I. *Hylobates agilis* (gibbon).
A. E. R. Herrera and H. Lehmann.
Biochim. Biophys. Acta, **251**, 482–488 (1971).

MYOGLOBIN—ORANGUTAN

```
        1               5                      10                      15
  1  GLY LEU SER ASP GLY GLU TRP GLN LEU VAL LEU ASN VAL TRP GLY   15
 16  LYS VAL GLU ALA ASP ILE PRO SER HIS GLY GLN GLU VAL LEU ILE   30
 31  ARG LEU PHE LYS GLY HIS PRO GLU THR LEU GLU LYS PHE ASP LYS   45
 46  PHE LYS HIS LEU LYS SER GLU ASP GLU MET LYS ALA SER GLU ASP   60
 61  LEU LYS LYS HIS GLY ALA THR VAL LEU THR ALA LEU GLY GLY ILE   75
 76  LEU LYS LYS LYS GLY HIS HIS GLU ALA GLU ILE LYS PRO LEU ALA   90
 91  GLN SER HIS ALA THR LYS HIS LYS ILE PRO VAL LYS TYR LEU GLU  105
106  PHE ILE SER GLU SER ILE ILE GLN VAL LEU GLN SER LYS HIS PRO  120
121  GLY ASP PHE GLY ALA ASP ALA GLN GLY ALA MET ASN LYS ALA LEU  135
136  GLU LEU PHE ARG LYS ASP MET ALA SER ASN TYR LYS GLU LEU GLY  150
151  PHE GLN GLY                                                  165
```

Myoglobin of the orangutan as a phylogenetic enigma.
A. E. Romero-Herrera, H. Lehmann, O. Castillo, K. A. Joysey and A. E. Friday.
Nature, **261**, 162–164 (1976).

MYOGLOBIN—RABBIT

	1			5					10					15		
1	GLY	LEU	SER	ASP	ALA	GLU	TRP	GLN	LEU	VAL	LEU	ASN	VAL	TRP	GLY	15
16	LYS	VAL	GLU	ALA	ASP	LEU	ALA	GLY	HIS	GLY	(GLN	GLU)	VAL	LEU	ILE	30
31	ARG	LEU	PHE	HIS	THR	HIS	PRO	GLU	THR	LEU	GLU	LYS	PHE	ASP	LYS	45
46	PHE	LYS	HIS	LEU	LYS	SER	GLU	ASP	GLU	MET	LYS	ALA	SER	GLU	ASP	60
61	LEU	LYS	LYS	HIS	GLY	ASN	THR	VAL	LEU	THR	ALA	LEU	GLY	ALA	ILE	75
76	LEU	LYS	LYS	LYS	GLY	HIS	HIS	GLU	ALA	GLU	ILE	LYS	PRO	LEU	ALA	90
91	GLN	SER	HIS	ALA	THR	LYS	HIS	LYS	ILE	PRO	VAL	LYS	TYR	LEU	GLU	105
106	PHE	ILE	SER	GLU	ALA	ILE	ILE	HIS	VAL	LEU	HIS	SER	LYS	HIS	PRO	120
121	GLY	ASP	PHE	GLY	ALA	ASP	ALA	GLN	ALA	ALA	MET	SER	LYS	ALA	LEU	135
136	GLU	LEU	PHE	ARG	ASN	ASP	ILE	ALA	ALA	GLN	TYR	LYS	GLU	LEU	GLY	150
151	PHE	GLN	GLY													165

The primary structure of the myoglobin of rabbit (*Oryctolagus cuniculus*).
A. E. Romero-Herrera, H. Lehmann and O. Castillo.
Biochim. Biophys. Acta, **439**, 51–54 (1976).

HORSE MYOGLOBIN

	1			5					10					15		
1	GLY	LEU	SER	ASP	GLY	GLU	TRP	GLN	GLN	VAL	LEU	ASN	VAL	TRP	GLY	15
16	LYS	VAL	GLU	ALA	ASP	ILE	ALA	GLY	HIS	GLY	GLN	GLU	VAL	LEU	ILE	30
31	ARG	LEU	PHE	THR	GLY	HIS	PRO	GLU	THR	LEU	GLU	LYS	PHE	ASP	LYS	45
46	PHE	LYS	HIS	LEU	LYS	THR	GLU	ALA	GLU	MET	LYS	ALA	SER	GLU	ASP	60
61	LEU	LYS	LYS	HIS	GLY	THR	VAL	VAL	LEU	THR	ALA	LEU	GLY	GLY	ILE	75
76	LEU	LYS	LYS	LYS	GLY	HIS	HIS	GLU	ALA	GLU	LEU	LYS	PRO	LEU	ALA	90
91	GLN	SER	HIS	ALA	THR	LYS	HIS	LYS	ILE	PRO	ILE	LYS	TYR	LEU	GLU	105
106	PHE	ILE	SER	ASP	ALA	ILE	ILE	HIS	VAL	LEU	HIS	SER	LYS	HIS	PRO	120
121	GLY	ASP	PHE	GLY	ALA	ASP	ALA	GLN	GLY	ALA	MET	THR	LYS	ALA	LEU	135
136	GLU	LEU	PHE	ARG	ASN	ASP	ILE	ALA	ALA	LYS	TYR	LYS	GLU	LEU	GLY	150
151	PHE	GLN	GLY													165

The covalent structure of horse myoglobin.
M. Dautrevaux, Y. Boulanger, K.-K. Han, and G. Biserte.
Eur. J. Biochem., **11**, 267–277 (1969).
And
Residue 122 of sperm whale and horse myoglobin.
A. E. R. Herrera and H. Lehmann.
Biochim. Biophys. Acta, **336**, 318–323 (1974).

GLOBINS

MYOGLOBIN—PIG

	1				5					10					15		
1	GLY	LEU	SER	ASP	GLY	GLU	TRP	GLN	LEU	VAL	LEU	ASN	VAL	TRP	GLY		15
16	LYS	VAL	GLU	ALA	ASP	VAL	ALA	GLY	HIS	GLY	GLN	GLU	VAL	LEU	ILE		30
31	ARG	LEU	PHE	LYS	GLY	HIS	PRO	GLU	THR	LEU	GLU	LYS	PHE	ASP	LYS		45
46	PHE	LYS	HIS	LEU	LYS	SER	GLU	ASP	GLU	MET	LYS	ALA	SER	GLU	ASP		60
61	LEU	LYS	LYS	HIS	GLY	ASN	THR	VAL	LEU	THR	ALA	LEU	GLY	GLY	ILE		75
76	LEU	LYS	LYS	LYS	GLY	HIS	HIS	GLU	ALA	GLU	LEU	THR	PRO	LEU	ALA		90
91	GLN	SER	HIS	ALA	THR	LYS	HIS	LYS	ILE	PRO	VAL	LYS	TYR	LEU	GLU		105
106	PHE	ILE	SER	GLU	ALA	ILE	ILE	GLN	VAL	LEU	GLN	SER	LYS	HIS	PRO		120
121	GLY	ASP	PHE	GLY	ALA	ASP	ALA	GLN	GLY	ALA	MET	SER	LYS	ALA	LEU		135
136	GLU	LEU	PHE	ARG	ASN	ASP	MET	ALA	ALA	LYS	TYR	LYS	GLU	LEU	GLY		150
151	PHE	GLN	GLY														165

Comparison of the amino acid sequence of pig heart myoglobin with other ungulate myoglobins.
J. Rousseaux, M. Dautrevaux, and K. Han.
Biochim. Biophys. Acta, **439**, 55–62 (1976).

MYOGLOBIN—SHEEP

	1				5					10					15		
1	GLY	LEU	SER	ASP	GLY	GLU	TRP	GLN	LEU	VAL	LEU	ASN	ALA	TRP	GLY		15
16	LYS	VAL	GLU	ALA	ASP	VAL	ALA	GLY	HIS	GLY	GLN	GLU	VAL	LEU	ILE		30
31	ARG	LEU	PHE	THR	GLY	HIS	PRO	GLU	THR	LEU	GLU	LYS	PHE	ASP	LYS		45
46	PHE	LYS	HIS	LEU	LYS	THR	GLU	ALA	GLU	MET	LYS	ALA	SER	GLU	ASP		60
61	LEU	LYS	LYS	HIS	GLY	ASN	THR	VAL	LEU	THR	ALA	LEU	GLY	GLY	ILE		75
76	LEU	LYS	LYS	LYS	GLY	HIS	HIS	GLU	ALA	GLU	VAL	LYS	HIS	LEU	ALA		90
91	GLU	SER	HIS	ALA	ASN	LYS	HIS	LYS	VAL	PRO	ILE	LYS	TYR	LEU	GLU		105
106	PHE	ILE	SER	ASP	ALA	ILE	ILE	HIS	VAL	LEU	HIS	ALA	LYS	HIS	PRO		120
121	SER	ASN	PHE	GLY	ALA	ASP	ALA	GLN	GLY	ALA	MET	SER	LYS	ALA·LEU			135
136	GLU	LEU	PHE	ARG	ASN	ASP	MET	ALA	ALA	GLU	TYR	LYS	VAL	LEU	GLY		150
151	PHE	GLN	GLY														165

The covalent structure of sheep-heart myoglobin.
K.-K. Han, D. Tetaert, Y. Moschetto, M. Dautrevaux, and C. Kopeyan.
Eur. J. Biochem., **27**, 585–592 (1972).

BEEF HEART MYOGLOBIN

	1				5					10					15		
1	GLY	LEU	SER	ASP	GLY	GLU	TRP	GLN	ALA	VAL	LEU	ASN	ALA	TRP	GLY	15
16	LYS	VAL	GLU	ALA	ASP	VAL	ALA	GLY	HIS	GLY	GLN	GLU	VAL	LEU	ILE	30
31	ARG	LEU	PHE	THR	GLY	HIS	PRO	GLU	THR	LEU	GLU	LYS	PHE	ASP	LYS	45
46	PHE	LYS	HIS	LEU	LYS	THR	GLU	ALA	GLU	MET	LYS	ALA	SER	GLU	ASP	60
61	LEU	LYS	LYS	HIS	GLY	ASN	THR	VAL	LEU	THR	ALA	LEU	GLY	GLY	ILE	75
76	LEU	LYS	LYS	LYS	GLY	HIS	HIS	GLU	ALA	GLU	VAL	LYS	HIS	LEU	ALA	90
91	GLU	SER	HIS	ALA	ASN	LYS	HIS	LYS	VAL	PRO	ILE	LYS	TYR	LEU	GLU	105
106	PHE	ILE	SER	ASP	ALA	ILE	ILE	HIS	VAL	LEU	HIS	ALA	LYS	HIS	PRO	120
121	SER	ASN	PHE	ALA	ALA	ASP	ALA	GLN	GLY	ALA	MET	SER	LYS	ALA	LEU	135
136	GLU	LEU	PHE	ARG	ASN	ASP	ALA	ALA	GLU	LYS	TYR	LYS	VAL	LEU	GLY	150
151	PHE	HIS	GLY													165

The Covalent Structure of Beef Heart Myoglobin.
K.-K. Han, M. Dautrevaux, X. Chaila, and G. Biserte.
Eur. J. Biochem., **16**, 465–471 (1970).

MYOGLOBIN—CHICKEN

	1				5					10					15		
1	GLY	LEU	SER	ASP	GLN	GLU	TRP	GLN	GLN	VAL	LEU	THR	ILE	TRP	GLY	15
16	LYS	VAL	GLU	ALA	ASP	ILE	ALA	GLY	HIS	GLY	HIS	GLU	VAL	LEU	MET	30
31	ARG	LEU	PHE	HIS	ASP	HIS	PRO	GLU	THR	LEU	ASP	ARG	PHE	ASP	LYS	45
46	PHE	LYS	GLY	LEU	LYS	THR	GLU	PRO	ASP	MET	LYS	GLY	SER	GLU	ASP	60
61	LEU	LYS	LYS	HIS	GLY	GLN	THR	VAL	LEU	THR	ALA	LEU	GLY	ALA	GLN	75
76	LEU	LYS	LYS	LYS	GLY	HIS	HIS	GLU	ALA	ASP	LEU	LYS	PRO	LEU	ALA	90
91	GLN	THR	HIS	ALA	THR	LYS	HIS	LYS	ILE	PRO	VAL	LYS	TYR	LEU	GLU	105
106	PHE	ILE	SER	GLU	VAL	ILE	ILE	LYS	VAL	ILE	ALA	GLU	LYS	HIS	ALA	120
121	ALA	ASP	PHE	GLY	ALA	ASP	SER	GLN	ALA	ALA	MET	LYS	LYS	ALA	LEU	135
136	GLU	LEU	PHE	ARG	ASP	ASP	MET	ALA	SER	LYS	TYR	LYS	GLU	PHE	GLY	150
151	PHE	GLN	GLY													165

The primary structure of chicken myoglobin (*Gallus gallus*).
M. Deconinck, S. Peiffer, J. Depreter, C. Paul, A. G. Schnek, and J. Leonis.
Biochim. Biophys. Acta, **386**, 567–575 (1975).

GLOBINS

MYOGLOBIN—DOG

	1				5					10					15		
1	GLY	LEU	SER	ASP	GLY	GLU	TRP	GLN	ILE	VAL	LEU	ASN	ILE	TRP	GLY		15
16	LYS	VAL	GLU	THR	ASP	LEU	ALA	GLY	HIS	GLY	GLN	GLU	VAL	LEU	ILE		30
31	ARG	LEU	PHE	LYS	ASN	HIS	PRO	GLU	THR	LEU	ASP	LYS	PHE	ASP	LYS		45
46	PHE	LYS	HIS	LEU	LYS	SER	GLU	ASP	GLU	MET	LYS	GLY	SER	GLU	ASP		60
61	LEU	LYS	LYS	HIS	GLY	ASN	THR	VAL	LEU	THR	ALA	LEU	GLY	GLY	ILE		75
76	LEU	LYS	LYS	LYS	GLY	HIS	HIS	GLU	ALA	GLU	LEU	LYS	PRO	LEU	ALA		90
91	GLN	SER	HIS	ALA	THR	LYS	HIS	LYS	ILE	PRO	VAL	LYS	TYR	LEU	GLU		105
106	PHE	ILE	SER	ASP	ALA	ILE	ILE	GLN	VAL	LEU	GLN	SER	LYS	HIS	SER		120
121	GLY	ASP	PHE	HIS	ALA	ASP	THR	GLU	ALA	ALA	MET	LYS	LYS	ALA	LEU		135
136	GLU	LEU	PHE	ARG	ASN	ASP	ILE	ALA	ALA	LYS	TYR	LYS	GLU	LEU	GLY		150
151	PHE	GLN	GLY														165

The covalent structure of dog myoglobin.
V. Dumur, M. Dautrevaux, and K. Han.
Biochim. Biophys. Acta, **420**, 376–386 (1976).

MYOGLOBIN—BADGER

	1				5					10					15		
1	GLU	LEU	SER	ASP	GLY	GLU	TRP	GLN	LEU	VAL	LEU	ASN	VAL	TRP	GLY		15
16	LYS	VAL	GLU	ALA	ASP	LEU	ALA	GLY	HIS	GLY	GLN	GLU	VAL	LEU	ILE		30
31	ARG	LEU	PHE	LYS	GLY	HIS	PRO	GLU	THR	LEU	GLU	LYS	PHE	ASP	LYS		45
46	PHE	LYS	HIS	LEU	LYS	SER	GLU	ASP	GLU	MET	LYS	GLY	SER	GLU	ASP		60
61	LEU	LYS	LYS	HIS	GLY	ASN	THR	VAL	LEU	THR	ALA	LEU	GLY	GLY	ILE		75
76	LEU	LYS	LYS	LYS	GLY	HIS	GLN	GLU	ALA	GLU	LEU	LYS	PRO	LEU	ALA		90
91	GLN	SER	HIS	ALA	THR	LYS	HIS	LYS	ILE	PRO	VAL	LYS	TYR	LEU	GLU		105
106	PHE	ILE	SER	ASP	ALA	ILE	ALA	GLN	VAL	LEU	GLN	SER	LYS	HIS	PRO		120
121	GLY	ASN	PHE	ALA	ALA	GLU	ALA	GLN	GLY	ALA	MET	LYS	LYS	ALA	LEU		135
136	GLU	LEU	PHE	ARG	ASN	ASP	ILE	ALA	ALA	LYS	TYR	LYS	GLU	LEU	GLY		150
151	PHE	GLN	GLY														165

The primary sequence of badger myoglobin.
D. Tetaert, K.-K. Han, M.-T. Plancot, M. Dautre-Vaux, S. Ducastaing, I. Hombrados, and E. Neuzil.
Biochim. Biophys. Acta, **351**, 317–324 (1974).

GLOBINS

MYOGLOBIN—TREE-SHREW

	1				5					10					15	
1	GLY	LEU	SER	ASP	GLY	GLU	TRP	GLN	LEU	VAL	LEU	ASN	VAL	TRP	GLY	15
16	LYS	VAL	GLU	ALA	ASP	VAL	ALA	GLY	HIS	GLY	GLN	GLU	VAL	LEU	ILE	30
31	ARG	LEU	PHE	LYS	GLY	HIS	PRO	GLU	THR	LEU	GLU	LYS	PHE	ASP	LYS	45
46	PHE	LYS	HIS	LEU	LYS	THR	GLU	ASP	GLU	MET	LYS	ALA	SER	GLU	ASP	60
61	LEU	LYS	LYS	HIS	GLY	ASN	THR	VAL	LEU	SER	ALA	LEU	GLY	GLY	ILE	75
76	LEU	LYS	LYS	LYS	GLY	GLN	HIS	GLU	ALA	GLU	ILE	LYS	PRO	LEU	ALA	90
91	GLN	SER	HIS	ALA	THR	LYS	HIS	LYS	ILE	PRO	VAL	LYS	TYR	LEU	GLU	105
106	PHE	ILE	SER	GLU	ALA	ILE	ILE	GLN	VAL	LEU	GLN	SER	LYS	HIS	PRO	120
121	GLY	ASP	PHE	GLY	ALA	ASP	ALA	GLN	ALA	ALA	MET	SER	LYS	ALA	LEU	135
136	GLU	LEU	PHE	ARG	ASN	ASP	ILE	ALA	ALA	LYS	TYR	LYS	GLU	LEU	GLY	150
151	PHE	GLN	GLY													165

The myoglobin of primates. VI. *Tupaia glis belangeri* (common treeshrew).
A. E. Romero-Herrera and H. Lehmann.
Biochim. Biophys. Acta, **359**, 236–241 (1974).

MYOGLOBIN—HEDGEHOG

	1				5					10					15	
1	GLY	LEU	SER	ASP	GLY	GLU	TRP	GLN	LEU	VAL	LEU	ASN	VAL	TRP	GLY	15
16	LYS	VAL	GLU	ALA	ASP	ILE	PRO	GLY	HIS	GLY	GLN	GLU	VAL	LEU	ILE	30
31	ARG	LEU	PHE	LYS	ASP	HIS	PRO	GLU	THR	LEU	GLU	LYS	PHE	ASP	LYS	45
46	PHE	LYS	HIS	LEU	LYS	SER	GLU	ASP	GLU	MET	LYS	SER	SER	GLU	ASP	60
61	LEU	LYS	LYS	HIS	GLY	THR	THR	VAL	LEU	THR	ALA	LEU	GLY	GLY	ILE	75
76	LEU	LYS	LYS	LYS	GLY	GLN	HIS	GLU	ALA	GLN	LEU	ALA	PRO	LEU	ALA	90
91	GLN	SER	HIS	ALA	ASN	LYS	HIS	LYS	ILE	PRO	VAL	LYS	TYR	LEU	GLU	105
106	PHE	ILE	SER	GLU	ALA	ILE	ILE	GLN	VAL	LEU	LYS	SER	LYS	HIS	ALA	120
121	GLY	ASP	PHE	GLY	ALA	ASP	ALA	GLN	GLY	ALA	MET	SER	LYS	ALA	LEU	135
136	GLU	LEU	PHE	ARG	ASN	ASP	ILE	ALA	ALA	LYS	TYR	LYS	GLU	LEU	GLY	150
151	PHE	GLN	GLY													165

The primary structure of the myoglobin of the insectivore *Erinaceus Europaeus* (Common European hedgehog).
A. E. Romero-Herrera, H. Lehmann, and W. Fakes.
Biochim. Biophys. Acta, **379**, 13–21 (1975).

270

GLOBINS

MYOGLOBIN—AMERICAN OPOSSUM

```
       1              5                    10                      15
  1  GLY LEU SER ASP GLY GLU TRP GLN LEU VAL LEU ASN ALA TRP GLY   15
 16  LYS VAL GLU ALA ASP ILE PRO GLY HIS GLY GLN GLU VAL LEU ILE   30
 31  ARG LEU PHE LYS GLY HIS PRO GLU THR LEU GLU LYS PHE ASP LYS   45
 46  PHE LYS HIS LEU LYS SER GLU ASP GLU MET LYS ALA SER GLU ASP   60
 61  LEU LYS LYS HIS GLY ALA THR VAL LEU THR ALA LEU GLY ASN ILE   75
 76  LEU LYS LYS LYS GLY ASN HIS GLU ALA GLU LEU LYS PRO LEU ALA   90
 91  GLN SER HIS ALA THR LYS HIS LYS ILE SER VAL GLN PHE LEU GLU  105
106  PHE ILE SER GLU ALA ILE ILE GLN VAL ILE GLN SER LYS HIS PRO  120
121  GLY ASP PHE GLY GLY ASP ALA GLN ALA ALA MET GLY LYS ALA LEU  135
136  GLU LEU PHE ARG ASN ASP MET ALA ALA LYS TYR LYS GLU LEU GLY  150
151  PHE GLN GLY                                                  165
```

The primary structure of the myoglobin of *Didelphis marsupialis*, (Virginia opossum).
A. E. Romero-Herrera, and H. Lehmann.
Biochim. Biophys. Acta, **400**, 387–398 (1975).

KANGAROO MYOGLOBIN

```
       1              5                    10                      15
  1  GLY LEU SER ASP GLY GLU TRP GLN LEU VAL LEU ASN ILE TRP GLY   15
 16  LYS VAL GLU THR ASP GLU GLY GLY HIS GLY LYS ASP VAL LEU ILE   30
 31  ARG LEU PHE LYS GLY HIS PRO GLU THR LEU GLU LYS PHE ASP LYS   45
 46  PHE LYS HIS LEU LYS SER GLU ASP GLU MET LYS ALA SER GLU ASP   60
 61  LEU LYS LYS HIS GLY ILE THR VAL LEU THR ALA LEU GLY ASN ILE   75
 76  LEU LYS LYS LYS GLY HIS HIS GLU ALA GLU LEU LYS PRO LEU ALA   90
 91  GLN SER HIS ALA THR LYS HIS LYS ILE PRO VAL GLN PHE LEU GLU  105
106  PHE ILE SER ASP ALA ILE ILE GLN VAL ILE GLN SER LYS HIS ALA  120
121  GLY ASN PHE GLY ALA ASP ALA GLN ALA ALA MET LYS LYS ALA LEU  135
136  GLU LEU PHE ARG HIS ASP MET ALA ALA LYS TYR LYS GLU PHE GLY  150
151  PHE GLN GLY                                                  165
```

Studies on Marsupial Proteins. IV. Amino Acid Sequence of the Myoglobin of the Red
Kangaroo *Megaleia rufa*.
G. M. Air and E. O. P. Thompson.
Aust. J. Biol. Sci., **24**, 75–95 (1971).

SPERM WHALE MYOGLOBIN

	1				5					10					15		
1	VAL	LEU	SER	GLU	GLY	GLU	TRP	GLN	LEU	VAL	LEU	HIS	VAL	TRP	ALA		15
16	LYS	VAL	GLU	ALA	ASP	VAL	ALA	GLY	HIS	GLY	GLN	ASP	ILE	LEU	ILE		30
31	ARG	LEU	PHE	LYS	SER	HIS	PRO	GLU	THR	LEU	GLU	LYS	PHE	ASP	ARG		45
46	PHE	LYS	HIS	LEU	LYS	THR	GLU	ALA	GLU	MET	LYS	ALA	SER	GLU	ASP		60
61	LEU	LYS	LYS	HIS	GLY	VAL	THR	VAL	LEU	THR	ALA	LEU	GLY	ALA	ILE		75
76	LEU	LYS	LYS	LYS	GLY	HIS	HIS	GLU	ALA	GLU	LEU	LYS	PRO	LEU	ALA		90
91	GLN	SER	HIS	ALA	THR	LYS	HIS	LYS	ILE	PRO	ILE	LYS	TYR	LEU	GLU		105
106	PHE	ILE	SER	GLU	ALA	ILE	ILE	HIS	VAL	LEU	HIS	SER	ARG	HIS	PRO		120
121	GLY	ASP	PHE	GLY	ALA	ASP	ALA	GLN	GLY	ALA	MET	ASN	LYS	ALA	LEU		135
136	GLU	LEU	PHE	ARG	LYS	ASP	ILE	ALA	ALA	LYS	TYR	LYS	GLU	LEU	GLY		150
151	TYR	GLN	GLY														165

Amino acid sequence of sperm whale myoglobin.
A. B. Edmundson.
Nature, **205**, 883–887 (1965).
And
Residue 122 of sperm whale and horse myoglobin.
A. E. R. Herrera and H. Lehmann.
Biochim. Biophys. Acta, **336**, 318–323 (1974).

MYOGLOBIN—CALIFORNIA GRAY WHALE

	1				5					10					15		
1	VAL	LEU	SER	ASP	ALA	GLU	TRP	GLN	LEU	VAL	LEU	ASN	ILE	TRP	ALA		15
16	LYS	VAL	GLU	ALA	ASP	VAL	ALA	GLY	HIS	GLY	GLN	ASP	ILE	LEU	ILE		30
31	ARG	LEU	PHE	LYS	GLY	HIS	PRO	GLU	THR	LEU	GLU	LYS	PHE	ASP	LYS		45
46	PHE	LYS	HIS	LEU	LYS	THR	GLU	ALA	GLU	MET	LYS	ALA	SER	GLU	ASP		60
61	LEU	LYS	LYS	HIS	GLY	ASN	THR	VAL	LEU	THR	ALA	LEU	GLY	GLY	ILE		75
76	LEU	LYS	LYS	LYS	GLY	HIS	HIS	GLU	ALA	GLU	LEU	LYS	PRO	LEU	ALA		90
91	GLN	SER	HIS	ALA	THR	LYS	HIS	LYS	ILE	PRO	ILE	LYS	TYR	LEU	GLU		105
106	PHE	ILE	SER	ASP	ALA	ILE	ILE	HIS	VAL	LEU	HIS	SER	ARG	HIS	PRO		120
121	GLY	ASP	PHE	GLY	ALA	ASP	ALA	GLN	ALA	ALA	MET	ASN	LYS	ALA	LEU		135
136	GLU	LEU	PHE	ARG	LYS	ASP	ILE	ALA	ALA	LYS	TYR	LYS	GLU	LEU	GLY		150
151	PHE	GLN	GLY														165

Complete primary structure of the major component myoglobin of California gray whale
(*Eschrichtius gibbosus*).
R. A. Bogardt, F. E. Dwulet, L. D. Lehman, B. N. Jones, and F. R. N. Gurd.
Biochemistry, **15**, 2597–2602 (1976).

GLOBINS

MYOGLOBIN—DWARF SPERM WHALE

	1				5					10					15	
1	VAL	LEU	SER	GLU	GLY	GLU	TRP	GLN	LEU	VAL	LEU	HIS	VAL	TRP	ALA	15
16	LYS	VAL	GLU	ALA	ASP	ILE	ALA	GLY	HIS	GLY	GLN	ASP	ILE	LEU	ILE	30
31	ARG	LEU	PHE	LYS	HIS	HIS	PRO	GLU	THR	LEU	GLU	LYS	PHE	ASP	ARG	45
46	PHE	LYS	HIS	LEU	LYS	SER	GLU	ALA	GLU	MET	LYS	ALA	SER	GLU	ASP	60
61	LEU	LYS	LYS	HIS	GLY	VAL	THR	VAL	LEU	THR	ALA	LEU	GLY	ALA	ILE	75
76	LEU	LYS	LYS	LYS	GLY	HIS	HIS	GLU	ALA	GLU	LEU	LYS	PRO	LEU	ALA	90
91	GLN	SER	HIS	ALA	THR	LYS	HIS	LYS	ILE	PRO	ILE	LYS	TYR	LEU	GLU	105
106	PHE	ILE	SER	GLU	ALA	ILE	ILE	HIS	VAL	LEU	HIS	SER	ARG	HIS	PRO	120
121	ALA	ASP	PHE	GLY	ALA	ASP	ALA	GLN	GLY	ALA	MET	SER	LYS	ALA	LEU	135
136	GLU	LEU	PHE	ARG	LYS	ASP	ILE	ALA	ALA	LYS	TYR	LYS	GLU	LEU	GLY	150
151	TYR	GLN	GLY													165

The complete amino acid sequence of the major component myoglobin of Dwarf Sperm whale (*Kogia simus*).
F. E. Dwulet, B. N. Jones, L. D. Lehman, and F. R. N. Gurd.
Biochemistry, **16**, 873–876 (1977).

MYOGLOBIN—HUMPBACK WHALE

	1				5					10					15	
1	VAL	LEU	SER	ASP	ALA	GLU	TRP	GLN	LEU	VAL	LEU	ASN	ILE	TRP	ALA	15
16	LYS	VAL	GLU	ALA	ASP	VAL	ALA	GLY	HIS	GLY	GLN	ASP	ILE	LEU	ILE	30
31	ARG	LEU	PHE	LYS	GLY	HIS	PRO	GLU	THR	LEU	GLU	LYS	PHE	ASP	LYS	45
46	PHE	LYS	HIS	LEU	LYS	THR	GLU	ALA	GLU	MET	LYS	ALA	SER	GLU	ASP	60
61	LEU	LYS	LYS	HIS	GLY	ASN	THR	VAL	LEU	THR	ALA	LEU	GLY	GLY	ILE	75
76	LEU	LYS	LYS	LYS	GLY	HIS	HIS	GLU	ALA	GLU	LEU	LYS	PRO	LEU	ALA	90
91	GLN	SER	HIS	ALA	THR	LYS	HIS	LYS	ILE	PRO	ILE	LYS	TYR	LEU	GLU	105
106	PHE	ILE	SER	ASP	ALA	ILE	ILE	HIS	VAL	LEU	HIS	SER	ARG	HIS	PRO	120
121	ALA	ASP	PHE	GLY	ALA	ASP	ALA	GLN	ALA	ALA	MET	ASN	LYS	ALA	LEU	135
136	GLU	LEU	PHE	ARG	LYS	ASP	ILE	ALA	ALA	LYS	TYR	LYS	GLU	LEU	GLY	150
151	PHE	GLN	GLY													165

Complete amino acid sequence of the major component Myoglobin from the Humpback Whale, *Megaptera novaeangliae*.
L. D. Lehman, F. E. Dwulet, B. N. Jones, R. A. Bogardt, S. T. Krueckeberg, R. B. Visscher, and F. R. N. Gurd.
Biochemistry, **17**, 3736–3739 (1978).

MYOGLOBIN—PILOT WHALE

	1				5					10					15		
1	GLY	LEU	SER	ASP	GLY	GLU	TRP	GLN	LEU	VAL	LEU	ASN	VAL	TRP	GLY	15
16	LYS	VAL	GLU	ALA	ASP	LEU	ALA	GLY	HIS	GLY	GLN	ASP	ILE	LEU	ILE	30
31	ARG	LEU	PHE	LYS	GLY	HIS	PRO	GLU	THR	LEU	GLU	LYS	PHE	ASP	LYS	45
46	PHE	LYS	HIS	LEU	LYS	THR	GLU	ALA	ASP	MET	LYS	ALA	SER	GLU	ASP	60
61	LEU	LYS	LYS	HIS	GLY	ASN	THR	VAL	LEU	THR	ALA	LEU	GLY	ALA	ILE	75
76	LEU	LYS	LYS	LYS	GLY	HIS	HIS	GLU	ALA	GLU	LEU	LYS	PRO	LEU	ALA	90
91	GLN	SER	HIS	ALA	THR	LYS	HIS	LYS	ILE	PRO	ILE	LYS	TYR	LEU	GLU	105
106	PHE	ILE	SER	GLU	ALA	ILE	ILE	HIS	VAL	LEU	HIS	SER	ARG	HIS	PRO	120
121	ALA	GLU	PHE	GLY	ALA	ASP	ALA	GLN	GLY	ALA	MET	ASN	LYS	ALA	LEU	135
136	GLU	LEU	PHE	ARG	LYS	ASP	ILE	ALA	ALA	LYS	TYR	LYS	GLU	LEU	GLY	150
151	PHE	HIS	GLY													165

Complete amino acid sequence of myoglobin from the pilot whale *Globicephala melaena*.
B. N. Jones, F. E. Dwulet, L. D. Lehman, M. H. Garner, R. A. Bogardt, W. H. Garner, and F. R. N. Gurd.
Biochemistry, **17**, 1971–1974 (1978).

HARBOR SEAL MYOGLOBIN

	1				5					10					15		
1	GLY	LEU	SER	ASP	GLY	GLU	TRP	HIS	LEU	VAL	LEU	ASN	VAL	TRP	GLY	15
16	LYS	VAL	GLU	THR	ASP	LEU	ALA	GLY	HIS	GLY	GLN	GLU	VAL	LEU	ILE	30
31	ARG	LEU	PHE	LYS	SER	HIS	PRO	GLU	THR	LEU	GLU	LYS	PHE	ASP	LYS	45
46	PHE	LYS	HIS	LEU	LYS	SER	GLU	ASP	ASP	MET	ARG	ARG	SER	GLU	ASP	60
61	LEU	ARG	LYS	HIS	GLY	ASN	THR	VAL	LEU	THR	ALA	LEU	GLY	GLY	ILE	75
76	LEU	LYS	LYS	LYS	GLY	HIS	HIS	GLU	ALA	GLU	LEU	LYS	PRO	LEU	ALA	90
91	GLN	SER	HIS	ALA	THR	LYS	HIS	LYS	ILE	PRO	ILE	LYS	TYR	LEU	GLU	105
106	PHE	ILE	SER	GLU	ALA	ILE	ILE	HIS	VAL	LEU	HIS	SER	LYS	HIS	PRO	120
121	ALA	GLU	PHE	GLY	ALA	ASP	ALA	GLN	ALA	ALA	MET	LYS	LYS	ALA	LEU	135
136	GLU	LEU	PHE	ARG	ASN	ASP	ILE	ALA	ALA	LYS	TYR	LYS	GLU	LEU	GLY	150
151	PHE	HIS	GLY													165

GLOBINS

PORPOISE MYOGLOBIN

	1			5					10					15		
1	GLY	LEU	SER	GLU	GLY	GLU	TRP	GLN	LEU	VAL	LEU	ASN	VAL	TRP	GLY	15
16	LYS	VAL	GLU	ALA	ASP	LEU	ALA	GLY	HIS	GLY	GLN	ASP	VAL	LEU	ILE	30
31	ARG	LEU	PHE	LYS	GLY	HIS	PRO	GLU	THR	LEU	GLU	LYS	PHE	ASP	LYS	45
46	PHE	LYS	HIS	LEU	LYS	THR	GLU	ALA	GLU	MET	LYS	ALA	SER	GLU	ASP	60
61	LEU	LYS	LYS	HIS	GLY	ASN	THR	VAL	LEU	THR	ALA	LEU	GLY	GLY	ILE	75
76	LEU	LYS	LYS	LYS	GLY	HIS	HIS	GLU	ALA	ASN	LEU	LYS	PRO	LEU	ALA	90
91	GLN	SER	HIS	ALA	THR	LYS	HIS	LYS	ILE	PRO	ILE	LYS	TYR	LEU	GLU	105
106	PHE	ILE	SER	GLU	ALA	ILE	ILE	HIS	VAL	LEU	HIS	SER	ARG	HIS	PRO	120
121	ALA	GLU	PHE	GLY	ALA	ASP	ALA	GLN	GLY	ALA	MET	ASN	LYS	ALA	LEU	135
136	GLU	LEU	PHE	ARG	LYS	ASP	ILE	ALA	THR	LYS	TYR	LYS	GLU	LEU	GLY	150
151	PHE	HIS	GLY													165

Comparison of Myoglobin from Harbor Seal, Porpoise and Sperm Whale. V. The Complete Amino Acid sequence of Harbor Seal, and Porpoise Myoglobins.
R. A. Bradshaw and F. R. N. Gurd.
J. Biol. Chem., **244**, 2167–2181 (1969).

MYOGLOBIN—CALIFORNIA SEA LION

	1			5					10					15		
1	GLY	LEU	SER	ASP	GLY	GLU	TRP	GLN	LEU	VAL	LEU	ASN	ILE	TRP	GLY	15
16	LYS	VAL	GLU	ALA	ASP	LEU	VAL	GLY	HIS	GLY	GLN	GLU	VAL	LEU	ILE	30
31	ARG	LEU	PHE	LYS	GLY	HIS	PRO	GLU	THR	LEU	GLU	LYS	PHE	ASP	LYS	45
46	PHE	LYS	HIS	LEU	LYS	SER	GLU	ASP	GLU	MET	LYS	ARG	SER	GLU	ASP	60
61	LEU	LYS	LYS	HIS	GLY	LYS	THR	VAL	LEU	THR	ALA	LEU	GLY	GLY	ILE	75
76	LEU	LYS	LYS	LYS	GLY	HIS	HIS	ASP	ALA	GLU	LEU	LYS	PRO	LEU	ALA	90
91	GLN	SER	HIS	ALA	THR	LYS	HIS	LYS	ILE	PRO	ILE	LYS	TYR	LEU	GLU	105
106	PHE	ILE	SER	GLU	ALA	ILE	ILE	HIS	VAL	LEU	GLN	SER	LYS	HIS	PRO	120
121	GLY	ASP	PHE	GLY	ALA	ASP	THR	HIS	ALA	ALA	MET	LYS	LYS	ALA	LEU	135
136	GLU	LEU	PHE	ARG	ASN	ASP	ILE	ALA	ALA	LYS	TYR	ARG	GLU	LEU	GLY	150
151	PHE	GLN	GLY													165

California sea lion myoglobin. Complete covalent structure of the polypeptide chain.
R. A. Vigna, L. J. Gurd, and F. R. N. Gurd.
J. Biol. Chem., **249**, 4144–4148 (1974).

MYOGLOBIN—DOLPHIN

	1				5					10					15	
1	GLY	LEU	SER	ASP	GLY	GLU	TRP	GLN	LEU	VAL	LEU	ASN	VAL	TRP	ALA	15
16	LYS	VAL	(GLX,	ALA,	ASX,	VAL,	ALA,	GLY,	HIS,	GLY,	GLX,	ASX,	LEU,	LEU,	ILE)	30
31	ARG	LEU	PHE	LYS	GLY	HIS	PRO	GLU	THR	LEU	GLU	LYS	PHE	ASP	LYS	45
46	PHE	LYS	HIS	LEU	LYS	THR	GLU	ALA	ASP	MET	LYS	ALA	SER	GLU	ASX	60
61	LEU	LYS	LYS	HIS	GLY	ASP	THR	VAL	LEU	THR	ALA	LEU	GLY	ALA	ILE	75
76	LEU	LYS	LYS	LYS	GLY	HIS	HIS	ASP	(ALA,	GLX)	LEU	LYS	PRO	LEU	ALA	90
91	GLN	SER	HIS	ALA	THR	LYS	HIS	LYS	ILE	PRO	ILE	LYS	TYR	LEU	GLU	105
106	PHE	ILE	SER	GLU	ALA	ILE	ILE	HIS	VAL	LEU	HIS	SER	ARG	HIS	PRO	120
121	ALA	GLN	PHE	GLY	ALA	ASP	ALA	GLN	GLY	ALA	MET	ASX	LYS	ALA	LEU	135
136	GLU	LEU	PHE	ARG	LYS	ASP	ILE	ALA	ALA	LYS	TYR	LYS	GLU	LEU	GLY	150
151	PHE	HIS	GLY													165

Differences in amino acid sequence between dolphin and sperm whale myoglobins.
M. Karadjova, P. Nedkov, A. Bakardjieva, and N. Genov.
Biochim. Biophys. Acta, **221**, 136–139 (1970).

MYOGLOBIN—AMAZON RIVER DOLPHIN

	1				5					10					15	
1	GLY	LEU	SER	ASP	GLY	GLU	TRP	GLN	LEU	VAL	LEU	ASN	ILE	TRP	GLY	15
16	LYS	VAL	GLU	ALA	ASP	LEU	ALA	GLY	HIS	GLY	GLN	ASP	VAL	LEU	ILE	30
31	ARG	LEU	PHE	LYS	GLY	HIS	PRO	GLU	THR	LEU	GLU	LYS	PHE	ASP	LYS	45
46	PHE	LYS	HIS	LEU	LYS	THR	GLU	ALA	GLU	MET	LYS	ALA	SER	GLU	ASP	60
61	LEU	LYS	LYS	HIS	GLY	ASN	THR	VAL	LEU	THR	ALA	LEU	GLY	GLY	ILE	75
76	LEU	LYS	LYS	LYS	GLY	HIS	HIS	GLU	ALA	GLU	LEU	LYS	PRO	LEU	ALA	90
91	GLN	SER	HIS	ALA	THR	LYS	HIS	LYS	ILE	PRO	ILE	LYS	TYR	LEU	GLU	105
106	PHE	ILE	SER	GLU	ALA	ILE	ILE	HIS	VAL	LEU	HIS	SER	ARG	HIS	PRO	120
121	GLY	ASP	PHE	GLY	ALA	ASP	ALA	GLN	ALA	ALA	MET	ASN	LYS	ALA	LEU	135
136	GLU	LEU	PHE	ARG	LYS	ASP	ILE	ALA	ALA	LYS	TYR	LYS	GLU	LEU	GLY	150
151	PHE	HIS	GLY													165

The complete amino acid sequence of the major component myoglobin of Amazon river dolphin (*Inia geoffrensis*).
F. E. Dwulet, R. A. Bogardt, B. N. Jones, L. D. Lehman, and F. R. N. Gurd.
Biochemistry, **14**, 5336–5343 (1975).

GLOBINS

MYOGLOBIN—ATLANTIC BOTTLENOSED DOLPHIN

	1			5					10					15		
1	GLY	LEU	SER	ASP	GLY	GLU	TRP	GLN	LEU	VAL	LEU	ASN	VAL	TRP	GLY	15
16	LYS	VAL	GLU	ALA	ASP	LEU	ALA	GLY	HIS	GLY	GLN	ASP	VAL	LEU	ILE	30
31	ARG	LEU	PHE	LYS	GLY	HIS	PRO	GLU	THR	LEU	GLU	LYS	PHE	ASP	LYS	45
46	PHE	LYS	HIS	LEU	LYS	THR	GLU	ALA	ASP	MET	LYS	ALA	SER	GLU	ASP	60
61	LEU	LYS	LYS	HIS	GLY	ASN	THR	VAL	LEU	THR	ALA	LEU	GLY	ALA	ILE	75
76	LEU	LYS	LYS	LYS	GLY	HIS	HIS	ASP	ALA	GLU	LEU	LYS	PRO	LEU	ALA	90
91	GLN	SER	HIS	ALA	THR	LYS	HIS	LYS	ILE	PRO	ILE	LYS	TYR	LEU	GLU	105
106	PHE	ILE	SER	GLU	ALA	ILE	ILE	HIS	VAL	LEU	HIS	SER	ARG	HIS	PRO	120
121	ALA	GLU	PHE	GLY	ALA	ASP	ALA	GLN	GLY	ALA	MET	ASN	LYS	ALA	LEU	135
136	GLU	LEU	PHE	ARG	LYS	ASP	ILE	ALA	ALA	LYS	TYR	LYS	GLU	LEU	GLY	150
151	PHE	HIS	GLY													165

Complete amino acid sequence of the myoglobin from the Atlantic bottlenosed dolphin, *Tursiops truncatus*.
B. N. Jones, R. A. Vigna, F. E. Dwulet, R. A. Bogardt, L. D. Lehman, and F. R. N. Gurd.
Biochemistry, **15**, 4418–4422 (1976).

MYOGLOBIN—PACIFIC COMMON DOLPHIN

	1			5					10					15		
1	GLY	LEU	SER	ASP	GLY	GLU	TRP	GLN	LEU	VAL	LEU	ASN	VAL	TRP	GLY	15
16	LYS	VAL	GLU	ALA	ASP	LEU	ALA	GLY	HIS	GLY	GLN	ASP	VAL	LEU	ILE	30
31	ARG	LEU	PHE	LYS	GLY	HIS	PRO	GLU	THR	LEU	GLU	LYS	PHE	ASP	LYS	45
46	PHE	LYS	HIS	LEU	LYS	THR	GLU	ALA	ASP	MET	LYS	ALA	SER	GLU	ASP	60
61	LEU	LYS	LYS	HIS	GLY	ASN	THR	VAL	LEU	THR	ALA	LEU	GLY	ALA	ILE	75
76	LEU	LYS	LYS	LYS	GLY	HIS	HIS	ASP	ALA	GLU	LEU	LYS	PRO	LEU	ALA	90
91	GLN	SER	HIS	ALA	THR	LYS	HIS	LYS	ILE	PRO	ILE	LYS	TYR	LEU	GLU	105
106	PHE	ILE	SER	GLU	ALA	ILE	ILE	HIS	VAL	LEU	HIS	SER	ARG	HIS	PRO	120
121	ALA	GLU	PHE	GLY	ALA	ASP	ALA	GLN	GLY	ALA	MET	ASN	LYS	ALA	LEU	135
136	GLU	LEU	PHE	ARG	LYS	ASP	ILE	ALA	ALA	LYS	TYR	LYS	GLU	LEU	GLY	150
151	PHE	HIS	GLY													165

Complete primary structure of the major component myoglobin of pacific common dolphin (*Delphinus delphis*).
C. C. Wang, R. Avila, B. N. Jones, and F. R. N. Gurd.
Biochemistry, **16**, 4978–4981 (1977).

MYOGLOBIN—DALL PORPOISE

	1				5					10					15	
1	GLY	LEU	SER	GLU	GLY	GLU	TRP	GLN	LEU	VAL	LEU	ASN	VAL	TRP	GLY	15
16	LYS	VAL	GLU	ALA	ASP	LEU	ALA	GLY	HIS	GLY	GLN	ASP	VAL	LEU	ILE	30
31	ARG	LEU	PHE	LYS	GLY	HIS	PRO	GLU	THR	LEU	GLU	LYS	PHE	ASP	LYS	45
46	PHE	LYS	HIS	LEU	LYS	THR	GLU	ALA	GLU	MET	LYS	ALA	SER	GLU	ASP	60
61	LEU	LYS	LYS	HIS	GLY	ASN	THR	VAL	LEU	THR	ALA	LEU	GLY	GLY	ILE	75
76	LEU	LYS	LYS	LYS	GLY	HIS	HIS	ASP	ALA	GLU	LEU	LYS	PRO	LEU	ALA	90
91	GLN	SER	HIS	ALA	THR	LYS	HIS	LYS	ILE	PRO	ILE	LYS	TYR	LEU	GLU	105
106	PHE	ILE	SER	GLU	ALA	ILE	ILE	HIS	VAL	LEU	HIS	SER	ARG	HIS	PRO	120
121	ALA	GLU	PHE	GLY	ALA	ASP	ALA	GLN	GLY	ALA	MET	ASN	LYS	ALA	LEU	135
136	GLU	LEU	PHE	ARG	LYS	ASP	ILE	ALA	THR	LYS	TYR	LYS	GLU	LEU	GLY	150
151	PHE	HIS	GLY													165

Complete amino acid sequence of the myoglobin from the Dall Porpoise (*Phocoenoides dalli dalli*) and reinvestigation of the primary structure of the myoglobin from common porpoise (*Phocoena phocoena*).
J. L. Meuth, B. N. Jones, W. H. Garner, and F. R. N. Gurd.
Biochemistry, **17**, 3429–3431 (1978).

MYOGLOBIN—MOLLUSC APLYSIA LIMACINA

	1				5					10					15	
1	AC	SER	LEU	SER	ALA	ALA	GLU	ALA	ASP	LEU	ALA	GLY	LYS	SER	TRP	15
16	ALA	PRO	VAL	PHE	ALA	ASN	LYS	ASN	ALA	ASN	GLY	ALA	ASP	PHE	LEU	30
31	VAL	ALA	LEU	PHE	GLU	LYS	PHE	PRO	ASP	SER	ALA	ASN	PHE	PHE	ALA	45
46	ASP	PHE	LYS	GLY	LYS	SER	VAL	ALA	ASP	ILE	LYS	ALA	SER	PRO	LYS	60
61	LEU	ARG	ASP	VAL	SER	SER	ARG	ILE	PHE	THR	ARG	LEU	ASN	GLU	PHE	75
76	VAL	ASN	ASP	ALA	ALA	ASN	ALA	GLY	LYS	MET	SER	ALA	MET	LEU	SER	90
91	GLN	PHE	ALA	LYS	GLU	HIS	VAL	GLY	PHE	GLY	VAL	GLY	SER	ALA	GLN	105
106	PHE	GLU	ASN	VAL	ARG	SER	MET	PHE	PRO	GLY	PHE	VAL	ALA	SER	VAL	120
121	ALA	ALA	PRO	PRO	ALA	GLY	ALA	ASP	ALA	TRP	THR	LYS	LEU	PHE	GLY	135
136	LEU	ILE	ILE	ASP	ALA	LEU	LYS	ALA	ALA	GLY	LYS					150

The amino acid sequence of myoglobin from mollusc *Aplysia limacina*.
L. Tentori, G. Vivaldi, S. Carta, M. Marinucci, A. Massa, E. Antonini, and M. Brunori.
Int. J. Peptide Protein Res., **5**, 187–200 (1973).

GLOBINS

SOYABEAN LEGHAEMOGLOBIN

	1			5					10					15		
1	VAL	ALA	PHE	THR	GLU	LYS	GLN	ASP	ALA	LEU	VAL	SER	SER	SER	PHE	15
16	GLU	ALA	PHE	LYS	ALA	ASN	ILE	PRO	GLN	TYR	SER	VAL	VAL	PHE	TYR	30
31	THR	SER	ILE	LEU	GLU	LYS	ALA	PRO	ALA	ALA	LYS	ASP	LEU	PHE	SER	45
46	PHE	LEU	ALA	ASN	PRO	THR	ASP	GLY	VAL	ASN	PRO	LYS	LEU	THR	GLY	60
61	HIS	ALA	GLU	LYS	LEU	PHE	ALA	LEU	VAL	ARG	ASP	SER	ALA	GLY	GLN	75
76	LEU	LYS	ALA	SER	GLY	THR	VAL	VAL	ALA	ASP	ALA	ALA	LEU	GLY	SER	90
91	VAL	HIS	ALA	GLN	LYS	ALA	VAL	THR	ASN	PRO	GLU	PHE	VAL	VAL	LYS	105
106	GLU	ALA	LEU	LEU	LYS	THR	ILE	LYS	ALA	ALA	VAL	GLY	ASP	LYS	TRP	120
121	SER	ASP	GLU	LEU	SER	ARG	ALA	TRP	GLU	VAL	ALA	TYR	ASP	GLU	LEU	135
136	ALA	ALA	ALA	ILE	LYS	ALA	LYS									150

The Primary Structure of Soybean Leghemoglobin.
N. Ellfolk and G. Sievers.
Acta Chem. Scand., **25**, 3532–3534 (1971).

SOYABEAN LEGHAEMOGLOBIN C_2

	1			5					10					15		
1	GLY	ALA	PHE	THR	ASP/GLU	LYS	GLN	GLU	ALA	LEU	VAL	SER	SER	SER	PHE	15
16	GLU	ALA	PHE	LYS	THR	ASN	ILE	PRO	GLN	TYR	SER	VAL	VAL	PHE	TYR	30
31	THR	SER	ILE	LEU	GLU	LYS	ALA	PHE	ALA	VAL	LYS	ASP	LEU	PHE	SER	45
46	PHE	LEU	ALA	ASN	GLY	VAL	ASN	PRO	THR	ASN	PRO	LYS	LEU	THR	GLY	60
61	HIS	ALA	GLU	LYS	LEU	PHE	GLY	LEU	VAL	ARG	ASP	SER	ALA	GLY	GLN	75
76	LEU	LYS	ALA	THR	VAL	VAL	ALA	ASP	ALA	ALA	SER	GLY	SER	ILE	HIS	90
91	ALA	GLN	LYS	ALA	ILE	THR	ASN	PRO	GLU	PHE	VAL	VAL	LYS	GLU	ALA	105
106	LEU	LEU	LYS	THR	ILE	LYS	GLU	ALA	VAL	GLY	ASP	LYS	TRP	SER	ASP	120
121	GLU	LEU	SER	SER	ALA	TRP	GLU	VAL	ALA	TYR	ASP	GLU	LEU	ALA	ALA	135
136	ALA	ILE	LYS	LYS	ALA	PHE										150

The amino acid sequence of soybean leghaemoglobin C_2.
J. G. R. Hurrell and S. J. Leach.
FEBS Letters, **80**, 23–26 (1977).

GLOBINS

LEGHAEMOGLOBIN I—BROAD BEAN

	1			5					10					15		
1	GLY	PHE	THR	GLU/ASP	LYS/GLN	GLN	GLU	ALA	LEU	VAL	ASN	SER	SER	SER	GLN	15
16	LEU	PHE	LYS	GLN	ASN	PRO	SER	ASN	TYR	SER	VAL	LEU	PHE	TYR	THR	30
31	ILE	ILE	LEU	GLN/LYS	LYS	ALA	PRO	THR	ALA	LYS	ALA	MET	PHE	SER	PHE	45
46	LEU	LYS	ASP	SER	ALA	GLY	VAL	VAL	ASP	SER	PRO	LYS	LEU	GLN	ALA	60
61	HIS	ALA	GLU	LYS/GLN	VAL	PHE	GLY	MET	VAL	ARG	ASP/GLU	SER	ALA	VAL/ILE	GLN	75
76	LEU	ARG/GLN	ALA	THR	GLY	GLU	VAL	VAL	LEU	ASP	GLY	LYS	ASP	GLY	SER	90
91	ILE	HIS	ILE	GLN	LYS	GLY	VAL	LEU	ASP	PRO	HIS	PHE	VAL	VAL	VAL	105
106	LYS	GLU	ALA	LEU	LEU	LYS	THR	ILE	LYS	GLU	ALA	SER	GLY	ASP	LYS	120
121	TRP	SER	GLU	GLU	LEU	SER/GLU	ALA	ALA/ILE	TRP	GLU	VAL	ALA	TYR	ASP/GLU	GLY	135
136	LEU	ALA	THR	ALA	ILE	LYS	ALA	ALA								150

Note: GLY is also found at positions 22, 23, 41, and 59.
The amino acid sequence of leghaemoglobin I from root nodules of broad bean (*Vicia faba* L.).
M. Richardson, M. J. Dilworth, and M. D. Scawen.
FEBS Letters, **51**, 33–37 (1975).

LEGHAEMOGLOBIN COMPONENT A—KIDNEY BEAN

	1			5					10					15		
1	GLY	ALA	PHE	THR	GLU	LYS	GLN	GLU	ALA	LEU	VAL	ASN	SER	SER	TRP	15
16	GLU	ALA	PHE	LYS	GLY	ASN	ILE	PRO	GLN	TYR	SER	VAL	VAL	PHE	TYR	30
31	THR	SER	ILE	LEU	GLU	LYS	ALA	PRO	ALA	ALA	LYS	ASN	LEU	PHE	SER	45
46	PHE	LEU	ALA	ASN	GLY	VAL	ASP	PRO	THR	ASN	PRO	LYS	LEU	THR	ALA	60
61	HIS	ALA	GLU	SER	LEU	PHE	GLY	LEU	VAL	ARG	ASP	SER	ALA	ALA	GLN	75
76	LEU	ARG	ALA	ASN	GLY	ALA	VAL	VAL	ALA	ASP	ALA	ALA	LEU	GLY	SER	90
91	ILE	HIS	SER	GLN	LYS	GLY	VAL	SER	ASN	ASP	GLN	PHE	LEU	VAL	VAL	105
106	LYS	GLU	ALA	LEU	LEU	LYS	THR	LEU	LYS	GLN	ALA	VAL	GLY	ASP	LYS	120
121	TRP	THR	ASP	GLN	LEU	SER	THR	ALA	LEU	GLU	LEU	ALA	TYR	ASP	GLU	135
136	LEU	ALA	ALA	ALA	ILE	LYS	LYS	ALA	TYR	ALA						150

The amino acid sequence of leghemoglobin component a from *Phaseolus vulgaris* (Kidney bean).
P. Lehtovaara and N. Ellfolk.
Eur. J. Biochem., **54**, 577–584 (1975).

CYTOCHROMES

HUMAN LIVER MICROSOMAL CYTOCHROME B₅

	1				5					10					15		
1	SER	ASP	GLU	ALA	VAL	LYS	TYR	TYR	THR	LEU	GLN	GLU	ILE	GLX	LYS	15
16	HIS	ASN	HIS	SER	LYS	SER	THR	TRP	LEU	ILE	LEU	HIS	HIS	LYS	VAL	30
31	TYR	ASP	LEU	THR	LYS	PHE	LEU	GLU	GLU	HIS	PRO	GLY	GLY	GLU	GLU	45
46	VAL	LEU	ARG	GLU	GLN	ALA	GLY	GLY	ASP	ALA	THR	GLU	ASN	PHE	GLU	60
61	ASP	VAL	GLY	HIS	SER	THR	ASP	ALA	ARG	GLU	MET	SER	LYS	THR	PHE	75
76	ILE	ILE	GLY	GLU	LEU	HIS	PRO	ASP	ASP	LYS	PRO	ARG				90

Amino acid sequences of tryptic peptides of cytochrome b_5 from the microsomes of human, monkey, porcine and chicken liver.
F. G. Nobrega and J. Ozols.
J. Biol. Chem., **246**, 1706–1717 (1971).
Structural studies of cytochrome b_5. III. Sequential studies on human liver cytochrome b_5.
M. A. Rashid, B. Hagihara, M. Kobayashi, S. Tani, and A. Tsugita.
J. Biochem., **74**, 985–1002 (1973).
The sequence reported in this paper is different from that previously published by the following: (i) HIS (residue 18) was not found. (ii) The N-terminus has three additional residues, GLN GLX ALA.

CALF LIVER MICROSOMAL CYTOCHROME B₅

	1				5					10					15		
1	SER	LYS	ALA	VAL	LYS	TYR	TYR	THR	LEU	GLU	GLN	GLU	ILE	LYS	HIS	15
16	ASN	ASN	SER	LYS	SER	THR	TRP	LEU	ILE	LEU	HIS	TYR	LYS	VAL	TYR	30
31	ASP	LEU	THR	LYS	PHE	LEU	GLU	GLU	HIS	PRO	GLY	GLY	GLU	GLU	VAL	45
46	LEU	ARG	GLU	GLN	ALA	GLY	GLY	ASP	ALA	THR	GLU	ASP	PHE	GLU	ASP	60
61	VAL	GLY	HIS	SER	THR	ASP	ALA	ARG	GLU	LEU	SER	LYS	THR	PHE	ILE	75
76	ILE	GLY	GLU	LEU	HIS	PRO	ASP	ASP	ARG	SER	LYS	ILE	THR	LYS	PRO	90
91	SER	GLU	SER													105

Correction of the Amino Acid Sequence of Calf Liver Microsomal Cytochrome b_5.
J. Ozols and P. Strittmatter.
J. Biol. Chem., **244**, 6617–6618 (1969).

CYTOCHROMES

MONKEY LIVER MICROSOMAL CYTOCHROME B₅

	1				5					10					15	
1	SER	ASP	GLU	ALA	VAL	LYS	TYR	TYR	THR	LEU	GLN	GLU	ILE	GLX	LYS	15
16	HIS	ASN	HIS	SER	LYS	SER	THR	TRP	LEU	ILE	LEU	HIS	HIS	LYS	VAL	30
31	TYR	ASP	LEU	THR	LYS	PHE	LEU	GLU	GLU	HIS	PRO	GLY	GLY	GLU	GLU	45
46	VAL	LEU	ARG	GLU	GLN	ALA	GLY	GLY	ASP	ALA	THR	GLU	ASN	PHE	GLU	60
61	ASP	VAL	GLY	HIS	SER	THR	ASP	ALA	ARG	GLU	LEU	SER	LYS	THR	TYR	75
76	ILE	ILE	GLY	GLU	LEU	HIS	PRO	ASP	ASP	LYS	PRO	ARG				90

PIG LIVER MICROSOMAL CYTOCHROME B₅

	1				5					10					15	
1	ALA	VAL	LYS	TYR	TYR	THR	LEU	GLN	GLU	ILE	GLX	LYS	HIS	ASN	ASN	15
16	SER	LYS	SER	THR	TRP	LEU	ILE	LEU	HIS	HIS	LYS	VAL	TYR	ASP	LEU	30
31	THR	LYS	PHE	LEU	GLU	GLU	HIS	PRO	GLY	GLY	GLU	GLU	VAL	LEU	ARG	45
46	GLU	GLN	ALA	GLY	GLY	ASP	ALA	THR	GLU	ASN	PHE	GLU	ASP	VAL	GLY	60
61	HIS	SER	THR	ASP	ALA	ARG	GLU	LEU	SER	LYS	THR	PHE	ILE	ILE	GLY	75
76	GLU	LEU	HIS	PRO	ASP	ASP	ARG									90

CHICKEN LIVER MICROSOMAL CYTOCHROME B₅

	1				5					10					15	
1	GLY	ARG	TYR	TYR	ARG	LEU	GLN	GLU	VAL	GLX	LYS	HIS	ASN	ASN	SER	15
16	GLN	SER	THR	TRP	ILE	ILE	VAL	HIS	HIS	ARG	ILE	TYR	ASP	ILE	THR	30
31	LYS	PHE	LEU	ASP	GLU	HIS	PRO	GLY	GLY	GLU	GLU	VAL	LEU	ARG	GLU	45
46	GLN	ALA	GLY	GLY	ASP	ALA	THR	GLU	ASN	PHE	GLU	ASP	VAL	GLY	HIS	60
61	SER	THR	ASP	ALA	ARG	ALA	LEU	SER	GLU	THR	PHE	ILE	ILE	GLY	GLU	75
76	LEU	HIS	PRO	ASP	ASP	LYS	PRO	ARG								90

Amino acid sequences of Tryptic peptides of cytochrome b₅ from the microsomes of Human, Monkey, Porcine and Chicken Liver.
F. G. Nóbrega and J. Ozols.
J. Biol. Chem., **246**, 1706–1717 (1971).

282

CYTOCHROMES

RABBIT LIVER MICROSOMAL CYTOCHROME b$_5$

	1			5					10					15		
1	(GLX, ALA, ALA)	SER	ASP	LYS	ASP	VAL	LYS	TYR/PHE	TYR	THR	LEU	GLN/GLU	GLU			15
16	ILE	LYS	LYS	HIS	ASN	HIS	SER	LYS	SER	THR	TRP	LEU	ILE	LEU	HIS	30
31	HIS	LYS	VAL	TYR	ASP	LEU	THR	LYS	PHE	LEU	GLU	GLU	HIS	PRO	GLY	45
46	GLY	GLU	GLU	VAL	LEU	ARG	GLU	GLN	ALA	GLY	GLY	ASP	ALA	THR	GLU	60
61	ASN	PHE	GLU	ASP	VAL	GLY	HIS	SER	THR	ASP	ALA	ARG	GLU	LEU	SER	75
76	LYS	THR	PHE	ILE	ILE	GLY	GLU	LEU	HIS	PRO	ASP	ASP	ARG	SER	LYS	90
91	LEU	SER	LYS	PRO	MET/THR	GLU	THR	OOO/GLX								

Amino Acid Sequence of Rabbit Liver Microsomal Cytochrome b$_5$.
J. Ozols.
J. Biol. Chem., **245**, 4863–4874 (1970).

YEAST CYTOCHROME b$_2$ CORE

	1			5					10					15		
1	LYS	GLN	LYS	ILE	SER	PRO	ALA	GLU	VAL	ALA	LYS	HIS	ASN	LYS	PRO	15
16	ASP	ASP	CYS	TRP	VAL	VAL	ILE	ASN	GLY	TYR	VAL	TYR	ASP	LEU	THR	30
31	ARG	PHE	LEU	PRO	ASN	HIS	PRO	GLY	GLY	GLN	ASP	VAL	ILE	LYS	PHE	45
46	ASN	ALA	GLY	LYS	ASP	VAL	THR	ALA	ILE	PHE	GLU	PRO	LEU	HIS	ALA	60
61	PRO	ASX	VAL	ILE	ASX	LYS	TYR	ILE	ALA	PRO	GLN	LYS	LEU	GLY	PRO	75
76	LEU	GLU	GLY	SER	MET	PRO	PRO	GLU	LEU	VAL	CYS	PRO	PRO	TYR	ALA	90
91	PRO	GLY	GLU	THR	LYS											105

Homology between bakers' yeast cytochrome b$_2$ and liver microsomal cytochrome b$_5$.
B. Guiard, O. Groudinsky, and F. Lederer.
Proc. Natn. Acad. Sci. U.S.A., **71**, 2539–2543 (1974).

CYTOCHROME b₅₆₂ OF ESCHERICHIA COLI

	1				5					10					15	
1	ALA	ASP	LEU	GLU	ASP	ASP	MET	GLN	THR	LEU	ASN	ASP	ASN	LEU	LYS	15
16	VAL	ILE	GLU	LYS	ALA	(ASX,	ASX,	GLX)	LYS	ALA	ASN	ASP	ALA	ALA	GLN	30
31	VAL	LYS	LEU	LYS	MET	ARG	ALA	ALA	ALA	LEU	ASN	ALA	GLN	LYS	LYS	45
46	ALA	THR	PRO	PRO	LYS	LEU	GLU	ASP	LYS	SER	PRO	ASN	SER	GLN	PRO	60
61	MET	LYS	ASP	PHE	ARG	HIS	GLY	PHE	ASP	ILE	LEU	VAL	GLY	GLU	ILE	75
76	ASP	ASP	ALA	LEU	LYS	LEU	ALA	ASN	GLU	GLY	LYS	VAL	LYS	GLU	ALA	90
91	GLN	ALA	ALA	GLU	ALA	GLN	LEU	LYS	THR	THR	ARG	ASN	ALA	TYR	LYS	105
106	HIS	GLN	LYS	TYR	ARG											120

The Amino Acid Sequence of Cytochrome b₅₆₂ of *Escherichia coli.*
E. Itagaki and L. P. Hager.
Biochem. Biophys. Res. Commun., **32**, 1013–1019 (1968).

HUMAN HEART CYTOCHROME c

	1				5					10					15	
1	AC	GLY	ASP	VAL	GLU	LYS	GLY	LYS	LYS	ILE	PHE	ILE	MET	LYS	CYS	15
16	(SER	GLN)	CYS	HIS	THR	VAL	GLU	LYS	GLY	GLY	LYS	HIS	LYS	THR	GLY	30
31	PRO	ASN	LEU	HIS	GLY	LEU	PHE	GLY	ARG	LYS	THR	GLY	GLN	ALA	PRO	45
46	GLY	TYR	SER	TYR	THR	ALA	ALA	ASN	LYS	ASN	LYS	GLY	ILE	ILE	TRP	60
61	GLY	GLU	ASP	THR	LEU	MET	GLU	TYR	LEU	GLU	ASN	PRO	LYS	LYS	TYR	75
76	ILE	PRO	GLY	THR	LYS	MET	ILE	PHE	VAL	GLY	ILE	LYS	LYS	LYS	GLU	90
91	GLU	ARG	ALA	ASP	LEU	ILE	ALA	TYR	LEU	LYS	LYS	ALA	THR	ASN	GLU	105

The Amino Acid Sequence of Human Heart Cytochrome c.
H. Matsubara and E. L. Smith.
J. Biol. Chem., **237**, 3575–3576 (1962).

BOVINE HEART CYTOCHROME c

	1				5					10					15	
1	AC	GLY	ASP	VAL	GLU	LYS	GLY	LYS	LYS	ILE	PHE	VAL	GLN	LYS	CYS	15
16	ALA	GLN	CYS	HIS	THR	VAL	GLU	LYS	GLY	GLY	LYS	HIS	LYS	THR	GLY	30
31	PRO	ASN	LEU	HIS	GLY	LEU	PHE	GLY	ARG	LYS	THR	GLY	GLN	ALA	PRO	45
46	GLY	PHE	SER	TYR	THR	ASP	ALA	ASN	LYS	ASN	LYS	GLY	ILE	THR	TRP	60
61	GLY	GLU	GLU	THR	LEU	MET	GLU	TYR	LEU	GLU	ASN	PRO	LYS	LYS	TYR	75
76	ILE	PRO	GLY	THR	LYS	MET	ILE	PHE	ALA	GLY	ILE	LYS	LYS	LYS	GLY	90
91	GLU	ARG	GLU	ASP	LEU	ILE	ALA	TYR	LEU	LYS	LYS	ALA	THR	ASN	GLU	105

The Amino Acid Sequence of Bovine Heart Cytochrome c.
T. Nakashima, H. Higa, H. Matsubara, A. M. Benson, and K. T. Yasunobu.
J. Biol. Chem., **241**, 1166–1177 (1966).

CYTOCHROMES

HORSE HEART CYTOCHROME c

	1			5					10					15		
1	AC	GLY	ASP	VAL	GLU	LYS	GLY	LYS	LYS	ILE	PHE	VAL	GLN	LYS	CYS	15
16	ALA	GLN	CYS	HIS	THR	VAL	GLU	LYS	GLY	GLY	LYS	HIS	LYS	THR	GLY	30
31	PRO	ASN	LEU	HIS	GLY	LEU	PHE	GLY	ARG	LYS	THR	GLY	GLN	ALA	PRO	45
46	GLY	PHE	THR	TYR	THR	ASP	ALA	ASN	LYS	ASN	LYS	GLY	ILE	THR	TRP	60
61	LYS	GLU	GLU	THR	LEU	MET	GLU	TYR	LEU	GLU	ASN	PRO	LYS	LYS	TYR	75
76	ILE	PRO	GLY	THR	LYS	MET	ILE	PHE	ALA	GLY	ILE	LYS	LYS	LYS	THR	90
91	GLU	ARG	GLU	ASP	LEU	ILE	ALA	TYR	LEU	LYS	LYS	ALA	THR	ASN	GLU	105

Amino acid sequence of Horse Heart Cytochrome c.
E. Margoliash, E. L. Smith, G. Kreil, and H. Tuppy.
Nature, **192**, 1121–1127 (1961).

ZEBRA CYTOCHROME c

	1			5					10					15		
1	AC	GLY	ASP	VAL	GLU	LYS	GLY	LYS	LYS	ILE	PHE	VAL	GLN	LYS	CYS	15
16	ALA	GLN	CYS	HIS	THR	VAL	GLU	LYS	GLY	GLY	LYS	HIS	LYS	THR	GLY	30
31	PRO	ASN	LEU	HIS	GLY	LEU	PHE	GLY	ARG	LYS	THR	GLY	GLN	ALA	PRO	45
46	GLY	PHE	SER	TYR	(THR,	ASX,	ALA,	ASX)	LYS	ASN	LYS	GLY	ILE	THR	TRP	60
61	LYS	GLU	GLU	THR	LEU	MET	GLU	TYR	LEU	GLU	ASN	PRO	LYS	LYS	TYR	75
76	ILE	PRO	GLY	THR	LYS	MET	ILE	PHE	ALA	GLY	ILE	LYS	LYS	LYS	THR	90
91	GLU	ARG	GLU	ASP	LEU	ILE	ALA	TYR	LEU	LYS	LYS	ALA	THR	ASN	GLU	105

Cytochrome c of the zebra (*Equus quagga boehmi*).
L. Gürtler and H. J. Horstmann.
FEBS Letters, **18**, 106–108 (1971).

CAMEL HEART CYTOCHROME c

	1			5					10					15		
1	AC	GLY	ASP	VAL	GLU	LYS	GLY	LYS	LYS	ILE	PHE	VAL	GLN	LYS	CYS	15
16	ALA	GLN	CYS	HIS	THR	VAL	GLU	LYS	GLY	GLY	LYS	HIS	LYS	THR	GLY	30
31	PRO	ASN	LEU	HIS	GLY	LEU	PHE	GLY	ARG	LYS	THR	GLY	GLN	ALA	VAL	45
46	GLY	PHE	SER	TYR	THR	ASP	ALA	ASN	LYS	ASN	LYS	GLY	ILE	THR	TRP	60
61	GLY	GLU	GLU	THR	LEU	MET	GLU	TYR	LEU	GLU	ASN	PRO	LYS	LYS	TYR	75
76	ILE	PRO	GLY	THR	LYS	MET	ILE	PHE	ALA	GLY	ILE	LYS	LYS	LYS	GLY	90
91	GLU	ARG	ALA	ASP	LEU	ILE	ALA	TYR	LEU	LYS	LYS	ALA	THR	ASN	GLU	105

Primary Structure of Cytochrome c from the Camel *Camelus dromedarius*.
M. Sokolovsky and M. Moldovan.
Biochemistry, **11**, 145–149 (1972).

CYTOCHROMES

RABBIT HEART CYTOCHROME c

	1				5					10					15		
1	AC	GLY	ASP	VAL	GLU	LYS	GLY	LYS	LYS	ILE	PHE	VAL	GLN	LYS	CYS		15
16	ALA	GLN	CYS	HIS	THR	VAL	GLU	LYS	GLY	GLY	LYS	HIS	LYS	THR	GLY		30
31	PRO	ASN	LEU	HIS	GLY	LEU	PHE	GLY	ARG	LYS	THR	GLY	GLN	ALA	VAL		45
46	GLY	PHE	SER	TYR	THR	ASP	ALA	ASN	LYS	ASN	LYS	GLY	ILE	THR	TRP		60
61	GLY	GLU	ASP	THR	LEU	MET	GLU	TYR	LEU	GLU	ASN	PRO	LYS	LYS	TYR		75
76	ILE	PRO	GLY	THR	LYS	MET	ILE	PHE	ALA	GLY	ILE	LYS	LYS	LYS	ASP		90
91	GLU	ARG	ALA	ASP	LEU	ILE	ALA	TYR	LEU	LYS	LYS	ALA	THR	ASN	GLU		105

Rabbit Heart Cytochrome c.
S. B. Needleman and E. Margoliash.
J. Biol. Chem., **241**, 853–863 (1966).

CYTOCHROME c—GUANACO

	1				5					10					15		
1	AC	GLY	ASP	VAL	GLU	LYS	GLY	LYS	LYS	ILE	PHE	VAL	GLN	LYS	CYS		15
16	ALA	GLN	CYS	HIS	THR	VAL	GLU	LYS	GLY	GLY	LYS	HIS	LYS	THR	GLY		30
31	PRO	ASN	LEU	HIS	GLY	LEU	PHE	GLY	ARG	LYS	THR	GLY	GLN	ALA	VAL		45
46	GLY	PHE	SER	TYR	THR	ASP	ALA	ASN	LYS	ASN	LYS	GLY	ILE	THR	TRP		60
61	GLY	GLU	GLU	THR	LEU	MET	GLU	TYR	LEU	GLU	ASN	PRO	LYS	LYS	TYR		75
76	ILE	PRO	GLY	THR	LYS	MET	ILE	PHE	ALA	GLY	ILE	LYS	LYS	LYS	GLY		90
91	GLU	ARG	ALA	ASP	LEU	ILE	ALA	TYR	LEU	LYS	LYS	ALA	THR	ASN	GLU		105

Complete amino acid sequence of Guanaco (*Lama guanicoe*) Cytochrome c.
R. L. Niece, E. Margoliash, and W. M. Fitch.
Biochemistry, **16**, 68–72 (1977).

HOG CYTOCHROME c

	1				5					10					15		
1	AC	GLY	ASP	VAL	GLU	LYS	GLY	LYS	LYS	ILE	PHE	VAL	GLN	LYS	CYS		15
16	ALA	GLN	CYS	HIS	THR	VAL	GLU	LYS	GLY	GLY	LYS	HIS	LYS	THR	GLY		30
31	PRO	ASN	LEU	HIS	GLY	LEU	PHE	GLY	ARG	LYS	THR	GLY	GLN	ALA	PRO		45
46	GLY	PHE	SER	TYR	THR	ASP	ALA	ASN	LYS	ASN	LYS	GLY	ILE	THR	TRP		60
61	GLY	GLU	GLU	THR	LEU	MET	GLU	TYR	LEU	GLU	ASN	PRO	LYS	LYS	TYR		75
76	ILE	PRO	GLY	THR	LYS	MET	ILE	PHE	ALA	GLY	ILE	LYS	LYS	LYS	GLY		90
91	GLU	ARG	GLU	ASP	LEU	ILE	ALA	TYR	LEU	LYS	LYS	ALA	THR	ASN	GLU		105

The Primary Structure of the Cytochrome c from various organs of the Hog.
J. W. Stewart and E. Margoliash.
Can. J. Biochem., **43**, 1187–1206 (1965).

CYTOCHROMES

ELEPHANT SEAL CYTOCHROME c

	1				5					10					15	
1	AC	GLY	ASP	VAL	GLU	LYS	GLY	LYS	LYS	ILE	PHE	VAL	GLU	LYS	CYS	15
16	ALA	GLN	CYS	HIS	THR	VAL	GLU	LYS	GLY	GLY	LYS	HIS	LYS	THR	GLY	30
31	PRO	ASN	LEU	HIS	GLY	LEU	PHE	GLY	ARG	LYS	THR	GLY	GLN	ALA	PRO	45
46	GLY	PHE	SER	TYR	THR	ASP	ALA	ASN	LYS	ASN	LYS	GLY	ILE	THR	TRP	60
61	GLY	GLU	GLU	THR	LEU	MET	GLU	TYR	LEU	GLU	ASN	PRO	LYS	LYS	TYR	75
76	ILE	PRO	GLY	THR	LYS	MET	ILE	PHE	ALA	GLY	ILE	LYS	LYS	THR	GLY	90
91	GLU	ARG	ALA	ASP	LEU	ILE	ALA	TYR	LEU	LYS	ILE	ALA	THR	LYS	GLU	105

Primary Structure of Cytochrome c from the Elephant Seal, *Mirounga Leonina*.
R. C. Augusteyn, M. A. McDowall, E. C. Webb, and B. Zerner.
Biochim. Biophys. Acta, **257**, 264–272 (1972).

KANGAROO CYTOCHROME c

	1				5					10					15	
1	AC	GLY	ASP	VAL	GLU	LYS	GLY	LYS	LYS	ILE	PHE	VAL	GLN	LYS	CYS	15
16	ALA	GLN	CYS	HIS	THR	VAL	GLU	LYS	GLY	GLY	LYS	HIS	LYS	THR	GLY	30
31	PRO	ASN	LEU	ASN	GLY	ILE	PHE	GLY	ARG	LYS	THR	GLY	GLN	ALA	PRO	45
46	GLY	PHE	THR	TYR	THR	ASP	ALA	ASN	LYS	ASN	LYS	GLY	ILE	ILE	TRP	60
61	GLY	GLU	ASP	THR	LEU	MET	GLU	TYR	LEU	GLU	ASN	PRO	LYS	LYS	TYR	75
76	ILE	PRO	GLY	THR	LYS	MET	ILE	PHE	ALA	GLY	ILE	LYS	LYS	LYS	GLY	90
91	GLU	ARG	ALA	ASP	LEU	ILE	ALA	TYR	LEU	LYS	LYS	ALA	THR	ASN	GLU	105

Primary Structure of Cytochrome c, from the Great Grey Kangaroo, *Macropus canguru*.
C. Nolan and E. Margoliash.
J. Biol. Chem., **241**, 1049–1059 (1966).

BAT CYTOCHROME c

	1				5					10					15	
1	GLY	ASP	VAL	GLU	LYS	GLY	LYS	LYS	ILE	PHE	VAL	GLN	LYS	CYS	ALA	15
16	GLN	CYS	HIS	THR	VAL	GLU	LYS	GLY	GLY	LYS	HIS	LYS	THR	GLY	PRO	30
31	ASN	LEU	HIS	GLY	LEU	PHE	GLY	ARG	LYS	THR	GLY	GLN	ALA	PRO	GLY	45
46	PHE	SER	TYR	THR	ASP	ALA	ASN	LYS	ASN	LYS	GLY	ILE	THR	TRP	GLY	60
61	GLU	ALA	THR	LEU	MET	GLU	TYR	LEU	GLU	ASN	PRO	LYS	LYS	TYR	ILE	75
76	PRO	GLY	THR	LYS	MET	ILE	PHE	ALA	GLY	ILE	LYS	LYS	SER	ALA	GLU	90
91	ARG	ALA	ASP	LEU	ILE	ALA	TYR	LEU	LYS	LYS	ALA	THR	LYS	GLU		105

The amino acid sequence of bat (*Miniopteris schreibersi*) cytochrome c.
D. J. Strydom, S. J. van der Walt, and D. P. Botes.
Comp. Biochem. Physiol., **42B**, 21–24 (1972).

CYTOCHROMES

WHALE HEART CYTOCHROME c

	1			5					10					15		
1	AC	GLY	ASP	VAL	GLU	LYS	GLY	LYS	LYS	ILE	PHE	VAL	GLN	LYS	CYS	15
16	ALA	GLN	CYS	HIS	THR	VAL	GLU	LYS	GLY	GLY	LYS	HIS	LYS	THR	GLY	30
31	PRO	ASN	LEU	HIS	GLY	LEU	PHE	GLY	ARG	LYS	THR	GLY	GLN	ALA	VAL	45
46	GLY	PHE	SER	TYR	THR	ASP	ALA	ASN	LYS	ASN	LYS	GLY	ILE	THR	TRP	60
61	GLY	GLU	GLU	THR	LEU	MET	GLU	TYR	LEU	GLU	ASN	PRO	LYS	LYS	TYR	75
76	ILE	PRO	GLY	THR	LYS	MET	ILE	PHE	ALA	GLY	ILE	LYS	LYS	LYS	GLY	90
91	GLU	ARG	ALA	ASP	LEU	ILE	ALA	TYR	LEU	LYS	LYS	ALA	THR	ASN	GLU	105

Amino acid sequence of Whale Heart Cytochrome c.
A. Goldstone and E. L. Smith.
J. Biol. Chem., **241**, 4480–4486 (1966).

SNAPPING TURTLE HEART CYTOCHROME c

	1			5					10					15		
1	AC	GLY	ASP	VAL	GLU	LYS	GLY	LYS	LYS	ILE	PHE	VAL	GLN	LYS	CYS	15
16	ALA	GLN	CYS	HIS	THR	VAL	GLU	LYS	GLY	GLY	LYS	HIS	LYS	THR	GLY	30
31	PRO	ASN	LEU	ASN	GLY	LEU	ILE	GLY	ARG	LYS	THR	GLY	GLN	ALA	GLU	45
46	GLY	PHE	SER	TYR	THR	GLU	ALA	ASN	LYS	ASN	LYS	GLY	ILE	THR	TRP	60
61	GLY	GLU	GLU	THR	LEU	MET	GLU	TYR	LEU	GLU	ASN	PRO	LYS	LYS	TYR	75
76	ILE	PRO	GLY	THR	LYS	MET	ILE	PHE	ALA	GLY	ILE	LYS	LYS	LYS	ALA	90
91	GLU	ARG	ALA	ASP	LEU	ILE	ALA	TYR	LEU	LYS	ASP	ALA	THR	SER	LYS	105

Primary Structure of the Cytochrome c from the Snapping Turtle, *Chelydra Serpentina*.
S. K. Chan, I. Tulloss and E. Margoliash.
Biochemistry, **5**, 2586–2597 (1966).

CHICKEN HEART CYTOCHROME c

	1			5					10					15		
1	AC	GLY	ASP	ILE	GLU	LYS	GLY	LYS	LYS	ILE	PHE	VAL	GLN	LYS	CYS	15
16	SER	GLN	CYS	HIS	THR	VAL	GLU	LYS	GLY	GLY	LYS	HIS	LYS	THR	GLY	30
31	PRO	ASN	LEU	HIS	GLY	LEU	PHE	GLY	ARG	LYS	THR	GLY	GLN	ALA	GLU	45
46	GLY	PHE	SER	TYR	THR	ASP	ALA	ASN	LYS	ASN	LYS	GLY	ILE	THR	TRP	60
61	GLY	GLU	ASP	THR	LEU	MET	GLU	TYR	LEU	GLU	ASN	PRO	LYS	LYS	TYR	75
76	ILE	PRO	GLY	THR	LYS	MET	ILE	PHE	ALA	GLY	ILE	LYS	LYS	LYS	SER	90
91	GLU	ARG	VAL	ASP	LEU	ILE	ALA	TYR	LEU	LYS	ASP	ALA	THR	SER	LYS	105

Amino Acid Sequence of Chicken Heart Cytochrome c.
S. K. Chan and E. Margoliash.
J. Biol. Chem., **241**, 507–515 (1966).

CYTOCHROMES

EMU CYTOCHROME c

	1				5					10					15	
1	AC	GLY	ASP	ILE	GLU	LYS	GLY	LYS	LYS	ILE	PHE	VAL	GLN	LYS	CYS	15
16	SER	GLN	CYS	HIS	THR	VAL	GLU	LYS	GLY	GLY	LYS	HIS	LYS	THR	GLY	30
31	PRO	ASN	LEU	ASN	GLY	LEU	PHE	GLY	ARG	LYS	THR	GLY	GLN	ALA	GLU	45
46	GLY	PHE	SER	TYR	THR	ASP	ALA	ASN	LYS	ASN	LYS	GLY	ILE	THR	TRP	60
61	GLY	GLU	ASP	THR	LEU	MET	GLU	TYR	LEU	GLU	ASN	PRO	LYS	LYS	TYR	75
76	ILE	PRO	GLY	THR	LYS	MET	ILE	PHE	ALA	GLY	ILE	LYS	LYS	LYS	SER	90
91	GLU	ARG	ALA	ASP	LEU	ILE	ALA	TYR	LEU	LYS	ASP	ALA	THR	SER	LYS	105

Primary structure of cytochrome c from the emu, *Dromaeus novaehollandiae*.
R. C. Augusteyn.
Biochim. Biophys. Acta, **303**, 1–7 (1973).

OSTRICH CYTOCHROME c

	1				5					10					15	
1	AC	GLY	ASP	ILE	GLU	LYS	GLY	LYS	LYS	ILE	PHE	VAL	GLN	LYS	CYS	15
16	SER	GLN	CYS	HIS	THR	VAL	GLU	LYS	GLY	GLY	LYS	HIS	LYS	THR	GLY	30
31	PRO	ASN	LEU	ASP	GLY	LEU	PHE	GLY	ARG	LYS	THR	GLY	GLN	ALA	GLU	45
46	GLY	PHE	SER	TYR	THR	ASP	ALA	ASN	LYS	ASN	LYS	GLY	ILE	THR	TRP	60
61	GLY	GLU	ASP	THR	LEU	MET	GLU	TYR	LEU	GLU	ASN	PRO	LYS	LYS	TYR	75
76	ILE	PRO	GLY	THR	LYS	MET	ILE	PHE	ALA	GLY	ILE	LYS	LYS	LYS	SER	90
91	GLU	ARG	ALA	ASP	LEU	ILE	ALA	TYR	LEU	LYS	ASP	ALA	THR	SER	LYS	105

The amino acid sequence of ostrich (*Struthio camelus*) cytochrome c.
N. L. Howard, F. J. Joubert, and D. J. Strydom.
Comp. Biochem. Physiol., **48B**, 75–85 (1974).

CARP CYTOCHROME c

	1				5					10					15	
1	AC	GLY	ASP	VAL	GLU / ASP	LYS	GLY	LYS	LYS	VAL	PHE	VAL	GLN	LYS	CYS	15
16	ALA	GLN	CYS	HIS	THR	VAL	GLX	ASX	GLY	GLY	LYS	HIS	LYS	VAL	GLY	30
31	PRO	ASN	LEU	TRP	GLY	LEU	PHE	GLY	ARG	LYS	THR	GLY	GLN	ALA	PRO	45
46	GLY	PHE	SER	TYR	THR	ASX	ALA	ASX	LYS	SER	LYS	GLY	ILE	VAL	TRP	60
61	ASX	GLX	GLX	THR	LEU	MET	GLU	TYR	LEU	GLX	ASX	PRO	LYS	LYS	TYR	75
76	ILE	PRO	GLY	THR	LYS	MET	ILE	PHE	ALA	GLY	ILE	LYS	LYS	LYS	GLY	90
91	GLU	ARG	ALA	ASP	LEU	ILE	ALA	TYR	LEU	LYS	SER	ALA	THR	SER		105

The Amino Acid Sequence of Carp Cytochrome c.
L. Gürtler and H. J. Horstmann.
Eur. J. Biochem., **12**, 48–57 (1970).

CYTOCHROMES

DOGFISH CYTOCHROME c

	1			5					10					15		
1	AC	GLY	ASP	VAL	GLU	LYS	GLY	LYS	LYS	VAL	PHE	VAL	GLN	LYS	CYS	15
16	ALA	GLN	CYS	HIS	THR	VAL	GLU	ASN	GLY	GLY	LYS	HIS	LYS	THR	GLY	30
31	PRO	ASN	LEU	SER	GLY	LEU	PHE	GLY	ARG	LYS	THR	GLY	GLN	ALA	GLN	45
46	GLY	PHE	SER	TYR	THR	ASP	ALA	ASN	LYS	SER	LYS	GLY	ILE	THR	TRP	60
61	GLN	GLN	GLU	THR	LEU	ARG	ILE	TYR	LEU	GLU	ASN	PRO	LYS	LYS	TYR	75
76	ILE	PRO	GLY	THR	LYS	MET	ILE	PHE	ALA	GLY	LEU	LYS	LYS	LYS	SER	90
91	GLU	ARG	GLN	ASP	LEU	ILE	ALA	TYR	LEU	LYS	LYS	THR	ALA	ALA	SER	105

Amino Acid Sequence of the Cytochrome c from the Dogfish *Squalus sucklii*.
A. Goldstone and E. L. Smith.
J. Biol. Chem., **242**, 4702–4710 (1967).

BONITO CYTOCHROME c

	1			5					10					15		
1	AC	GLY	ASP	VAL	ALA	LYS	GLY	LYS	LYS	THR	PHE	VAL	GLN	LYS	CYS	15
16	ALA	GLN	CYS	HIS	THR	VAL	GLU	ASN	GLY	GLY	LYS	HIS	LYS	VAL	GLY	30
31	PRO	ASN	LEU	TRP	GLY	LEU	PHE	GLY	ARG	LYS	THR	GLY	GLN	ALA	GLU	45
46	GLY	TYR	SER	TYR	THR	ASP	ALA	ASN	LYS	SER	LYS	GLY	ILE	VAL	TRP	60
61	ASN	GLU	ASN	THR	LEU	MET	GLU	TYR	LEU	GLU	ASN	PRO	LYS	LYS	TYR	75
76	ILE	PRO	GLY	THR	LYS	MET	ILE	PHE	ALA	GLY	ILE	LYS	LYS	LYS	GLY	90
91	GLU	ARG	GLN	ASP	LEU	VAL	ALA	TYR	LEU	LYS	SER	ALA	THR	SER		105

The Amino Acid Sequence of Cytochrome c from Bonito (*Katsuwonus pelamis, Linnaeus*).
T. Nakayama, K. Titani and K. Narita.
J. Biochem., **70**, 311–326 (1971).

LAMPREY CYTOCHROME c

	1			5					10					15		
1	AC	GLY	ASP	VAL	GLU	LYS	GLY	LYS	LYS	VAL	PHE	VAL	GLN	LYS	CYS	15
16	SER	GLN	CYS	HIS	THR	VAL	GLU	LYS	ALA	GLY	LYS	HIS	LYS	THR	GLY	30
31	PRO	ASN	LEU	SER	GLY	LEU	PHE	GLY	ARG	LYS	THR	GLY	GLN	ALA	PRO	45
46	GLY	PHE	SER	TYR	THR	ASP	ALA	ASN	LYS	SER	LYS	GLY	ILE	VAL	TRP	60
61	ASN	GLN	GLU	THR	LEU	PHE	VAL	TYR	LEU	GLU	ASN	PRO	LYS	LYS	TYR	75
76	ILE	PRO	GLY	THR	LYS	MET	ILE	PHE	ALA	GLY	ILE	LYS	LYS	GLU	GLY	90
91	GLU	ARG	LYS	ASP	LEU	ILE	ALA	TYR	LEU	LYS	LYS	SER	THR	SER	GLU	105

Amino acid sequence of a Cytochrome c from the Common Pacific Lamprey, *Entosphenus tridentatus*.
C. Nolan, W. M. Fitch, T. Uzzell, L. J. Weiss, and E. Margoliash.
Biochemistry, **12**, 4052–4060 (1973).

CYTOCHROMES

SNAIL CYTOCHROME c

	1				5					10					15	
1	GLY	GLX	ALA	GLX	LYS	GLY	LYS	LYS	ILE	PHE	THR	GLN	LYS	CYS	LEU	15
16	GLN	CYS	HIS	THR	VAL	GLU	ALA	GLY	GLY	LYS	HIS	LYS	THR	GLY	PRO	30
31	ASN	LEU	SER	GLY	LEU	PHE	GLY	ARG	LYS	GLN	GLY	GLN	ALA	PRO	GLY	45
46	PHE	ALA	TYR	THR	ASP	ALA	ASN	LYS	GLY	LYS	GLY	ILE	THR	TRP	LYS	60
61	ASN	GLN	THR	LEU	PHE	GLU	TYR	LEU	GLU	ASN	PRO	LYS	LYS	TYR	ILE	75
76	PRO	GLY	THR	LYS	MET	VAL	PHE	ALA	GLY	LEU	LYS	ASX	GLX	THR	GLU	90
91	ARG	VAL	HIS	LEU	ILE	ALA	TYR	LEU	GLX	GLX	ALA	THR	LYS	LYS		105

The Amino Acid Sequence of Cytochrome c from *Helix aspersa* Müller (Garden Snail).
R. H. Brown, M. Richardson, D. Boulter, J. A. M. Ramshaw, and R. P. S. Jefferies.
Biochem. J., **128**, 971–974 (1972).

CYTOCHROME c—STARFISH

	1				5					10					15	
1	GLY	GLN	VAL	GLU	LYS	GLY	LYS	LYS	ILE	PHE	VAL	GLN	ARG	CYS	ALA	15
16	GLN	CYS	HIS	THR	VAL	GLU	LYS	ALA	GLY	LYS	HIS	LYS	THR	GLY	PRO	30
31	ASN	LEU	ASN	GLY	ILE	LEU	GLY	ARG	LYS	THR	GLY	GLN	ALA	ALA	GLY	45
46	PHE	SER	TYR	THR	ASP	ALA	ASN	ARG	ASN	LYS	GLY	ILE	THR	TRP	LYS	60
61	ASN	GLU	THR	LEU	PHE	GLU	TYR	LEU	GLU	ASN	PRO	LYS	LYS	TYR	ILE	75
76	PRO	GLY	THR	LYS	MET	VAL	PHE	ALA	GLY	LEU	LYS	LYS	GLN	LYS	GLU	90
91	ARG	GLN	ASP	LEU	ILE	ALA	TYR	LEU	GLU	ALA	ALA	THR	LYS			105

The amino acid sequence of cytochrome c from *Asterias rubens* L. (Common starfish).
A. Lyddiatt and D. Boulter.
FEBS Letters, **67**, 331–334 (1976).

SILKWORM CYTOCHROME c

	1			5					10					15		
1	GLY	VAL	PRO	ALA	GLY	ASN	ALA	GLU	ASN	GLY	LYS	LYS	ILE	PHE	VAL	15
16	GLN	ARG	CYS	ALA	GLN	CYS	HIS	THR	VAL	GLU	ALA	GLY	GLY	LYS	HIS	30
31	LYS	VAL	GLY	PRO	ASN	LEU	HIS	GLY	PHE	TYR	GLY	ARG	LYS	THR	GLY	45
46	GLN	ALA	PRO	GLY	PHE	SER	TYR	SER	ASN	ALA	ASN	LYS	ALA	LYS	GLY	60
61	ILE	THR	TRP	GLY	ASP	ASP	THR	LEU	PHE	GLU	TYR	LEU	GLU	ASN	PRO	75
76	LYS	LYS	TYR	ILE	PRO	GLY	THR	LYS	MET	VAL	PHE	ALA	GLY	LEU	LYS	90
91	LYS	ALA	ASN	GLU	ARG	ALA	ASP	LEU	ILE	ALA	TYR	LEU	LYS	GLU	SER	105
106	THR	LYS														120

Properties and Primary Structure of the Cytochrome c from the Flight Muscles of the Moth, *Samia cynthia*.
S. K. Chan and E. Margoliash.
J. Biol. Chem., **241**, 335–348 (1966).

TOBACCO MOTH CYTOCHROME c

	1			5					10					15		
1	GLY	VAL	PRO	ALA	GLY	ASN	ALA	ASP	ASN	GLY	LYS	LYS	ILE	PHE	VAL	15
16	GLN	ARG	CYS	ALA	GLN	CYS	HIS	THR	VAL	GLU	ALA	GLY	GLY	LYS	HIS	30
31	LYS	VAL	GLY	PRO	ASN	LEU	HIS	GLY	PHE	PHE	GLY	ARG	LYS	THR	GLY	45
46	GLN	ALA	PRO	GLY	PHE	SER	TYR	SER	ASN	ALA	ASN	LYS	ALA	LYS	GLY	60
61	ILE	THR	TRP	GLN	ASP	ASP	THR	LEU	PHE	GLU	TYR	LEU	GLU	ASN	PRO	75
76	LYS	LYS	TYR	ILE	PRO	GLY	THR	LYS	MET	VAL	PHE	ALA	GLY	LEU	LYS	90
91	LYS	ALA	ASN	GLU	ARG	ALA	ASP	LEU	ILE	ALA	TYR	LEU	LYS	GLN	ALA	105
106	THR	LYS														120

Biochemical Studies in the Developing Thoracic Muscles of the Tobacco Horn Worm. 4. Primary Structure of Cytochrome c.
S. K. Chan.
Biochim. Biophys. Acta, **221**, 497–501 (1970).

CYTOCHROMES

CYTOCHROME c—INSECT CERATITIS CAPITATA

	1				5					10					15	
1	GLY	VAL	PRO	ALA	GLY	ASP	VAL	GLU	LYS	GLY	LYS	LYS	LEU	PHE	VAL	15
16	GLN	ARG	CYS	ALA	GLN	CYS	HIS	THR	VAL	GLU	ALA	GLY	GLY	LYS	HIS	30
31	LYS	VAL	GLY	PRO	ASN	LEU	HIS	GLY	LEU	ILE	GLY	ARG	LYS	THR	GLY	45
46	GLN	ALA	ALA	GLY	PHE	ALA	TYR	THR	ASP	ALA	ASN	LYS	ALA	LYS	GLY	60
61	ILE	THR	TRP	ASN	GLU	ASP	THR	LEU	PHE	GLU	TYR	LEU	GLU	ASN	PRO	75
76	LYS	LYS	TYR	ILE	PRO	GLY	THR	LYS	MET	ILE	PHE	ALA	GLY	LEU	LYS	90
91	LYS	PRO	ASN	GLU	ARG	GLY	ASP	LEU	ILE	ALA	TYR	LEU	LYS	SER	ALA	105
106	THR	LYS														120

Primary structure of cytochrome c from the insect *Ceratitis capitata*.
J. M. Fernández-Sousa, J. G. Gavilanes, A. M. Municio, J. A. Paredes, A. Pérez-Aranda, and R. Rodriguez.
Biochim. Biophys. Acta, **393**, 358–367 (1975).

CYTOCHROME c—LOCUST

	1				5					10					15	
1	GLY	VAL	PRO	GLN	GLY	ASP	VAL	GLU	LYS	GLY	LYS	LYS	ILE	PHE	VAL	15
16	GLN	ARG	CYS	ALA	GLN	CYS	HIS	THR	VAL	GLU	ALA	GLY	GLY	LYS	HIS	30
31	LYS	THR	GLY	PRO	ASN	LEU	HIS	GLY	LEU	PHE	GLY	ARG	LYS	THR	GLY	45
46	GLN	ALA	PRO	GLY	PHE	SER	TYR	THR	ASP	ALA	ASN	LYS	SER	LYS	GLY	60
61	ILE	THR	TRP	ASP	GLU	ASN	THR	LEU	PHE	ILE	TYR	LEU	GLU	ASN	PRO	75
76	LYS	LYS	TYR	ILE	PRO	GLY	THR	LYS	MET	VAL	PHE	ALA	GLY	LEU	LYS	90
91	LYS	PRO	GLU	GLU	ARG	ALA	ASP	LEU	ILE	ALA	TYR	LEU	LYS	GLU	SER	105
106	THR	LYS														120

The amino acid sequence of cytochrome c from the locust, *Schistocerca gregaria* Forskal.
A. Lyddiatt and D. Boulter.
Biochem. J., **163**, 333–338 (1977).

CYTOCHROME c—BLOWFLY

	1				5					10					15		
1	GLY	VAL	PRO	ALA	GLY	ASP	VAL	GLU	LYS	GLY	LYS	LYS	ILE	PHE	VAL		15
16	GLN	ARG	CYS	ALA	GLN	CYS	HIS	THR	VAL	GLU	ALA	GLY	GLY	LYS	HIS		30
31	LYS	VAL	GLY	PRO	ASN	LEU	HIS	GLY	LEU	PHE	GLY	ARG	LYS	THR	GLY		45
46	GLN	ALA	PRO	GLY	PHE	ALA	TYR	THR	ASN	ALA	ASN	LYS	ALA	LYS	GLY		60
61	ILE	THR	TRP	GLN	ASP	ASP	THR	LEU	PHE	GLU	TYR	LEU	GLU	ASN	PRO		75
76	LYS	LYS	TYR	ILE	PRO	GLY	THR	LYS	MET	ILE	PHE	ALA	GLY	LEU	LYS		90
91	LYS	PRO	ASN	GLU	ARG	GLY	ASP	LEU	ILE	ALA	TYR	LEU	LYS	SER	ALA		105
106	THR	LYS															120

The amino acid sequence of cytochrome c from the blowfly *Lucilia cuprina*.
D. C. Shaw, K. L. Williams, E. Smith, and L. M. Birt.
Biochim. Biophys. Acta, **532**, 179–184 (1978).

CYTOCHROME c—COMMON BRANDLING WORM

	1				5					10					15		
1	GLY	GLY	ILE	PRO	ALA	GLY	ASP	VAL	GLU	LYS	GLY	LYS	THR	ILE	PHE		15
16	LYS	GLN	ARG	CYS	ALA	GLN	CYS	HIS	THR	VAL	ASP	LYS	GLY	GLY	PRO		30
31	HIS	LYS	THR	GLY	PRO	ASN	LEU	HIS	GLY	ILE	FHE	GLY	ARG	ALA	THR		45
46	GLY	GLN	ALA	ALA	GLY	PHE	ALA	TYR	THR	ASP	ALA	ASN	LYS	SER	LYS		60
61	GLY	ILE	THR	TRP	THR	LYS	ASP	THR	LEU	TYR	GLU	TYR	LEU	GLU	ASN		75
76	PRO	LYS	LYS	TYR	ILE	PRO	GLY	THR	LYS	MET	VAL	PHE	ALA	GLY	LEU		90
91	LYS	ASN	GLU	LYS	GLN	ARG	ALA	ASN	LEU	ILE	ALA	TYR	LEU	GLU	GLN		105
106	GLU	THR	LYS														120

The amino acid sequence of cytochrome c from *Eisenia foetida* (Savigny) (Common brandling worm).
A. Lyddiatt and D. Boulter.
FEBS Letters, **62**, 85–88 (1976).

CYTOCHROMES

WHEAT GERM CYTOCHROME c

```
      1              5                    10                   15
  1  AC   ALA SER PHE SER GLU ALA PRO PRO GLY ASN PRO ASP ALA GLY   15
 16  ALA LYS ILE  PHE LYS THR LYS CYS ALA GLN CYS HIS  THR VAL ASP   30
 31  ALA GLY ALA GLY HIS  LYS GLN GLY PRO ASN LEU HIS  GLY LEU PHE   45
 46  GLY ARG GLN SER GLY THR THR ALA GLY TYR SER TYR SER ALA ALA   60
 61  ASN LYS ASN LYS ALA VAL GLU TRP GLU GLU ASN THR LEU TYR ASP   75
 76  TYR LEU LEU ASN PRO LYS LYS TYR ILE  PRO GLY THR LYS MET VAL   90
 91  PHE PRO GLY LEU LYS LYS PRO GLN ASP ARG ALA ASP LEU ILE  ALA  105
106  TYR LEU LYS LYS ALA THR SER SER                                120
```

The Amino Acid Sequence of Wheat Germ Cytochrome c.
F. C. Stevens, A. N. Glazer, and E. L. Smith.
J. Biol. Chem., **242**, 2764–2779 (1967).

BUCKWHEAT CYTOCHROME c

```
      1              5                    10                   15
  1  AC   ALA THR PHE SER GLU ALA PRO PRO GLY ASN ILE  LYS SER GLY   15
 16  GLU LYS ILE  PHE LYS THR LYS CYS ALA GLN CYS HIS  THR VAL GLU   30
 31  LYS GLY ALA GLY HIS  LYS GLN GLY PRO ASN LEU ASN GLY LEU PHE   45
 46  GLY ARG GLN SER GLY THR THR ALA GLY TYR SER TYR SER ALA ALA   60
 61  ASN LYS ASN LYS ALA VAL THR TRP GLY GLU ASP THR LEU TYR GLU   75
 76  TYR LEU LEU ASN PRO TML LYS TYR ILE  PRO GLY THR LYS MET VAL   90
 91  PHE PRO GLY LEU TML LYS PRO GLN GLU ARG ALA ASP LEU ILE  ALA  105
106  TYR LEU LYS ASX SER THR GLX                                    120
```

CAULIFLOWER CYTOCHROME c

```
      1              5                    10                   15
  1  AC   ALA SER PHE ASX GLU ALA PRO PRO GLY ASX SER LYS ALA GLY   15
 16  GLU LYS ILE  PHE LYS THR LYS CYS ALA GLN CYS HIS  THR VAL ASP   30
 31  LYS GLY ALA GLY HIS  LYS GLN GLY PRO ASN LEU ASN GLY LEU PHE   45
 46  GLY ARG GLN SER GLY THR THR ALA GLY TYR SER TYR SER ALA ALA   60
 61  ASN LYS ASN LYS ALA VAL GLU TRP GLU GLU LYS THR LEU TYR ASP   75
 76  TYR LEU LEU ASN PRO TML LYS TYR ILE  PRO GLY THR LYS MET VAL   90
 91  PHE PRO GLY LEU TML LYS PRO GLN ASP ARG ALA ASP LEU ILE  ALA  105
106  TYR LEU LYS GLU ALA THR ALA                                    120
```

The Amino Acid Sequence of Cytochrome c of *Fagopyrum esculentum* Moench (Buckwheat)
and *Brassica oleracea* L. (Cauliflower).
E. W. Thompson, M. Richardson, and D. Boulter.
Biochem. J., **124**, 783–785 (1971).

PUMPKIN CYTOCHROME c

	1			5					10				15			
1	AC	ALA	SER	PHE	ASN	GLU	ALA	PRO	PRO	GLY	ASN	SER	LYS	ALA	GLY	15
16	GLU	LYS	ILE	PHE	LYS	THR	LYS	CYS	ALA	GLN	CYS	HIS	THR	VAL	ASP	30
31	LYS	GLY	ALA	GLY	HIS	LYS	GLN	GLY	PRO	ASN	LEU	ASN	GLY	LEU	PHE	45
46	GLY	ARG	GLN	SER	GLY	THR	THR	PRO	GLY	TYR	SER	TYR	SER	ALA	ALA	60
61	ASN	LYS	ASN	ARG	ALA	VAL	ILE	TRP	GLU	GLU	LYS	THR	LEU	TYR	ASP	75
76	TYR	LEU	LEU	ASN	PRO	TML	LYS	TYR	ILE	PRO	GLY	THR	LYS	MET	VAL	90
91	PHE	PRO	GLY	LEU	TML	LYS	PRO	GLN	ASP	ARG	ALA	ASP	LEU	ILE	ALA	105
106	TYR	LEU	LYS	GLU	ALA	THR	ALA									120

The Amino Acid Sequence of Cytochrome c from *Cucurbita maxima* L. (Pumpkin).
E. W. Thompson, M. Richardson, and D. Boulter.
Biochem. J., **124**, 779–781 (1971).

LEEK CYTOCHROME c

	1			5					10				15			
1	AC	ALA	THR	PHE	SER	GLX	ALA	PRO	PRO	GLY	ASX	GLX	LYS	ALA	GLY	15
16	GLN	LYS	ILE	PHE	LYS	LEU	LYS	CYS	ALA	GLN	CYS	HIS	THR	VAL	GLU	30
31	LYS	GLY	ALA	GLY	HIS	LYS	GLN	GLY	PRO	ASN	LEU	ASN	GLY	LEU	PHE	45
46	GLY	ARG	GLN	SER	GLY	THR	ALA	ALA	GLY	TYR	SER	TYR	SER	ALA	ALA	60
61	ASN	LYS	ASN	MET	ALA	VAL	VAL	TRP	GLX	GLX	ASX	THR	LEU	TYR	ASP	75
76	TYR	LEU	LEU	ASN	PRO	TML	LYS	TYR	ILE	PRO	GLY	THR	LYS	MET	VAL	90
91	PHE	PRO	GLY	LEU	TML	LYS	PRO	GLN	ASP	ARG	ALA	ASP	LEU	ILE	ALA	105
106	TYR	LEU	LYS	GLU	SER	THR	ALA									120

The Amino Acid Sequence of Cytochrome c from *Allium porrum* L. (Leek).
R. H. Brown and D. Boulter.
Biochem. J., **131**, 247–251 (1973).

CYTOCHROMES

SPINACH CYTOCHROME c

	1				5					10					15	
1	AC	ALA	THR	PHE	SER	GLU	ALA	PRO	PRO	GLY	ASN	LYS	ASP	VAL	GLY	15
16	ALA	LYS	ILE	PHE	LYS	THR	LYS	CYS	ALA	GLN	CYS	HIS	THR	VAL	ASP	30
31	LEU	GLY	ALA	GLY	HIS	LYS	GLN	GLY	PRO	ASN	LEU	ASN	GLY	LEU	PHE	45
46	GLY	ARG	GLN	SER	GLY	THR	ALA	ALA	SER	TYR	SER	TYR	SER	ALA	ALA	60
61	ASN	LYS	ASN	LYS	ALA	VAL	ILE	TRP	SER	GLU	ASP	THR	LEU	TYR	GLU	75
76	TYR	LEU	LEU	ASN	PRO	TML	LYS	TYR	ILE	PRO	GLY	THR	LYS	MET	VAL	90
91	PHE	PRO	GLY	LEU	TML	LYS	PRO	GLN	ASP	ARG	ALA	ASP	LEU	ILE	ALA	105
106	TYR	LEU	LYS	ASP	SER	THR	GLN									120

The Amino Acid Sequence of Cytochrome c from *Spinacea oleracea* L. (Spinach).
R. H. Brown, M. Richardson, R. Scogin, and D. Boulter.
Biochem. J., **131**, 253–256 (1973).

CYTOCHROME c FROM NASTURTIUM (TROPAEOLUM MAJUS L.)

	1				5					10					15	
1	AC	ALA	SER	PHE	ALA	GLU	ALA	PRO	ALA	GLY	ASP	ASN	LYS	ALA	GLY	15
16	ASP	LYS	ILE	PHE	LYS	ASN	LYS	CYS	ALA	GLN	CYS	HIS	THR	VAL	ASP	30
31	LYS	GLY	ALA	GLY	HIS	LYS	GLN	GLY	PRO	ASN	LEU	ASN	GLY	LEU	PHE	45
46	GLY	ARG	GLN	SER	GLY	THR	THR	ALA	GLY	TYR	SER	TYR	SER	ALA	ALA	60
61	ASN	LYS	ASN	LYS	ALA	VAL	LEU	TRP	GLX	GLX	ALA	THR	LEU	TYR	ASP	75
76	TYR	LEU	LEU	ASN	PRO	TML	LYS	TYR	ILE	PRO	GLY	THR	LYS	MET	VAL	90
91	PHE	PRO	GLY	LEU	TML	LYS	PRO	GLN	ASP	ARG	ALA	ASP	LEU	ILE	ALA	105
106	TYR	LEU	LYS	GLU	SER	THR	ALA									120

CYTOCHROME c FROM BOX-ELDER (ACER NEGUNDO L.)

	1				5					10					15	
1	AC	ALA	SER	PHE	ALA	GLU	ALA	PRO	PRO	GLY	ASN	PRO	ALA	ALA	GLY	15
16	GLU	LYS	ILE	PHE	LYS	THR	LYS	CYS	ALA	GLN	CYS	HIS	THR	VAL	ASP	30
31	LYS	GLY	ALA	GLY	HIS	LYS	GLN	GLY	PRO	ASN	LEU	ASN	GLY	LEU	PHE	45
46	GLY	ARG	GLN	SER	GLY	THR	THR	ALA	GLY	TYR	SER	TYR	SER	ALA	ALA	60
61	ASN	LYS	ASN	MET	ALA	VAL	ASN	TRP	GLY	TYR	ASN	THR	LEU	TYR	ASP	75
76	TYR	LEU	LEU	ASN	PRO	TML	LYS	TYR	ILE	PRO	GLY	THR	LYS	MET	VAL	90
91	PHE	PRO	GLY	LEU	TML	LYS	PRO	GLN	ASP	ARG	ALA	ASP	LEU	ILE	ALA	105
106	TYR	LEU	LYS	GLN	SER	THR	ALA	ALA/SER								

CYTOCHROMES

CYTOCHROME c FROM ELDER (SAMBUCUS NIGRA *L.*)

	1		5						10					15		
1	AC	ALA	SER	PHE	ALA	GLU	ALA	PRO	PRO	GLY	ASN	PRO	LYS	ALA	GLY	15
16	GLU	LYS	ILE	PHE	LYS	THR	LYS	CYS	ASN	GLN	CYS	HIS	THR	VAL	ASP	30
31	LYS	GLY	ALA	GLY	HIS	LYS	GLN	GLY	PRO	ASN	LEU	ASN	GLY	LEU	PHE	45
46	GLY	ARG	GLN	SER	GLY	THR	THR	ALA	GLY	TYR	SER	TYR	SER	ALA	ALA	60
61	ASN	LYS	ASN	MET	ALA	VAL	ASN	TRP	GLU	GLU	LYS	THR	LEU	TYR	ASP	75
76	TYR	LEU	LEU	ASN	PRO	TML	LYS	TYR	ILE	PRO	GLY	THR	LYS	MET	VAL	90
91	PHE	PRO	GLY	LEU	TML	LYS	PRO	GLN	ASP	ARG	ALA	ASP	LEU	ILE	ALA	105
106	TYR	LEU	LYS	GLN	SER	THR	ALA									120

CYTOCHROME c FROM PARSNIP (PASTINACA SATIVA *L.*)

	1		5						10					15		
1	AC	ALA	SER	PHE	ALA	GLU	ALA	PRO	PRO	GLY	ASP	LYS	ASP	VAL	GLY	15
16	GLY	LYS	ILE	PHE	LYS	THR	LYS	CYS	ALA	GLX	CYS	HIS	THR	VAL	GLX	30
31	LEU	GLY	ALA	GLY	HIS	LYS	GLN	GLY	PRO	ASN	LEU	ASN	GLY	LEU	PHE	45
46	GLY	ARG	GLN	SER	GLY	THR	THR	ALA	GLY	TYR	SER	TYR	SER	ALA	ALA	60
61	ASN	LYS	ASN	LYS	ALA	VAL	LEU	TRP	ALA	ASX	ASX	THR	LEU	TYR	ASP	75
76	TYR	LEU	LEU	ASN	PRO	TML	LYS	TYR	ILE	PRO	GLY	THR	LYS	MET	VAL	90
91	PHE	PRO	GLY	LEU	TML	LYS	PRO	GLN	ASP	ARG	ALA	ASP	LEU	ILE	ALA	105
106	TYR	LEU	LYS	HIS	ALA	THR	ALA									120

The amino acid sequences of cytochrome c from four plant sources.
R. H. Brown and D. Boulter.
Biochem. J., **137**, 93–100 (1974).

CYTOCHROMES

CYTOCHROME c—POTATO

	1				5					10					15	
1	AC	ALA	SER	PHE	GLY	GLU	ALA	PRO	PRO	GLY	ASN	PRO	LYS	ALA	GLY	15
16	GLU	LYS	ILE	PHE	LYS	THR	LYS	CYS	ALA	GLN	CYS	HIS	THR	VAL	ASP	30
31	LYS	GLY	ALA	GLY	HIS	LYS	GLU	GLY	PRO	ASN	LEU	ASN	GLY	LEU	PHE	45
46	GLY	ARG	GLN	SER	GLY	THR	THR	ALA	GLY	TYR	SER	TYR	SER	ASN	ALA	60
61	ASN	LYS	ASN	MET	ALA	VAL	THR	TRP	GLY	GLU	ASN	THR	LEU	TYR	ASP	75
76	TYR	LEU	LEU	ASN	PRO	TML	LYS	TYR	ILE	PRO	GLY	THR	LYS	MET	VAL	90
91	PHE	PRO	GLY	LEU	TML	LYS	PRO	GLN	ASP GLU	ARG	ALA	ASP	LEU	ILE	ALA	105
106	TYR	LEU	LYS	GLU	ALA	THR	ALA									120

The amino acid sequence of cytochrome c from *Solanum tuberosum* (Potato).
G. Martinez, H. Rochat, and G. Ducet.
FEBS Letters, **47**, 212–217 (1974).
And
A re-examination of the amino acid sequence data of cytochromes c from *Solanum tuberosum* (potato) and *Lycopersicon esculentum* (Tomato).
R. Brown and D. Boulter.
FEBS Letters, **51**, 66–67 (1975).
This paper reports the finding of GLU at position 98 in potato cytochrome c.

TOMATO CYTOCHROME c

	1				5					10					15	
1	AC	ALA	SER	PHE	ASN	GLU	ALA	PRO	PRO	GLY	ASN	PRO	LYS	ALA	GLY	15
16	GLU	LYS	ILE	PHE	LYS	THR	LYS	CYS	ALA	GLN	CYS	HIS	THR	VAL	GLU	30
31	LYS	GLY	ALA	GLY	HIS	LYS	GLU	GLY	PRO	ASN	LEU	ASN	GLY	LEU	PHE	45
46	GLY	ARG	GLN	SER	GLY	THR	THR	ALA	GLY	TYR	SER	TYR	SER	ALA	ALA	60
61	ASN	LYS	ASN	MET	ALA	VAL	ASN	TRP	GLY	GLU	ASN	THR	LEU	TYR	ASP	75
76	TYR	LEU	LEU	ASN	PRO	TML	LYS	TYR	ILE	PRO	GLY	THR	LYS	MET	VAL	90
91	PHE	PRO	GLY	LEU	TML	LYS	PRO	GLN	GLU	ARG	ALA	ASP	LEU	ILE	ALA	105
106	TYR	LEU	LYS	GLU	ALA	THR	ALA									120

The Amino Acid Sequence of Cytochrome c from tomato (*Lycopersicon esculentum*).
R. Scogin, M. Richardson, and D. Boulter.
Arch. Biochem. Biophys., **150**, 489–492 (1972).
And
A re-examination of the amino acid sequence data of cytochromes c from *Solanum tuberosum* (potato) and *Lycopersicon esculentum* (Tomato).
R. Brown and D. Boulter.
FEBS Letters, **51**, 66–67 (1975).

ABUTILON CYTOCHROME c

	1			5					10				15			
1	AC	ALA	SER	PHE	GLN	GLU	ALA	PRO	PRO	GLY	ASN	ALA	LYS	ALA	GLY	15
16	GLU	LYS	ILE	PHE	LYS	THR	LYS	CYS	ALA	GLN	CYS	HIS	THR	VAL	GLU	30
31	LYS	GLY	ALA	GLY	HIS	LYS	GLN	GLY	PRO	ASN	LEU	ASN	GLY	LEU	PHE	45
46	GLY	ARG	GLN	SER	GLY	THR	THR	PRO	GLY	TYR	SER	TYR	SER	ALA	ALA	60
61	ASN	LYS	ASN	MET	ALA	VAL	ASN	TRP	GLY	GLU	ASN	THR	LEU	TYR	ASP	75
76	TYR	LEU	LEU	ASN	PRO	TML	LYS	TYR	ILE	PRO	GLY	THR	LYS	MET	VAL	90
91	PHE	PRO	GLY	LEU	TML	LYS	PRO	GLN	ASP	ARG	ALA	ASP	LEU	ILE	ALA	105
106	TYR	LEU	LYS	GLU	SER	THR	ALA									120

COTTON CYTOCHROME c

	1			5					10				15			
1	AC	ALA	SER	PHE	GLN	GLU	ALA	PRO	PRO	GLY	ASN	ALA	LYS	ALA	GLY	15
16	GLU	LYS	ILE	PHE	LYS	THR	LYS	CYS	ALA	GLN	CYS	HIS	THR	VAL	ASP	30
31	LYS	GLY	ALA	GLY	HIS	LYS	GLN	GLY	PRO	ASN	LEU	ASN	GLY	LEU	PHE	45
46	GLY	ARG	GLN	SER	GLY	THR	THR	ALA	GLY	TYR	SER	TYR	SER	ALA	ALA	60
61	ASN	LYS	ASN	MET	ALA	VAL	GLN	TRP	GLY	GLU	ASN	THR	LEU	TYR	ASP	75
76	TYR	LEU	LEU	ASN	PRO	TML	LYS	TYR	ILE	PRO	GLY	THR	LYS	MET	VAL	90
91	PHE	PRO	GLY	LEU	TML	LYS	PRO	GLN	ASP	ARG	ALA	ASP	LEU	ILE	ALA	105
106	TYR	LEU	LYS	GLU	SER	THR	ALA									120

The Amino Acid Sequence of Cytochrome c from *Abutilon theophrasti* Medic. and *Gossypium barbadense* L. (Cotton).
E. W. Thompson, B. A. Notton, M. Richardson, and D. Boulter.
Biochem. J., **124**, 787–791 (1971).

MAIDENHAIR TREE CYTOCHROME c

	1			5					10				15			
1	AC	ALA	THR	PHE	SER	GLU	ALA	PRO	PRO	GLY	ASP	PRO	LYS	ALA	GLY	15
16	GLU	LYS	ILE	PHE	LYS	THR	LYS	CYS	ALA	GLX	(CYS,	HIS)	THR	VAL	GLX	30
31	LYS	GLY	ALA	GLY	HIS	LYS	GLN	GLY	PRO	ASN	LEU	HIS	GLY	LEU	PHE	45
46	GLY	ARG	GLN	SER	GLY	THR	THR	ALA	GLY	TYR	SER	TYR	SER	THR	GLY	60
61	ASN	LYS	ASN	LYS	ALA	VAL	ASN	TRP	GLY	GLX	GLX	THR	LEU	TYR	GLU	75
76	TYR	LEU	LEU	ASN	PRO	TML	LYS	TYR	ILE	PRO	GLY	THR	LYS	MET	VAL	90
91	PHE	PRO	GLY	LEU	TML	LYS	PRO	GLX	GLX	ARG	ALA	ASP	LEU	ILE	SER	105
106	TYR	LEU	LYS	GLN	ALA	THR	SER	GLN	GLU							120

The Amino Acid Sequence of the Cytochrome c of *Ginkgo biloba* L.
J. A. M. Ramshaw, M. Richardson, and D. Boulter.
Eur. J. Biochem., **23**, 475–483 (1971).

CYTOCHROMES

CASTOR CYTOCHROME c

	1				5					10					15	
1	AC	ALA	SER	PHE	ASX	GLX	ALA	PRO	PRO	GLY	ASX	VAL	LYS	ALA	GLY	15
16	GLU	LYS	ILE	PHE	LYS	THR	LYS	CYS	ALA	GLN	CYS	HIS	THR	VAL	GLU	30
31	LYS	GLY	ALA	GLY	HIS	LYS	GLN	GLY	PRO	ASN	LEU	ASN	GLY	LEU	PHE	45
46	GLY	ARG	GLN	SER	GLY	THR	THR	ALA	GLY	TYR	SER	TYR	SER	ALA	ALA	60
61	ASN	LYS	ASN	MET	ALA	VAL	GLN	TRP	GLY	GLU	ASN	THR	LEU	TYR	ASP	75
76	TYR	LEU	LEU	ASN	PRO	TML	LYS	TYR	ILE	PRO	GLY	THR	LYS	MET	VAL	90
91	PHE	PRO	GLY	LEU	TML	LYS	PRO	GLN	ASP	ARG	ALA	ASP	LEU	ILE	ALA	101
106	TYR	LEU	LYS	GLU GLN	ALA	THR	ALA									120

SESAME CYTOCHROME c

	1				5					10					15	
1	AC	ALA	SER	PHE	ASX	GLX	ALA	PRO	PRO	GLY	ASX	VAL	LYS	SER	GLY	15
16	GLU	LYS	ILE	PHE	LYS	THR	LYS	CYS	ALA	GLN	CYS	HIS	THR	VAL	ASP	30
31	LYS	GLY	ALA	GLY	HIS	LYS	GLN	GLY	PRO	ASN	LEU	ASN	GLY	LEU	PHE	45
46	GLY	ARG	GLN	SER	GLY	THR	THR	PRO	GLY	TYR	SER	TYR	SER	ALA	ALA	60
61	ASN	LYS	ASN	MET	ALA	VAL	ILE	TRP	GLY	GLU	ASN	THR	LEU	TYR	ASP	75
76	TYR	LEU	LEU	ASN	PRO	TML	LYS	TYR	ILE	PRO	GLY	THR	LYS	MET	VAL	90
91	PHE	PRO	GLY	LEU	TML	LYS	PRO	GLN	GLU	ARG	ALA	ASP	LEU	ILE	ALA	105
106	TYR	LEU	LYS	GLU	ALA	THR	ALA									120

The Amino Acid Sequence of Sesame (*Sesamum indicum* L.) and Castor (*Ricinus communis* L.) Cytochrome c.
E. W. Thompson, M. Richardson, and D. Boulter.
Biochem. J., **121**, 439–446 (1971).

SUNFLOWER CYTOCHROME c

		1			5				10					15			
1	AC	ALA	SER	PHE	ALA	GLU	ALA	PRO	ALA	GLY	ASP	PRO	THR	THR	GLY		15
16	ALA	LYS	ILE	PHE	LYS	THR	LYS	CYS	ALA	GLN	CYS	HIS	THR	VAL	GLU		30
31	LYS	GLY	ALA	GLY	HIS	LYS	GLN	GLY	PRO	ASN	LEU	ASN	GLY	LEU	PHE		45
46	GLY	ARG	GLN	SER	GLY	THR	THR	ALA	GLY	TYR	SER	TYR	SER	ALA	ALA		60
61	ASN	LYS	ASN	MET	ALA	VAL	ILE	TRP	GLU	GLU	ASN	THR	LEU	TYR	ASP		75
76	TYR	LEU	LEU	ASN	PRO	TML	LYS	TYR	ILE	PRO	GLY	THR	LYS	MET	VAL		90
91	PHE	PRO	GLY	LEU	TML	LYS	PRO	GLN	GLU	ARG	ALA	ASP	LEU	ILE	ALA	105
106	TYR	LEU	LYS	THR	SER	THR	ALA									120

The Amino Acid Sequence of *Helianthus annuus* L. (Sunflower) Cytochrome c. Deduced from Chymotryptic Peptides.
J. A. M. Ramshaw, E. W. Thompson, and D. Boulter.
Biochem. J., **119**, 535–539 (1970).

CYTOCHROME c—HEMP

		1			5				10					15			
1	AC	ALA	SER	PHE	ASX	GLX	ALA	PRO	PRO	GLY	ASX	SER	LYS	ALA	GLY		15
16	GLU	LYS	ILE	PHE	LYS	THR	LYS	CYS	ALA	GLU	CYS	HIS	THR	VAL	GLY		30
31	ARG	GLY	ALA	GLY	HIS	LYS	GLN	GLY	PRO	ASN	LEU	ASN	GLY	LEU	PHE		45
46	GLY	ARG	GLN	SER	GLY	THR	THR	ALA	GLY	TYR	SER	TYR	SER	ALA	ALA		60
61	ASN	LYS	ASN	MET	ALA	VAL	THR	TRP	GLX	GLX	LYS	THR	LEU	TYR	ASP		75
76	TYR	LEU	LEU	ASN	PRO	TML	LYS	TYR	ILE	PRO	GLY	THR	LYS	MET	VAL		90
91	PHE	PRO	GLY	LEU	TML	LYS	PRO	GLX	ASX	ARG	ALA	ASP	LEU	ILE	ALA	105
106	TYR	LEU	LYS	GLU	SER	THR	ALA									120

The amino acid sequence of *Cannabis sativa* cytochrome c.
D. G. Wallace, R. H. Brown, and D. Boulter.
Phytochemistry, **12**, 2617–2622 (1973).

CYTOCHROMES

RAPE CYTOCHROME c

	1			5					10					15		
1	AC	ALA	SER	PHE	ASP	GLU	ALA	PRO	PRO	GLY	ASN	SER	LYS	ALA	GLY	15
16	GLU	LYS	ILE	PHE	LYS	THR	LYS	CYS	ALA	GLN	CYS	HIS	THR	VAL	ASP	30
31	LYS	GLY	ALA	GLY	HIS	LYS	GLN	GLY	PRO	ASN	LEU	ASN	GLY	LEU	PHE	45
46	GLY	ARG	GLN	SER	GLY	THR	THR	ALA	GLY	TYR	SER	TYR	SER	ALA	ALA	60
61	ASN	LYS	ASN	LYS	ALA	VAL	GLU	TRP	GLU	GLU	LYS	THR	LEU	TYR	ASP	75
76	TYR	LEU	LEU	ASN	PRO	TML	LYS	TYR	ILE	PRO	GLY	THR	LYS	MET	VAL	90
91	PHE	PRO	GLY	LEU	TML	LYS	PRO	GLN	ASP	ARG	ALA	ASP	LEU	ILE	ALA	105
106	TYR	LEU	LYS	GLU	ALA	THR	ALA									120

The Amino Acid Sequence of Rape (*Brassica Napus* L) Cytochrome c.
M. Richardson, J. A. M. Ramshaw and D. Boulter.
Biochim. Biophys. Acta, **251**, 331–333 (1971).

MUNG-BEAN CYTOCHROME c

	1			5					10					15		
1	AC	ALA	SER	PHE	ASX	GLX	ALA	PRO	PRO	GLY	ASX	SER	LYS	SER	GLY	15
16	GLU	LYS	ILE	PHE	LYS	THR	LYS	CYS	ALA	GLN	CYS	HIS	THR	VAL	ASP	30
31	LYS	GLY	ALA	GLY	HIS	LYS	GLN	GLY	PRO	ASN	LEU	ASN	GLY	LEU	PHE	45
46	GLY	ARG	GLN	SER	GLY	THR	THR	ALA	GLY	TYR	SER	TYR	SER	THR	ALA	60
61	ASN	LYS	ASN	MET	ALA	VAL	ILE	TRP	GLU	GLU	LYS	THR	LEU	TYR	ASP	75
76	TYR	LEU	LEU	ASN	PRO	TML	LYS	TYR	ILE	PRO	GLY	THR	LYS	MET	VAL	90
91	PHE	PRO	GLY	LEU	TML	LYS	PRO	GLN	ASP	ARG	ALA	ASP	LEU	ILE	ALA	105
106	TYR	LEU	LYS	GLU	SER	THR	ALA									120

The Amino Acid Sequence of Mung-bean Cytochrome c.
E. W. Thompson, M. V. Laycock, J. A. M. Ramshaw, and D. Boulter.
Biochem. J., **117**, 183 (1970).
In corrected form:
E. W. Thompson, M. Richardson, and D. Boulter.
Biochem. J., **121**, 439–446 (1971).

CYTOCHROME c FROM NIGELLA DAMASCENA L.

```
        1              5                  10                    15
  1  AC  ALA SER PHE ASX GLX ALA PRO ALA GLY ASX SER ALA SER GLY   15
 16  GLU LYS ILE PHE LYS THR LYS CYS ALA GLX CYS HIS THR VAL ASX   30
 31  GLX GLY ALA GLY HIS LYS GLX GLY PRO ASN LEU HIS GLY LEU PHE   45
 46  GLY ARG GLN SER GLY THR VAL ALA GLY TYR SER TYR SER ALA ALA   60
 61  ASN LYS ASN LYS ALA VAL ASN TRP GLU GLU LYS THR LEU TYR ASP   75
 76  TYR LEU LEU ASN PRO TML LYS TYR ILE PRO GLY THR LYS MET VAL   90
 91  PHE PRO GLY LEU TML LYS PRO GLX GLX ARG ALA ASX LEU LEU ALA  105
106  TYR LEU LYS GLU SER THR ALA                                   120
```

The amino acid sequence of Cytochrome c from *Nigella damascena* L. (Love-in-a-mist).
R. H. Brown and D. Boulter.
Biochem. J., **133**, 251–254 (1973).

BAKER'S YEAST CYTOCHROME c

```
        1              5                  10                    15
  1  THR GLU PHE LYS ALA GLY SER ALA LYS LYS GLY ALA THR LEU PHE   15
 16  LYS THR ARG CYS LEU GLN CYS HIS THR VAL GLU LYS GLY GLY PRO   30
 31  HIS LYS VAL GLY PRO ASN LEU HIS GLY ILE PHE GLY ARG HIS SER   45
 46  GLY GLN ALA GLU GLY TYR SER TYR THR ASP ALA ASN ILE LYS LYS   60
 61  ASN VAL LEU TRP ASP GLU ASN ASN MET SER GLU TYR LEU THR ASN   75
 76  PRO LYS LYS TYR ILE PRO GLY THR LYS MET ALA PHE GLY GLY LEU   90
 91  LYS LYS GLU LYS ASP ARG ASN ASP LEU ILE THR TYR LEU LYS LYS  105
106  ALA CYS GLU                                                   120
```

The Complete Amino Acid Sequence in Baker's Yeast Cytochrome c.
K. Narita and K. Titani.
J. Biochem., **65**, 259–267 (1969).
And
Saccharomyces cerevisiae iso-cytochromes c: revision of the amino acid sequence between the cysteine residues.
F. Lederer, A.-M. Simon, and J. Verdiere.
Biochem. Biophys. Res. Commun., **47**, 55–58 (1972).

CYTOCHROMES

DEBARYOMYCES KLOECKERI *CYTOCHROME c*

	1				5					10					15	
1	PRO	ALA	PRO	TYR	GLU	LYS	GLY	SER	GLU	LYS	LYS	GLY	ALA	ASN	LEU	15
16	PHE	LYS	THR	ARG	CYS	LEU	GLN	CYS	HIS	THR	VAL	GLU	GLU	GLY	GLY	30
31	PRO	HIS	LYS	VAL	GLY	PRO	ASN	LEU	HIS	GLY	VAL	VAL	GLY	ARG	THR	45
46	SER	GLY	GLN	ALA	GLN	GLY	PHE	SER	TYR	THR	ASP	ALA	ASN	LYS	LYS	60
61	LYS	GLY	VAL	GLU	TRP	THR	GLU	GLN	ASP	LEU	SER	ASP	TYR	LEU	GLU	75
76	ASN	PRO	TML	LYS	TYR	ILE	PRO	GLY	THR	LYS	MET	ALA	PHE	GLY	GLY	90
91	LEU	LYS	LYS	ALA	LYS	ASP	ARG	ASN	ASP	LEU	ILE	THR	TYR	LEU	VAL	105
106	LYS	ALA	THR	LYS												120

The Amino Acid Sequence of Cytochrome c from *Debaryomyces kloeckeri*.
K. Sugeno, K. Narita and K. Titani.
J. Biochem., **70**, 659–682 (1971).

CYTOCHROME c FROM USTILAGO SPHAEROGENA

	1				5					10					15	
1	GLY	PHE	GLU	ASP	GLY	ASP	ALA	LYS	LYS	GLY	ALA	ARG	ILE	PHE	LYS	15
16	THR	ARG	CYS	ALA	GLN	CYS	HIS	THR	LEU	GLY	ALA	GLY	GLU	PRO	ASN	30
31	LYS	VAL	GLY	PRO	ASN	LEU	HIS	GLY	LEU	PHE	GLY	ARG	LYS	SER	GLY	45
46	THR	VAL	GLU	GLY	PHE	SER	TYR	THR	ASP	ALA	ASN	LYS	LYS	ALA	GLY	60
61	GLN	VAL	TRP	GLU	GLU	GLU	THR	PHE	LEU	GLU	TYR	LEU	GLU	ASN	PRO	75
76	LYS	LYS	TYR	ILE	PRO	GLY	THR	LYS	MET	ALA	PHE	GLY	GLY	LEU	LYS	90
91	LYS	GLU	LYS	ASP	ARG	ASN	ASP	LEU	VAL	THR	TYR	LEU	ARG	GLU	GLU	105
106	THR	LYS														120

The primary structure of cytochrome c from the rust fungus *Ustilago sphaerogena*.
K. G. Bitar, S. N. Vinogradov, C. Nolan, L. J. Weiss, and E. Margoliash.
Biochem. J., **129**, 561–569 (1972).

NEUROSPORA CRASSA *CYTOCHROME c*

	1				5					10					15		
1	GLY	PHE	SER	ALA	GLY	ASP	SER	LYS	LYS	GLY	ALA	ASN	LEU	PHE	LYS		15
16	THR	ARG	CYS	ALA	GLU	CYS	HIS	GLY	GLU	GLY	GLY	ASN	LEU	THR	GLN		30
31	LYS	ILE	GLY	PRO	ALA	LEU	HIS	GLY	LEU	PHE	GLY	ARG	LYS	THR	GLY		45
46	SER	VAL	ASP	GLY	TYR	ALA	TYR	THR	ASP	ALA	ASN	LYS	GLN	LYS	GLY		60
61	ILE	THR	TRP	ASP	GLU	ASN	THR	LEU	PHE	GLU	TYR	LEU	GLU	ASN	PRO		75
76	LYS	LYS	TYR	ILE	PRO	GLY	THR	LYS	MET	ALA	PHE	GLY	GLY	LEU	LYS		90
91	LYS	ASP	LYS	ASP	ARG	ASN	ASP	ILE	ILE	THR	PHE	MET	LYS	GLU	ALA		105
106	THR	ALA															120

Neurospora crassa, Cytochrome c.
J. Heller and E. L. Smith.
J. Biol. Chem., **241**, 3165–3180 (1966).
And dispute:
Neurospora crassa and *Humicola lanuginosa* cytochrome c: more homology in the heme region.
F. Lederer and A. M. Simon.
Biochem. Biophys. Res. Commun., **56**, 317–323 (1974).
This paper reports that the sequence of residues 20–30 is:
GLN CYS HIS THR LEU GLU GLU GLY GLY GLY ASN.

HUMICOLA LANUGINOSA *CYTOCHROME c*

	1				5					10					15		
1	ALA	LYS	GLY	GLY	SER	PHE	GLU	PRO	GLY	ASP	SER	ALA	LYS	GLY	ALA		15
16	ASN	LEU	PHE	LYS	THR	ARG	CYS	ALA	GLU	CYS	HIS	GLY	GLU	GLY	ALA		30
31	ASN	VAL	SER	GLN	LYS	ILE	GLY	PRO	ASN	LEU	HIS	GLY	LEU	PHE	GLY		45
46	ARG	LYS	THR	GLY	SER	VAL	GLU	GLY	TYR	SER	TYR	THR	ASP	ALA	ASN		60
61	LYS	GLN	ALA	GLY	ILE	THR	TRP	ASN	GLU	ASP	THR	LEU	PHE	GLU	TYR		75
76	LEU	GLU	ASN	PRO	DML	LYS	PHE	ILE	PRO	GLY	THR	LYS	MET	ALA	PHE		90
91	GLY	GLY	LEU	TML	LYS	ASN	LYS	ASP	ARG	ASN	ASP	LEU	ILE	THR	TYR		105
106	LEU	LYS	GLU	ALA	THR	LYS											120

Proteins of the Thermophilic Fungus *Humicola lanuginosa* I. Isolation and Amino Acid Sequence of a Cytochrome c.
W. T. Morgan, C. P. Hensley, Jr, and J. P. Riehm.
J. Biol. Chem., **247**, 6555–6565 (1972).
Note: The above sequence is that of the major component, c_A.
And dispute:
Neurospora crassa and *Humicola lanuginosa* cytochrome c: more homology in the heme region.
F. Lederer and A. M. Simon.
Biochem. Biophys. Res. Commun., **56**, 317–323 (1974).
This paper reports the following differences:
residue 11 is ALA, 12 is SER, 24 is GLN, and residues 28–33 are VAL GLU GLN GLY GLY ALA.

CYTOCHROMES

CANDIDA KRUSEI *CYTOCHROME* c

	1				5					10					15	
1	PRO	ALA	PRO	PHE	GLU	GLN	GLY	SER	ALA	LYS	LYS	GLY	ALA	THR	LEU	15
16	PHE	LYS	THR	ARG	CYS	ALA	GLN	CYS	HIS	THR	ILE	GLU	ALA	GLY	GLY	30
31	PRO	HIS	LYS	VAL	GLY	PRO	ASN	LEU	HIS	GLY	ILE	PHE	SER	ARG	HIS	45
46	SER	GLY	GLN	ALA	GLU	GLY	TYR	SER	TYR	THR	ASP	ALA	ASN	LYS	ARG	60
61	ALA	GLY	VAL	GLU	TRP	ALA	GLU	PRO	THR	MET	SER	ASP	TYR	LEU	GLU	75
76	ASN	PRO	LYS	LYS	TYR	ILE	PRO	GLY	THR	LYS	MET	ALA	PHE	GLY	GLY	90
91	LEU	LYS	LYS	ALA	LYS	ASP	ARG	ASN	ASP	LEU	VAL	THR	TYR	MET	LEU	105
106	GLU	ALA	SER	LYS												120

The Amino Acid Sequence of Cytochrome c from *Candida krusei*.
K. Narita and K. Titani.
J. Biochem., **63**, 226–241 (1968).
And
Candida krusei cytochrome c: a correction to the sequence. Glutamine-16, an invariant residue in mitochondrial cytochrome c?
F. Lederer.
Eur. J. Biochem., **31**, 144–147 (1972).

CYTOCHROME c—TETRAHYMENA PYRIFORMIS

	1				5					10					15	
1	GLY	PRO	LYS	GLU	PRO	GLU	VAL	THR	VAL	PRO	GLU	GLY	ASP	ALA	SER	15
16	ALA	GLY	ARG	ASP	ILE	PHE	ASP	SER	GLN	CYS	SER	ALA	CYS	HIS	ALA	30
31	ILE	GLU	GLY	ASP	SER	THR	ALA	ALA	PRO	VAL	LEU	GLY	GLY	VAL	ILE	45
46	GLY	ARG	LYS	ALA	GLY	GLN	GLU	LYS	PHE	ALA	TYR	SER	LYS	GLY	MET	60
61	LYS	GLY	SER	GLY	ILE	THR	TRP	ASN	GLU	LYS	HIS	LEU	PHE	VAL	PHE	75
76	LEU	LYS	ASN	PRO	SER	LYS	HIS	VAL	PRO	GLY	THR	LYS	MET	ALA	PHE	90
91	ALA	GLY	LEU	PRO	ALA	ASP	LYS	ASP	ARG	ALA	ASP	LEU	ILE	ALA	TYR	105
106	LEU	LYS	SER	VAL												120

Amino acid sequence of cytochrome c from *Tetrahymena pyriformis* Phenoset A.
G. E. Tarr and W. M. Fitch.
Biochem. J., **159**, 193–199 (1976).

CYTOCHROMES

EUGLENA GRACILIS *CYTOCHROME c*

	1				5					10					15				
1	AC		GLY	ASP	ALA	GLU	ARG	GLY	LYS	LYS	LEU	PHE	GLU	SER	ARG	ALA			15
16	ALA	GLN	CYS	HIS	SER	ALA	GLN	LYS	GLY	VAL	ASN	SER	THR	GLY	PRO				30
31	SER	LEU	TRP	GLY	VAL	TYR	GLY	ARG	THR	SER	GLY	SER	VAL	PRO	GLY				45
46	TYR	ALA	TYR	SER	ASN	ALA	ASN	LYS	ASN	ALA	ALA	ILE	VAL	TRP	GLU				60
61	GLU	GLU	THR	LEU	HIS	LYS	PHE	LEU	GLU	ASN	PRO	LYS	LYS	TYR	VAL				75
76	PRO	GLY	THR	LYS	MET	ALA	PHE	ALA	GLY	ILE	TML	ALA	LYS	LYS	ASP				90
91	ARG	GLN	ASP	ILE	ILE	ALA	TYR	MET	LYS	THR	LEU	LYS	ASP						105

The Amino Acid Sequence of Cytochrome c from *Euglena gracilis*.
G. W. Pettigrew.
Nature, **241**, 531–533 (1973).
And
The Properties and Amino Acid Sequence of Cytochrome c from *Euglena gracilis*.
D. K. Lin, R. L. Niece and W. M. Fitch.
Nature, **241**, 533–535 (1973).
And
Purification, properties and amino acid sequence of atypical cytochrome c from two protozoa, *Euglena gracilis* and *Crithidia oncopelti*.
G. W. Pettigrew, J. L. Leaver, T. E. Meyer, and A. P. Ryle.
Biochem. J., **147**, 291–302 (1975).

CRITHIDIA ONCOPELTI *CYTOCHROME c*

	1				5					10					15	
1	PRO	TML	ALA	ARG	GLU	PRO	LEU	PRO	PRO	GLY	ASP	ALA	ALA	LYS	GLY	15
16	GLU	LYS	ILE	PHE	LYS	GLY	ARG	ALA	ALA	GLN	CYS	HIS	THR	GLY	ALA	30
31	LYS	GLY	GLY	ALA	ASN	GLY	VAL	GLY	PRO	ASN	LEU	PHE	GLY	ILE	VAL	45
46	ASN	ARG	HIS	SER	GLY	THR	VAL	GLU	GLY	PHE	ALA	TYR	SER	LYS	ALA	60
61	ASN	ALA	ASP	SER	GLY	VAL	VAL	TRP	THR	PRO	GLU	VAL	LEU	ASP	VAL	75
76	TYR	LEU	GLU	ASN	PRO	TML	LYS	PHE	MET	PRO	GLY	THR	LYS	MET	SER	90
91	PHE	ALA	GLY	ILE	LYS	LYS	PRO	GLN	GLU	ARG	ALA	ASP	LEU	ILE	ALA	105
106	TYR	LEU	GLU	ASN	LEU	LYS										120

The Amino Acid Sequence of a Cytochrome c from a protozoan *Crithidia oncopelti*.
G. W. Pettigrew.
FEBS Letters, **22**, 64–66 (1972).
Note: The N-terminus of this protein is blocked by an unknown group.

CYTOCHROMES

CYTOCHROME c—SCHIZOSACCHAROMYCES POMBE

	1				5					10					15		
1	PRO	TYR	ALA	PRO	GLY	ASP	GLU	LYS	LYS	GLY	ALA	SER	LEU	PHE	LYS		15
16	THR	ARG	CYS	ALA	GLN	CYS	HIS	THR	VAL	GLU	LYS	GLY	GLY	ALA	ASN		30
31	LYS	VAL	GLY	PRO	ASN	LEU	HIS	GLY	VAL	PHE	GLY	ARG	LYS	THR	GLY		45
46	GLN	ALA	GLU	GLY	PHE	SER	TYR	THR	GLU	ALA	ASN	LYS	ASP	ARG	GLY		60
61	ILE	THR	TRP	ASX	GLX	GLX	THR	LEU	PHE	ALA	TYR	LEU	GLU	ASN	PRO		75
76	TML	LYS	TYR	ILE	PRO	GLY	THR	LYS	MET	ALA	PHE	ALA	GLY	PHE	LYS		90
91	LYS	PRO	ALA	ASP	ARG	ASN	ASN	VAL	ILE	THR	TYR	LEU	LYS	LYS	ALA		105
106	THR	SER	GLU														120

Cytochrome c from *Schizosaccharomyces pombe*. 2. The Amino Acid Sequence.
A. Simon-Becam, M. Claisse, and F. Lederer.
Eur. J. Biochem., **86**, 407–416 (1978).

CYTOCHROME c'—RHODOSPIRILLUM RUBRUM *S1*

	1				5					10					15		
1	ALA	ASP	PRO	ALA	ALA	TYR	VAL	GLU	TYR	ARG	LYS	SER	VAL	LEU	SER		15
16	ALA	THR	SER	ASN	TYR	MET	LYS	ALA	ILE	GLY	ILE	THR	LEU	LYS	GLU		30
31	ASP	LEU	ALA	VAL	PRO	ASN	GLN	THR	ALA	ASP	HIS	ALA	LYS	ALA	ILE		45
46	ALA	SER	ILE	MET	GLU	THR	LEU	PRO	ALA	ALA	PHE	PRO	GLU	GLY	THR		60
61	ALA	GLY	ILE	ALA	LYS	THR	GLU	ALA	LYS	ALA	ALA	ILE	TRP	LYS	ASP		75
76	PHE	GLU	ALA	PHE	LYS	VAL	ALA	SER	LYS	LYS	SER	GLN	ASP	ALA	ALA		90
91	LEU	GLU	LEU	ALA	SER	ALA	ALA	GLU	THR	GLY	ASP	LYS	ALA	ALA	ILE		105
106	GLY	ALA	LYS	LEU	GLN	ALA	LEU	GLY	GLY	THR	CYS	LYS	ALA	CYS	HIS		120
121	LYS	GLU	PHE	LYS	ALA	ASP											135

Amino acid sequence of cytochrome c' from the purple photosynthetic bacterium *Rhodospirillum rubrum* S1.
T. E. Meyer, R. P. Ambler, R. G. Bartsch, and M. D. Kamen.
J. Biol. Chem., **250**, 8416–8421 (1975).

CYTOCHROME c' FROM ALCALIGENES

	1				5					10					15	
1	PYG	PHE	ALA	LYS	PRO	GLU	ASP	ALA	VAL	LYS	TYR	ARG	GLN	SER	ALA	15
16	LEU	THR	LEU	MET	ALA	SER	HIS	PHE	GLY	ARG	MET	THR	PRO	VAL	VAL	30
31	LYS	GLY	GLN	ALA	PRO	TYR	ASP	ALA	ALA	GLN	ILE	LYS	ALA	ASN	VAL	45
46	GLU	VAL	LEU	LYS	THR	LEU	SER	ALA	LEU	PRO	TRP	ALA	ALA	PHE	GLY	60
61	PRO	GLY	THR	GLU	GLY	GLY	ASP	ALA	ARG	PRO	GLU	ILE	TRP	SER	ASP	75
76	ALA	ALA	SER	PHE	LYS	GLN	LYS	GLN	GLN	ALA	PHE	GLN	ASP	ASN	ILE	90
91	VAL	LYS	LEU	SER	ALA	ALA	ALA	ASP	ALA	GLY	ASP	LEU	ASP	LYS	LEU	105
106	ARG	ALA	ALA	PHE	GLY	ASP	VAL	GLY	ALA	SER	CYS	LYS	ALA	CYS	HIS	120
121	ASP	ALA	TYR	ARG	LYS	LYS	LYS									135

The amino acid sequence of Cytochrome c' from Alcaligenes sp. N.C.I.B. 11015.
R. P. Ambler.
Biochem. J., **135**, 751–758 (1973).

CYTOCHROME c₂—RHODOMICROBIUM VANNIELII

	1				5					10					15	
1	ALA	GLY	ASP	PRO	VAL	LYS	GLY	GLU	GLN	VAL	PHE	LYS	GLN	CYS	LYS	15
16	ILE	CYS	HIS	GLN	VAL	GLY	PRO	THR	ALA	LYS	ASN	GLY	VAL	GLY	PRO	30
31	GLU	GLN	ASN	ASP	VAL	PHE	GLY	GLN	LYS	ALA	GLY	ALA	ARG	PRO	GLY	45
46	PHE	ASN	TYR	SER	ASP	ALA	MET	LYS	ASN	SER	GLY	LEU	THR	TRP	ASP	60
61	GLU	ALA	THR	LEU	ASP	LYS	TYR	LEU	GLU	ASN	PRO	LYS	ALA	VAL	VAL	75
76	PRO	GLY	THR	LYS	MET	VAL	PHE	VAL	GLY	LEU	LYS	ASN	PRO	GLN	ASP	90
91	ARG	ALA	ASP	VAL	ILE	ALA	TYR	LEU	LYS	GLN	LEU	SER	GLY	LYS		105

CYTOCHROME c₂—RHODOPSEUDOMONAS VIRIDIS

	1				5					10					15	
1	PYG	ASP	ALA	ALA	SER	GLY	GLU	GLN	VAL	PHE	LYS	GLN	CYS	LYS	VAL	15
16	CYS	HIS	SER	ILE	GLY	PRO	GLY	ALA	LYS	ASN	LYS	VAL	GLY	PRO	VAL	30
31	LEU	ASN	GLY	LEU	PHE	GLY	ARG	HIS	SER	GLY	THR	ILE	GLU	GLY	PHE	45
46	SER	TYR	SER	ASP	ALA	ASN	LYS	ASN	SER	GLY	ILE	THR	TRP	THR	GLU	60
61	GLU	VAL	PHE	ARG	GLU	TYR	ILE	ARG	ASP	PRO	LYS	ALA	LYS	ILE	PRO	75
76	GLY	THR	LYS	MET	ILE	PHE	ALA	GLY	ILE	LYS	ASP	GLU	GLN	LYS	VAL	90
91	SER	ASP	LEU	ILE	ALA	TYR	LEU	LYS	GLN	PHE	ASN	ALA	ASP	GLY	SER	105
106	LYS	LYS														120

Primary structure determination of two cytochromes c₂: close similarity to functionally unrelated mitochondrial cytochrome c.
R. P. Ambler, T. E. Meyer, and M. D. Kamen.
Proc. Natn. Acad. Sci., U.S.A., **73**, 472–475 (1976).

CYTOCHROMES

RHODOSPIRILLUM RUBRUM *CYTOCHROME* c_2

	1				5					10					15		
1	GLU	GLY	ASP	ALA	ALA	ALA	GLY	GLU	LYS	VAL	SER	LYS	LYS	CYS	LEU		15
16	ALA	CYS	HIS	THR	PHE	ASP	GLN	GLY	GLY	ALA	ASN	LYS	VAL	GLY	PRO		30
31	ASN	LEU	PHE	GLY	VAL	PHE	GLU	ASN	THR	ALA	ALA	HIS	LYS	ASP	ASN		45
46	TYR	ALA	TYR	SER	GLU	SER	TYR	THR	GLU	MET	LYS	ALA	LYS	GLY	LEU		60
61	THR	TRP	THR	GLU	ALA	ASN	LEU	ALA	ALA	TYR	VAL	LYS	ASN	PRO	LYS		75
76	ALA	PHE	VAL	LEU	GLU	LYS	SER	GLY	ASP	PRO	LYS	ALA	LYS	SER	LYS		90
91	MET	THR	PHE	LYS	LEU	THR	LYS	ASP	ASP	GLU	ILE	GLU	ASN	VAL	ILE		105
106	ALA	TYR	LEU	LYS	THR	LEU	LYS										120

Cytochrome c_2 of *Rhodospirillum rubrum*. II Complete Amino Acid Sequence and Phylogenetic relationships.
K. Dus, K. Sletten, and M. D. Kamen.
J. Biol. Chem., **243**, 5507–5518 (1968).

DESULFOVIBRIO VULGARIS *CYTOCHROME* c_3

	1				5					10					15		
1	ALA	PRO	LYS	ALA	PRO	ALA	ASP	GLY	LEU	LYS	MET	GLU	ALA	THR	LYS		15
16	GLN	PRO	VAL	VAL	PHE	ASN	HIS	SER	THR	HIS	LYS	SER	VAL	LYS	CYS		30
31	GLY	ASP	CYS	HIS	HIS	PRO	VAL	ASN	GLY	LYS	GLU	ASP	TYR	ARG	LYS		45
46	CYS	GLY	THR	ALA	GLY	CYS	HIS	ASP	SER	MET	ASP	LYS	LYS	ASP	LYS		60
61	SER	ALA	LYS	GLY	TYR	TYR	HIS	VAL	MET	HIS	ASP	LYS	ASN	THR	LYS		75
76	PHE	LYS	SER	CYS	VAL	GLY	CYS	HIS	VAL	GLU	VAL	ALA	GLY	ALA	ASP		90
91	ALA	ALA	LYS	LYS	LYS	ASP	LEU	THR	GLY	CYS	LYS	LYS	SER	LYS	CYS		105
106	HIS	GLU															120

The Amino Acid Sequence of Cytochrome c_3 from *Desulfovibrio vulgaris* (N.C.I.B. 8303).
R. P. Ambler.
Biochem. J., **109**, 47p–48p (1968).
And
Amino acid sequence of cytochrome c_3 from *Desulfovibrio vulgaris*.
E. B. Trousil and L. L. Campbell.
J. Biol. Chem., **249**, 386–393 (1974).

DESULFOVIBRIO DESULFURICANS *CYTOCHROME* c_3

	1				5					10					15	
1	VAL	ASP	ALA	PRO	ALA	ASP	MET	VAL	ILE	LYS	ALA	PRO	ALA	GLY	ALA	15
16	LYS	VAL	THR	LYS	ALA	PRO	VAL	ALA	PHE	SER	HIS	LYS	GLY	HIS	ALA	30
31	SER	MET	ASP	CYS	LYS	THR	CYS	HIS	HIS	LYS	TRP	ASP	GLY	ALA	GLY	45
46	ALA	ILE	GLN	PRO	CYS	GLN	ALA	SER	GLY	CYS	HIS	ALA	ASN	THR	GLU	60
61	SER	LYS	LYS	GLY	ASP	ASP	SER	PHE	TYR	MET	ALA	PHE	HIS	GLU	ARG	75
76	LYS	SER	GLU	LYS	SER	CYS	VAL	GLY	CYS	HIS	LYS	SER	MET	LYS	LYS	90
91	GLY	PRO	THR	LYS	CYS	THR	GLU	CYS	HIS	PRO	LYS	ASN				105

The Amino Acid Sequence of Cytochrome c_3 from *Desulfovibrio desulfuricans* (Strain EL Agheila Z, N.C.I.B. 8380).
R. P. Ambler, M. Bruschi, and J. LeGall.
FEBS Letters, **18**, 347–350 (1971).

PSEUDOMONAS MENDOCINA *CH-110 CYTOCHROME* c_5

	1				5					10					15	
1	ALA	ALA	SER	ALA	GLY	GLY	GLY	ALA	ARG	SER	ALA	ASP	ASP	ILE	ILE	15
16	ALA	LYS	HIS	CYS	ASN	ALA	CYS	HIS	GLY	ALA	GLY	VAL	LEU	GLY	ALA	30
31	PRO	LYS	ILE	GLY	ASP	THR	ALA	ALA	TRP	LYS	GLU	ARG	ALA	ASP	HIS	45
46	GLN	GLY	GLY	LEU	ASP	GLY	ILE	LEU	ALA	LYS	ALA	ILE	SER	GLY	ILE	60
61	ASN	ALA	MET	PRO	PRO	LYS	GLY	THR	CYS	ALA	ASP	CYS	SER	ASP	ASP	75
76	GLU	LEU	ARG	GLU	ALA	ILE	GLN	LYS	MET	SER	GLY	LEU				90

Amino Acid Sequence of Cytochrome c_5 from *Pseudomonas mendocina*.
R. P. Ambler and E. Taylor.
Trans. Biochem. Soc., **1**, 166–168 (1973).

CHLOROPSEUDOMONAS ETHYLICA *CYTOCHROME* c-551.5

	1				5					10					15	
1	ALA	ASP	VAL	VAL	THR	TYR	GLU	ASN	LYS	LYS	GLY	ASN	VAL	THR	PHE	15
16	ASP	HIS	LYS	ALA	HIS	ALA	GLU	LYS	LEU	GLY	CYS	ASP	ALA	CYS	HIS	30
31	GLU	GLY	THR	PRO	ALA	LYS	ILE	ALA	ILE	ASP	LYS	LYS	SER	ALA	HIS	45
46	LYS	ASP	ALA	CYS	LYS	THR	CYS	HIS	LYS	SER	ASN	ASN	GLY	PRO	THR	60
61	LYS	CYS	GLY	GLY	CYS	HIS	ILE	LYS								75

The Amino Acid Sequence of Cytochrome c-551.5 (Cytochrome c_7) from the green photosynthetic Bacterium *Chloropseudomonas ethylica*.
R. P. Ambler.
FEBS Letters, **18**, 351–353 (1971).

312

CYTOCHROMES

CYTOCHROME c-550—PARACOCCUS DENITRIFICANS

	1		5				10				15				
1	AC	ASN	GLU	GLY	ASP	ALA	ALA	LYS	GLY	GLU	LYS	GLU	PHE	ASN	LYS	15
16	CYS	LYS	ALA	CYS	HIS	MET	ILE	GLN	ALA	PRO	ASP	GLY	THR	ASP	ILE	30
31	LYS	GLY	GLY	LYS	THR	GLY	PRO	ASN	LEU	TYR	GLY	VAL	VAL	GLY	ARG	45
46	LYS	ILE	ALA	SER	GLU	GLU	GLY	PHE	LYS	TYR	GLY	GLU	GLY	ILE	LEU	60
61	GLU	VAL	ALA	GLU	LYS	ASN	PRO	ASP	LEU	THR	TRP	THR	GLU	ALA	ASN	75
76	LEU	ILE	GLU	TYR	VAL	THR	ASP	PRO	LYS	PRO	LEU	VAL	LYS	LYS	MET	90
91	THR	ASP	ASP	LYS	GLY	ALA	LYS	THR	LYS	MET	THR	PHE	LYS	MET	GLY	105
106	LYS	ASN	GLN	ALA	ASP	VAL	VAL	ALA	PHE	LEU	ALA	GLN	ASX	ASX	PRO	120
121	ASX	ALA	GLY	GLX	GLY	GLX	ALA	ALA	GLY	ALA	GLY	SER	ASX	SER	GLX	135

Amino acid sequence of *Paracoccus denitrificans* Cytochrome c-550.
R. Timkovich, R. E. Dickerson, and E. Margoliash.
J. Biol. Chem., **251**, 2197–2206 (1976).

CYTOCHROME c-551 FROM PSEUDOMONAS AERUGINOSA

The amino acid sequence of the protein from strain 6009 is recorded below. Eight other strains of *Pseudomonas aeruginosa* (54, 292, 950, 1896, 2000, and 2195) have been found to have cytochromes of identical sequence. Strains 129 and 1224 have a modified cytochrome, having the replacement of ALA for ASP (residue 2).

	1		5				10				15				
1	GLU	ASP	PRO	GLU	VAL	LEU	PHE	LYS	ASN	LYS	GLY	CYS	VAL	ALA	CYS	15
16	HIS	ALA	ILE	ASP	THR	LYS	MET	VAL	GLY	PRO	ALA	TYR	LYS	ASP	VAL	30
31	ALA	ALA	LYS	PHE	ALA	GLY	GLN	ALA	GLY	ALA	GLU	ALA	GLU	LEU	ALA	45
46	GLN	ARG	ILE	LYS	ASN	GLY	SER	GLN	GLY	VAL	TRP	GLY	PRO	ILE	PRO	60
61	MET	PRO	PRO	ASN	ALA	VAL	SER	ASP	ASP	GLU	ALA	GLN	THR	LEU	ALA	75
76	LYS	TRP	VAL	LEU	SER	GLN	LYS									90

The Amino Acid Sequence of *Pseudomonas* Cytochrome c-551.
R. P. Ambler.
Biochem. J., **89**, 349–378 (1963).

PSEUDOMONAS FLUORESCENS *C-18 CYTOCHROME c-551*

	1				5					10					15	
1	GLU	ASP	GLY	ALA	ALA	LEU	PHE	LYS	SER	LYS	PRO	CYS	ALA	ALA	CYS	15
16	HIS	THR	ILE	ASP	SER	LYS	MET	VAL	GLY	PRO	ALA	LEU	LYS	GLU	VAL	30
31	ALA	ALA	LYS	ASN	ALA	GLY	VAL	LYS	ASP	ALA	ASP	LYS	THR	LEU	ALA	45
46	GLY	HIS	ILE	LYS	ASN	GLY	THR	GLN	GLY	ASN	TRP	GLY	PRO	ILE	PRO	60
61	MET	PRO	PRO	ASN	GLN	VAL	THR	ASP	ALA	GLU	ALA	LEU	THR	LEU	ALA	75
76	GLN	TRP	VAL	LEU	SER	LEU	LYS									90

The Amino Acid Sequences of Cytochrome c-551, from Three Species of *Pseudomonas*.
R. P. Ambler and M. Wynn.
Biochem. J., **131**, 485–498 (1973).
Note: The amino acid sequence of the protein from strain C-18 is recorded above. The protein from strain C-8376 has an identical sequence. The sequence differences of the other strains, so far examined, are recorded below:

STRAIN (C-type)	RESIDUE							
	1	18	29	46	47	63	65	70
18/8376	GLU	ILE	GLU	GLY	HIS	PRO	GLN	GLU
50	GLU	VAL	ASP	GLY	ARG	PRO	GLN	GLU
181/217	ASP	ILE	GLU	SER	HIS	ALA	PRO	GLU
191	ASP	ILE	GLU	ASP	HIS	PRO	GLN	GLN
204	ASP	ILE	GLU	GLY	HIS	PRO	PRO	GLU

The evolutionary stability of cytochrome c-551 in *Pseudomonas aeruginosa* and *Pseudomonas fluorescens* Biotype C.
R. P. Ambler.
Biochem. J., **137**, 3–14 (1974).

PSEUDOMONAS MENDOCINA *CH110 CYTOCHROME c-551*

	1				5					10					15	
1	ALA	SER	GLY	GLU	GLU	LEU	PHE	LYS	SER	LYS	PRO	CYS	GLY	ALA	CYS	15
16	HIS	SER	VAL	GLN	ALA	LYS	LEU	VAL	GLY	PRO	ALA	LEU	LYS	ASP	VAL	30
31	ALA	ALA	LYS	ASN	ALA	GLY	VAL	ASP	GLY	ALA	ALA	ASP	VAL	LEU	ALA	45
46	GLY	HIS	ILE	LYS	ASN	GLY	SER	THR	GLY	VAL	TRP	GLY	ALA	MET	PRO	60
61	MET	PRO	PRO	ASN	PRO	VAL	THR	GLU	GLU	GLU	ALA	LYS	THR	LEU	ALA	75
76	GLU	TRP	VAL	LEU	THR	LEU	LYS									90

CYTOCHROMES

PSEUDOMONAS STUTZERI *221 CYTOCHROME c-551*

```
     1           5              10             15
 1  GLN ASP GLY GLU ALA LEU PHE LYS SER LYS PRO CYS ALA ALA CYS  15
16  HIS SER ILE ASP ALA LYS LEU VAL GLY PRO ALA PHE LYS GLU VAL  30
31  ALA ALA LYS TYR ALA GLY GLN ASP GLY ALA ALA ASP LEU LEU ALA  45
46  GLY HIS ILE LYS ASN GLY SER GLN GLY VAL TRP GLY PRO ILE PRO  60
61  MET PRO PRO ASN PRO VAL THR GLU GLU GLU ALA LYS ILE LEU ALA  75
76  GLU TRP ILE LEU SER GLN LYS                                  90
```

The amino acid sequences of cytochrome c-551, from three species of Pseudomonas.
R. P. Ambler and M. Wynn.
Biochem. J., **131**, 485–498 (1973).

CYTOCHROME c-552 FROM EUGLENA GRACILIS

```
     1           5              10             15
 1  GLY GLY ALA ASP VAL PHE ALA ASP ASN CYS SER THR CYS HIS VAL  15
16  ASN GLY GLY ASN VAL ILE SER ALA GLY LYS VAL LEU SER LYS THR  30
31  ALA ILE GLU GLU TYR LEU ASP GLY GLY TYR THR LYS GLU ALA ILE  45
46  GLU TYR GLN VAL ARG ASN GLY LYS GLY PRO MET PRO ALA TRP GLU  60
61  GLY VAL LEU SER GLU ASP GLU ILE VAL ALA VAL THR ASP TYR VAL  75
76  TYR THR GLN ALA GLY GLY ALA TRP ALA ASN VAL SER              90
```

The purification and amino acid sequence of cytochrome c-552 from *Euglena gracilis*.
G. W. Pettigrew.
Biochem. J., **139**, 449–459 (1974).

CYTOCHROME c-553 FROM MONOCHRYSIS LUTHERI

```
     1           5              10             15
 1  GLY ASX ILE ALA ASX GLY GLX GLX VAL PHE THR GLY ASP CYS ALA  15
16  ALA CYS HIS SER VAL GLX GLX GLX MML THR LEU GLU LEU SER SER  30
31  LEU TRP LYS ALA LYS SER TYR LEU ALA ASN PHE ASN GLY ASP GLU  45
46  SER ALA ILE VAL TYR GLN VAL THR ASN GLY LYS ASN ALA MET PRO  60
61  ALA PHE GLY GLY ARG LEU GLU ASP ASP GLU ILE ALA ASX VAL ALA  75
76  SER TYR VAL LEU SER LYS ALA GLY                              90
```

The amino acid sequence of cytochrome c-553 from the chrysophycean alga *Monochrysis lutheri*.
M. V. Laycock.
Can. J. Biochem., **50**, 1311–1325 (1972).

CYTOCHROMES

DESULFOVIBRIO VULGARIS *CYTOCHROME c-553*

```
    1           5              10                15
 1  ALA ASP GLY ALA ALA LEU TYR LYS SER CYS ILE GLY CYS HIS SER   15
16  ALA ASP GLY GLY LYS ALA MET MET THR ASN ALA VAL LYS GLY LYS   30
31  TYR SER ASP GLU GLU LEU LYS ALA LEU ALA ASP TYR MET LYS ALA   45
46  ALA MET GLY SER ALA LYS PRO VAL LYS GLY GLN GLY ALA GLU GLU   60
61  LEU TYR LYS MET LYS GLY TYR ALA ASP GLY SER TYR GLY GLY GLU   75
76  ARG LYS ALA MET SER LYS LEU                                   90
```

C-Type Cytochromes of *Desulfovibrio vulgaris*. The Primary Structure of cytochrome c_{553}.
M. Bruschi and J. LeGall.
Biochim. Biophys. Acta, **271**, 48–60 (1972).

CYTOCHROME c-555—CRITHIDIA FASCICULATA

```
     1           5              10                15
  1  PRO TML ALA ARG ALA PRO LEU PRO PRO GLY ASP ALA ALA ARG GLY   15
 16  GLU LYS LEU PHE LYS GLY ARG ALA ALA GLN CYS HIS THR ALA ASN   30
 31  GLN GLY GLY ALA ASN GLY VAL GLY (PRO, ASN, LEU, TYR, GLY, LEU, VAL,   45
 46  GLY, ARG)HIS, SER GLY THR ILE GLU GLY TYR ALA TYR SER LYS ALA   60
```

```
 61  ASN ALA  ASP  SER GLY VAL VAL TRP THR PRO ASP VAL LEU ASP VAL   75
              GLU
```

```
 76  TYR LEU GLU ASN PRO TML LYS PHE MET PRO GLY THR LYS MET SER   90
 91  PHE ALA GLY MET LYS LYS PRO GLN GLU ARG ALA ASP VAL ILE ALA  105
106  TYR LEU GLU THR LEU LYS GLY                                  120
```

Note: The N-terminus of this protein is blocked by an unidentified group.
Evidence for the amino acid sequence of *Crithidia fasciculata* Cytochrome c_{555}.
G. C. Hill and G. W. Pettigrew.
Eur. J. Biochem., **57**, 265–270 (1975).

CYTOCHROME f—ALARIA ESCULENTA

```
    1           5              10                15
 1  ILE ASP ILE ASN ASN GLY GLU ASN ILE PHE THR ALA ASN CYS SER   15
16  ALA CYS HIS ALA GLY GLY ASN ASN VAL ILE MET PRO GLU LYS THR   30
31  LEU LYS LYS ASP ALA LEU ALA ASP ASN LYS MET VAL SER VAL ASN   45
46  ALA ILE THR TYR GLN VAL THR ASN GLY LYS ASN ALA MET PRO ALA   60
61  PHE GLY SER ARG LEU ALA GLU THR ASP ILE GLU ASP VAL ALA ASN   75
76  PHE VAL LEU THR GLN SER ASP LYS GLY TRP ASP                   90
```

The amino acid sequence of cytochrome f from the brown alga *Alaria esculenta* (L.) Grev.
M. V. Laycock.
Biochem. J., **149**, 271–279 (1975).

CYTOCHROMES

CYTOCHROME f—SPIRULINA MAXIMA

	1				5					10					15	
1	GLY	ASP	VAL	ALA	ALA	GLY	ALA	SER	VAL	PHE	SER	ALA	ASN	CYS	ALA	15
16	ALA	CYS	HIS	MET	GLY	GLY	ARG	ASN	VAL	ILE	VAL	ALA	ASN	LYS	THR	30
31	LEU	SER	LYS	SER	ASP	LEU	ALA	LYS	TYR	LEU	LYS	GLY	PHE	ASP	ASP	45
46	ASP	ALA	VAL	ALA	ALA	VAL	ALA	TYR	GLN	VAL	THR	ASN	GLY	LYS	ASN	60
61	ALA	MET	PRO	GLY	PHE	ASN	GLY	ARG	LEU	SER	PRO	LYS	GLN	ILE	GLU	75
76	ASP	VAL	ALA	ALA	TYR	VAL	VAL	ASP	GLN	ALA	GLU	LYS	GLY	TRP		90

Amino acid sequence similarity between cytochrome f from a blue-green bacterium and algal chloroplasts.
R. P. Ambler and R. G. Bartsch.
Nature, **253**, 285–288 (1975).

FERREDOXIN I—POKEWEED

```
     1            5                  10                    15
 1   ALA THR TYR LYS VAL THR LEU VAL THR PRO SER GLY THR GLN THR    15
16   ILE ASP CYS PRO ASP ASP THR TYR VAL LEU ASP ALA ALA GLU GLU    30
31   ALA GLY LEU ASP LEU PRO TYR SER CYS ARG ALA GLY SER CYS SER    45
46   SER CYS THR GLY LYS VAL THR ALA GLY THR VAL ASP GLN GLU ASP    60
61   GLN SER PHE LEU ASP ASP ASP GLN ILE GLU ALA GLY PHE VAL LEU    75
76   THR CYS VAL ALA PHE PRO LYS GLY ASP VAL THR ILE GLU THR HIS    90
91   LYS GLU GLU ASP ILE VAL                                       105
```

FERREDOXIN II—POKEWEED

```
     1            5                  10                    15
 1   ALA ALA SER TYR LYS VAL THR PHE VAL THR PRO SER GLY THR ASN    15
16   THR ILE THR CYS PRO ALA ASP THR TYR VAL LEU ASP ALA ALA GLU    30
31   GLU SER GLY LEU ASP LEU PRO TYR SER CYS ARG ALA GLY ALA CYS    45
46   SER SER CYS ALA GLY LYS VAL THR ALA GLY ALA VAL ASN GLN GLU    60
61   ASP GLY SER PHE LEU GLU GLU GLU GLN MET GLU ALA GLY TRP VAL    75
76   LEU THR CYS VAL ALA TYR PRO THR SER ASP VAL THR ILE GLU THR    90
91   HIS LYS GLU GLU ASP LEU THR ALA                              105
```

Amino acid sequences of two ferredoxins from pokeweed, *Phytolacca americana*.
S. Wakabayashi, T. Hase, K. Wada, H. Matsubara, K. Suzuki, and S. Takaichi.
J. Biochem., **83**, 1305–1319 (1978).

FERREDOXIN I—HORSETAIL

```
     1            5                  10                    15
 1   ALA TYR LYS THR VAL LEU LYS THR PRO SER GLY GLU PHE THR LEU    15
16   ASP VAL PRO GLU GLY THR THR ILE LEU ASP ALA ALA GLU GLU ALA    30
31   GLY TYR ASP LEU PRO PHE SER CYS ARG ALA GLY ALA CYS SER SER    45
46   CYS LEU GLY LYS VAL VAL SER GLY SER VAL ASP GLN SER GLU GLY    60
61   SER PHE LEU ASP ASP GLY GLN MET GLU GLU GLY PHE VAL LEU THR    75
76   CYS ILE ALA ILE PRO GLU SER ASP LEU VAL ILE GLU THR HIS LYS    90
91   GLU GLU GLU LEU PHE                                           105
```

318

FERREDOXINS

FERREDOXIN II—HORSETAIL

	1				5					10					15	
1	ALA	TYR	LYS	VAL	THR	LEU	LYS	THR	PRO	ASP	GLY	ASP	ILE	THR	PHE	15
16	ASP	VAL	GLU	PRO	GLY	GLU	ARG	LEU	ILE	ASP	ILE	ALA	SER	GLU	LYS	30
31	ALA	ASP	LEU	PRO	LEU	SER	CYS	GLN	ALA	GLY	ALA	CYS	SER	THR	CYS	45
46	LEU	GLY	LYS	ILE	VAL	SER	GLY	THR	VAL	ASP	GLN	SER	GLU	GLY	SER	60
61	PHE	LEU	ASP	ASP	GLU	GLN	ILE	GLU	GLN	GLY	TYR	VAL	LEU	THR	CYS	75
76	ILE	ALA	ILE	PRO	GLU	SER	ASP	VAL	VAL	ILE	GLU	THR	HIS	LYS	GLU	90
91	ASP	GLU	LEU													105

Horsetail (*Equisetum telmateia*) Ferredoxins I and II.
T. Hase, K. Wada, and H. Matsubara.
J. Biochem., **82**, 267–276 (1977).

ALFALFA FERREDOXIN

	1				5					10					15	
1	ALA	SER	TYR	LYS	VAL	LYS	LEU	VAL	THR	PRO	GLU	GLY	THR	GLN	GLU	15
16	PHE	GLU	CYS	PRO	ASP	ASP	VAL	TYR	ILE	LEU	ASP	HIS	ALA	GLU	GLU	30
31	GLU	GLY	ILE	VAL	LEU	PRO	TYR	SER	CYS	ARG	ALA	GLY	SER	CYS	SER	45
46	SER	CYS	ALA	GLY	LYS	VAL	ALA	ALA	GLY	GLU	VAL	ASN	GLN	SER	ASP	60
61	GLY	SER	PHE	LEU	ASP	ASP	ASP	GLN	ILE	GLU	GLU	GLY	TRP	VAL	LEU	75
76	THR	CYS	VAL	ALA	TYR	ALA	LYS	SER	ASP	VAL	THR	ILE	GLU	THR	HIS	90
91	LYS	GLU	GLU	GLU	LEU	THR	ALA									105

Primary Structure of Alfalfa Ferredoxin.
S. Keresztes-Nagy, F. Perini, and E. Margoliash.
J. Biol. Chem., **244**, 981–995 (1969).

SPINACH FERREDOXIN

	1				5					10					15	
1	ALA	ALA	TYR	LYS	VAL	THR	LEU	VAL	THR	PRO	THR	GLY	ASN	VAL	GLU	15
16	PHE	GLN	CYS	PRO	ASP	ASP	VAL	TYR	ILE	LEU	ASP	ALA	ALA	GLU	GLU	30
31	GLU	GLY	ILE	ASP	LEU	PRO	TYR	SER	CYS	ARG	ALA	GLY	SER	CYS	SER	45
46	SER	CYS	ALA	GLY	LYS	LEU	LYS	THR	GLY	SER	LEU	ASN	GLN	ASP	ASP	60
61	GLN	SER	PHE	LEU	ASP	ASP	ASP	GLN	ILE	ASP	GLU	GLY	TRP	VAL	LEU	75
76	THR	CYS	ALA	ALA	TYR	PRO	VAL	SER	ASP	VAL	THR	ILE	GLU	THR	HIS	90
91	LYS	GLU	GLU	GLU	LEU	THR	ALA									105

Spinach Ferredoxin. II. Tryptic, Chymotryptic and Thermolytic Peptides and Complete Amino Acid Sequence.
H. Matsubara and R. M. Sasaki.
J. Biol. Chem., **243**, 1732–1757 (1968).

TARO FERREDOXIN

	1				5					10					15	
1	ALA	THR	TYR	LYS	VAL	LYS	LEU	VAL	THR	PRO	SER	GLY	GLN	GLN	GLU	15
16	PHE	GLN	CYS	PRO	ASP	ASP	VAL	TYR	ILE	LEU	ASP	GLN	ALA	GLU	GLU	30
31	VAL	GLY	ILE	ASP	LEU	PRO	TYR	SER	CYS	ARG	ALA	GLY	SER	CYS	SER	45
46	SER	CYS	ALA	GLY	LYS	VAL	LYS	VAL	GLY	ASP	VAL	ASP	GLN	SER	ASP	60
61	GLY	SER	PHE	LEU	ASP	ASP	GLU	GLN	ILE	GLY	GLU	GLY	TRP	VAL	LEU	75
76	THR	CYS	VAL	ALA	TYR	PRO	VAL	SER	ASP	GLY	THR	ILE	GLU	THR	HIS	90
91	LYS	GLU	GLU	GLU	LEU	THR	ALA									105

The Amino Acid Sequence of Taro Ferredoxin.
K. K. Rao and H. Matsubara.
Biochem. Biophys. Res. Commun., **38**, 500–506 (1970).

LEUCAENA GLAUCA *FERREDOXIN*

	1				5					10					15	
1	ALA	PHE	LYS	VAL	LYS	LEU/VAL	LEU	THR	PRO	ASP	GLY	PRO/ALA	LYS	GLU	PHE	15
16	GLU	CYS	PRO	ASP	ASP	VAL	TYR	ILE	LEU	ASP	GLN	ALA	GLU	GLU	LEU	30
31	GLY	ILE	ASP/GLU	LEU	PRO	TYR	SER	CYS	ARG	ALA	GLY	SER	CYS	SER	SER	45
46	CYS	ALA	GLY	LYS	LEU	VAL	GLU	GLY	ASP	LEU	ASP	GLN	SER	ASP	GLN	60
61	SER	PHE	LEU	ASP	ASP	GLU	GLN	ILE	GLU	GLU	GLY	TRP	VAL	LEU	THR	75
76	CYS	ALA	ALA	TYR	PRO	ARG	SER	ASP	VAL	VAL	ILE	GLU	THR	HIS	LYS	90
91	GLU	GLU	GLU	LEU	THR	GLY/ALA										105

Non-heme Iron Proteins. 10. The Amino Acid Sequence of Ferredoxins from *Leucaena glauca*.
A. M. Benson and K. T. Yasunobu.
J. Biol. Chem., **244**, 955–963 (1969).

FERREDOXINS

CHROMATIUM *FERREDOXIN*

```
        1               5                    10                   15
 1   ALA MET ILE  THR ASP GLN CYS  ILE  ASN CYS ASN VAL CYS  GLN PRO    15
16   GLU CYS PRO  ASN GLY ALA ILE  SER  GLN GLY ASP GLU THR  TYR VAL    30
31   ILE  GLU PRO SER LEU CYS THR  GLU  CYS VAL GLY HIS  TYR GLU THR    45
46   SER GLN CYS  VAL ASP CYS VAL  GLU  VAL CYS PRO ILE  LYS ASP PRO    60
61   SER HIS  GLU GLU THR GLU ASP  GLU  LEU ARG ALA LYS  TYR GLU ARG    75
76   ILE  THR GLY GLU GLY                                               90
```

The Amino Acid Sequence of *Chromatium* Ferredoxin.
H. Matsubara, R. M. Sasaki, D. K. Tsuchiya and M. C. W. Evans.
J. Biol. Chem., **245**, 2121–2131 (1970).

CLOSTRIDIUM PASTEURIANUM *FERREDOXIN*

```
        1               5                    10                   15
 1   ALA TYR LYS  ILE  ALA ASP SER  CYS  VAL SER CYS GLY ALA CYS  ALA   15
16   SER GLU CYS  PRO VAL ASN ALA  ILE  SER GLN GLY ASP SER ILE  PHE    30
31   VAL ILE  ASP ALA ASP THR CYS  ILE  ASP CYS GLY ASN CYS ALA ASN     45
46   VAL CYS PRO  VAL GLY ALA PRO  VAL  GLN GLU                         60
```

The Amino Acid Sequence of *Clostridium Pasteurianum* Ferredoxin.
M. Tanaka, T. Nakashima, A. M. Benson, H. F. Mower and K. T. Yasunobu.
Biochemistry, **5**, 1666–1681 (1966).

DESULFOVIBRIO GIGAS *FERREDOXIN*

```
        1               5                    10                   15
 1   PRO ILE  GLN VAL ASP ASN CYS  MET  ALA CYS GLN ALA CYS ILE  ASN    15
16   GLU CYS PRO  VAL ASP VAL PHE  GLN  MET ASP GLU GLN GLY ASP LYS     30
31   ALA VAL ASN  ILE  PRO ASN SER ASN  LEU ASP ASP GLN CYS VAL GLU     45
46   ALA ILE  GLN SER CYS PRO ALA ALA  ILE  ARG SER                    60
```

The Amino Acid Sequence of Ferredoxin from the sulphate reducing Bacterium *Desulfovibrio Gigas*.
J. Travis, D. J. Newman, J. LeGall and H. D. Peck, Jr.
Biochem. Biophys. Res. Commun., **45**, 452–458 (1971).

SCENEDESMUS *FERREDOXIN*

	1				5					10					15		
1	ALA	THR	TYR	LYS	VAL	THR	LEU	LYS	THR	PRO	SER	GLY	ASP	GLN	THR		15
16	ILE	GLU	CYS	PRO	ASP	ASP	THR	TYR	ILE	LEU	ASP	ALA	ALA	GLU	GLU		30
31	ALA	GLY	LEU	ASP	LEU	PRO	TYR	SER	CYS	ARG	ALA	GLY	ALA	CYS	SER		45
46	SER	CYS	ALA	GLY	LYS	VAL	GLU	ALA	GLY	THR	VAL	ASP	GLN	SER	ASP		60
61	GLN	SER	PHE	LEU	ASP	ASP	SER	GLN	MET	ASP	GLY	GLY	PHE	VAL	LEU		75
76	THR	CYS	VAL	ALA	TYR	PRO	THR	SER	ASP	CYS	THR	ILE	ALA	THR	HIS		90
91	LYS	GLU	GLU	ASP	LEU	PHE											105

The Amino Acid Sequence of *Scenedesmus* Ferredoxin.
K. Sugeno and H. Matsubara.
Biochem. Biophys. Res. Commun., **32**, 951–955 (1968).

CLOSTRIDIUM BUTYRICUM *FERREDOXIN*

	1				5					10					15		
1	ALA	PHE	VAL	ILE	ASN	ASP	SER	CYS	VAL	SER	CYS	GLY	ALA	CYS	ALA		15
16	GLY	GLU	CYS	PRO	VAL	SER	ALA	ILE	THR	GLN	GLY	ASP	THR	GLN	PHE		30
31	VAL	ILE	ASP	ALA	ASP	THR	CYS	ILE	ASP	CYS	GLY	ASN	CYS	ALA	ASN		45
46	VAL	CYS	PRO	VAL	GLY	ALA	PRO	ASN	GLN	GLU							60

The Amino Acid Sequence of *Clostridium butyricum* Ferredoxin.
A. M. Benson, H. F. Mower, and K. T. Yasunobu.
Proc. Natn. Acad. Sci., U.S.A., **55**, 1532–1535 (1966).

MICROCOCCUS AEROGENES *FERREDOXIN*

	1				5					10					15		
1	ALA	TYR	VAL	ILE	ASN	ASP	SER	CYS	ILE	ALA	CYS	GLY	ALA	CYS	LYS		15
16	PRO	GLU	CYS	PRO	VAL	ASN	ILE	GLN	GLN	GLY	SER	ILE	TYR	ALA	ILE		30
31	ASP	ALA	ASP	SER	CYS	ILE	ASP	CYS	GLY	SER	CYS	ALA	SER	VAL	CYS		45
46	PRO	VAL	GLY	ALA	PRO	ASN	PRO	GLU	ASP								60

Non-heme Iron Proteins. IX. The amino acid sequence of ferredoxin from *Micrococcus Aerogenes*.
J. N. Tsunoda, K. T. Yasunobu, and H. R. Whiteley.
J. Biol. Chem., **243**, 6262–6272 (1968).

FERREDOXINS

CLOSTRIDIUM ACIDI-URICI *FERREDOXIN*

```
     1              5                    10                   15
 1   ALA TYR VAL ILE  ASN GLU ALA CYS ILE  SER CYS GLY ALA CYS ASP   15
16   PRO GLU CYS PRO  VAL ASP ALA ILE  SER GLN GLY ASP SER ARG TYR   30
31   VAL ILE ASP ALA ASP  THR CYS ILE  ASP CYS GLY ALA CYS ALA GLY   45
46   VAL CYS PRO VAL ASP  ALA PRO VAL GLN ALA                        60
```

The Amino Acid Sequence of Ferredoxin from *Clostridium acidi-urici*.
S. C. Rall, R. E. Bolinger, and R. D. Cole.
Biochemistry, **8**, 2486–2496 (1969).

CLOSTRIDIUM TARTARIVORUM *FERREDOXIN*

```
     1              5                    10                   15
 1   ALA HIS ILE ILE  THR ASP GLU CYS ILE  SER CYS GLY ALA CYS ALA   15
16   ALA GLU CYS PRO  VAL GLU ALA ILE  HIS GLU GLY THR GLY LYS TYR   30
31   GLN VAL ASP ALA ASP  THR CYS ILE  ASP CYS GLY ALA CYS GLN ALA   45
46   VAL CYS PRO THR  GLY ALA VAL LYS ALA GLU                        60
```

The primary structure of the *Clostridium tartarivorum* Ferredoxin, a heat-stable ferredoxin.
M. Tanaka, M. Haniu, G. Matsueda, K. T. Yasunobu, R. H. Himes, J. M. Akagi, E. M. Barnes, and T. Devanathan.
J. Biol. Chem., **246**, 3953–3960 (1971).

CLOSTRIDIUM THERMOSACCHAROLYTICUM *FERREDOXIN*

```
     1              5                    10                   15
 1   ALA HIS ILE ILE  THR ASP GLU CYS ILE  SER CYS GLY ALA CYS ALA   15
16   ALA GLU CYS PRO  VAL GLU ALA ILE  HIS GLU GLY THR GLY LYS TYR   30
31   GLU VAL ASP ALA ASP  THR CYS ILE  ASP CYS GLY ALA CYS GLU ALA   45
46   VAL CYS PRO THR  GLY ALA VAL LYS ALA GLU                        60
```

The primary structure of the *Clostridium thermosaccharolyticum* Ferredoxin, a heat-stable ferredoxin.
M. Tanaka, M. Haniu, K. T. Yasunobu, R. H. Himes, and J. M. Akagi.
J. Biol. Chem., **248**, 5215–5217 (1973).

PEPTOSTREPTOCOCCUS ELSDENII *FERREDOXIN*

	1				5					10					15	
1	MET	HIS	VAL	ILE	SER	ASP	GLU	CYS	VAL	LYS	CYS	GLY	ALA	CYS	ALA	15
16	SER	THR	CYS	PRO	THR	GLY	ALA	ILE	GLU	GLU	GLY	GLU	THR	LYS	TYR	30
31	VAL	VAL	THR	ASP	SER	CYS	ILE	ASP	CYS	GLY	ALA	CYS	GLU	ALA	VAL	45
46	CYS	PRO	THR	GLY	ALA	ILE	SER	ALA	GLU							60

The above sequence is quoted in the review:
The evolution of iron-sulfur protein containing organisms.
K. T. Yasunobu and M. Tanaka.
Systematic Zoology, **22**, 570–589 (1973).

FERREDOXIN—CLOSTRIDIUM M-E

	1				5					10					15	
1	ALA	TYR	LYS	ILE	THR	ASP	GLY	CYS	ILE	ASN	CYS	GLY	ALA	CYS	GLU	15
16	PRO	GLU	CYS	PRO	VAL	GLU	ALA	ILE	SER	GLU	SER	ASP	ALA	VAL	ARG	30
31	VAL	ILE	ASP	ALA	ASP	LYS	CYS	ILE	ASP	CYS	GLY	ALA	CYS	ALA	ASN	45
46	THR	CYS	PRO	VAL	ASP	ALA	ILE	VAL	GLU	GLY						60

Amino acid sequence determination of the Clostridium M-E ferredoxin and a comment on the role of the aromatic residues in the Clostridial ferredoxins.
M. Tanaka, M. Haniu, K. T. Yasunobu, J. B. Jones, and T. C. Stadtman.
Biochemistry, **13**, 5284–5289 (1974).

FERREDOXIN—CHLOROBIUM LIMICOLA

	1				5					10					15	
1	ALA	LEU	TYR	ILE	THR	GLU	GLU	CYS	THR	TYR	CYS	GLY	ALA	CYS	GLU	15
16	PRO	GLU	CYS	PRO	VAL	THR	ALA	ILE	SER	ALA	GLY	ASP	ASP	ILE	TYR	30
31	VAL	ILE	ASP	ALA	ASN	THR	CYS	ASN	GLU	CYS	ALA	GLY	LEU	ASP	GLU	45
46	GLN	ALA	CYS	VAL	ALA	VAL	CYS	PRO	ALA	GLU	CYS	ILE	VAL	GLN	GLY	60

Amino acid sequence of ferredoxin from a photosynthetic green bacterium, *Chlorobium limicola*.
M. Tanaka, M. Haniu, K. T. Yasunobu, M. C. W. Evans, and K. K. Rao.
Biochemistry, **13**, 2953–2959 (1974).

324

FERREDOXINS

FERREDOXIN II—CHLOROBIUM LIMICOLA

	1				5					10					15	
1	ALA	HIS	ARG	ILE	THR	GLU	GLU	CYS	THR	TYR	CYS	ALA	ALA	CYS	GLU	15
16	PRO	GLU	CYS	PRO	VAL	ASN	ALA	ILE	SER	ALA	GLY	ASP	GLU	ILE	TYR	30
31	ILE	VAL	ASP	GLU	SER	VAL	CYS	THR	ASP	CYS	GLU	GLY	TYR	TYR	ASP	45
46	GLU	PRO	ALA	CYS	VAL	ALA	VAL	CYS	PRO	VAL	ASP	CYS	ILE	ILE	LYS	60
61	VAL															75

The amino acid sequence of ferredoxin II from *Chlorobium limicola* a photosynthetic green bacterium.
M. Tanaka, M. Haniu, K. T. Yasunobu, M. C. W. Evans, and K. K. Rao.
Biochemistry, **14**, 1938–1943 (1975).

FERREDOXIN—CHLOROBIUM THIOSULFATOPHILUM

	1				5					10					15	
1	ALA	LEU	TYR	ILE	THR	GLU	GLU	CYS	THR	TYR	CYS	GLY	ALA	CYS	GLU	15
16	PRO	GLU	CYS	PRO	THR	ASN	ALA	ILE	SER	ALA	GLY	SER	GLU	ILE	TYR	30
31	VAL	ILE	ASP	ALA	ALA	GLY	CYS	THR	GLU	CYS	VAL	GLY	PHE	ALA	ASP	45
46	ALA	PRO	ALA	CYS	ALA	ALA	VAL	CYS	PRO	ALA	GLU	CYS	ILE	VAL	GLN	60
61	GLY															75

Amino acid sequence of a ferredoxin from *Chlorobium thiosulfatophilum* strain Tassajara, a photosynthetic green sulfur bacterium.
T. Hase, S. Wakabayashi, H. Matsubara, M. C. W. Evans, and J. V. Jennings.
J. Biochem., **83**, 1321–1325 (1978).

FERREDOXIN—B. STEAROTHERMOPHILUS

	1				5					10					15	
1	PRO	LYS	TYR	THR	ILE	VAL	ASP	LYS	GLU	THR	CYS	ILE	ALA	CYS	GLY	15
16	ALA	CYS	GLY	ALA	ALA	ALA	PRO	ASP	ILE	TYR	ASP	TYR	ASP	GLU	ASP	30
31	GLY	ILE	ALA	TYR	VAL	THR	LEU	ASP	ASP	ASN	GLN	GLY	ILE	VAL	GLU	45
46	VAL	PRO	ASP	ILE	LEU	ILE	ASP	ASP	MET	MET	ASP	ALA	PHE	GLU	GLY	60
61	CYS	PRO	THR	GLU	SER	ILE	LYS	VAL	ALA	ASP	GLU	PRO	PHE	ASP	GLY	75
76	ASP	PRO	ASN	LYS	PHE	ASP										90

Amino acid sequence of a four-iron-four-sulphur ferredoxin isolated from *Bacillus stearothermophilus*.
T. Hase, N. Ohmiya, H. Matsubara, R. N. Mullinger, K. K. Rao, and D. O. Hall.
Biochem. J., **159**, 55–63 (1976).

FERREDOXIN—APHANOTHECE SACRUM

	1			5					10					15		
1	ALA	SER	TYR	LYS	VAL	THR	LEU	LYS	THR	PRO	ASP	GLY	ASP	ASN	VAL	15
16	ILE	THR	VAL	PRO	ASP	ASP	GLU	TYR	ILE	LEU	ASP	VAL	ALA	GLU	GLU	30
31	GLU	GLY	LEU	ASP	LEU	PRO	TYR	SER	CYS	ARG	ALA	GLY	ALA	CYS	SER	45
46	THR	CYS	ALA	GLY	LYS	LEU	VAL	SER	GLY	PRO	ALA	PRO	ASP	GLU	ASP	60
61	GLN	SER	PHE	LEU	ASP	ASP	ASP	GLN	ILE	GLN	ALA	GLY	TYR	ILE	LEU	75
76	THR	CYS	VAL	ALA	TYR	PRO	THR	GLY	ASP	CYS	VAL	ILE	GLU	THR	HIS	90
91	LYS	GLU	GLU	ALA	LEU	TYR										105

Amino acid sequence of the major component of *Aphanothece sacrum* Ferredoxin.
T. Hase, K. Wada, and H. Matsubara.
J. Biochem., **79**, 329–343 (1976).

FERREDOXIN—NOSTOC MUSCORUM

	1			5					10					15		
1	ALA	THR	PHE	LYS	VAL	THR	LEU	ILE	ASN	GLU	ALA	GLU	GLY	THR	LYS	15
16	HIS	GLU	ILE	GLU	VAL	PRO	ASP	ASP	GLU	TYR	ILE	LEU	ASP	ALA	ALA	30
31	GLU	GLU	GLU	GLY	TYR	ASP	LEU	PRO	PHE	SER	CYS	ARG	ALA	GLY	ALA	45
46	CYS	SER	THR	CYS	ALA	GLY	LYS	LEU	VAL	SER	GLY	THR	VAL	ASP	GLN	60
61	SER	ASP	GLN	SER	PHE	LEU	ASP	ASP	ASP	GLN	ILE	GLU	ALA	GLY	TYR	75
76	VAL	LEU	THR	CYS	VAL	ALA	TYR	PRO	THR	SER	ASP	VAL	VAL	ILE	GLN	90
91	THR	HIS	LYS	GLU	GLU	ASP	LEU	TYR								105

Amino acid sequence of the major component of *Nostoc muscorum* Ferredoxin.
T. Hase, K. Wada, M. Ohmiya, and H. Matsubara.
J. Biochem., **80**, 993–999 (1976).

FERREDOXIN—SPIRULINA MAXIMA

	1			5					10					15		
1	ALA	THR	TYR	LYS	VAL	THR	LEU	ILE	SER	GLU	ALA	GLU	GLY	ILE	ASN	15
16	GLU	THR	ILE	ASP	CYS	ASP	ASP	ASP	THR	TYR	ILE	LEU	ASP	ALA	ALA	30
31	GLU	GLU	ALA	GLY	LEU	ASP	LEU	PRO	TYR	SER	CYS	ARG	ALA	GLY	ALA	45
46	CYS	SER	THR	CYS	ALA	GLY	LYS	ILE	THR	SER	GLY	SER	ILE	ASP	GLN	60
61	SER	ASP	GLN	SER	PHE	LEU	ASP	ASP	ASP	GLN	ILE	GLU	ALA	GLY	TYR	75
76	VAL	LEU	THR	CYS	VAL	ALA	TYR	PRO	THR	SER	ASP	CYS	THR	ILE	GLN	90
91	THR	HIS	GLN	GLU	GLU	GLY	LEU	TYR								105

Modification of the automated sequence determination as applied to the sequence determination of the *Spirulina maxima* Ferredoxin.
M. Tanaka, M. Haniu, K. T. Yasunobu, K. K. Rao, and D. O. Hall.
Biochemistry, **14**, 5535–5540 (1975).

FERREDOXINS

FERREDOXIN—SPIRULINA PLATENSIS

	1				5					10					15	
1	ALA	THR	TYR	LYS	VAL	THR	LEU	ILE	ASN	GLU	ALA	GLU	GLY	ILE	ASN	15
16	GLU	THR	ILE	ASP	CYS	ASP	ASP	ASP	THR	TYR	ILE	LEU	ASP	ALA	ALA	30
31	GLU	GLU	ALA	GLY	LEU	ASP	LEU	PRO	TYR	SER	CYS	ARG	ALA	GLY	ALA	45
46	CYS	SER	THR	CYS	ALA	GLY	THR	ILE	THR	SER	GLY	THR	ILE	ASP	GLN	60
61	SER	ASP	GLN	SER	PHE	LEU	ASP	ASP	ASP	GLN	ILE	GLU	ALA	GLY	TYR	75
76	VAL	LEU	THR	CYS	VAL	ALA	TYR	PRO	THR	SER	ASP	CYS	THR	ILE	LYS	90
91	THR	HIS	GLN	GLU	GLU	GLY	LEU	TYR								105

Amino acid sequence of *Spirulina platensis* ferredoxin: a far divergency of blue-green algal ferredoxins.
K. Wada, T. Hase, H. Tokunaga, and H. Matsubara.
FEBS Letters, **55**, 102–104 (1975).
The complete amino acid sequence of the *Spirulina Platensis* ferredoxin.
M. Tanaka, M. Haniu, and K. T. Yasunobu.
Biochem. Biophys. Res. Commun., **69**, 759–764 (1976).

FERREDOXIN—HALOBACTERIUM HALOBIUM

	1				5					10					15	
1	PRO	THR	VAL	GLU	TYR	LEU	ASN	TYR	GLU	THR	LEU	ASP	ASP	GLN	GLY	15
16	TRP	ASP	MET	ASP	ASP	ASP	ASP	LEU	PHE	GLU	LYS	ALA	ALA	ASP	ALA	30
31	GLY	LEU	ASP	GLY	GLU	ASP	TYR	GLY	THR	MET	GLU	VAL	ALA	GLU	GLY	45
46	GLU	TYR	ILE	LEU	GLU	ALA	ALA	GLU	ALA	GLN	GLY	TYR	ASP	TRP	PRO	60
61	PHE	SER	CYS	ARG	ALA	GLY	ALA	CYS	ALA	ASN	CYS	ALA	SER	ILE	VAL	75
76	LYS	GLU	GLY	GLU	ILE	ASP	MET	ASP	MET	GLN	GLN	ILE	LEU	SER	ASP	90
91	GLU	GLU	VAL	GLU	GLU	LYS	ASP	VAL	ARG	LEU	THR	CYS	ILE	GLY	SER	105
106	PRO	ALA	ALA	ASP	GLU	VAL	LYS	ILE	VAL	TYR	ASN	ALA	ACL	HIS	LEU	120
121	ASP	TYR	LEU	GLN	ASN	ARG	VAL	ILE								135

Complete amino acid sequence of *Halobacterium halobium* Ferredoxin containing an Nε-Acetyl lysine residue.
T. Hase, S. Wakabayashi, H. Matsubara, L. Kerscher, D. Oesterhelt, K. K. Rao, and D. O. Hall.
J. Biochem., **83**, 1657–1670 (1978).

FERREDOXIN—PSEUDOMONAS OVALIS

	1				5					10					15	
1	THR	PHE	VAL	VAL	THR	ASP	ASN	CYS	ILE	LYS	CYS	LYS	TYR	THR	ASP	15
16	CYS	VAL	GLU	VAL	CYS	PRO	VAL	ASP	CYS	PHE	TYR	GLU	GLY	PRO	ASN	30
31	PHE	LEU	VAL	ILE	HIS	PRO	ASP	GLU	CYS	ILE	ASP	CYS	ALA	LEU	CYS	45
46	GLU	PRO	GLU	CYS	PRO	ALA	GLN	ALA	ILE	PHE	SER	GLU	ASP	GLU	VAL	60
61	PRO	SER	GLY	MET	GLU	ASN	PHE	ILE	GLU	LEU	ASN	ALA	GLU	LEU	ALA	75
76	GLU	ILE	TRP	PRO	ASN	ILE	THR	GLU	ARG	LYS	ASP	ALA	LEU	PRO	ASP	90
91	ALA	GLU	GLU	TRP	ASP	GLY	LYS	PRO	GLY	LYS	ILE	ALA	ASP	LEU	GLU	105
106	ARG															120

Pseudomonas ovalis Ferredoxin: similarity to *Azotobacter* and *chromatium* ferredoxins.
T. Hase, S. Wakabayashi, H. Matsubara, D. Ohmori, and K. Suzuki.
FEBS Letters, **91**, 315–319 (1978).

OTHER METALLOPROTEINS

RUBREDOXIN FROM PSEUDOMONAS OLEOVORANS

	1			5					10					15			
1	ALA	SER	TYR	LYS	CYS	PRO	ASP	CYS	ASN	TYR	VAL	TYR	ASP	GLU	SER		15
16	ALA	GLY	ASN	VAL	HIS	GLU	GLY	PHE	SER	PRO	GLY	THR	PRO	TRP	HIS		30
31	LEU	ILE	PRO	GLU	ASP	TRP	ASP	CYS	PRO	CYS	CYS	ALA	VAL	ARG	ASP		45
46	LYS	LEU	ASP	PHE	MET	LEU	ILE	GLU	SER	GLY	VAL	GLY	GLU	LYS	GLY		60
61	VAL	THR	SER	THR	HIS	THR	SER	PRO	ASN	LEU	SER	GLU	VAL	SER	GLY		75
76	THR	SER	LEU	THR	ALA	GLU	ALA	VAL	VAL	ALA	PRO	THR	SER	LEU	GLU		90
91	LYS	LEU	PRO	SER	ALA	ASP	VAL	LYS	GLY	GLN	ASP	LEU	TYR	LYS	THR		105
106	GLU	PRO	PRO	ARG	SER	ASP	ALA	GLU	GLY	GLY	LYS	ALA	TYR	LEU	LYS		120
121	TRP	ILE	CYS	ILE	THR	CYS	GLY	HIS	ILE	TYR	ASP	TRP	GLU	ALA	LEU		135
136	GLY	ASP	GLU	ALA	GLU	GLY	PHE	THR	PRO	GLY	THR	ARG	PHE	GLU	ASP		150
151	ILE	PRO	ASP	TRP	ASP	CYS	CYS	TRP	CYS	(ASX, PRO)		GLY	ALA	THR	LYS		165
166	GLU	ASN	TYR	VAL	LEU	TYR	GLU	GLU	LYS								180

Evolutionary and phylogenetic relationships of rubredoxin-containing microbes.
A. Benson, K. Tomoda, J. Chang, G. Matsueda, E. T. Lode, M. J. Coon, and K. T. Yasunobu.
Biochem. Biophys. Res. Commun., **42**, 640–646 (1971).

RUBREDOXIN FROM CLOSTRIDIUM PASTEURIANUM

	1			5					10					15			
1	MET	LYS	LYS	TYR	THR	CYS	THR	VAL	CYS	GLY	TYR	ILE	TYR	ASP	PRO		15
16	GLU	ASP	GLY	ASP	PRO	ASP	ASP	GLY	VAL	ASN	PRO	GLY	THR	ASP	PHE		30
31	LYS	ASP	ILE	PRO	ASP	ASP	TRP	VAL	CYS	PRO	LEU	CYS	GLY	VAL	GLY		45
46	LYS	ASP	GLU	PHE	GLU	GLU	VAL	GLU	GLU								60

Note: The N-terminal residue is N-formylated.
K. McCarthy (1972), Ph.D. Dissertation, George Washington University.
Quoted in:
Sequence of Rubredoxin by X-ray diffraction.
J. R. Herriott, K. D. Watenpaugh, L. C. Sieker, and L. H. Jensen.
J. Mol. Biol., **80**, 423–432 (1973).

OTHER METALLOPROTEINS

RUBREDOXIN—DESULFOVIBRIO VULGARIS

	1				5					10					15		
1	MET	LYS	LYS	TYR	VAL	CYS	THR	VAL	CYS	GLY	TYR	GLU	TYR	ASP	PRO	15
16	ALA	GLU	GLY	ASP	PRO	THR	ASN	GLY	VAL	LYS	PRO	GLY	THR	SER	PHE	30
31	ASP	ASP	LEU	PRO	ALA	ASP	TRP	VAL	CYS	PRO	VAL	CYS	GLY	ALA	PRO	45
46	LYS	SER	GLU	PHE	GLU	ALA	ALA									60

Non-heme iron proteins. The amino acid sequence of rubredoxin from *Desulfovibrio vulgaris*.
M. Bruschi.
Biochim. Biophys. Acta, **434**, 4–17 (1976).

RUBREDOXIN—DESULFOVIBRIO GIGAS

	1				5					10					15		
1	MET	ASP	ILE	TYR	VAL	CYS	THR	VAL	CYS	GLY	TYR	GLU	TYR	ASP	PRO	15
16	ALA	LYS	GLY	ASP	PRO	ASP	SER	GLY	ILE	LYS	PRO	GLY	THR	LYS	PHE	30
31	GLU	ASP	LEU	PRO	ASP	ASP	TRP	ALA	CYS	PRO	VAL	CYS	GLY	ALA	SER	45
46	LYS	ASP	ALA	PHE	GLU	LYS	GLN									60

The amino acid sequence of rubredoxin from the sulfate reducing bacterium, *Desulfovibrio gigas*.
M. Bruschi.
Biochem. Biophys. Res. Commun., **70**, 615–621 (1976).

RUBREDOXIN FROM MICROCOCCUS AEROGENES

	1				5					10					15		
1	MET	GLN	LYS	PHE	GLU	CYS	THR	LEU	CYS	GLY	TYR	ILE	TYR	ASP	PRO	15
16	ALA	LEU	VAL	GLY	PRO	ASP	THR	PRO	ASP	GLN	ASP	GLY	ALA	PHE	GLU	30
31	ASP	VAL	SER	GLU	ASN	TRP	VAL	CYS	PRO	LEU	CYS	GLY	ALA	GLY	LYS	45
46	GLU	ASP	PHE	GLU	VAL	TYR	GLU	ASP								60

Non-heme Iron Proteins. IV. Structural studies of *Micrococcus aerogenes* Rubredoxin.
H. Bachmayer, A. M. Benson, K. T. Yasunobu, W. T. Garrard, and H. R. Whiteley.
Biochemistry, **7**, 986–996 (1968).

OTHER METALLOPROTEINS

RUBREDOXIN FROM PEPTOSTREPTOCOCCUS ELSDENII

	1				5					10					15	
1	MET	ASP	LYS	TYR	GLU	CYS	SER	ILE	CYS	GLY	TYR	ILE	TYR	ASP	GLU	15
16	ALA	GLU	GLY	ASP	ASP	GLY	ASN	VAL	ALA	ALA	GLY	THR	LYS	PHE	ALA	30
31	ASP	LEU	PRO	ALA	ASP	TRP	VAL	CYS	PRO	THR	CYS	GLY	ALA	ASP	LYS	45
46	ASP	ALA	PHE	VAL	LYS	MET	ASP									60

Non-heme Iron Proteins. 5. The Amino Acid Sequence of Rubredoxin from *Peptostreptococcus elsdenii*.
H. Bachmayer, K. T. Yasunobu, J. L. Peel, and S. Mayhew.
J. Biol. Chem., **243**, 1022–1030 (1968).

STELLACYANIN

	1				5					10					15	
1	THR	VAL	TYR	THR	VAL	GLY	ASP	SER	ALA	GLY	TRP	LYS	VAL	PRO	PHE	15
16	PHE	GLY	ASP	VAL	ASP	TYR	ASP	TRP	LYS	TRP	ALA	SER	ASN	LYS	THR	30
31	PHE	HIS	ILE	GLY	ASP	VAL	LEU	VAL	PHE	LYS	TYR	ASP	ARG	ARG	PHE	45
46	HIS	ASN	VAL	ASP	LYS	VAL	THR	GLN	LYS	ASN	TYR	GLN	SER	CYS	ASN	60
61	ASP	THR	THR	PRO	ILE	ALA	SER	TYR	ASN	THR	GLY	ASX	ASX	ARG	ILE	75
76	ASN	LEU	LYS	THR	VAL	GLY	GLN	LYS	TYR	TYR	ILE	CYS	GLY	VAL	PRO	90
91	LYS	HIS	CYS	ASP	LEU	GLY	GLN	LYS	VAL	HIS	ILE	ASN	VAL	THR	VAL	105

The amino acid sequence of Stellacyanin, from the Lacquer tree.
C. Bergman, E. Gandvik, P. O. Nyman and L. Strid.
Biochem. Biophys. Res. Commun., **77**, 1052–1059 (1977).

AZURIN OF PSEUDOMONAS FLUORESCENS

	1				5					10					15	
1	ALA	GLU	CYS	SER	VAL	ASP	ILE	GLN	GLY	ASN	ASP	GLN	MET	GLN	PHE	15
16	ASN	THR	ASN	ALA	ILE	THR	VAL	ASP	LYS	SER	CYS	LYS	GLN	PHE	THR	30
31	VAL	ASN	LEU	SER	HIS	PRO	GLY	ASN	LEU	PRO	LYS	ASN	VAL	MET	GLY	45
46	HIS	ASN	TRP	VAL	LEU	SER	THR	ALA	ALA	ASP	MET	GLN	GLY	VAL	VAL	60
61	THR	ASP	GLY	MET	ALA	SER	GLY	LEU	ASP	LYS	ASP	TYR	LEU	LYS	PRO	75
76	ASP	ASP	SER	ARG	VAL	ILE	ALA	HIS	THR	LYS	LEU	ILE	GLY	SER	GLY	90
91	GLU	LYS	ASP	SER	VAL	THR	PHE	ASP	VAL	SER	LYS	LEU	LYS	GLU	GLY	105
106	GLU	GLN	TYR	MET	PHE	PHE	CYS	THR	PHE	PRO	GLY	HIS	SER	ALA	LEU	120
121	MET	LYS	GLY	THR	LEU	THR	LEU	LYS								135

Note: Disulphide bridge between CYS 3 and 26.
The Amino Acid Sequence of *Pseudomonas fluorescens* Azurin.
R. P. Ambler and L. H. Brown.
Biochem. J., **104**, 784–825 (1967).

OTHER METALLOPROTEINS

AZURIN FROM BORDETELLA BRONCHISEPTICA

	1			5					10					15	
1	ALA	GLU	CYS	SER	VAL	ASP	ILE	ALA	GLY	THR	ASP	GLN	MET	GLN	PHE	15
16	ASP	LYS	LYS	ALA	ILE	GLU	VAL	SER	LYS	SER	CYS	LYS	GLN	PHE	THR	30
31	VAL	ASN	LEU	LYS	HIS	THR	GLY	LYS	LEU	PRO	ARG	ASN	VAL	MET	GLY	45
46	HIS	ASN	TRP	VAL	LEU	THR	LYS	THR	ALA	ASP	MET	GLN	ALA	VAL	GLU	60
61	LYS	ASP	GLY	ILE	ALA	ALA	GLY	LEU	ASP	ASN	GLN	TYR	LEU	LYS	ALA	75
76	GLY	ASP	THR	ARG	VAL	LEU	ALA	HIS	THR	LYS	VAL	LEU	GLY	GLY	GLY	90
91	GLU	SER	ASP	SER	VAL	THR	PHE	ASP	VAL	ALA	LYS	LEU	ALA	ALA	GLY	105
106	ASP	ASP	TYR	THR	PHE	PHE	CYS	SER	PHE	PRO	GLY	HIS	GLY	ALA	LEU	120
121	MET	LYS	GLY	THR	LEU	LYS	LEU	VAL	ASP							135

Species differences in the Amino Acid Sequences of Bacterial Proteins.
R. P. Ambler.
In: *Chemotaxonomy and Serotaxonomy*, The Systematics Association Special Volume, No. 2, Ed. J. G. Hawkes (Academic Press, New York, 1968) pp. 57–64.

THIOREDOXIN OF ESCHERICHIA COLI *B*

	1			5					10					15	
1	SER	ASP	LYS	ILE	ILE	HIS	LEU	THR	ASP	ASP	SER	PHE	ASP	THR	ASP	15
16	LEU	VAL	LYS	ALA	ASP	GLY	ALA	ILE	LEU	VAL	ASP	PHE	TRP	ALA	GLU	30
31	TRP	CYS	GLY	PRO	CYS	LYS	MET	ILE	ALA	PRO	ILE	LEU	ASP	GLU	ILE	45
46	ALA	ASP	GLU	TYR	GLN	GLY	LYS	LEU	THR	VAL	ALA	LYS	LEU	ASN	ILE	60
61	ASP	GLN	ASN	PRO	GLY	THR	ALA	PRO	LYS	TYR	ILE	GLY	ARG	GLY	ILE	75
76	PRO	THR	LEU	LEU	LEU	PHE	LYS	ASN	GLY	GLU	VAL	ALA	ALA	THR	LYS	90
91	VAL	GLY	ALA	LEU	SER	LYS	GLY	GLN	LEU	LYS	GLU	PHE	LEU	ASP	ALA	105
106	ASN	LEU	ALA													120

Thioredoxin 6. The amino acid sequence of the Protein from *Escherichia coli* B.
A. Holmgren.
Eur. J. Biochem., **6**, 475–484 (1968).

332

OTHER METALLOPROTEINS

T4 THIOREDOXIN

	1				5					10					15	
1	MET	PHE	LYS	VAL	TYR	GLY	TYR	ASP	SER	ASN	ILE	HIS	LYS	CYS	VAL	15
16	TYR	CYS	ASP	ASN	ALA	LYS	ARG	LEU	LEU	THR	VAL	LYS	LYS	GLN	PRO	30
31	PHE	GLU	PHE	ILE	ASN	ILE	MET	PRO	GLU	LYS	GLY	VAL	PHE	ASP	ASP	45
46	GLU	LYS	ILE	ALA	GLU	LEU	LEU	THR	LYS	LEU	GLY	ARG	ASP	THR	GLN	60
61	ILE	GLY	LEU	THR	MET	PRO	GLN	VAL	PHE	ALA	PRO	ASP	GLY	SER	HIS	75
76	ILE	GLY	GLY	PHE	ASP	GLN	LEU	ARG	GLU	TYR	PHE	LYS				90

Studies on the Structure of T4 Thioredoxin. II. Amino acid sequence of the protein and
comparison with thioredoxin from *Escherichia Coli*.
B.-M. Sjöberg and A. Holmgren.
J. Biol. Chem., **247**, 8063–8068 (1972).

FLAVODOXIN FROM DESULFOVIBRIO VULGARIS

	1				5					10					15	
1	MET	PRO	LYS	ALA	LEU	ILE	VAL	TYR	GLY	SER	THR	THR	GLY	ASN	THR	15
16	GLU	TYR	THR	ALA	GLU	THR	ILE	ALA	ARG	GLU	LEU	ALA	ASX	ALA	GLY	30
31	TYR	GLU	VAL	ASP	SER	ARG	ASP	ALA	ALA	SER	VAL	GLU	ALA	GLY	GLY	45
46	LEU	PHE	GLU	GLY	PHE	ASP	LEU	VAL	LEU	LEU	GLY	CYS	SER	THR	TRP	60
61	GLY	ASP	ASP	SER	ILE	GLX	LEU	GLX	ASX	ASX	PHE	ILE	PRO	LEU	PHE	75
76	ASP	SER	LEU	GLX	GLX	THR	GLY	ALA	GLX	GLY	ARG	LYS	VAL	ALA	CYS	90
91	PHE	GLY	CYS	GLY	ASX	SER	SER	TYR	GLU	TYR	PHE	CYS	GLY	ALA	VAL	105
106	ASP	ALA	ILE	GLU	GLU	LYS	LEU	LYS	ASN	LEU	GLY	ALA	GLX	ILE	VAL	120
121	GLX	ASX	GLY	LEU	ARG	ILE	ASP	GLY	ASP	PRO	ARG	ALA	ALA	ARG	ASX	135
136	ASX	ILE	VAL	GLY	TRP	ALA	HIS	ASP	VAL	ARG	GLY	ALA	ILE			150

The amino acid sequence of *Desulfovibrio vulgaris* flavodoxin.
M. Dubourdieu, J. Le Gall, and J. L. Fox.
Biochem. Biophys. Res. Commun., **52**, 1418–1425 (1973).

OTHER METALLOPROTEINS

FLAVODOXIN—CLOSTRIDIUM MP

	1			5					10					15		
1	MET	LYS	ILE	VAL	TYR	TRP	SER	GLY	THR	GLY	ASN	THR	GLU	LYS	MET	15
16	ALA	GLU	LEU	ILE	ALA	LYS	GLY	ILE	ILE	GLU	SER	GLY	LYS	ASP	VAL	30
31	ASN	THR	ILE	ASN	VAL	SER	ASP	VAL	ASN	ILE	ASP	GLU	LEU	LEU	ASN	45
46	GLU	ASP	ILE	LEU	ILE	LEU	GLY	CYS	SER	ALA	MET	GLY	ASP	GLU	VAL	60
61	LEU	GLU	GLU	SER	GLU	PHE	GLU	PRO	PHE	ILE	GLU	GLU	ILE	SER	THR	75
76	LYS	ILE	SER	GLY	LYS	LYS	VAL	ALA	LEU	PHE	GLY	SER	TYR	GLY	TRP	90
91	GLY	ASP	GLY	LYS	TRP	MET	ARG	ASP	PHE	GLU	GLU	ARG	MET	ASN	GLY	105
106	TYR	GLY	CYS	VAL	VAL	VAL	GLU	THR	PRO	LEU	ILE	VAL	GLN	ASN	GLU	120
121	PRO	ASP	GLU	ALA	GLU	GLN	ASP	CYS	ILE	GLU	PHE	GLY	LYS	LYS	ILE	135
136	ALA	ASN	ILE													150

The amino acid sequence of the *Clostridium* MP flavodoxin.
M. Tanaka, M. Haniu, K. T. Yasunobu, and S. G. Mayhew.
J. Biol. Chem., **249**, 4393–4396 (1974).

FLAVODOXIN FROM PEPTOSTREPTOCOCCUS ELSDENII

	1			5					10					15		
1	MET	VAL	GLU	ILE	VAL	TYR	TRP	SER	GLY	THR	GLY	ASN	THR	GLU	ALA	15
16	MET	ALA	ASN	GLU	ILE	GLU	ALA	ALA	VAL	LYS	ALA	ALA	GLY	ALA	ASP	30
31	VAL	GLU	SER	VAL	ARG	PHE	GLU	ASP	THR	ASN	VAL	ASP	ASP	VAL	ALA	45
46	SER	LYS	ASP	VAL	ILE	LEU	LEU	GLY	CYS	PRO	ALA	MET	GLY	SER	GLU	60
61	GLU	LEU	GLU	ASP	SER	VAL	VAL	GLU	PRO	PHE	PHE	THR	ASP	LEU	ALA	75
76	PRO	LYS	LEU	LYS	GLY	LYS	LYS	VAL	GLY	LEU	PHE	GLY	SER	TYR	GLY	90
91	TRP	GLY	SER	GLY	GLU	TRP	MET	ASP	ALA	TRP	LYS	GLN	ARG	THR	GLU	105
106	ASP	THR	GLY	ALA	THR	VAL	ILE	GLY	THR	ALA	ILE	VAL	ASN	GLU	MET	120
121	PRO	ASP	ASN	ALA	PRO	GLU	CYS	LYS	GLU	LEU	GLY	GLU	ALA	ALA	ALA	135
136	LYS	ALA														150

The primary structure of *Peptostreptococcus elsdenii* Flavodoxin.
M. Tanaka, M. Haniu, K. T. Yasunobu, S. Mayhew, and V. Massey.
J. Biol. Chem., **248**, 4354–4366 (1973).
And
Correction of the amino acid sequence of *Peptostreptococcus elsdenii* flavodoxin.
M. Tanaka, M. Haniu, K. T. Yasunobu, S. G. Mayhew, and V. Massey.
J. Biol. Chem., **249**, 4397 (1974).

OTHER METALLOPROTEINS

FLAVODOXIN—AZOTOBACTER VINELANDII

	1			5					10					15	
1	ALA	LYS	ILE	GLY	LEU	PHE	PHE	GLY	SER	ASN	THR	GLY	LYS	THR	ARG	15
16	LYS	VAL	ALA	LYS	SER	ILE	LYS	LYS	ARG	PHE	ASP	ASP	GLU	THR	MET	30
31	SER	ASP	ALA	LEU	ASN	VAL	ASN	ARG	VAL	SER	ALA	GLU	ASP	PHE	ALA	45
46	GLN	TYR	GLN	PHE	LEU	ILE	LEU	GLY	THR	PRO	THR	LEU	GLY	GLU	GLY	60
61	GLU	LEU	PRO	GLY	LEU	SER	SER	ASP	CYS	GLU	ASN	GLU	SER	TRP	GLU	75
76	GLU	PHE	LEU	PRO	LYS	ILE	GLU	GLY	LEU	ASP	PHE	SER	GLY	LYS	THR	90
91	VAL	ALA	LEU	PHE	GLY	LEU	GLY	ASP	GLN	VAL	GLY	TYR	PRO	GLU	ASP	105
106	TYR	LEU	ASP	ALA	LEU	GLY	GLU	LEU	TYR	SER	PHE	PHE	LYS	ASP	ARG	120
121	GLY	ALA	LYS	ILE	VAL	GLY	SER	TRP	SER	THR	ASP	GLY	TYR	GLU	PHE	135
136	GLU	SER	SER	GLU	ALA	VAL	VAL	ASP	GLY	LYS	PHE	VAL	GLY	LEU	ALA	150
151	LEU	ASP	LEU	ASP	ASN	GLN	SER	GLY	LYS	THR	ASP	GLU	ARG	VAL	ALA	165
166	ALA	TRP	LEU	ALA	GLN	ILE	ALA	PRO	GLU	PHE	GLY	LEU	SER	LEU		180

Complete amino acid sequence of Azotoflavin, a flavodoxin from *Azotobacter vinelandii*.
M. Tanaka, M. Haniu, K. T. Yasunobu, and D. C. Yoch.
Biochemistry, **16**, 3525–3537 (1977).

HIGH POTENTIAL IRON–SULPHUR PROTEIN FROM THIOCAPSA PFENNIGII

	1			5					10					15	
1	GLU	ASP	LEU	PRO	HIS	VAL	ASP	ALA	ALA	THR	ASN	PRO	ILE	ALA	GLN	15
16	SER	LEU	HIS	TYR	ILE	GLU	ASP	ALA	ASN	ALA	SER	GLU	ARG	ASN	PRO	30
31	VAL	THR	LYS	THR	GLU	LEU	PRO	GLY	SER	GLU	GLN	PHE	CYS	HIS	ASN	45
46	CYS	SER	PHE	ILE	GLN	ALA	ASP	SER	GLY	ALA	TRP	ARG	PRO	CYS	THR	60
61	LEU	TYR	PRO	GLY	TYR	THR	VAL	SER	GLU	ASP	GLY	TRP	CYS	LEU	SER	75
76	TRP	ALA	HIS	LYS	THR	ALA										90

Primary structure of a high potential iron–sulfur protein from the photosynthetic bacterium
Thiocapsa pfennigii.
S. M. Tedro, T. E. Meyer, and M. D. Kamen.
J. Biol. Chem., **249**, 1182–1188 (1974).

HIGH POTENTIAL IRON–SULPHUR PROTEIN FROM CHROMATIUM VINOSUM

	1				5				10					15		
1	SER	ALA	PRO	ALA	ASN	ALA	VAL	ALA	ALA	ASP	ASN	ALA	THR	ALA	ILE	15
16	ALA	LEU	LYS	TYR	ASN	GLN	ASP	ALA	THR	LYS	SER	GLU	ARG	VAL	ALA	30
31	ALA	ALA	ARG	PRO	GLY	LEU	PRO	PRO	GLU	GLU	GLN	HIS	CYS	ALA	ASP	45
46	CYS	GLN	PHE	MET	GLN	ALA	ASP	ALA	ALA	GLY	ALA	THR	ASP	GLU	TRP	60
61	LYS	GLY	CYS	GLN	LEU	PHE	PRO	GLY	LYS	LEU	ILE	ASN	VAL	ASN	GLY	75
76	TRP	CYS	ALA	SER	TRP	THR	LEU	LYS	ALA	GLY						90

The complete amino acid sequence of Chromatium high potential iron sulfur protein.
K. Dus, S. Tedro, and R. G. Bartsch.
J. Biol. Chem., **248**, 7318–7331 (1973).

PLASTOCYANIN—VEGETABLE MARROW

	1				5				10					15		
1	ILE	GLU	VAL	LEU	LEU	GLY	GLY	ASP	ASP	GLY	SER	LEU	ALA	PHE	ILE	15
16	PRO	ASN	ASP	PHE	SER	VAL	ALA	ALA	GLY	GLU	LYS	ILE	VAL	PHE	LYS	30
31	ASN	ASN	ALA	GLY	PHE	PRO	HIS	ASN	VAL	VAL	PHE	ASP	GLU	ASP	GLU	45
46	ILE	PRO	SER	GLY	VAL	ASP	ALA	GLY	LYS	ILE	SER	MET	ASN	GLU	GLU	60
61	ASP	LEU	LEU	ASN	ALA	PRO	GLY	GLU	VAL	TYR	LYS	VAL	ASN	LEU	THR	75
76	GLU	LYS	GLY	SER	TYR	SER	PHE	TYR	CYS	SER	PRO	HIS	GLN	GLY	ALA	90
91	GLY	MET	VAL	GLY	LYS	VAL	THR	VAL	ASN							105

The amino acid sequence of plastocyanin from *Cucurbita pepo* (vegetable marrow).
M. D. Scawen and D. Boulter.
Biochem. J., **143**, 257–264 (1974).

PLASTOCYANIN—BROAD BEAN

	1				5				10					15		
1	VAL	GLU	VAL	LEU	LEU	GLY	ALA	SER	ASP	GLY	GLY	LEU	ALA	PHE	VAL	15
16	PRO	ASN	SER	PHE	GLU	VAL	SER	ALA	GLY	ASP	THR	ILE	VAL	PHE	LYS	30
31	ASN	ASN	ALA	GLY	PHE	PRO	HIS	ASN	VAL	VAL	PHE	ASP	GLU	ASP	GLU	45
46	ILE	PRO	SER	GLY	VAL	ASP	ALA	ALA	LYS	ILE	SER	MET	PRO	GLU	GLU	60
61	ASP	LEU	LEU	ASN	ALA	PRO	GLY	GLU	THR	TYR	SER	VAL	LYS	LEU	ASP	75
76	ALA	LYS	GLY	THR	TYR	LYS	PHE	TYR	CYS	SER	PRO	HIS	GLN	GLY	ALA	90
91	GLY	MET	VAL	GLY	GLN	VAL	THR	VAL	ASN							105

The amino acid sequence of plastocyanin from *Vicia faba* L. (Broad bean).
J. A. M. Ramshaw, M. D. Scawen, and D. Boulter.
Biochem. J., **141**, 835–843 (1974).

336

OTHER METALLOPROTEINS

PLASTOCYANIN—FRENCH BEAN

	1				5					10					15	
1	LEU	GLU	VAL	LEU	LEU	GLY	SER	GLY	ASP	GLY	SER	LEU	VAL	PHE	VAL	15
16	PRO	SER	GLU	PHE	SER	VAL	PRO	SER	GLY	GLU	LYS	ILE	VAL	PHE	LYS	30
31	ASN	ASN	ALA	GLY	PHE	PRO	HIS	ASN	VAL	VAL	PHE	ASP	GLU	ASP	GLU	45
46	ILE	PRO	ALA	GLY	VAL	ASP	ALA	VAL	LYS	ILE	SER	MET	PRO	GLU	GLU	60
61	GLU	LEU	LEU	ASN	ALA	PRO	GLY	GLU	THR	TYR	VAL	VAL	THR	LEU	ASP	75
76	THR	LYS	GLY	THR	TYR	SER	PHE	TYR	CYS	SER	PRO	HIS	GLN	GLY	ALA	90
91	GLY	MET	VAL	GLY	LYS	VAL	THR	VAL	ASN							105

The amino acid sequence of plastocyanin from French bean (*Phaseolus vulgaris*).
P. R. Milne, J. R. E. Wells, and R. P. Ambler.
Biochem. J., **143**, 691–701 (1974).

ELDER PLASTOCYANIN

	1				5					10					15	
1	VAL	GLU	ILE	LEU	LEU	GLY	GLY	GLU	ASP	GLY	SER	LEU	ALA	PHE	VAL/ILE	16
16	PRO	GLY/SER	ASN	PHE	SER	VAL	PRO	SER	GLY	GLU	LYS	ILE	THR	PHE	LYS	30
31	ASN	ASN	ALA	GLY	PHE	PRO	HIS	ASN	VAL	VAL	PHE	ASP	GLU	ASP	GLU	45
46	VAL	PRO	SER	GLY	VAL	ASP	SER	ALA	LYS	ILE	SER	MET	SER	GLU	ASP	60
61	ASP	LEU	LEU	ASN	ALA	PRO	GLY	GLU	THR	TYR	SER	VAL	THR	LEU	THR	75
76	GLU	SER	GLY	THR	TYR	LYS	PHE	TYR	CYS	SER	PRO	HIS	GLN	GLY	ALA	90
91	GLY	MET	VAL	GLY	LYS	VAL	THR	VAL	ASN							105

The amino acid sequence of Plastocyanin from *Sambucus nigra* L. (Elder).
M. D. Scawen, J. A. M. Ramshaw, R. H. Brown, and D. Boulter.
Eur. J. Biochem., **44**, 299–303 (1974).

POTATO PLASTOCYANIN

	1				5					10					15	
1	LEU	ASP	VAL	LEU	LEU	GLY	GLY	ASP	ASP	GLY	SER	LEU	ALA	PHE	ILE	15
16	PRO	GLY	ASN	PHE	SER	VAL	SER	ALA	GLY	GLU	LYS	ILE	THR	PHE	LYS	30
31	ASN	ASN	ALA	GLY	PHE	PRO	HIS	ASN	VAL	VAL	PHE	ASP	GLU	ASP	GLU	45
46	ILE	PRO	ALA	GLY	VAL	ASP	ALA	SER	LYS	ILE	SER	MET	ALA	GLU	GLU	60
61	ASP	LEU	LEU	ASN	ALA	ALA	GLY	GLU	THR	TYR	SER	VAL	THR	LEU	SER	75
76	GLU	LYS	GLY	THR	TYR	THR	PHE	TYR	CYS	ALA	PRO	HIS	GLN	GLY	ALA	90
91	GLY	MET	VAL	GLY	LYS	VAL	THR	VAL	ASN							105

The amino acid sequence of Plastocyanin from *Solanum tuberosum* L. (Potato).
J. A. M. Ramshaw, M. D. Scawen, C. J. Bailey, and D. Boulter.
Biochem. J., **139**, 583–592 (1974).

OTHER METALLOPROTEINS

PLASTOCYANIN—SPINACH

	1				5					10					15	
1	VAL	GLU	VAL	LEU	LEU	GLY	GLY	GLY	ASP	GLY	SER	LEU	ALA	PHE	LEU	15
16	PRO	GLY	ASP	PHE	SER	VAL	ALA	SER	GLY	GLU	GLU	ILE	VAL	PHE	LYS	30
31	ASN	ASN	ALA	GLY	PHE	PRO	HIS	ASN	VAL	VAL	PHE	ASP	GLU	ASP	GLU	45
46	ILE	PRO	SER	GLY	VAL	ASP	ALA	ALA	LYS	ILE	SER	MET	SER	GLU	GLU	60
61	ASP	LEU	LEU	ASN	ALA	PRO	GLY	GLU	THR	TYR	LYS	VAL	THR	LEU	THR	75
76	GLU	LYS	GLY	THR	TYR	LYS	PHE	TYR	CYS	SER	PRO	HIS	GLN	GLY	ALA	90
91	GLY	MET	VAL	GLY	LYS	VAL	THR	VAL	ASN							105

The amino acid sequence of plastocyanin from spinach (*Spinacia oleracea*).
M. D. Scawen, J. A. M. Ramshaw, and D. Boulter.
Biochem. J., **147**, 343–349 (1975).

PLASTOCYANIN—ANABAENA VARIABILIS

	1				5					10					15	
1	GLU	THR	TYR	THR	VAL	LYS	LEU	GLY	SER	ASP	LYS	GLY	LEU	LEU	VAL	15
16	PHE	GLU	PRO	ALA	LYS	LEU	THR	ILE	LYS	PRO	GLY	ASP	THR	VAL	GLU	30
31	PHE	LEU	ASN	ASN	LYS	VAL	PRO	PRO	HIS	ASN	VAL	VAL	PHE	ASP	ALA	45
46	ALA	LEU	ASN	PRO	ALA	LYS	SER	ALA	ASP	LEU	ALA	LYS	SER	LEU	SER	60
61	HIS	LYS	GLN	LEU	LEU	MET	SER	PRO	GLY	GLN	SER	THR	SER	THR	THR	75
76	PHE	PRO	ALA	ASP	ALA	PRO	ALA	GLY	GLU	TYR	THR	PHE	TYR	CYS	GLU	90
91	PRO	HIS	ARG	GLY	ALA	GLY	MET	VAL	GLY	LYS	ILE	THR	VAL	ALA	GLY	105

Prokaryote–eukaryote relationships and the amino acid sequence of plastocyanin from
Anabaena variabilis.
A. Aitken.
Biochem. J., **149**, 675–683 (1975).

CHLORELLA FUSCA *PLASTOCYANIN*

	1				5					10					15	
1	ASP	VAL	THR	VAL	LYS	LEU	GLY	ALA	ASP	SER	GLY	ALA	LEU	VAL	PHE	15
16	GLU	PRO	SER	SER	VAL	THR	ILE	LYS	ALA	GLY	GLU	THR	VAL	THR	TRP	30
31	VAL	ASN	ASN	ALA	GLY	PHE	PRO	HIS	ASN	ILE	VAL	PHE	ASP	GLU	ASP	45
46	GLU	VAL	PRO	SER	GLY	ALA	ASN	ALA	GLU	ALA	LEU	SER	HIS	GLU	ASP	60
61	TYR	LEU	ASN	ALA	PRO	GLY	GLU	SER	TYR	SER	ALA	LYS	PHE	ASP	THR	75
76	ALA	GLY	THR	TYR	GLY	TYR	PHE	CYS	GLU	PRO	HIS	GLN	GLY	ALA	GLY	90
91	MET	LYS	GLY	THR	ILE	THR	VAL	GLN								105

The amino acid sequence of plastocyanin from *Chlorella fusca*.
J. Kelly and R. P. Ambler.
Biochem. J., **143**, 681–690 (1974).

OTHER METALLOPROTEINS

MYOHEMERYTHRIN

	1				5					10					15		
1	GLY	TRP	GLU	ILE	PRO	GLU	PRO	TYR	VAL	TRP	ASP	GLU	SER	PHE	ARG		15
16	VAL	PHE	TYR	GLU	GLN	LEU	ASP	GLU	GLU	HIS	LYS	LYS	ILE	PHE	LYS		30
31	GLY	ILE	PHE	CYS	ASP	ILE	ARG	ASP	ASN	SER	ALA	PRO	ASN	LEU	ALA		45
46	THR	LEU	VAL	LYS	VAL	THR	THR	ASN	HIS	PHE	THR	HIS	GLU	GLU	ALA		60
61	MET	MET	ASP	ALA	ALA	LYS	TYR	SER	GLU	VAL	VAL	PRO	HIS	LYS	LYS		75
76	MET	HIS	LYS	ASP	PHE	LEU	GLU	LYS	ILE	GLY	GLY	LEU	SER	ALA	PRO		90
91	VAL	ASP	ALA	LYS	ASN	VAL	ASP	TYR	CYS	LYS	GLU	TRP	LEU	VAL	ASN		105
106	HIS	ILE	LYS	GLY	THR	ASP	PHE	LYS	TYR	LYS	GLY	LYS	LEU				120

The primary structure of myohemerythrin.
G. L. Klippenstein, J. L. Cote, and S. E. Ludlam.
Biochemistry, **15**, 1128–1136 (1976).

HEMERYTHRIN

	1				5					10					15		
1	GLY	PHE	PRO	ILE	PRO	ASP	PRO	TYR	VAL	ASP	TRP	PRO	SER	PHE	ARG		15
16	THR	PHE	TYR	SER	ILE	ILE	ASP	ASP	GLU	HIS	LYS	THR	LEU	PHE	ASN		30
31	GLY	ILE	PHE	HIS	LEU	ALA	ILE	ASP	ASP	ASN	ALA	ASP	ASN	LEU	GLY		45
46	GLU	LEU	ARG	ARG	CYS	THR	GLY	LYS	HIS	PHE	LEU	ASN	GLN	GLU	VAL		60
61	LEU	MET	GLN	ALA	SER	GLN	TYR	GLN	PHE	TYR	ASP	GLU	HIS	LYS	LYS		75
76	GLU	HIS	GLU	GLY	PHE	ILE	HIS	ALA	LEU	ASP	ASN	TRP	LYS	GLY	ASP		90
91	VAL	LYS	TRP	ALA	LYS	SER	TRP	LEU	VAL	ASN	HIS	ILE	LYS	THR	ILE		105
106	ASP	PHE	LYS	TYR	LYS	GLY	LYS	ILE									120

Note: Variants have at positions 79 and 96, THR and ALA respectively.
The Primary Structure of *Golfingia gouldii* Hemerythrin. Order of peptides in fragments produced by tryptic digestion of succinylated hemerythrin. Complete Amino Acid Sequence.
G. L. Klippenstein, J. W. Holleman, and I. M. Klotz.
Biochemistry, **7**, 3868–3878 (1968).

OTHER METALLOPROTEINS

HEMERYTHRIN—THEMISTE DYSCRITUM

	1				5					10					15		
1	GLY	PHE	PRO	ILE	PRO	ASP	PRO	TYR	CYS	TRP	ASP	ILE	SER	PHE	ARG		15
16	THR	PHE	TYR	THR	ILE	ILE VAL	ASP	ASP	GLU	HIS	LYS	THR	LEU	PHE	ASN		30
31	GLY	ILE	LEU	LEU	LEU	SER	GLN	ALA	ASP	ASN	ALA	ASP	HIS	LEU	ASN		45
46	GLU	LEU	ARG	ARG	CYS	THR	GLY	LYS	HIS	PHE	LEU	ASN	GLU	GLN	GLN		60
61	LEU	MET	GLN	ALA	SER	GLN	TYR	ALA	GLY	TYR	ALA	GLU	HIS	LYS	LYS		75
76	ALA	HIS	ASP	ASP	PHE	ILE	HIS	LYS	LEU	ASP	THR	TRP	ASP	GLY	ASP		90
91	VAL	THR	TYR	ALA	LYS	ASN	TRP	LEU	VAL	ASN	HIS	ILE	LYS	THR	ILE		105
106	ASP	PHE	LYS	TYR	ARG	GLY	LYS	ILE									120

Note: Micro-heterogeneity exists at position 64 and the evidence for position 65 (SER) is rather poor.
Amino acid sequence of Hemerythrin from *Themiste dyscritum*.
J. S. Loehr, P. J. Lammers, B. Brimhall, and M. A. Hermodson.
J. Biol. Chem., **253**, 5726–5731 (1978).

C-PHYCOCYANIN—MASTIGOCLADUS LAMINOSUS α-CHAIN

	1				5					10					15		
1	VAL	LYS	THR	PRO	ILE	THR	ASP	ALA	ILE	ALA	ALA	ALA	ASP	THR	GLN		15
16	GLY	ARG	PHE	LEU	SER	ASN	THR	GLU	LEU	GLN	ALA	VAL	ASN	GLY	ARG		30
31	TYR	GLN	ARG	ALA	ALA	ALA	SER	LEU	GLU	ALA	ALA	ARG	ALA	LEU	THR		45
46	ALA	ASN	ALA	GLN	ARG	LEU	ILE	ASP	GLY	ALA	ALA	GLN	ALA	VAL	TYR		60
61	GLN	LYS	PHE	PRO	TYR	LEU	ILE	GLN	THR	SER	GLY	PRO	ASN	TYR	ALA		75
76	ALA	ASP	ALA	ARG	GLY	LYS	SER	LYS	CYS	ALA	ARG	ASP	ILE	GLY	HIS		90
91	TYR	LEU	ARG	ILE	ILE	THR	TYR	SER	LEU	VAL	ALA	GLY	GLY	THR	GLY		105
106	PRO	LEU	ASP	GLU	TYR	LEU	ILE	ALA	GLY	LEU	ASN	GLU	ILE	ASN	ASP		120
121	ALA	PHE	GLU	LEU	SER	PRO	SER	TRP	TYR	ILE	GLU	ALA	LEU	LYS	TYR		135
136	ILE	LYS	ALA	ASN	HIS	GLY	LEU	SER	GLY	GLN	ALA	ALA	ASN	GLU	ALA		150
151	ASN	THR	TYR	ILE	ASP	TYR	VAL	ILE	ASN	ALA	LEU	SER					165

OTHER METALLOPROTEINS

β-CHAIN

	1				5					10					15	
1	ALA	TYR	ASP	VAL	PHE	THR	LYS	VAL	VAL	SER	GLN	ALA	ASP	SER	ARG	15
16	GLY	GLU	PHE	LEU	SER	ASN	GLU	GLN	LEU	ASP	ALA	LEU	ALA	ASN	VAL	30
31	VAL	LYS	GLU	GLY	ASN	LYS	ARG	LEU	ASP	VAL	VAL	ASN	ARG	ILE	THR	45
46	SER	ASN	ALA	SER	THR	ILE	VAL	THR	ASN	ALA	ALA	ARG	ALA	LEU	PHE	60
61	GLU	GLU	GLN	PRO	GLN	LEU	ILE	ALA	PRO	GLY	GLY	SER	ALA	THR	ARG	75
76	ASN	GLY	THR	MET	ALA	ALA	CYS	LEU	ARG	ASP	MET	GLU	ILE	ILE	LEU	90
91	ARG	TYR	ILE	THR	TYR	ALA	ILE	LEU	ALA	GLY	ASP	ALA	SER	ILE	LEU	105
106	ASP	ASP	ARG	CYS	LEU	ASN	GLY	LEU	ARG	GLU	THR	TYR	GLN	ALA	LEU	120
121	GLY	THR	PRO	GLY	SER	SER	VAL	ALA	VAL	GLY	ILE	GLN	LYS	MET	LYS	135
136	GLU	ALA	ALA	ILE	ASN	ILE	ALA	ASN	ASP	PRO	ASN	GLY	ILE	THR	LYS	150
151	GLY	ASP	CYS	SER	ALA	LEU	ILE	SER	GLU	VAL	ALA	SER	TYR	PHE	ASP	165
166	ARG	ALA	ALA	ALA	ALA	VAL	ALA									180

The Complete amino acid sequence of both subunits of C-Phycocyanin from the cyanobacterium *Mastigocladus laminosus*.
G. Frank, W. Sidler, H. Widmer, and H. Zuber.
Hoppe-Seyler's Z. Physiol. Chem., **359**, 1491–1507 (1978).

PUTIDAREDOXIN

	1				5					10					15	
1	SER	LYS	VAL	VAL	TYR	VAL	SER	HIS	ASP	GLY	THR	ARG	ARG	GLN	LEU	15
16	ASP	VAL	ALA	ASP	GLY	VAL	SER	LEU	MET	GLN	ALA	ALA	VAL	SER	ASN	30
31	GLY	ILE	TYR	ASP	ILE	VAL	GLY	ASP	CYS	GLY	GLY	SER	ALA	SER	CYS	45
46	ALA	THR	CYS	HIS	VAL	TYR	VAL	ASN	GLU	ALA	PHE	THR	ASP	LYS	VAL	60
61	PRO	ALA	ALA	ASN	GLU	ARG	GLU	ILE	GLY	MET	LEU	GLU	CYS	VAL	THR	75
76	ALA	GLU	LEU	LYS	PRO	ASN	SER	ARG	LEU	CYS	CYS	GLN	ILE	ILE	MET	90
91	THR	PRO	GLU	LEU	ASP	GLY	ILE	VAL	VAL	ASP	VAL	PRO	ASP	ARG	GLN	105
106	TRP															120

The amino acid sequence of Putidaredoxin, an iron–sulfur protein from *Pseudomonas putida*.
M. Tanaka, M. Haniu, K. T. Yasunobu, K. Dus, and I. C. Gunsalus.
J. Biol. Chem., **249**, 3689–3701 (1974).

OTHER METALLOPROTEINS

BOVINE ADRENODOXIN

	1				5					10					15	
1	SER	SER	SER	GLN	ASP	LYS	ILE	THR	VAL	HIS	PHE	ILE	ASN	ARG	ASP	15
16	GLY	GLU	THR	LEU	THR	THR	LYS	GLY	LYS	ILE	GLY	ASP	SER	LEU	LEU	30
31	ASP	VAL	VAL	VAL	GLX	ASX	ASN	LEU	ASP	ILE	ASP	GLY	PHE	GLY	ALA	45
46	CYS	GLU	GLY	THR	LEU	ALA	CYS	SER	THR	CYS	HIS	LEU	ILE	PHE	GLU	60
61	GLN	HIS	ILE	PHE	GLU	LYS	LEU	GLU	ALA	ILE	THR	ASN	GLU	GLU	ASN	75
76	ASN	MET	ASX	GLX	LEU	LEU	ASP	LEU	ALA	TYR	GLY	LEU	THR	ASP	ARG	90
91	SER	ARG	LEU	GLY	CYS	GLN	ILE	CYS	LEU	THR	LYS	ALA	MET	ASP	ASN	105
106	MET	ASP	THR	VAL	ARG	VAL	PRO	ASP	ALA	VAL	SER	ASP	ALA			120

The Primary Structure of Bovine Adrenodoxin.
M. Tanaka, M. Haniu, and K. T. Yasunobu.
Biochem. Biophys. Res. Commun., **39**, 1182–1188 (1970).

IRON-PROTEIN: COMPONENT OF NITROGENASE

	1				5					10					15	
1	MET	ARG	GLN	VAL	ALA	ILE	TYR	GLY	LYS	GLY	GLY	ILE	GLY	LYS	SER	15
16	THR	THR	THR	GLN	ASN	LEU	THR	SER	GLY	LEU	HIS	ALA	MET	GLY	LYS	30
31	THR	ILE	MET	VAL	VAL	GLY	CYS	ASP	PRO	LYS	ALA	ASP	SER	THR	ARG	45
46	LEU	LEU	LEU	GLY	GLY	LEU	ALA	GLN	LYS	SER	VAL	LEU	ASP	THR	LEU	60
61	ARG	GLU	GLU	GLY	GLU	ASP	VAL	GLU	LEU	ASP	SER	ILE	LEU	LYS	GLU	75
76	GLY	TYR	GLY	GLY	ILE	ARG	CYS	VAL	GLU	SER	GLY	GLY	PRO	GLU	PRO	90
91	GLY	VAL	GLY	CYS	ALA	GLY	ARG	GLY	ILE	ILE	THR	SER	ILE	ASN	MET	105
106	LEU	GLU	GLN	LEU	GLY	ALA	TYR	THR	ASP	ASP	LEU	ASP	TYR	VAL	PHE	120
121	TYR	ASP	VAL	LEU	GLY	ASP	VAL	VAL	CYS	GLY	GLY	PHE	ALA	MET	PRO	135
136	ILE	ARG	GLU	GLY	LYS	ALA	GLN	GLU	ILE	TYR	ILE	VAL	ALA	SER	GLY	150
151	GLU	MET	MET	ALA	LEU	TYR	ALA	ALA	ASN	ASN	ILE	SER	LYS	GLY	ILE	165
166	GLN	LYS	TYR	ALA	LYS	SER	GLY	GLY	VAL	ARG	LEU	GLY	GLY	ILE	ILE	180
181	CYS	ASN	SER	ARG	LYS	VAL	ALA	ASN	GLU	TYR	GLU	LEU	LEU	ASP	ALA	195
196	PHE	ALA	LYS	GLU	LEU	GLY	SER	GLN	LEU	ILE	HIS	PHE	VAL	PRO	ARG	210
211	SER	PRO	MET	VAL	THR	LYS	ALA	GLU	ILE	ASN	LYS	GLN	THR	VAL	ILE	225
226	GLU	TYR	ASP	PRO	THR	CYS	GLU	GLN	ALA	GLU	GLU	TYR	ARG	GLU	LEU	240
241	ALA	ARG	LYS	VAL	ASP	ALA	ASN	GLU	LEU	PHE	VAL	ILE	PRO	LYS	PRO	255
256	MET	THR	GLN	GLU	ARG	LEU	GLU	GLU	ILE	LEU	MET	GLN	TYR	GLY	LEU	270
271	MET	ASP	LEU													285

The amino acid sequence of *Clostridium pasteurianum* Iron protein, a component of Nitrogenase.
M. Tanaka, M. Haniu, K. T. Yasunobu, and L. E. Mortenson.
J. Biol. Chem., **252**, 7093–7100 (1977).

OTHER METALLOPROTEINS

CALCIUM-BINDING PROTEIN—BOVINE INTESTINE

```
         1              5                    10                      15
 1  AC   LYS GLN SER PRO LEU GLU LYS TYR ALA ALA GLU LYS SER ILE    15
16  GLN  LYS GLU ILE GLU LYS GLY PHE PHE LYS GLN LEU LEU VAL SER    30
31  VAL  GLN LYS ALA GLY ASP LYS GLU SER LEU GLN PRO LEU PHE THR    45
46  LEU  LEU LYS SER GLY PRO GLU GLU ASN LEU LYS GLU SER GLN ASN    60
61  GLY  PRO ASP LEU LYS SER GLY PRO GLN ASN ASP LEU GLU GLU LYS    75
76  GLY  THR ASP PHE VAL LEU PHE SER LEU LYS GLN                    90
```

Note: Serine was also found at position 76.
Calcium-binding protein of bovine intestine. The complete amino acid sequence.
W. Huang, D. V. Cohn, J. W. Hamilton, C. Fullmer, and R. H. Wasserman.
J. Biol. Chem., **250**, 7647–7655 (1975).

METALLOTHIONEIN—HORSE

```
         1              5                    10                      15
 1  AC   MET ASP PRO ASN CYS SER CYS VAL ALA GLY GLU SER CYS THR    15
16  CYS  ALA GLY SER CYS LYS CYS LYS GLN CYS ARG CYS ALA SER CYS    30
31  LYS  LYS SER CYS CYS SER CYS CYS PRO VAL GLY CYS ALA LYS CYS    45
46  ALA  GLN GLY CYS VAL CYS LYS GLY ALA SER ASP LYS CYS CYS SER    60
61  CYS  ALA                                                        75
```

Amino acid sequence of equine renal metallothionein-1B.
Y. Kojima, C. Berger, B. L. Vallee, and J. H. R. Kagi.
Proc. Natn. Acad. Sci., U.S.A., **73**, 3413–3417 (1976).

METALLOTHIONEIN—HUMAN LIVER

```
         1              5                    10                      15
 1  AC   MET ASP PRO ASN CYS SER CYS ALA ALA GLY ASP SER CYS THR    15
16  CYS  ALA GLY SER CYS LYS CYS LYS GLU CYS LYS CYS THR SER CYS    30
31  LYS  LYS SER CYS CYS SER CYS CYS PRO VAL GLY CYS ALA LYS CYS    45
46  ALA  GLN GLY CYS ILE CYS LYS GLY ALA SER ASP LYS CYS CYS SER    60
61  CYS  ALA                                                        75
```

Primary structure of human hepatic metallothionein.
M. M. Kissling and J. H. R. Kägi.
FEBS Letters, **82**, 247–250 (1977).

IMMUNOGLOBULINS

IMMUNOGLOBULIN γ-CHAIN—HUMAN EU

	1				5					10					15	
1	PYG	VAL	GLN	LEU	VAL	GLN	SER	GLY	ALA	GLU	VAL	LYS	LYS	PRO	GLY	15
16	SER	SER	VAL	LYS	VAL	SER	CYS	LYS	ALA	SER	GLY	GLY	THR	PHE	SER	30
31	ARG	SER	ALA	ILE	ILE	TRP	VAL	ARG	GLN	ALA	PRO	GLY	GLN	GLY	LEU	45
46	GLU	TRP	MET	GLY	GLY	ILE	VAL	PRO	MET	PHE	GLY	PRO	PRO	ASN	TYR	60
61	ALA	GLN	LYS	PHE	GLN	GLY	ARG	VAL	THR	ILE	THR	ALA	ASP	GLU	SER	75
76	THR	ASN	THR	ALA	TYR	MET	GLU	LEU	SER	SER	LEU	ARG	SER	GLU	ASP	90
91	THR	ALA	PHE	TYR	PHE	CYS	ALA	GLY	GLY	TYR	GLY	ILE	TYR	SER	PRO	105
106	GLU	GLU	TYR	ASN	GLY	GLY	LEU	VAL	THR	VAL	SER	SER	ALA	SER	THR	120
121	LYS	GLY	PRO	SER	VAL	PHE	PRO	LEU	ALA	PRO	SER	SER	LYS	SER	THR	135
136	SER	GLY	GLY	THR	ALA	ALA	LEU	GLY	CYS	LEU	VAL	LYS	ASP	TYR	PHE	150
151	PRO	GLU	PRO	VAL	THR	VAL	SER	TRP	ASN	SER	GLY	ALA	LEU	THR	SER	165
166	GLY	VAL	HIS	THR	PHE	PRO	ALA	VAL	LEU	GLN	SER	SER	GLY	LEU	TYR	180
181	SER	LEU	SER	SER	VAL	VAL	THR	VAL	PRO	SER	SER	SER	LEU	GLY	THR	195
196	GLN	THR	TYR	ILE	CYS	ASN	VAL	ASN	HIS	LYS	PRO	SER	ASN	THR	LYS	210
211	VAL	ASP	LYS	ARG	VAL	GLU	PRO	LYS	SER	CYS	ASP	LYS	THR	HIS	THR	225
226	CYS	PRO	PRO	CYS	PRO	ALA	PRO	GLU	LEU	LEU	GLY	GLY	PRO	SER	VAL	240
241	PHE	LEU	PHE	PRO	PRO	LYS	PRO	LYS	ASP	THR	LEU	MET	ILE	SER	ARG	255
256	THR	PRO	GLU	VAL	THR	CYS	VAL	VAL	VAL	ASP	VAL	SER	HIS	GLU	ASP	270
271	PRO	GLN	VAL	LYS	PHE	ASN	TRP	TYR	VAL	ASP	GLY	VAL	GLN	VAL	HIS	285
286	ASN	ALA	LYS	THR	LYS	PRO	ARG	GLU	GLN	GLN	TYR	ASX	SER	THR	TYR	300
301	ARG	VAL	VAL	SER	VAL	LEU	THR	VAL	LEU	HIS	GLN	ASN	TRP	LEU	ASP	315
316	GLY	LYS	GLU	TYR	LYS	CYS	LYS	VAL	SER	ASN	LYS	ALA	LEU	PRO	ALA	330
331	PRO	ILE	GLU	LYS	THR	ILE	SER	LYS	ALA	LYS	GLY	GLN	PRO	ARG	GLU	345
346	PRO	GLN	VAL	TYR	THR	LEU	PRO	PRO	SER	ARG	GLU	GLU	MET	THR	LYS	360
361	ASN	GLN	VAL	SER	LEU	THR	CYS	LEU	VAL	LYS	GLY	PHE	TYR	PRO	SER	375
376	ASP	ILE	ALA	VAL	GLU	TRP	GLU	SER	ASN	ASP	GLY	GLU	PRO	GLU	ASN	390
391	TYR	LYS	THR	THR	PRO	PRO	VAL	LEU	ASP	SER	ASP	GLY	SER	PHE	PHE	405
406	LEU	TYR	SER	LYS	LEU	THR	VAL	ASP	LYS	SER	ARG	TRP	GLN	GLU	GLY	420
421	ASN	VAL	PHE	SER	CYS	SER	VAL	MET	HIS	GLU	ALA	LEU	HIS	ASN	HIS	435
436	TYR	THR	GLN	LYS	SER	LEU	SER	LEU	SER	PRO	GLY					450

Note: Intrachain disulphide bridges are between residues CYS 22 and 96; CYS 144 and 200; CYS 261 and 321; CYS 367 and 425. Inter-heavy chain disulphide bridges are from CYS 226 and CYS 229; heavy to light chain bridge is from CYS 220.

The Covalent Structure of an Entire γG Immunoglobulin Molecule.
G. M. Edelman, B. A. Cunningham, W. E. Gall, P. D. Gottlieb, U. Rutishauser, and M. J. Waxdal.
Proc. Natn. Acad. Sci., U.S.A., **63**, 78–85 (1969).
The Covalent Structure of a Human γG-Immunoglobulin.
G. M. Edelman.
Biochemistry, **9**, 3197–3205 (1970).

IMMUNOGLOBULINS

IMMUNOGLOBULIN μ-CHAIN—HUMAN OU

```
         1              5                      10                        15
  1  PYG VAL THR LEU THR GLU SER GLY PRO ALA LEU VAL LYS PRO LYS    15
 16  GLN PRO LEU THR LEU THR CYS THR PHE SER GLY PHE SER LEU SER    30
 31  THR SER ARG MET ARG VAL SER TRP ILE ARG ARG PRO PRO GLY LYS    45
 46  ALA LEU GLU TRP LEU ALA ARG ILE ASX ASX ASX ASP LYS PHE TYR    60
 61  TRP SER THR SER LEU ARG THR ARG LEU SER ILE SER LYS ASN ASP    75
 76  SER LYS ASN GLN VAL VAL LEU ILE MET ILE ASN VAL ASN PRO VAL    90
 91  ASP THR ALA THR TYR TYR CYS ALA ARG VAL VAL ASN SER VAL MET   105
106  ALA GLY TYR TYR TYR TYR TYR MET ASP VAL TRP GLY LYS GLY THR   120
121  THR VAL THR VAL SER SER GLY SER ALA SER ALA PRO THR LEU PHE   135
136  PRO LEU VAL SER CYS GLU ASN SER (ASX, PRO, SER, SER, THR) VAL ALA   150
151  VAL GLY CYS LEU ALA GLX ASP PHE LEU PRO ASP SER ILE THR PHE   165
166  SER TRP LYS TYR (ASN, ASX, SER, ASX, LYS) ILE SER SER THR ARG GLY   180
181  PHE PRO SER VAL LEU ARG GLY GLY LYS TYR ALA ALA THR (SER, GLX)   195
196  VAL LEU LEU PRO SER LYS ASP VAL MET GLN GLY THR ASP GLU HIS   210
211  VAL CYS LYS TRP VAL GLN HIS PRO ASN GLY ASX LYS GLN LYS ASX   225
226  VAL PRO LEU PRO VAL ILE ALA GLU LEU PRO PRO LYS VAL SER VAL   240
241  PHE VAL PRO PRO ARG ASX GLY PHE PHE GLY ASX PRO ARG LYS SER   255
256  LYS LEU ILE CYS GLN ALA THR GLY PHE SER PRO ARG GLN VAL TRP   270
271  SER LEU ARG GLU GLY LYS GLN VAL GLY SER GLY VAL THR THR ASX   285
286  GLX VAL GLX ALA GLX ALA LYS GLX SER GLY PRO THR THR TYR LYS   300
301  VAL THR SER THR LEU THR ILE LYS GLX SER ASP TRP LEU GLY GLU   315
316  SER MET PHE THR CYS ARG VAL ASP HIS ARG GLY LEU THR PHE GLN   330
331  GLN ASN ALA SER SER MET CYS VAL PRO ASP GLN ASP THR ALA ILE   345
346  ARG VAL PHE ALA ILE PRO PRO SER PHE ALA SER ILE PHE LEU THR   360
361  LYS SER THR LYS LEU THR CYS LEU VAL THR ASP LEU THR THR TYR   375
376  ASX SER VAL THR ILE SER TRP THR ARG GLU GLU ASN GLY ALA VAL   390
391  LYS THR HIS THR ASN ILE SER GLU SER HIS PRO ASN ALA THR PHE   405
406  SER ALA VAL GLY GLU ALA SER ILE CYS GLU ASP ASX ASP TRP SER   420
421  GLY GLU ARG PHE THR CYS THR VAL THR HIS THR ASP LEU PRO SER   435
436  PRO LEU LYS GLN THR ILE SER ARG PRO LYS GLY VAL ALA LEU HIS   450
451  ARG PRO ASX VAL TYR LEU LEU PRO PRO ALA ARG GLX GLX LEU ASN   465
466  LEU ARG GLU SER ALA THR ILE THR CYS LEU VAL THR GLY PHE SER   480
481  PRO ALA ASP VAL PHE VAL GLU TRP MET GLN ARG GLY GLU PRO LEU   495
496  SER PRO GLN LYS TYR VAL THR SER ALA PRO MET PRO GLU PRO GLN   510
511  ALA PRO GLY ARG TYR PHE ALA HIS SER ILE LEU THR VAL SER GLU   525
526  GLU GLU TRP ASN THR GLY GLN THR TYR THR CYS VAL VAL ALA HIS   540
541  GLU ALA LEU PRO ASN ARG VAL THR GLU ARG THR VAL ASP LYS SER   555
556  THR GLY LYS PRO THR LEU TYR ASN VAL SER LEU VAL MET SER ASP   570
571  THR ALA GLY THR CYS TYR                                        585
```

Note: Intrachain disulphide bridges link CYS 22 and 97; CYS 153 and 212; CYS 259 and 320; CYS 367 and 426; CYS 474 and 536.
Complete amino acid sequence of the Mu heavy chain of a human IgM.
F. W. Putman, G. Florent, C. Paul, T. Shinoda and A. Shimizu.
Science, **182**, 287–291 (1973).

IMMUNOGLOBULIN μ-CHAIN—HUMAN Gal

	1				5					10					15	
1	GLU	VAL	GLN	LEU	VAL	GLU	SER	GLY	GLY	ASP	LEU	VAL	GLN	PRO	GLY	15
16	ARG	SER	LEU	ARG	LEU	SER	CYS	ALA	ALA	SER	GLY	PHE	(ASX,	VAL,	LEU,	30
31	ASX,	ASX,	PHE)	MET	THR	TRP	VAL	ARG	GLN	ALA	PRO	GLY	LYS	GLY	LEU	45
46	GLU	TRP	VAL	ALA	ASN	ILE	LYS	GLX	ASX	GLY	SER	GLX	GLX	ASX	TYR	60
61	VAL	ASP	SER	VAL	LYS	GLY	ARG	PHE	THR	ILE	SER	ARG	ASP	ASN	ALA	75
76	LYS	ASN	SER	LEU	TYR	LEU	GLN	MET	ASN	SER	LEU	ARG	VAL	GLU	ASP	90
91	THR	ALA	LEU	TYR	TYR	CYS	ALA	ARG	GLY	TRP	GLY	GLY	GLY	ASP	TYR	105
106	TRP	GLY	GLN	GLY	THR	LEU	VAL	THR	VAL	SER	THR	GLY	SER	ALA	SER	120
121	ALA	PRO	THR	LEU	PHE	PRO	LEU	VAL	SER	CYS	GLU	ASX	SER	ASX	PRO	135
136	SER	SER	THR	VAL	ALA	VAL	GLY	CYS	LEU	ALA	GLN	ASP	PHE	LEU	PRO	150
151	ASP	SER	ILE	THR	PHE	SER	TRP	LYS	TYR	LYS	ASX	ASN	SER	ASP	ILE	165
166	SER	SER	THR	ARG	GLY	PHE	PRO	SER	VAL	LEU	ARG	GLY	GLY	LYS	TYR	180
181	ALA	ALA	THR	SER	GLN	VAL	LEU	LEU	PRO	SER	LYS	ASP	VAL	MET	GLN	195
196	GLY	THR	ASN	GLU	HIS	VAL	VAL	CYS	LYS	VAL	GLX	HIS	PRO	ASX	GLY	210
211	ASX	LYS	GLU	LYS	ASP	VAL	PRO	LEU	PRO	VAL	ILE	ALA	GLX	LEU	PRO	225
226	PRO	LYS	VAL	SER	VAL	PHE	VAL	PRO	PRO	ARG	ASP	GLY	PHE	PHE	GLY	240
241	ASX	PRO	ARG	LYS	SER	LYS	LEU	ILE	CYS	GLN	ALA	THR	GLY	PHE	SER	255
256	PRO	ARG	GLN	ILE	GLN	VAL	SER	TRP	LEU	ARG	GLU	GLY	LYS	GLN	VAL	270
271	GLY	SER	GLY	VAL	THR	THR	ASN	GLU	VAL	GLX	ALA	GLX	ALA	LYS	GLU	285
286	SER	GLY	PRO	THR	THR	TYR	LYS	VAL	THR	SER	THR	LEU	THR	ILE	LYS	300
301	GLU	SER	ASX	TRP	LEU	SER	GLN	SER	MET	PHE	THR	CYS	ARG	VAL	ASP	315
316	HIS	ARG	GLY	LEU	THR	PHE	GLN	GLN	ASX	ALA	SER	SER	MET	CYS	VAL	330
331	PRO	ASP	GLX	ASX	THR	ALA	ILE	ARG	VAL	PHE	ALA	ILE	PRO	PRO	SER	345
346	PHE	ALA	SER	ILE	PHE	LEU	THR	LYS	SER	THR	LYS	LEU	THR	CYS	LEU	360
361	VAL	THR	ASP	LEU	THR	TYR	ASP	SER	VAL	THR	ILE	SER	TRP	THR	ARG	375
376	GLN	ASP	GLY	GLU	ALA	VAL	LYS	THR	HIS	THR	ASX	ILE	SER	GLX	SER	390
391	HIS	PRO	ASX	ALA	THR	PHE	SER	ALA	VAL	GLY	GLU	ALA	SER	ILE	CYS	405
406	GLU	ASX	ASX	TRP	ASN	SER	GLY	GLU	ARG	PHE	THR	CYS	THR	VAL	THR	420
421	HIS	THR	ASP	LEU	PRO	SER	PRO	LEU	LYS	GLN	THR	ILE	SER	ARG	PRO	435
436	LYS	GLY	VAL	ALA	LEU	HIS	ARG	PRO	ASP	VAL	TYR	LEU	LEU	PRO	PRO	450
451	ALA	ARG	GLU	GLN	LEU	ASN	LEU	ARG	GLU	SER	ALA	THR	ILE	THR	CYS	465
466	LEU	VAL	THR	GLY	PHE	SER	PRO	ALA	ASP	VAL	PHE	VAL	GLN	TRP	GLN	480
481	MET	GLN	ARG	GLY	GLN	PRO	LEU	SER	PRO	GLU	LYS	TYR	VAL	THR	SER	495
496	ALA	PRO	MET	PRO	GLU	PRO	GLN	ALA	PRO	GLY	ARG	TYR	PHE	ALA	HIS	510
511	SER	ILE	LEU	THR	VAL	SER	GLU	GLU	GLU	TRP	ASN	THR	GLY	GLU	THR	525
526	TYR	THR	CYS	VAL	VAL	ALA	HIS	GLU	ALA	LEU	PRO	ASN	ARG	VAL	THR	540
541	GLU	ARG	THR	VAL	ASP	LYS	SER	THR	GLY	LYS	PRO	THR	LEU	TYR	ASX	555
556	VAL	SER	LEU	VAL	MET	SER	ASX	THR	ALA	GLY	THR	CYS	TYR			570

The primary structure of a monoclonal IgM-immunoglobulin (macroglobulin Gal.) II: The amino acid sequence of the H-chain (μ-type).
S. Watanabe, H. U. Barnikol, J. Horn, J. Bertram, and N. Hilschmann.
Hoppe-Seyler's Z. Physiol. Chem., **354**, 1505–1509 (1973).

IMMUNOGLOBULINS

IMMUNOGLOBULIN κ-CHAIN—HUMAN EU

	1				5					10					15	
1	ASP	ILE	GLN	MET	THR	GLN	SER	PRO	SER	THR	LEU	SER	ALA	SER	VAL	15
16	GLY	ASP	ARG	VAL	THR	ILE	THR	CYS	ARG	ALA	SER	GLN	SER	ILE	ASN	30
31	THR	TRP	LEU	ALA	TRP	TYR	GLN	GLN	LYS	PRO	GLY	LYS	ALA	PRO	LYS	45
46	LEU	LEU	MET	TYR	LYS	ALA	SER	SER	LEU	GLU	SER	GLY	VAL	PRO	SER	60
61	ARG	PHE	ILE	GLY	SER	GLY	SER	GLY	THR	GLU	PHE	THR	LEU	THR	ILE	75
76	SER	SER	LEU	GLN	PRO	ASP	ASP	PHE	ALA	THR	TYR	TYR	CYS	GLN	GLN	90
91	TYR	ASN	SER	ASP	SER	LYS	MET	PHE	GLY	GLN	GLY	THR	LYS	VAL	GLU	105
106	VAL	LYS	GLY	THR	VAL	ALA	ALA	PRO	SER	VAL	PHE	ILE	PHE	PRO	PRO	120
121	SER	ASP	GLU	GLN	LEU	LYS	SER	GLY	THR	ALA	SER	VAL	VAL	CYS	LEU	135
136	LEU	ASN	ASN	PHE	TYR	PRO	ARG	GLU	ALA	LYS	VAL	GLN	TRP	LYS	VAL	150
151	ASP	ASN	ALA	LEU	GLN	SER	GLY	ASN	SER	GLN	GLU	SER	VAL	THR	GLU	165
166	GLN	ASP	SER	LYS	ASP	SER	THR	TYR	SER	LEU	SER	SER	THR	LEU	THR	180
181	LEU	SER	LYS	ALA	ASP	TYR	GLU	LYS	HIS	LYS	VAL	TYR	ALA	CYS	GLU	195
196	VAL	THR	HIS	GLN	GLY	LEU	SER	SER	PRO	VAL	THR	LYS	SER	PHE	ASN	210
211	ARG	GLY	GLU	CYS												225

The Covalent Structure of an entire γG Immunoglobulin molecule.
G. M. Edelman, B. A. Cunningham, W. E. Gall, P. D. Gottlieb, U. Rutishauser, and M. J. Waxdal.
Proc. Natn. Acad. Sci., U.S.A., **63**, 78–85 (1969).

IMMUNOGLOBULIN κ-CHAIN—HUMAN AG

	1				5					10					15	
1	ASP	ILE	GLN	MET	THR	GLN	SER	PRO	SER	SER	LEU	SER	ALA	SER	VAL	15
16	GLY	ASP	ARG	VAL	THR	ILE	THR	CYS	GLN	ALA	SER	GLN	ASP	ILE	ASN	30
31	HIS	TYR	LEU	ASN	TRP	TYR	GLN	GLN	GLY	PRO	LYS	LYS	ALA	PRO	LYS	45
46	ILE	LEU	ILE	TYR	ASP	ALA	SER	ASN	LEU	GLU	THR	GLY	VAL	PRO	SER	60
61	ARG	PHE	SER	GLY	SER	GLY	PHE	GLY	THR	ASP	PHE	THR	PHE	THR	ILE	75
76	SER	GLY	LEU	GLN	PRO	GLU	ASP	ILE	ALA	THR	TYR	TYR	CYS	GLN	GLN	90
91	TYR	ASP	THR	LEU	PRO	ARG	THR	PHE	GLY	GLN	GLY	THR	LYS	LEU	GLU	105
106	ILE	LYS	ARG	THR	VAL	ALA	ALA	PRO	SER	VAL	PHE	ILE	PHE	PRO	PRO	120
121	SER	ASN	GLU	GLN	LEU	LYS	SER	GLY	THR	ALA	SER	VAL	VAL	CYS	LEU	135
136	LEU	ASN	ASN	PHE	TYR	PRO	ARG	GLU	ALA	LYS	VAL	GLN	TRP	LYS	VAL	150
151	ASP	ASN	ALA	LEU	GLN	SER	GLY	ASN	SER	GLN	GLU	SER	VAL	THR	GLU	165
166	GLN	ASP	SER	LYS	ASP	SER	THR	TYR	SER	LEU	SER	SER	THR	LEU	THR	180
181	LEU	SER	LYS	ALA	ASP	TYR	GLU	LYS	HIS	LYS	VAL	TYR	ALA	CYS	GLU	195
196	VAL	THR	HIS	GLN	GLY	LEU	SER	SER	PRO	VAL	THR	LYS	SER	PHE	ASN	210
211	ARG	GLY	GLU	CYS												225

Note: Disulphide bridges are between CYS 134 and 194; CYS 23 and 88.
The Amino Acid Sequence of a κ-Type Bence-Jones Protein. III. The Complete Sequence and location of the disulfide bridges.
K. Titani, T. Shinoda, and F. W. Putman.
J. Biol. Chem., **244**, 3550–3560 (1969).

IMMUNOGLOBULINS

IMMUNOGLOBULIN κ-CHAIN—HUMAN BI

	1				5					10					15	
1	ASP	ILE	GLN	MET	THR	GLN	SER	PRO	SER	PRO	LEU	SER	ALA	SER	VAL	15
16	GLY	ASP	SER	VAL	THR	ILE	THR	CYS	GLN	ALA	SER	GLN	ASP	ILE	ARG	30
31	ASN	SER	LEU	ILE	TRP	TYR	GLN	GLN	LYS	PRO	GLY	LYS	ALA	PRO	LYS	45
46	PHE	LEU	ILE	TYR	ASP	ALA	GLU	ASN	LEU	GLU	ILE	GLY	VAL	PRO	SER	60
61	ARG	PHE	ARG	GLY	SER	GLY	SER	GLY	THR	ASP	PHE	ALA	LEU	SER	ILE	75
76	SER	SER	LEU	GLN	PRO	GLN	ASP	PHE	ALA	THR	TYR	TYR	CYS	GLN	GLN	90
91	TYR	TYR	ASN	LEU	PRO	TYR	THR	PHE	GLY	GLN	GLY	THR	LYS	LEU	GLU	105
106	ILE	LYS	ARG	THR	VAL	ALA	ALA	PRO	SER	VAL	PHE	ILE	PHE	PRO	PRO	120
121	SER	ASP	GLU	GLN	LEU	LYS	SER	GLY	THR	ALA	SER	VAL	VAL	CYS	LEU	135
136	LEU	ASN	ASN	PHE	TYR	PRO	ARG	GLU	ALA	LYS	VAL	GLN	TRP	LYS	VAL	150
151	ASP	ASN	ALA	LEU	GLN	SER	GLY	ASX	SER	GLX	GLX	SER	VAL	THR	GLX	165
166	GLX	ASX	SER	LYS	ASP	SER	THR	TYR	SER	LEU	SER	SER	THR	LEU	THR	180
181	LEU	SER	LYS	ALA	ASP	TYR	GLU	LYS	HIS	LYS	VAL	TYR	ALA	CYS	GLU	195
196	VAL	THR	HIS	GLN	GLY	LEU	SER	SER	PRO	VAL	THR	LYS	SER	PHE	ASN	210
211	ARG	GLY	GLU	CYS												225

The primary structure of the L-chain immunoglobulin κ-Type sub-group I (Bence-Jones Protein BI).
M. Braun, W. Leibold, H.-U. Barnikol and N. Hilschmann.
Hoppe-Seyler's Z. Physiol. Chem., **352**, 647–651 (1971).

IMMUNOGLOBULIN κ-CHAIN—HUMAN HAU

	1				5					10					15	
1	ASP	ILE	GLN	MET	THR	GLN	SER	PRO	SER	SER	LEU	SER	ALA	SER	VAL	15
16	GLY	ASP	ARG	VAL	THR	ILE	THR	CYS	ARG	ALA	SER	GLN	SER	ILE	SER	30
31	SER	TYR	LEU	SER	TRP	TYR	GLN	GLN	LYS	PRO	GLY	LYS	ALA	PRO	GLN	45
46	VAL	LEU	ILE	TYR	ALA	ALA	SER	SER	LEU	PRO	SER	GLY	VAL	PRO	SER	60
61	ARG	PHE	SER	GLY	SER	GLY	SER	GLY	THR	ASP	PHE	THR	LEU	THR	ILE	75
76	SER	SER	LEU	GLN	PRO	GLU	ASP	PHE	ALA	THR	TYR	TYR	CYS	GLN	GLN	90
91	ASN	TYR	ILE	THR	PRO	THR	SER	PHE	GLY	GLN	GLY	THR	ARG	VAL	GLU	105
106	ILE	LYS	ARG	THR	VAL	ALA	ALA	PRO	SER	VAL	PHE	ILE	PHE	PRO	PRO	120
121	SER	ASX	GLX	GLX	LEU	LYS	SER	GLY	THR	ALA	SER	VAL	VAL	CYS	LEU	135
136	LEU	ASX	ASX	PHE	TYR	PRO	ARG	GLX	ALA	LYS	VAL	GLX	TRP	LYS	VAL	150
151	ASX	ASX	ALA	LEU	GLX	SER	GLY	ASX	SER	GLX	GLX	SER	VAL	THR	GLX	165
166	GLX	ASX	SER	LYS	ASX	SER	THR	TYR	SER	LEU	SER	SER	THR	LEU	THR	180
181	LEU	SER	LYS	ALA	ASX	TYR	GLX	LYS	HIS	LYS	VAL	TYR	ALA	CYS	GLX	195
196	VAL	THR	HIS	GLX	GLY	LEU	SER	SER	PRO	VAL	THR	LYS	SER	PHE	ASX	210
211	ARG	GLY	GLX	CYS												225

The primary structure of the L-chain immunoglobulin κ-Type sub-group I (Bence-Jones Protein HAU).
S. Watanabe and N. Hilschmann.
Hoppe-Seyler's Z. Physiol. Chem., **351**, 1291–1295 (1970).

IMMUNOGLOBULINS

IMMUNOGLOBULIN κ-CHAIN—HUMAN Roy

	1				5					10					15	
1	ASP	ILE	GLN	MET	THR	GLN	SER	PRO	SER	SER	LEU	SER	ALA	SER	VAL	15
16	GLY	ASP	ARG	VAL	THR	ILE	THR	CYS	GLX	ALA	SER	GLX	ASX	ILE	SER	30
31	ILE	PHE	LEU	ASN	TRP	TYR	GLN	GLN	GLY	PRO	LYS	LYS	ALA	PRO	LYS	45
46	LEU	LEU	ILE	TYR	ASP	ALA	SER	LYS	LEU	GLU	ALA	GLY	VAL	PRO	SER	60
61	ARG	PHE	SER	GLY	THR	GLY	SER	GLY	THR	ASP	PHE	THR	PHE	THR	ILE	75
76	SER	SER	LEU	GLN	PRO	GLU	ASP	ILE	ALA	THR	TYR	TYR	CYS	GLN	GLN	90
91	PHE	ASP	ASN	LEU	PRO	LEU	THR	PHE	GLY	GLY	GLY	THR	LYS	VAL	ASP	105
106	PHE	LYS	ARG	THR	VAL	ALA	ALA	PRO	SER	VAL	PHE	ILE	PHE	PRO	PRO	120
121	SER	ASP	GLU	GLN	LEU	LYS	SER	GLY	THR	ALA	SER	VAL	VAL	CYS	LEU	135
136	LEU	ASN	ASN	PHE	TYR	PRO	ARG	GLU	ALA	LYS	VAL	GLN	TRP	LYS	VAL	150
151	ASP	ASN	ALA	LEU	GLN	SER	GLY	ASN	SER	GLN	GLU	SER	VAL	THR	GLU	165
166	GLN	ASP	SER	LYS	ASP	SER	THR	TYR	SER	LEU	SER	SER	THR	LEU	THR	180
181	LEU	SER	LYS	ALA	ASP	TYR	GLU	LYS	HIS	LYS	LEU	TYR	ALA	CYS	GLU	195
196	VAL	THR	HIS	GLN	GLY	LEU	SER	SER	PRO	VAL	THR	LYS	SER	PHE	ASN	210
211	ARG	GLY	GLU	CYS												225

The Chemical Structure of the Bence-Jones Protein Roy and Cum of the κ-Type.
N. Hilschmann.
Hoppe-Seyler's Z. Physiol. Chem., **348**, 1077–1080 (1967).

IMMUNOGLOBULIN κ-CHAIN—HUMAN Ti

	1				5					10					15	
1	GLU	ILE	VAL	LEU	THR	GLN	SER	PRO	GLY	THR	LEU	SER	LEU	SER	PRO	15
16	GLY	GLU	ARG	ALA	THR	LEU	SER	CYS	ARG	ALA	SER	GLN	SER	VAL	SER	30
31	ASN	SER	PHE	LEU	ALA	TRP	TYR	GLN	GLN	LYS	PRO	GLY	GLN	ALA	PRO	45
46	ARG	LEU	LEU	ILE	TYR	VAL	ALA	SER	SER	ARG	ALA	THR	GLY	ILE	PRO	60
61	ASP	ARG	PHE	SER	GLY	SER	GLY	SER	GLY	THR	ASP	PHE	THR	LEU	THR	75
76	ILE	SER	ARG	LEU	GLU	PRO	GLU	ASP	PHE	ALA	VAL	TYR	TYR	CYS	GLN	90
91	GLN	TYR	GLY	SER	SER	PRO	SER	THR	PHE	GLY	GLN	GLY	THR	LYS	VAL	105
106	GLU	LEU	LYS	ARG	THR	VAL	ALA	ALA	PRO	SER	VAL	PHE	ILE	PHE	PRO	120
121	PRO	SER	ASP	GLU	GLN	LEU	LYS	SER	GLY	THR	ALA	SER	VAL	VAL	CYS	135
136	LEU	LEU	ASN	ASN	PHE	TYR	PRO	ARG	GLU	ALA	LYS	VAL	GLN	TRP	LYS	150
151	VAL	ASP	ASN	ALA	LEU	GLN	SER	GLY	ASN	SER	GLN	GLU	SER	VAL	THR	165
166	GLU	GLN	ASP	SER	LYS	ASP	SER	THR	TYR	SER	LEU	SER	SER	THR	LEU	180
181	THR	LEU	SER	LYS	ALA	ASP	TYR	GLU	LYS	HIS	LYS	VAL	TYR	ALA	CYS	195
196	GLU	VAL	THR	HIS	GLN	GLY	LEU	SER	SER	PRO	VAL	THR	LYS	SER	PHE	210
211	ASN	ARG	GLY	GLU	CYS											225

The primary structure of a monoclonal immunoglobulin L-chain of the κ-type, sub-group III (Bence-Jones protein Ti).
L. Suter, H.-U. Barnikol, S. Watanabe, and N. Hilschmann.
Hoppe-Seyler's Z. Physiol. Chem., **353**, 189–208 (1972).

IMMUNOGLOBULIN κ-CHAIN—HUMAN Dee

	1				5					10					15	
1	ASX	ILE	GLX	MET	THR	GLN	SER	PRO	SER	SER	LEU	SER	ALA	SER	VAL	15
16	GLY	ASP	ARG	VAL	THR	ILE	THR	CYS	ARG	ALA	GLY	GLN	SER	VAL	ASN	30
31	LYS	TYR	LEU	ASN	TRP	TYR	GLN	GLN	LYS	PRO	GLY	LYS	ALA	PRO	LYS	45
46	VAL	LEU	(ILE,	PHE)	ALA	ALA	SER	SER	LEU	LYS	SER	GLY	VAL	PRO	SER	60
61	ARG	PHE	SER	GLY	SER	GLY	SER	GLY	THR	ASP	PHE	THR	LEU	THR	ILE	75
76	SER	GLY	LEU	LEU	PRO	GLU	ASP	PHE	ALA	THR	TYR	TYR	CYS	GLX	GLX	90
91	SER	TYR	THR	THR	PRO	TYR	THR	PHE	GLY	PRO	GLY	THR	LYS	VAL	GLU	105
106	MET	THR	ARG	THR	VAL	(ALA,	ALA)	PRO	(SER,	VAL,	PHE)	ILE	PHE	PRO	PRO	120
121	SER	ASP	GLU	GLN	LEU	LYS	SER	GLY	THR	ALA	SER	VAL	(VAL,	CYS,	LEU)	135
136	LEU	ASN	ASN	PHE	TYR	PRO	ARG	GLU	ALA	LYS	VAL	(GLN,	TRP)	LYS	VAL	150
151	ASX	ASX	ALA	LEU	GLX	SER	GLY	ASX	SER	GLX	GLX	SER	VAL	THR	GLX	165
166	GLX	ASP	SER	LYS	ASX	SER	THR	TYR	SER	LEU	SER	SER	THR	LEU	THR	180
181	LEU	SER	LYS	ALA	ASP	TYR	GLU	LYS	HIS	LYS	VAL	TYR	(ALA,	CYS,	GLX)	195
196	VAL	(THR,	HIS,	GLN,	GLY,	LEU,	SER,	SER,	PRO,	VAL,	THR)	LYS	SER	PHE	ASN	210
211	ARG	GLY	GLU	CYS												225

The Amino Acid Sequence of a Human κ Light Chain.
C. P. Milstein and E. V. Deverson.
Biochem. J., **123**, 945–958 (1971).

IMMUNOGLOBULIN κ-CHAIN—HUMAN Cum

	1				5					10					15	
1	GLU	ASP	ILE	VAL	MET	THR	GLN	THR	PRO	LEU	SER	LEU	PRO	VAL	THR	15
16	PRO	GLY	GLU	PRO	ALA	SER	ILE	SER	CYS	ARG	SER	SER	GLN	SER	LEU	30
31	LEU	ASP	SER	GLY	ASP	GLY	ASN	THR	TYR	LEU	ASN	TRP	TYR	LEU	GLN	45
46	LYS	ALA	GLY	GLN	GLN	PRO	SER	LEU	LEU	ILE	TYR	THR	LEU	SER	TYR	60
61	ARG	ALA	SER	GLY	VAL	PRO	ASP	ARG	PHE	SER	GLY	SER	GLY	SER	GLY	75
76	THR	ASP	PHE	THR	LEU	LYS	ILE	SER	ARG	VAL	GLN	ALA	GLU	ASP	VAL	90
91	GLY	VAL	TYR	TYR	CYS	GLN	MET	ARG	LEU	GLU	ILE	PRO	TYR	THR	PHE	105
106	GLY	GLN	GLY	THR	LYS	LEU	GLU	ILE	ARG	ARG	THR	VAL	ALA	ALA	PRO	120
121	SER	VAL	PHE	ILE	PHE	PRO	PRO	SER	ASP	GLU	GLN	LEU	LYS	SER	GLY	135
136	THR	ALA	SER	VAL	VAL	CYS	LEU	LEU	ASN	ASN	PHE	TYR	PRO	ARG	GLU	150
151	ALA	LYS	VAL	GLN	TRP	LYS	VAL	ASP	ASN	ALA	LEU	GLN	SER	GLY	ASN	165
166	SER	GLN	GLU	SER	VAL	THR	GLN	GLN	ASP	SER	LYS	ASP	SER	THR	TYR	180
181	SER	LEU	SER	SER	THR	LEU	THR	LEU	SER	LYS	ALA	ASP	TYR	GLU	LYS	195
196	HIS	LYS	VAL	TYR	ALA	CYS	GLU	VAL	THR	HIS	GLN	GLY	LEU	SER	SER	210
211	PRO	VAL	THR	LYS	SER	PHE	ASN	ARG	GLY	GLU	CYS					225

The Amino Acid Sequence of the Bence-Jones protein Cum (κ-Type).
N. Hilschmann.
Hoppe-Seyler's Z. Physiol. Chem., **348**, 1718–1722 (1967).

IMMUNOGLOBULINS

IMMUNOGLOBULIN κ-CHAIN—HUMAN Rei

	1			5					10					15		
1	ASP	ILE	GLN	MET	THR	GLN	SER	PRO	SER	SER	LEU	SER	ALA	SER	VAL	15
16	GLY	ASP	ARG	VAL	THR	ILE	THR	CYS	GLN	ALA	SER	GLN	ASP	ILE	ILE	30
31	LYS	TYR	LEU	ASN	TRP	TYR	GLN	GLN	THR	PRO	GLY	LYS	ALA	PRO	LYS	45
46	LEU	LEU	ILE	TYR	GLU	ALA	SER	ASN	LEU	GLN	ALA	GLY	VAL	PRO	SER	60
61	ARG	PHE	SER	GLY	SER	GLY	SER	GLY	THR	ASP	TYR	THR	PHE	THR	ILE	75
76	SER	SER	LEU	GLN	PRO	GLU	ASP	ILE	ALA	THR	TYR	TYR	CYS	GLN	GLN	90
91	TYR	GLN	SER	LEU	PRO	TYR	THR	PHE	GLY	GLN	GLY	THR	LYS	LEU	GLN	105
106	ILE	THR	ARG	THR	VAL	ALA	ALA	PRO	SER	VAL	PHE	ILE	PHE	PRO	PRO	120
121	SER	ASX	GLX	GLX	LEU	LYS	SER	GLY	THR	ALA	SER	VAL	VAL	CYS	LEU	135
136	LEU	ASX	ASX	PHE	TYR	PRO	ARG	GLU	ALA	LYS	VAL	GLN	TRP	LYS	VAL	150
151	ASX	ASX	ALA	LEU	GLX	SER	GLY	ASX	SER	GLX	GLX	SER	VAL	THR	GLX	165
166	GLX	ASX	SER	LYS	ASP	SER	THR	TYR	SER	LEU	SER	SER	THR	LEU	THR	180
181	LEU	SER	LYS	ALA	ASP	TYR	GLU	LYS	HIS	LYS	LEU	TYR	ALA	CYS	GLU	195
196	VAL	THR	HIS	GLN	GLY	LEU	SER	SER	PRO	VAL	THR	LYS	SER	PHE	ASN	210
211	ARG	GLY	GLU	CYS												225

The primary structure of a crystalline monoclonal immunoglobulin κ-type L-chain, subgroup I (Bence-Jones protein Rei); isolation and characterization of the tryptic peptides; the complete amino acid sequence of the protein; a contribution to the elucidation of the three-dimensional structure of antibodies, in particular their combining site.
W. Palm and N. Hilschmann.
Hoppe-Seyler's Z. Physiol. Chem., **356**, 167–191 (1975).

IMMUNOGLOBULINS

IMMUNOGLOBULIN κ-CHAIN—HUMAN Gal

	1			5					10					15		
1	ASP	ILE	GLN	MET	THR	GLN	SER	PRO	SER	SER	LEU	SER	ALA	SER	VAL	15
16	GLY	ASP	ARG	VAL	THR	ILE	ILE	CYS	ARG	ALA	SER	GLN	GLY	ILE	ARG	30
31	ASN	ASP	LEU	THR	TRP	TYR	GLN	GLN	LYS	PRO	GLY	LYS	ALA	PRO	LYS	45
46	GLU	LEU	ILE	TYR	ALA	ALA	SER	ASN	LEU	GLN	SER	GLY	VAL	PRO	SER	60
61	ARG	PHE	SER	GLY	SER	GLY	ALA	GLY	THR	GLU	PHE	THR	LEU	THR	ILE	75
76	SER	SER	LEU	GLN	PRO	GLU	ASP	PHE	ALA	THR	TYR	TYR	CYS	LEU	GLN	90
91	GLN	ASN	SER	TYR	PRO	ARG	SER	PHE	GLY	GLN	GLY	THR	LYS	VAL	GLU	105
106	ILE	LYS	ARG	THR	VAL	ALA	ALA	PRO	SER	VAL	PHE	ILE	PHE	PRO	PRO	120
121	SER	ASX	GLX	GLX	LEU	LYS	SER	GLY	THR	ALA	SER	VAL	VAL	CYS	LEU	135
136	LEU	ASX	ASX	PHE	TYR	PRO	ARG	GLX	ALA	LYS	VAL	GLX	TRP	LYS	VAL	150
151	ASX	ASX	ALA	LEU	GLX	SER	GLY	ASX	SER	GLX	GLX	SER	VAL	THR	GLX	165
166	GLX	ASX	SER	LYS	ASX	SER	THR	TYR	SER	LEU	SER	SER	THR	LEU	THR	180
181	LEU	SER	LYS	ALA	ASX	TYR	GLX	LYS	HIS	LYS	VAL	TYR	ALA	CYS	GLX	195
196	VAL	THR	HIS	GLX	GLY	LEU	SER	SER	PRO	VAL	THR	LYS	SER	PHE	ASX	210
211	ARG	GLY	GLX	CYS												225

The primary structure of a monoclonal IgM-immunoglobulin (macroglobulin Gal.). The amino acid sequence of the L-chain κ-type.
C. J. Laure, S. Watanabe, and N. Hilschmann.
Hoppe-Seyler's Z. Physiol. Chem., **354**, 1503–1504 (1973).

IMMUNOGLOBULIN κ-CHAIN—HUMAN Car

	1			5					10					15		
1	ASP	ILE	GLN	MET	THR	GLN	SER	PRO	SER	THR	LEU	SER	ALA	SER	VAL	15
16	GLY	ASP	ARG	VAL	ALA	ILE	THR	CYS	ARG	ALA	SER	GLN	ASN	ILE	SER	30
31	SER	TRP	LEU	ALA	TRP	TYR	GLN	GLN	LYS	PRO	GLY	LYS	ALA	PRO	LYS	45
46	VAL	LEU	ILE	TYR	LYS	SER	SER	SER	LEU	GLU	SER	GLY	VAL	PRO	SER	60
61	ARG	PHE	SER	GLY	SER	GLY	SER	GLY	THR	ASP	PHE	THR	LEU	THR	ILE	75
76	SER	SER	LEU	GLX	PRO	ASX	ASX	PHE	ALA	THR	TYR	TYR	CYS	GLN	GLN	90
91	TYR	ASN	THR	PHE	PHE	THR	PHE	GLY	PRO	GLY	THR	LYS	VAL	ASP	ILE	105
106	LYS	ARG	THR	VAL	ALA	ALA	PRO	SER	VAL	PHE	ILE	PHE	PRO	PRO	SER	120
121	(ASP,	GLU,	GLN,	LEU)	LYS	SER	GLY	THR	ALA	SER	VAL	(VAL,	CYS,	LEU)	LEU	135
136	ASN	ASN	PHE	TYR	PRO	ARG	GLU	ALA	LYS	VAL	GLN	TRP	LYS	VAL	ASX	150
151	ASX	ALA	LEU	(GLX,	SER,	GLY,	ASX,	SER,	GLX,	GLX)	SER	(VAL,	THR,	GLX,	GLX,	165
166	ASX,	SER)	LYS	(ASX,	SER,	THR)	TYR	SER	LEU	SER	SER	THR	LEU	THR	LEU	180
181	SER	LYS	ALA	ASP	(TYR,	GLU)	LYS	HIS	LYS	LEU	TYR	ALA	CYS	GLU	VAL	195
196	THR	(HIS,	GLU,	GLY,	LEU,	SER,	SER,	PRO,	VAL,	THR)	LYS	SER	PHE	ASN	ARG	210
211	GLY	GLU	CYS													225

Primary structure of κ light chain from a human myeloma protein.
C. P. Milstein and E. V. Deverson.
Eur. J. Biochem., **49**, 377–391 (1974).

IMMUNOGLOBULINS

IMMUNOGLOBULIN κ-CHAIN—HUMAN Len

```
       1              5                  10                 15
  1  ASP ILE VAL MET THR GLN SER PRO ASN SER LEU ALA VAL SER LEU   15
 16  GLY GLU ARG ALA THR ILE ASN CYS LYS SER SER GLN SER VAL LEU   30
 31  TYR SER SER ASN SER LYS ASN TYR LEU ALA TRP TYR GLN GLN LYS   45
 46  PRO GLY GLN PRO PRO LYS LEU LEU ILE TYR TRP ALA SER THR ARG   60
 61  GLU SER GLY VAL PRO ASP ARG PHE SER GLY SER GLY SER GLY THR   75
 76  ASP PHE THR LEU THR ILE SER SER LEU GLN ALA GLU ASP VAL ALA   90
 91  VAL TYR TYR CYS GLN GLN TYR TYR SER THR PRO TYR SER PHE GLY  105
106  GLN GLY THR LYS LEU GLU ILE LYS ARG THR VAL ALA ALA PRO SER  120
121  VAL PHE ILE PHE PRO PRO SER ASX GLX GLX LEU LYS SER GLY THR  135
136  ALA SER VAL VAL CYS LEU LEU ASN ASN PHE TYR PRO ARG GLU ALA  150
151  LYS VAL GLN TRP LYS VAL ASX ASX ALA LEU GLX SER GLY ASX SER  165
166  GLX GLX SER VAL THR GLX GLX ASX SER LYS ASX SER THR TYR SER  180
181  LEU SER SER THR LEU THR LEU SER LYS ALA ASP TYR GLU LYS HIS  195
196  LYS VAL TYR ALA CYS GLX VAL THR HIS GLX GLY LEU SER SER PRO  210
211  VAL THR LYS SER PHE ASN ARG GLY GLU CYS                      225
```

The primary structure of the monoclonal immunoglobulin light chain κ-type, subgroup IV, (Bence-Jones protein Len).
M. Schneider and N. Hilschmann.
Hoppe-Seyler's Z. Physiol. Chem., **356**, 507–557 (1975).

IMMUNOGLOBULIN κ-CHAIN—HUMAN Scw

```
       1              5                  10                 15
  1  ASP ILE GLN MET THR GLN SER PRO SER SER LEU SER ALA SER VAL   15
 16  GLY ASP ARG VAL THR ILE THR CYS GLN ALA SER GLN ASP ILE ARG   30
 31  LYS HIS LEU ASN TRP TYR ASP GLN LYS PRO GLY LYS ALA PRO ARG   45
 46  LEU LEU ILE TYR GLY ALA SER THR LEU GLU THR GLY VAL PRO SER   60
 61  ARG PHE SER GLY SER GLY SER GLY THR ASP PHE THR LEU THR ILE   75
 76  SER THR LEU GLN PRO GLU ASP ILE GLY ASN TYR TYR CYS GLN GLN   90
 91  TYR ASP ASN VAL PRO ILE THR PHE GLY GLN GLY THR ARG VAL GLU  105
106  ASN LYS GLY THR VAL ALA ALA PRO SER VAL PHE ILE PHE PRO PRO  120
121  SER ASX GLX GLX LEU LYS SER GLY THR ALA SER VAL VAL CYS LEU  135
136  LEU ASX ASX PHE TYR PRO ARG GLX ALA LYS VAL GLX TRP LYS VAL  150
151  ASX ASX ALA LEU GLX SER GLY ASX SER GLX GLX SER VAL THR GLX  165
166  GLX ASX SER LYS ASX SER THR TYR SER LEU SER SER THR LEU THR  180
181  LEU SER LYS ALA ASX TYR GLX LYS HIS LYS LEU TYR ALA CYS GLX  195
196  VAL THR HIS GLX GLY LEU SER SER PRO VAL THR LYS SER PHE ASX  210
211  ARG GLY GLX CYS                                              225
```

The primary structure of a human immunoglobulin L-chain of the K-type (Bence-Jones protein Scw). II: The chymotryptic peptides and the complete amino acid sequence.
M. Eulitz and N. Hilschmann.
Hoppe-Seyler's Z. Physiol. Chem., **355**, 842–866 (1974).

IMMUNOGLOBULIN κ-CHAIN—HUMAN Ka

```
        1            5               10              15
  1   ASP ILE GLN MET THR GLN SER PRO SER THR LEU SER VAL SER VAL    15
 16   GLY ASP ARG VAL THR ILE THR CYS GLU ALA SER GLN THR VAL LEU    30
 31   SER TYR LEU ASN TRP TYR GLN GLN LYS PRO GLY LYS ALA PRO LYS    45
 46   LEU LEU ILE TYR ALA ALA SER SER LEU GLU THR GLY VAL PRO SER    60
 61   ARG PHE SER GLY GLN GLY SER GLY THR ASX PHE THR PHE THR ILE    75
 76   SER SER VAL GLX PRO GLX ASX PHE ALA THR TYR TYR CYS GLN GLX    90
 91   TYR LEU ASP LEU PRO ARG THR PHE GLY GLN GLY THR LYS VAL ASP   105
106   LEU LYS ARG THR VAL ALA ALA PRO SER VAL PHE (ILE, PHE, PRO, PRO, 120
121   SER, ASX, GLX, GLX, LEU) LYS SER GLY THR (ALA, SER, VAL, VAL) CYS LEU 135
136   LEU (ASX, ASX, PHE, TYR, PRO) ARG GLU ALA LYS VAL GLN TRP LYS VAL 150
151   ASX ASX ALA (LEU, GLX, SER, GLY, ASX, SER, GLX, GLX, SER, VAL, THR, GLX, 165
166   GLX, ASX, SER) LYS ASP SER THR TYR (SER, LEU, SER, SER, THR, LEU, THR, 180
181   LEU, SER) LYS ALA ASP TYR GLU LYS HIS LYS VAL TYR ALA CYS GLU   195
196   VAL THR (HIS, GLX, GLY, LEU, SER, SER, PRO, VAL, THR) LYS SER PHE ASN 210
211   ARG GLY GLU CYS                                                225
```

Comparative structural studies on the light chains of human immunoglobulins. I. Protein Ka with the Inv(3) allotypic marker.
T. Shinoda.
J. Biochem., **77**, 1277–1296 (1975).

IMMUNOGLOBULIN κ-CHAIN—HUMAN Ni

```
        1            5               10              15
  1   ASP ILE GLN MET THR GLN SER PRO SER SER LEU SER ALA THR VAL    15
 16   GLY ASP ARG VAL THR LEU LEU CYS GLU ALA SER GLN SER VAL LEU    30
 31   GLU SER GLY ASN THR PHE LEU ALA TRP TYR GLN GLN LYS PRO LYS    45
 46   LYS ALA PRO LYS LEU LEU ILE TYR ASP ALA SER ASN LEU GLU THR    60
 61   GLY VAL PRO SER ARG PHE SER GLU SER GLY SER GLY THR ASP PHE    75
 76   THR PHE THR ILE SER GLY LEU GLX PRO GLX ASX PHE ALA VAL TYR    90
 91   TYR CYS GLN GLX TYR ASP THR LEU PRO SER THR PHE GLY VAL ALA   105
106   SER LYS VAL GLU SER LYS ARG THR VAL ALA ALA (PRO, SER) VAL PHE 120
121   ILE PHE (PRO, PRO, SER, ASX, GLX, GLX) LEU LYS SER GLY THR (ALA, SER, 135
136   VAL) VAL CYS LEU LEU ASN ASN PHE (TYR, PRO) ARG GLU ALA LYS VAL 150
151   GLN TRP LYS VAL ASP ASN ALA LEU GLN SER (GLY, ASX, SER, GLX, GLX, 165
166   SER, VAL, THR, GLX, GLX, ASX, SER) LYS ASP SER THR TYR SER LEU SER 180
181   SER THR LEU THR LEU SER LYS ALA ASP TYR GLU LYS HIS LYS VAL   195
196   TYR ALA CYS GLU VAL THR (HIS, GLX) GLY LEU SER SER PRO (VAL, THR) 210
211   LYS SER PHE ASN ARG GLY GLU CYS                                225
```

Amino acid sequence of a human kappa type Bence-Jones protein. II. Chymotryptic peptides and sequence of protein Ni.
T. Shinoda.
J. Biochem., **73**, 433–446 (1973).

IMMUNOGLOBULINS

IMMUNOGLOBULIN κ-CHAIN—MOUSE MOPC 21

	1				5					10					15	
1	ASN	ILE	VAL	MET	THR	GLN	SER	PRO	LYS	SER	MET	SER	MET	SER	VAL	15
16	GLY	GLU	ARG	VAL	THR	LEU	THR	CYS	LYS	ALA	SER	GLU	ASN	VAL	VAL	30
31	THR	TYR	VAL	SER	TRP	TYR	GLN	GLN	LYS	PRO	GLU	GLN	SER	PRO	LYS	45
46	LEU	LEU	ILE	TYR	GLY	ALA	SER	ASN	ARG	TYR	THR	GLY	VAL	PRO	ASP	60
61	ARG	PHE	THR	GLY	SER	GLY	SER	ALA	THR	ASP	PHE	THR	LEU	THR	ILE	75
76	SER	SER	VAL	GLN	ALA	GLU	ASP	LEU	ALA	ASP	TYR	HIS	CYS	GLY	GLN	90
91	GLY	TYR	SER	TYR	PRO	TYR	THR	PHE	GLY	GLY	GLY	THR	LYS	LEU	GLU	105
106	ILE	LYS	ARG	ALA	ASP	ALA	ALA	PRO	THR	VAL	SER	ILE	PHE	PRO	PRO	120
121	SER	SER	GLU	GLN	LEU	THR	SER	GLY	GLY	ALA	SER	VAL	VAL	CYS	PHE	135
136	LEU	ASN	ASN	PHE	TYR	PRO	LYS	ASP	ILE	ASN	VAL	LYS	TRP	LYS	ILE	150
151	ASP	GLY	SER	GLU	ARG	GLN	ASN	GLY	VAL	LEU	ASX	SER	ASX	THR	GLX	165
166	TRP	ASX	SER	LYS	ASP	SER	THR	TYR	SER	MET	SER	SER	THR	LEU	THR	180
181	LEU	THR	LYS	ASP	GLU	TYR	GLU	ARG	HIS	ASN	SER	TYR	THR	CYS	GLU	195
196	ALA	THR	HIS	LYS	THR	SER	THR	SER	PRO	ILE	VAL	LYS	SER	PHE	ASN	210
211	ARG	ASN	GLU	CYS												225

The Complete Amino Acid Sequence of a Mouse κ Light Chain.
J. Svasti and C. Milstein.
Biochem. J., **128**, 427–444 (1972).

IMMUNOGLOBULIN κ-CHAIN—MOUSE MOPC 173

	1				5					10					15	
1	ASP	ILE	GLN	MET	THR	GLN	THR	THR	SER	SER	LEU	SER	ALA	SER	LEU	15
16	GLY	ASP	ARG	VAL	THR	ILE	SER	CYS	SER	ALA	SER	GLN	SER	ILE	GLY	30
31	ASN	TYR	(LEU, ASX, TRP)		TYR	GLN	GLN	LYS	PRO	ASP	GLY	THR	VAL	LYS	45
46	LEU	LEU	ILE	TYR	TYR	THR	SER	SER	LEU	HIS	SER	GLY	VAL	PRO	SER	60
61	ARG	PHE	SER	GLY	SER	GLY	SER	GLY	THR	ASP	TYR	SER	LEU	THR	ILE	75
76	SER	ASX	LEU	GLX	PRO	GLX	ASX	ILE	ALA	THR	TYR	TYR	CYS	GLN	GLN	90
91	TYR	SER	LYS	LEU	PRO	ARG	THR	PHE	GLY	GLY	GLY	THR	LYS	LEU	GLU	105
106	ILE	LYS	ARG	ALA	ASX	ALA	ALA	PRO	THR	VAL	SER	ILE	PHE	PRO	PRO	120
121	SER	SER	GLX	GLX	LEU	THR	SER	GLY	GLY	ALA	SER	VAL	VAL	CYS	PHE	135
136	LEU	ASN	ASN	PHE	TYR	PRO	LYS	ASP	ILE	ASN	VAL	LYS	TRP	LYS	ILE	150
151	ASP	GLY	SER	GLU	ARG	GLN	ASX	GLY	VAL	LEU	ASX	SER	ASN	THR	GLU	165
166	TRP	ASP	SER	LYS	ASP	SER	THR	TYR	SER	MET	SER	SER	THR	LEU	THR	180
181	LEU	THR	LYS	ASP	GLU	TYR	GLU	ARG	HIS	ASN	SER	TYR	THR	CYS	GLU	195
196	ALA	THR	HIS	LYS	THR	SER	THR	SER	PRO	ILE	VAL	LYS	SER	PHE	ASN	210
211	ARG	ASN	GLU	CYS												225

Determination of the primary structure of a mouse IgG2a immunoglobulin. Amino acid sequence of the light chain.
C. Schiff and M. Fougereau.
Eur. J. Biochem., **59**, 525–537 (1975).

RABBIT 2717 IMMUNOGLOBULIN LIGHT CHAIN

	1				5					10					15	
1	VAL	GLU	VAL	LEU	THR	GLN	THR	PRO	SER	PRO	VAL	SER	ALA	ALA	VAL	15
16	GLY	GLY	THR	VAL	THR	ILE	SER	CYS	GLN	SER	THR	LYS	SER	ILE	TYR	30
31	ASX	ASX	ASX	TYR	LEU	ALA	TRP	TYR	GLN	GLX	LYS	PRO	GLY	GLN	PRO	45
46	PRO	LYS	ALA	LEU	ILE	TYR	THR	ALA	SER	SER	LEU	ALA	SER	GLY	VAL	60
61	PRO	SER	ARG	PHE	THR	GLY	SER	GLY	SER	GLY	THR	GLX	PHE	THR	LEU	75
76	THR	LEU	SER	ASP	VAL	GLX	CYS	ASP	ASP	ALA	ALA	THR	TYR	TYR	CYS	90
91	GLY	GLY	ALA	ASP	TYR	THR	GLY	TYR	SER	PHE	GLY	GLY	GLY	THR	GLU	105
106	VAL	VAL	VAL	LYS	GLY	ASX	PRO	VAL	ALA	PRO	THR	VAL	LEU	ILE	PHE	120
121	PRO	PRO	ALA	ALA	ASN	GLN	VAL	ALA	THR	GLY	THR	THR	VAL	ILE	VAL	135
136	CYS	VAL	ALA	ASX	LYS	TYR	PHE	PRO	ASP	VAL	THR	VAL	THR	SER	GLX	150
151	VAL	ASP	GLY	THR	TRP	VAL	SER	GLX (ASP,	GLY,	THR,	THR)	ILE		GLX	SER	165
166	LYS	ILE	SER	GLX	ASP	SER	ASP	ASP	CYS	THR	TYR	LEU	SER	SER	THR	180
181	LEU	THR	LEU	THR	SER	THR	GLX	TYR	ASP	SER	HIS	LYS	GLX	TYR	THR	195
196	CYS	LYS	GLY	THR	VAL	LYS	GLX (SER,	THR,	GLY,	THR,	VAL,	VAL,	GLX)		SER	210
211	PHE	ASN	ARG	GLY	ASX	CYS										225

Amino acid sequence of the light chain derived from a rabbit anti-*p*-azobenzoate antibody of restricted heterogeneity.
E. Appella, O. A. Roholt, A. Chersi, G. Radzimski, and D. Pressman.
Biochem. Biophys. Res. Commun., **53**, 1122–1129 (1973).

IMMUNOGLOBULIN LIGHT CHAIN ALLOTYPE B4—RABBIT

	1				5					10					15	
1	ALA	ASP	ILE	VAL	MET	THR	GLN	THR	PRO	ALA	SER	VAL	SER	GLU	PRO	15
16	VAL	GLY	GLY	THR	VAL	THR	ILE	LYS	CYS	GLN	THR	SER	GLN	SER	ILE	30
31	ASP	ASP	TYR	LEU	SER	TRP	TYR	GLN	GLN	LYS	PRO	GLY	GLN	PRO	PRO	45
46	LYS	GLY	LEU	ILE	TYR	ARG	ALA	SER	THR	LEU	ALA	SER	GLY	VAL	PRO	60
61	SER	ARG	PHE	ARG	GLY	SER	GLY	SER	GLY	THR	TIIR	ASP	PHE	THR	LEU	THR	75
76	ILE	SER	ASP	LEU	GLU	CYS	ALA	ASP	ALA	ALA	THR	TYR	TYR	CYS	GLN	90
91	SER	THR	TYR	GLY	VAL	GLY	PHE	GLY	GLY	GLY	THR	GLU	VAL	VAL	VAL	105
106	LYS	GLY	ASP	PRO	VAL	ALA	PRO	THR	VAL	LEU	ILE	PHE	PRO	PRO	ALA	120
121	ALA	ASP	GLN	VAL	ALA	THR	GLY	THR	VAL	THR	ILE	VAL	CYS	VAL	ALA	135
136	ASN	LYS	TYR	PHE	PRO	ASP	VAL	THR	VAL	THR	TRP	GLU	VAL	ASP	GLY	150
151	THR	THR	GLN	THR	THR	GLY	ILE	GLU	ASN	SER	LYS	THR	PRO	GLN	ASP	165
166	SER	ALA	ASP	CYS	THR	TYR	ASN	LEU	SER	SER	THR	LEU	THR	LEU	THR	180
181	SER	THR	GLN	TYR	ASN	SER	HIS	LYS	GLU	TYR	THR	CYS	LYS	VAL	THR	195
196	GLN	GLY	THR	THR	SER	VAL	VAL	GLN	SER	PHE	ASN	ARG	GLY	ASP	CYS	210

Primary structure of the L chain from a rabbit homogeneous antibody to streptococcal carbohydrate.
K. C. S. Chen, T. J. Kindt, and R. M. Krause.
J. Biol. Chem., **250**, 3289–3296 (1975).

IMMUNOGLOBULINS

IMMUNOGLOBULIN LIGHT CHAIN (L120)—RABBIT

	1				5					10					15	
1	ALA	PHE	GLU	LEU	THR	GLN	THR	PRO	SER	SER	VAL	GLU	ALA	ALA	VAL	15
16	THR	GLY	THR	VAL	THR	ILE	LYS	CYS	GLN	SER	SER	GLN	SER	ILE	GLY	30
31	THR	TYR	LEU	ALA	TRP	TYR	GLX	GLX	LYS	PRO	GLY	SER	PRO	PRO	LYS	45
46	LEU	LEU	ILE	TYR	ARG	ALA	SER	THR	LEU	SER	GLY	VAL	SER	SER	ARG	60
61	PHE	LYS	GLY	SER	GLY	SER	GLY	THR	GLU	PHE	THR	LEU	THR	ILE	SER	75
76	GLY	VAL	GLU	CYS	ALA	ASP	ALA	ALA	THR	TYR	TYR	CYS	GLN	GLY	THR	90
91	TYR	TYR	GLX	SER	ALA	SER	PHE	GLY	GLY	GLY	THR	GLU	VAL	VAL	VAL	105
106	LYS	GLY	ASP	PRO	VAL	ALA	PRO	THR	VAL	LEU	ILE	PHE	PRO	PRO	ALA	120
121	ALA	ASP	GLN	VAL	ALA	THR	GLY	THR	VAL	THR	ILE	VAL	CYS	VAL	ALA	135
136	ASN	LYS	TYR	PHE	PRO	ASP	VAL	THR	VAL	THR	TRP	GLU	VAL	ASP	GLY	150
151	THR	THR	GLN	THR	THR	GLY	ILE	GLU	ASN	SER	LYS	THR	PRO	GLN	ASN	165
166	SER	ALA	ASP	CYS	THR	TYR	ASN	LEU	SER	SER	THR	LEU	THR	LEU	THR	180
181	SER	THR	GLN	TYR	ASN	SER	HIS	LYS	GLU	TYR	THR	CYS	LYS	VAL	THR	195
196	GLN	GLY	THR	THR	SER	VAL	VAL	GLN	SER	PHE	ASN	ARG	GLY	ASP	CYS	210

Sequence of a rabbit anti-*Micrococcus lysodeikticus* antibody light chain.
M. Van Hoegaerden and A. D. Strosberg.
Biochemistry, **17**, 4311–4317 (1978).

IMMUNOGLOBULIN λ-CHAIN—HUMAN KERN

	1				5					10					15	
1	TYR	ALA	LEU	THR	GLN	PRO	PRO	SER	VAL	SER	VAL	SER	PRO	GLY	GLN	15
16	THR	ALA	VAL	ILE	THR	CYS	SER	GLY	ASP	ASN	LEU	GLU	LYS	THR	PHE	30
31	VAL	SER	TRP	PHE	GLN	GLN	ARG	PRO	GLY	GLN	SER	PRO	LEU	LEU	VAL	45
46	ILE	TYR	HIS	THR	SER	GLU	ARG	PRO	SER	GLU	ILE	PRO	GLU	ARG	PHE	60
61	SER	GLY	SER	SER	SER	GLY	ALA	THR	ALA	THR	LEU	THR	ILE	SER	GLY	75
76	ALA	GLN	SER	VAL	ASP	GLU	ALA	ASP	TYR	PHE	CYS	GLN	THR	TRP	ASP	90
91	THR	ILE	THR	ALA	ILE	PHE	GLY	GLY	GLY	THR	LYS	LEU	THR	VAL	LEU	105
106	SER	GLN	PRO	LYS	ALA	ALA	PRO	SER	VAL	THR	LEU	PHE	PRO	PRO	SER	120
121	SER	GLU	GLU	LEU	GLN	ALA	ASN	LYS	ALA	THR	LEU	VAL	CYS	LEU	ILE	135
136	SER	ASP	PHE	TYR	PRO	GLY	ALA	VAL	THR	VAL	ALA	TRP	LYS	ALA	ASP	150
151	GLY	SER	PRO	VAL	LYS	ALA	GLY	VAL	GLU	THR	THR	THR	PRO	SER	LYS	165
166	GLN	SER	ASN	ASN	LYS	TYR	ALA	ALA	SER	SER	TYR	LEU	SER	LEU	THR	180
181	PRO	GLU	GLN	TRP	LYS	SER	HIS	ARG	SER	TYR	SER	CYS	GLN	VAL	THR	195
196	HIS	GLU	GLY	SER	THR	VAL	GLU	LYS	THR	VAL	ALA	PRO	THR	GLU	CYS	210
211	SER															225

The Primary Structure of the monoclonal Immunoglobin L-Chain of the λ-Type, Sub-group IV. (Bence-Jones Protein KERN).
H. Ponstingl, M. Hess, and N. Hilschmann.
Hoppe-Seyler's Z. Physiol. Chem., **352**, 247–266 (1971).

IMMUNOGLOBULIN λ-CHAIN—HUMAN NEI

	1				5					10					15	
1	PYG	SER	ALA	LEU	THR	GLN	PRO	ALA	SER	VAL	SER	GLY	SER	PRO	GLY	15
16	GLN	SER	ILE	THR	ILE	SER	CYS	THR	GLY	THR	THR	SER	ASP	VAL	GLY	30
31	SER	TYR	ASN	PHE	VAL	SER	TRP	TYR	GLN	GLN	ASN	PRO	GLY	LYS	ALA	45
46	PRO	LYS	LEU	MET	ILE	TYR	GLU	GLY	ASN	LYS	ARG	PRO	SER	GLY	VAL	60
61	SER	ASN	ARG	PHE	SER	GLY	SER	LYS	SER	GLY	LYS	THR	ALA	SER	LEU	75
76	THR	ILE	SER	GLY	LEU	GLN	VAL	GLU	ASP	GLU	ALA	ASP	TYR	TYR	CYS	90
91	CYS	SER	TYR	ALA	GLY	ASX	SER	THR	ARG	VAL	PHE	GLY	GLY	GLY	THR	105
106	ARG	VAL	THR	VAL	LEU	SER	GLN	PRO	LYS	ALA	ALA	PRO	SER	VAL	THR	120
121	LEU	PHE	PRO	PRO	SER	SER	GLX	GLX	LEU	GLN	ALA	ASN	LYS	ALA	THR	135
136	LEU	VAL	CYS	LEU	ILE	SER	ASP	PHE	TYR	PRO	GLY	ALA	VAL	THR	VAL	150
151	ALA	TRP	LYS	ALA	ASP	SER	SER	PRO	VAL	LYS	ALA	GLY	VAL	GLU	THR	165
166	THR	THR	PRO	SER	LYS	GLX	SER	ASX	ASX	LYS	TYR	ALA	ALA	SER	SER	180
181	TYR	LEU	SER	LEU	THR	PRO	GLX	GLX	TRP	LYS	SER	HIS	ARG	SER	TYR	195
196	SER	CYS	GLX	VAL	THR	HIS	GLX	GLY	SER	THR	VAL	GLX	LYS	THR	VAL	210
211	ALA	PRO	THR	GLU	CYS	SER										225

The Primary Structure of a Monoclonal Human λ-Type Immunoglobulin L-Chain of Sub-group II. (Bence-Jones Protein NEI).
F. A. Garver and N. Hilschmann.
Eur. J. Biochem., **26**, 10–32 (1972).

IMMUNOGLOBULIN λ-CHAIN—HUMAN PET (X)

	1				5					10					15	
1	TYR	ASP	LEU	THR	GLN	PRO	PRO	SER	VAL	SER	VAL	SER	PRO	GLY	GLN	15
16	THR	ALA	SER	ILE	THR	CYS	SER	GLY	ASP	LYS	LEU	GLY	ASP	LYS	ASP	30
31	VAL	CYS	TRP	TYR	GLN	GLN	ARG	PRO	GLY	GLN	SER	PRO	VAL	LEU	VAL	45
46	ILE	TYR	GLN	ASP	ASN	GLN	ARG	SER	SER	GLY	ILE	PRO	GLU	ARG	PHE	60
61	SER	GLY	SER	ASN	SER	GLY	ASN	THR	ALA	THR	LEU	THR	ILE	SER	GLY	75
76	THR	GLN	ALA	MET	ASP	GLU	ALA	ASP	TYR	TYR	CYS	GLN	ALA	TRP	ASP	90
91	SER	MET	SER	VAL	VAL	PHE	GLY	GLY	GLY	THR	ARG	LEU	THR	VAL	LEU	105
106	SER	GLN	PRO	LYS	ALA	ALA	PRO	SER	VAL	THR	LEU	PHE	PRO	PRO	SER	120
121	SER	GLU	GLU	LEU	GLN	ALA	ASN	LYS	ALA	THR	LEU	VAL	CYS	LEU	ILE	135
136	SER	ASP	PHE	TYR	PRO	GLY	ALA	VAL	THR	VAL	ALA	TRP	LYS	ALA	ASP	150
151	SER	SER	PRO	VAL	LYS	ALA	GLY	VAL	GLU	THR	THR	THR	PRO	SER	LYS	165
166	GLN	SER	ASN	ASN	LYS	TYR	ALA	ALA	SER	SER	TYR	LEU	SER	LEU	THR	180
181	PRO	GLU	GLN	TRP	LYS	SER	HIS	ARG	SER	TYR	SER	CYS	GLN	VAL	THR	195
196	HIS	GLU	GLY	SER	THR	VAL	GLU	LYS	THR	VAL	ALA	PRO	THR	GLU	CYS	210
211	SER															225

Immunoglobulin λ-Chains. The Complete Amino Acid Sequence of a Bence-Jones Protein.
C. Milstein, J. B. Clegg, and J. M. Jarvis.
Biochem. J., **110**, 631–652 (1968).

IMMUNOGLOBULINS

IMMUNOGLOBULIN λ-CHAIN—HUMAN NEW

	1				5					10					15	
1	PYG	SER	VAL	LEU	THR	GLN	PRO	PRO	SER	VAL	SER	ALA	ALA	PRO	GLY	15
16	GLN	LYS	VAL	THR	ILE	SER	CYS	SER	GLY	GLY	SER	THR	ASN	ILE	GLY	30
31	ASN	ASN	TYR	VAL	SER	TRP	HIS	GLN	HIS	LEU	PRO	GLY	THR	ALA	PRO	45
46	LYS	LEU	LEU	ILE	TYR	GLU	ASP	ASN	LYS	ARG	PRO	SER	GLY	ILE	PRO	60
61	ASP	ARG	ILE	SER	ALA	SER	LYS	SER	GLY	THR	SER	ALA	THR	LEU	GLY	75
76	ILE	THR	GLY	LEU	ARG	THR	GLY	ASP	GLU	ALA	ASP	TYR	TYR	CYS	ALA	90
91	THR	TRP	ASP	SER	SER	LEU	ASN	ALA	VAL	VAL	PHE	GLY	GLY	GLY	THR	105
106	LYS	VAL	THR	VAL	LEU	GLY	GLN	PRO	LYS	ALA	ALA	PRO	SER	VAL	THR	120
121	LEU	PHE	PRO	PRO	SER	SER	GLU	GLU	LEU	GLN	ALA	ASN	LYS	ALA	THR	135
136	LEU	VAL	CYS	LEU	ILE	SER	ASP	PHE	TYR	PRO	GLY	ALA	VAL	THR	VAL	150
151	ALA	TRP	LYS	ALA	ASP	SER	SER	PRO	VAL	LYS	ALA	GLY	VAL	GLU	THR	165
166	THR	THR	PRO	SER	LYS	GLN	SER	ASN	ASN	LYS	TYR	ALA	ALA	SER	SER	180
181	TYR	LEU	SER	LEU	THR	PRO	GLU	GLN	TRP	LYS	SER	HIS	ARG	SER	TYR	195
196	SER	CYS	GLN	VAL	THR	HIS	GLU	GLY	SER	THR	VAL	GLU	LYS	THR	VAL	210
211	ALA	PRO	THR	GLU	CYS	SER										225

The Complete Amino Acid Sequence of a Bence-Jones NEW (λ-Type). Sub-groups in the variable part of immunoglobulin L-Chain, λ-Type.
B. Langer, M. Steinmetz-Kayne, and N. Hilschmann.
Hoppe-Seyler's Z. Physiol. Chem., **349**, 945–951 (1968).

IMMUNOGLOBULIN λ-CHAIN—HUMAN WIN

	1				5					10					15	
1	PYG	SER	ALA	LEU	THR	GLN	PRO	PRO	ARG	VAL	SER	GLY	SER	PRO	GLY	15
16	GLN	SER	VAL	THR	ILE	SER	CYS	THR	GLY	SER	TYR	SER	ASN	VAL	THR	30
31	GLY	TYR	ASN	HIS	VAL	SER	TRP	TYR	GLN	GLN	ASP	PRO	GLY	LYS	VAL	45
46	PRO	LYS	LEU	MET	ILE	TYR	ASP	VAL	ASP	LYS	ARG	PRO	SER	GLY	VAL	60
61	PRO	ASP	ARG	PHE	SER	GLY	SER	LYS	SER	ALA	ASN	THR	ALA	SER	LEU	75
76	THR	ILE	SER	GLY	LEU	GLN	ALA	ASN	ASN	GLU	ALA	ASP	TYR	TYR	CYS	90
91	SER	SER	TYR	GLY	GLY	THR	TYR	SER	LEU	ILE	PHE	GLY	GLY	GLY	THR	105
106	LYS	LEU	THR	VAL	LEU	GLY	GLN	PRO	LYS	ALA	ALA	PRO	SER	VAL	THR	120
121	LEU	PHE	PRO	PRO	SER	SER	GLU	GLU	LEU	GLN	ALA	ASN	LYS	ALA	THR	135
136	LEU	VAL	CYS	LEU	ILE	SER	ASP	PHE	TYR	PRO	GLY	ALA	VAL	THR	VAL	150
151	ALA	TRP	LYS	ALA	ASP	SER	SER	PRO	VAL	LYS	ALA	GLY	VAL	GLU	THR	165
166	THR	THR	PRO	SER	LYS	GLN	SER	ASN	ASN	LYS	TYR	ALA	ALA	SER	SER	180
181	TYR	LEU	SER	LEU	THR	PRO	GLU	GLN	TRP	LYS	SER	HIS	ARG	SER	TYR	195
196	SER	CYS	GLN	VAL	THR	HIS	GLU	GLY	SER	THR	VAL	GLU	LYS	THR	VAL	210
211	ALA	PRO	THR	GLU	CYS	SER										225

Amino acid sequence of the human myeloma lambda chain WIN.
B. L. Chen, Y. H. Chiu, R. L. Humphrey, and R. J. Poljak.
Biochim. Biophys. Acta, **537**, 9–21 (1978).

IMMUNOGLOBULINS

IMMUNOGLOBULIN λ-CHAIN—HUMAN SH

```
        1           5              10             15
  1  SER GLU LEU THR GLN ASP PRO ALA VAL SER VAL ALA LEU GLY GLN   15
 16  THR VAL ARG ILE THR CYS GLN GLY ASP SER LEU ARG GLY TYR ASP   30
 31  ALA ALA TRP TYR GLN GLN LYS PRO GLY GLN ALA PRO LEU LEU VAL   45
 46  ILE TYR GLY ARG ASN ASN ARG PRO SER GLY ILE PRO ASP ARG PHE   60
 61  SER GLY SER SER SER GLY HIS THR ALA SER LEU THR ILE THR GLY   75
 76  ALA GLN ALA GLU ASP GLU ALA ASP TYR TYR CYS ASN SER ARG ASP   90
 91  SER SER GLY LYS HIS VAL LEU PHE GLY GLY GLY THR LYS LEU THR  105
106  VAL LEU GLY GLN PRO LYS ALA ALA PRO SER VAL THR LEU PHE PRO  120
121  PRO SER SER GLU GLU LEU GLN ALA ASN LYS ALA THR LEU VAL CYS  135
136  LEU ILE SER ASP PHE TYR PRO GLY ALA VAL THR VAL ALA TRP LYS  150
151  ALA ASP SER SER PRO VAL LYS ALA GLY VAL GLU THR THR THR PRO  165
166  SER LYS GLN SER ASN ASN LYS TYR ALA ALA SER SER TYR LEU SER  180
181  LEU THR PRO GLU GLN TRP LYS SER HIS ARG SER TYR SER CYS GLN  195
196  VAL THR HIS GLU GLY SER THR VAL GLU LYS THR VAL ALA PRO THR  210
211  GLU CYS SER                                                  225
```

The Amino Acid Sequence of a λ-Type Bence-Jones Protein. III. The Complete Amino Acid Sequence and Location of the Disulfide Bridges.
K. Titani, M. Wikler, T. Shinoda and F. W. Putnam.
J. Biol. Chem., **245**, 2171–2176 (1970).

IMMUNOGLOBULIN λ-CHAIN—HUMAN VIL

```
        1           5              10             15
  1  HIS SER ALA LEU THR GLN PRO ALA SER VAL SER GLY SER LEU GLY   15
 16  GLN SER ILE THR ILE SER CYS THR GLY THR SER SER ASP VAL GLY   30
 31  GLY TYR ASN TYR VAL SER TRP PHE GLN GLN HIS PRO GLY THR ALA   45
 46  PRO LYS LEU ILE ILE SER GLU VAL ARG ASN ARG PRO SER GLY VAL   60
 61  SER ASP ARG PHE SER GLY SER LYS SER ALA ASN THR ALA SER LEU   75
 76  THR ILE SER GLY LEU GLN ALA GLU ASP GLU ALA ASP TYR TYR CYS   90
 91  SER SER TYR THR SER SER ASN SER VAL VAL PHE GLY GLY GLY THR  105
106  LYS LEU THR VAL LEU GLY GLN PRO LYS ALA ALA PRO SER VAL THR  120
121  LEU PHE PRO PRO SER SER GLU GLU LEU GLN ALA ASN LYS ALA THR  135
136  LEU VAL CYS LEU ILE SER ASP PHE TYR PRO GLY ALA VAL THR VAL  150
151  ALA TRP LYS ALA ASP SER SER PRO VAL LYS ALA GLY VAL GLU THR  165
166  THR THR PRO SER LYS GLN SER ASN ASN LYS TYR ALA ALA SER SER  180
181  TYR LEU SER LEU THR PRO GLU GLN TRP LYS SER HIS ARG SER TYR  195
196  SER CYS GLN VAL THR HIS GLU GLY SER THR VAL GLU LYS THR VAL  210
211  ALA PRO THR GLU CYS SER                                      225
```

The primary structure of a monoclonal immunoglobulin L-chain, of the λ-Type, sub-group II. (Bence-Jones Protein VIL).
H. Ponstingl and N. Hilschmann.
Hoppe-Seyler's Z. Physiol. Chem., **352**, 859–877 (1971).

360

IMMUNOGLOBULINS

IMMUNOGLOBULIN λ-CHAIN—HUMAN NewM

```
       1              5                    10                    15
  1  PYG SER VAL LEU THR GLN PRO PRO SER VAL SER GLY ALA PRO GLY   15
 16  GLN ARG VAL THR ILE  SER CYS THR GLY SER SER SER ASN ILE  GLY  30
 31  ALA GLY ASN HIS VAL LYS TRP TYR GLN GLN LEU PRO GLY THR ALA   45
 46  PRO LYS LEU LEU ILE  PHE HIS ASN ASN ALA ARG PHE SER VAL SER  60
 61  LYS SER GLY SER SER ALA THR LEU ALA ILE  THR GLY LEU GLN ALA  75
 76  GLU ASP GLU ALA ASP TYR TYR CYS GLN SER TYR ASP ARG SER LEU   90
 91  ARG VAL PHE GLY GLY GLY THR LYS LEU THR VAL LEU ARG GLN PRO  105
106  LYS ALA ALA PRO SER VAL THR LEU PHE PRO PRO SER SER GLX GLX  120
121  LEU GLN ALA ASN LYS ALA THR LEU VAL CYS LEU ILE  SER ASP PHE 135
136  TYR PRO GLY ALA VAL THR VAL ALA TRP LYS ALA ASP SER SER PRO  150
151  VAL LYS ALA GLY VAL GLU THR THR THR PRO SER LYS GLN SER ASN  165
166  ASN LYS TYR ALA ALA SER SER TYR LEU SER LEU THR PRO GLU GLN  180
181  TRP LYS SER HIS LYS SER TYR SER CYS GLX VAL THR HIS GLU GLY  195
196  SER THR VAL GLU LYS THR VAL ALA PRO THR GLU CYS SER          210
```

Amino acid sequence of the (λ) light chain of a human myeloma immunoglobulin (IgG New).
B. L. Chen and R. J. Poljak.
Biochemistry, **13**, 1295–1302 (1974).

IMMUNOGLOBULIN λ-CHAIN—HUMAN Vor

```
       1              5                    10                    15
  1  PYG SER VAL LEU THR GLN PRO PRO SER ALA SER GLY THR PRO GLY   15
 16  GLN ARG VAL THR ILE  SER CYS SER GLY GLY ASN PHE ASP ILE  GLY  30
 31  ARG ASN SER VAL ASN TRP TYR GLN VAL HIS PRO GLY THR ALA PRO  45
 46  ARG LEU LEU ILE  TYR SER SER ASP GLN ARG SER SER GLY VAL PRO  60
 61  ASP ARG PHE SER GLY SER LYS SER GLY THR SER ALA SER LEU ALA  75
 76  ILE  SER GLY LEU GLN SER GLU ASN GLU ALA ASP TYR PHE CYS ALA  90
 91  THR TRP ASP ASP SER LEU ASP GLY PRO VAL PHE GLY GLY GLY THR  105
106  LYS VAL THR VAL LEU GLY GLN PRO LYS ALA ALA PRO SER VAL THR  120
121  LEU PHE PRO PRO SER SER GLX GLX LEU GLX ALA ASX LYS ALA THR  135
136  LEU VAL CYS LEU ILE  SER ASP PHE TYR PRO GLY ALA VAL THR VAL  150
151  ALA TRP LYS ALA ASP SER SER PRO VAL LYS ALA GLY VAL GLU THR  165
166  THR THR PRO SER LYS GLX SER ASX ASX LYS TYR ALA ALA SER SER  180
181  TYR LEU SER LEU THR PRO GLX GLX TRP LYS SER HIS LYS SER TYR  195
196  SER CYS GLX VAL THR HIS GLX GLY SER THR VAL GLX LYS THR VAL  210
211  ALA PRO THR GLU CYS SER                                      225
```

The primary structure of a monoclonal immunoglobulin L-chain of λ-type subgroup I
(Bence-Jones protein Vor).
M. Engelhard, M. Hess, and N. Hilschmann.
Hoppe-Seyler's Z. Physiol. Chem., **355**, 85–88 (1974).

IMMUNOGLOBULINS

IMMUNOGLOBULIN λ-CHAIN—HUMAN DEL

	1				5					10					15	
1	TYR	VAL	LEU	SER	GLN	PRO	PRO	SER	VAL	SER	VAL	ALA	PRO	GLY	GLN	15
16	THR	ALA	ARG	ILE	THR	CYS	GLY	GLY	ASP	GLY	ILE	GLY	GLY	LYS	SER	30
31	VAL	HIS	TRP	TYR	GLN	GLN	LYS	PRO	GLY	GLN	ALA	PRO	VAL	LEU	VAL	45
46	VAL	HIS	GLU	ASP	ASN	ASP	ARG	PRO	ALA	GLY	ILE	PRO	GLU	ARG	PHE	60
61	SER	GLY	SER	ASN	SER	GLY	ASN	THR	ALA	ALA	LEU	THR	ILE	SER	ARG	75
76	VAL	GLU	ALA	GLY	ASP	GLU	ALA	ASP	TYR	TYR	CYS	GLU	VAL	TRP	ASP	90
91	ASP	ARG	THR	ALA	HIS	VAL	VAL	PHE	GLY	GLY	GLY	THR	LYS	LEU	THR	105
106	VAL	LEU	GLY	GLN	PRO	LYS	ALA	ALA	PRO	SER	VAL	THR	LEU	PHE	PRO	120
121	PRO	SER	SER	GLX	GLX	LEU	GLX	ALA	ASN	LYS	ALA	THR	LEU	VAL	CYS	135
136	LEU	ILE	SER	ASX	PHE	TYR	PRO	GLY	ALA	VAL	THR	VAL	ALA	TRP	LYS	150
151	ALA	ASX	SER	SER	PRO	VAL	LYS	ALA	GLY	VAL	GLX	THR	THR	THR	PRO	165
166	SER	LYS	GLN	SER	ASX	ASX	LYS	TYR	ALA	ALA	SER	SER	TYR	LEU	SER	180
181	LEU	THR	PRO	GLX	GLX	TRP	LYS	SER	HIS	ARG	SER	TYR	SER	CYS	GLX	195
196	VAL	THR	HIS	GLX	GLY	SER	THR	VAL	GLX	LYS	THR	VAL	ALA	PRO	THR	210
211	GLX	CYS	SER													225

A new subgroup of human L-chains of the λ-type. The primary structure of Bence-Jones protein DEL.
M. Eulitz.
Eur. J. Biochem., **50**, 49–69 (1974).

IMMUNOGLOBULIN λ-CHAIN—HUMAN BAU

	1				5					10					15	
1	TYR	GLY	LEU	THR	GLN	PRO	PRO	SER	LEU	SER	VAL	SER	PRO	GLY	GLN	15
16	THR	ALA	SER	ILE	THR	CYS	SER	GLY	ASP	LYS	LEU	GLY	GLU	GLN	TYR	30
31	VAL	CYS	TRP	TYR	GLN	GLN	LYS	PRO	GLY	GLN	SER	PRO	VAL	LEU	VAL	45
46	ILE	TYR	HIS	ASP	SER	LYS	ARG	PRO	SER	GLY	ILE	PRO	GLU	ARG	PHE	60
61	SER	GLY	SER	ASN	SER	GLY	THR	THR	ALA	THR	LEU	THR	ILE	SER	GLY	75
76	THR	GLN	ALA	MET	ASP	GLU	ALA	ASP	TYR	TYR	CYS	GLN	ALA	TRP	ASP	90
91	SER	TYR	THR	VAL	ILE	PHE	GLY	GLY	GLY	THR	LYS	LEU	THR	VAL	LEU	105
106	GLY	GLN	PRO	LYS	ALA	(ALA,	PRO,	SER,	VAL,	THR,	LEU,	PHE,	PRO,	PRO,	SER,	120
121	SER,	GLX,	GLX,	LEU,	GLX,	ALA,	ASX)	LYS	ALA	THR	LEU	VAL	CYS	LEU	(ILE,	135
136	SER,	ASP,	PHE,	TYR,	PRO,	GLY,	ALA,	VAL,	THR,	VAL,	ALA)	TRP	LYS	ALA	ASP	150
151	SER	SER	PRO	VAL	LYS	ALA	(GLY,	VAL,	GLU,	THR,	THR,	THR,	PRO,	SER)	LYS	165
166	(GLX,	SER,	ASN,	ASN)	LYS	TYR	(ALA,	ALA,	SER,	SER,	TYR,	LEU,	SER,	LEU,	THR,	180
181	PRO,	GLX,	GLX)	TRP	LYS	SER	HIS	ARG	SER	TYR	SER	CYS	(GLX,	VAL,	THR,	195
196	HIS,	GLX,	GLY,	SER,	THR,	VAL,	GLX)	LYS	THR	(VAL,	ALA,	PRO,	THR,	GLU,	CYS)	210
211	SER															225

Pattern of antibody structure. The primary structure of a monoclonal immunoglobulin L-chain of the λ-type, subgroup IV (Bence Jones protein BAU).
K. Baczko, D. Braun, and N. Hilschmann.
Hoppe-Seyler's Z. Physiol. Chem., **355**, 131–154 (1974).

IMMUNOGLOBULINS

IMMUNOGLOBULIN λ-CHAIN—HUMAN Mcg

	1				5					10					15	
1	PYG	SER	ALA	LEU	THR	GLN	PRO	PRO	SER	ALA	SER	GLY	SER	LEU	GLY	15
16	GLN	SER	VAL	THR	ILE	SER	CYS	THR	GLY	THR	SER	SER	ASP	VAL	GLY	30
31	GLY	TYR	ASN	TYR	VAL	SER	TRP	TYR	GLN	GLN	HIS	ALA	GLY	LYS	ALA	45
46	PRO	LYS	VAL	ILE	ILE	TYR	GLU	VAL	ASN	LYS	ARG	PRO	SER	GLY	VAL	60
61	PRO	ASP	ARG	PHE	SER	GLY	SER	LYS	SER	GLY	ASN	THR	ALA	SER	LEU	75
76	THR	VAL	SER	GLY	LEU	GLN	ALA	GLU	ASP	GLU	ALA	ASP	TYR	TYR	CYS	90
91	SER	SER	TYR	GLU	GLY	SER	ASP	ASN	PHE	VAL	PHE	GLY	THR	GLY	THR	105
106	LYS	VAL	THR	VAL	LEU	GLY	GLN	PRO	LYS	ALA	ASN	PRO	THR	VAL	THR	120
121	LEU	PHE	PRO	PRO	SER	SER	GLU	GLU	LEU	GLN	ALA	ASN	LYS	ALA	THR	135
136	LEU	VAL	CYS	LEU	ILE	SER	ASP	PHE	TYR	PRO	GLY	ALA	VAL	THR	VAL	150
151	ALA	TRP	LYS	ALA	ASP	GLY	SER	PRO	VAL	LYS	ALA	GLY	VAL	GLU	THR	165
166	THR	LYS	PRO	SER	LYS	GLN	SER	ASN	ASN	LYS	TYR	ALA	ALA	SER	SER	180
181	TYR	LEU	SER	LEU	THR	PRO	GLU	GLN	TRP	LYS	SER	HIS	ARG	SER	TYR	195
196	SER	CYS	GLN	VAL	THR	HIS	GLU	GLY	SER	THR	VAL	GLU	LYS	THR	VAL	210
211	ALA	PRO	THR	GLU	CYS	SER										225

Primary structure of the Mcg λ-chain.
J. W. Fett and H. F. Deutsch.
Biochemistry, **13**, 4102–4114 (1974).

IMMUNOGLOBULIN LAMBDA CHAIN Sm

	1				5					10					15	
1	PYG	SER	ALA	LEU	THR	GLN	PRO	ALA	SER	VAL	SER	GLU	SER	PRO	GLY	15
16	GLN	SER	ILE	THR	ILE	SER	CYS	THR	GLY	ASX	SER	SER	VAL	VAL	GLY	30
31	GLN	PRO	LYS	ALA	ALA	PRO	SER	VAL	THR	LEU	PHE	PRO	PRO	SER	SER	45
46	GLU	GLU	LEU	GLN	ALA	ASN	LYS	ALA	THR	LEU	VAL	CYS	LEU	ILE	SER	60
61	ASP	PHE	TYR	PRO	GLY	ALA	VAL	THR	VAL	ALA	TRP	LYS	ALA	ASP	GLY	75
76	SER	PRO	VAL	LYS	ALA	GLY	VAL	GLU	THR	THR	THR	PRO	SER	LYS	GLN	90
91	SER	ASN	ASN	LYS	TYR	ALA	ALA	SER	SER	TYR	LEU	SER	LEU	THR	PRO	105
106	GLU	GLN	TRP	LYS	SER	HIS	ARG	SER	TYR	SER	CYS	GLN	VAL	THR	HIS	120
121	GLU	GLY	SER	THR	VAL	GLU	LYS	THR	VAL	ALA	PRO	THR	GLU	CYS	SER	135

Primary structure of a deleted human lambda type immunoglobulin light chain containing carbohydrate: protein Sm λ.
F. A. Garver, L. Chang, J. Mendicino, T. Isobe, and E. F. Osserman.
Proc. Natn. Acad. Sci., U.S.A., **72**, 4559–4563 (1975).

IMMUNOGLOBULIN λ-CHAIN—MOUSE PROTEIN MOPC 104E

	1				5					10					15	
1	PYG	ALA	VAL	VAL	THR	GLN	GLN	SER	ALA	LEU	THR	THR	SER	PRO	GLY	15
16	GLU	THR	THR	VAL	LEU	THR	CYS	ARG	SER	SER	THR	GLY	ALA	VAL	THR	30
31	THR	SER	ASN	TYR	ALA	ASN	TRP	VAL	GLN	GLN	PRO	ASP	LYS	HIS	LEU	45
46	PHE	THR	GLY	LEU	ILE	GLY	GLY	THR	ASN	ASN	ARG	ALA	PRO	GLY	VAL	60
61	PRO	ALA	ARG	PHE	SER	GLY	SER	LEU	ILE	GLY	ASN	LYS	ALA	ALA	LEU	75
76	THR	ILE	THR	GLY	ALA	GLN	THR	GLU	ASP	GLU	ALA	ILE	TYR	PHE	CYS	90
91	ALA	LEU	TRP	TYR	SER	ASN	HIS	TRP	VAL	PHE	GLY	GLY	GLY	THR	LYS	105
106	LEU	THR	VAL	LEU	GLY	GLN	PRO	LYS	SER	SER	PRO	SER	VAL	THR	LEU	120
121	PHE	PRO	PRO	SER	SER	GLU	GLU	LEU	THR	GLU	ASN	LYS	ALA	THR	LEU	135
136	VAL	CYS	THR	ILE	THR	ASP	PHE	TYR	PRO	GLY	VAL	VAL	THR	VAL	ASP	150
151	TRP	LYS	VAL	ASP	GLY	THR	PRO	VAL	THR	GLN	GLY	MET	GLU	THR	THR	165
166	GLU	PRO	SER	LYS	GLN	SER	ASN	ASN	LYS	TYR	MET	ALA	SER	SER	TYR	180
181	LEU	THR	LEU	THR	ARG	ALA	TRP	GLU	ARG	SER	HIS	SER	TYR	SER	SER	195
196	CYS	GLN	VAL	THR	(HIS,	GLX,	GLY,	HIS,	THR)	VAL	GLN	LYS	SER	LEU	SER	210
211	ARG	ALA	ASP	CYS	SER											225

Amino Acid Sequences of Two Mouse Immunoglobulin Lambda Chains.
E. Appella.
Proc. Natn. Acad. Sci., U.S.A., **68**, 590–594 (1971).

IMMUNOGLOBULIN λ-CHAIN—MOUSE MOPC 315

	1				5					10					15	
1	PYG	ALA	VAL	VAL	THR	GLU	GLU	SER	ALA	LEU	THR	THR	SER	PRO	GLY	15
16	GLY	THR	(VAL,	ILE)	LEU	THR	CYS	ARG	SER	SER	THR	GLY	ALA	VAL	THR	30
31	THR	SER	ASN	TYR	ALA	ASN	TRP	ILE	GLX	GLX	LYS	PRO	ASX	HIS	LEU	45
46	PHE	THR	GLY	LEU	ILE	GLY	GLY	THR	SER	ASP	ARG	ALA	PRO	GLY	VAL	60
61	PRO	VAL	ARG	PHE	SER	GLY	SER	LEU	ILE	GLY	ASP	LYS	ALA	ALA	LEU	75
76	THR	ILE	THR	GLY	ALA	GLX	THR	GLX	ASP	ASP	ALA	MET	TYR	PHE	CYS	90
91	ALA	LEU	TRP	PHE	ARG	ASX	HIS	PHE	VAL	PHE	GLY	GLY	GLY	THR	LYS	105
106	VAL	THR	VAL	LEU	GLY	GLN	PRO	LYS	SER	THR	PRO	THR	LEU	THR	VAL	120
121	PHE	PRO	PRO	SER	SER	GLU	GLU	LEU	LYS	GLU	ASN	LYS	ALA	THR	LEU	135
136	VAL	CYS	LEU	ILE	SER	ASN	PHE	SER	PRO	GLY	SER	(VAL,	THR)	VAL	ALA	150
151	TRP	LYS	ALA	ASN	GLY	THR	PRO	ILE	THR	GLN	GLY	VAL	ASX	THR	(THR,	165
166	ASX,	PRO,	SER)	LYS	GLU	GLY	ASN	LYS	PHE	MET	ALA	SER	SER	PHE	LEU	180
181	HIS	LEU	THR	ASP	SER	GLN	TRP	ARG	SER	HIS	ASX	SER	PHE	THR	CYS	195
196	GLN	VAL	THR	HIS	GLN	GLY	ASN	THR	VAL	GLU	LYS	SER	LEU	SER	PRO	210
211	ALA	GLU	CYS	LEU												225

Amino acid sequence of the light chain of a mouse myeloma protein.
E. S. Dugan, R. A. Bradshaw, E. S. Simms, and H. N. Eisen.
Biochemistry, **12**, 5400–5416 (1973).

FIBRINOPEPTIDES

FIBRINOPEPTIDE A—BOVINE

```
       1              5                    10                      15
 1   GLU ASP GLY SER ASP PRO PRO SER GLY ASP PHE LEU THR GLU GLY    15
16   GLY GLY VAL ARG                                                30
```

Thrombin-induced Formation of Co-fibrin. III. Acid Degradation studies and Summary of sequential evidence on Peptide A.
J. E. Folk, J. A. Gladner, and Y. Levin.
J. Biol. Chem., **234**, 2317–2320 (1959).

FIBRINOPEPTIDE A—HUMAN

```
       1              5                    10                      15
 1   ALA ASP SER GLY GLU GLY ASP PHE LEU ALA GLU GLY GLY GLY VAL    15
16   ARG                                                            30
```

Amino Acid Sequence and the Occurrence of Phosphorus in Human Fibrinopeptides.
B. Blombäck, M. Blombäck, P. Edman, and B. Hessel.
Nature, **193**, 883–884 (1962).

FIBRINOPEPTIDE A—DOG

```
       1              5                    10                      15
 1   THR ASN SER LYS GLU GLY GLU PHE ILE ALA GLU GLY GLY GLY VAL    15
16   ARG                                                            30
```

FIBRINOPEPTIDE A—RABBIT

```
       1              5                    10                      15
 1   VAL ASP PRO GLY GLU SER THR PHE ILE ASP GLU GLY ALA THR GLY    15
16   ARG                                                            30
```

FIBRINOPEPTIDE A—CAT

```
       1              5                    10                      15
 1   GLY ASP VAL GLN GLU GLY GLU PHE ILE ALA GLU GLY GLY GLY VAL    15
16   ARG                                                            30
```

FIBRINOPEPTIDE A—GUINEA PIG

```
    1        5              10              15
1   THR ASP THR GLU PHE GLU ALA ALA GLY GLY GLY VAL ARG         15
```

Studies on Fibrinopeptides from Mammals.
B. Blombäck, M. Blombäck, and N. J. Gröndahl.
Acta Chem. Scand., **19**, 1789–1791 (1965).

FIBRINOPEPTIDE A—CHICKEN

```
    1        5              10              15
1   PYG ASP GLY LYS THR THR PHE GLU LYS GLU GLY GLY GLY GLY ARG  15
```

Amino Acid sequence of chicken fibrinopeptide A.
T. Takagi, J. S. Finlayson, and S. Iwanaga.
Biochim. Biophys. Acta, **534**, 161–164 (1978).

FIBRINOPEPTIDE A—SIKA DEER

```
    1        5              10              15
1   ALA ASP GLY SER ASP PRO ALA SER SER GLU PHE (LEU ALA GLU GLY  15
16  GLY GLY VAL ARG)                                              30
```


FIBRINOPEPTIDE A—CAMEL

```
    1        5              10              15
1   THR ASP PRO ASP ALA ASP GLU GLY GLU PHE (LEU, ALA, GLU, GLY, GLY,  15
16  GLY, VAL, ARG)                                                30
```

Structure of fibrinopeptides—its relation to enzyme specificity and phylogeny and
classification of species.
B. Blombäck, M. Blombäck, N. J. Gröndahl, and E. Holmberg.
Arkiv Kemi., **25**, 411–428 (1966).

FIBRINOPEPTIDE A—GREEN MONKEY

```
    1        5              10              15
1   ALA ASP THR GLY GLU GLY ASP PHE LEU ALA GLU GLY GLY GLY VAL  15
16  ARG                                                          30
```

FIBRINOPEPTIDES

FIBRINOPEPTIDE A—MACAQUE

```
       1              5                  10                    15
 1  ALA ASP THR GLY GLU GLY ASP PHE LEU ALA GLU GLY GLY GLY VAL   15
16  ARG                                                            30
```

Studies on Fibrinopeptides from Primates.
B. Blombäck, M. Blombäck, N. J. Gröndahl, C. Guthrie, and M. Hinton.
Acta Chem. Scand., **19**, 1788–1789 (1965).

FIBRINOPEPTIDE A—LAMPREY

```
       1              5                  10                    15
 1  ASP ASP ILE SER LEU ARG                                        15
```

Amino acid sequences of lamprey fibrinopeptides A and B and characterization of the junctions split by lamprey and mammalian thrombins.
B. A. Cottrell and R. F. Doolittle.
Biochim. Biophys. Acta, **453**, 426–438 (1976).

FIBRINOPEPTIDE B—CAMEL

```
       1              5                  10                    15
 1  ALA THR ASP TYR ASP GLU GLU GLU ASP ASP ARG VAL LYS VAL ARG    15
16  LEU ASP ALA ARG                                                30
```

Structure of fibrinopeptides—its relation to enzyme specificity and phylogeny and classification of species.
B. Blombäck, M. Blombäck, N. J. Gröndahl, and E. Holmberg.
Arkiv. Kemi., **25**, 411–428 (1966).

FIBRINOPEPTIDE B—HUMAN

```
       1              5                  10                    15
 1  PYG GLY VAL ASN ASP ASN GLU GLU GLY PHE PHE SER ALA ARG        15
```

FIBRINOPEPTIDE B—GREEN MONKEY

```
       1              5                  10                    15
 1  ASN GLU GLU GLY LEU PHE GLY GLY ARG                            15
```

FIBRINOPEPTIDE B—MACAQUE

	1			5				10				15	
1	ASN	GLU	GLU	SER	PRO	PHE	SER	GLY	ARG				15

Studies on Fibrinopeptides from Primates.
B. Blombäck, M. Blombäck, N. J. Gröndahl, C. Guthrie, and M. Hinton.
Acta Chem. Scand., **19**, 1788–1789 (1965).

FIBRINOPEPTIDE B—DOG

	1			5				10				15	
1	HIS	TYR	TYR	ASP	ASP	THR	ASP	GLU	GLU	GLU	ARG	ILE	VAL	SER	THR	15
16	VAL	ASP	ALA	ARG												30

FIBRINOPEPTIDE B—RABBIT

	1			5				10				15	
1	ALA	ASP	ASP	TYR	ASP	ASP	GLU	VAL	LEU	PRO	ASP	ALA	ARG	15

Studies on Fibrinopeptides from Mammals.
B. Blombäck, M. Blombäck, and N. J. Gröndahl.
Acta Chem. Scand., **19**, 1789–1791 (1965).

FIBRINOPEPTIDE B—BOVINE

	1			5				10				15	
1	AC	THR	GLU	PHE	PRO	ASP	TYR	ASP	GLU	GLY	GLU	ASP	ASP	ARG	PRO	15
16	LYS	VAL	GLY	LEU	GLY	ALA	ARG									30

The Amino Acid Sequence of Peptide B of Co-Fibrin.
J. E. Folk and J. A. Gladner.
Biochim. Biophys. Acta, **44**, 383–385 (1960).

FIBRINOPEPTIDES

FIBRINOPEPTIDE B—LAMPREY

	1				5					10					15	
1	GLU	ASP	LEU	SER	LEU	VAL	GLY	GLN	PRO	GLU	ASN	ASP	TYR	ASP	THR	15
16	GLY	ASP	ASP	ASX	THR	ALA	ALA	ASP	PRO	ASP	SER	ASN	ASN	THR	ALA	30
31	ALA	ALA	LEU	ASP	VAL	ARG										45

Note: Residue 13 is Tyrosine-O-sulphate.
Amino acid sequences of lamprey fibrinopeptides A and B; characterization of the junctions split by lamprey and mammalian thrombins.
B. A. Cottrell and R. F. Doolittle.
Biochim. Biophys. Acta, **453**, 426–438 (1976).

HORMONES AND OTHER ACTIVE PEPTIDES

PHYLLOMEDUSIN

1		5			10			15	

1 PYG ASN PRO ASN ARG PHE ILE GLY LEU MET NH_2 15

Occurrence of Phyllomedusin, a Physalaemin-Like Decapeptide, in the skin of *Phyllomedusa bicolor*.
A. Anastasi and G. F. Erspamer.
Experientia, **26**, 866–867 (1970).

PHYSALAEMIN

1		5			10			15	

1 PYG ALA ASP PRO ASN LYS PHE TYR GLY LEU MET NH_2 15

Isolation and Amino Acid Sequence of Physalaemin, the Main Active Polypeptide of the skin of *Physalaemus fuscumaculatus*.
A. Anastasi, V. Erspamer, and J. M. Cei.
Arch. Biochem. Biophys., **108**, 341–348 (1964).

CAERULEIN

1		5			10			15	

1 PYG GLN ASP TYR THR GLY TRP MET ASP PHE NH_2 15

Note: TYR position 4 is sulphated.
Isolation and Amino Acid Sequence of Caerulein, the active decapeptide of the skin of *Hyla caerulea*.
A. Anastasi, V. Erspamer, and R. Endean.
Arch. Biochem. Biophys., **125**, 57–68 (1968).

BOMBININ

1		5			10			15	

1 GLY ILE GLY ALA LEU SER ALA LYS GLY ALA LEU LYS GLY LEU ALA   15
16 LYS GLY LEU ALA GLX HIS PHE ALA ASN NH_2 30

Isolation and Structure of an Hemolytic Polypeptide from the Defensive Secretion of European Bombina species.
A. Csordás and H. Michl.
Monatsh., **101**, 182–189 (1970).

HORMONES AND OTHER ACTIVE PEPTIDES

ELEDOISIN

1				5					10			15
1 PYG	PRO	SER	LYS	ASP	ALA	PHE	ILE	GLY	LEU	MET	NH$_2$	15

The Isolation and Amino Acid Sequence of Eledoisin, the active endecapeptide of the posterior salivary glands of *Eledone*.
A. Anastasi and V. Erspamer.
Arch. Biochem. Biophys., **101**, 56–65 (1963).

ALYTESIN

1				5					10					15
1 PYG	GLY	ARG	LEU	GLY	THR	GLN	TRP	ALA	VAL	GLY	HIS	LEU	MET	NH$_2$ 15

BOMBESIN

1				5					10					15
1 PYG	GLN	ARG	LEU	GLY	ASN	GLN	TRP	ALA	VAL	GLY	HIS	LEU	MET	NH$_2$ 15

Isolation and Amino Acid Sequence of Alytesin and Bombesin, two Analogous Active Tetradecapeptides from the skin of European Frogs.
A. Anastasi, V. Erspamer, and M. Bucci.
Arch. Biochem. Biophys., **148**, 443–446 (1972).

PEPTIDE BO-III—BOMBINA ORIENTALIS

1				5					10			15
1 ARG	PRO	PRO	GLY	PHE	SER	PRO	PHE	ARG	GLY	LYS	PHE HIS	15

Active peptides on smooth muscle in the skin of *Bombina orientalis* Boulenger and characterization of a new bradykinin analogue.
T. Yasuhara, M. Hira, T. Nakajima, N. Yanaihara, C. Yanaihara, T. Hashimoto, N. Sakura, S. Tachibana, K. Araki, M. Bessho, and T. Yamanaka.
Chem. Pharm. Bull., **21**, 1388–1391 (1973).

HORMONES AND OTHER ACTIVE PEPTIDES

UPEROLEIN

```
     1              5                   10                      15
 1   PYG PRO ASP PRO ASN ALA PHE TYR GLY LEU MET NH2                    15
```

Structure of uperolein a physalaemin-like endecapeptide occurring in the skin of *Uperoleia rugosa* and *Uperoleia marmorata*.
A. Anastasi, V. Erspamer, and R. Endean.
Experientia, **31**, 394–395 (1975).

XENOPSIN

```
     1              5                   10                      15
 1   PYG GLY LYS ARG PRO TRP ILE  LEU                                   15
```

Isolation and structure of a new active peptide 'Xenopsin' on the smooth muscle, especially on a strip of fundus from a rat stomach, from the skin of *Xenopus laevis*.
K. Araki, S. Tachibana, M. Uchiyama, T. Nakajima, and T. Yasuhara.
Chem. Pharm. Bull. (Japan), **21**, 2801–2804 (1973).

BRADYKININ—BOVINE

```
     1              5                   10                      15
 1   ARG PRO PRO GLY PHE SER PRO PHE ARG                                15
```

The Structure of Bradykinin-A plasma Kinin from Ox Blood.
D. F. Elliott, G. P. Lewis, and E. W. Horton.
Biochem. Biophys. Res. Commun., **3**, 87–91 (1960).

KALLIDIN II—BOVINE

```
     1              5                   10                      15
 1   LYS ARG PRO PRO GLY PHE SER PRO PHE ARG                           15
```

Isolation and Structure of Kallidins.
E. Werle, I. Trautschold and G. Leysath.
Hoppe-Seyler's Z. Physiol. Chem., **326**, 174–176 (1961).

HORMONES AND OTHER ACTIVE PEPTIDES

MET–LYS-BRADYKININ—BOVINE

```
    1              5                    10                       15
1   MET LYS  ARG PRO  PRO GLY PHE  SER PRO PHE ARG                      15
```

Methionyl–lysyl-bradykinin, a New Kinin from Ox Blood.
D. F. Elliott and G. P. Lewis.
Biochem. J., **95**, 437–447 (1965).

KALLIDIN II—HUMAN

```
    1              5                    10                       15
1   LYS  ARG PRO  PRO GLY PHE  SER PRO PHE  ARG                         15
```

Human Plasma Kallidins: Isolation and Chemical Studies.
J. V. Pierce and M. E. Webster.
Biochem. Biophys. Res. Commun., **5**, 353–357 (1961).

KININ PEPTIDE III—FROG

```
    1              5                    10                       15
1   ARG PRO  PRO GLY PHE  SER PRO PHE  ARG VAL ALA PRO ALA SER          15
```

On the third Active Peptide on Smooth Muscle in the Skin of *Rana nigromaculata*.
T. Nakajima.
Chem. Pharm. Bull. (*Japan*), **16**, 2088–2089 (1968).

VAL (1)-THR (6)-BRADYKININ

```
    1              5                    10                       15
1   VAL PRO  PRO GLY PHE  THR PRO PHE  ARG                              15
```

Occurrence of a New Active Peptides on Smooth Muscle and Bradykinin in the Skin of *Rana nigromaculata*.
T. Nakajima.
Chem. Pharm. Bull. (*Japan*), **16**, 769–770 (1968).

HORMONES AND OTHER ACTIVE PEPTIDES

RELAXIN—PIG (A-CHAIN)

	1		5				10				15					
1	ARG	MET	THR	LEU	SER	GLU	LYS	CYS	CYS	GLU	VAL	GLY	CYS	ILE	ARG	15
16	LYS	ASP	ILE	ALA	ARG	LEU	CYS									30

Primary structure of the A chain of porcine relaxin.
C. Schwabe, J. K. McDonald, and B. G. Steinetz.
Biochem. Biophys. Res. Commun., **70**, 397–405 (1976).

AMELETIN

	1				5		10	15	
1	PYG	ALA	GLY	TYR	SER	LYS			15

Sequential analysis is subnanomolar amounts of peptides. Determination of the structure of a habituation induced brain peptide (Ameletin).
S. R. Burzynski.
Anal. Biochem., **70**, 359–365 (1976).

PORCINE COLIPASE II

	1		5				10				15					
1	GLY	ILE	ILE	ILE	ASN	LEU	ASP	GLU	GLY	GLU	LEU	CYS	LEU	ASN	SER	15
16	ALA	GLN	CYS	LYS	SER	ASN	CYS	CYS	GLN	HIS	ASP	THR	ILE	LEU	SER	30
31	LEU	ARG	CYS	ALA	LEU	LYS	ALA	ARG	GLU	ASN	SER	GLU	CYS	ALA	PHE	45
46	THR	LEU	TYR	GLY	VAL	TYR	TYR	LYS	CYS	PRO	CYS	GLU	ARG	GLY	LEU	60
61	THR	CYS	GLU	GLY	ASP	LYS	SER	LEU	VAL	GLY	SER	ILE	THR	ASN	THR	75
76	ASN	PHE	GLY	ILE	CYS	HIS	ASN	VAL	GLY							90

The primary structure of porcine colipase II. Part 1. The amino acid sequence.
M. Charles, C. Erlanson, J. Bianchetta, J. Joffre, A. Guidoni, and M. Rovery.
Biochim. Biophys. Acta, **359**, 186–197 (1974).

TUFTSIN

	1				5	10	15	
1	THR	LYS	PRO	ARG				15

Characteristics and isolation of the phagocytosis-stimulating peptide, Tuftsin.
K. Nishioka, A. Constantopoulos, P. S. Satoh, W. M. Mitchell, and V. A. Najjar.
Biochim. Biophys. Acta, **310**, 217–229 (1973).

PORCINE MOTILIN

	1				5					10					15	
1	PHE	VAL	PRO	ILE	PHE	THR	TYR	GLY	GLU	LEU	GLN	ARG	MET	GLN	GLU	15
16	LYS	GLU	ARG	ASN	LYS	GLY	GLN									30

Correction to the amino acid sequence of porcine motilin.
H. Schubert and J. C. Brown.
Can. J. Biochem., **52**, 7–8 (1974).

NEUROTENSIN

	1				5					10					15
1	PYG	LEU	TYR	GLU	ASN	LYS	PRO	ARG	ARG	PRO	TYR	ILE	LEU		15

The amino acid sequence of a hypothalamic peptide neurotensin.
R. Carraway and S. E. Leeman.
J. Biol. Chem., **250**, 1907–1911 (1975).

INHIBITORY PEPTIDE FROM CAT SPINAL CORD

	1		5		10		15
1	HIS	(GLY, LYS)					15

An inhibitory tripeptide from cat spinal cord.
C. J. Lote, J. P. Gent, J. H. Wolstencroft, and M. Szelke.
Nature, **264**, 188–189 (1976).

GROWTH HORMONE-RELEASING ACTIVE PEPTIDE

	1				5					10		15
1	VAL	HIS	LEU	SER	ALA	GLU	GLU	LYS	GLU	ALA		15

The amino acid sequence of a peptide with growth hormone-releasing activity isolated from Porcine Hypothalmus.
A. V. Schally, Y. Baba, R. M. G. Nair, and C. D. Bennett.
J. Biol. Chem., **246**, 6647–6650 (1971).

HORMONES AND OTHER ACTIVE PEPTIDES

GASTRIC INHIBITORY PEPTIDE

	1				5					10					15		
1	TYR	ALA	GLU	GLY	THR	PHE	ILE	SER	ASP	TYR	SER	ILE	ALA	MET	ASP		15
16	LYS	ILE	ARG	GLN	GLN	ASP	PHE	VAL	ASN	TRP	LEU	LEU	ALA	GLN	GLN		30
31	LYS	GLY	LYS	LYS	SER	ASP	TRP	LYS	HIS	ASN	ILE	THR	GLN				45

A Gastric Inhibitory Polypeptide II: The Complete Amino Acid Sequence.
J. C. Brown and J. R. Dryburgh.
Can. J. Biochem., **49**, 867–872 (1971).

UROGASTRONE

	1				5					10					15		
1	ASN	SER	ASP	SER	GLU	CYS	PRO	LEU	SER	HIS	ASP	GLY	TYR	CYS	LEU		15
16	HIS	ASP	GLY	VAL	CYS	MET	TYR	ILE	GLU	ALA	LEU	ASP	LYS	TYR	ALA		30
31	CYS	ASN	CYS	VAL	VAL	GLY	TYR	ILE	GLY	GLU	ARG	CYS	GLN	TYR	ARG		45
46	ASP	LEU	LYS	TRP	TRP	GLU	LEU	ARG									60

Note: Urogastrone is a mixture of two peptides, a beta peptide which is shown above, and a gamma peptide identical with the beta peptide in sequence but having residue 53 (ARG) deleted.
Isolation and structure of urogastrone and its relationship to epidermal growth factor.
H. Gregory.
Nature, **257**, 325–327 (1975).

ANTHOPLEURIN A

	1				5					10					15		
1	GLY	VAL	SER	CYS	LEU	CYS	ASP	SER	ASP	GLY	PRO	SER	VAL	ARG	GLY		15
16	ASN	THR	LEU	SER	GLY	THR	LEU	TRP	LEU	TYR	PRO	SER	GLY	CYS	PRO		30
31	SER	GLY	TRP	HIS	ASN	CYS	LYS	ALA	HIS	GLY	PRO	THR	ILE	GLY	TRP		45
46	CYS	CYS	LYS	GLN													60

Amino acid sequence of the *Anthopleura xanthogrammica* heart stimulant, Anthopleurin A.
M. Tanaka, M. Haniu, K. T. Yasunobu, and T. R. Norton.
Biochemistry, **16**, 204–208 (1977).

HORMONES AND OTHER ACTIVE PEPTIDES

SUBSTANCE P—HORSE

```
   1              5                  10                      15
1  ARG PRO LYS  PRO GLN GLN PHE  PHE  GLY LEU MET NH₂                    15
```

The isolation and amino acid sequence of substance P from horse intestine.
R. O. Studer, A. Trzeciak, and W. Lergier.
Helv. Chim. Acta., **56**, 860–866 (1973).

SUBSTANCE P—BOVINE

```
   1              5                  10                      15
1  ARG PRO LYS  PRO GLN GLN PHE  PHE  GLY LEU MET NH₂                    15
```

Amino acid sequence of Substance P.
M. M. Chang, S. E. Leeman, and H. D. Niall.
Nature (New Biol.), **232**, 86–87 (1971).

SUBSTANCE PS1

```
   1              5                          10                     15
1  ASP VAL  PRO SER  ALA ASN ALA ASN ALA ASN ASN GLN ARG THR ALA    15
       LEU
16 ALA ALA LYS  PRO GLN ALA ASN ALA GLU ALA SER SER                 30
```

The amino acid sequence of a peptide from *Drosophila funebris*: a paragonial peptide from
males which reduces the receptivity of females.
H. Baumann, K. J. Wilson, P. S. Chen, and R. E. Humbel.
Eur. J. Biochem., **52**, 521–529 (1975).

α-ENDORPHIN—PIG

```
   1              5                  10                      15
1  TYR GLY GLY PHE  MET THR SER  GLU LYS  SER GLN THR PRO LEU VAL    15
16 THR                                                               30
```

HORMONES AND OTHER ACTIVE PEPTIDES

γ-ENDORPHIN—PIG

```
 1                    5                          10                        15
 1  TYR GLY GLY PHE MET THR SER GLU LYS SER GLN THR PRO LEU VAL    15
16  THR LEU                                                        30
```

Isolation, primary structure, and synthesis of α-endorphin and γ-endorphin, two peptides of hypothalamic-hypophysial origin with morphinomimetic activity.
N. Ling, R. Burgus, and R. Guillemin.
Proc. Natn. Acad. Sci., U.S.A., **73**, 3942–3946 (1976).

ENKEPHALIN

COMPONENT I

```
 1              5                  10                    15
 1            TYR GLY GLY PHE MET                         15
```

COMPONENT II

```
 1              5                  10                    15
 1            TYR GLY GLY PHE LEU                         15
```

Identification of two related pentapeptides from the brain with potent opiate agonist activity.
J. Hughes, T. W. Smith, H. W. Kosterlitz, L. A. Fothergill, B. A. Morgan, and H. R. Morris.
Nature, **258**, 577–579 (1975).

PEPTIDE WITH OPIATE ACTIVITY FROM CAMEL PITUITARY GLANDS

```
 1              5                      10                    15
 1  TYR GLY GLY PHE MET THR SER GLU LYS SER GLN THR PRO LEU VAL    15
16  THR LEU PHE LYS ASN ALA ILE ILE LYS ASN ALA HIS LYS LYS GLY   30
31  GLN                                                           45
```

Isolation and structure of an untriakontapeptide with opiate activity from camel pituitary glands.
C. H. Li and D. Chung.
Proc. Natn. Acad. Sci., U.S.A., **73**, 1145–1148 (1976).

HORMONES AND OTHER ACTIVE PEPTIDES

PORCINE GASTRIN

	1			5				10					15	
1	PYG	GLY	PRO	TRP	MET	GLU	GLU	GLU	GLU	GLU	ALA	TYR	GLY	TRP	MET	15
16	ASP	PHE	NH$_2$												30

Note: The above sequence is Gastrin I: Gastrin II has a sulphate ester on TYR 12.
The Antral Hormone Gastrin.
H. Gregory. P. M. Hardy, D. S. Jones, G. W. Kenner, and R. C. Sheppard.
Nature, **204**, 931–933 (1964).

HUMAN GASTRIN

	1			5				10					15	
1	PYG	GLY	PRO	TRP	LEU	GLU	GLU	GLU	GLU	GLU	ALA	TYR	GLY	TRP	MET	15
16	ASP	PHE	NH$_2$												30

Note: The above sequence is Gastrin I: Gastrin II has a sulphate ester on TYR 12.
Human Gastrin: Isolation, Structure and Synthesis. Structures of Human Gastrins I and II.
P. H. Bentley, G. W. Kenner, and R. C. Sheppard.
Nature, **209**, 583–585 (1966).

OVINE AND BOVINE GASTRINS

	1			5				10					15	
1	PYG	GLY	PRO	TRP	VAL	GLU	GLU	GLU	GLU	ALA	ALA	TYR	GLY	TRP	MET	15
16	ASP	PHE	NH$_2$												30

Note: The above sequence is Gastrin I: Gastrin II has a sulphate ester on TYR 12.
Isolation, structure and synthesis of ovine and bovine gastrins.
K. L. Agarwal, J. Beacham, P. H. Bentley, R. A. Gregory, G. W. Kenner, R. C. Sheppard, and H. J. Tracy.
Nature, **219**, 614–615 (1968).

HORMONES AND OTHER ACTIVE PEPTIDES

FELINE GASTRIN

	1				5					10					15	
1	PYG	GLY	PRO	TRP	LEU	GLU	GLU	GLU	GLU	ALA	ALA	TYR	GLY	TRP	MET	15
16	ASP	PHE	NH₂													30

Note: Feline gastrin exists with TYR 12 sulphated and unsulphated.
Feline Gastrin. An Example of Peptide Sequence Analysis by Mass Spectrometry.
K. L. Agarwal, G. W. Kenner, and R. C. Sheppard.
J. Amer. Chem. Soc., **91**, 3096–3097 (1969).

LH- AND FSH-RELEASING HORMONE

	1				5					10				
1	PYG	HIS	TRP	SER	TYR	GLY	LEU	ARG	PRO	GLY	NH₂			15

Structure of the Porcine LH- and FSH-releasing Hormone. I. The proposed amino acid sequence.
H. Matsuo, Y. Baba, R. M. G. Nair, A. Arimura and A. V. Schally.
Biochem. Biophys. Res. Commun., **43**, 1334–1339 (1971).

AVIAN PANCREATIC POLYPEPTIDE

	1				5					10					15	
1	GLY	PRO	SER	GLN	PRO	THR	TYR	PRO	GLY	ASP	ASP	ALA	PRO	VAL	GLU	15
16	ASP	LEU	ILE	ARG	PHE	TYR	ASP	ASN	LEU	GLN	GLN	TYR	LEU	ASN	VAL	30
31	VAL	THR	ARG	HIS	ARG	TYR	NH₂									45

Isolation and characterization of a new pancreatic polypeptide hormone.
J. R. Kimmel, J. Hayden, and H. G. Pollock.
J. Biol. Chem., **250**, 9369–9376 (1975)

LOCUST ADIPOKINETIC HORMONE

	1				5					10				
1	PYG	LEU	ASN	PHE	THR	PRO	ASN	TRP	GLY	THR	NH₂			15

Structure of locust adipokinetic hormone, a neurohormone that regulates lipid utilisation during flight.
J. V. Stone, W. Mordue, K. E. Batley, and H. R. Morris.
Nature, **263**, 207–211 (1976).

HORMONES AND OTHER ACTIVE PEPTIDES

BLANCHING HORMONE

	1		5						10					15	
1	PYG	LEU	ASN	PHE	SER	PRO	GLY	TRP	NH₂						15

Structure of the red-pigment concentrating hormone of the shrimp, *Pandalus borealis*.
P. Fernlund.
Biochim. Biophys. Acta, **371**, 304–311 (1974).

PORCINE VASOACTIVE INTESTINAL PEPTIDE

	1			5						10					15	
1	HIS	SER	ASP	ALA	VAL	PHE	THR	ASP	ASN	TYR	THR	ARG	LEU	ARG	LYS	15
16	GLN	MET	ALA	VAL	LYS	LYS	TYR	LEU	ASN	SER	ILE	LEU	ASN	NH₂		30

Structure of the porcine vasoactive intestinal octacosapeptide. The amino acid sequence. Use of kallikrein in its determination.
V. Mutt and S. I. Said.
Eur. J. Biochem., **42**, 581–589 (1974).

BOVINE GLUCAGON

	1			5						10					15	
1	HIS	SER	GLN	GLY	THR	PHE	THR	SER	ASP	TYR	SER	LYS	TYR	LEU	ASP	15
16	SER	ARG	ARG	ALA	GLN	ASP	PHE	VAL	GLN	TRP	LEU	MET	ASN	THR		30

Amino Acid Sequence of Bovine Glucagon.
W. W. Bromer, M. E. Boucher, and J. E. Koffenberger, Jr.
J. Biol. Chem., **246**, 2822–2827 (1971).

HUMAN GLUCAGON

	1			5						10					15	
1	HIS	SER	GLN	GLY	THR	PHE	THR	SER	ASP	TYR	SER	LYS	TYR	LEU	ASP	15
16	SER	ARG	ARG	ALA	GLN	ASP	PHE	VAL	GLN	TRP	LEU	MET	ASN	THR		30

The Amino Acid Sequence of Human Glucagon.
J. Thomsen, K. Kristiansen, K. Brunfeldt, and F. Sundby.
FEBS Letters, **21**, 315–319 (1972).

PORCINE SECRETIN

	1				5					10					15		
1	HIS	SER	ASP	GLY	THR	PHE	THR	SER	GLU	LEU	SER	ARG	LEU	ARG	ASP		15
16	SER	ALA	ARG	LEU	GLN	ARG	LEU	LEU	GLN	GLY	LEU	VAL.	NH$_2$				30

Structure of Porcine Secretin. The Amino Acid Sequence.
V. Mutt, J. E. Jorpes, and S. Magnusson.
Eur. J. Biochem., **15**, 513–519 (1970).

SHEEP OXYTOCIN

	1			5					10		15
1	CYS	TYR	ILE	GLN	ASN	CYS	PRO	LEU	GLY	NH$_2$	15

Note: A disulphide bridge links residues CYS 1 and 6.
Purification and structure of oxytocin and vasopressin of the sheep.
R. Acher, J. Chauvet, and M.-T. Lenci.
Compt. rend., **248**, 1435–1438 (1959).

BOVINE VASOPRESSIN

	1			5					10		15
1	CYS	TYR	PHE	GLN	ASN	CYS	PRO	ARG	GLY	NH$_2$	15

Note: A disulphide bridge links residues CYS 1 and 6.
Enzymatic Cleavage of Glycinamide from Vasopressin and a proposed structure for this pressor–antidiuretic Hormone of the Posterior Pituitary.
V. du Vigneaud, H. C. Lawler and E. A. Popenoe.
J. Amer. Chem. Soc., **75**, 4880–4881 (1953).

BOVINE VASOTOCIN

	1			5					10		15
1	CYS	TYR	ILE	GLN	ASN	CYS	PRO	ARG	GLY	NH$_2$	15

Note: A disulphide bridge links residues CYS 1 and 6.
Structural Elucidation of a Gonadotropin-inhibiting substance from the bovine pineal gland.
D. W. Cheesman.
Biochim. Biophys. Acta, **207**, 247–253 (1970).

```
                    5                  10                     15
1   L       R ILE  SER ASN CYS PRO ILE  GLY NH2                    15
```

Note: A disulphide bridge links residues CYS 1 and 6. Isolation of isotocin, a new hypothalamus hormone, from bony fishes.
R. Acher, J. Chauvet, M. T. Chauvet and D. Crepy.
Biochim. Biophys. Acta, **58**, 624–625 (1962).

GLUMITOCIN

```
     1              5                  10                     15
1  CYS TYR ILE  SER ASN CYS PRO GLN GLY NH2                    15
```

Note: A disulphide bridge links residues CYS 1 and 6.
Isolation of glumitocin, a new hypothalamus hormone, from the cartilaginous fish the ray (*Raia clavata*).
R. Acher, J. Chauvet, M. T. Chauvet, and D. Crepy.
Biochim. Biophys. Acta, **107**, 393–396 (1965).

MESOTOCIN

```
     1              5                  10                     15
1  CYS TYR ILE  GLN ASN CYS PRO ILE  GLY NH2                    15
```

Note: A disulphide bridge links residues CYS 1 and 6.
Isolation of mesotocin from the frog, intermediate between the isotocin of fishes and oxytocin of mammals.
R. Acher, J. Chauvet, M. T. Chauvet, and D. Crepy.
Biochim. Biophys. Acta, **90**, 613–615 (1964).

ANGIOTENSIN BOVINE

```
     1              5                  10                     15
1  ASP ARG VAL TYR VAL HIS  PRO PHE HIS  LEU                   15
```

The Amino Acid Sequence of a Hypertensin.
D. F. Elliott and W. S. Peart.
Biochem. J., **65**, 246–254 (1957).

HORMONES AND OTHER ACTIVE PEPTIDES

HISTIDINE-RICH PEPTIDE FROM BOVINE KININOGEN

	1				5					10					15	
1	SER	HIS	GLY	LEU	GLY	HIS	GLY	HIS	GLN	LYS	GLN	HIS	GLY	LEU	GLY	15
16	HIS	GLY	HIS	LYS	HIS	GLY	HIS	GLY	HIS	GLY	LYS	HIS	LYS	ASN	LYS	30
31	GLY	LYS	ASN	ASN	GLY	LYS	HIS	TYR	ASP	TRP	ARG					45

Studies on the primary structure of bovine high-molecular weight kininogen. Amino acid sequence of a fragment ("histidine-rich peptide") released by plasma kallikrein.
Y. N. Han, M. Komiya, S. Iwanaga, and T. Suzuki.
J. Biochem., **77**, 55–68 (1975).

HUMAN CALCITONIN

	1				5					10					15	
1	CYS	GLY	ASN	LEU	SER	THR	CYS	MET	LEU	GLY	THR	TYR	THR	GLN	ASP	15
16	PHE	ASN	LYS	PHE	HIS	THR	PHE	PRO	GLN	THR	ALA	ILE	GLY	VAL	GLY	30
31	ALA	PRO	NH$_2$													45

Note: The above sequence is Calcitonin M, a disulphide bridge links residues CYS 1 and 7.
Calcitonin D is the antiparallel dimer of Calcitonin M, joined by disulphide bridges.
Human Calcitonin III. Structure of Calcitonin M and D.
R. Neher, B. Riniker, W. Rittel, and H. Zuber.
Helv. Chim. Acta, **51**, 1900–1905 (1968).

PORCINE CALCITONIN

	1				5					10					15	
1	CYS	SER	ASN	LEU	SER	THR	CYS	VAL	LEU	SER	ALA	TYR	TRP	ARG	ASN	15
16	LEU	ASN	ASN	PHE	HIS	ARG	PHE	SER	GLY	MET	GLY	PHE	GLY	PRO	GLU	30
31	THR	PRO	NH$_2$													45

Note: A disulphide bridge links residues CYS 1 and 7.
Purification and Structure of Porcine Calcitonin.
P. H. Bell, W. F. Barg, Jr, D. F. Colucci, M. C. Davies, C. Dziobkowski, M. E. Englert, E. Heyder, R. Paul, and E. H. Snedeker.
J. Amer. Chem. Soc., **90**, 2704–2706 (1968).
The Amino Acid Sequence of Porcine Thyrocalcitonin.
J. T. Potts, Jr, H. D. Niall, H. T. Keutmann, H. B. Brewer, and L. J. Deftos.
Proc. Natn. Acad. Sci., U.S.A., **59**, 1321–1328 (1968).

HORMONES AND OTHER ACTIVE PEPTIDES

EEL CALCITONIN

	1				5					10					15	
1	CYS	SER	ASN	LEU	SER	THR	CYS	VAL	LEU	GLY	LYS	LEU	SER	GLN	GLU	15
16	LEU	HIS	LYS	LEU	GLN	THR	TYR	PRO	ARG	THR	ASP	VAL	GLY	ALA	GLY	30
31	THR	PRO	NH₂													45

Amino acid sequence of eel calcitonin.
T. Noda and K. Narita.
J. Biochem., **79**, 353–359 (1976).

SALMON CALCITONIN

	1				5					10					15	
1	CYS	SER	ASN	LEU	SER	THR	CYS	VAL	LEU	GLY	LYS	LEU	SER	GLN	GLU	15
16	LEU	HIS	LYS	LEU	GLN	THR	TYR	PRO	ARG	THR	ASN	THR	GLY	SER	GLY	30
31	THR	PRO	NH₂													45

Note: A disulphide bridge links residues CYS 1 and 7.
Amino Acid Sequence of Salmon Ultimobranchial Calcitonin.
H. D. Niall, D. H. Copp, H. T. Keutmann, and J. T. Potts, Jr.
Proc. Natn. Acad. Sci., U.S.A., **64**, 771–778 (1969).

CALCITONIN—RAT

	1				5					10					15	
1	CYS	GLY	ASN	LEU	SER	THR	CYS	MET	LEU	GLY	THR	TYR	THR	GLN	ASP	15
16	LEU	ASN	LYS	PHE	HIS	THR ALA	PHE	PRO	GLN	ALA THR	SER	ILE	GLY	VAL	GLY	30
31	ALA	PRO	NH₂													45

A proposed structure for rat calcitonin.
P. G. H. Byfield, J. L. McLoughlin, E. W. Matthews, and I. MacIntyre.
FEBS Letters, **65**, 242–245 (1976).

RAT THYROCALCITONIN

	1				5					10					15	
1	CYS	GLY	ASN	LEU	SER	THR	CYS	MET	LEU	GLY	THR	TYR	THR	GLN	ASP	15
16	LEU	ASN	LYS	PHE	HIS	THR	PHE	PRO	GLN	THR	SER	ILE	GLY	VAL	GLY	30
31	ALA	PRO	NH₂													45

The complete amino acid sequence of rat thyrocalcitonin.
D. Raulais, J. Hagaman, D. A. Ontjes, R. L. Lundblad, and H. S. Kingdon.
Eur. J. Biochem., **64**, 607–611 (1976).

HORMONES AND OTHER ACTIVE PEPTIDES

MONKEY α-MSH

	1		5					10					15		
1	AC	SER	TYR	SER	MET	GLU	HIS	PHE	ARG	TRP	GLY	LYS	PRO	VAL	NH$_2$	15

The Isolation and Structure of α- and β-Melanocyte-stimulating Hormones from Monkey Pituitary Glands.
T. H. Lee, A. B. Lerner, and V. Buettner-Janusch.
J. Biol. Chem., **236**, 1390–1394 (1961).

SHEEP α-MSH

	1		5					10					15		
1	AC	SER	TYR	SER	MET	GLU	HIS	PHE	ARG	TRP	GLY	LYS	PRO	VAL	NH$_2$	15

Melanocyte-Stimulating Hormones from Sheep Pituitary Glands.
T. H. Lee, A. B. Lerner, and V. Buettner-Janusch.
Biochim. Biophys. Acta, **71**, 706–709 (1963).

PORCINE α-MSH

	1		5					10					15		
1	AC	SER	TYR	SER	MET	GLU	HIS	PHE	ARG	TRP	GLY	LYS	PRO	VAL	NH$_2$	15

Amino Acid Sequence of the α-melanocyte-stimulating Hormone.
J. I. Harris and A. B. Lerner.
Nature, **179**, 1346–1347 (1957).

HORSE α-MSH

	1		5					10			15		
1	AC	SER	TYR	SER	MET	GLU	HIS	PHE	ARG	TRP	GLY	(LYS, PRO)	VAL	NH$_2$	15

The Isolation and Structure of α-Melanocyte-stimulating Hormone from Horse Pituitaries.
J. S. Dixon and C. H. Li.
J. Amer. Chem. Soc., **82**, 4568–4572 (1960).

HORMONES AND OTHER ACTIVE PEPTIDES

DOGFISH MSH

	1		5					10					15
1	TYR OOO	SER	MET	GLU	HIS	PHE	ARG	TRP	GLY	LYS	PRO	MET NH$_2$	15

Note: A deamidated form is also isolated.
Purification and Amino Acid Sequence of Melanocyte-Stimulating Hormone from Dogfish, *Squalus acanthias*.
P. J. Lowry and A. Chadwick.
Biochem. J., **118**, 713–718 (1970).

DOGFISH β-MSH

	1				5					10					15
1	ASP	GLY	ASP	ASP	TYR	LYS	PHE	GLY	HIS	PHE	ARG	TRP	SER	VAL	PRO	15
16	LEU															30

Structural studies of a α-melanocyte stimulating hormone and a novel β-melanocyte stimulating hormone from the neurointermediate lobe of the pituitary of the dogfish *Squalus acanthias*.
H. P. J. Bennett, P. J. Lowry, C. McMartin, and A. P. Scott.
Biochem. J., **141**, 439–444 (1974).

CAMEL α-MSH

	1			5					10					15
1	AC	SER	TYR	SER	MET	GLU	HIS	PHE	ARG	TRP	GLY	LYS	PRO	VAL NH$_2$	15

CAMEL β-MSH

	1				5				10					15
1	ASP	GLY	GLY	PRO	TYR	LYS	MET	GLU GLN	HIS	PHE	ARG	TRP	GLY	SER	PRO	15
16	PRO	LYS	ASP													30

Isolation, characterization and amino acid sequence of melanotropins from camel pituitary glands.
C. H. Li, W. O. Danho, D. Chung, and A. J. Rao.
Biochemistry, **14**, 947–952 (1975).

HORMONES AND OTHER ACTIVE PEPTIDES

HUMAN β-MSH

	1				5					10					15	
1	ALA	GLU	LYS	LYS	ASP	GLU	GLY	PRO	TYR	ARG	MET	GLU	HIS	PHE	ARG	15
16	TRP	GLY	SER	PRO	PRO	LYS	ASP									30

Structure of a Melanocyte-Stimulating Hormone from the Human Pituitary gland.
J. I. Harris.
Nature, **184**, 167–169 (1959).

MONKEY β-MSH

	1				5					10					15	
1	ASP	GLU	GLY	PRO	TYR	ARG	MET	GLU	HIS	PHE	ARG	TRP	GLY	SER	PRO	15
16	PRO	LYS	ASP													30

The Isolation and Structure of a α- and β-Melanocyte-stimulating Hormones from Monkey Pituitary Glands.
T. H. Lee, A. B. Lerner and V. Buettner-Janusch.
J. Biol. Chem., **236**, 1390–1394 (1961).

BOVINE β-MSH

	1				5					10					15	
1	ASP	SER	GLY	PRO	TYR	LYS	MET	GLU	HIS	PHE	ARG	TRP	GLY	SER	PRO	15
16	PRO	LYS	ASP													30

The Isolation and Structure of a Melanocyte-Stimulating Hormone from Bovine Pituitary Glands.
I. I. Geschwind, C. H. Li and L. Barnafi.
J. Amer. Chem. Soc., **79**, 1003–1004 (1957).

PORCINE β-MSH

	1				5					10					15	
1	ASP	GLU	GLY	PRO	TYR	LYS	MET	GLU	HIS	PHE	ARG	TRP	GLY	SER	PRO	15
16	PRO	LYS	ASP													30

Amino acid Sequence of a Melanophore stimulating peptide.
J. I. Harris and P. Roos.
Nature, **178**, 90 (1956).

HORMONES AND OTHER ACTIVE PEPTIDES

BOVINE PROINSULIN

	1				5					10					15		
1	PHE	VAL	ASN	GLN	HIS	LEU	CYS	GLY	SER	HIS	LEU	VAL	GLU	ALA	LEU		15
16	TYR	LEU	VAL	CYS	GLY	GLU	ARG	GLY	PHE	PHE	TYR	THR	PRO	LYS	ALA		30
31	ARG	ARG	GLU	VAL	GLU	GLY	PRO	GLN	VAL	GLY	ALA	LEU	GLU	LEU	ALA		45
46	GLY	GLY	PRO	GLY	ALA	GLY	GLY	LEU	GLU	GLY	PRO	PRO	GLN	LYS	ARG		60
61	GLY	ILE	VAL	GLU	GLN	CYS	CYS	ALA	SER	VAL	CYS	SER	LEU	TYR	GLN		75
76	LEU	GLU	ASN	TYR	CYS	ASN											90

Note: Disulphide bridges are between CYS 7 and 67; CYS 19 and 80; CYS 66 and 71.
Proinsulin Intermediate Form 1 lacks residues 59 and 60; Intermediate Form 2 lacks residues 31 and 32.
The Structure of Bovine Proinsulin.
C. Nolan, E. Margoliash, J. D. Peterson, and D. F. Steiner.
J. Biol. Chem., **246**, 2780–2795 (1971).

PIG PROINSULIN

	1				5					10					15		
1	PHE	VAL	ASN	GLN	HIS	LEU	CYS	GLY	SER	HIS	LEU	VAL	GLU	ALA	LEU		15
16	TYR	LEU	VAL	CYS	GLY	GLU	ARG	GLY	PHE	PHE	TYR	THR	PRO	LYS	ALA		30
31	ARG	ARG	GLU	ALA	GLN	ASN	PRO	GLN	ALA	GLY	ALA	VAL	GLU	LEU	GLY		45
46	GLY	GLY	LEU	GLY	GLY	LEU	GLN	ALA	LEU	ALA	LEU	GLU	GLY	PRO	PRO		60
61	GLN	LYS	ARG	GLY	ILE	VAL	GLU	GLN	CYS	CYS	THR	SER	ILE	CYS	SER		75
76	LEU	TYR	GLN	LEU	GLU	ASN	TYR	CYS	ASN								90

Note: Disulphide bridges are between CYS 7 and 70; CYS 19 and 83; CYS 69 and 74.
Porcine Proinsulin: Characterization and Amino Acid Sequence.
R. E. Chance, R. M. Ellis and W. W. Bromer.
Science, **161**, 165–167 (1968).

HUMAN INSULIN

A-CHAIN

	1				5					10					15		
1	GLY	ILE	VAL	GLU	GLN	CYS	CYS	THR	SER	ILE	CYS	SER	LEU	TYR	GLN		15
16	LEU	GLU	ASN	TYR	CYS	ASN											30

HORMONES AND OTHER ACTIVE PEPTIDES

B-CHAIN

	1				5					10					15	
1	PHE	VAL	ASN	GLN	HIS	LEU	CYS	GLY	SER	HIS	LEU	VAL	GLU	ALA	LEU	15
16	TYR	LEU	VAL	CYS	GLY	GLU	ARG	GLY	PHE	PHE	TYR	THR	PRO	LYS	THR	30

Amino acid Sequence of Human Insulin.
D. S. H. W. Nicol and L. F. Smith.
Nature, **187**, 483–485 (1960).

BOVINE INSULIN

A-CHAIN

	1				5					10					15	
1	GLY	ILE	VAL	GLU	GLN	CYS	CYS	ALA	SER	VAL	CYS	SER	LEU	TYR	GLN	15
16	LEU	GLU	ASN	TYR	CYS	ASN										30

B-CHAIN

	1				5					10					15	
1	PHE	VAL	ASN	GLN	HIS	LEU	CYS	GLY	SER	HIS	LEU	VAL	GLU	ALA	LEU	15
16	TYR	LEU	VAL	CYS	GLY	GLU	ARG	GLY	PHE	PHE	TYR	THR	PRO	LYS	ALA	30

Note: Disulphide bonds are between residues CYS A_6 and A_{11}; CYS A_7 and B_7; CYS A_{20} and B_{19}.

The Amino acid sequence in the Phenylalanyl chain of Insulin. 1. The identification of lower peptides from partial hydrolysates.
F. Sanger and H. Tuppy.
Biochem. J., **49**, 463–481 (1951).
The Amino acid Sequence in the Phenylalanyl chain of Insulin. 2. Investigation of peptides from enzymic hydrolysates.
F. Sanger and H. Tuppy.
Biochem. J., **49**, 481–490 (1951).
The Amino acid sequence in the Glycyl chain of Insulin. 1. The identification of lower peptides from partial hydrolysates.
F. Sanger and E. O. P. Thompson.
Biochem. J., **53**, 353–366 (1953).
The Amino acid sequence in the glycyl chain of Insulin. 2. Investigation of peptides from enzymic hydrolysates.
F. Sanger and E. O. P. Thompson.
Biochem. J., **53**, 366–374 (1953).
The Disulphide Bonds of Insulin.
A. P. Ryle, F. Sanger, L. F. Smith, and R. Kitai.
Biochem. J., **60**, 541–556 (1955).
The Amide Groups of Insulin.
F. Sanger, E. O. P. Thompson, and R. Kitai.
Biochem. J., **59**, 509–518 (1955).

HORMONES AND OTHER ACTIVE PEPTIDES

PIG INSULIN

A-CHAIN

	1			5						10					15	
1	GLY	ILE	VAL	GLU	GLN	CYS	CYS	THR	SER	ILE	CYS	SER	LEU	TYR	GLN	15
16	LEU	GLU	ASN	TYR	CYS	ASN										30

B-CHAIN

	1			5						10					15	
1	PHE	VAL	ASN	GLN	HIS	LEU	CYS	GLY	SER	HIS	LEU	VAL	GLU	ALA	LEU	15
16	TYR	LEU	VAL	CYS	GLY	GLU	ARG	GLY	PHE	PHE	TYR	THR	PRO	LYS	ALA	30

SHEEP INSULIN

A-CHAIN

	1			5						10					15	
1	GLY	ILE	VAL	GLU	GLN	CYS	CYS	ALA	GLY	VAL	CYS	SER	LEU	TYR	GLN	15
16	LEU	GLU	ASN	TYR	CYS	ASN										30

B-CHAIN

	1			5						10					15	
1	PHE	VAL	ASN	GLN	HIS	LEU	CYS	GLY	SER	HIS	LEU	VAL	GLU	ALA	LEU	15
16	TYR	LEU	VAL	CYS	GLY	GLU	ARG	GLY	PHE	PHE	TYR	THR	PRO	LYS	ALA	30

The Structure of Pig and Sheep Insulins.
H. Brown, F. Sanger, and R. Kitai.
Biochem. J., **60**, 556–565 (1955).

HORMONES AND OTHER ACTIVE PEPTIDES

HORSE INSULIN

A-CHAIN

	1				5					10					15		
1	GLY	ILE	VAL	GLU	GLN	CYS	CYS	THR	GLY	ILE	CYS	SER	LEU	TYR	GLN	15
16	LEU	GLU	ASN	TYR	CYS	ASN										30

B-CHAIN

	1				5					10					15		
1	PHE	VAL	ASN	GLN	HIS	LEU	CYS	GLY	SER	HIS	LEU	VAL	GLU	ALA	LEU	15
16	TYR	LEU	VAL	CYS	GLY	GLU	ARG	GLY	PHE	PHE	TYR	THR	PRO	LYS	ALA	30

WHALE INSULIN

A-CHAIN

	1				5					10					15		
1	GLY	ILE	VAL	GLU	GLN	CYS	CYS	THR	SER	ILE	CYS	SER	LEU	TYR	GLN	15
16	LEU	GLU	ASN	TYR	CYS	ASN										30

B-CHAIN

	1				5					10					15		
1	PHE	VAL	ASN	GLN	HIS	LEU	CYS	GLY	SER	HIS	LEU	VAL	GLU	ALA	LEU	15
16	TYR	LEU	VAL	CYS	GLY	GLU	ARG	GLY	PHE	PHE	TYR	THR	PRO	LYS	ALA	30

Species differences in Insulin.
J. I. Harris, F. Sanger, and M. A. Naughton.
Arch. Biochem. Biophys., **65**, 427–438 (1956).

HORMONES AND OTHER ACTIVE PEPTIDES

DOG INSULIN

A-CHAIN

```
    1                   5                   10                      15
 1  GLY ILE  VAL GLU GLN CYS CYS ALA SER VAL CYS SER LEU TYR GLN   15
16  LEU GLU ASN TYR CYS ASN                                        30
```

B-CHAIN

```
    1                   5                   10                      15
 1  PHE VAL ASN GLN HIS  LEU CYS GLY SER HIS  LEU VAL GLU ALA LEU  15
16  TYR LEU VAL CYS GLY GLU ARG GLY PHE PHE TYR THR PRO LYS ALA    30
```

ELEPHANT INSULIN

A-CHAIN

```
    1                   5                   10                      15
 1  GLY ILE  VAL GLU GLN CYS CYS ALA GLY VAL CYS SER LEU TYR GLN   15
16  LEU GLU ASN TYR CYS ASN                                        30
```

B-CHAIN

```
    1                   5                   10                      15
 1  PHE VAL ASN GLN HIS LEU CYS GLY SER HIS  LEU VAL GLU ALA LEU   15
16  TYR LEU VAL CYS GLY GLU ARG GLY PHE PHE TYR THR PRO LYS THR    30
```

RABBIT INSULIN

A-CHAIN

```
    1                   5                   10                      15
 1  GLY ILE  VAL GLU GLN CYS CYS ALA SER VAL CYS SER LEU TYR GLN   15
16  LEU GLU ASN TYR CYS ASN                                        30
```

B-CHAIN

```
    1                   5                   10                      15
 1  PHE VAL ASN GLN HIS LEU CYS GLY SER HIS  LEU VAL GLU ALA LEU   15
16  TYR LEU VAL CYS GLY GLU ARG GLY PHE PHE TYR THR PRO LYS SER    30
```

HORMONES AND OTHER ACTIVE PEPTIDES

GOAT INSULIN

A-CHAIN

	1				5					10					15		
1	GLY	ILE	VAL	GLU	GLN	CYS	CYS	ALA	GLY	VAL	CYS	SER	LEU	TYR	GLN		15
16	LEU	GLU	ASN	TYR	CYS	ASN											30

B-CHAIN

	1				5					10					15		
1	PHE	VAL	ASN	GLN	HIS	LEU	CYS	GLY	SER	HIS	LEU	VAL	GLU	ALA	LEU		15
16	TYR	LEU	VAL	CYS	GLY	GLU	ARG	GLY	PHE	PHE	TYR	THR	PRO	LYS	ALA		30

RAT INSULIN

A-CHAIN

	1				5					10					15		
1	GLY	ILE	VAL	ASP	GLN	CYS	CYS	ALA	SER	VAL	CYS	SER	LEU	TYR	GLN		15
16	LEU	GLU	ASN	TYR	CYS	ASN											30

B-CHAIN

	1				5					10					15		
1	PHE	VAL	LYS	GLN	HIS	LEU	CYS	GLY	SER	HIS	LEU	VAL	GLU	ALA	LEU		15
16	TYR	LEU	VAL	CYS	GLY	GLU	ARG	GLY	PHE	PHE	TYR	THR	PRO	LYS/MET	SER		30

HORMONES AND OTHER ACTIVE PEPTIDES

CHICKEN INSULIN

A-CHAIN

	1			5					10					15	
1	GLY	ILE	VAL	GLU	GLN	CYS	CYS	HIS	ASN	THR	CYS	SER	LEU	TYR	GLN	15
16	LEU	GLU	ASN	TYR	CYS	ASN										30

B-CHAIN

	1			5					10					15	
1	ALA	ALA	ASN	GLN	HIS	LEU	CYS	GLY	SER	HIS	LEU	VAL	GLU	ALA	LEU	15
16	TYR	LEU	VAL	CYS	GLY	GLU	ARG	GLY	PHE	PHE	TYR	SER	PRO	LYS	ALA	30

Species Variation in Amino Acid Sequence of Insulin.
L. F. Smith.
Amer. J. Med., **40**, 662–666 (1966).

SPERM WHALE INSULIN

A-CHAIN

	1			5					10					15	
1	GLY	ILE	VAL	GLU	GLN	CYS	CYS	THR	SER	ILE	CYS	SER	LEU	TYR	GLN	15
16	LEU	GLU	ASN	TYR	CYS	ASN										30

B-CHAIN

	1			5					10					15	
1	PHE	VAL	ASN	GLN	HIS	LEU	CYS	GLY	SER	HIS	LEU	VAL	GLU	ALA	LEU	15
16	TYR	LEU	VAL	CYS	GLY	GLU	ARG	GLY	PHE	PHE	TYR	THR	PRO	LYS	ALA	30

HORMONES AND OTHER ACTIVE PEPTIDES

SEI-WHALE INSULIN

A-CHAIN

```
      1              5                   10                  15
 1  GLY ILE  VAL GLU GLN CYS CYS ALA SER THR CYS SER LEU TYR GLN   15
16  LEU GLU ASN TYR CYS ASN                                        30
```

B-CHAIN

```
      1              5                   10                  15
 1  PHE VAL ASN GLN HIS  LEU CYS GLY SER HIS  LEU VAL GLU ALA LEU   15
16  TYR LEU VAL CYS GLY GLU ARG GLY PHE PHE TYR THR PRO LYS ALA     30
```

Note: The above two sequences have B_{21} GLU inserted which is missed in the original paper.
Structure of Sperm- and Sei-Whale Insulins.
Y. Ishihara, T. Saito, Y. Ito, and M. Fujino.
Nature, **181**, 1468–1469 (1958).

MOUSE INSULIN

A-CHAIN

```
      1              5                   10                  15
 1  GLY ILE  VAL ASP GLN CYS CYS THR SER ILE  CYS SER LEU TYR GLN   15
16  LEU GLU ASN TYR CYS ASN                                        30
```

B-CHAIN

```
      1              5                   10                  15
                                         PRO
 1  PHE VAL LYS GLN HIS  LEU CYS GLY  SER  HIS  LEU VAL GLU ALA LEU   15
                                                         LYS
16  TYR LEU VAL CYS GLY GLU ARG GLY PHE PHE TYR THR PRO  MET  SER     30
```

Amino Acid Sequence of the two Insulins from Mouse (*Mus musculus*).
H. F. Bünzli, B. Glatthaar, P. Kunz, E. Mülhaupt, and R. E. Humbel.
Hoppe-Seyler's Z. Physiol. Chem., **353**, 451–458 (1972).

HORMONES AND OTHER ACTIVE PEPTIDES

INSULIN—DUCK

A-CHAIN

```
       1            5                   10                    15
 1  GLY ILE  VAL GLU GLN CYS CYS GLU ASN PRO CYS SER LEU TYR GLN   15
16  LEU GLU ASN TYR CYS ASN                                        30
```

B-CHAIN

```
       1            5                   10                    15
 1  ALA ALA ASN GLN HIS  LEU CYS GLY SER HIS  LEU VAL GLU ALA LEU   15
16  TYR LEU VAL CYS GLY GLU ARG GLY PHE PHE TYR SER PRO LYS THR     30
```

Duck Insulin. Isolation, crystallization and amino acid sequence.
J. Markussen and F. Sundby.
Int. J. Peptide Protein Res., **5**, 37–48 (1973).

TURKEY INSULIN

A-CHAIN

```
       1            5                   10                    15
 1  GLY ILE  VAL GLU GLN CYS CYS HIS  ASN THR CYS SER LEU TYR GLN   15
16  LEU GLU ASN TYR CYS ASN                                        30
```

B-CHAIN

```
       1            5                   10                    15
 1  ALA ALA ASN GLN HIS  LEU CYS GLY SER HIS  LEU VAL GLU ALA LEU   15
16  TYR LEU VAL CYS GLY GLU ARG GLY PHE PHE TYR SER PRO LYS ALA     30
```

Isolation of thermolytic peptides and determination of the primary structure by a modified
paper strip technique.
J. Jentsch.
Proc. First Int. Conf. on Solid-Phase Methods in Protein Sequence Analysis, May 1975,
Ed. R. A. Laursen (Pierce Chem. Corp., Rockford, Ill., U.S.A.) pp 193–202 (1975).

HORMONES AND OTHER ACTIVE PEPTIDES

COD INSULIN

A-CHAIN

```
     1                    5                   10                      15
 1  GLY ILE  VAL ASP GLN CYS CYS HIS  ARG PRO CYS ASP ILE  PHE ASP   15
16  LEU GLN ASN TYR CYS ASN                                          30
```

B-CHAIN

```
     1                    5                   10                      15
 1  MET ALA PRO PRO GLN HIS  LEU CYS GLY SER HIS  LEU VAL ASP ALA    15
16  LEU TYR LEU VAL CYS GLY ASP  ARG GLY PHE PHE TYR ASN PRO LYS     30
```

The Sequence of Amino Acids in Insulin Isolated from Islet Tissue of the Cod (*Gadus callarias*).
K. B. M. Reid, P. T. Grant, and A. Youngson.
Biochem. J., **110**, 289–296 (1968).

INSULIN—HAGFISH

A-CHAIN

```
     1                    5                   10                      15
 1  GLY ILE  VAL GLU GLN CYS CYS HIS  LYS ARG CYS SER ILE  TYR ASN   15
16  LEU GLN ASN TYR CYS ASN                                          30
```

B-CHAIN

```
     1                    5                   10                      15
 1  ARG THR THR GLY HIS  LEU CYS GLY LYS  ASP LEU VAL ASN ALA LEU    15
16  TYR ILE  ALA CYS GLY VAL ARG GLY PHE PHE TYR ASP PRO THR LYS     30
31  MET                                                              45
```

The amino acid sequence of the insulin from a primitive vertebrate the Atlantic hagfish (*Myxine glutinosa*).
J. D. Peterson, D. F. Steiner, S. O. Emdin, and S. Falkmer.
J. Biol. Chem., **250**, 5183–5191 (1975).

HORMONES AND OTHER ACTIVE PEPTIDES

HUMAN PANCREATIC C-PEPTIDE

```
      1              5                  10                    15
 1  GLU ALA GLU ASP LEU GLN VAL GLY GLN VAL GLU LEU GLY GLY GLY    15
16  PRO GLY ALA GLY SER LEU GLN PRO LEU ALA LEU GLU GLY SER LEU    30
31  GLN                                                            45
```

Studies on Human Proinsulin. Isolation and Amino Acid Sequence of the Human Pancreatic C-Peptide.
P. E. Oyer, S. Cho, J. D. Peterson, and D. F. Steiner.
J. Biol. Chem., **246**, 1375–1386 (1971).
Also
The Amino Acid Sequence of the C-Peptide of Human Proinsulin.
A. S. C. Ko, D. G. Smyth, J. Markussen, and F. Sundby.
Eur. J. Biochem., **20**, 190–199 (1971).

HORSE PROINSULIN C-PEPTIDE

```
      1              5                  10                    15
 1  GLU ALA GLU ASP PRO GLN VAL GLY GLU VAL GLU LEU GLY GLY GLY    15
16  PRO GLY LEU GLY GLY LEU GLN PRO LEU ALA LEU ALA GLY PRO GLN    30
31  GLN                                                            45
```

Primary Structures of the Proinsulin Connecting Peptides of the Rat and the Horse.
H. S. Tager and D. F. Steiner.
J. Biol. Chem., **247**, 7936–7940 (1972).

RAT PROINSULIN C-PEPTIDE

```
      1              5                  10                    15
 1  GLU VAL GLU ASP PRO GLN VAL  PRO  GLN LEU GLU LEU GLY GLY GLY   15
                                 ALA
16  PRO  GLU  ALA ASP GLY LEU GLN THR LEU ALA LEU GLU VAL ALA ARG   30
         GLY
31  GLN                                                            45
```

Rat-Proinsulin C-Peptides, Amino-acid Sequences.
J. Markussen and F. Sundby.
Eur. J. Biochem., **25**, 153–162 (1972).

HORMONES AND OTHER ACTIVE PEPTIDES

C-PEPTIDE—DUCK

```
     1           5                   10                  15
 1  ASP VAL GLU GLN PRO LEU VAL ASN GLY PRO LEU HIS  GLY GLU VAL   15
16  GLY GLU LEU PRO PHE GLN HIS  GLU GLU TYR GLN                   30
```

Isolation and amino acid sequence of the C-peptide of Duck Proinsulin.
J. Markussen and F. Sundby.
Eur. J. Biochem., **34**, 401–408 (1973).

C-PEPTIDE—GUINEA PIG

```
     1           5                   10                  15
 1  GLU LEU GLU ASP PRO GLN VAL GLU GLN THR GLU LEU GLY MET GLY    15
16  LEU GLY ALA GLY GLY LEU GLN PRO LEU GLN GLY ALA LEU GLN        30
```

The amino acid sequence of guinea pig C-peptide.
D. G. Smyth, J. Markussen, and F. Sundby.
Nature, **248**, 151–152 (1974).
And
Guinea pig proinsulin. Primary structure of the C-peptide isolated from pancreas.
D. E. Massey and D. G. Smyth.
J. Biol. Chem., **250**, 6288–6290 (1975).

INSULIN-LIKE GROWTH FACTOR I (IGF-I)

```
     1           5                   10                  15
 1  GLY PRO GLU THR LEU CYS GLY ALA GLU LEU VAL ASP ALA LEU GLN    15
16  PHE VAL CYS GLY ASP ARG GLY PHE TYR PHE ASN LYS PRO THR GLY    30
31  TYR GLY SER SER SER ARG ARG ALA PRO GLN THR GLY ILE VAL ASP    45
46  GLU CYS CYS PHE ARG SER CYS ASP LEU ARG ARG LEU GLU MET TYR    60
61  CYS ALA PRO LEU LYS PRO ALA LYS SER ALA                        75
```

The amino acid sequence of human Insulin-like growth factor I and its structural homology
with proinsulin.
E. Rinderknecht and R. E. Humbel.
J. Biol. Chem., **253**, 2769–2776 (1978).

HORMONES AND OTHER ACTIVE PEPTIDES

BOVINE NEUROPHYSIN I

```
         1              5              10                15
 1  ALA VAL LEU ASP LEU ASP VAL ARG THR CYS LEU PRO CYS GLY PRO   15
16  GLY GLY LYS GLY ARG CYS PHE GLY PRO SER ILE CYS CYS GLY ASP   30
31  GLU LEU GLY CYS PHE VAL GLY THR ALA GLU ALA LEU ARG CYS GLN   45
46  GLU GLU ASN TYR LEU PRO SER PRO CYS GLN SER GLY GLN LYS PRO   60
61  CYS GLY SER GLY GLY ARG CYS ALA ALA ALA GLY ILE CYS CYS ASP   75
76  PRO ASP GLY CYS ALA PRO ASP PRO GLU CYS HIS GLU SER ALA SER   90
91  PHE LEU                                                      105
```

Note: Disulphide bridges join residues CYS 10 and 85; CYS 13 and 34; CYS 21 and 27; CYS 28 and 44; CYS 54 and 61; CYS 67 and 73; CYS 74 and 79.
Structural studies of bovine neurophysin—I.
W. G. North, R. Walter, D. H. Schlesinger, E. Breslow, and J. D. Capra.
Ann. N.Y. Acad. Sci., **248**, 408–422 (1975).

PORCINE NEUROPHYSIN I

```
         1              5              10                15
 1  ALA MET SER ASP LEU GLU LEU ARG GLN CYS LEU PRO CYS GLY PRO   15
16  GLY GLY LYS GLY ARG CYS PHE GLY PRO SER ILE CYS GLY CYS ASP   30
31  GLU LEU GLY CYS PHE VAL GLY THR ALA GLU ALA LEU ARG CYS GLN   45
46  GLU GLU ASN TYR LEU PRO SER PRO CYS GLN SER GLY GLN LYS PRO   60
61  CYS GLY SER GLY GLY ARG CYS ALA ALA ALA GLY ILE CYS CYS ASN   75
76  ASP GLU SER CYS VAL THR GLU PRO GLU CYS ARG GLU GLY ALA SER   90
91  PHE LEU                                                      105
```

Amino Acid Sequence of Porcine Neurophysin I.
T. C. Wuu, S. Crumm, and M. Saffran.
J. Biol. Chem., **246**, 6043–6063 (1971).

HORMONES AND OTHER ACTIVE PEPTIDES

NEUROPHYSIN II—BOVINE

	1				5					10					15	
1	ALA	MET	SER	ASP	LEU	GLU	LEU	ARG	GLN	CYS	LEU	PRO	CYS	GLY	PRO	15
16	GLY	GLY	LYS	GLY	ARG	CYS	PHE	GLY	PRO	SER	ILE	CYS	CYS	GLY	ASP	30
31	GLU	LEU	GLY	CYS	PHE	VAL	GLY	THR	ALA	GLU	ALA	LEU	ARG	CYS	GLN	45
46	GLU	GLU	ASN	TYR	LEU	PRO	SER	PRO	CYS	GLN	SER	GLY	GLN	LYS	PRO	60
61	CYS	GLY	SER	GLY	GLY	ARG	CYS	ALA	ALA	ALA	GLY	ILE	CYS	CYS	ASN	75
76	ASP	GLU	SER	CYS	VAL	THR	GLU	PRO	GLU	CYS	ARG	GLU	GLY	ILE/VAL	GLY	90
91	PHE	PRO	ARG	ARG	VAL											105

Foetal bovine MSEL-Neurophysin: comparison with adult homologous neurophysin.
M. T. Chauvet, J. Chauvet, and R. Acher.
FEBS Letters, **62**, 89–92 (1976).

BOVINE NEUROPHYSIN II

	1				5					10					15	
1	ALA	MET	SER	ASP	LEU	GLU	LEU	ARG	GLN	CYS	LEU	PRO	CYS	GLY	PRO	15
16	GLY	GLY	LYS	GLY	ARG	CYS	PHE	GLY	PRO	SER	ILE	CYS	CYS	GLY	ASN	30
31	GLU	LEU	GLY	GLN	PHE	VAL	GLY	THR	ALA	GLU	ALA	LEU	ARG	CYS	GLN	45
46	GLU	GLU	ASN	TYR	LEU	PRO	SER	PRO	CYS	GLN	SER	GLY	GLN	ARG	PRO	60
61	CYS	GLY	SER	GLY	GLY	ARG	CYS	ALA	ALA	ALA	THR	ILE	CYS	CYS	SER	75
76	ASP	GLU	GLU	CYS	VAL	PRO	ASP	GLU	GLN	VAL	LYS	PRO	GLY	GLY	ARG	90
91	GLY	GLY	CYS	PHE	CYS	ARG	VAL									105

Complete Amino Acid Sequence of Bovine Neurophysin II.
R. Walter, D. H. Schlesinger, I. L. Schwartz, and J. D. Capra.
Biochem. Biophys. Res. Commun., **44**, 293–298 (1971).
Determination of the complete amino acid sequence of bovine neurophysin II.
D. H. Schlesinger, J. D. Capra, and R. Walter.
Int. J. Peptide Protein Res., **6**, 1–12 (1974).

HORMONES AND OTHER ACTIVE PEPTIDES

NEUROPHYSIN II—OVINE

	1				5					10					15	
1	ALA	MET	SER	ASP	LEU	GLU	LEU	ARG	GLN	CYS	LEU	PRO	CYS	GLY	PRO	15
16	GLY	GLY	LYS	GLY	ARG	CYS	PHE	GLY	PRO	SER	ILE	CYS	CYS	GLY	ASP	30
31	GLU	LEU	GLY	CYS	PHE	VAL	GLY	THR	ALA	GLU	ALA	LEU	ARG	CYS	GLN	45
46	GLU	GLU	ILE	TYR	LEU	PRO	SER	PRO	CYS	GLN	SER	GLY	GLN	LYS	PRO	60
61	CYS	GLY	SER	GLY	GLY	ARG	CYS	ALA	ALA	ALA	GLY	ILE	CYS	CYS	ASN	75
76	ASP	GLU	SER	CYS	VAL	THR	GLU	PRO	GLU	CYS	ARG	GLU	GLY	ILE	GLY	90
91	PHE	PRO	ARG	ARG	VAL											105

The complete amino acid sequence of the major ovine neurophysin (MSEL-neurophysin): comparison with a re-investigated bovine MSEL-neurophysin.
M. T. Chauvet, J. Chauvet, and R. Acher.
FEBS Letters, **58**, 234–237 (1975).

OVINE NEUROPHYSIN III

	1				5					10					15	
1	ALA	MET	SER	ASP	LEU	GLU	LEU	ARG	GLN	CYS	LEU	PRO	CYS	GLY	PRO	15
16	GLY	GLY	LYS	GLY	ARG	CYS	PHE	GLY	PRO	SER	ILE	CYS	CYS	GLY	ASP	30
31	GLU	LEU	GLY	CYS	PHE	VAL	GLY	THR	ALA	GLU	ALA	LEU	ARG	CYS	GLN	45
46	GLU	GLU	ILE	TYR	LEU	PRO	SER	PRO	CYS	GLN	SER	GLY	GLN	LYS	PRO	60
61	CYS	GLY	SER	GLY	GLY	ARG	CYS	ALA	ALA	ALA	GLY	ILE	CYS	CYS	ASN	75
76	SER	GLU	ALA	CYS	VAL	THR	GLU	PRO	GLU	CYS	ARG	GLU	GLY	ILE	GLY	90
91	PHE	PRO	ARG	VAL												105

Complete amino acid sequence of ovine neurophysin-III.
D. H. Schlesinger, M. Ernst, A. Nicholas, W. B. Watkins, and R. Walter.
FEBS Letters, **57**, 55–59 (1975).

HORMONES AND OTHER ACTIVE PEPTIDES

NEUROPHYSIN—WHALE

	1				5					10					15	
1	ALA	MET	SER	ASP	LEU	GLU	LEU	ARG	GLN	CYS	LEU	PRO	CYS	GLY	PRO	15
16	GLY	GLY	LYS	GLY	ARG	CYS	PHE	GLY	PRO	SER	ILE	CYS	CYS	GLY	ASP	30
31	GLU	LEU	GLY	CYS	PHE	MET	GLY	THR	ALA	GLU	ALA	LEU	ARG	CYS	GLN	45
46	GLU	GLU	ASN	TYR	LEU	PRO	SER	PRO	CYS	GLN	SER	GLY	GLN	LYS	PRO	60
61	CYS	GLY	SER	GLY	GLY	ARG	CYS	ALA	ALA	ALA	GLY	ILE	CYS	CYS	ASN	75
76	ASP	GLU	SER	CYS	VAL	THR	GLU	PRO	GLU	CYS	ARG	GLU	GLY	ALA	SER	90
91	PHE	PRO	ARG	ARG	ALA											105

Phylogeny of Neurophysins. Complete amino acid sequence of whale (*Balaenoptera physalus*) MSEL-neurophysin.
M. T. Chauvet, P. Codogno, J. Chauvet, and R. Acher.
FEBS Letters, **88**, 91–93 (1978).

HUMAN ANDRENOCORTICOTROPIN

	1				5					10					15	
1	SER	TYR	SER	MET	GLU	HIS	PHE	ARG	TRP	GLY	LYS	PRO	VAL	GLY	LYS	15
16	LYS	ARG	ARG	PRO	VAL	LYS	VAL	TYR	PRO	ASN	GLY	ALA	GLU	ASP	GLU	30
31	SER	ALA	GLU	ALA	PHE	PRO	LEU	GLU	PHE							45

On the structure of human corticotropin (Adrenocorticotropic hormone).
T. H. Lee, A. B. Lerner, and V. Buettner-Janusch.
J. Biol. Chem., **236**, 2970–2974 (1961).
In corrected form:
Revised Amino Acid Sequence for Porcine and Human Adrenocorticotropic Hormone.
B. Riniker, P. Sieber, W. Rittel, and H. Zuber.
Nature (*New Biol.*), **235**, 114–115 (1972).
Confirmation of the 1–20 amino acid sequence of human adrenocorticotrophin.
H. P. J. Bennett, P. J. Lowry, and C. McMartin.
Biochem. J., **133**, 11–13 (1973).

HORMONES AND OTHER ACTIVE PEPTIDES

PORCINE ADRENOCORTICOTROPIN

	1				5					10					15	
1	SER	TYR	SER	MET	GLU	HIS	PHE	ARG	TRP	GLY	LYS	PRO	VAL	GLY	LYS	15
16	LYS	ARG	ARG	PRO	VAL	LYS	VAL	TYR	PRO	ASN	GLY	ALA	GLU	ASP	GLU	30
31	LEU	ALA	GLU	ALA	PHE	PRO	LEU	GLU	PHE							45

Revised Amino Acid Sequence for Porcine and Human Adrenocorticotropic Hormone.
B. Riniker, P. Sieber, W. Rittel, and H. Zuber.
Nature (New Biol.), **235**, 114–115 (1972).
Revised Amide Location for Porcine and Human Adrenocorticotropic Hormone.
L. Gráf, S. Bujusz, A. Patthy, E. Barát, and G. Cseh.
Acta Biochim. Biophys. Acad. Sci. Hung., **6**, 415–418 (1971).
Re-examination of the sequence of the C-terminal tryptic fragment from porcine adrenocorticotropic hormone.
L. Gráf.
Acta Biochim. Biophys. Acad. Sci. Hung., **7**, 293–297 (1972).

BOVINE ADRENOCORTICOTROPIN

	1				5					10					15	
1	SER	TYR	SER	MET	GLU	HIS	PHE	ARG	TRP	GLY	LYS	PRO	VAL	GLY	LYS	15
16	LYS	ARG	ARG	PRO	VAL	LYS	VAL	TYR	PRO	ASN	GLY	ALA	GLU	ASP	GLU	30
31	SER	ALA	GLN	ALA	PHE	PRO	LEU	GLU	PHE							45

Adrenocorticotropins XXI. The Amino Acid Sequence of Bovine Adrenocorticotropin.
C. H. Li, J. S. Dixon, and D. Chung.
Biochim. Biophys. Acta, **46**, 324–334 (1961).
In corrected form:
Adrenocorticotropin 45. Revised Amino Acid Sequences for Sheep and Bovine Hormones.
C. H. Li.
Biochem. Biophys. Res. Comm., **49**, 835–839 (1972).

HORMONES AND OTHER ACTIVE PEPTIDES

OVINE ADRENOCORTICOTROPIN

	1				5					10					15	
1	SER	TYR	SER	MET	GLU	HIS	PHE	ARG	TRP	GLY	LYS	PRO	VAL	GLY	LYS	15
16	LYS	ARG	ARG	PRO	VAL	LYS	VAL	TYR	PRO	ASN	GLY	ALA	GLU	ASP	GLU	30
31	SER	ALA	GLN	ALA	PHE	PRO	LEU	GLU	PHE							45

Adrenocorticotropin 45. Revised Amino Acid Sequences for Sheep and Bovine Hormones.
C. H. Li.
Biochem. Biophys. Res. Comm., **49**, 835–839 (1972).
And
Identity of structure of ovine and bovine ACTH: correction of revised structure of the ovine hormone.
A. Jöhl, B. Riniker, and L. Schenkel-Hulliger.
FEBS Letters, **45**, 172–174 (1974).

DOGFISH ADRENOCORTICOTROPIN

	1				5					10					15	
1	SER	TYR	SER	MET	GLU	HIS	PHE	ARG	TRP	GLY	LYS	PRO	MET	GLY	ARG	15
16	LYS	ARG	ARG	PRO	ILE	LYS	VAL	TYR	PRO	ASN	SER	PHE	GLU	ASP	GLU	30
31	SER	VAL	GLU	ASN	MET	GLY	PRO	GLU	LEU							45

The isolation and amino acid sequence of an adrenocorticotrophin from the pars distalis and a corticotrophin-like intermediate-lobe peptide from the neurointermediate lobe of the pituitary of the dogfish.
P. J. Lowry, H. P. J. Bennett, C. McMartin, and A. P. Scott.
Biochem. J., **141**, 427–437 (1974).

PEPTIDE WITH IN VITRO ACTH-RELEASING ACTIVITY

	1				5					10					15	
1	PHE	LEU	GLY	PHE	PRO	THR	THR	LYS	THR	TYR	PHE	PRO	HIS	PHE		15

Isolation, structural elucidation and synthesis of a tetradecapeptide with *in vitro* ACTH-releasing activity corresponding to residues 33–46 of the α-chain of porcine hemoglobin.
A. V. Schally, W. Y. Huang, T. W. Redding, A. Arimura, D. H. Coy, K. Chihara, R. C. C. Chang, V. Raymond, and F. Labrie.
Biochem. Biophys. Res. Commun., **82**, 582–588 (1978).

HORMONES AND OTHER ACTIVE PEPTIDES

HUMAN CHORIONIC SOMATOMAMMOTROPIN (HCS)

	1				5					10					15	
1	VAL	GLN	THR	VAL	PRO	LEU	SER	ARG	LEU	PHE	ASP	HIS	ALA	MET	LEU	15
16	GLN	ALA	HIS	ARG	ALA	HIS	GLN	LEU	ALA	ILE	ASP	THR	TYR	GLN	GLU	30
31	PHE	GLU	GLU	THR	TYR	ILE	PRO	LYS	ASP	GLN	LYS	TYR	SER	PHE	LEU	45
46	HIS	ASP	SER	GLN	THR	SER	PHE	CYS	PHE	SER	ASP	SER	ILE	PRO	THR	60
61	PRO	SER	ASN	MET	GLU	GLU	THR	GLN	GLN	LYS	SER	ASN	LEU	GLU	LEU	75
76	LEU	ARG	ILE	SER	LEU	LEU	LEU	ILE	GLU	SER	TRP	LEU	GLU	PRO	VAL	90
91	ARG	PHE	LEU	ARG	SER	MET	PHE	ALA	ASN	ASN	LEU	VAL	TYR	ASP	THR	105
106	SER	ASP	SER	ASP	ASP	TYR	HIS	LEU	LEU	LYS	ASP	LEU	GLU	GLU	GLY	120
121	ILE	GLN	THR	LEU	MET	GLY	ARG	LEU	GLU	ASP	GLY	SER	ARG	ARG	THR	135
136	GLY	GLN	ILE	LEU	LYS	GLN	THR	TYR	SER	LYS	PHE	ASP	THR	ASN	SER	150
151	HIS	ASN	HIS	ASP	ALA	LEU	LEU	LYS	ASN	TYR	GLY	LEU	LEU	TYR	CYS	165
166	PHE	ARG	LYS	ASP	MET	ASP	LYS	VAL	GLU	THR	PHE	LEU	ARG	MET	VAL	180
181	GLN	CYS	ARG	SER	VAL	GLU	GLY	SER	CYS	GLY	PHE					195

Primary structure of human chorionic somatomammotropin (HCS) molecule.
C. H. Li, J. S. Dixon, and D. Chung.
Science, **173**, 56–58 (1971); and *Arch. Biochem. Biophys.*, **155**, 95–110 (1973).

HUMAN PITUITARY GROWTH HORMONE

	1				5					10					15	
1	PHE	PRO	THR	ILE	PRO	LEU	SER	ARG	LEU	PHE	ASP	ASN	ALA	MET	LEU	15
16	ARG	ILE	SER	LEU	LEU	LEU	ILE	GLN	SER	TRP	LEU	GLU	PRO	VAL	GLU	30
31	PHE	ALA	HIS	ARG	LEU	HIS	GLN	LEU	ALA	PHE	ASP	THR	TYR	GLU	GLU	45
46	PHE	GLU	GLU	ALA	TYR	ILE	PRO	LYS	GLU	GLN	LYS	TYR	SER	PHE	LEU	60
61	GLN	ASP	PRO	GLU	THR	SER	LEU	CYS	PHE	SER	GLU	SER	ILE	PRO	THR	75
76	PRO	SER	ASN	ARG	GLU	GLU	THR	GLN	LYS	SER	ASN	LEU	GLN	LEU	LEU	90
91	ARG	SER	VAL	PHE	ALA	ASN	SER	LEU	VAL	TYR	GLY	ALA	SER	ASN	SER	105
106	ASP	VAL	TYR	ASP	LEU	LEU	LYS	ASP	LEU	GLU	GLU	GLY	ILE	GLU	THR	120
121	LEU	MET	GLY	ARG	LEU	GLU	ASP	PRO	SER	GLY	ARG	THR	GLY	GLN	ILE	135
136	PHE	LYS	GLN	THR	TYR	SER	LYS	PHE	ASP	THR	ASN	SER	HIS	ASN	ASP	150
151	ASP	ALA	LEU	LEU	LYS	ASN	TYR	GLY	LEU	LEU	TYR	CYS	PHE	ARG	LYS	165
166	ASP	MET	ASP	LYS	VAL	GLU	THR	PHE	LEU	ARG	ILE	VAL	GLN	CYS	ARG	180
181	SER	VAL	GLU	GLY	SER	CYS	GLY	PHE								195

Note: Disulphide bridges are between CYS 68 and 162; CYS 186 and 179.
Human Pituitary Growth Hormone. 19. The Primary Structure of the Hormone.
C. H. Li, J. S. Dixon, and W.-K. Liu.
Arch. Biochem. Biophys., **133**, 70–91 (1969).
Note: This sequence has been reinvestigated by Niall, who transposes the fragment, residues 17–31.
Revised Primary Structure for Human Growth Hormone.
H. D. Niall.
Nature (*New Biol.*), **230**, 90–91 (1971).

HORMONES AND OTHER ACTIVE PEPTIDES

EQUINE GROWTH HORMONE

```
         1              5                      10                     15
  1   PHE PRO ALA MET PRO LEU SER SER LEU PHE ALA ASN ALA VAL LEU     15
 16   ARG ALA GLN HIS LEU HIS GLN LEU ALA ALA ASP THR TYR LYS GLU     30
 31   PHE GLU ARG ALA TYR ILE PRO GLU GLY GLN ARG TYR SER ILE GLN     45
 46   ASN ALA GLN ALA ALA PHE CYS PHE SER GLU THR ILE PRO ALA PRO     60
 61   THR GLY LYS ASP GLU ALA GLN GLN ARG SER ASP MET GLU LEU LEU     75
 76   ARG PHE SER LEU LEU LEU ILE GLN SER TRP LEU GLY PRO VAL GLN     90
 91   LEU LEU SER ARG VAL PHE THR ASN SER LEU VAL PHE GLY THR SER    105
106   ASP ARG VAL TYR GLU LYS LEU ARG ASP LEU GLU GLU GLY ILE GLN    120
121   ALA LEU MET ARG GLU LEU GLU ASP GLY SER PRO ARG ALA GLY GLN    135
136   ILE LEU LYS GLN THR TYR ASP LYS PHE ASP THR ASN LEU ARG SER    150
151   ASP ASP ALA LEU LEU LYS ASN TYR GLY LEU LEU SER CYS PHE LYS    165
166   LYS ASP LEU HIS LYS ALA GLU THR TYR LEU ARG VAL MET LYS CYS    180
181   ARG ARG PHE VAL GLU SER SER CYS ALA PHE                        195
```

Primary structure of equine growth hormone.
M. M. Zakin, E. Poskus, A. A. Langton, P. Ferrara, J. A. Santomé, J. M. Dellacha, and A. C. Paladini.
Int. J. Peptide Protein Res., **8**, 435–444 (1976).

SHEEP PITUITARY GROWTH HORMONE

```
         1              5                      10                     15
  1   ALA PHE PRO ALA MET SER LEU SER GLY LEU PHE ALA ASN ALA VAL     15
 16   LEU ARG ALA GLN HIS LEU HIS GLN LEU ALA ALA ASP THR PHE LYS     30
 31   GLU PHE GLU ARG THR TYR ILE PRO GLU GLY GLN ARG TYR SER ILE     45
 46   GLN ASN THR GLN VAL ALA PHE CYS PHE SER GLU THR ILE PRO ALA     60
 61   PRO THR GLY LYS ASN GLU ALA GLN GLN LYS SER ASP LEU GLU LEU     75
 76   LEU ARG ILE SER LEU LEU LEU ILE GLN SER TRP LEU GLY PRO LEU     90
 91   GLN PHE LEU SER ARG VAL PHE THR ASP SER LEU VAL PHE GLY THR    105
106   SER ASP ARG VAL TYR GLU LYS LEU LYS ASP LEU GLU GLU GLY ILE    120
121   LEU ALA LEU MET ARG GLU LEU GLU ASP VAL THR PRO ARG ALA GLY    135
136   GLN ILE LEU LYS GLN THR TYR ASP LYS PHE ASP THR ASN MET ARG    150
151   SER ASP ASP ALA LEU LEU LYS ASN TYR GLY LEU LEU SER CYS PHE    165
166   ARG LYS ASP LEU HIS LYS THR GLU THR TYR LEU ARG VAL MET LYS    180
181   CYS ARG ARG PHE GLY GLU ALA SER CYS ALA PHE                    195
```

Amino Acid Sequence of Sheep Pituitary Growth Hormone.
C. H. Li, J. S. Dixon, D. Gordon, and J. Knorr.
Int. J. Peptide Protein Res., **4**, 151–153 (1972).
The primary structure of sheep pituitary growth hormone.
C. H. Li, D. Gordon, and J. Knorr.
Arch. Biochem. Biophys., **156**, 493–508 (1973).

HORMONES AND OTHER ACTIVE PEPTIDES

BOVINE GROWTH HORMONE

	1			5						10					15	
1	ALA OOO	PHE	PRO	ALA	MET	SER	LEU	SER	GLY	LEU	PHE	ALA	ASN	ALA	VAL	15
16	LEU	ARG	ALA	GLN	HIS	LEU	HIS	GLN	LEU	ALA	ALA	ASP	THR	PHE	LYS	30
31	GLU	PHE	GLU	ARG	THR	TYR	ILE	PRO	GLU	GLY	GLN	ARG	TYR	SER	ILE	45
46	GLN	ASN	THR	GLN	VAL	ALA	PHE	CYS	PHE	SER	GLU	THR	ILE	PRO	ALA	60
61	PRO	THR	GLY	LYS	ASN	GLU	ALA	GLN	GLN	LYS	SER	ASP	LEU	GLU	LEU	75
76	LEU	ARG	ILE	SER	LEU	LEU	LEU	ILE	GLN	SER	TRP	LEU	GLY	PRO	LEU	90
91	GLN	PHE	LEU	SER	ARG	VAL	PHE	THR	ASN	SER	LEU	VAL	PHE	GLY	THR	105
106	SER	ASP	ARG	VAL	TYR	GLU	LYS	LEU	LYS	ASP	LEU	GLU	GLU	GLY	ILE	120
121	LEU	ALA	LEU	MET	ARG	GLU	VAL LEU	GLU	ASP	GLY	THR	PRO	ARG	ALA	GLY	135
136	GLN	ILE	LEU	LYS	GLN	THR	TYR	ASP	LYS	PHE	ASP	THR	ASN	MET	ARG	150
151	SER	ASP	ASP	ALA	LEU	LEU	LYS	ASN	TYR	GLY	LEU	LEU	SER	CYS	PHE	165
166	ARG	LYS	ASP	LEU	HIS	LYS	THR	GLU	THR	TYR	LEU	ARG	VAL	MET	LYS	180
181	CYS	ARG	ARG	PHE	GLY	GLU	ALA	SER	CYS	ALA	PHE					195

Notes: (i) Disulphide bridges link CYS 53 and 164; CYS 181 and 189. (ii) This sequence is different from that published by Santomé *et al*.
The primary structure of bovine growth hormone.
M. Wallis.
FEBS Letters, **35**, 11–14 (1973).
Studies on the common active site of growth hormone. Revision of the amino acid sequence of an active fragment of bovine growth hormone.
N. Yamasaki, J. Shimanaka, and M. Sonenberg.
J. Biol. Chem., **250**, 2510–2514 (1975).
(This paper confirms residues 96–133 of the sequence of bovine growth hormone as proposed by M. Wallis, and reported above.)

HORMONES AND OTHER ACTIVE PEPTIDES

BOVINE GROWTH HORMONE

	1				5					10					15		
1	ALA	PHE	PRO	ALA	MET	SER	LEU	SER	GLY	LEU	PHE	ALA	ASN	ALA	VAL	15
16	LEU	ARG	ALA	GLN	HIS	LEU	GLN	ALA	(THR, ASP)	ALA	LEU	HIS	PHE	LYS		30
31	GLU	PHE	GLU	ARG	THR	TYR	ILE	GLU	PRO	GLY	GLN	ARG	TYR	SER	ILE	45
46	GLN	ASP	THR	GLN	VAL	ALA	PHE	CYS	PHE	SER	GLU	THR	ILE	PRO	ALA	60
61	PRO	THR	GLY	LYS	ASN	GLU	ALA	GLN	GLU	LYS	SER	ASP	LEU	GLU	LEU	75
76	LEU	ARG	ILE	SER	LEU	LEU	LEU	ILE	SER	GLU	TRP	LEU	(GLX, PRO)	GLY		90
91	PHE	LEU	ARG	VAL	PHE	THR	ASN	SER	LEU	VAL	PHE	GLY	THR	SER	ASP	105
106	ARG	VAL	TYR	GLU	LYS	ASN	GLU	LYS	LYS	LEU	GLU	GLU	GLY	ILE	LEU	120
121	MET	ARG	GLU	LEU/VAL	GLU	ASP	GLY	THR	PRO	ARG	ALA	GLY	GLN	ILE	LEU	135
136	LYS	GLN	THR	TYR	ASP	LYS	PHE	ASP	THR	ASN	MET	ARG	SER	ASN	ASP	150
151	ALA	LEU	LEU	LYS	ASN	TYR	GLY	LEU	LEU	SER	CYS	PHE	ARG	LYS	ASN	165
166	LEU	HIS	THR	LYS	GLU	THR	TYR	LEU	ARG	VAL	MET	LYS	CYS	ARG	ARG	180
181	PHE	GLY	GLU	ALA	SER	CYS	ALA	PHE								195

The amino acid sequence of bovine growth hormone.
J. A. Santomé, J. M. Dellacha, A. C. Paladini, C. E. M. Wolfenstein, C. Pena, E. Poskus, S. T. Daurat, M. J. Biscoglio, Z. M. M. De Sesé, and A. V. F. De Sangüesa.
FEBS Letters, **16**, 198–200 (1971).

BOVINE POSTERIOR PITUITARY PEPTIDE

	1				5					10					15		
1	ARG	GLY	GLU	VAL	LYS	ASP	ALA	SER	GLY	GLU	LEU	GLU	PRO	PRO	PRO	15
16	GLY	PRO	PHE	ILE	GLN	ARG	GLY	ARG	ALA	SER	CYS	TRP	LEU	GLY	ARG	30
31	THR	GLY	SER	CYS	GLN	ASN	CYS	TRP	LEU	CYS	SER	GLN	GLY	ASN	CYS	45
46	ALA	GLY	VAL													60

Note: Disulphide bridges link CYS 34 and 37; CYS 40 and 45.
Structure of a large polypeptide of bovine posterior pituitary tissue.
E. C. Preddie.
J. Biol. Chem., **240**, 4194–4203 (1965).

HORMONES AND OTHER ACTIVE PEPTIDES

BOVINE PARATHYROID HORMONE

	1				5					10					15	
1	ALA	VAL	SER	GLU	ILE	GLN	PHE	MET	HIS	ASN	LEU	GLY	LYS	HIS	LEU	15
16	SER	SER	MET	GLU	ARG	VAL	GLU	TRP	LEU	ARG	LYS	LYS	LEU	GLN	ASP	30
31	VAL	HIS	ASN	PHE	VAL	ALA	LEU	GLY	ALA	SER	ILE	ALA	TYR	ARG	ASP	45
46	GLY	SER	SER	GLN	ARG	PRO	ARG	LYS	LYS	GLU	ASP	ASN	VAL	LEU	VAL	60
61	GLU	SER	HIS	GLN	LYS	SER	LEU	GLY	GLU	ALA	ASP	LYS	ALA	ASP	VAL	75
76	ASP	VAL	LEU	ILE	LYS	ALA	LYS	PRO	GLN							90

The Amino Acid Sequence of Bovine Parathyroid Hormone. 1.
H. D. Niall, H. T. Keutmann, R. Sauer, M. Hogan, B. F. Dawson, G. D. Aurbach, and J. T. Potts, Jr.
Hoppe-Seyler's Z. Physiol. Chem., **351**, 1586–1588 (1970).
And
Bovine Parathyroid Hormone: Amino Acid Sequence.
H. B. Brewer and R. Ronan.
Proc. Natn. Acad. Sci., U.S.A., **67**, 1862–1869 (1970).

PORCINE PARATHYROID HORMONE

	1				5					10					15	
1	SER	VAL	SER	GLU	ILE	GLN	LEU	MET	HIS	ASN	LEU	GLY	LYS	HIS	LEU	15
16	SER	SER	LEU	GLU	ARG	VAL	GLU	TRP	LEU	ARG	LYS	LYS	LEU	GLN	ASP	30
31	VAL	HIS	ASN	PHE	VAL	ALA	LEU	GLY	ALA	SER	ILE	VAL	HIS	ARG	ASP	45
46	GLY	GLY	SER	GLN	ARG	PRO	ARG	LYS	LYS	GLU	ASP	ASN	VAL	LEU	VAL	60
61	GLU	SER	HIS	GLN	LYS	SER	LEU	GLY	GLU	ALA	ASP	LYS	ALA	ALA	VAL	75
76	ASP	VAL	LEU	ILE	LYS	ALA	LYS	PRO	GLN							90

The amino acid sequence of porcine parathyroid hormone.
R. T. Sauer, H. D. Niall, M. L. Hogan, H. T. Keutmann, J. L. H. O'Riordan, and J. T. Potts.
Biochemistry, **13**, 1994–1999 (1974).

HORMONES AND OTHER ACTIVE PEPTIDES

PORCINE PROLACTIN

	1			5					10					15		
1	LEU	PRO	ILE	CYS	PRO	SER	GLY	ALA	VAL	ASN	CYS	GLN	VAL	SER	LEU	15
16	ARG	ASP	LEU	PHE	ASP	ARG	ALA	VAL	ILE	LEU	SER	HIS	TYR	ILE	HIS	30
31	ASN	LEU	SER	SER	GLU	MET	PHE	ASN	GLU	PHE	ASP	LYS	ARG	TYR	ALA	45
46	GLN	GLY	ARG	GLY	PHE	ILE	THR	LYS	ALA	ILE	ASN	SER	CYS	HIS	THR	60
61	SER	SER	LEU	SER	THR	PRO	GLU	ASP	LYS	GLU	GLN	ALA	GLN	GLN	ILE	75
76	HIS	HIS	GLU	VAL	LEU	LEU	ASN	LEU	ILE	LEU	ARG	VAL	LEU	ARG	SER	90
91	TRP	ASN	ASP	PRO	LEU	TYR	HIS	LEU	VAL	THR	GLU	VAL	ARG	GLY	MET	105
106	GLN	GLU	ALA	PRO	ASP	ALA	ILE	LEU	SER	ARG	ALA	ILE	GLU	ILE	GLU	120
121	GLU	GLU	ASN	LYS	ARG	LEU	LEU	GLU	GLY	MET	GLU	LYS	ILE	VAL	GLY	135
136	GLN	VAL	HIS	PRO	GLY	ILE	LYS	GLU	ASN	GLU	VAL	TYR	SER	VAL	TRP	150
151	SER	GLY	LEU	PRO	SER	LEU	GLN	MET	ALA	ASP	GLU	ASP	THR	ARG	LEU	165
166	PHE	ALA	PHE	TYR	ASN	LEU	LEU	HIS	CYS	LEU	ARG	ARG	ASP	SER	HIS	180
181	LYS	ILE	ASP	ASN	TYR	LEU	LYS	LEU	LEU	LYS	CYS	ARG	ILE	ILE	TYR	195
196	ASN	SER	ASN	CYS												210

Studies on pituitary lactogenic hormone. The primary structure of the porcine hormone.
C. H. Li.
Int. J. Peptide Protein Res., **8**, 205–224 (1976).

BOVINE PROLACTIN

	1			5					10					15		
1	THR	PRO	VAL	CYS	PRO	ASN	GLY	PRO	GLY	ASX	CYS	GLN	VAL	SER	LEU	15
16	ARG	ASP	LEU	PHE	ASP	ARG	ALA	VAL	MET	VAL	SER	HIS	TYR	ILE	HIS	30
31	ASN	LEU	SER	SER	GLU	MET	PHE	ASN	GLU	PHE	ASP	LYS	ARG	TYR	ALA	45
46	GLN	GLY	LYS	GLY	PHE	ILE	THR	MET	ALA	LEU	ASN	SER	CYS	HIS	THR	60
61	SER	SER	LEU	PRO	THR	PRO	GLU	ASP	LYS	GLX	GLX	ALA	GLX	GLX	THR	75
76	HIS	HIS	GLX	VAL	LEU	MET	SER	LEU	ILE	LEU	GLY	LEU	LEU	ARG	SER	90
91	TRP	ASX	ASX	PRO	LEU	TYR	HIS	LEU	VAL	THR	GLU	VAL	ARG	GLY	MET	105
106	LYS	GLY	ALA	PRO	ASP	ALA	ILE	LEU	SER	ARG	ALA	ILE	GLX	ILE	GLX	120
121	GLX	GLX	ASX	LYS	ARG	LEU	LEU	GLU	GLY	MET	GLU	MET	ILE	PHE	GLY	135
136	GLN	VAL	ILE	PRO	GLY	ALA	LYS	GLX	THR	GLX	PRO	TYR	PRO	VAL	TRP	150
151	SER	GLY	LEU	PRO	SER	LEU	GLN	THR	LYS	ASP	GLU	ASP	ALA	ARG	TYR	165
166	SER	ALA	PHE	TYR	ASN	LEU	LEU	HIS	CYS	LEU	ARG	ARG	ASP	SER	SER	180
181	LYS	ILE	ASP	THR	TYR	LEU	LYS	LEU	LEU	ASN	CYS	ARG	ILE	ILE	TYR	195
196	ASN	ASN	ASN	CYS												210

Note: Disulphide bridges link residues CYS 4 and 11; CYS 58 and 174; CYS 191 and 199.
The primary structure of bovine prolactin.
M. Wallis.
FEBS Letters, **44**, 205–208 (1974).

412

HORMONES AND OTHER ACTIVE PEPTIDES

SHEEP PROLACTIN

	1				5					10					15	
1	THR	PRO	VAL	CYS	PRO	ASN	GLY	PRO	GLY	ASP	CYS	GLN	VAL	SER	LEU	15
16	ARG	ASP	LEU	PHE	ASP	ARG	ALA	VAL	MET	VAL	SER	HIS	TYR	ILE	HIS	30
31	ASN	LEU	SER	SER	GLU	MET	PHE	ASN	GLU	PHE	ASP	LYS	ARG	TYR	ALA	45
46	GLN	GLY	LYS	GLY	PHE	ILE	THR	MET	ALA	LEU	ASN	SER	CYS	HIS	THR	60
61	SER	SER	LEU	PRO	THR	PRO	GLU	ASP	LYS	GLU	GLN	ALA	GLN	GLN	THR	75
76	HIS	HIS	GLU	VAL	LEU	MET	SER	LEU	ILE	LEU	GLY	LEU	ARG	SER	TRP	90
91	ASN	ASP	PRO	LEU	TYR	HIS	LEU	VAL	THR	GLU	VAL	ARG	GLY	MET	LYS	105
106	GLY	VAL	PRO	ASP	ALA	ILE	LEU	SER	ARG	ALA	ILE	GLU	ILE	GLU	GLU	120
121	GLU	ASN	LYS	ARG	LEU	LEU	GLU	GLY	MET	GLU	MET	ILE	PHE	GLY	GLN	135
136	VAL	ILE	PRO	GLY	ALA	LYS	GLU	THR	GLU	PRO	TYR	PRO	VAL	TRP	SER	150
151	GLY	LEU	PRO	SER	LEU	GLN	THR	LYS	ASP	GLU	ASP	ALA	ARG	HIS	SER	165
166	ALA	PHE	TYR	ASN	LEU	LEU	HIS	CYS	LEU	ARG	ARG	ASP	SER	SER	LYS	180
181	ILE	ASP	THR	TYR	LEU	LYS	LEU	LEU	ASN	CYS	ARG	ILE	ILE	TYR	ASN	195
196	ASN	ASN	CYS													210

Note: Disulphide bridges link residues CYS 4 and 11; CYS 58 and 173; CYS 190 and 198.
Studies on Pituitary Lactogenic Hormone. 30. The Primary structure of Sheep Hormone.
C. H. Li, J. S. Dixon, T.-B. Lo, K. D. Schmidt, and Y. A. Pankov.
Arch. Biochem. Biophys., **141**, 705–737 (1970).

HUMAN PLACENTAL LACTOGEN

	1				5					10					15	
1	VAL	GLN	THR	VAL	PRO	LEU	SER	ARG	LEU	PHE	ASP	HIS	ALA	MET	LEU	15
16	GLN	ALA	HIS	ARG	ALA	HIS	GLN	LEU	ALA	ILE	ASP	THR	TYR	GLN	GLU	30
31	PHE	GLU	GLU	THR	TYR	ILE	PRO	LYS	ASP	GLN	LYS	TYR	SER	PHE	LEU	45
46	HIS	ASP	SER	GLX	THR	SER	PHE	CYS	PHE	SER	ASX	SER	THR	PRO	THR	60
61	PRO	SER	ASX	MET	GLX	GLX	THR	GLX	LYS	SER	ASX	LEU	GLX	LEU	LEU	75
76	ARG	ILE	SER	LEU	LEU	LEU	ILE	GLX	SER	TRP	LEU	GLX	PRO	VAL	ARG	90
91	PHE	LEU	ARG	SER	MET	PHE	ALA	ASX	ASX	LEU	VAL	TYR	ASX	THR	SER	105
106	ASX	ASX	ASX	SER	TYR	HIS	LEU	LEU	LYS	ASX	LEU	GLX	GLX	GLY	ILE	120
121	GLX	THR	LEU	MET	GLY	ARG	LEU	GLX	ASX	GLY	SER	ARG	THR	GLY	GLX	135
136	ILE	LEU	LYS	GLX	THR	TYR	SER	LYS	PHE	ASX	THR	ASX	SER	HIS	ASX	150
151	HIS	ASX	ALA	LEU	LEU	LYS	ASX	TYR	GLY	LEU	LEU	TYR	CYS	PHE	ARG	165
166	LYS	ASX	MET	ASX	LYS	VAL	GLX	THR	PHE	LEU	ARG	MET	VAL	GLN	CYS	180
181	ARG	SER	VAL	GLU	GLY	SER	CYS	GLY	PHE							195

Amino acid sequence of Human Placental Lactogen.
L. M. Sherwood, S. Handwerger, W. D. McLaurin, and M. Lanner.
Nature (*New Biol.*), **233**, 59–61 (1971).

HORMONES AND OTHER ACTIVE PEPTIDES

SHEEP β-LIPOTROPIC HORMONE

	1				5					10					15	
1	GLU	LEU	GLY	THR	GLU	ARG	LEU	GLU	GLN	ALA	ARG	GLY	PRO	GLU	ALA	15
16	ALA	GLU	GLU	SER	ALA	ALA	ALA	ARG	ALA	GLU	LEU	GLU	TYR	GLY	LEU	30
31	VAL	ALA	GLU	ALA	GLN	ALA	ALA	GLU	LYS	LYS	ASP	SER	GLY	PRO	TYR	45
46	LYS	MET	GLU	HIS	PHE	ARG	TRP	GLY	SER	PRO	PRO	LYS	ASP	LYS	ARG	60
61	TYR	GLY	GLY	PHE	MET	THR	SER	GLU	LYS	SER	GLN	THR	PRO	LEU	VAL	75
76	THR	LEU	PHE	LYS	ASN	ALA	ILE	LYS	LYS	ASN	HIS	ALA	LYS	GLY	GLN	90

Isolation and Amino acid sequence of β-LPH from Sheep Pituitary Glands.
C. H. Li, L. Barnafi, M. Chrétien, and D. Chung.
Nature, **208**, 1093–1094 (1965).

SHEEP β-LIPOTROPIC HORMONE (REVISED STRUCTURE)

	1				5					10					15	
1	GLU	LEU	THR	GLY	GLU	ARG	LEU	GLU	GLN	ALA	ARG	GLY	PRO	GLU	ALA	15
16	GLN	ALA	GLU	SER	ALA	ALA	ALA	ARG	ALA	GLU	LEU	GLU	TYR	GLY	LEU	30
31	VAL	ALA	GLU	ALA	GLU	ALA	ALA	GLU	LYS	LYS	ASP	SER	GLY	PRO	TYR	45
46	LYS	MET	GLU	HIS	PHE	ARG	TRP	GLY	SER	PRO	PRO	LYS	ASP	LYS	ARG	60
61	TYR	GLY	GLY	PHE	MET	THR	SER	GLU	LYS	SER	GLN	THR	PRO	LEU	VAL	75
76	THR	LEU	PHE	LYS	ASN	ALA	ILE	LYS	LYS	ASN	HIS	ALA	LYS	GLY	GLN	90

Revised Structure of Sheep Beta-Lipotropic Hormone.
M. Chrétien, C. Gilardeau, and C. H. Li.
Int. J. Peptide Protein Res., **4**, 263–265 (1972).

PORCINE β-LIPOTROPIC HORMONE

	1				5					10					15	
1	GLU	LEU	ALA	GLY	ALA	PRO	PRO	GLU	PRO	ALA	ARG	ASP	PRO	GLU	ALA	15
16	PRO	ALA	GLU	GLY	ALA	ALA	ALA	ARG	ALA	GLU	LEU	GLU	TYR	GLY	LEU	30
31	VAL	ALA	GLU	ALA	GLN	ALA	ALA	GLU	LYS	LYS	ASP	GLU	GLY	PRO	TYR	45
46	LYS	MET	GLU	HIS	PHE	ARG	TRP	GLY	SER	PRO	PRO	LYS	ASP	LYS	ARG	60
61	TYR	GLY	GLY	PHE	MET	THR	SER	GLU	LYS	SER	GLN	THR	PRO	LEU	VAL	75
76	THR	LEU	PHE	LYS	ASN	ALA	ILE	VAL	LYS	ASN	ALA	HIS	LYS	LYS	GLY	90
91	GLN															105

Amino acid sequence of porcine β-lipotropic hormone.
L. Gráf, E. Barát, G. Cseh, and M. Sajgó.
Biochim. Biophys. Acta, **229**, 276–278 (1971).

HORMONES AND OTHER ACTIVE PEPTIDES

FOLLICLE-STIMULATING HORMONE—HUMAN (α-SUBUNIT)

	1				5					10					15	
1	ALA	PRO	ASP	VAL	GLU	ASP	CYS	PRO	GLU	CYS	THR	LEU	GLN	GLU	ASN	15
16	PRO	PHE	PHE	SER	GLN	PRO	GLY	ALA	PRO	ILE	LEU	GLN	CYS	(MET	GLY	30
31	CYS	CYS)	PHE	SER	ARG	ALA	TYR	PRO	THR	PRO	LEU	ARG	SER	LYS	LYS	45
46	THR	MET	LEU	VAL	GLN	LYS	ASN	VAL	THR	SER	GLU	SER	THR	CYS	CYS	60
61	(VAL	ALA	LYS	SER	TYR	ASN	ARG)VAL	THR	VAL	MET	GLY	GLY	PHE	LYS		75
76	VAL	GLU	ASN	HIS	THR	ALA	CYS	HIS	CYS	SER	THR	CYS	TYR	TYR	HIS	90
91	LYS	SER														105

Primary amino acid sequence of follicle-stimulating hormone from human pituitary glands. I. α-Subunit.
P. Rathnam and B. B. Saxena.
J. Biol. Chem., **250**, 6735–6746 (1975).

FOLLICLE-STIMULATING HORMONE—HUMAN (β-SUBUNIT)

	1				5					10					15	
1	ASN	SER	CYS	GLU	LEU	THR	ASN	ILE	THR	ILE	ALA	ILE	GLU	LYS	GLU	15
16	GLU	CYS	ARG	PHE	CYS	LEU	THR	ILE	ASN	THR	THR	TRP	CYS	ALA	GLY	30
31	TYR	CYS	TYR	THR	ARG	ASP	LEU	VAL	TYR	LYS	ASN	PRO	ALA	ARG	PRO	45
46	LYS	ILE	GLN	LYS	THR	CYS	THR	PHE	LYS	GLU	LEU	VAL	TYR	GLU	THR	60
61	VAL	ARG	VAL	PRO	GLY	CYS	ALA	HIS	HIS	ALA	ASP	SER	LEU	TYR	THR	75
76	TYR	PRO	VAL	ALA	THR	GLN	CYS	HIS	CYS	GLY	LYS	CYS	ASP	SER	ASP	90
91	SER	THR	ASP	CYS	THR	VAL	ARG	GLY	LEU	GLY	PRO	SER	TYR	CYS	SER	105
106	PHE	GLY	GLU	MET	LYS	GLN	TYR	PRO	THR	ALA	LEU	SER	TYR			120

Amino acid sequence of the β-subunit of follicle-stimulating hormone from human pituitary glands.
B. B. Saxena and P. Rathnam.
J. Biol. Chem., **251**, 993–1005 (1976).

HORMONES AND OTHER ACTIVE PEPTIDES

FOLLICLE-STIMULATING HORMONE, β-SUBUNIT—PIG

	1				5					10					15	
1	CYS	GLX	LEU	THR	ASN	ILE	THR	ILE	THR	VAL	GLX	VAL	LYS	CYS	LEU	15
16	THR	PHE	CYS	ILE	SER	ILE	ASN	THR	THR	TRP	CYS	ALA	GLY	TYR	CYS	30
31	THR	THR	GLY	ARG	ASX	LEU	VAL	TYR	LYS	ASX	PRO	ALA	ARG	PRO	ASX	45
46	ILE	GLX	LYS	THR	CYS	THR	TYR	ARG	GLX	LEU	VAL	TYR	GLX	THR	VAL	60
61	LYS	VAL	PRO	GLY	CYS	ALA	HIS	HIS	ALA	ASX	SER	LEU	TYR	THR	TYR	75
76	PRO	VAL	ALA	THR	GLX	CYS	HIS	CYS	GLY	LYS	CYS	ASX	SER	ASX	SER	90
91	THR	ASX	CYS	THR	VAL	ARG	GLY	LEU	GLY	PRO	SER	TYR	CYS	SER	PHE	105
106	GLY	GLU														120

Porcine Follitropin. The amino acid sequence of the β-subunit.
J. Closset, G. Maghuin-Rogister, G. Hennen, and A. D. Strosberg.
Eur. J. Biochem., **86**, 115–120 (1978).

PORCINE THYROTROPIN—BETA SUBUNIT

	1				5					10					15	
1	PHE	CYS	ILE	PRO	THR	GLU	TYR	MET	MET	HIS	VAL	GLU	ARG	LYS	GLU	15
16	CYS	ALA	TYR	CYS	LEU	THR	ILE/VAL	ASN	SER	THR	ILE	CYS	ALA	GLY	TYR	30
31	CYS	MET	THR	ARG	ASP	PHE	ASP	GLY	LYS	LEU	PHE	LEU	PRO	LYS	TYR	45
46	ALA	LEU	SER	GLN	ASP	VAL	CYS	THR	TYR	ARG	ASP	PHE	MET	TYR	LYS	60
61	THR	VAL	GLU	ILE	PRO	GLY	(CYS	PRO	HIS	HIS)	VAL	THR	PRO	TYR	PHE	75
76	SER	TYR	PRO	VAL	ALA	ILE	SER	CYS	LYS	CYS	GLY	LYS	CYS	ASP	THR	90
91	ASP	TYR	SER	ASP	CYS	ILE	HIS	GLU	ALA	ILE	LYS	THR	ASN	TYR	CYS	105
106	THR	LYS	PRO	GLU	LYS	SER	TYR									120

Porcine thyrotropin. The amino acid sequence of the α- and β-subunits.
G. Maghuin-Rogister, G. Hennen, J. Closset, and C. Kopeyan.
Eur. J. Biochem., **61**, 157–163 (1976).

HORMONES AND OTHER ACTIVE PEPTIDES

BOVINE THYROTROPIN

	1				5					10					15	
1	PHE	CYS	ILE	PRO	THR	GLU	TYR	MET	MET	HIS	VAL	GLU	ARG	LYS	GLU	15
16	CYS	ALA	TYR	CYS	LEU	THR	ILE	ASN	THR	THR	VAL	CYS	ALA	GLY	TYR	30
31	CYS	MET	THR	ARG	ASX	VAL	ASX	GLY	LYS	LEU	PHE	LEU	PRO	LYS	TYR	45
46	ALA	LEU	SER	GLN	ASP	VAL	CYS	THR	TYR	ARG	ASP	PHE	MET	TYR	LYS	60
61	THR	ALA	GLU	ILE	PRO	GLY	CYS	PRO	ARG	HIS	VAL	THR	PRO	TYR	PHE	75
76	SER	TYR	PRO	VAL	ALA	ILE	SER	CYS	LYS	CYS	GLY	LYS	CYS	ASX	THR	90
91	ASX	TYR	SER	ASX	CYS	ILE	HIS	GLU	ALA	ILE	LYS	THR	ASN	TYR	CYS	105
106	THR	LYS	PRO	GLN	LYS	SER	TYR	MET								120

The Primary Structure of Bovine Thyrotropin. II. The Amino acid sequence of the reduced, S-carboxymethyl α- and β-chains.
T.-H. Liao and J. G. Pierce.
J. Biol. Chem., **246**, 850–865 (1971).

OVINE ICSH (α-SUBUNIT)

	1				5					10					15	
1	PHE	PRO	ASP	GLY	GLU	PHE	THR	MET	GLN	GLY	CYS	PRO	GLU	CYS	LYS	15
16	LEU	LYS	GLU	ASN	LYS	TYR	PHE	SER	LYS	PRO	ASP	ALA	PRO	ILE	TYR	30
31	GLN	CYS	MET	GLY	CYS	CYS	PHE	SER	ARG	ALA	TYR	PRO	THR	PRO	ALA	45
46	ARG	SER	LYS	LYS	THR	MET	LEU	VAL	PRO	LYS	ASN	ILE	THR	SER	GLU	60
61	ALA	THR	CYS	CYS	VAL	ALA	LYS	ALA	PHE	THR	LYS	ALA	THR	VAL	MET	75
76	GLY	ASN	VAL	ARG	VAL	GLU	ASN	HIS	THR	GLU	CYS	HIS	SER	CYS	THR	90
91	CYS	TYR	TYR	HIS	LYS	SER										108

Notes: (i) Heterogeneity at the N-terminus has been reported, with additional N-terminal ASP, GLY and possibly PRO. (ii) Disulphide bridges link residues CYS 14 and 86; CYS 11 and 64; CYS 35 and 63; CYS 32 and 89; CYS 36 and 91.
The primary structure of ovine interstitial cell-stimulating hormone. Part 1. The α-subunit.
M. R. Sairam, H. Papkoff, and C. H. Li.
Arch. Biochem. Biophys., **153**, 551–571 (1972).
The primary structure of the ovine interstitial cell-stimulating hormone. Part 3. Disulfide bridges of the α-subunit.
D. Chung, M. R. Sairam, and C. H. Li.
Arch. Biochem. Biophys., **159**, 678–682 (1973).

HORMONES AND OTHER ACTIVE PEPTIDES

OVINE ICSH (β-SUBUNIT)

```
        1           5              10              15
 1  SER ARG GLY PRO LEU ARG PRO LEU CYS GLU PRO ILE ASN ALA THR   15
16  LEU ALA ALA GLU LYS GLU ALA CYS PRO VAL CYS ILE THR PHE THR   30
31  THR SER ILE GLY ALA TYR CYS CYS PRO SER MET LYS ARG VAL LEU   45
46  PRO VAL PRO PRO LEU ILE PRO MET PRO GLN ARG VAL CYS THR TYR   60
61  HIS GLN LEU ARG PHE ALA SER VAL ARG LEU PRO GLY PRO CYS PRO   75
76  VAL ASP PRO GLY MET VAL SER PHE PRO VAL ALA LEU SER CYS HIS   90
91  GLY PRO CYS CYS ARG LEU SER SER THR ASP CYS GLY PRO GLY ARG  105
106 THR GLU PRO LEU ALA CYS ASP HIS PRO PRO LEU PRO ASP ILE LEU  120
```

Amino Acid Sequence of the Subunits of Ovine Pituitary Interstitial Cell-Stimulating Hormone.
H. Papkoff, M. R. Sairam, and C. H. Li.
J. Amer. Chem. Soc., **93**, 1531–1532 (1971).
The primary structure of ovine interstitial cell-stimulating hormone.
M. R. Sairam, T. S. A. Samy, H. Papkoff, and C. H. Li.
Arch. Biochem. Biophys., **153**, 572–586 (1972).

OVINE LUTEINIZING HORMONE S-SUBUNIT

```
        1           5              10              15
     *   *   *   *   *   *   *
 1  PHE PRO ASN GLY GLX PHE THR MET GLN GLY CYS PRO GLX CYS LYS   15
16  LEU LYS GLX ASX LYS TYR PHE SER LYS PRO ASX ALA PRO ILE TYR   30
31  GLX CYS MET GLY CYS CYS PHE SER ARG ALA TYR PRO THR PRO ALA   45
46  ARG SER LYS LYS THR MET LEU VAL PRO LYS ASN ILE THR SER GLX   60
61  ALA THR CYS CYS VAL ALA LYS ALA PHE THR LYS ALA THR VAL MET   75
76  GLY ASN VAL ARG VAL GLX ASN HIS THR GLX CYS HIS CYS SER THR   90
91  CYS TYR TYR HIS LYS SER                                      105
```

Note: The N-terminal residue may be any one of the residues marked with an asterisk, thus the chain length of this subunit varies from 90 to 96 residues.
The Primary Structure of Ovine Luteinizing Hormone. 1. The amino acid sequence of the reduced and S-aminoethylated S-subunit. (LH-α).
W.-K. Liu, H. S. Nahm, C. M. Sweeney, W. M. Lamkin, H. N. Baker, and D. N. Ward.
J. Biol. Chem., **247**, 4351–4364 (1972).

418

HORMONES AND OTHER ACTIVE PEPTIDES

PORCINE LUTEINIZING HORMONE α-SUBUNIT

	1				5					10					15		
1	THR	MET	GLN	GLY	CYS	PRO	GLU	CYS	LYS	LEU	LYS	GLU	ASN	LYS	TYR	15
16	PHE	SER	LYS	LEU	GLY	ALA	PRO	ILE	TYR	GLN	CYS	MET	GLY	CYS	CYS	30
31	PHE	SER	ARG	ALA	TYR	PRO	THR	PRO	ALA	ARG	SER	LYS	LYS	THR	MET	45
46	LEU	VAL	PRO	LYS	ASN	ILE	THR	SER	GLU	ALA	THR	CYS	CYS	VAL	ALA	60
61	LYS	ALA	PHE	THR	LYS	ALA	THR	VAL	MET	GLY	ASN	ALA	ARG	VAL	GLU	75
76	ASN	HIS	THR	GLU	CYS	HIS	CYS	SER	THR	CYS	TYR	TYR	HIS	LYS	SER	90

The primary structure of the porcine luteinizing-hormone α-subunit.
G. Maghuin-Rogister, Y. Combarnous, and G. Hennen.
Eur. J. Biochem., **39**, 255–263 (1973).

HUMAN LUTROPIN β-SUBUNIT

	1				5					10					15		
1	SER	ARG	GLU	PRO	LEU	ARG	PRO	TRP	CYS	HIS	PRO	ILE	ASN	ALA	ILE	15
16	LEU	ALA	VAL	GLN	LYS	GLU	GLY	CYS	PRO	VAL	CYS	ILE	THR	VAL	ASN	30
31	THR	THR	ILE	CYS	ALA	GLY	TYR	CYS	PRO	THR	MET	MET	ARG	VAL	LEU	45
46	GLN	ALA	VAL	LEU	PRO	PRO	LEU	PRO	GLN	VAL	CYS	THR	TYR	ARG	ASP	60
61	VAL	ARG	PHE	GLU	SER	ILE	ARG	LEU	PRO	GLY	CYS	PRO	ARG	GLY	VAL	75
76	ASP	PRO	VAL	VAL	SER	PHE	PRO	VAL	ALA	LEU	SER	CYS	ARG	CYS	GLY	90
91	PRO	CYS	ARG	ARG	SER	THR	SER	ASP	CYS	GLY	GLY	PRO	LYS	ASP	HIS	105
106	PRO	LEU	THR	CYS	ASP	PRO	GLN	HIS	SER	GLY						120

Human pituitary lutropin. Isolation, properties and the complete amino acid sequence of the β-subunit.
M. R. Sairam and C. H. Li.
Biochim. Biophys. Acta, **412**, 70–81 (1975).

HORMONES AND OTHER ACTIVE PEPTIDES

BOVINE LUTEINIZING HORMONE β-SUBUNIT

	1				5					10					15	
1	SER	ARG	GLY	PRO	LEU	ARG	PRO	LEU	CYS	GLX	PRO	ILE	ASN	ALA	THR	15
16	LEU	ALA	ALA	GLX	LYS	GLX	ALA	CYS	PRO	VAL	CYS	ILE	THR	PHE	THR	30
31	THR	SER	ILE	CYS	ALA	GLY	TYR	CYS	PRO	SER	MET	LYS	ARG	VAL	LEU	45
46	PRO	VAL	ILE	LEU	PRO	PRO	MET	PRO	GLX	ARG	VAL	CYS	THR	TYR	HIS	60
61	GLU	LEU	ARG	PHE	ALA	SER	VAL	ARG	LEU	PRO	GLY	CYS	PRO	PRO	GLY	75
76	VAL	ASX	PRO	MET	VAL	SER	PHE	PRO	VAL	ALA	LEU	SER	CYS	(HIS,	CYS,	90
91	GLY,	PRO)	CYS	ARG	LEU	SER	SER	THR	ASX	CYS	GLY	PRO	GLY	ARG	THR	105
106	GLX	PRO	LEU	ALA	CYS	ASX	HIS	PRO	PRO	LEU	PRO	ASP	ILE	LEU		120

Note: The amino terminus of this protein is blocked.

The Amino Acid Sequence of Bovine Luteinizing Hormone β-Subunit.
G. Maghuin-Rogister and A. Dockier.
FEBS Letters, **19**, 209–213 (1971).

PORCINE LUTEINIZING HORMONE β-SUBUNIT

	1				5					10					15	
1	SER	ARG	GLY	PRO	LEU	ARG	PRO	LEU	CYS	ARG/GLX	PRO	ILE	ASN	ALA	THR	15
16	LEU	ALA	ALA	GLU	ASP	GLU	ALA	CYS	PRO	VAL	CYS	ILE	THR	PHE	THR	30
31	THR	SER	ILE	CYS	ALA	GLY	TYR	CYS	PRO	SER	MET	ARG	ARG	VAL	LEU	45
46	PRO	ALA	ALA	LEU	PRO	PRO	VAL	PRO	GLN	PRO	VAL	CYS	THR	TYR	ARG	60
61	GLU	LEU	ILE	PHE	ALA	SER	SER	ARG	LEU	PRO	GLY	CYS	PRO	PRO	GLY	75
76	VAL	ASP	PRO	THR	VAL	SER	PHE	PRO	VAL	ALA	LEU	SER	CYS	HIS	CYS	90
91	GLY	PRO	CYS	ARG	LEU	SER	SER	SER	ASP	CYS	GLY	PRO	GLY	ARG	ALA	105
106	GLN	PRO	LEU	ALA	CYS	ASP	ARG	PRO	PRO	LEU	PRO	GLY	LEU	LEU		120

Note: The N-terminal residue is blocked by an unknown group.

Luteinizing hormone. The primary structures of the β-subunit from bovine and porcine species.
G. Maghuin-Rogister and G. Hennen.
Eur. J. Biochem., **39**, 235–253 (1973).

HORMONES AND OTHER ACTIVE PEPTIDES

OVINE LUTEINIZING HORMONE A-SUBUNIT

	1				5					10					15	
1	AC	SER	ARG	GLY	PRO	LEU	ARG	PRO	LEU	CYS	GLN	PRO	ILE	ASN	ALA	15
16	THR	LEU	ALA	ALA	GLU	LYS	GLU	ALA	CYS	PRO	VAL	CYS	ILE	THR	PHE	30
31	THR	THR	SER	ILE	CYS	ALA	GLY	TYR	CYS	PRO	SER	MET	LYS	ARG	VAL	45
46	LEU	PRO	VAL	ILE	LEU	PRO	PRO	MET	PRO	GLN	ARG	VAL	CYS	THR	TYR	60
61	HIS	GLU	LEU	ARG	PHE	ALA	SER	VAL	ARG	LEU	PRO	GLY	CYS	PRO	PRO	75
76	GLY	VAL	ASP	PRO	MET	VAL	SER	PHE	PRO	VAL	ALA	LEU	SER	CYS	HIS	90
91	CYS	GLY	PRO	CYS	ARG	LEU	SER	SER	THR	ASP	CYS	GLY	PRO	GLY	ARG	105
106	THR	GLX	PRO	LEU	ALA	CYS	ASX	HIS	PRO	PRO	LEU	PRO	ASP	ILE	LEU	120

The Primary structure of Ovine Luteinizing Hormone. 2. The Amino Acid Sequence of the reduced S-carboxymethylated A-Subunit (LH-β).
W.-K. Liu, H. S. Nahm, C. M. Sweeney, G. N. Holcomb, and D. N. Ward.
J. Biol. Chem., **247**, 4365–4381 (1972).

MOUSE NERVE GROWTH FACTOR

	1				5					10					15	
1	SER	SER	THR	HIS	PRO	VAL	PHE	HIS	MET	GLY	GLU	PHE	SER	VAL	CYS	15
16	ASP	SER	VAL	SER	VAL	TRP	VAL	GLY	ASP	LYS	THR	THR	ALA	THR	ASN	30
31	ILE	LYS	GLY	LYS	GLU	VAL	THR	VAL	LEU	ALA	GLU	VAL	ASN	ILE	ASN	45
46	ASN	SER	VAL	PHE	ARG	GLN	TYR	PHE	PHE	GLU	THR	LYS	CYS	ARG	ALA	60
61	SER	ASN	PRO	VAL	GLU	SER	GLY	CYS	ARG	GLY	ILE	ASP	SER	LYS	HIS	75
76	TRP	ASN	SER	TYR	CYS	THR	THR	THR	HIS	THR	PHE	VAL	LYS	ALA	LEU	90
91	THR	THR	ASP	GLU	LYS	GLN	ALA	ALA	TRP	ARG	PHE	ILE	ARG	ILE	ASN	105
106	THR	ALA	CYS	VAL	CYS	VAL	LEU	SER	ARG	LYS	ALA	THR	ARG			120

Note: Disulphide bridges are between CYS 15 and 80; CYS 58 and 108; CYS 68 and 110.
Nerve Growth Factor from mouse submaxillary Gland: Amino Acid Sequence.
R. H. Angeletti and R. A. Bradshaw.
Proc. Natn. Acad. Sci., U.S.A., **68**, 2417–2420 (1971).
Amino acid sequence of mouse 2.5S nerve growth factor. II. Isolation and characterization of the thermolytic and peptic peptides and the complete covalent structure.
R. H. Angeletti, M. A. Hermodson, and R. A. Bradshaw.
Biochemistry, **12**, 100–115 (1973).

HORMONES AND OTHER ACTIVE PEPTIDES

HUMAN CHORIONIC GONADOTROPIN
α-SUBUNIT

	1				5					10					15	
1	ALA	PRO	ASP	VAL	GLN	ASP	CYS	PRO	GLU	CYS	THR	LEU	GLN	GLU	ASP	15
16	PRO	PHE	PHE	SER	GLN	PRO	GLY	ALA	PRO	ILE	LEU	GLX	CYS	MET	GLY	30
31	CYS	CYS	PHE	SER	ARG	ALA	TYR	PRO	THR	PRO	LEU	ARG	SER	LYS	LYS	45
46	THR	MET	LEU	VAL	GLN	LYS	ASN	VAL	THR	SER	GLU	SER	THR	CYS	CYS	60
61	VAL	ALA	LYS	SER	TYR	ASN	ARG	VAL	THR	VAL	MET	GLY	GLY	PHE	LYS	75
76	VAL	GLU	ASN	HIS	THR	ALA	CYS	HIS	CYS	SER	THR	CYS	TYR	TYR	HIS	90
91	LYS	SER														105

Note: Residues at positions 1, 3 and 4 are found in varying proportions as the N-terminal residue.

β-SUBUNIT

	1				5					10					15	
1	SER	LYS	GLU	PRO	LEU	ARG	PRO	ARG	CYS	ARG	PRO	ILE	ASN	ALA	THR	15
16	LEU	ALA	VAL	GLU	LYS	GLU	GLY	CYS	PRO	VAL	CYS	ILE	THR	VAL	ASN	30
31	THR	THR	ILE	CYS	ALA	GLY	TYR	CYS	PRO	THR	MET	THR	ARG	VAL	LEU	45
46	GLN	GLY	VAL	LEU	PRO	ALA	LEU	PRO	GLN	VAL	VAL	CYS	ASN	TYR	ARG	60
61	ASP	VAL	ARG	PHE	GLU	SER	ILE	ARG	LEU	PRO	GLY	CYS	PRO	ARG	GLY	75
76	VAL	ASN	PRO	VAL	VAL	SER	TYR	ALA	VAL	ALA	LEU	SER	CYS	GLN	CYS	90
91	ALA	LEU	CYS	ARG	ARG	SER	THR	THR	ASP	CYS	GLY	GLY	PRO	LYS	ASP	105
106	HIS	PRO	LEU	THR	CYS	ASP	ASP	PRO	ARG	PHE	GLN	ASP	SER	SER	SER	120
121	SER	LYS	ALA	PRO	PRO	PRO	SER	LEU	PRO	SER	PRO	SER	ARG	LEU	PRO	135
136	GLY	PRO	SER	ASP	THR	PRO	ILE	LEU	PRO	GLN						150

Human chorionic gonadotropin: A proposal for the amino acid sequence.
F. J. Morgan, S. Birkin, and R. E. Canfield.
Molecular & Cellular Biochem., **2**, 97–99 (1973).
And
The amino acid sequence of human chorionic gonadotropin. The α-subunit and β-subunit.
F. J. Morgan, S. Birken, and R. E. Canfield.
J. Biol. Chem., **250**, 5247–5258 (1975).
And
Human chorionic gonadotropin. Linear amino acid sequence of the α-subunit.
R. Bellisario, R. B. Carlsen, and O. P. Bahl.
J. Biol. Chem., **248**, 6796–6809 (1973).
Human chorionic gonadotropin. Linear amino acid sequence of the β-subunit.
R. B. Carlsen, O. P. Bahl, and N. Swaminathan.
J. Biol. Chem., **248**, 6810–6827 (1973).
The sequence reported in this paper is different from that reported by Canfield *et al*. in the following aspects:
(i) It has an additional tripeptide sequence at the C-terminus, (SER LEU PRO).
(ii) Residue 55 is LEU (not VAL).
(iii) Residue 138 is PRO (not SER).
(iv) Residue 121 (SER) was not found.

TOXINS

CHOLERA TOXIN B SUBUNIT

	1				5					10					15	
1	THR	PRO	GLU	ASN	ILE	THR	ASP	LEU	CYS	ALA	GLU	TYR	HIS	ASN	THR	15
16	GLN	ILE	HIS	THR	LEU	ASN	ASN	LYS	ILE	PHE	SER	TYR	THR	GLU	SER	30
31	LEU	ALA	GLY	LYS	ARG	GLU	MET	ALA	ILE	ILE	THR	PHE	LYS	ASP	GLY	45
46	ALA	THR	PHE	GLU	VAL	GLU	VAL	PRO	GLY	SER	GLU	HIS	ILE	ASP	SER	60
61	GLU	LYS	LYS	ALA	ILE	GLU	ARG	MET	LYS	ASP	THR	LEU	ARG	ILE	ALA	75
76	TYR	LEU	THR	GLU	ALA	LYS	VAL	GLU	LYS	LEU	CYS	VAL	TRP	ASN	ASN	90
91	LYS	THR	PRO	HIS	ALA	ILE	ALA	ALA	ILE	SER	MET	ALA	ASN			105

Note: A disulphide bridge joins residues CYS 9 and 86.
Primary structure of cholera toxin B-subunit.
C. Y. Lai, E. Mendez, D. Chang, and M. Wang.
Biochem. Biophys. Res. Commun., **74**, 215–222 (1977).

ENTEROTOXIN B

	1				5					10					15	
1	GLU	SER	GLN	PRO	ASP	PRO	LYS	PRO	ASP	GLU	LEU	HIS	LYS	SER	SER	15
16	LYS	PHE	THR	GLY	LEU	MET	GLU	ASN	MET	LYS	VAL	LEU	TYR	ASN	ASN	30
31	ASP	HIS	VAL	SER	ALA	ILE	ASN	VAL	LYS	SER	ILE	ASN	GLU	PHE	PHE	45
46	ASP	LEU	ILE	TYR	LEU	TYR	SER	ILE	LYS	ASP	THR	LYS	LEU	GLY	ASN	60
61	TYR	ASP	ASN	VAL	ARG	VAL	GLU	PHE	LYS	ASN	LYS	ASP	LEU	ALA	ASP	75
76	LYS	TYR	LYS	ASP	LYS	TYR	VAL	ASP	VAL	PHE	GLY	ALA	ASN	TYR	TYR	90
91	GLN	CYS	TYR	PHE	SER	LYS	LYS	THR	ASN	ASN	ILE	ASP	SER	HIS	GLU	105
106	ASN	THR	LYS	ARG	LYS	THR	CYS	MET	TYR	GLY	GLY	VAL	THR	GLU	HIS	120
121	GLY	ASN	ASN	GLN	LEU	ASP	LYS	TYR	TYR	ARG	SER	ILE	THR	VAL	ARG	135
136	VAL	PHE	GLU	ASP	GLY	LYS	ASN	LEU	LEU	SER	PHE	ASP	VAL	GLN	THR	150
151	ASN	LYS	LYS	LYS	VAL	THR	ALA	GLU	GLN	LEU	ASP	TYR	LEU	THR	ARG	165
166	HIS	TYR	LEU	VAL	LYS	ASN	LYS	LYS	LEU	TYR	GLU	PHE	ASN	ASN	SER	180
181	PRO	TYR	GLU	THR	GLY	TYR	ILE	LYS	PHE	ILE	GLU	ASN	GLU	ASN	SER	195
196	PHE	TRP	TYR	ASP	MET	MET	PRO	ALA	PRO	GLY	ASN	LYS	PHE	ASP	GLN	210
211	SER	LYS	TYR	LEU	MET	MET	TYR	ASN	ASN	ASP	LYS	MET	VAL	ASP	SER	225
226	LYS	ASP	VAL	LYS	ILE	GLU	VAL	TYR	LEU	THR	THR	LYS	LYS	LYS		240

The Primary Structure of Staphylococcal Enterotoxin B.
I.-Y. Huang and M. S. Bergdoll.
J. Biol. Chem., **245**, 3518–3525 (1970).

VISCOTOXIN A2

	1			5					10					15		
1	LYS	SER	CYS	CYS	PRO	ASN	THR	THR	GLY	ARG	ASN	ILE	TYR	ASN	THR	15
16	CYS	ARG	PHE	GLY	GLY	GLY	SER	ARG	GLU	VAL	CYS	ALA	SER	LEU	SER	30
31	GLY	CYS	LYS	ILE	ILE	SER	ALA	SER	THR	CYS	PRO	SER	TYR	PRO	ASP	45
46	LYS															60

The Amino Acid Sequence of Viscotoxin A2 from the European Mistletoe (*Viscum album* L., Loranthaceae).
T. Olson and G. Samuelsson.
Acta. Chem. Scand., **26**, 585–595 (1972).

VISCOTOXIN A3

	1			5					10					15		
1	LYS	SER	CYS	CYS	PRO	ASN	THR	THR	GLY	ARG	ASN	ILE	TYR	ASN	ALA	15
16	CYS	ARG	LEU	THR	GLY	ALA	PRO	ARG	PRO	THR	CYS	ALA	LYS	LEU	SER	30
31	GLY	CYS	LYS	ILE	ILE	SER	GLY	SER	THR	CYS	PRO	SER	TRP	PRO	ASP	45
46	LYS															60

The Amino Acid Sequence of Oxidized Viscotoxin A3 from the European Mistletoe (*Viscum album* L., Loranthaceae).
G. Samuelsson, L. Seger, and T. Olson.
Acta Chem. Scand., **22**, 2624–2642 (1968).

VISCOTOXIN B

	1			5					10					15		
1	LYS	SER	CYS	CYS	PRO	ASN	THR	THR	GLY	ARG	ASN	ILE	TYR	ASN	THR	15
16	CYS	ARG	LEU	GLY	GLY	GLY	SER	ARG	GLU	ARG	CYS	ALA	SER	LEU	SER	30
31	GLY	CYS	LYS	ILE	ILE	SER	ALA	SER	THR	CYS	PRO	SER	TYR	PRO	ASP	45
46	LYS															60

The Amino Acid Sequence of Viscotoxin B from the European Mistletoe (*Viscum album* L., Loranthaceae).
G. Samuelsson and B. M. Pettersson.
Eur. J. Biochem., **21**, 86–89 (1971).

TOXINS

PHORATOXIN

	1			5					10				15			
1	LYS	SER	CYS	CYS	PRO	THR	THR	THR	ALA	ARG	ASN	ILE	TYR	ASN	THR	15
16	CYS	ARG	PHE	GLY	GLY	GLY	SER	ARG	PRO	VAL	CYS	ALA	LYS	LEU	SER	30
31	GLY	CYS	LYS	ILE	ILE	SER	GLY	THR	LYS	CYS	ASP	SER	GLY	TRP	ASN	45
46	HIS															60

Phoratoxin, a toxic protein from the mistletoe *Phoradendron tomentosum* subsp. *macrophyllum* (Loranthaceae). The amino acid sequence.
S. T. Mellstrand and G. Samuelsson.
Acta Pharm. Succica, **11**, 347–360 (1974).

TOXIN III—ANEMONIA SULCATA

	1			5					10				15			
1	ARG	SER	CYS	CYS	PRO	CYS	TYR	TRP	GLY	GLY	CYS	PRO	TRP	GLY	GLN	15
16	ASN	CYS	TYR	PRO	GLU	GLY	CYS	SER	GLY	PRO	LYS	VAL				30

Toxin III from *Anemonia sulcata*: Primary structure.
G. Martinez, C. Kopeyan, H. Schweitz, and M. Lazdunski.
FEBS Letters, **84**, 247–252 (1977).

TOXIN I—ANEMONIA SULCATA

	1			5					10				15			
1	GLY	ALA	ALA PRO	CYS	LEU	CYS	LYS	SER	ASP	GLY	PRO	ASN	THR	ARG	GLY	15
16	ASN	SER	MET	SER	GLY	THR	ILE	TRP	VAL	PHE	GLY	CYS	PRO	SER	GLY	30
31	TRP	ASN	ASN	CYS	GLU	GLY	ARG	ALA	ILE	ILE	GLY	TYR	CYS	CYS	LYS	45
46	GLN															60

Amino acid sequence of toxin I from *Anemonia sulcata*.
G. Wunderer and M. Eulitz.
Eur. J. Biochem., **89**, 11–17 (1978).

TOXIN II—ANEMONIA SULCATA

	1			5					10					15	
1	GLY	ILE VAL	PRO	CYS	LEU	CYS	ASP	SER	ASP	GLY	PRO	SER	VAL	ARG	GLY	15
16	ASN	THR	LEU	SER	GLY	ILE	ILE	TRP	LEU	ALA	GLY	CYS	PRO	SER	GLY	30
31	TRP	HIS	ASN	CYS	LYS	LYS	HIS	GLY	PRO	THR	ILE	GLY	TRP	CYS	CYS	45
46	LYS	GLN														60

Amino acid sequence of a coelenterate toxin: toxin II from *Anemonia sulcata*.
G. Wunderer, H. Fritz, E. Wachter, and W. Machleidt.
Eur. J. Biochem., **68**, 193–198 (1976).

MAST-CELL DEGRANULATING PEPTIDE

	1			5					10					15	
1	ILE	LYS	CYS	ASN	CYS	LYS	ARG	HIS	VAL	ILE	LYS	PRO	HIS	ILE	CYS	15
16	ARG	LYS	ILE	CYS	GLY	LYS	ASN	NH$_2$								30

The Amino Acid Sequence of the specific mast-cell degranulating peptide of bee venom.
P. Haux.
Hoppe-Seyler's Z. Physiol. Chem., **350**, 536–546 (1969).

APAMIN

	1			5					10					15	
1	CYS	ASN	CYS	LYS	ALA	PRO	GLU	THR	ALA	LEU	CYS	ALA	ARG	ARG	CYS	15
16	GLN	GLN	HIS	NH$_2$												30

Note: Disulphide bridges link residues CYS 1 and 11; CYS 3 and 15.
The Structure of Apamin.
R. Shipolini, A. F. Bradbury, G. L. Callewaert, and C. A. Vernon.
Chem. Commun., 679–680 (1967).
The Disulphide Bridges of Apamin.
G. L. Callewaert, R. Shipolini and C. A. Vernon.
FEBS Letters, **1**, 111–113 (1968).

TOXINS

MELITTIN

	1			5					10					15		
1	GLY	ILE	GLY	ALA	VAL	LEU	LYS	VAL	LEU	THR	THR	GLY	LEU	PRO	ALA	15
16	LEU	ILE	SER	TRP	ILE	LYS	ARG	LYS	ARG	GLN	GLN	NH_2				30

Sequence analysis of mellittins.
E. Habermann and J. Jentsch.
Hoppe-Seyler's Z. Physiol. Chem., **348**, 37–50 (1967).

MELITTIN FROM APIS DORSATA

	1			5					10					15		
1	GLY	ILE	GLY	ALA	ILE	LEU	LYS	VAL	LEU	SER	THR	GLY	LEU	PRO	ALA	15
16	LEU	ILE	SER	TRP	ILE	LYS	ARG	LYS	ARG	GLN	GLU	NH_2				30

The structure of *Apis dorsata* melittin: phylogenetic relationships between honeybees as deduced from sequence data.
G. Kreil.
FEBS Letters, **54**, 100–102 (1975).

MELITTIN FROM APIS FLOREA

	1			5					10					15		
1	GLY	ILE	GLY	ALA	ILE	LEU	LYS	VAL	LEU	ALA	THR	GLY	LEU	PRO	THR	15
16	LEU	ILE	SER	TRP	ILE	LYS	ASN	LYS	ARG	LYS	GLN	NH_2				30

Structure of melittin isolated from two species of honey bees.
G. Kreil.
FEBS Letters, **33**, 241–244 (1973).

MELITTIN B

	1			5					10					15		
1	GLY	ILE	GLY	ALA	VAL	LEU	LYS	VAL	LEU	THR	THR	GLY	LEU	PRO	ALA	15
16	LEU	ILE	SER	TRP	ILE	LYS	ARG	LYS	ARG	GLN	GLN	NH_2				30

Note: The N-terminus of the above peptide is blocked by a formyl group.

MELITTIN II

	1		5					10					15			
1	GLY	ILE	GLY	ALA	VAL	LEU	LYS	VAL	LEU	THR	THR	GLY	LEU	PRO	ALA	15
16	LEU	ILE	SER	TRP	ILE	SER	ARG	LYS	LYS	ARG	GLN	GLN				30

Note: The N-terminus of the above peptide is blocked by an unknown group.
The chemistry of melittin from bee venom.
J. Jentsch.
Chemie in unserer Zeit, **8**, 177–183 (1974).
And
On Melittin XI.—Three melittins in Bee Venom.
J. Jentsch.
Ann. Chem., **757**, 193–195 (1972).

PROMELITTIN

	1		5					10					15			
1	GLU	PRO	GLU	PRO	ASP	PRO	GLU	ALA	GLY	ILE	GLY	ALA	VAL	LEU	LYS	15
16	VAL	LEU	THR	THR	GLY	LEU	PRO	ALA	LEU	ILE	SER	TRP	ILE	LYS	ARG	30
31	LYS	ARG	GLN	GLN	NH$_2$											45

Biosynthesis of Melittin, a toxic peptide from bee venom. Amino acid sequence of the precursor.
G. Kreil.
Eur. J. Biochem., **33**, 558–566 (1973).

SECAPIN FROM BEE VENOM

	1		5					10					15			
1	TYR	ILE	ILE	ASP	VAL	PRO	PRO	ARG	CYS	PRO	PRO	GLY	SER	LYS	PHE	15
16	ILE	LYS	ASN	ARG	CYS	ARG	VAL	PRO	VAL							30

MELITTIN F FROM BEE VENOM

	1		5					10					15			
1	VAL	LEU	THR	THR	GLY	LEU	PRO	ALA	LEU	ILE	SER	TRP	ILE	LYS	ARG	15
16	LYS	ARG	GLN	GLN	NH$_2$											30

TOXINS

PEPTIDE 401 (MCD PEPTIDE) FROM BEE VENOM

	1				5					10					15	
1	ILE	LYS	CYS	ASN	CYS	LYS	ARG	HIS	VAL	ILE	LYS	PRO	HIS	ILE	CYS	15
16	ARG	LYS	ILE	CYS	GLY	LYS	ASN	NH₂								30

The structures of some peptides from bee venom.
J. Gauldie, J. M. Hanson, R. A. Shipolini, and C. A. Vernon.
Eur. J. Biochem., **83**, 405–410 (1978).

NEUROTOXIN VARIANT 1 FROM SCORPION VENOM

	1				5					10					15	
1	LYS	GLU	GLY	TYR	LEU	VAL	LYS	LYS	SER	ASP	GLY	CYS	LYS	TYR	ASP	15
16	CYS	PHE	TRP	LEU	GLY	LYS	ASN	GLU	HIS	ASN	THR	CYS	GLU	CYS	LYS	30
31	ALA	LYS	ASN	GLN	GLY	GLY	SER	TYR	GLY	TYR	CYS	TYR	ALA	PHE	ALA	45
46	CYS	TRP	CYS	GLU	GLY	LEU	PRO	GLU	SER	THR	PRO	THR	TYR	PRO	LEU	60
61	PRO	ASN	LYS	CYS	SER											75

NEUROTOXIN VARIANT 2 FROM SCORPION VENOM

	1				5					10					15	
1	LYS	GLU	GLY	TYR	LEU	VAL	ASN	LYS	SER	THR	GLY	CYS	LYS	TYR	GLY	15
16	CYS	LEU	LYS	LEU	GLY	GLU	ASN	GLU	GLY	ASN	LYS	CYS	GLU	CYS	LYS	30
31	ALA	LYS	ASN	GLN	GLY	GLY	SER	TYR	GLY	TYR	CYS	TYR	ALA	PHE	ALA	45
46	CYS	TRP	CYS	GLU	GLY	LEU	PRO	GLU	SER	THR	PRO	THR	TYR	PRO	LEU	60
61	PRO	ASN	LYS	CYS	SER	SER										75

NEUROTOXIN VARIANT 3 FROM SCORPION VENOM

	1				5					10					15	
1	LYS	GLU	GLY	TYR	LEU	VAL	LYS	LYS	SER	ASP	GLY	CYS	LYS	TYR	GLY	15
16	CYS	LEU	LYS	LEU	GLY	GLU	ASN	GLU	GLY	ASN	THR	CYS	GLU	CYS	LYS	30
31	ALA	LYS	ASN	GLN	GLY	GLY	SER	TYR	GLY	TYR	CYS	TYR	ALA	PHE	ALA	45
46	CYS	TRP	CYS	GLU	GLY	LEU	PRO	GLU	SER	THR	PRO	THR	TYR	PRO	LEU	60
61	PRO	ASN	LYS	CYS	SER											75

Amino acid sequences of neurotoxic protein variants from the venom of *Centruroides sculpturatus* Ewing.
D. R. Babin, D. D. Watt, S. M. Goos, and R. V. Mlejnek.
Arch. Biochem. Biophys., **164**, 694–706 (1974).

NEUROTOXIN I FROM SCORPION VENOM

	1				5					10					15	
1	LYS	ASP	GLY	TYR	LEU	VAL	GLU	LYS	THR	GLY	CYS	LYS	LYS	THR	CYS	15
16	TYR	LYS	LEU	GLY	GLU	ASN	ASP	PHE	CYS	ASN	ARG	GLU	CYS	LYS	TRP	30
31	LYS	HIS	ILE	GLY	GLY	SER	TYR	GLY	TYR	CYS	TYR	GLY	PHE	GLY	CYS	45
46	TYR	CYS	GLU	GLY	LEU	PRO	ASP	SER	THR	GLN	THR	TRP	PRO	LEU	PRO	60
61	ASN	LYS	CYS	THR												75

Amino acid sequence of neurotoxin I from *Centruroides sculpturatus* Ewing.
D. R. Babin, D. D. Watt, S. M. Goos, and R. V. Mlejnek.
Arch. Biochem. Biophys., **166**, 125–134 (1975).

NEUROTOXIN I—SCORPION

	1				5					10					15	
1	LYS	ARG	ASP	GLY	TYR	ILE	VAL	TYR	PRO	ASN	ASN	CYS	VAL	TYR	HIS	15
16	CYS	VAL	PRO	PRO	CYS	ASP	GLY	LEU	CYS	LYS	LYS	ASN	GLY	GLY	SER	30
31	SER	GLY	SER	SER	CYS	PHE	LEU	VAL	PRO	SER	GLY	LEU	ALA	CYS	TRP	45
46	CYS	LYS	ASP	LEU	PRO	ASP	ASN	VAL	PRO	ILE	LYS	ASP	THR	SER	ARG	60
61	LYS	CYS	THR													75

The Amino Acid Sequence of Neurotoxin I of *Androctonus australis*.
H. Rochat, C. Rochat, F. Miranda, S. Lissitzky, and P. Edman.
Eur. J. Biochem., **17**, 262–266 (1970).

NEUROTOXIN II—SCORPION

	1				5					10					15	
1	VAL	LYS	ASP	GLY	TYR	ILE	VAL	ASP	ASP	VAL	ASN	CYS	THR	TYR	PHE	15
16	CYS	GLY	ARG	ASN	ALA	TYR	CYS	ASN	GLU	GLU	CYS	THR	LYS	LEU	LYS	30
31	GLY	GLU	SER	GLY	TYR	CYS	GLN	TRP	ALA	SER	PRO	TYR	GLY	ASN	ALA	45
46	CYS	TYR	CYS	TYR	LYS	LEU	PRO	ASP	HIS	VAL	ARG	THR	LYS	GLY	PRO	60
61	GLY	ARG	CYS	HIS	NH$_2$											75

The Amino Acid Sequence of Neurotoxin II of *Androctonus australis*.
H. Rochat, C. Rochat, F. Sampieri, F. Miranda, and S. Lissitzky.
Eur. J. Biochem., **28**, 381–388 (1972).

430

TOXINS

NEUROTOXIN V—SCORPION

```
         1              5                    10                        15
  1  LEU LYS ASP GLY TYR ILE  VAL ASP ASP LYS ASN CYS THR PHE PHE   15
 16  CYS GLY ARG ASN ALA TYR CYS ASN ASP GLU CYS LYS LYS LYS GLY   30
 31  GLY GLU SER GLY TYR CYS GLN TRP ALA SER PRO TYR GLY ASN ALA   45
 46  CYS TRP CYS TYR LYS LEU PRO ASP ARG VAL SER ILE  LYS GLU LYS  60
 61  GLY ARG CYS ASN NH2                                            75
```

Amino acid sequence of Neurotoxin V from the scorpion *Leiurus quinquestriatus quinquestriatus*.
C. Kopeyan, G. Martinez, and H. Rochat.
FEBS Letters, **89**, 54–57 (1978).

NOTEXIN—AUSTRALIAN TIGER SNAKE

```
          1              5                    10                       15
   1  ASN LEU VAL GLN PHE SER TYR LEU ILE  GLN CYS ALA ASN HIS GLY   15
  16  LYS ARG PRO THR TRP HIS TYR MET ASP TYR GLY CYS TYR CYS GLY   30
  31  ALA GLY GLY SER GLY THR PRO VAL ASP GLU LEU ASP ARG CYS CYS   45
  46  LYS ILE  HIS ASP ASP CYS TYR ASP GLU ALA GLY LYS LYS GLY CYS  60
  61  PHE PRO LYS MET SER ALA TYR ASP TYR TYR CYS GLY GLU ASN GLY   75
  76  PRO TYR CYS ARG ASN ILE  LYS LYS LYS CYS LEU ARG PHE VAL CYS  90
  91  ASP CYS ASP VAL GLU ALA ALA PHE CYS PHE ALA LYS ALA PRO TYR  105
 106  ASN ASN ALA ASN TRP ASN ILE  ASP THR LYS LYS ARG CYS GLN     120
```

Amino acid sequence of a presynaptic Neurotoxin from the venom of *Notechis scutatus scutatus* (Australian tiger snake).
J. Halpert and D. Eaker.
J. Biol. Chem., **250**, 6990–6997 (1975).

CROTAMINE FROM THE SOUTH AMERICAN RATTLESNAKE

```
         1              5                    10                        15
  1  TYR LYS GLN CYS HIS LYS LYS GLY GLY HIS CYS PHE PRO LYS GLU   15
 16  LYS ILE  CYS LEU PRO PRO SER SER ASP PHE GLY LYS MET ASP CYS  30
 31  ARG TRP ARG TRP LYS CYS CYS LYS LYS GLY SER GLY              45
```

The primary structure of Crotamine.
C. J. Laure.
Hoppe-Seyler's Z. Physiol. Chem., **356**, 213–215 (1975).

TOXIN II—RINGHALS

	1			5					10					15	
1	LEU	GLU	CYS	HIS	ASN	GLN	GLN	SER	SER	GLN	PRO	PRO	THR	THR	LYS	15
16	SER	CYS	PRO	GLY	ASP	THR	ASN	CYS	TYR	ASN	LYS	ARG	TRP	ARG	ASP	30
31	HIS	ARG	GLY	THR	ILE	ILE	GLU	ARG	GLY	CYS	GLY	CYS	PRO	THR	VAL	45
46	LYS	PRO	GLY	ILE	ASN	LEU	LYS	CYS	CYS	THR	THR	ASP	ARG	CYS	ASN	60
61	ASN															75

TOXIN IV—RINGHALS

	1			5					10					15	
1	LEU	GLU	CYS	HIS	ASN	GLN	GLN	SER	SER	GLN	THR	PRO	THR	THR	GLN	15
16	THR	CYS	PRO	GLY	GLU	THR	ASN	CYS	TYR	LYS	LYS	GLN	TRP	SER	ASP	30
31	HIS	ARG	GLY	SER	ARG	THR	GLU	ARG	GLY	CYS	GLY	CYS	PRO	THR	VAL	45
46	LYS	PRO	GLY	ILE	LYS	LEU	LYS	CYS	CYS	THR	THR	ASP	ARG	CYS	ASN	60
61	LYS															75

Snake Venom Toxins. Purification, properties and complete amino acid sequence of two toxins from Ringhals (*Hemachatus haemachatus*) venom.
A. J. C. Strydom and D. P. Botes.
J. Biol. Chem., **246**, 1341–1349 (1971).

HEMOLYTIC PROTEIN 12 B OF AFRICAN RINGHALS COBRA VENOM

	1			5					10					15	
1	LEU	LYS	CYS	HIS	ASN	LYS	LEU	VAL	PRO	PHE	LEU	SER	LYS	THR	CYS	15
16	PRO	GLU	GLY	LYS	ASN	LEU	CYS	TYR	LYS	MET	THR	MET	LEU	LYS	MET	30
31	PRO	LYS	ILE	PRO	ILE	LYS	ARG	GLY	CYS	THR	ASP	ALA	CYS	PRO	LYS	45
46	SER	SER	LEU	LEU	VAL	LYS	VAL	VAL	CYS	CYS	ASN	LYS	ASP	LYS	CYS	60
61	ASN															75

Complete amino acid sequence of a non-neurotoxic hemolytic protein from the venom of *Haemachatus haemachatus* (African Ringhals cobra).
L. Fryklund and D. Eaker.
Biochemistry, **12**, 661–667 (1973).

TOXINS

TOXIN (a) OF KING COBRA VENOM

	1				5					10					15	
1	THR	LYS	CYS	TYR	VAL	THR	PRO	ASP	VAL	LYS	SER	GLU	THR	CYS	PRO	15
16	ALA	GLY	GLN	ASP	ILE	CYS	TYR	THR	GLU	THR	TRP	CYS	ASP	ALA	TRP	30
31	CYS	THR	SER	ARG	GLY	LYS	ARG	VAL	ASP	LEU	GLY	CYS	ALA	ALA	THR	45
46	CYS	PRO	ILE	VAL	LYS	PRO	GLY	VAL	GLU	ILE	LYS	CYS	CYS	SER	THR	60
61	ASP	ASN	CYS	ASN	PRO	PHE	PRO	THR	TRP	ARG	LYS	ARG	PRO			75

TOXIN (b) OF KING COBRA VENOM

	1				5					10					15	
1	THR	LYS	CYS	TYR	VAL	THR	PRO	ASP	ALA	THR	SER	GLN	THR	CYS	PRO	15
16	ASP	GLY	GLN	ASP	ILE	CYS	TYR	THR	LYS	THR	TRP	CYS	ASP	GLY	PHE	30
31	CYS	SER	SER	ARG	GLY	LYS	ARG	ILE	ASP	LEU	GLY	CYS	ALA	ALA	THR	45
46	CYS	PRO	LYS	VAL	LYS	PRO	GLY	VAL	ASP	ILE	LYS	CYS	CYS	SER	THR	60
61	ASP	ASN	CYS	ASN	PRO	PHE	PRO	THR	TRP	LYS	ARG	LYS	HIS			75

Snake Venom Toxins. The amino acid sequences of two toxins from *Ophiophagus hannah* (King Cobra) venom.
F. J. Joubert.
Biochim. Biophys. Acta, **317**, 85–98 (1973).

CARDIOTOXIN FROM NAJA NIGRICOLLIS *VENOM*

	1				5					10					15	
1	LEU	LYS	CYS	ASN	GLN	LEU	ILE	PRO	PRO	PHE	TRP	LYS	THR	CYS	PRO	15
16	LYS	GLY	LYS	ASN	LEU	CYS	TYR	LYS	MET	THR	MET	ARG	ALA	ALA	PRO	30
31	MET	VAL	PRO	VAL	LYS	ARG	GLY	CYS	ILE	ASP	VAL	CYS	PRO	LYS	SER	45
46	SER	LEU	LEU	ILE	LYS	TYR	MET	CYS	CYS	ASN	THR	ASP	LYS	CYS	ASN	60

Note: Disulphide bridges join residues CYS 3 and 21; CYS 14 and 38; CYS 42 and 53; CYS 54 and 59.
The complete covalent structure of a cardiotoxin from the venom of *Naja nigricollis* (African black-necked spitting cobra).
L. Fryklund and D. Eaker.
Biochemistry, **14**, 2865–2871 (1975).

CARDIOTOXIN—BUNGARUS FASCIATUS VENOM

	1				5					10					15	
1	ASN	LEU	TYR	GLN	PHE	LYS	ASN	MET	ILE	GLU	CYS	ALA	GLY	THR	ARG	15
16	ASN	ILE	ALA	GLY	PHE	THR	ASN	TRP	GLN	ALA	LEU	VAL	LYS	LYS	TYR	30
31	GLY	CYS	TYR	CYS	GLY	PRO	GLY	THR	HIS	ASP	PRO	ASP	ALA	LEU	GLU	45
46	LYS	ASN	GLY	CYS	TYR	THR	GLY	PRO	LEU	ARG	PHE	GLY	ASN	ILE	TYR	60
61	ASN	LEU	ALA	ALA	LYS	CYS	CYS	GLY	SER	PRO	ASN	ARG	LYS	THR	TYR	75
76	VAL	TYR	THR	CYS	ASN	ALA	PRO	ALA	PHE	GLY	ILE	LYS	THR	VAL	CYS	90
91	ASP	CYS	ASP	ARG	ASP	CYS	GLN	THR	CYS	ASP	ALA	TYR	HIS	LYS	THR	105
106	ALA	LEU	ALA	TYR	GLY	ILE	ASP	GLU	THR	LYS	HIS	CYS	GLN			120

Complete amino acid sequence of a new type of cardiotoxin of *Bungarus fasciatus* venom.
H.-S. Lu and T.-B. Lo.
Int. J. Peptide Protein Res., **12**, 181–183 (1978).

TOXIN V^II 1—CAPE COBRA

	1				5					10					15	
1	LEU	LYS	CYS	HIS	LYS	LEU	VAL	PRO	PRO	VAL	TRP	LYS	THR	CYS	PRO	15
16	GLU	GLY	LYS	ASN	LEU	CYS	TYR	LYS	MET	PHE	MET	VAL	SER	THR	SER	30
31	THR	VAL	PRO	VAL	LYS	ARG	GLY	CYS	ILE	ASP	VAL	CYS	PRO	LYS	ASP	45
46	SER	ALA	LEU	VAL	LYS	TYR	VAL	CYS	CYS	SER	THR	ASP	LYS	CYS	ASN	60

TOXIN V^II 2—CAPE COBRA

	1				5					10					15	
1	LEU	LYS	CYS	HIS	GLN	LEU	ILE	PRO	PRO	PHE	TRP	LYS	THR	CYS	PRO	15
16	GLU	GLY	LYS	ASN	LEU	CYS	TYR	LYS	MET	TYR	MET	VAL	ALA	THR	PRO	30
31	MET	ILE	PRO	VAL	LYS	ARG	GLY	CYS	ILE	ASP	VAL	CYS	PRO	LYS	ASN	45
46	SER	ALA	LEU	VAL	LYS	TYR	MET	CYS	CYS	ASN	THR	ASP	LYS	CYS	ASN	60

TOXIN V^II 3—CAPE COBRA

	1				5					10					15	
1	LEU	LYS	CYS	ASN	GLN	LEU	ILE	PRO	PRO	PHE	TRP	LYS	THR	CYS	PRO	15
16	LYS	GLY	LYS	ASN	LEU	CYS	TYR	ASN	MET	TYR	MET	VAL	SER	THR	SER	30
31	THR	VAL	PRO	VAL	LYS	ARG	GLY	CYS	ILE	ASP	VAL	CYS	PRO	LYS	ASN	45
46	SER	ALA	LEU	VAL	LYS	TYR	VAL	CYS	CYS	ASN	THR	ASP	ARG	CYS	ASN	60

The amino acid sequence of three non-curarimimetic toxins from *Naja nivea* venom.
D. P. Botes and C. C. Viljoen.
Biochim. Biophys. Acta, **446**, 1–9 (1976).

TOXINS

CARDIOTOXIN FROM THE CAMBODIAN COBRA

	1				5					10					15	
1	LEU	LYS	CYS	ASN	LYS	LEU	ILE	PRO	ILE	ALA	SER	LYS	THR	CYS	PRO	15
16	ALA	GLY	LYS	ASN	LEU	CYS	TYR	LYS	MET	PHE	MET	MET	SER	ASP	LEU	30
31	THR	ILE	PRO	VAL	LYS	ARG	GLY	CYS	ILE	ASP	VAL	CYS	PRO	LYS	ASN	45
46	SER	LEU	LEU	VAL	LYS	TYR	VAL	CYS	CYS	ASN	THR	ASP	ARG	CYS	ASN	60

The complete amino acid sequence of a Cardiotoxin from the venom of *Naja naja* (Cambodian cobra).
L. Fryklund and D. Eaker.
Biochemistry, **14**, 2860–2865 (1975).

TOXIN α OF CAPE COBRA VENOM

	1				5					10					15	
1	ILE	ARG	CYS	PHE	ILE	THR	PRO	ASP	VAL	THR	SER	GLN	ALA	CYS	PRO	15
16	ASP	GLY	HIS	VAL	CYS	TYR	THR	LYS	MET	TRP	CYS	ASP	ASN	PHE	CYS	30
31	GLY	MET	ARG	GLY	LYS	ARG	VAL	ASP	LEU	GLY	CYS	ALA	ALA	THR	CYS	45
46	PRO	LYS	VAL	LYS	PRO	GLY	VAL	ASN	ILE	LYS	CYS	CYS	SER	ARG	ASP	60
61	ASN	CYS	ASN	PRO	PHE	PRO	THR	ARG	LYS	ARG	SER					75

TOXIN β OF CAPE COBRA VENOM

	1				5					10					15	
1	MET	ILE	CYS	HIS	ASN	GLN	GLN	SER	SER	GLN	ARG	PRO	THR	ILE	LYS	15
16	THR	CYS	PRO	GLY	GLU	THR	ASN	CYS	TYR	LYS	LYS	ARG	TRP	ARG	ASP	30
31	HIS	ARG	GLY	THR	ILE	ILE	GLU	ARG	GLY	CYS	GLY	CYS	PRO	SER	VAL	45
46	LYS	LYS	GLY	VAL	GLY	ILE	TYR	CYS	CYS	LYS	THR	ASP	LYS	CYS	ASN	60
61	ARG															75

Snake Venom toxins. The amino acid sequences of toxins *α* and *β* from *Naja nivea* venom and the disulfide bonds of toxin *α*.
D. P. Botes.
J. Biol. Chem., **246**, 7383–7391 (1971).

TOXIN δ OF CAPE COBRA VENOM

	1				5					10					15	
1	LEU	GLN	CYS	HIS	ASN	GLN	GLN	SER	SER	GLN	PRO	PRO	THR	THR	LYS	15
16	THR	CYS	PRO	GLY	GLU	THR	ASN	CYS	TYR	LYS	LYS	ARG	TRP	ARG	ASP	30
31	HIS	ARG	GLY	SER	ILE	THR	GLU	ARG	GLY	CYS	GLY	CYS	PRO	SER	VAL	45
46	LYS	LYS	GLY	ILE	GLU	ILE	ASN	CYS	CYS	THR	THR	ASP	LYS	CYS	ASN	60
61	ASN															75

Snake Venom Toxins. Purification and properties of three toxins from *Naja nivea* (Cape Cobra) venom and the amino acid sequence of toxin δ.
D. P. Botes, D. J. Strydom, C. G. Anderson, and P. A. Christensen.
J. Biol. Chem., **246**, 3132–3139 (1971).

CYTOTOXIN I—INDIAN COBRA VENOM

	1				5					10					15	
1	LEU	LYS	CYS	ASN	LYS	LEU	ILE	PRO	LEU	ALA	TYR	LYS	THR	CYS	PRO	15
16	ALA	GLY	LYS	ASN	LEU	CYS	TYR	LYS	MET	TYR	MET	VAL	SER	ASN	LYS	30
31	THR	VAL	PRO	VAL	LYS	ARG	GLY	CYS	ILE	ASP	VAL	CYS	PRO	LYS	ASN	45
46	SER	LEU	VAL	LEU	LYS	TYR	GLU	CYS	CYS	ASN	THR	ASP	ARG	CYS	ASN	60

Amino Acid Sequence of Cytotoxin I from the venom of the Indian Cobra, (*Naja naja*).
K. Hayashi, M. Takechi, and T. Sasaki.
Biochem. Biophys. Res. Commun., **45**, 1357–1362 (1971).

CYTOTOXIN II OF THE INDIAN COBRA

	1				5					10					15	
1	LEU	LYS	CYS	ASN	LYS	LEU	VAL	PRO	LEU	PHE	TYR	LYS	THR	CYS	PRO	15
16	ALA	GLY	LYS	ASN	LEU	CYS	TYR	LYS	MET	TYR	MET	VAL	ALA	THR	PRO	30
31	LYS	VAL	PRO	VAL	LYS	ARG	GLY	CYS	ILE	ASP	VAL	CYS	PRO	LYS	SER	45
46	SER	LEU	VAL	LEU	LYS	TYR	VAL	CYS	CYS	ASN	THR	ASP	ARG	CYS	ASN	60

Note: Disulphide bridges link residues CYS 3 and 21; CYS 14 and 38; CYS 42 and 53; CYS 54 and 59.
Localization of the four disulfide bridges in Cytotoxin II from the Indian cobra (*Naja naja*).
M. Takechi and K. Hayashi.
Biochem. Biophys. Res. Commun., **49**, 584–590 (1972).

TOXINS

TOXIN A—INDIAN COBRA VENOM

	1				5					10					15	
1	ILE	ARG	CYS	PHE	ILE	THR	PRO	ASP	ILE	THR	SER	LYS	ASP	CYS	PRO	15
16	ASN	GLY	HIS	VAL	CYS	TYR	THR	LYS	THR	TRP	CYS	ASP	GLY	PHE	CYS	30
31	SER	ILE	ARG	GLY	LYS	ARG	VAL	ASP	LEU	GLY	CYS	ALA	ALA	THR	CYS	45
46	PRO	THR	VAL	ARG	THR	GLY	VAL	ASP	ILE	GLN	CYS	CYS	SER	THR	ASP	60
61	ASP	CYS	ASP	PRO	PHE	PRO	THR	ARG	LYS	ARG	PRO					75

Amino Acid Sequence of Toxin A from the venom of the Indian Cobra, (*Naja naja*).
K. Nakai, T. Sasaki, and K. Hayashi.
Biochem. Biophys. Res. Commun., **44**, 893–897 (1971).

TOXIN V^{II}1 OF BANDED EGYPTIAN COBRA VENOM

	1				5					10					15	
1	LEU	LYS	CYS	HIS	LYS	LEU	VAL	PRO	PRO	VAL	TRP	LYS	THR	CYS	PRO	15
16	GLU	GLY	LYS	ASN	LEU	CYS	TYR	LYS	MET	PHE	MET	VAL	SER	THR	SER	30
31	THR	VAL	PRO	VAL	LYS	ARG	GLY	CYS	ILE	ASP	VAL	CYS	PRO	LYS	ASN	45
46	SER	ALA	LEU	VAL	LYS	TYR	VAL	CYS	CYS	SER	THR	ASP	LYS	CYS	ASN	60

The purification of Toxins V^{II}1 and V^{II}2, two cytotoxin homologues, from Banded Egyptian Cobra (*Naja haje annulifera*) venom, and the complete amino acid sequence of toxin V^{II}1.
K. H. K. Weise, F. H. H. Carlsson, F. J. Joubert, and D. J. Strydom.
Hoppe-Seyler's Z. Physiol. Chem., **354**, 1317–1326 (1973).

TOXIN V^{II}2 OF BANDED EGYPTIAN COBRA

	1				5					10					15	
1	LEU	LYS	CYS	HIS	LYS	LEU	VAL	PRO	PRO	PHE	TRP	LYS	THR	CYS	PRO	15
16	GLU	GLY	LYS	ASN	LEU	CYS	TYR	LYS	MET	TYR	MET	VAL	ALA	THR	PRO	30
31	MET	LEU	PRO	VAL	LYS	ARG	GLY	CYS	ILE	ASP	VAL	CYS	PRO	LYS	ASP	45
46	SER	ALA	LEU	VAL	LYS	TYR	MET	CYS	CYS	ASN	THR	ASP	LYS	CYS	ASN	60

Note: The amino acids VAL and SER were also found at positions 52, and 55, respectively, indicating the presence of a minor species homologous to toxin V^{II}2, designated toxin V^{II}2A. The amino acid sequence of toxin V^{II}2, a cytotoxin homologue from Banded Egyptian cobra (*Naja haje annulifera*) venom.
F. J. Joubert.
Hoppe-Seyler's Z. Physiol. Chem., **356**, 1893–1900 (1975).

TOXIN III FROM NAJA HAJE

	1				5					10					15	
1	ILE	ARG	CYS	PHE	ILE	THR	PRO	ASP	VAL	THR	SER	GLN	ALA	CYS	PRO	15
16	ASP	GLY	GLN	ASN	ILE	CYS	TYR	THR	LYS	THR	TRP	CYS	ASP	ASN	PHE	30
31	CYS	GLY	MET	ARG	GLY	LYS	ARG	VAL	ASP	LEU	GLY	CYS	ALA	ALA	THR	45
46	CYS	PRO	THR	VAL	LYS	PRO	GLY	VAL	ASP	ILE	LYS	CYS	CYS	SER	THR	60
61	ASP	ASN	CYS	ASN	PRO	PHE	PRO	THR	ARG	GLU	ARG	SER				75

Amino acid sequence of toxin III of *Naja haje*.
C. Kopeyan, F. Miranda, and H. Rochat.
Eur. J. Biochem., **58**, 117–122 (1975).

TOXIN CM-5 FROM NAJA HAJE HAJE

	1				5					10					15	
1	ILE	ARG	CYS	PHE	ILE	THR	PRO	ASP	VAL	THR	SER	GLN	ALA	CYS	PRO	15
16	ASP	GLY	HIS	VAL	CYS	TYR	THR	LYS	MET	TRP	CYS	ASP	ASN	PHE	CYS	30
31	GLY	MET	ARG	GLY	LYS	ARG	VAL	ASP	LEU	GLY	CYS	ALA	ALA	THR	CYS	45
46	PRO	THR	VAL	LYS	PRO	GLY	VAL	ASP	ILE	LYS	CYS	CYS	SER	THR	ASP	60
61	ASN	CYS	ASN	PRO	PHE	PRO	THR	ARG	LYS	ARG	SER					75

TOXIN CM-6 FROM NAJA HAJE HAJE

	1				5					10					15	
1	LEU	GLU	CYS	HIS	ASN	GLN	GLN	SER	SER	GLN	PRO	PRO	THR	THR	LYS	15
16	THR	CYS	PRO	GLY	GLU	THR	ASN	CYS	TYR	LYS	LYS	ARG	TRP	ARG	ASP	30
31	HIS	ARG	GLY	SER	ILE	THR	GLU	ARG	GLY	CYS	GLY	CYS	PRO	SER	VAL	45
46	LYS	LYS	GLY	ILE	GLU	ILE	ASN	CYS	CYS	THR	THR	ASP	LYS	CYS	ASN	60
61	ASN															75

438

TOXINS

TOXIN CM-10a FROM NAJA HAJE HAJE

```
     1                    5                         10                      15
 1   MET ILE CYS HIS  ASN GLN GLN SER SER  GLN PRO PRO THR ILE LYS    15
16   THR CYS PRO GLY  GLU THR ASN CYS TYR  LYS LYS GLN TRP ARG ASP    30
31   HIS ARG GLY THR  ILE ILE GLU ARG GLY  CYS GLY CYS PRO SER VAL    45
46   LYS LYS GLY VAL  GLY ILE TYR CYS CYS  LYS THR ASP LYS CYS ASN    60
61   ARG                                                              75
```

Purification, some properties and the primary structures of three reduced and
S-carboxymethylated toxins (CM-5, CM-6 and CM-10a) from *Naja haje haje* (Egyptian cobra)
venom.
F. Joubert and N. Taljaard.
Biochim. Biophys. Acta, **537**, 1–8 (1978).

TOXIN CM-8 FROM NAJA HAJE HAJE *VENOM*

```
     1                    5                         10                      15
 1   LEU LYS CYS HIS  GLN LEU VAL PRO PRO  PHE TRP LYS THR CYS PRO    15
16   GLU GLY LYS ASN  LEU CYS TYR LYS MET  TYR MET VAL SER SER SER    30
31   THR VAL PRO VAL  LYS ARG GLY CYS ILE  ASP VAL CYS PRO LYS ASN    45
46   SER ALA LEU VAL  LYS TYR VAL CYS CYS  ASN THR ASP LYS CYS ASN    60
```

TOXIN CM-9 FROM NAJA HAJE HAJE *VENOM*

```
     1                    5                         10                      15
 1   LEU LYS CYS HIS  GLN LEU VAL PRO PRO  PHE TRP LYS THR CYS PRO    15
16   ALA GLY LYS ASN  LEU CYS TYR LYS MET  TYR MET VAL ALA THR PRO    30
31   MET ILE PRO VAL  LYS ARG GLY CYS ILE  ASP VAL CYS PRO LYS ASN    45
46   SER ALA LEU VAL  LYS TYR MET CYS CYS  ASN THR ASP LYS CYS ASN    60
```

TOXIN CM-10b FROM NAJA HAJE HAJE *VENOM*

```
     1                    5                         10                      15
 1   LEU LYS CYS HIS  LYS LEU VAL PRO PRO  PHE TRP LYS THR CYS PRO    15
16   GLU GLY LYS ASN  LEU CYS TYR LYS MET  TYR MET VAL ALA THR PRO    30
31   MET ILE PRO VAL  LYS ARG GLY CYS ILE  ASP VAL CYS PRO LYS ASN    45
46   SER ALA LEU VAL  LYS TYR VAL CYS CYS  ASN THR ASP LYS CYS ASN    60
```

TOXIN CM-7 FROM NAJA HAJE HAJE VENOM

	1				5					10					15	
1	LEU	LYS	CYS	HIS	GLN	LEU	VAL	PRO	PRO	PHE	TRP	LYS	THR	CYS	PRO	15
16	GLU	GLY	LYS	ASN	LEU	CYS	TYR	LYS	MET	TYR	MET	VAL	ALA	THR	PRO	30
31	MET	ILE	PRO	VAL	LYS	ARG	GLY	CYS	ILE	ASP	VAL	CYS	PRO	LYS	ASN	45
46	SER	ALA	LEU	VAL	LYS	TYR	MET	CYS	CYS	ASN	THR	ASP	LYS	CYS	ASN	60

Naja haje haje (Egyptian cobra) Venom. Purification, some properties and the amino acid sequences of four toxins (CM-7, CM-8, CM-9 and CM-10b).
F. Joubert and N. Taljaard.
Biochim. Biophys. Acta., **534**, 331–340 (1978).

TOXIN CM-8 FROM EGYPTIAN COBRA VENOM

	1				5					10					15	
1	LEU	LYS	CYS	TYR	LYS	LEU	VAL	PRO	PRO	PHE	TRP	LYS	THR	CYS	PRO	15
16	GLU	GLY	LYS	ASN	LEU	CYS	TYR	LYS	MET	TYR	MET	VAL	SER	THR	LEU	30
31	THR	VAL	PRO	VAL	LYS	ARG	GLY	CYS	ILE	ASP	VAL	CYS	PRO	LYS	ASN	45
46	SER	ALA	LEU	VAL	LYS	TYR	VAL	CYS	CYS	ASN	THR	ASP	LYS	CYS	ASN	60

Note: A related toxin was also found, designated toxin CM-8A, that differed from CM-8 in having HIS at position 4.

TOXIN CM-11 FROM EGYPTIAN COBRA VENOM

	1				5					10					15	
1	LEU	LYS	CYS	ASN	LYS	LEU	ILE	PRO	PRO	PHE	TRP	LYS	THR	CYS	PRO	15
16	LYS	GLY	LYS	ASN	LEU	CYS	TYR	LYS	MET	TYR	MET	VAL	SER	THR	LEU	30
31	THR	VAL	PRO	VAL	LYS	ARG	GLY	CYS	ILE	ASP	VAL	CYS	PRO	LYS	ASN	45
46	SER	ALA	LEU	VAL	LYS	TYR	VAL	CYS	CYS	ASN	THR	ASN	LYS	CYS	ASN	60

TOXINS

TOXIN CM-13a FROM EGYPTIAN COBRA VENOM

	1				5					10					15	
1	LEU	LYS	CYS	HIS	ASN	THR	GLN	LEU	PRO	PHE	ILE	TYR	LYS	THR	CYS	15
16	PRO	GLU	GLY	LYS	ASN	LEU	CYS	PHE	LYS	THR	THR	LEU	LYS	LYS	LEU	30
31	PRO	LEU	LYS	ILE	PRO	ILE	LYS	ARG	GLY	CYS	ALA	ALA	THR	CYS	PRO	45
46	LYS	SER	SER	ALA	LEU	LEU	LYS	SER	VAL	CYS	CYS	ASN	THR	ASP	LYS	60
61	CYS															75

Snake venom toxins. The amino acid sequences of three toxins (CM-8, CM-11 and CM-13a) from *Naja haje annulifera* (Egyptian cobra) venom.
F. J. Joubert.
Eur. J. Biochem., **64**, 219–232 (1976).

TOXIN CM-10 FROM EGYPTIAN COBRA VENOM

	1				5					10					15	
1	MET	ILE	CYS	TYR	LYS	GLN	GLN	SER	LEU	GLN	PHE	PRO	ILE	THR	THR	15
16	VAL	CYS	PRO	GLY	GLU	LYS	ASN	CYS	TYR	LYS	LYS	GLN	TRP	SER	GLY	30
31	HIS	ARG	GLY	THR	ILE	ILE	GLU	ARG	GLY	CYS	GLY	CYS	PRO	SER	VAL	45
46	LYS	LYS	GLY	ILE	GLU	ILE	ASN	CYS	CYS	THR	THR	ASP	LYS	CYS	ASN	60
61	ARG															75

TOXIN CM-12 FROM EGYPTIAN COBRA VENOM

	1				5					10					15	
1	MET	ILE	CYS	TYR	LYS	GLN	ARG	SER	LEU	GLN	PHE	PRO	ILE	THR	THR	15
16	VAL	CYS	PRO	GLY	GLU	LYS	ASN	CYS	TYR	LYS	LYS	GLN	TRP	SER	GLY	30
31	HIS	ARG	GLY	THR	ILE	ILE	GLU	ARG	GLY	CYS	GLY	CYS	PRO	SER	VAL	45
46	LYS	LYS	GLY	ILE	GLU	ILE	ASN	CYS	CYS	THR	THR	ASP	LYS	CYS	ASN	60
61	ARG															75

TOXIN CM-14 FROM EGYPTIAN COBRA VENOM

	1				5					10					15	
1	MET	ILE	CYS	HIS	ASN	GLN	GLN	SER	SER	GLN	PRO	PRO	THR	ILE	LYS	15
16	THR	CYS	PRO	GLY	GLU	THR	ASN	CYS	TYR	LYS	LYS	ARG	TRP	ARG	ASP	30
31	HIS	ARG	GLY	THR	ILE	ILE	GLU	ARG	GLY	CYS	GLY	CYS	PRO	SER	VAL	45
46	LYS	LYS	GLY	VAL	GLY	ILE	TYR	CYS	CYS	LYS	THR	ASN	LYS	CYS	ASN	60
61	ARG															75

The amino acid sequences of three toxins (CM-10, CM-12 and CM-14) from *Naja haje annulifera* (Egyptian Cobra) venom.
F. J. Joubert.
Hoppe-Seyler's Z. Physiol. Chem., **356**, 53–72 (1975).

TOXIN CM-13b FROM THE EGYPTIAN COBRA

	1				5					10					15	
1	LEU	THR	CYS	PHE	ASN	CYS	PRO	GLU	VAL	TYR	CYS	ASN	ARG	PHE	HIS	15
16	THR	CYS	ARG	ASN	GLY	GLU	LYS	ILE	CYS	PHE	LYS	ARG	PHE	ASN	GLU	30
31	ARG	LYS	LEU	LEU	GLY	LYS	ARG	TYR	THR	ARG	GLY	CYS	ALA	ALA	THR	45
46	CYS	PRO	VAL	ALA	LYS	PRO	ARG	GLU	ILE	VAL	GLU	CYS	CYS	SER	THR	60
61	ASP	ARG	CYS	ASN	HIS											75

The purification and amino acid sequence of Toxin CM-13b from *Naja haje annulifera* (Egyptian Cobra) venom.
F. J. Joubert.
Hoppe-Seyler's Z. Physiol. Chem., **356**, 1901–1908 (1975).

TOXIN $V^{II}1$ OF FOREST COBRA VENOM

	1				5					10					15	
1	LEU ILE	GLU	CYS	ASN	LYS	LEU	VAL	PRO	ILE	ALA	HIS	LYS	THR	CYS	PRO	15
16	ALA	GLY	LYS	ASN	LEU	CYS	TYR	GLN	MET	TYR	MET	VAL	SER	LYS	SER	30
31	THR	ILE	PRO	VAL	LYS	ARG	GLY	CYS	ILE	ASP	VAL	CYS	PRO	LYS	SER	45
46	SER	LEU	LEU	VAL	LYS	TYR	VAL	CYS	CYS	ASN	THR	ASP	ARG	CYS	ASN	60

Snake Venom Toxins. The isolation and purification of three cytotoxin homologues from the venom of the forest cobra (*Naja melanoleuca*) and the complete amino acid sequence of toxin $V^{II}1$.
F. H. H. Carlsson and F. J. Joubert.
Biochim. Biophys. Acta, **336**, 453–469 (1974).

TOXINS $V^{II}2$ AND $V^{II}3$ OF FOREST COBRA VENOM

	1				5					10					15	
1	ILE	LYS	CYS	HIS	ASN	THR	LEU	LEU	PRO	PHE	ILE	TYR	LYS	THR	CYS	15
16	PRO	GLU	GLY	GLN	ASN	LEU	CYS	PHE	LYS	GLY	THR	LEU	LYS	PHE	PRO	30
31	LYS	LYS	THR	THR	TYR	ASN LYS	ARG	GLY	CYS	ALA	ALA	THR	CYS	PRO	LYS	45
46	SER	SER	LEU	LEU	VAL	LYS	TYR	VAL	CYS	CYS	ASN	THR	ASN	LYS	CYS	60
61	ASN															75

Note: Toxin $V^{II}2$ has ASN at position 36, and Toxin $V^{II}3$ has LYS.
Snake venom toxins. The primary structures of two novel cytotoxin homologues from the venom of the forest cobra (*Naja melanoleuca*).
F. H. H. Carlsson.
Biochem. Biophys. Res. Commun., **59**, 269–276 (1974).

TOXINS

TOXIN(3.9.4) OF NAJA MELANOLEUCA *VENOM*

	1				5					10					15	
1	LYS	ARG	CYS	TYR	ARG	THR	PRO	ASP	LEU	LYS	SER	GLN	THR	CYS	PRO	15
16	PRO	GLY	GLU	ASP	LEU	CYS	TYR	THR	LYS	LYS	TRP	CYS	ALA	ASP	TRP	30
31	CYS	THR	SER	ARG	GLY	LYS	VAL	ILE	GLU	LEU	GLY	CYS	VAL	ALA	THR	45
46	CYS	PRO	LYS	VAL	LYS	PRO	TYR	GLU	GLN	ILE	THR	CYS	CYS	SER	THR	60
61	ASP	ASN	CYS	ASN	PRO	HIS	PRO	LYS	MET	LYS	PRO					75

The separation of a neurotoxin from the venom of *Naja melanoleuca* and the primary sequence determination.
R. A. Shipolini, G. S. Bailey, and B. E. C. Banks.
Eur. J. Biochem., **42**, 203–211 (1974).

*TOXIN B—*NAJA MELANOLEUCA

	1				5					10					15	
1	ILE	ARG	CYS	PHE	ILE	THR	PRO	ASP	VAL	THR	SER	GLN	ILE	CYS	ALA	15
16	ASP	GLY	HIS	VAL	CYS	TYR	THR	LYS	THR	TRP	CYS	ASP	ASN	PHE	CYS	30
31	ALA	SER	ARG	GLY	LYS	ARG	VAL	ASP	LEU	GLY	CYS	ALA	ALA	THR	CYS	45
46	PRO	THR	VAL	LYS	PRO	GLY	VAL	ASN	ILE	LYS	CYS	CYS	SER	THR	ASP	60
61	ASN	PRO	PHE	PRO	THR	ARG	ASN	ARG	PRO							75

*TOXIN D—*NAJA MELANOLEUCA

	1				5					10					15	
1	MET	GLU	CYS	HIS	ASN	GLN	GLN	SER	SER	GLN	PRO	PRO	THR	THR	LYS	15
16	THR	CYS	PRO	GLY	GLU	THR	ASN	CYS	TYR	LYS	LYS	GLN	TRP	SER	ASP	30
31	HIS	ARG	GLY	THR	ILE	ILE	GLU	ARG	GLY	CYS	GLY	CYS	PRO	SER	VAL	45
46	LYS	LYS	GLY	VAL	LYS	ILE	ASN	CYS	CYS	THR	THR	ASP	ARG	CYS	ASN	60
61	ASN															75

Snake Venom Toxins. The amino acid sequences of Toxins b and d from *Naja melanoleuca* venom.
D. P. Botes.
J. Biol. Chem., **247**, 2866–2871 (1972).

PROTEIN S₄C₁₁ FROM FOREST COBRA VENOM

			5					10					15		
1	LEU	THR	CYS	LEU	ILE	CYS	PRO	GLU	LYS	TYR	CYS	ASN	LYS	VAL	HIS	15
16	THR	CYS	ARG	ASN	GLY	GLU	ASN	ILE	CYS	PHE	LYS	ARG	PHE	TYR	GLU	30
31	GLY	ASN	LEU	LEU	GLY	LYS	ARG	TYR	PRO	ARG	GLY	CYS	ALA	ALA	THR	45
46	CYS	PRO	GLU	ALA	LYS	PRO	ARG	GLU	ILE	VAL	GLU	CYS	CYS	SER	THR	60
61	ASP	LYS	CYS	ASN	HIS											75

Snake venom toxins, the primary structure of protein S₄C₁₁. A neurotoxin homologue from the venom of forest cobra (*Naja melanoleuca*).
F. H. H. Carlsson.
Biochim. Biophys. Acta, **400**, 310–321 (1975).

CYTOTOXIN FROM NAJA NAJA OXIANA VENOM

			5					10					15		
1	LEU	LYS	CYS	LYS	LYS	LEU	VAL	PRO	LEU	PHE	SER	LYS	THR	CYS	PRO	15
16	ALA	GLY	LYS	ASN	LEU	CYS	TYR	LYS	MET	PHE	MET	VAL	ALA	ALA	PRO	30
31	HIS	VAL	PRO	VAL	LYS	ARG	GLY	CYS	ILE	ASP	VAL	CYS	PRO	LYS	SER	45
46	SER	LEU	LEU	VAL	LYS	TYR	VAL	CYS	CYS	ASN	THR	ASP	LYS	CYS	ASN	60

The isolation and sequence determination of a cytotoxin from the venom of the middle-asian cobra *Naja naja oxiana*.
E. V. Grishin, A. P. Sukhikh, T. B. Adamovich, Yu. A. Ovchinnikov, and L. Ya. Yukelson.
FEBS Letters, **48**, 179–183 (1974).

NEUROTOXIN I FROM NAJA NAJA OXIANA VENOM

			5					10					15		
1	ILE	THR	CYS	TYR	LYS	THR	PRO	ILE	PRO	ILE	THR	SER	GLU	THR	CYS	15
16	ALA	PRO	GLY	GLN	ASN	LEU	CYS	TYR	THR	LYS	THR	TRP	CYS	ASP	ALA	30
31	TRP	CYS	GLY	SER	ARG	GLY	LYS	VAL	ILE	GLU	LEU	GLY	CYS	ALA	ALA	45
46	THR	CYS	PRO	THR	VAL	GLU	SER	TYR	GLN	ASP	ILE	LYS	CYS	CYS	SER	60
61	THR	ASP	ASP	CYS	ASN	PRO	HIS	PRO	LYS	GLN	LYS	ARG	PRO			75

Amino acid sequence of neurotoxin I from *Naja naja oxiana* venom.
E. V. Grishin, A. P. Sukhikh, L. N. Slobodyan, Yu. A. Ovchinnikov, and V. M. Sorokin.
FEBS Letters, **45**, 118–121 (1974).

TOXINS

NEUROTOXIN II FROM NAJA NAJA OXIANA *VENOM*

	1				5					10					15	
1	LEU	GLU	CYS	HIS	ASN	GLN	GLN	SER	SER	GLN	PRO	PRO	THR	THR	LYS	15
16	THR	CYS	SER	GLY	GLU	THR	ASN	CYS	TYR	LYS	LYS	TRP	TRP	SER	ASP	30
31	HIS	ARG	GLY	THR	ILE	ILE	GLU	ARG	GLY	CYS	GLY	CYS	PRO	LYS	VAL	45
46	LYS	PRO	GLY	VAL	ASN	LEU	ASN	CYS	CYS	ARG	THR	ASP	ARG	CYS	ASN	60
61	ASN															75

Amino acid sequence of Neurotoxin II from *Naja naja oxiana* venom.
E. V. Grishin, A. P. Sukhikh, N. N. Lukyanchuk, L. N. Slobodyan, V. M. Lipkin, Y. A. Ovchinnikov, and V. M. Sorokin.
FEBS Letters, **36**, 77–78 (1973).
Amino acid sequence of Oxiana α, the main neurotoxin of the venom of *Naja naja oxiana*.
H. Arnberg, D. Eaker, L. Fryklund, and E. Karlsson.
Biochim. Biophys. Acta, **359**, 222–232 (1974).

COBROTOXIN—NAJA NAJA ATRA

	1				5					10					15	
1	LEU	GLU	CYS	HIS	ASN	GLN	GLN	SER	SER	GLN	THR	PRO	THR	THR	THR	15
16	GLY	CYS	SER	GLY	GLY	GLU	THR	ASN	CYS	TYR	LYS	LYS	ARG	TRP	ARG	30
31	ASP	HIS	ARG	GLY	TYR	ARG	THR	GLU	ARG	GLY	CYS	GLY	CYS	PRO	SER	45
46	VAL	LYS	ASN	GLY	ILE	GLU	ILE	ASN	CYS	CYS	THR	THR	ASP	ARG	CYS	60
61	ASN	ASN														75

Note: Disulphide bridges link residues CYS 3 and 24; CYS 17 and 41; CYS 43 and 54; CYS 55 and 60.
The Position of Disulfide Bonds in Cobrotoxin.
C. C. Yang, H. J. Yang, and R. H. C. Chiu.
Biochim. Biophys. Acta, **214**, 355–365 (1970).

CARDIOTOXIN-ANALOGUE I—NAJA NAJA ATRA

	1				5					10					15	
1	LEU	LYS	CYS	ASN	LYS	LEU	ILE	PRO	ILE	ALA	SER	LYS	THR	CYS	PRO	15
16	ALA	GLY	LYS	ASN	LEU	CYS	TYR	LYS	MET	PHE	MET	MET	SER	ASP	LEU	30
31	THR	ILE	PRO	VAL	LYS	ARG	GLY	CYS	ILE	ASP	VAL	CYS	PRO	LYS	SER	45
46	ASN	LEU	LEU	VAL	LYS	TYR	VAL	CYS	CYS	ASN	THR	ASP	ARG	CYS	ASN	60

Amino acid sequence of cardiotoxin-analogue I from the venom of *Naja naja atra*.
K. Hayashi, M. Takechi, T. Sasaki, and C. Y. Lee.
Biochem. Biophys. Res. Commun., **64**, 360–365 (1975).

CARDIOTOXIN-ANALOGUE IV—NAJA NAJA ATRA

	1				5					10					15		
1	ARG	LYS	CYS	ASN	LYS	LEU	VAL	PRO	LEU	PHE	TYR	LYS	THR	CYS	PRO	15
16	ALA	GLY	LYS	ASN	LEU	CYS	TYR	LYS	MET	PHE	MET	VAL	SER	ASN	LEU	30
31	THR	VAL	PRO	VAL	LYS	ARG	GLY	CYS	ILE	ASP	VAL	CYS	PRO	LYS	ASN	45
46	SER	ALA	LEU	VAL	LYS	TYR	VAL	CYS	CYS	ASN	THR	ASP	ARG	CYS	ASN	60

The amino acid sequence of cardiotoxin-analogue IV from the venom of *Naja naja atra*.
N. Kaneda, T. Sasaki, and K. Hayashi.
FEBS Letters, **70**, 217–222 (1976).

CYTOTOXIN V^{II}1 FROM N.M. MOSSAMBICA VENOM

	1				5					10					15		
1	LEU	LYS	CYS	ASN	GLN	LEU	ILE	PRO	PRO	PHE	TRP	LYS	THR	CYS	PRO	15
16	LYS	GLY	LYS	ASN	LEU	CYS	TYR	LYS	MET	THR	MET	ARG	ALA	ALA	PRO	30
31	MET	VAL	PRO	VAL	LYS	ARG	GLY	CYS	ILE	ASP	VAL	CYS	PRO	LYS	SER	45
46	SER	LEU	LEU	ILE	LYS	TYR	MET	CYS	CYS	ASN	THR	ASN	LYS	CYS	ASN	60

CYTOTOXIN V^{II}2 FROM N.M. MOSSAMBICA VENOM

	1				5					10					15		
1	LEU	LYS	CYS	ASN	GLN	LEU	ILE	PRO	PRO	PHE	TRP	LYS	THR	CYS	PRO	15
16	LYS	GLY	LYS	ASN	LEU	CYS	TYR	LYS	MET	THR	MET	ARG	GLY	ALA	SER	30
31	LYS	VAL	PRO	VAL	LYS	ARG	GLY	CYS	ILE	ASP	VAL	CYS	PRO	LYS	SER	45
46	SER	LEU	LEU	ILE	LYS	TYR	MET	CYS	CYS	ASN	THR	ASP	LYS	CYS	ASN	60

CYTOTOXIN V^{II}3 FROM N.M. MOSSAMBICA VENOM

	1				5					10					15		
1	LEU	LYS	CYS	ASN	ARG	LEU	ILE	PRO	PRO	PHE	TRP	LYS	THR	CYS	PRO	15
16	GLU	GLY	LYS	ASN	LEU	CYS	TYR	LYS	MET	THR	MET	ARG	LEU	ALA	PRO	30
31	LYS	VAL	PRO	VAL	LYS	ARG	GLY	CYS	ILE	ASP	VAL	CYS	PRO	LYS	SER	45
46	SER	LEU	LEU	ILE	LYS	TYR	MET	CYS	CYS	ASN	THR	ASN	LYS	CYS	ASN	60

Snake Venom Toxins. The amino acid sequences of three cytotoxin homologues from *Naja mossambica mossambica* venom.
A. I. Louw.
Biochim. Biophys. Acta, **336**, 481–495 (1974).

TOXINS

CYTOTOXIN V^II^4 FROM N.M. MOSSAMBICA *VENOM*

	1				5				10					15	
1	LEU	LYS	CYS	ASN	LYS	LEU	ILE	PRO	ILE	ALA	TYR	LYS	THR	CYS	PRO	15
16	GLU	GLY	LYS	ASN	LEU	CYS	TYR	LYS	MET	MET	LEU	ALA	SER	LYS	LYS	30
31	MET	VAL	PRO	VAL	LYS	ARG	GLY	CYS	ILE	ASN	VAL	CYS	PRO	LYS	ASN	45
46	SER	ALA	LEU	VAL	LYS	TYR	VAL	CYS	CYS	SER	THR	ASP	ARG	CYS	ASN	60

Snake venom toxins. The complete amino acid sequence of cytotoxin $V^{II}4$ from the venom of *Naja mossambica mossambica*.
A. I. Louw.
Biochem. Biophys. Res. Commun., **58**, 1022–1029 (1974).

TOXIN α-BLACK MAMBA VENOM

	1				5				10					15	
1	ARG	ILE	CYS	TYR	ASN	HIS	GLN	SER	THR	THR	ARG	ALA	THR	THR	LYS	15
16	SER	CYS	GLU	GLU	ASN	SER	CYS	TYR	LYS	LYS	TYR	TRP	ARG	ASP	HIS	30
31	ARG	GLY	THR	ILE	ILE	GLU	ARG	GLY	CYS	GLY	CYS	PRO	LYS	VAL	LYS	45
46	PRO	GLY	VAL	GLY	ILE	HIS	CYS	CYS	GLN	SER	ASP	LYS	CYS	ASN	TYR	60

TOXIN γ-BLACK MAMBA VENOM

	1				5				10					15	
1	ARG	THR	CYS	ASN	LYS	THR	PHE	SER	ASP	GLN	SER	LYS	ILE	CYS	PRO	15
16	PRO	GLY	GLU	ASN	ILE	CYS	TYR	THR	LYS	THR	TRP	CYS	ASP	ALA	TRP	30
31	CYS	SER	GLN	ARG	GLY	LYS	ARG	VAL	GLU	LEU	GLY	CYS	ALA	ALA	THR	45
46	CYS	PRO	LYS	VAL	LYS	ALA	GLY	VAL	GLU	ILE	LYS	CYS	CYS	SER	THR	60
61	ASP	ASP	CYS	ASP	LYS	PHE	GLN	PHE	GLY	LYS	PRO	ARG				75

Snake Venom Toxins. The Amino Acid Sequences of Two Toxins from *Dendroaspis polylepis* (Black Mamba Venom).
D. J. Strydom.
J. Biol. Chem., **247**, 4029–4042 (1972).

POLYPEPTIDE FROM DENDROASPIS VIRIDIS VENOM

	1			5					10					15	
1	MET	ILE	CYS	TYR	SER	HIS	LYS	THR	PRO	GLN	ASN	SER	ALA	THR	ILE	15
16	THR	CYS	GLU	GLU	LYS	THR	CYS	TYR	LYS	PHE	VAL	THR	LYS	LEU	PRO	30
31	GLY	VAL	ILE	LEU	ALA	ARG	GLY	CYS	GLY	CYS	PRO	LYS	LYS	GLU	ILE	45
46	PHE	ARG	LYS	SER	ILE	HIS	CYS	CYS	ARG	SER	ASP	LYS	CYS	ASN	GLU	60

The amino acid sequence of a polypeptide from the venom of *Dendroaspis viridis*.
R. A. Shipolini and B. E. C. Banks.
Eur. J. Biochem., **49**, 399–405 (1974).

NEUROTOXIN (4.11.3) FROM VENOM OF WEST AFRICAN GREEN MAMBA

	1			5					10					15	
1	ARG	ILE	CYS	TYR	ASN	HIS	GLN	SER	THR	THR	PRO	ALA	THR	THR	LYS	15
16	SER	CYS	GLY	GLU	ASN	SER	CYS	TYR	LYS	LYS	THR	TRP	SER	ASP	HIS	30
31	ARG	GLY	THR	ILE	ILE	GLU	ARG	GLY	CYS	GLY	CYS	PRO	LYS	VAL	LYS	45
46	ARG	GLY	VAL	HIS	LEU	HIS	CYS	CYS	GLN	SER	ASP	LYS	CYS	ASN	ASN	60

NEUROTOXINS (4.7.3; 4.9.3) FROM VENOM OF WEST AFRICAN GREEN MAMBA

	1			5					10					15	
1	ARG	THR	CYS	TYR	LYS	THR	PRO	SER	VAL	LYS	PRO	GLU	THR	CYS	PRO	15
16	HIS	GLY	GLU	ASN	ILE	CYS	TYR	THR	GLU	THR	TRP	CYS	ASP	ALA	TRP	30
31	CYS	SER	GLN	ARG	GLY	LYS	ARG	GLU	GLU	LEU	GLY	CYS	ALA	ALA	THR	45
46	CYS	PRO	LYS	VAL	LYS	ALA	GLY	VAL	GLY	ILE	LYS	CYS	CYS	SER	THR	60
61	ASP	ASN	CYS	ASP	PRO	PHE	PRO	VAL	LYS	ASN	PRO	ARG				75

Note: It is suggested that the only difference between toxins (4.7.3) and (4.9.3), is that the former toxin contains a partially photo-oxidised tryptophan residue.
The primary structure and neuromuscular effects of three neurotoxic polypeptides from the venom of *Dendroaspis viridis*.
B. E. C. Banks, R. Miledi, and R. A. Shipolini.
Eur. J. Biochem., **45**, 457–468 (1974).

TOXINS

NEUROTOXIN I OF DENDROASPIS VIRIDIS *VENOM*

	1	5				10				15					
1	ARG	THR	CYS	TYR	LYS	THR	PRO	SER	VAL	LYS	PRO	GLU	THR	CYS	PRO	15
16	HIS	GLY	GLU	ASN	ILE	CYS	TYR	THR	GLU	THR	TRP	CYS	ASP	ALA	TRP	30
31	CYS	SER	GLN	ARG	GLY	LYS	ARG	VAL	GLU	LEU	GLY	CYS	ALA	ALA	THR	45
46	CYS	PRO	LYS	VAL	LYS	ALA	GLY	VAL	GLY	ILE	LYS	CYS	CYS	SER	THR	60
61	ASP	ASN	CYS	ASN	PRO	PHE	PRO	VAL	TRP	ASN	PRO	ARG	GLY			75

NEUROTOXIN V OF DENDROASPIS VIRIDIS *VENOM*

Neurotoxin V has identical sequence to that shown above for Neurotoxin I except that it lacks GLY 73.

Purification of six neurotoxins from the venom of *Dendroaspis viridis*. Primary structure of two long toxins.
G. Bechis, C. Granier, J. van Rietschoten, E. Jover, H. Rochat, and F. Miranda.
Eur. J. Biochem., **68**, 445–456 (1976).

TOXIN Ta2 OF GREEN MAMBA VENOM

	1	5				10				15					
1	MET	ILE	CYS	TYR	SER	HIS	LYS	THR	PRO	GLN	PRO	SER	ALA	THR	ILE	15
16	THR	CYS	GLU	GLU	LYS	THR	CYS	TYR	LYS	LYS	SER	VAL	ARG	LYS	LEU	30
31	PRO	ALA	VAL	VAL	ALA	GLY	ARG	GLY	CYS	GLY	CYS	PRO	SER	LYS	GLU	45
46	MET	LEU	VAL	ALA	ILE	HIS	CYS	CYS	ARG	SER	ASP	LYS	CYS	ASN	GLU	60

Snake Venom Toxins. The purification and amino acid sequence of toxin Ta2 from *Dendroaspis angusticeps* venom.
C. C. Viljoen and D. P. Botes.
J. Biol. Chem., **249**, 366–372 (1974).

TOXIN F$_{VII}$ OF GREEN MAMBA VENOM

	1	5				10				15					
1	THR	MET	CYS	TYR	SER	HIS	THR	THR	THR	SER	ARG	ALA	ILE	LEU	THR	15
16	ASN	CYS	GLY	GLU	ASN	SER	CYS	TYR	ARG	LYS	SER	ARG	ARG	HIS	PRO	30
31	PRO	LYS	MET	VAL	LEU	GLY	ARG	GLY	CYS	GLY	CYS	PRO	PRO	GLY	ASP	45
46	ASP	ASN	LEU	GLU	VAL	LYS	CYS	CYS	THR	SER	PRO	ASP	LYS	CYS	ASN	60
61	TYR															75

Snake Venom Toxins. The purification and amino acid sequence of toxin F$_{VII}$ from *Dendroaspis angusticeps* venom.
C. C. Viljoen and D. P. Botes.
J. Biol. Chem., **248**, 4915–4919 (1973).

TOXIN V_n^I I OF JAMESON'S MAMBA VENOM

	1				5					10					15	
1	ARG	ILE	CYS	TYR	ASN	HIS	GLN	SER	THR	THR	PRO	ALA	THR	THR	LYS	15
16	SER	CYS	GLY	GLU	ASN	SER	CYS	TYR	LYS	LYS	THR	TRP	SER	ASP	HIS	30
31	ARG	GLY	THR	ILE	ILE	GLU	ARG	GLY	CYS	GLY	CYS	PRO	LYS	VAL	LYS	45
46	GLN	GLY	ILE	HIS	LEU	HIS	CYS	CYS	GLN	SER	ASP	LYS	CYS	ASN	ASN	60

TOXIN V_n^{III} I OF JAMESON'S MAMBA VENOM

	1				5					10					15	
1	ARG	THR	CYS	TYR	LYS	THR	TYR	SER	ASP	LYS	SER	LYS	THR	CYS	PRO	15
16	ARG	GLY	GLU	ASP	ILE	CYS	TYR	THR	LYS	THR	TRP	CYS	ASP	GLY	PHE	30
31	CYS	SER	GLN	ARG	GLY	LYS	ARG	VAL	GLU	LEU	GLY	CYS	ALA	ALA	THR	45
46	CYS	PRO	LYS	VAL	LYS	THR	GLY	VAL	GLU	ILE	LYS	CYS	CYS	SER	THR	60
61	ASP	TYR	CYS	ASN	PRO	PHE	PRO	VAL	TRP	ASN	PRO	ARG				75

Snake Venom Toxins. The amino acid sequences of two toxins from *Dendroaspis jamesoni kaimosae* (Jameson's mamba) venom.
A. J. C. Strydom.
Biochim. Biophys. Acta, **328**, 491–509 (1973).

PROTEIN S_5C_4 OF JAMESON'S MAMBA VENOM

	1				5					10					15	
1	MET	ILE	CYS	TYR	SER	HIS	LYS	THR	PRO	GLN	ASN	SER	ALA	THR	ILE	15
16	THR	CYS	GLU	GLU	LYS	THR	CYS	TYR	LYS	LYS	PHE	VAL	THR	ASN	VAL	30
31	PRO	GLY	VAL	ILE	LEU	ALA	ARG	GLY	CYS	GLY	CYS	PRO	LYS	LYS	GLU	45
46	ILE	PHE	ARG	SER	ILE	HIS	CYS	CYS	ARG	SER	ASP	LYS	CYS	ASN	GLU	60

The amino acid sequence of protein S_5C_4 from *Dendroaspis jamesoni kaimosae* (Jameson's mamba) venom.
F. J. Joubert, A. J. C. Strydom, and N. Taljaard.
Hoppe-Seyler's Z. Physiol. Chem., **359**, 741–749 (1978).

TOXINS

β₁-BUNGAROTOXIN

A-CHAIN

	1			5					10					15		
1	ASN	LEU	ILE	ASN	PHE	MET	GLU	MET	ILE	ARG	TYR	THR	ILE	PRO	CYS	15
16	GLU	LYS	THR	TRP	GLY	GLU	TYR	ALA	ASP	TYR	GLY	CYS	TYR	CYS	GLY	30
31	ALA	GLY	GLY	SER	GLY	ARG	PRO	ILE	ASP	ALA	LEU	ASP	ARG	CYS	CYS	45
46	TYR	VAL	HIS	ASP	ASN	CYS	TYR	GLY	ASP	ALA	GLU	LYS	LYS	HIS	LYS	60
61	CYS	ASN	PRO	LYS	THR	SER	GLN	TYR	SER	TYR	LYS	LEU	THR	LYS	ARG	75
76	THR	ILE	ILE	CYS	TYR	GLY	ALA	ALA	GLY	GLY	THR	CYS	ARG	ILE VAL	VAL	90
91	CYS	ASP	CYS	ASP	ARG	THR	ALA	ALA	LEU	CYS	PHE	GLY	GLN	SER	ASP	105
106	TYR	ILE	GLU	GLU	HIS	LYS	ASN	ILE	ASP	THR	ALA	ARG	PHE	CYS	GLN	120

B-CHAIN

	1			5					10					15		
1	ARG	GLN	ARG	HIS	ARG	ASP	CYS	ASP	LYS	PRO	PRO	ASP	LYS	GLY	ASN	15
16	CYS	GLY	PRO	VAL	ARG	ALA	PHE	TYR	TYR	ASP	THR	ARG	LEU	LYS	THR	30
31	CYS	LYS	ALA	PHE	GLN	TYR	ARG	GLY	CYS	ASP	GLY	ASP	HIS	GLY	ASN	45
46	PHE	LYS	THR	GLU	THR	LEU	CYS	ARG	CYS	GLU	CYS	LEU	VAL	TYR	PRO	60

Amino acid sequences of the two polypeptide chains in $β_1$-Bungarotoxin from the venom of *Bungarus multicinctus*.
K. Kondo, K. Narita, and C.-Y. Lee.
J. Biochem., **83**, 101–115 (1978).

α-BUNGAROTOXIN

	1			5					10					15		
1	ILE	VAL	CYS	HIS	THR	THR	ALA	THR	ILE	PRO	SER	SER	ALA	VAL	THR	15
16	CYS	PRO	PRO	GLY	GLU	ASN	LEU	CYS	TYR	ARG	LYS	MET	TRP	CYS	ASP	30
31	ALA	PHE	CYS	SER	SER	ARG	GLY	LYS	VAL	VAL	GLU	LEU	GLY	CYS	ALA	45
46	ALA	THR	CYS	PRO	SER	LYS	LYS	PRO	TYR	GLU	GLU	VAL	THR	CYS	CYS	60
61	SER	THR	ASP	LYS	CYS	ASN	HIS	PRO	PRO	LYS	ARG	GLN	PRO	GLY		75

Purification, Properties and Amino Acid Sequence of α-Bungarotoxin from the Venom of *Bungarus multicinctus*.
D. Mebs, K. Narita, S. Iwanaga, Y. Samejima, and C.-Y. Lee.
Hoppe-Seyler's Z. Physiol. Chem., **353**, 243–262 (1972).

NEUROTOXINS 4 AND 5 FROM SCHISTOSA VENOM

	1			5					10					15	
1	MET	THR	CYS	CYS	ASN	GLN	GLN	SER	SER	GLN	PRO	LYS	THR	THR	THR	15
16	ASN	CYS	ALA	GLU	SER	SER	CYS	TYR	LYS	LYS	THR	TRP	SER	ASP	HIS	30
31	ARG	GLY	THR	ARG	ILE	GLU	ARG	GLY	CYS	GLY	CYS	PRO	GLN	VAL	LYS	45
46	PRO/SER	GLY	ILE	LYS	LEU	GLU	CYS	CYS	HIS	THR	ASN	GLU	CYS	ASN	ASN	60

Note: Residue 46 in toxin 5 is SER, and in toxin 4 is PRO.
Amino acid sequences of two principal neurotoxins of *Enhydrina schistosa* venom.
L. Fryklund, D. Eaker, and E. Karlsson.
Biochemistry, **11**, 4633–4640 (1972).

ERABUTOXINS a AND b

	1		5						10					15	
1	ARG	ILE	CYS	PHE	ASN	GLN	HIS	SER	SER	GLN	PRO	GLN	THR	THR	LYS	15
16	THR	CYS	PRO	SER	GLY	SER	GLU	SER	CYS	TYR	ASN/HIS	LYS	GLN	TRP	SER	30
31	ASP	PHE	ARG	GLY	THR	ILE	ILE	GLU	ARG	GLY	CYS	GLY	CYS	PRO	THR	45
46	VAL	LYS	PRO	GLY	ILE	LYS	LEU	SER	CYS	CYS	GLU	SER	GLU	VAL	CYS	60
61	ASN	ASN														75

Note: Erabutoxin a has ASN for residue 26, and erabutoxin b has HIS.
The Amino Acid Sequences of Erabutoxins, Neurotoxic Proteins of Sea-Snake (*Laticauda semifasciata*) Venom.
S. Sato and N. Tamiya.
Biochem. J., **122**, 453–461 (1971).

ERABUTOXIN c

	1		5						10					15	
1	ARG	ILE	CYS	PHE	ASN	GLN	HIS	SER	SER	GLN	PRO	GLN	THR	THR	LYS	15
16	THR	CYS	PRO	SER	GLY	SER	GLU	SER	CYS	TYR	HIS	LYS	GLN	TRP	SER	30
31	ASP	PHE	ARG	GLY	THR	ILE	ILE	GLU	ARG	GLY	CYS	GLY	CYS	PRO	THR	45
46	VAL	LYS	PRO	GLY	ILE	ASN	LEU	SER	CYS	CYS	GLU	SER	GLU	VAL	CYS	60
61	ASN	ASN														75

Note: Erabutoxins a, b and c have disulphide bridges linking residues CYS 3 and 24; CYS 17 and 41; CYS 43 and 54; CYS 55 and 60.
The Isolation, Properties and Amino Acid Sequence of Erabutoxin c, a Minor Neurotoxin Component of the venom of a Sea Snake *Laticanda semifasciata*.
N. Tamiya and H. Abe.
Biochem. J., **130**, 547–555 (1972).

TOXINS

NEUROTOXIN a OF SEA SNAKE VENOM (AIPYSURUS LAEVIS)

	1	5		10		15	
1	LEU THR CYS CYS ASN	GLN GLN SER SER GLN	PRO LYS THR THR THR	15
16	ASP CYS ALA ASP ASN	SER CYS TYR LYS LYS	THR TRP GLN ASP HIS	30
31	ARG GLY THR ARG ILE	GLU ARG GLY CYS GLY	CYS PRO GLN VAL LYS	45
46	PRO GLY ILE LYS LEU	GLU CYS CYS LYS THR	ASN GLU CYS ASN ASN	60

NEUROTOXIN b OF SEA SNAKE VENOM (AIPYSURUS LAEVIS)

	1	5		10		15	
1	LEU THR CYS CYS ASN	GLN GLN SER SER GLN	PRO LYS THR THR THR	15
16	ASP CYS ALA ASP ASN	SER CYS TYR LYS MET	THR TRP ARG ASP HIS	30
31	ARG GLY THR ARG ILE	GLU ARG GLY CYS GLY	CYS PRO GLN VAL LYS	45
46	PRO GLY ILE LYS LEU	GLU CYS CYS LYS THR	ASN GLU CYS ASN ASN	60

NEUROTOXIN c OF SEA SNAKE VENOM (AIPYSURUS LAEVIS)

	1	5		10		15	
1	LEU THR CYS CYS ASN	GLN GLN SER SER GLN	PRO LYS THR THR THR	15
16	ASP CYS ALA ASP ASN	SER CYS TYR LYS LYS	THR TRP LYS ASP HIS	30
31	ARG GLY THR ARG ILE	GLU ARG GLY CYS GLY	CYS PRO GLN VAL LYS	45
46	PRO GLY ILE LYS LEU	GLU CYS CYS LYS THR	ASN GLU CYS ASN ASN	60

Isolation, properties and amino acid sequences of three neurotoxins from the venom of a sea snake, *Aipysurus laevis*.
N. Maeda and N. Tamiya.
Biochem. J., **153**, 79–87 (1976).

TOXIN LS III FROM SEA SNAKE VENOM

	1	5		10		15	
1	ARG GLU CYS TYR LEU	ASN PRO HIS ASP THR	GLN THR CYS PRO SER	15
16	GLY GLN GLU ILE CYS	TYR VAL LYS SER TRP	CYS ASN ALA TRP CYS	30
31	SER SER ARG GLY LYS	VAL LEU GLU PHE GLY	CYS ALA ALA THR CYS	45
46	PRO SER VAL ASN THR	GLY THR GLU ILE LYS	CYS CYS SER ALA ASP	60
61	LYS CYS ASN THR TYR	PRO			75

The primary structure of the toxin Laticauda semifasciata III, a weak and reversibly acting neurotoxin from the venom of a sea snake *Laticauda semifasciata*.
N. Maeda and N. Tamiya.
Biochem. J., **141**, 389–400 (1974).

BLACK MAMBA VENOM COMPONENT FS2 OF LOW TOXICITY

```
    1               5                   10                      15
 1  ARG ILE  CYS TYR SER HIS  LYS ALA SER LEU PRO ARG ALA THR LYS    15
16  THR CYS VAL GLU ASN THR CYS TYR LYS MET PHE ILE  ARG THR HIS    30
31  ARG GLN TYR ILE  SER GLU ARG GLY CYS GLY CYS PRO THR ALA MET    45
46  TRP PRO TYR GLN THR GLU CYS CYS LYS GLY ASP ARG CYS ASN LYS     60
```

Snake venom toxins. The amino acid sequence of a short-neurotoxin homologue from *Dendroaspis polylepis polylepis* (Black Mamba) Venom.
D. J. Strydom.
Eur. J. Biochem., **76**, 99–106 (1977).

PEPTIDE DE-1 OF KING COBRA VENOM (NON-TOXIN)

```
    1               5                   10                      15
 1  LEU ILE  CYS PHE ASN GLN GLU THR TYR ARG PRO GLU THR THR THR    15
16  THR CYS PRO ASP GLY GLU ASN CYS TYR SER THR PHE TRP HIS ASN     30
31  ASP GLY HIS  VAL LYS ILE  GLU ARG GLY CYS GLY CYS PRO ARG VAL   45
46  ASN PRO PRO ILE  SER ILE  CYS CYS LYS THR ASP LYS CYS ASN ASN   60
```

The amino acid sequence of polypeptide DE-1 from *Ophiophagus hannah* (King Cobra) venom.
F. J. Joubert.
Hoppe-Seyler's Z. Physiol. Chem., **358**, 565–574 (1977).

454

VIRUS COAT PROTEINS

ALFALFA MOSAIC VIRUS COAT PROTEIN STRAIN 425

```
          1              5                    10                   15
   1   AC  SER SER SER GLN LYS LYS ALA GLY GLY LYS ALA GLY LYS PRO   15
  16   THR LYS ARG SER GLN ASN TYR ALA ALA LEU ARG LYS ALA GLN LEU   30
  31   PRO LYS PRO PRO ALA LEU LYS VAL PRO VAL VAL LYS PRO THR ASN   45
  46   THR ILE LEU PRO GLN THR GLY CYS VAL TRP GLN SER LEU GLY THR   60
  61   PRO LEU SER LEU SER SER PHE ASN GLY LEU GLY ALA ARG PHE LEU   75
  76   TYR SER PHE LEU LYS ASP PHE VAL GLY PRO ARG ILE LEU GLU GLU   90
  91   ASP LEU ILE TYR ARG MET VAL PHE SER ILE THR PRO SER HIS ALA  105
 106   GLY THR PHE CYS LEU THR ASP ASP VAL THR THR GLU ASP GLY ARG  120
 121   ALA VAL ALA HIS GLY ASN PRO MET GLN GLU PHE PRO HIS GLY ALA  135
 136   PHE HIS ALA ASN GLU LYS PHE GLY PHE GLU LEU VAL PHE THR ALA  150
 151   PRO THR HIS ALA GLY MET GLN ASN GLN ASN PHE LYS HIS SER TYR  165
 166   ALA VAL ALA LEU CYS LEU ASP PHE ASP ALA GLN PRO GLU GLY SER  180
 181   LYS ASN PRO SER PHE ARG PHE ASN GLU VAL TRP VAL GLU ARG LYS  195
 196   ALA PHE PRO ARG ALA GLY PRO LEU ARG SER LEU ILE THR VAL GLY  210
 211   LEU PHE ASP GLU ALA ASP ASN LEU ASP ARG HIS              225
```

Structural studies on the coat protein of alfalfa mosaic virus. The complete primary structure.
G. M. A. van Beynum, J. M. de Graaf, B. Kraal, and L. Bosch.
Eur. J. Biochem., **72**, 63–78 (1977).

TOBACCO MOSAIC VIRUS COAT PROTEIN STRAIN COWPEA

```
          1              5                    10                   15
   1   AC  ALA TYR SER ILE PRO THR PRO SER GLN LEU VAL TYR PHE THR   15
  16   GLU ASN TYR ALA ASP TYR ILE PRO PHE VAL ASN ARG LEU ILE ASN   30
  31   ALA ARG SER ASN SER PHE GLN THR GLN SER GLY ARG ASP GLU LEU   45
  46   ARG GLU ILE LEU ILE LYS SER GLN VAL SER VAL VAL SER PRO ILE   60
  61   SER ARG PHE PRO ALA GLU PRO ALA TYR TYR ILE TYR LEU ARG ASP   75
  76   PRO SER ILE SER THR VAL TYR THR ALA LEU LEU GLN SER THR ASP   90
  91   THR ARG ASN ARG VAL ILE GLU VAL GLU ASN SER THR ASP VAL THR  105
 106   THR ALA GLU GLN LEU ASN ALA VAL ARG ARG THR ASP ASP ALA SER  120
 121   THR ALA ILE HIS ASN ASN LEU GLU GLN LEU LEU SER LEU LEU THR  135
 136   ASN GLY THR GLY VAL PHE ASN ARG THR SER PHE GLU SER ALA SER  150
 151   GLY LEU TRP LEU VAL THR THR PRO THR ARG THR ALA          165
```

The amino acid sequence of the cowpea strain of tobacco mosaic virus protein.
M. W. Rees and M. N. Short.
Biochim. Biophys. Acta, **393**, 15–23 (1975).

VIRUS COAT PROTEINS

TOBACCO MOSAIC VIRUS COAT PROTEIN STRAIN OM

	1				5					10					15		
1	AC	SER	TYR	SER	ILE	THR	THR	PRO	SER	GLN	PHE	VAL	PHE	LEU	SER	15
16	SER	ALA	TRP	ALA	ASP	PRO	ILE	GLU	LEU	ILE	ASN	LEU	CYS	THR	ASN	30
31	ALA	LEU	GLY	ASN	GLN	PHE	GLN	THR	GLN	GLN	ALA	ARG	THR	VAL	VAL	45
46	GLN	ARG	GLN	PHE	SER	GLU	VAL	TRP	LYS	PRO	SER	PRO	GLN	VAL	THR	60
61	VAL	ARG	PHE	PRO	ASP	SER	ASP	PHE	LYS	VAL	TYR	ARG	TYR	ASN	ALA	75
76	VAL	LEU	ASP	PRO	LEU	VAL	THR	ALA	LEU	LEU	GLY	ALA	PHE	ASP	THR	90
91	ARG	ASN	ARG	ILE	ILE	GLU	VAL	GLU	ASN	GLN	ALA	ASN	PRO	THR	THR	105
106	ALA	GLU	THR	LEU	ASP	ALA	THR	ARG	ARG	VAL	ASP	ASP	ALA	THR	VAL	120
121	ALA	ILE	ARG	SER	ALA	ILE	ASN	ASN	LEU	VAL	VAL	GLU	LEU	ILE	ARG	135
136	GLY	THR	GLY	SER	TYR	ASN	ARG	SER	SER	PHE	GLU	SER	SER	SER	GLY	150
151	LEU	VAL	TRP	ASN	SER	GLY	PRO	ALA	THR							165

Note: The sequences of O and Kokubu strains differ from the above in that residue 153 is THR.

Amino Acid Sequences of Some Common Japanese Strains of Tobacco Mosaic Virus.
Y. Nozu, T. Ohno, and Y. Okada.
J. Biochem., **68**, 39–52 (1970).

TOBACCO MOSAIC VIRUS COAT PROTEIN STRAIN VULGARE

	1				5					10					15		
1	AC	SER	TYR	SER	ILE	THR	THR	PRO	SER	GLN	PHE	VAL	PHE	LEU	SER	15
16	SER	ALA	TRP	ALA	ASP	PRO	ILE	GLU	LEU	ILE	ASN	LEU	CYS	THR	ASN	30
31	ALA	LEU	GLY	ASN	GLN	PHE	GLN	THR	GLN	GLN	ALA	ARG	THR	VAL	VAL	45
46	GLN	ARG	GLN	PHE	SER	GLN	VAL	TRP	LYS	PRO	SER	PRO	GLN	VAL	THR	60
61	VAL	ARG	PHE	PRO	ASP	SER	ASP	PHE	LYS	VAL	TYR	ARG	TYR	ASN	ALA	75
76	VAL	LEU	ASP	PRO	LEU	VAL	THR	ALA	LEU	LEU	GLY	ALA	PHE	ASP	THR	90
91	ARG	ASN	ARG	ILE	ILE	GLU	VAL	GLU	ASN	GLN	ALA	ASN	PRO	THR	THR	105
106	ALA	GLU	THR	LEU	ASP	ALA	THR	ARG	ARG	VAL	ASP	ASP	ALA	THR	VAL	120
121	ALA	ILE	ARG	SER	ALA	ILE	ASN	ASN	LEU	ILE	VAL	GLU	LEU	ILE	ARG	135
136	GLY	THR	GLY	SER	TYR	ASN	ARG	SER	SER	PHE	GLU	SER	SER	SER	GLY	150
151	LEU	VAL	TRP	THR	SER	GLY	PRO	ALA	THR							165

A reinvestigation of the amino acid sequence of tobacco mosaic virus strain, vulgare.
F. A. Anderer, B. Wittmann-Liebold, and H. G. Wittmann.
Z. Naturforsch., **20B**, 1203–1213 (1965).

VIRUS COAT PROTEINS

TOBACCO MOSAIC VIRUS COAT PROTEIN STRAIN DAHLEMENSE

	1				5					10					15	
1	AC	SER	TYR	SER	ILE	THR	SER	PRO	SER	GLN	PHE	VAL	PHE	LEU	SER	15
16	SER	VAL	TRP	ALA	ASP	PRO	ILE	GLU	LEU	LEU	ASN	VAL	CYS	THR	SER	30
31	SER	LEU	GLY	ASN	GLN	PHE	GLN	THR	GLN	GLN	ALA	ARG	THR	THR	VAL	45
46	GLN	GLN	GLN	PHE	SER	GLU	VAL	TRP	LYS	PRO	PHE	PRO	GLN	SER	THR	60
61	VAL	ARG	PHE	PRO	GLY	ASP	VAL	TYR	LYS	VAL	TYR	ARG	TYR	ASN	ALA	75
76	VAL	LEU	ASP	PRO	LEU	ILE	THR	ALA	LEU	LEU	GLY	THR	PHE	ASP	THR	90
91	ARG	ASN	ARG	ILE	ILE	GLU	VAL	GLU	ASN	GLN	GLN	SER	PRO	THR	THR	105
106	ALA	GLU	THR	LEU	ASP	ALA	THR	ARG	ARG	VAL	ASP	ASP	ALA	THR	VAL	120
121	ALA	ILE	ARG	SER	ALA	ILE	ASN	ASN	LEU	VAL	ASN	GLU	LEU	VAL	ARG	135
136	GLY	THR	GLY	LEU	TYR	ASN	GLN	ASN	THR	PHE	GLU	SER	MET	SER	GLY	150
151	LEU	VAL	TRP	THR	SER	ALA	PRO	ALA	SER							165

Coat Proteins of strains of two RNA viruses: comparison of their amino acid sequences.
B. Wittmann-Liebold and H. G. Wittmann.
Molec. Gen. Genetics, **100**, 358–363 (1967).

TURNIP YELLOW MOSAIC VIRUS PROTEIN

	1				5					10					15	
1	AC	MET	GLU	ILE	ASP	LYS	GLU	LEU	ALA	PRO	GLN	ASP	ARG	THR	VAL	15
16	THR	VAL	ALA	THR	VAL	LEU	PRO	ALA	VAL	PRO	GLY	PRO	SER	PRO	LEU	30
31	THR	ILE	LYS	GLN	PRO	PHE	GLN	SER	GLU	VAL	LEU	PHE	ALA	GLY	THR	45
46	LYS	ASP	ALA	GLU	ALA	SER	LEU	THR	ILE	ALA	ASN	ILE	ASP	SER	VAL	60
61	SER	THR	LEU	THR	THR	PHE	TYR	ARG	HIS	ALA	SER	LEU	GLU	SER	LEU	75
76	TRP	VAL	THR	ILE	HIS	PRO	THR	LEU	GLN	ALA	PRO	THR	PHE	PRO	THR	90
91	THR	VAL	GLY	VAL	CYS	TRP	VAL	PRO	ALA	ASN	SER	PRO	VAL	THR	PRO	105
106	ALA	GLN	ILE	THR	LYS	THR	TYR	GLY	GLY	GLN	ILE	PHE	CYS	ILE	GLY	120
121	GLY	ALA	ILE	ASN	THR	LEU	SER	PRO	LEU	ILE	VAL	LYS	CYS	PRO	LEU	135
136	GLU	MET	MET	ASN	PRO	ARG	VAL	LYS	ASP	SER	ILE	GLN	TYR	LEU	ASP	150
151	SER	PRO	LYS	LEU	LEU	ILE	SER	ILE	THR	ALA	GLN	PRO	THR	ALA	PRO	165
166	PRO	ALA	SER	THR	CYS	ILE	ILE	THR	VAL	SER	GLY	THR	LEU	SER	MET	180
181	HIS	SER	PRO	LEU	ILE	THR	ASP	THR	SER	THR						195

Studies on the primary structure of turnip yellow mosaic virus protein.
D. Stehelin, R. Peter, and H. Duranton.
Biochim. Biophys. Acta, **293**, 253–265 (1973).

VIRUS COAT PROTEINS

BACTERIOPHAGE COAT PROTEIN STRAIN Fr

	1				5					10					15	
1	ALA	SER	ASN	PHE	GLU	GLU	PHE	VAL	LEU	VAL	ASN	ASP	GLY	GLY	THR	15
16	GLY	ASP	VAL	LYS	VAL	ALA	PRO	SER	ASN	PHE	ALA	ASN	GLY	VAL	ALA	30
31	GLU	TRP	ILE	SER	SER	ASN	SER	ARG	SER	GLN	ALA	TYR	LYS	VAL	THR	45
46	CYS	SER	VAL	ARG	GLN	SER	SER	ALA	ASN	ASN	ARG	LYS	TYR	THR	VAL	60
61	LYS	VAL	GLU	VAL	PRO	LYS	VAL	ALA	THR	GLN	VAL	GLN	GLY	GLY	VAL	75
76	GLU	LEU	PRO	VAL	ALA	ALA	TRP	ARG	SER	TYR	MET	ASN	MET	GLU	LEU	90
91	THR	ILE	PRO	VAL	PHE	ALA	THR	ASX	ASP	ASP	CYS	ALA	LEU	ILE	VAL	105
106	LYS	ALA	LEU	GLN	GLY	THR	PHE	LYS	THR	GLY	ILE	ALA	PRO	ASN	THR	120
121	ALA	ILE	ALA	ALA	ASN	SER	GLY	ILE	TYR							135

Coat Proteins of Strains of two RNA Viruses: Comparison of their Amino Acid Sequences.
B. Wittmann-Liebold and H. G. Wittmann.
Molec. Gen. Genetics, **100**, 358–363 (1967).

BACTERIOPHAGE COAT PROTEIN STRAIN f2

	1				5					10					15	
1	ALA	SER	ASN	PHE	THR	GLN	PHE	VAL	LEU	VAL	ASN	ASP	GLY	GLY	THR	15
16	GLY	ASN	VAL	THR	VAL	ALA	PRO	SER	ASN	PHE	ALA	ASN	GLY	VAL	ALA	30
31	GLU	TRP	ILE	SER	SER	ASN	SER	ARG	SER	GLN	ALA	TYR	LYS	VAL	THR	45
46	CYS	SER	VAL	ARG	GLN	SER	SER	ALA	GLN	ASN	ARG	LYS	TYR	THR	ILE	60
61	LYS	VAL	GLU	VAL	PRO	LYS	VAL	ALA	THR	GLN	THR	VAL	GLY	GLY	VAL	75
76	GLU	LEU	PRO	VAL	ALA	ALA	TRP	ARG	SER	TYR	LEU	ASN	LEU	GLU	LEU	90
91	THR	ILE	PRO	ILE	PHE	ALA	THR	ASN	SER	ASP	CYS	GLU	LEU	ILE	VAL	105
106	LYS	ALA	MET	GLN	GLY	LEU	LEU	LYS	ASP	GLY	ASN	PRO	ILE	PRO	SER	120
121	ALA	ILE	ALA	ALA	ASN	SER	GLY	ILE	TYR							135

Amino Acid Sequence of the f2 Coat Protein.
K. Weber and W. Konigsberg.
J. Biol. Chem., **242**, 3563–3578 (1967).

458

VIRUS COAT PROTEINS

BACTERIOPHAGE COAT PROTEIN STRAIN Qβ

	1			5					10					15	
1	ALA	LYS	LEU	GLU	THR	VAL	THR	LEU	GLY	ASN	ILE	GLY	LYS	ASP	GLY	15
16	LYS	GLN	THR	LEU	VAL	LEU	ASP	PRO	ARG	GLY	VAL	ASN	PRO	THR	ASN	30
31	GLY	VAL	ALA	SER	LEU	SER	GLN	ALA	GLY	ALA	VAL	PRO	ALA	LEU	GLU	45
46	LYS	ARG	VAL	THR	VAL	SER	VAL	SER	GLN	PRO	ARG	ASN	ARG	LYS	ASN	60
61	TYR	LYS	VAL	GLN	VAL	LYS	ILE	GLN	ASN	PRO	THR	ALA	CYS	THR	ALA	75
76	ASN	GLY	SER	CYS	ASP	PRO	SER	VAL	THR	ARG	GLN	ALA	TYR	ALA	ASP	90
91	VAL	THR	PHE	SER	PHE	THR	GLN	TYR	SER	THR	ASP	GLU	GLU	ARG	ALA	105
106	PHE	VAL	ARG	THR	GLU	LEU	ALA	ALA	LEU	LEU	ALA	SER	PRO	LEU	LEU	120
121	ILE	ASP	ALA	ILE	ASP	GLN	LEU	ASN	PRO	ALA	TYR					135

The Amino Acid Sequence of the Qβ Coat Protein.
T. Maita and W. Konigsberg.
J. Biol. Chem., **246**, 5003–5024 (1971).

BACTERIOPHAGE COAT PROTEIN STRAIN ZJ-2

	1			5					10					15	
1	ALA	GLU	GLY	ASP	ASP	PRO	ALA	LYS	ALA	ALA	PHE	ASP	SER	LEU	GLN	15
16	ALA	SER	ALA	THR	GLU	TYR	ILE	GLY	TYR	ALA	TRP	ALA	MET	VAL	VAL	30
31	VAL	ILE	VAL	GLY	ALA	ALA	ILE	GLY	ILE	LYS	LEU	PHE	LYS	LYS	PHE	45
46	THR	SER	LYS	ALA	SER											60

The Amino Acid Sequence of the B-Protein of Bacteriophage ZJ-2.
D. T. Snell and R. E. Offord.
Biochem. J., **127**, 167–178 (1972).

BACTERIOPHAGE COAT PROTEIN STRAIN fd

	1			5					10					15	
1	ALA	GLU	GLY	ASP	ASP	PRO	ALA	LYS	ALA	ALA	PHE	ASP	SER	LEU	GLN	15
16	ALA	SER	ALA	THR	GLU	TYR	ILE	GLY	TYR	ALA	TRP	ALA	MET	VAL	VAL	30
31	VAL	ILE	VAL	GLY	ALA	THR	ILE	GLY	ILE	LYS	LEU	PHE	LYS	LYS	PHE	45
46	THR	SER	LYS	ALA	SER											60

Virus proteins IV. The constitution of the coat protein of the fd phage.
F. Asbeck, K. Beyreuther, H. Köhler, G. v. Wettstein, and G. Braunitzer.
Hoppe-Seyler's Z. Physiol. Chem., **350**, 1047–1066 (1969).
And
Reinvestigation of a region of the fd bacteriophage coat protein sequence.
Y. Nakashima and W. Konigsberg.
J. Mol. Biol., **88**, 598–600 (1974).

HISTONE H1—TROUT

	1			5					10					15		
1	AC	ALA	GLU	VAL	ALA	PRO	ALA	PRO	ALA	ALA	ALA	ALA	PRO	ALA	LYS	15
16	ALA	PRO	LYS	LYS	LYS	ALA	ALA	ALA	LYS	PRO	LYS	LYS	SER	GLY	PRO	30
31	ALA	VAL	GLY	GLU	LEU	ALA	GLY	LYS	ALA	VAL	ALA	ALA	SER	LYS	GLU	45
46	ARG	SER	GLY	VAL	SER	LEU	ALA	ALA	LEU	LYS	LYS	SER	LEU	ALA	ALA	60
61	GLY	GLY	TYR	ASP	VAL	GLU	LYS	ASN	ASN	SER	ARG	VAL	LYS	ILE	ALA	75
76	VAL	LYS	SER	LEU	VAL	THR	LYS	GLY	THR	LEU	VAL	GLU	THR	LYS	GLY	90
91	THR	GLY	ALA	SER	GLY	SER	PHE	LYS	LEU	ASN	LYS	LYS	ALA	VAL	GLU	105
106	ALA	LYS	LYS	PRO	ALA	LYS	LYS	ALA	ALA	ALA	PRO	LYS	ALA	LYS	LYS	120
121	VAL	ALA	ALA	LYS	LYS	PRO	ALA	ALA	ALA	LYS	LYS	PRO	LYS	LYS	VAL	135
136	ALA	ALA	LYS	LYS	ALA	VAL	ALA	ALA	LYS	LYS	SER	PRO	LYS	LYS	ALA	150
151	LYS	LYS	PRO	ALA	THR	PRO	LYS	LYS	ALA	ALA	LYS	SER	PRO	LYS	LYS	165
166	ALA	THR	LYS	ALA	ALA	LYS	PRO	LYS	ALA	ALA	LYS	PRO	LYS	LYS	ALA	180
181	ALA	LYS	SER	PRO	LYS	LYS	VAL	LYS	LYS	PRO	ALA	ALA	ALA	LYS	LYS	195

The amino acid sequence of trout-testis Histone H1.
A. R. Macleod, N. C. W. Wong, and G. H. Dixon.
Eur. J. Biochem., **78**, 281–291 (1977).

HISTONE H2A—CALF THYMUS

	1			5					10					15		
1	AC	SER	GLY	ARG	GLY	LYS	GLN	GLY	GLY	LYS	ALA	ARG	ALA	LYS	ALA	15
16	LYS	THR	ARG	SER	SER	ARG	ALA	GLY	LEU	GLN	PHE	PRO	VAL	GLY	ARG	30
31	VAL	HIS	ARG	LEU	LEU	ARG	LYS	GLY	ASN	TYR	ALA	GLU	ARG	VAL	GLY	45
46	ALA	GLY	ALA	PRO	VAL	TYR	LEU	ALA	ALA	VAL	LEU	GLU	TYR	LEU	THR	60
61	ALA	GLU	ILE	LEU	GLU	LEU	ALA	GLY	ASN	ALA	ALA	ARG	ASP	ASN	LYS	75
76	LYS	THR	ARG	ILE	ILE	PRO	ARG	HIS	LEU	GLN	LEU	ALA	ILE	ARG	ASN	90
91	ASP	GLU	GLU	LEU	ASN	LYS	LEU	LEU	GLY	LYS	VAL	THR	ILE	ALA	GLN	105
106	GLY	GLY	VAL	LEU	PRO	ASN	ILE	GLN	ALA	VAL	LEU	LEU	PRO	LYS	LYS	120
121	THR	GLU	SER	HIS	HIS	LYS	ALA	LYS	GLY	LYS						135

Amino Acid Sequence of the Center of the Arginine–Lysine-rich Histone from Calf Thymus.
The Total Sequence.
L. C. Yeoman, M. O. J. Olson, N. Sugano, J. J. Jordan, C. W. Taylor, W. C. Starbuck, and H. Busch.
J. Biol. Chem., **247**, 6018–6023 (1972).
And
Covalent structure of calf-thymus ALK-histone.
P. Sautière, D. Tyrou, B. Laine, J. Mizon, P. Ruffin, and G. Biserte.
Eur. J. Biochem., **41**, 563–576 (1974).
And
Calf Thymus Histone H2A. Purification and Tryptic peptides.
H. Hayashi and K. Iwai.
J. Biochem., **80**, 681–692 (1976).

HISTONES

HISTONE H2A—RAT CHLOROLEUKEMIA

```
        1                5                    10                      15
   1  AC   SER  GLY ARG GLY LYS GLN GLY GLY LYS ALA ARG ALA LYS ALA    15
  16  LYS  SER  ARG SER SER ARG ALA GLY LEU GLN PHE PRO VAL GLY ARG     30
             THR
  31  VAL  HIS  ARG LEU LEU ARG LYS GLY ASN TYR ALA GLU ARG VAL GLY    45
  46  ALA  GLY  ALA PRO VAL TYR LEU ALA ALA VAL LEU GLU TYR LEU THR    60
  61  ALA  GLU  ILE LEU GLU LEU ALA GLY ASN ALA ALA ARG ASP ASN LYS    75
  76  LYS  THR  ARG ILE ILE PRO ARG HIS LEU GLN LEU ALA ILE ARG ASN    90
  91  ASP  GLU  GLU LEU ASN LYS LEU LEU GLY LYS VAL THR ILE ALA GLN   105
                                             ARG
 106  GLY  GLY  VAL LEU PRO ASN ILE GLN ALA VAL LEU LEU PRO LYS LYS   120
 121  THR  GLU  SER HIS HIS LYS ALA LYS GLY LYS                       135
```

Primary structure and microheterogeneities of rat chloroleukemia Histone H2A (Histone ALK, IIb1, or F2a2).
B. Laine, P. Sautière, and G. Biserte.
Biochemistry, **15**, 1640–1645 (1976).

HISTONE H2B$_{(1)}$—SEA URCHIN

```
        1               5                   10                      15
   1  PRO SER GLN LYS SER PRO THR LYS ARG SER PRO THR LYS ARG SER    15
  16  PRO THR LYS ARG SER PRO GLN LYS GLY GLY LYS GLY GLY LYS GLY    30
  31  ALA LYS ARG GLY GLY LYS ALA GLY LYS ARG ARG ARG GLY VAL GLN    45
  46  VAL LYS ARG ARG ARG ARG ARG ARG GLU SER TYR GLY ILE TYR ILE    60
  61  TYR LYS VAL LEU LYS GLN VAL HIS PRO ASP THR GLY ILE SER SER    75
  76  ARG ALA MET SER VAL MET ASN SER PHE VAL ASN ASP VAL PHE GLU    90
  91  ARG ILE ALA ALA GLU ALA GLY ARG LEU THR THR TYR ASN ARG ARG   105
 106  SER THR VAL SER SER ARG GLU VAL GLN THR ALA VAL ARG LEU LEU   120
 121  LEU PRO GLY GLU LEU ALA LYS HIS ALA VAL SER GLU GLY THR LYS   135
 136  ALA VAL THR LYS TYR THR THR SER ARG                           150
```

The complete amino acid sequence of Histone H2B$_{(1)}$ from the sperm of the Sea Urchin *Parechinus angulosus*.
M. Strickland, W. N. Strickland, W. F. Brandt, and C. von Holt.
Eur. J. Biochem., **77**, 263–275 (1977).

HISTONE H2B—BROWN TROUT

	1				5					10					15	
1	PRO	GLU	PRO	ALA	LYS	SER	ALA	PRO	LYS	LYS	GLY	SER	LYS	LYS	ALA	15
16	VAL	THR	LYS	THR	ALA	GLY	LYS	GLY	GLY	LYS	LYS	ARG	LYS	ARG	SER	30
31	ARG	LYS	GLU	SER	TYR	ALA	ILE	TYR	VAL	TYR	LYS	VAL	LEU	LYS	GLN	45
46	VAL	HIS	PRO	ASP	THR	GLY	ILE	SER	SER	LYS	ALA	MET	GLY	ILE	MET	60
61	ASN	SER	PHE	VAL	ASN	ASP	ILE	PHE	GLU	ARG	ILE	ALA	GLY	GLU	SER	75
76	SER	ARG	LEU	ALA	HIS	TYR	ASN	LYS	ARG	SER	THR	ILE	THR	SER	ARG	90
91	GLU	ILE	GLN	THR	ALA	VAL	ARG	LEU	LEU	LEU	PRO	GLY	GLU	LEU	ALA	105
106	LYS	HIS	ALA	VAL	SER	GLU	GLY	THR	LYS	ALA	VAL	THR	LYS	TYR	THR	120
121	SER	SER	LYS													135

The primary structure of Histone H2B from brown trout (*Salmo trutta*) Testes.
A. Kootstra and G. S. Bailey.
FEBS Letters, **68**, 76–78 (1976).

HISTONE H2B—CALF THYMUS

	1				5					10					15	
1	PRO	GLN	PRO	ALA	LYS	SER	ALA	PRO	ALA	PRO	LYS	LYS	GLY	SER	LYS	15
16	ALA	VAL	THR	LYS	LYS	ALA	GLN	LYS	LYS	ASP	GLY	LYS	LYS	ARG	LYS	30
31	ARG	SER	ARG	LYS	GLU	SER	TYR	SER	VAL	TYR	VAL	TYR	LYS	VAL	LEU	45
46	LYS	GLN	VAL	HIS	PRO	ASP	THR	GLY	ILE	SER	SER	LYS	ALA	MET	GLY	60
61	ILE	MET	ASN	SER	PHE	VAL	ASN	ASP	ILE	PHE	GLU	ARG	ILE	ALA	GLY	75
76	GLU	ALA	SER	ARG	LEU	ALA	HIS	TYR	ASN	LYS	ARG	SER	THR	ILE	THR	90
91	SER	ARG	GLU	ILE	GLN	THR	ALA	VAL	ARG	LEU	LEU	LEU	PRO	GLY	GLU	105
106	LEU	ALA	LYS	HIS	ALA	VAL	SER	GLU	GLY	THR	LYS	ALA	VAL	THR	LYS	120
121	TYR	THR	SER	SER	LYS											135

Amino acid Sequence of Slightly Lysine-rich Histone.
K. Iwai, K. Ishikawa, and H. Hayashi.
Nature, **226**, 1056–1058 (1970).

HISTONES

HISTONE H2B(2)—SEA URCHIN

```
      1              5                    10                        15
  1  PRO ARG SER PRO ALA LYS THR SER PRO ARG LYS GLY SER PRO ARG   15
 16  LYS GLY SER PRO SER ARG LYS ALA SER PRO LYS ARG GLY GLY LYS   30
 31  GLY ALA LYS ARG ALA GLY LYS GLY GLY ARG ARG ARG ARG VAL VAL   45
 46  LYS ARG ARG ARG ARG ARG ARG GLU SER TYR GLY ILE TYR ILE TYR   60
 61  LYS VAL LEU LYS GLN VAL HIS PRO ASP THR GLY ILE SER SER ARG   75
 76  ALA MET SER VAL MET ASN SER PHE VAL ASN ASP VAL PHE GLU ARG   90
 91  ILE ALA GLY GLU ALA SER ARG LEU THR SER ALA ASN ARG ARG SER  105
106  THR VAL SER SER ARG GLU ILE GLN THR ALA VAL ARG LEU LEU LEU  120
121  PRO GLY GLU LEU ALA LYS HIS ALA VAL SER GLU GLY THR LYS ALA  135
136  VAL THR LYS TYR THR THR SER ARG                              150
```

The complete amino acid sequence of Histone H2B(2) from sperm of the sea urchin *Parechinus angulosus*.
W. N. Strickland, M. Strickland, W. F. Brandt, and C. von Holt.
Eur. J. Biochem., **77**, 277–286 (1977).

HISTONE H3—CHICKEN ERYTHROCYTES

```
      1              5                    10                        15
  1  ALA ARG THR LYS GLN THR ALA ARG MML/DML SER THR GLY GLY LYS ALA   15
 16  PRO ARG LYS GLN LEU ALA THR LYS ALA ALA ARG MML/DML SER ALA PRO   30
 31  ALA THR GLY GLY VAL MML/DML LYS PRO HIS ARG TYR ARG PRO GLY THR   45
 46  VAL ALA LEU ARG GLU ILE ARG ARG TYR GLN LYS SER THR GLU LEU   60
 61  LEU ILE ARG LYS LEU PRO PHE GLN ARG LEU VAL ARG GLX ILE ALA   75
 76  GLX ASX PHE LYS THR ASX LEU ARG PHE GLX SER SER ALA VAL MET   90
 91  ALA LEU GLN GLU ALA SER GLU ALA TYR LEU VAL GLY LEU PHE GLU  105
106  ASP THR ASN LEU CYS ALA ILE HIS ALA LYS ARG VAL THR ILE MET  120
121  PRO LYS ASP ILE GLN LEU ALA ARG ARG ILE ARG GLY GLU ARG ALA  135
```

Notes: (i) LYS and TML may occur at positions 9, 27 and 36. (ii) ACL may occupy positions 14 and 23.
The determination of the primary structure of histone F3 from chicken erythrocytes by automatic Edman degradation.
W. F. Brandt and C. von Holt.
Eur. J. Biochem., **46**, 419–429 (1974).

HISTONE H3—CARP

	1				5					10					15	
1	ALA	ARG	THR	LYS	GLN	THR	ALA	ARG	MML/DML	SER	THR	GLY	GLY	LYS	ALA	15
16	PRO	ARG	LYS	GLN	LEU	ALA	THR	LYS	ALA	ALA	ARG	MML/DML	SER	ALA	PRO	30
31	ALA	THR	GLY	GLY	VAL	LYS	LYS	PRO	HIS	ARG	TYR	ARG	PRO	GLY	THR	45
46	VAL	ALA	LEU	ARG	GLU	ILE	ARG	ARG	TYR	GLN	LYS	SER	THR	GLU	LEU	60
61	LEU	ILE	ARG	LYS	LEU	PRO	PHE	GLN	ARG	LEU	VAL	ARG	GLU	ILE	ALA	75
76	GLN	ASP	PHE	LYS	THR	ASP	LEU	ARG	PHE	GLN	SER	SER	ALA	VAL	MET	90
91	ALA	LEU	GLN	GLU	ALA	SER	GLU	ALA	TYR	LEU	VAL	GLY	LEU	PHE	GLU	105
106	ASP	THR	ASN	LEU	CYS	ALA	ILE	HIS	ALA	LYS	ARG	VAL	THR	ILE	MET	120
121	PRO	LYS	ASP	ILE	GLN	LEU	ALA	ARG	ARG	ILE	ARG	GLY	GLU	ARG	ALA	135

Note: LYS and TML may occur at positions 9 and 27.
Amino acid sequence of histone III of the testes of the carp, *Letiobus bubalus*.
J. A. Hooper, E. L. Smith, K. R. Sommer, and R. Chalkley.
J. Biol. Chem., **248**, 3275–3279 (1973).

HISTONE H3—SHARK ERYTHROCYTES

	1				5					10					15	
1	ALA	ARG	THR	LYS	GLN	THR	ALA	ARG	MML/DML	SER	THR	GLY	GLY	LYS	ALA	15
16	PRO	ARG	LYS	GLN	LEU	ALA	THR	LYS	ALA	ALA	ARG	MML/DML	SER	ALA	PRO	30
31	ALA	THR	GLY	GLY	VAL	MML/DML	LYS	PRO	HIS	ARG	TYR	ARG	PRO	GLY	THR	45
46	VAL	ALA	LEU	ARG	GLU	ILE	ARG	ARG	TYR	GLN	LYS	SER	THR	GLU	LEU	60
61	LEU	ILE	ARG	LYS	LEU	PRO	PHE	GLN	ARG	LEU	VAL	ARG	GLX	ILE	ALA	75
76	GLX	ASX	PHE	LYS	THR	ASX	LEU	ARG	PHE	GLX	SER	SER	ALA	VAL	MET	90
91	ALA	LEU	GLN	GLU	ALA	SER	GLU	ALA	TYR	LEU	VAL	GLY	LEU	PHE	GLU	105
106	ASP	THR	ASN	LEU	CYS	ALA	ILE	HIS	ALA	LYS	ARG	VAL	THR	ILE	MET	120
121	PRO	LYS	ASP	ILE	GLN	LEU	ALA	ARG	ARG	ILE	ARG	GLY	GLU	ARG	ALA	135

Notes: (i) LYS and TML may also occupy positions 9, 27 and 36. (ii) ACL may occupy
positions 14 and 23.
The primary structure of histone F3 from shark erythrocytes.
W. F. Brandt, W. N. Strickland, and C. von Holt.
FEBS Letters, **40**, 349–352 (1974).

HISTONES

HISTONE H3—PEA EMBRYO

	1				5					10					15		
1	ALA	ARG	THR	LYS	GLN	THR	ALA	ARG	MML DML	SER	THR	GLY	GLY	LYS	ALA		15
16	PRO	ARG	LYS	GLN	LEU	ALA	THR	LYS	ALA	ALA	ARG	MML DML	SER	ALA	PRO		30
31	ALA	THR	GLY	GLY	VAL	LYS	LYS	PRO	HIS	ARG	PHE	ARG	PRO	GLY	THR		45
46	VAL	ALA	LEU	ARG	GLU	ILE	ARG	LYS	TYR	GLN	LYS	SER	THR	GLU	LEU		60
61	LEU	ILE	ARG	LYS	LEU	PRO	PHE	GLN	ARG	LEU	VAL	ARG	GLU	ILE	ALA		75
76	GLN	ASP	PHE	LYS	THR	ASP	LEU	ARG	PHE	GLN	SER	SER	ALA	VAL	SER		90
91	ALA	LEU	GLN	GLU	ALA	ALA SER	GLU	ALA	TYR	LEU	VAL	GLY	LEU	PHE	GLU		105
106	ASP	THR	ASN	LEU	CYS	ALA	ILE	HIS	ALA	LYS	ARG	VAL	THR	ILE	MET		120
121	PRO	LYS	ASP	ILE	GLN	LEU	ALA	ARG	ARG	ILE	ARG	GLY	GLU	ARG	ALA		135

Histone III. Part 5. The amino acid sequence of pea embryo histone III.
L. Patthy, E. L. Smith, and J. Johnson.
J. Biol. Chem., **248**, 6834–6840 (1973).

HISTONE H3—CALF THYMUS

	1				5					10					15		
1	ALA	ARG	THR	LYS	GLN	THR	ALA	ARG	MML DML	SER	THR	GLY	GLY	ACL	ALA		15
16	PRO	ARG	LYS	GLN	LEU	ALA	THR	ACL	ALA	ALA	ARG	MML DML	SER	ALA	PRO		30
31	ALA	THR	GLY	GLY	VAL	LYS	LYS	PRO	HIS	ARG	TYR	ARG	PRO	GLY	THR		45
46	VAL	ALA	LEU	ARG	GLU	ILE	ARG	ARG	TYR	GLN	LYS	SER	THR	GLU	LEU		60
61	LEU	ILE	ARG	LYS	LEU	PRO	PHE	GLN	ARG	LEU	VAL	ARG	GLU	ILE	ALA		75
76	GLN	ASP	PHE	LYS	THR	ASP	LEU	ARG	PHE	GLN	SER	SER	ALA	VAL	MET		90
91	ALA	LEU	GLN	GLU	ALA	CYS	GLU	ALA	TYR	LEU	VAL	GLY	LEU	PHE	GLU		105
106	ASP	THR	ASN	LEU	CYS	ALA	ILE	HIS	ALA	LYS	ARG	VAL	THR	ILE	MET		120
121	PRO	LYS	ASP	ILE	GLN	LEU	ALA	ARG	ARG	ILE	ARG	GLY	GLU	ARG	ALA		135

Complete Amino Acid Sequence of Calf-Thymus Histone III.
R. J. DeLange, J. A. Hooper, and E. L. Smith.
Proc. Natn. Acad. Sci., U.S.A., **69**, 882–884 (1972).
Note: LYS may also occupy positions 9 and 27.
Histone III. Part 3. Sequence studies on the cyanogen bromide peptides and complete amino acid sequence of calf thymus histone III.
R. J. DeLange, J. A. Hooper, and E. L. Smith.
J. Biol. Chem., **248**, 3261–3274 (1973).
Histone III. Part 4. Two forms of calf thymus histone III.
L. Patthy and E. L. Smith.
J. Biol. Chem., **250**, 1919–1920 (1975).
This paper reports the finding of two forms of Histone III, one having at position 96 the residue CYS, and the other SER.

HISTONE H4—PIG THYMUS

	1				5					10					15	
1	AC	SER	GLY	ARG	GLY	LYS	GLY	GLY	LYS	GLY	LEU	GLY	LYS	GLY	GLY	15
16	ALA	ACL	ARG	HIS	ARG	MML	VAL	LEU	ARG	ASP	ASN	ILE	GLN	GLY	ILE	30
31	THR	LYS	PRO	ALA	ILE	ARG	ARG	LEU	ALA	ARG	ARG	GLY	GLY	VAL	LYS	45
46	ARG	ILE	SER	GLY	LEU	ILE	TYR	GLU	GLU	THR	ARG	GLY	VAL	LEU	LYS	60
61	VAL	PHE	LEU	GLU	ASN	VAL	ILE	ARG	ASP	ALA	VAL	THR	TYR	THR	GLU	75
76	HIS	ALA	LYS	ARG	LYS	THR	VAL	THR	ALA	MET	ASP	VAL	VAL	TYR	ALA	90
91	LEU	LYS	ARG	GLN	GLY	ARG	THR	LEU	TYR	GLY	PHE	GLY	GLY			105

Glycine-rich and Arginine-rich Histone of Pig Thymus: Study of the Tryptic Peptides and Complete Sequence.
P. Sautière, M-D. Lambelin-Breynaert, Y. Moschetto, and G. Biserte.
Biochimie, **53**, 711–715 (1971).

HISTONE H4—CALF THYMUS

	1				5					10					15	
1	AC	SER	GLY	ARG	GLY	LYS	GLY	GLY	LYS	GLY	LEU	GLY	LYS	GLY	GLY	15
16	ALA	ACL	ARG	HIS	ARG	MML	VAL	LEU	ARG	ASP	ASN	ILE	GLN	GLY	ILE	30
31	THR	LYS	PRO	ALA	ILE	ARG	ARG	LEU	ALA	ARG	GLY	GLY	VAL	LYS	ARG	45
46	ARG	ILE	SER	GLY	LEU	ILE	TYR	GLU	GLU	THR	ARG	GLY	VAL	LEU	LYS	60
61	VAL	PHE	LEU	GLU	ASN	VAL	ILE	ARG	ASP	ALA	VAL	THR	TYR	THR	GLU	75
76	HIS	ALA	LYS	ARG	LYS	THR	VAL	THR	ALA	MET	ASP	VAL	VAL	TYR	ALA	90
91	LEU	LYS	ARG	GLN	GLY	ARG	THR	LEU	TYR	GLY	PHE	GLY	GLY			105

Calf and Pea Histone IV. 2. The Complete Amino Acid Sequence of Calf Thymus Histone IV; Presence of ε-N-Acetyl Lysine.
R. J. DeLange, D. M. Fambrough, E. L. Smith, and J. Bonner.
J. Biol. Chem., **244**, 319–334 (1969).

HISTONES

HISTONE H4—PEA SEEDLING

	1		5				10				15					
1	AC	SER	GLY	ARG	GLY	LYS	GLY	GLY	LYS	GLY	LEU	GLY	LYS	GLY	GLY	15
16	ALA	ACL	ARG	HIS	ARG	LYS	VAL	LEU	ARG	ASP	ASN	ILE	GLN	GLY	ILE	30
31	THR	LYS	PRO	ALA	ILE	ARG	ARG	LEU	ALA	ARG	ARG	GLY	GLY	VAL	LYS	45
46	ARG	ILE	SER	GLY	LEU	ILE	TYR	GLU	GLU	THR	ARG	GLY	VAL	LEU	LYS	60
61	ILE	PHE	LEU	GLU	ASN	VAL	ILE	ARG	ASP	ALA	VAL	THR	TYR	THR	GLU	75
76	HIS	ALA	ARG	ARG	LYS	THR	VAL	THR	ALA	MET	ASP	VAL	VAL	TYR	ALA	90
91	LEU	LYS	ARG	GLN	GLY	ARG	THR	LEU	TYR	GLY	PHE	GLY	GLY			105

Calf and Pea Histone IV. 3. Complete amino Acid Sequence of Pea Seedling Histone IV; Comparison with the Homologous Calf Thymus Histone.
R. J. DeLange, D. M. Fambrough, E. L. Smith, and J. Bonner.
J. Biol. Chem., **244**, 5669–5679 (1969).

HISTONE H4—BOVINE THYMUS

	1		5				10				15					
1	AC	SER	GLY	ARG	GLY	LYS	GLY	GLY	LYS	GLY	LEU	GLY	LYS	GLY	GLY	15
16	ALA	ACL	ARG	HIS	ARG	MML	VAL	LEU	ARG	ASP	ASN	ILE	GLN	GLY	ILE	30
31	THR	LYS	PRO	ALA	ILE	ARG	ARG	LEU	ALA	ARG	ARG	GLY	GLY	VAL	LYS	45
46	ARG	ILE	SER	GLY	LEU	ILE	TYR	GLU	GLU	THR	ARG	GLY	VAL	LEU	LYS	60
61	VAL	PHE	LEU	GLU	ASN	VAL	ILE	ARG	ASP	ALA	VAL	THR	TYR	THR	GLU	75
76	HIS	ALA	LYS	ARG	LYS	THR	VAL	THR	ALA	MET	ASP	VAL	VAL	TYR	ALA	90
91	LEU	LYS	ARG	GLN	GLY	ARG	THR	LEU	TYR	GLY	PHE	GLY	GLY			105

Structural Analysis of the Glycine-rich, Arginine-rich Histone.
Y. Ogawa, G. Quagliarotti, J. Jordan, C. W. Taylor, W. C. Starbuck, and H. Busch.
J. Biol. Chem., **244**, 4387–4392 (1969).

HISTONE H4—RAT

	1		5				10				15					
1	AC	SER	GLY	ARG	GLY	LYS	GLY	GLY	LYS	GLY	LEU	GLY	LYS	GLY	GLY	15
16	ALA	ACL	ARG	HIS	ARG	MML	VAL	LEU	ARG	ASP	ASN	ILE	GLN	GLY	ILE	30
31	THR	LYS	PRO	ALA	ILE	ARG	ARG	LEU	ALA	ARG	ARG	GLY	GLY	VAL	LYS	45
46	ARG	ILE	SER	GLY	LEU	ILE	TYR	GLU	GLU	THR	ARG	GLY	VAL	LEU	LYS	60
61	VAL	PHE	LEU	GLU	ASN	VAL	ILE	ARG	ASP	ALA	VAL	THR	TYR	THR	GLU	75
76	HIS	ALA	LYS	ARG	LYS	THR	VAL	THR	ALA	MET	ASP	VAL	VAL	TYR	ALA	90
91	LEU	LYS	ARG	GLN	GLY	ARG	THR	LEU	TYR	GLY	PHE	GLY	GLY			105

The primary structure of rat glycine and arginine rich histone, isolated from the chloroleukaemic tumour.
P. Sautière, D. Tyrou, Y. Moschetto, and G. Biserte.
Biochimie, **53**, 479–483 (1971).

HISTONE H4—SEA URCHIN

	1		5					10					15			
1	AC	SER	GLY	ARG	GLY	LYS	GLY	GLY	LYS	GLY	LEU	GLY	LYS	GLY	GLY	15
16	ALA	ACL	ARG	HIS	ARG	MML	VAL	LEU	ARG	ASP	ASN	ILE	GLN	GLY	ILE	30
31	THR	LYS	PRO	ALA	ILE	ARG	ARG	LEU	ALA	ARG	ARG	GLY	GLY	VAL	LYS	45
46	ARG	ILE	SER	GLY	LEU	ILE	TYR	GLU	GLY	THR	ARG	GLY	VAL	LEU	LYS	60
61	VAL	PHE	LEU	GLU	ASN	VAL	ILE	ARG	ASP	ALA	VAL	THR	TYR	CYS	GLU	75
76	HIS	ALA	LYS	ARG	LYS	THR	VAL	THR	ALA	MET	ASP	VAL	VAL	TYR	ALA	90
91	LEU	LYS	ARG	GLN	GLY	ARG	THR	LEU	TYR	GLY	PHE	GLY	GLY			105

Covalent structure of the sea urchin histone H4.
D. Wouters-Tyrou, P. Sautière, and G. Biserte.
FEBS Letters, **65**, 225–228 (1976).

468

PROTAMINES AND RELATED PROTEINS

GALLINE

```
        1              5                10                    15
 1  ALA ARG TYR ARG SER  ARG GLY ARG SER  ARG SER  ARG ARG THR ARG    15
16  ARG ARG ARG SER  PRO ARG SER  GLY ARG ARG ARG SER  PRO ARG ARG    30
31  ARG ARG SER  ARG ARG ARG ARG ARG TYR  GLY SER  ALA ARG ARG SER    45
46  ARG ARG SER  GLY GLY VAL ARG ARG ARG ARG TYR  GLY SER  ARG ARG    60
61  ARG ARG ARG ARG TYR                                               75
```

Studies on a protamine (Galline) from fowl sperm. The total amino acid sequence of the intact galline molecule.
M. Nakano, T. Tobita, and T. Ando.
Int. J. Peptide Protein Res., **8**, 565–578 (1976).

THYNNIN Y1

```
        1              5                10                    15
 1  PRO ARG ARG ARG ARG GLU ALA SER  ARG PRO VAL ARG ARG ARG ARG    15
16  ARG TYR ARG ARG SER  THR ALA ALA ARG ARG ARG ARG ARG VAL VAL    30
31  ARG ARG ARG ARG                                                 45
```

Thynnin, the protamine of the tuna fish: The sequence of component Y1.
G. Bretzel.
Hoppe-Seyler's Z. Physiol. Chem., **353**, 1362–1364 (1972).

THYNNIN Y2

```
        1              5                10                    15
 1  PRO ARG ARG ARG ARG GLN ALA SER  ARG PRO VAL ARG ARG ARG ARG    15
16  ARG TYR ARG ARG SER  THR ALA ALA ARG ARG ARG ARG ARG VAL VAL    30
31  ARG ARG ARG ARG                                                 45
```

Thynnin, the protamine of the tunafish: The sequence of component Y2.
G. Bretzel.
Hoppe-Seyler's Z. Physiol. Chem., **353**, 1362–1364 (1972).

PROTAMINES AND RELATED PROTEINS

THYNNIN Z1

```
    1              5                  10                 15
 1  PRO ARG ARG ARG ARG ARG SER  SER  ARG PRO VAL ARG ARG ARG ARG   15
16  ARG TYR ARG ARG SER  THR VAL ALA ARG ARG ARG ARG ARG VAL VAL    30
31  ARG ARG ARG ARG                                                  45
```

Thynnin, the protamine of the tuna fish: The amino acid sequence of Z1.
G. Bretzel.
Hoppe-Seyler's Z. Physiol. Chem., **354**, 312–320 (1973).

THYNNIN Z2

```
    1              5                  10                 15
 1  PRO ARG ARG ARG ARG ARG SER  SER  ARG PRO VAL ARG ARG ARG ARG   15
16  ARG TYR ARG ARG SER  THR ALA ALA ARG ARG ARG ARG ARG VAL VAL    30
31  ARG ARG ARG ARG                                                  45
```

Thynnin, the protamine of the tuna fish: The sequence of component Z2.
G. Bretzel.
Hoppe-Seyler's Z. Physiol. Chem., **354**, 543–549 (1973).

CLUPEINE Z

```
    1              5                  10                 15
 1  ALA ARG ARG ARG ARG SER  ARG ARG ALA SER  ARG PRO VAL ARG ARG   15
16  ARG ARG PRO ARG ARG VAL SER  ARG ARG ARG ARG ALA ARG ARG ARG    30
31  ARG                                                              45
```

Studies on Protamines. XV. The Complete Amino Acid Sequence of the Z component of Clupeine. Application of N to O acyl rearrangement and selective hydrolysis in sequence determination.
K. Iwai, C. Nakahara, and T. Ando.
J. Biochem., **69**, 493–509 (1971).

PROTAMINES AND RELATED PROTEINS

CLUPEINE YI

```
     1              5                   10                      15
 1   ALA ARG ARG ARG ARG SER  SER  SER  ARG PRO ILE  ARG ARG ARG ARG    15
16   PRO ARG ARG ARG THR THR ARG ARG ARG ARG ALA GLY ARG ARG ARG        30
31   ARG                                                                45
```

The Amino Acid Sequence of the third component of Clupeine.
T. Ando and K. Suzuki.
Biochim. Biophys. Acta, **140**, 375–377 (1967).
Studies on protamines XVII. The complete amino acid sequence of clupeine Y1.
K. Suzuki and T. Ando.
J. Biochem., **72**, 1433–1446 (1972).

CLUPEINE YII

```
     1              5                   10                      15
 1   PRO ARG ARG ARG THR ARG ARG ALA SER  ARG PRO VAL ARG ARG ARG    15
16   ARG PRO ARG ARG VAL SER  ARG ARG ARG ARG ALA ARG ARG ARG ARG    30
```

The Amino Acid Sequence of the Second Component of Clupeine.
T. Ando and K. Suzuki.
Biochim. Biophys. Acta, **121**, 427–429 (1966).
Studies on protamines XVI. The complete amino acid sequence of clupeine Y2.
K. Suzuki and T. Ando.
J. Biochem., **72**, 1419–1432 (1972).

SALMINE AI

```
     1              5                   10                      15
 1   PRO ARG ARG ARG ARG SER  SER  SER  ARG PRO VAL ARG ARG ARG ARG    15
16   ARG PRO ARG VAL SER  ARG ARG ARG ARG ARG ARG GLY GLY ARG ARG      30
31   ARG ARG                                                           45
```

IRIDINE I (a)

```
     1              5                   10                      15
 1   PRO ARG ARG ARG ARG SER  SER  SER  ARG PRO VAL ARG ARG ARG ARG    15
16   ARG PRO ARG ARG VAL SER  ARG ARG ARG ARG ARG ARG GLY GLY ARG      30
31   ARG ARG ARG                                                       45
```

PROTAMINES AND RELATED PROTEINS

IRIDINE I (b)

```
    1              5                   10                  15
 1  PRO ARG ARG ARG ARG ARG ARG SER SER SER ARG PRO ILE ARG ARG   15
16  ARG ARG PRO ARG ARG VAL SER ARG ARG ARG ARG ARG GLY GLY ARG   30
31  ARG ARG ARG                                                   45
```

IRIDINE II

```
    1              5                   10                  15
 1  PRO ARG ARG ARG ARG SER SER SER ARG PRO VAL ARG ARG ARG ARG   15
16  ALA ARG ARG VAL SER ARG ARG ARG ARG ARG ARG GLY GLY ARG ARG   30
31  ARG ARG                                                      45
```

A New Method for Fractionation of Protamines and the Amino Acid Sequences of Salmine and Three Components of Iridine.
T. Ando and S. Watanabe.
Int. J. Prot. Res., **1**, 221–224 (1969).

BASIC NUCLEAR PROTEIN OF BULL SPERMATOZOA

```
    1              5                   10                  15
 1  ALA ARG TYR ARG CYS CYS LEU THR HIS SER GLY SER ARG CYS ARG   15
16  ARG ARG ARG ARG ARG ARG CYS ARG ARG ARG ARG ARG ARG PHE GLY   30
31  ARG ARG ARG ARG ARG ARG VAL CYS TYR THR VAL ILE ARG CYS THR   45
46  ARG GLN                                                      60
```

The Complete Amino Acid Sequence of the Basic Nuclear Protein of Bull Spermatozoa.
J. P. Coelingh, C. H. Monfoort, T. H. Rozijn, J. A. G. Leuven, R. Schiphof, E. P. Steyn-Parvé, G. Braunitzer, B. Schrank, and A. Ruhfus.
Biochim. Biophys. Acta, **285**, 1–14 (1972).

RIBOSOMAL PROTEINS

RIBOSOMAL PROTEIN L7 OF ESCHERICHIA COLI

	1			5					10					15	
1	AC	SER	ILE	THR	LYS	ASP	GLN	ILE	ILE	GLU	ALA	VAL	ALA	ALA	MET	15
16	SER	VAL	MET	ASP	VAL	VAL	GLU	LEU	ILE	SER	ALA	MET	GLU	GLU	LYS	30
31	PHE	GLY	VAL	SER	ALA	ALA	ALA	ALA	VAL	ALA	VAL	ALA	ALA	GLY	PRO	45
46	VAL	GLU	ALA	ALA	GLU	GLU	LYS	THR	GLU	PHE	ASP	VAL	ILE	LEU	LYS	60
61	ALA	ALA	GLY	ALA	ASN	LYS	VAL	ALA	VAL	ILE	LYS	ALA	VAL	ARG	GLY	75
76	ALA	THR	GLY	LEU	GLY	LEU	MML LYS	GLU	ALA	LYS	ASP	LEU	VAL	GLU	SER	90
91	ALA	PRO	ALA	ALA	LEU	LYS	GLU	GLY	VAL	SER	LYS	ASP	ASP	ALA	GLU	105
106	ALA	LEU	LYS	LYS	ALA	LEU	GLU	GLU	ALA	GLY	ALA	GLU	VAL	GLU	VAL	120
121	LYS															135

The Primary Structure of an Acidic Protein from 50-S Ribosomes of *Escherichia coli* which is involved in GTP Hydrolysis Dependent on Elongation Factors G and T.
C. Terhorst, W. Möller, R. Laursen, and B. Wittmann-Liebold.
Eur. J. Biochem., **34**, 138–152 (1973).

RIBOSOMAL PROTEIN L16 OF ESCHERICHIA COLI

	1			5					10					15	
1	NMM LEU	GLN	PRO	LYS	ARG	THR	LYS	PHE	ARG	LYS	MET	HIS	LYS	GLY	15
16	ARG	ASN	ARG	GLY	LEU	ALA	GLN	GLY	THR	ASP	VAL	SER	PHE	GLY	SER	30
31	PHE	GLY	LEU	LYS	ALA	VAL	GLY	ARG	GLY	ARG	LEU	THR	ALA	ARG	GLN	45
46	ILE	GLU	ALA	ALA	ARG	ARG	ALA	MET	THR	ARG	ALA	VAL	LYS	ARG	GLN	60
61	GLY	LYS	ILE	TRP	ILE	ARG	VAL	PHE	PRO	ASP	LYS	PRO	ILE	THR	GLU	75
76	LYS	PRO	LEU	ALA	VAL	XXX	MET	GLY	LYS	GLY	LYS	GLY	ASN	VAL	GLU	90
91	TYR	TRP	VAL	ALA	LEU	ILE	GLN	PRO	GLY	LYS	VAL	LEU	TYR	GLU	MET	105
106	ASP	GLY	VAL	PRO	GLU	GLU	LEU	ALA	ARG	GLU	ALA	PHE	LYS	LEU	ALA	120
121	ALA	ALA	LYS	LEU	PRO	ILE	LYS	THR	THR	PHE	VAL	THR	LYS	THR	VAL	135
136	MET															150

The primary structure of protein L16 located at the peptidyltransferase center of *Escherichia coli* ribosomes.
J. Brosius and R. Chen.
FEBS Letters, **68**, 105–109 (1976).

RIBOSOMAL PROTEIN L19 OF ESCHERICHIA COLI

```
      1               5                  10                 15
  1  SER ASN ILE ILE LYS GLN LEU GLU GLN GLU GLN MET LYS GLN ASP   15
 16  VAL PRO SER PHE ARG PRO GLY ASP THR VAL GLU VAL LYS VAL TRP   30
 31  VAL VAL GLU GLY SER LYS LYS ARG LEU GLN ALA PHE GLU GLY VAL   45
 46  VAL ILE ALA ILE ARG ASN ARG GLY LEU HIS SER ALA PHE THR VAL   60
 61  ARG LYS ILE SER ASN GLY GLU GLY VAL GLU ARG VAL PHE GLN THR   75
 76  HIS SER PRO VAL VAL ASP SER ILE SER VAL LYS ARG ARG GLY ALA   90
 91  VAL ARG LYS ALA LYS LEU TYR TYR LEU ARG GLU ARG THR GLY LYS  105
106  ALA ALA ARG ILE LYS GLU ARG LEU ASN                          120
```

Primary structure of Protein L19 from the large subunit of *Escherichia coli* ribosomes.
J. Brosius and U. Arfsten.
Biochemistry, **17**, 508–516 (1978).

RIBOSOMAL PROTEIN L25 OF ESCHERICHIA COLI

```
      1               5                  10                 15
  1  MET PHE THR ILE ASN ALA GLU VAL ARG LYS GLU GLN GLY LYS GLY   15
 16  ALA SER ARG ARG LEU ARG ALA ALA ASN LYS PHE PRO ALA ILE ILE   30
 31  TYR GLY GLY LYS GLU ALA PRO LEU ALA ILE GLU LEU ASP HIS ASP   45
 46  LYS VAL MET ASN MET GLN ALA LYS ALA GLU PHE TYR SER GLU VAL   60
 61  LEU THR ILE VAL VAL ASP GLY LYS GLU ILE LYS VAL LYS ALA GLN   75
 76  ASP VAL GLN ARG HIS PRO TYR LYS PRO LYS LEU GLN HIS ILE ASP   90
 91  PHE VAL ARG ALA                                              105
```

The primary structure of the 5S rRNA binding protein L25 from *E. coli*.
N. V. Dovgas, L. F. Markova, T. A. Mednikova, L. M. Vinokurov, Yu. B. Alakhov, and Yu. A. Ovchinnikov.
FEBS Letters, **53**, 351–354 (1975); *FEBS Letters*, **57**, 305 (1975).
Confirmation:
The primary structure of the 5S rRNA binding protein L25 of *Escherichia coli* ribosomes.
K. G. Bitar and B. Wittmann-Liebold.
Hoppe-Seyler's Z. Physiol. Chem., **356**, 1343–1352 (1975).

474

RIBOSOMAL PROTEINS

RIBOSOMAL PROTEIN L27 FROM ESCHERICHIA COLI

	1			5					10					15		
1	ALA	HIS	LYS	LYS	ALA	GLY	GLY	SER	THR	ARG	ASN	GLY	ARG	ASP	SER	15
16	GLU	ALA	LYS	ARG	LEU	GLY	VAL	LYS	ARG	PHE	GLY	GLY	GLU	SER	VAL	30
31	LEU	ALA	GLY	SER	ILE	ILE	VAL	ARG	GLN	ARG	GLY	THR	LYS	PHE	HIS	45
46	ALA	GLY	ALA	ASN	VAL	GLY	CYS	GLY	ARG	ASP	HIS	THR	LEU	PHE	ALA	60
61	LYS	ALA	ASP	GLY	LYS	VAL	LYS	PHE	GLU	VAL	LYS	GLY	PRO	LYS	ASN	75
76	ARG	LYS	PHE	ILE	SER	ILE	GLU	ALA	GLU							90

The primary structure of protein L27 from the peptidyl-tRNA binding site of *Escherichia coli* ribosomes.
R. Chen, L. Mende, and U. Arfsten.
FEBS Letters, **59**, 96–99 (1975).

RIBOSOMAL PROTEIN L28 OF ESCHERICHIA COLI

	1			5					10					15		
1	SER	ARG	VAL	CYS	GLN	VAL	THR	GLY	LYS	ARG	PRO	VAL	THR	GLY	ASN	15
16	ASN	ARG	SER	HIS	ALA	LEU	ASN	ALA	THR	LYS	ARG	ARG	PHE	LEU	PRO	30
31	ASN	LEU	HIS	SER	HIS	ARG	PHE	TRP	VAL	GLU	SER	GLU	LYS	ARG	PHE	45
46	VAL	THR	LEU	ARG	VAL	SER	ALA	LYS	GLY	MET	ARG	VAL	ILE	ASP	LYS	60
61	LYS	GLY	ILE	ASP	THR	VAL	LEU	ALA	GLU	LEU	ARG	ALA	ARG	GLY	GLU	75
76	LYS	TYR														90

Primary structure of protein L28 from the large subunit of *Escherichia coli* ribosomes.
B. Wittmann-Liebold and E. Marzinzig.
FEBS Letters, **81**, 214–217 (1977).

RIBOSOMAL PROTEIN L29 OF ESCHERICHIA COLI

	1			5					10					15		
1	MET	LYS	ALA	LYS	GLU	LEU	ARG	GLU	LYS	SER	VAL	GLU	GLU	LEU	ASN	15
16	THR	GLU	LEU	LEU	ASN	LEU	LEU	ARG	GLU	GLN	PHE	ASN	LEU	ARG	MET	30
31	GLN	ALA	ALA	SER	GLY	GLN	LEU	GLN	GLN	SER	HIS	LEU	LEU	LYS	LEU	45
46	GLN	LEU	ASN	THR	LYS	GLN	VAL	ARG	ARG	ASP	VAL	ALA	ARG	VAL	LYS	60
61	ALA	GLY	ALA													75

The primary structure of the ribosomal protein L29 from *Escherichia coli*.
K. G. Bitar.
Biochim. Biophys. Acta, **386**, 99–106 (1974).

RIBOSOMAL PROTEINS

RIBOSOMAL PROTEIN L30 OF ESCHERICHIA COLI

```
     1                    5                    10                        15
 1   ALA LYS THR ILE  LYS ILE  THR GLN THR ARG SER ALA ILE  GLY ARG   15
16   LEU PRO LYS HIS  LYS ALA THR LEU LEU GLY LEU GLY LEU ARG ARG     30
31   ILE  GLY HIS  THR VAL GLU ARG GLU ASP THR PRO ALA ILE  ARG GLY   45
46   MET ILE  ASN ALA VAL SER PHE MET VAL LYS VAL GLU GLU             60
```

The primary structure of protein L30 from *Escherichia coli* ribosomes.
E. Ritter and B. Wittmann-Liebold.
FEBS Letters, **60**, 153–155 (1975).

RIBOSOMAL PROTEIN L32 OF ESCHERICHIA COLI

```
     1                    5                    10                        15
 1   ALA VAL GLN GLN ASN LYS PRO THR ARG SER LYS  ARG GLY MET ARG    15
16   ARG SER HIS  ASP ALA LEU THR ALA VAL THR SER LEU SER VAL ASP    30
31   LYS THR SER GLY GLU LYS HIS  LEU ARG HIS  HIS  ILE  THR ALA ASP  45
46   GLY TYR TYR ARG GLY ARG LYS VAL ILE  ALA LYS                    60
```

The primary structure of protein L32 from the 50S subunit of *Escherichia coli* ribosomes.
B. Wittmann-Liebold, B. Greuer and R. Pannenbecker.
Hoppe-Seyler's Z. Physiol. Chem., **356**, 1977–79 (1975).

RIBOSOMAL PROTEIN L33 OF ESCHERICHIA COLI

```
     1                    5                    10                        15
 1   NMA LYS GLY ILE  ARG GLU LYS ILE  LYS LEU VAL SER SER ALA GLY   15
16   THR GLY HIS  PHE TYR THR THR THR LYS ASN LYS ARG THR LYS PRO    30
31   GLU LYS LEU GLU LEU LYS LYS PHE ASP PRO VAL VAL ARG GLN HIS     45
46   VAL TYR ILE  LYS GLU ALA LYS ILE  LYS                           60
```

Primary structure of protein L33 from the large subunit of the *Escherichia coli* ribosome.
B. Wittmann-Liebold and R. Pannenbecker.
FEBS Letters, **68**, 115–118 (1976).

476

RIBOSOMAL PROTEINS

RIBOSOMAL PROTEIN L34 OF ESCHERICHIA COLI

	1				5					10					15	
1	MET	LYS	ARG	THR	PHE	GLN	PRO	SER	VAL	LEU	LYS	ARG	ASN	ARG	SER	15
16	HIS	GLY	PHE	ARG	ALA	ARG	MET	ALA	THR	LYS	ASN	GLY	ARG	GLN	VAL	30
31	LEU	ALA	ARG	ARG	ARG	ALA	LYS	GLY	ARG	ALA	ARG	LEU	THR	VAL	SER	45
46	LYS															60

The primary structure of protein L34 from the large ribosomal subunit of *Escherichia coli*.
R. Chen and G. Ehrke.
FEBS Letters, **63**, 215–217 (1976).
And
The sequence determination of a protein on a micro scale: The sequence analysis of ribosomal protein L34 of *Escherichia coli*.
R. Chen and G. Ehrke.
Hoppe-Seyler's Z. Physiol. Chem., **357**, 873–886 (1976).

RIBOSOMAL PROTEIN S4 OF ESCHERICHIA COLI

	1				5					10					15	
1	ALA	ARG	TYR	LEU	GLY	PRO	LYS	LEU	LYS	LEU	SER	ARG	ARG	GLU	GLY	15
16	THR	ASP	LEU	PHE	LEU	LYS	SER	GLY	VAL	ARG	ALA	ILE	ASP	THR	LYS	30
31	CYS	LYS	ILE	GLU	GLN	ALA	PRO	GLY	GLN	HIS	GLY	ALA	ARG	LYS	PRO	45
46	ARG	LEU	SER	ASP	TYR	GLY	VAL	GLN	LEU	ARG	GLU	LYS	GLN	LYS	VAL	60
61	ARG	ARG	ILE	TYR	GLY	VAL	LEU	GLU	ARG	GLN	PHE	ARG	ASN	TYR	TYR	75
76	LYS	GLU	ALA	ALA	ARG	LEU	LYS	GLY	ASN	THR	GLY	GLU	ASN	LEU	ALA	90
91	LEU	LEU	GLN	GLY	ARG	LEU	ASP	ASN	VAL	VAL	TYR	ARG	MET	GLY	PHE	105
106	GLY	ALA	THR	ARG	ALA	GLU	ALA	ARG	GLN	LEU	VAL	SER	HIS	LYS	ALA	120
121	ILE	MET	VAL	ASN	GLY	ARG	VAL	VAL	ASN	ILE	ALA	SER	TYR	GLN	VAL	135
136	ASP	PRO	ASN	SER	VAL	VAL	ILE	ARG	GLU	LYS	ALA	LYS	LYS	GLU	SER	150
151	ARG	VAL	LYS	ALA	ALA	LEU	GLU	LEU	ALA	GLU	GLN	ARG	GLU	LYS	PRO	165
166	THR	TRP	LEU	GLU	VAL	ASP	ALA	GLY	LYS	MET	GLU	GLY	THR	PHE	LYS	180
181	ARG	LYS	PRO	GLU	ARG	SER	ASP	LEU	SER	ALA	ASP	ILE	ASN	GLU	HIS	195
196	LEU	ILE	VAL	GLU	LEU	TYR	SER	LYS								210

The primary structure of ribosomal protein S4 from *Escherichia coli*.
J. Reinbolt and E. Schiltz.
FEBS Letters, **36**, 250–252 (1973).
Determination of the complete amino acid sequence of protein S4 from *Escherichia coli* ribosomes.
E. Schiltz and J. Reinbolt.
Eur. J. Biochem., **56**, 467–481 (1975).

RIBOSOMAL PROTEINS

RIBOSOMAL PROTEIN S6 OF ESCHERICHIA COLI

	1			5					10					15	
1	MET	ARG	HIS	TYR	GLU	ILE	VAL	PHE	MET	VAL	HIS	PRO	ASP	GLN	SER	15
16	GLU	GLN	VAL	PRO	GLY	MET	ILE	GLU	ARG	TYR	THR	ALA	ALA	ILE	THR	30
31	GLY	ALA	GLU	GLY	LYS	ILE	HIS	ARG	LEU	GLU	ASP	TRP	GLY	ARG	ARG	45
46	GLN	LEU	ALA	TYR	PRO	ILE	ASN	LYS	LEU	HIS	LYS	ALA	HIS	TYR	VAL	60
61	LEU	MET	ASN	VAL	GLU	ALA	PRO	GLN	GLU	VAL	ILE	ASP	GLU	LEU	GLU	75
76	THR	THR	PHE	ARG	PHE	ASN	ASP	ALA	VAL	ILE	ARG	SER	MET	VAL	MET	90
91	ARG	THR	LYS	HIS	ALA	VAL	THR	GLU	ALA	SER	PRO	MET	VAL	LYS	ALA	105
106	LYS	ASP	GLU	ARG	ARG	GLU	ARG	ARG	ASP	ASP	PHE	ALA	ASN	GLU	THR	120
121	ALA	ASP	ASP	ALA	GLU	ALA	GLY	ASP	SER	GLU	(GLU)$_n$					

Note: Protein S6 occurs in five different forms: S6-2, S6-3, S6-4, S6-5 and S6-6, in the proportion of $1:4:7:3:1$; the proteins differ in the number of glutamic acid residues at the C-terminus, viz, S6-2 ($n = 1$), S6-3 ($n = 2$), S6-4 ($n = 3$), S6-5 ($n = 4$) and S6-6 ($n = 5$).

Primary structure of ribosomal protein S6 from the wild type and a mutant of *Escherichia coli*.
H. Hitz, D. Schafer, and B. Wittmann-Liebold.
FEBS Letters, **56**, 259–262 (1975).

RIBOSOMAL PROTEIN S8 OF ESCHERICHIA COLI

	1			5					10					15	
1	SER	MET	GLN	ASP	PRO	ILE	ALA	ASP	MET	LEU	THR	ARG	ILE	ARG	ASN	15
16	GLY	GLN	ALA	ALA	ASN	LYS	ALA	ALA	VAL	THR	MET	PRO	SER	SER	LYS	30
31	LEU	LYS	VAL	ALA	ILE	ALA	ASN	VAL	LEU	LYS	GLU	GLU	GLY	PHE	ILE	45
46	GLU	ASP	PHE	LYS	VAL	GLU	GLY	ASP	THR	LYS	PRO	GLU	LEU	GLU	LEU	60
61	THR	LEU	LYS	TYR	PHE	GLN	GLY	LYS	VAL	VAL	ALA	GLU	ILE	SER	GLN	75
76	ARG	VAL	SER	ARG	PRO	GLY	LEU	ARG	ILE	TYR	LYS	LEU	GLN	ASP	LYS	90
91	PRO	LYS	ARG	VAL	MET	GLY	ASP	THR	ARG	ALA	ARG	LYS	LEU	GLN	ILE	105
106	CYS	VAL	ALA	TYR												120

The primary structure of the 16S rRNA binding protein from *Escherichia coli* ribosomes.
H. Stadler.
FEBS Letters, **48**, 114–116 (1974).
Determination of the amino acid sequence of the ribosomal protein S8 of *Escherichia coli*.
H. Stadler and B. Wittmann-Liebold.
Eur. J. Biochem., **66**, 49–56 (1976).

RIBOSOMAL PROTEINS

RIBOSOMAL PROTEIN S9 OF ESCHERICHIA COLI

```
       1           5                    10                       15
  1  ALA GLU ASN GLN TYR TYR GLY THR GLY ARG ARG LYS SER SER ALA   15
 16  ALA ARG VAL PHE ILE LYS PRO GLY ASN GLY LYS ILE VAL ILE ASN   30
 31  GLN ARG SER LEU GLU GLN TYR PHE GLY ARG GLU THR ALA ARG MET   45
 46  VAL VAL ARG GLN PRO LEU GLU LEU VAL ASN MET VAL GLU LYS LEU   60
 61  ASP LEU TYR ILE THR VAL LYS GLY GLY GLY ILE SER GLY GLN ALA   75
 76  GLY ALA ILE ARG HIS GLY ILE THR ARG ALA LEU MET GLU TYR ASP   90
 91  GLU SER LEU ARG SER GLU LEU ARG LYS ALA GLY PHE VAL THR ARG  105
106  ASP ALA ARG GLN VAL GLU ARG LYS LYS VAL GLY LEU ARG LYS ALA  120
121  ARG ARG PRO GLU PHE SER LYS ARG                              135
```

The primary structure of protein S9 from the 30S subunit of *Escherichia coli* ribosomes.
R. Chen and B. Wittmann-Liebold.
FEBS Letters, **52**, 139–140 (1975).

RIBOSOMAL PROTEIN S12 OF ESCHERICHIA COLI

```
       1           5                    10                       15
  1  ALA THR VAL ASN GLN LEU VAL ARG LYS PRO ARG ALA ARG LYS VAL   15
 16  ALA LYS SER ASN VAL PRO ALA LEU GLU ALA CYS PRO GLN LYS ARG   30
 31  GLY VAL CYS THR ARG VAL TYR THR THR THR PRO LYS LYS PRO ASN   45
 46  SER ALA LEU ARG LYS VAL CYS ARG VAL ARG LEU THR ASN GLY PHE   60
 61  GLU VAL THR SER TYR ILE GLY GLY GLU GLY HIS ASN LEU GLN GLU   75
 76  HIS SER VAL ILE LEU ILE ARG GLY GLY ARG VAL LYS XXX LEU PRO   90
 91  GLY VAL ARG TYR HIS THR VAL ARG GLY ALA LEU ASP CYS SER GLY  105
106  VAL LYS ASP ARG LYS GLN ALA ARG SER LYS TYR GLY VAL LYS ARG  120
121  PRO LYS ALA                                                  135
```

Primary structure of protein S12 from the small *Escherichia coli* ribosomal subunit.
G. Funatsu, M. Yaguchi, and B. Wittmann-Liebold.
FEBS Letters, **73**, 12–17 (1977).

RIBOSOMAL PROTEIN S13 OF ESCHERICHIA COLI

	1				5					10					15	
1	ALA	ARG	ILE	ALA	GLY	ILE	ASN	ILE	PRO	ASP	HIS	LYS	HIS	ALA	VAL	15
16	ILE	ALA	LEU	THR	SER	ILE	TYR	GLY	VAL	GLY	LYS	THR	ARG	SER	LYS	30
31	ALA	ILE	LEU	ALA	ALA	ALA	GLY	ILE	ALA	GLU	ASP	VAL	LYS	ILE	SER	45
46	GLU	LEU	SER	GLU	GLY	GLN	ILE	ASP	THR	LEU	ARG	ASP	GLU	VAL	ALA	60
61	LYS	PHE	VAL	VAL	GLU	GLY	ASP	LEU	ARG	ARG	GLU	ILE	SER	MET	SER	75
76	ILE	LYS	ARG	LEU	MET	ASP	LEU	GLY	CYS	TYR	ARG	GLY	LEU	ARG	HIS	90
91	ARG	ARG	GLY	LEU	PRO	VAL	ARG	GLY	GLN	ARG	THR	LYS	THR	ASN	ALA	105
106	ARG	THR	ARG	LYS	GLY	PRO	ARG	LYS	PRO	ILE	LYS	LYS				120

Primary structure of Protein S13 from the small subunit of *Escherichia coli* Ribosomes.
H. Lindemann and B. Wittmann-Liebold.
Hoppe-Seyler's Z. Physiol. Chem., **358**, 843–863 (1977).

RIBOSOMAL PROTEIN S15 OF ESCHERICHIA COLI

	1				5					10					15	
1	SER	LEU	SER	THR	GLU	ALA	THR	ALA	LYS	ILE	VAL	SER	GLU	PHE	GLY	15
16	ARG	ASP	ALA	ASN	ASP	THR	GLY	SER	THR	GLU	VAL	GLN	VAL	ALA	LEU	30
31	LEU	THR	ALA	GLN	ILE	ASN	HIS	LEU	GLN	GLY	HIS	PHE	ALA	GLU	LYS	45
46	LYS	ASP	HIS	HIS	SER	ARG	ARG	GLY	LEU	LEU	ARG	MET	VAL	SER	GLN	60
61	ARG	ARG	LYS	LEU	LEU	ASP	TYR	LEU	LYS	ARG	LYS	ASP	VAL	ALA	ARG	75
76	TYR	THR	GLN	LEU	ILE	GLU	ARG	LEU	GLY	LEU	ARG	ARG				90

Primary structure of the 16S rRNA binding protein S15 from *Escherichia coli* ribosomes.
T. Morinaga, G. Funatsu, M. Funatsu, and H. G. Wittmann.
FEBS Letters, **64**, 307–309 (1976).

RIBOSOMAL PROTEIN S16 OF ESCHERICHIA COLI

	1				5					10					15	
1	MET	VAL	THR	ILE	ARG	LEU	ALA	ARG	HIS	GLY	ALA	LYS	LYS	ARG	PRO	15
16	PHE	TYR	GLN	VAL	VAL	VAL	ALA	ASP	SER	ARG	ASN	ALA	ARG	ASN	GLY	30
31	ARG	PHE	ILE	GLU	ARG	VAL	GLY	PHE	PHE	ASN	PRO	ILE	ALA	SER	GLU	45
46	LYS	GLU	GLU	GLY	THR	ARG	LEU	ASP	LEU	ASP	ARG	ILE	ALA	HIS	TRP	60
61	VAL	GLY	GLN	GLY	ALA	THR	ILE	SER	ASP	ARG	VAL	ALA	ALA	LEU	ILE	75
76	LYS	GLU	VAL	ASN	LYS	ALA	ALA									90

The primary structure of protein S16 from *Escherichia coli* ribosomes.
J. Vandekerckhove, W. Rombauts, and B. Wittmann-Liebold.
FEBS Letters, **73**, 18–21 (1977).

RIBOSOMAL PROTEINS

RIBOSOMAL PROTEIN S17 OF ESCHERICHIA COLI

```
     1            5              10                    15
 1  THR ASP LYS ILE  ARG THR LEU GLN GLY ARG VAL VAL SER ASP LYS  15
16  MET GLU LYS SER ILE  VAL VAL ALA ILE  GLU ARG PHE VAL LYS HIS  30
31  PRO ILE TYR GLY LYS PHE ILE  LYS ARG THR THR LYS LEU HIS VAL  45
46  HIS ASP GLU ASN ASN GLU GLY ILE  GLY ASP VAL VAL CYS GLU ILE  60
61  ARG GLU ARG PRO CYS LEU SER LYS THR LYS SER TRP THR LEU VAL  75
76  ARG VAL VAL GLU LYS ALA VAL LEU                               90
```

The Primary structure of protein S17 from the small ribosomal subunit of *Escherichia coli*.
M. Yaguchi and H. G. Wittmann.
FEBS Letters, **87**, 37–40 (1978).

RIBOSOMAL PROTEIN S18 OF ESCHERICHIA COLI

```
     1            5              10                    15
 1  AC  ALA ARG TYR PHE ARG ARG ARG LYS PHE CYS ARG PHE THR ALA  15
16  GLN GLY VAL GLN GLU ILE  ASP TYR LYS ASP ILE  ALA THR LEU LYS  30
31  ASN TYR ILE  THR GLU SER GLY LYS ILE  VAL PRO SER ARG ILE  THR  45
46  GLY THR ARG ALA LYS TYR GLN ARG GLN LEU ALA ARG ALA ILE  LYS  60
61  ARG ALA ARG TYR LEU SER LEU LEU PRO TYR THR ASP ARG HIS GLN  75
```

Primary structure of protein S18 from the small *Escherichia coli* ribosomal subunit.
M. Yaguchi.
FEBS Letters, **59**, 217–220 (1975).

RIBOSOMAL PROTEIN S19 OF ESCHERICHIA COLI

```
     1            5              10                    15
 1  PRO ARG SER LEU LYS LYS GLY PRO PHE ILE  ASP LEU HIS LEU LEU  15
16  LYS LYS VAL GLU LYS ALA VAL GLU SER GLY ASP LYS LYS PRO LEU  30
31  ARG THR TRP SER ARG SER THR ILE  PHE PRO ASP ARG MET ILE  GLY  45
46  LEU THR ILE  ALA VAL HIS ASN GLY ARG GLN HIS VAL PRO VAL PHE  60
61  VAL THR ASP GLU MET VAL GLY HIS LYS LEU GLY GLU PHE ALA PRO  75
76  THR ARG THR TYR ARG GLY HIS ALA ALA ASN LYS LYS ALA LYS LYS  90
91  LYS                                                          105
```

Primary structure of protein S19 from the small ribosomal subunit of *Escherichia coli*.
M. Yaguchi and H. G. Wittman.
FEBS Letters, **88**, 227–230 (1978).

RIBOSOMAL PROTEINS

RIBOSOMAL PROTEIN S20 OF ESCHERICHIA COLI

	1				5					10					15	
1	ALA	ASN	ILE	LYS	SER	ALA	LYS	LYS	ARG	ALA	ILE	GLN	SER	GLU	LYS	15
16	ALA	ARG	LYS	HIS	ASN	ALA	SER	ARG	ARG	SER	MET	MET	ARG	THR	PHE	30
31	ILE	LYS	LYS	VAL	TYR	ALA	ALA	ILE	GLU	ALA	GLY	ASP	LYS	ALA	ALA	45
46	ALA	GLN	LYS	ALA	PHE	ASN	GLU	MET	GLN	PRO	ILE	VAL	ASP	ARG	GLN	60
61	ALA	ALA	LYS	GLY	LEU	ILE	HIS	LYS	ASN	LYS	ALA	ALA	ARG	HIS	LYS	75
76	ALA	ASN	LEU	THR	ALA	GLN	ILE	ASN	LYS	LEU	ALA					90

Primary structure of protein S20 from the small ribosomal subunit of *Escherichia coli*.
B. Wittmann-Liebold, E. Marzinzig, and A. Lehmann.
FEBS Letters, **68**, 110–114 (1976).

RIBOSOMAL PROTEIN S21 OF ESCHERICHIA COLI

	1				5					10					15	
1	PRO	VAL	ILE	LYS	VAL	ARG	GLU	ASN	GLU	PRO	PHE	ASP	VAL	ALA	LEU	15
16	ARG	ARG	PHE	LYS	ARG	SER	CYS	GLU	LYS	ALA	GLY	VAL	LEU	ALA	GLU	30
31	VAL	ARG	ARG	ARG	GLU	PHE	TYR	GLU	LYS	PRO	THR	THR	GLU	ARG	LYS	45
46	ARG	ALA	LYS	ALA	SER	ALA	VAL	LYS	ARG	HIS	ALA	LYS	LYS	LEU	ALA	60
61	ARG	GLU	ASN	ALA	ARG	ARG	THR	ARG	LEU	TYR						75

Determination of the complete amino acid sequence of protein S21 from *Escherichia coli* ribosomes.
J. Vandekerckhove, W. Rombauts, B. Peeters, and B. Wittmann-Liebold.
Hoppe-Seyler's Z. Physiol. Chem., **356**, 1955–1976 (1975).

KERATINS

PROTEIN SCMK–B2A OF WOOL KERATIN

	1				5					10					15		
1	AC	ALA	CMC	CMC	SER	THR	SER	PHE	CMC	GLY	PHE	PRO	ILE	CMC	SER		15
16	THR	GLY	GLY	THR	CMC	GLY	SER	SER	PRO	CMC	GLN	PRO	THR	CMC	CMC		30
31	GLN	THR	SER	CMC	CMC	GLN	PRO	THR	SER	ILE	GLN	THR	SER	CMC	CMC		45
46	GLN	PRO	ILE	SER	ILE	GLN	THR	SER	CMC	CMC	GLN	PRO	THR	SER	ILE		60
61	GLN	THR	SER	CMC	CMC	GLN	PRO	THR	CMC	LEU	GLN	THR	SER	GLY	CMC		75
76	GLU	THR	GLY	CMC	GLY	ILE	GLY	GLY	SER	ILE	GLY	TYR	GLY	GLN	VAL		90
91	GLY	SER	SER	GLY	ALA	VAL	SER	SER	ARG	THR	ARG	TRP	CMC	ARG	PRO		105
106	ASP	CMC	ARG	VAL	GLU	GLY	THR	SER	LEU	PRO	PRO	CMC	CMC	VAL	VAL		120
121	SER	CMC	THR	PRO	PRO	SER	CMC	CMC	GLN	LEU	TYR	TYR	ALA	GLN	ALA		135
136	SER	CMC	CMC	ARG	PRO	SER	TYR	CMC	GLY	GLN	SER	CMC	CMC	ARG	PRO		150
151	ALA	CMC	CMC	CMC	GLN	PRO	THR	CMC	ILE	GLU	PRO	ILE	CMC	GLU	PRO		165
166	SER	CMC	CMC	GLU	PRO	THR	CMC										180

The Amino Acid Sequence of Protein SCMK–B2A from the High-Sulphur Fraction of Wool Keratin.
T. C. Elleman.
Biochem. J., **130**, 833–845 (1972).

PROTEIN SCMK-B2B OF WOOL KERATIN

	1				5					10					15		
1	AC	ALA	CMC	CMC	SER	THR	SER	PHE	CMC	GLY	PHE	PRO	ILE	CMC	SER		15
16	SER	VAL	GLY	THR	CMC	GLY	SER	SER	CMC	GLY	GLN	PRO	THR	CMC	SER		30
31	GLN	THR	SER	CMC	CMC	GLN	PRO	THR	SER	ILE	GLN	THR	SER	CMC	CMC		45
46	GLN	PRO	ILE	SER	ILE	GLN	THR	SER	CMC	CMC	GLN	PRO	THR	CMC	LEU		60
61	GLN	THR	SER	GLY	CMC	GLU	THR	GLY	CMC	GLY	ILE	GLY	GLY	SER	ILE		75
76	GLY	TYR	GLY/ASP	GLN	VAL	GLY	SER	SER	GLY	ALA	VAL	SER	SER	ARG	THR		90
91	ARG	TRP	CMC	ARG	PRO	ASP	CMC	ARG	VAL	GLU	GLY	THR	SER	LEU	PRO		105
106	PRO	CMC	CMC	VAL	VAL	SER	CMC	THR	SER	PRO	SER	CMC	CMC	GLN	LEU		120
121	TYR	TYR	ALA	GLN	ALA	SER	CMC	CMC	ARG	PRO	SER	TYR	CMC	GLY	GLN		135
136	SER	CMC	CMC	ARG	PRO	ALA	CMC	CMC	CMC	GLN	PRO	THR	CMC	ILE	GLU		150
151	PRO	VAL	CMC	GLU	PRO	THR	CMC										165

The Sequence of SCMK–B2B, a High-Sulphur Protein from Wool Keratin.
T. C. Elleman and T. A. Dopheide.
J. Biol. Chem., **247**, 3900–3909 (1972).

PROTEIN SCMK–B2C OF WOOL KERATIN

	1		5					10					15		
1	AC	ALA	CMC	CMC	SER	THR	SER	PHE	CMC	GLY	PHE	PRO	ILE	CMC	SER	15
16	THR	ALA	GLY	THR	CMC	GLY	SER	SER	CMC	CMC	ARG	SER	THR	CMC	SER	30
31	GLN	THR	SER	CMC	CMC	GLN	PRO	THR	SER	ILE	GLN	THR	SER	CMC	CMC	45
46	GLN	PRO	THR	CMC	LEU	GLN	THR	SER	GLY	CMC	GLU	THR	GLY	CMC	GLY	60
61	ILE	GLY	GLY	SER	ILE THR	GLY	TYR	GLY	GLN	VAL	GLY	SER	SER	GLY	ALA	75
76	VAL	SER	SER	ARG	THR	ARG	TRP	CMC	ARG	PRO	ASP	CMC	ARG	VAL	GLU	90
91	GLY	THR	SER	LEU	PRO	PRO	CMC	CMC	VAL	VAL	SER	CMC	THR	SER	PRO	105
106	SER	CMC	CMC	GLN	LEU	TYR	TYR	ALA	GLN	ALA	SER	CMC	CMC	ARG	PRO	120
121	SER	TYR	CMC	GLY	GLN	SER	CMC	CMC	ARG	PRO	ALA	CMC	CMC	CMC	GLN	135
136	PRO	THR	CMC	THR	GLU	PRO	VAL	CMC	GLU	PRO	THR	CMC	SER	GLN	PRO	150
151	ILE	CMC														165

The Amino Acid Sequence of Protein SCMK–B2C from the High Sulphur Fraction of Wool Keratin.
T. C. Elleman.
Biochem. J., **128**, 1229–1239 (1972).

PROTEIN SCMKB–IIIA3 OF WOOL KERATIN

	1		5					10					15		
1	THR	GLY	SER	CMC	CMC	GLY	PRO	THR	PHE	SER	SER	LEU	SER	CMC	GLY	15
16	GLY	GLY	CMC	LEU	GLN	PRO	ARG	TYR	TYR	ARG	ASP	PRO	CMC	CMC	CMC	30
31	ARG	PRO	VAL	SER	CMC	GLN	THR	VAL	SER	ARG	PRO	VAL	THR	PHE	VAL	45
46	PRO	ARG	CMC	THR	ARG	PRO	ILE	CMC	GLU	PRO	CMC	ARG	ARG	PRO	VAL	60
61	CMC	CMC	ASP	PRO	CMC	SER	LEU	GLN	GLU	GLY	CMC	CMC	ARG	PRO	ILE	75
76	THR	CMC	CMC	PRO	THR	SER	CMC	GLN	ALA	VAL	VAL	CMC	ARG	PRO	CMC	90
91	CMC	TRP	ALA	THR	THR	CMC	CMC	GLN	PRO	VAL	SER	VAL	GLN	CMC	PRO	105
106	CMC	CMC	ARG	PRO	THR	SER	CMC	GLN	PRO	ALA	PRO	CMC	SER	ARG	THR	120
121	THR	CMC	ARG	THR	PHE	ARG	THR	SER	PRO	CMC	CMC					135

KERATINS

PROTEIN SCMKB–IIIA3A OF WOOL KERATIN

	1			5					10					15		
1	THR	GLY	SER	CMC	CMC	GLY	PRO	THR	PHE	SER	SER	LEU	SER	CMC	GLY	15
16	GLY	GLY	CMC	LEU	GLN	PRO	CMC	CMC	TYR	ARG	ASP	PRO	CMC	CMC	CMC	30
31	ARG	PRO	VAL	SER	SER	GLN	THR	THR	VAL	SER	ARG	PRO	VAL	THR	PHE	45
46	VAL	SER	ARG	CMC	THR	ARG	PRO	ILE	CMC	GLU	PRO	CMC	ARG	ARG	PRO	60
61	VAL	CMC	CMC	ASP	PRO	CMC	SER	LEU	GLN	GLU	GLY	CMC	CMC	ARG	PRO	75
76	ILE	THR	CMC	CMC	PRO	THR	SER	CMC	GLN	ALA	VAL	VAL	CMC	ARG	PRO	90
91	CMC	CMC	TRP	ALA	THR	THR	CMC	CMC	GLN	PRO	VAL	SER	VAL	GLN	CMC	105
106	PRO	CMC	CMC	ARG	PRO	THR	SER	CMC	PRO	SER	ALA	PRO	ARG	THR	THR	120
121	CMC	ARG	THR	PHE	ARG	THR	SER	PRO	CMC	CMC						135

Studies on the high-sulphur proteins of reduced Merino wool. Amino acid sequence of protein
SCMKB–IIIA3.
L. S. Swart and T. Haylett.
Biochem. J., **133**, 641–654 (1973).

PROTEIN SCMKB–IIIB2 OF WOOL KERATIN

	1			5					10					15		
1	AC	ALA	CMC	CMC	ALA	PRO	ARG	CMC	CMC	SER	VAL	ARG	THR	GLY	PRO	15
16	ALA	THR	THR	ILE	CMC	SER	SER	ASP	LYS	PHE	CMC	ARG	CMC	GLY	VAL	30
31	CMC	LEU	PRO	SER	THR	CMC	PRO	HIS	ASN	ILE	SER	LEU	LEU	GLN	PRO	45
46	THR	CMC	CMC	ASP	ASN	SER	PRO	VAL	PRO	CMC	VAL	TYR	PRO	ASP	THR	60
61	TYR	VAL	PRO	THR	CMC	PHE	LEU	LEU	ASN	SER	SER	HIS	PRO	THR	PRO	75
76	GLY	LEU	SER	GLY	ILE	ASN	LEU	THR	THR	PHE	ILE	GLN	PRO	GLY	CMC	90
91	GLU	ASN	VAL	CMC	GLU	PRO	ARG	CMC								105

Studies on the High-Sulfur Proteins of Reduced Merino Wool. Part III: The Amino Acid
Sequence of Protein SCMKB–IIIB2.
T. Haylett and L. S. Swart.
Textile Res. J., **39**, 917–925 (1969).

PROTEIN SCMKB–IIIB3 OF WOOL KERATIN

	1			5					10					15		
1	AC	ALA	CMC	CMC	ALA	ARG	LEU	CMC	CMC	SER	VAL	PRO	THR	SER	PRO	15
16	ALA	THR	THR	ILE	CMC	SER	SER	ASP	LYS	PHE	CMC	ARG	CMC	GLY	VAL	30
31	CMC	LEU	PRO	SER	THR	CMC	PRO	HIS	THR	VAL	TRP	LEU	LEU	GLN	PRO	45
46	THR	CMC	CMC	CMC	ASP	ASN	ARG	PRO	PRO	PRO	TYR	HIS	VAL	PRO	GLN	60
61	PRO	SER	VAL	PRO	THR	CMC	PHE	LEU	LEU	ASN	SER	SER	GLN	PRO	THR	75
76	PRO	GLY	LEU	GLU	SER	ILE	ASN	LEU	THR	THR	TYR	THR	GLN	SER	SER	90
91	CMC	GLU	PRO	CMC	ILE	PRO	SER	CMC	CMC							105

Studies on the High-Sulphur Proteins of Reduced Merino Wool. Amino Acid Sequence of Protein SCMKB–IIIB3.
T. Haylett, L. S. Swart, and D. Parris.
Biochem. J., **123**, 191–200 (1971).

PROTEIN SCMKB–IIIB4 OF WOOL KERATIN

	1			5					10					15		
1	AC	ALA	CMC	CMC	ALA	ARG	LEU	CMC	CMC	SER	VAL	PRO	THR	SER	PRO	15
16	ALA	THR	THR	ILE	CMC	SER	SER	ASP	LYS	PHE	CMC	ARG	CMC	GLY	VAL	30
31	CMC	LEU	PRO	SER	THR	CMC	PRO	HIS	THR	VAL	TRP	PHE	LEU	GLN	PRO	45
46	THR	CMC	CMC	CMC	ASP	ASN	ARG	PRO	PRO	PRO	CMC	HIS	ILE	PRO	GLN	60
61	PRO	SER	VAL	PRO	THR	CMC	PHE	LEU	LEU	ASN	SER	SER	GLN	PRO	THR	75
76	PRO	GLY	LEU	GLU	SER	ILE	ASN	LEU	THR	THR	TYR	THR	GLN	PRO	SER	90
91	CMC	GLU	PRO	CMC	ILE	PRO	SER	CMC	CMC							105

Studies on the High-Sulphur Proteins of Reduced Merino Wool. Amino Acid Sequence of Protein SCMKB–IIIB4.
L. S. Swart and T. Haylett.
Biochem. J., **123**, 201–210 (1971).

486

KERATINS

MOHAIR PROTEIN SCMKB–M1.2

	1				5					10					15	
1	AC	ALA	CMC	CMC	ALA	PRO	ARG	CMC	CMC	SER	VAL	ARG	THR	GLY	PRO	15
16	ALA	THR	THR	ILE	CMC	SER	SER	ASP	LYS	PHE	CMC	ARG	CMC	GLY	VAL	30
31	CMC	LEU	PRO	SER	THR	CMC	PRO	HIS	ASP	ILE	SER	LEU	LEU	GLN	PRO	45
46	THR	PHE	CMC	ASP	ASN	SER	PRO	VAL	PRO	TYR	HIS	VAL	PRO	ASP	THR	60
61	TYR	VAL	PRO	THR	CMC	PHE	LEU	LEU	ASN	SER	SER	HIS	PRO	THR	PRO	75
76	GLY	LEU	SER	GLY	ILE	ASN	LEU	THR	THR	PHE	ILE	GLN	PRO	GLY	CMC	90
91	GLU	ASN	ALA	CMC	GLU	PRO	ARG	CYS								105

Studies on the high-sulphur proteins of reduced mohair. The isolation and amino acid sequence of protein SCMKB–M1.2.
D. Parris and L. S. Swart.
Biochem. J., **145**, 459–467 (1975).

FEATHER KERATIN FROM SILVER GULL

	1				5					10					15	
1	AC	ALA	CMC	ASN	ASP	LEU	CMC	THR GLY	PRO	CMC	GLY	PRO	THR	PRO	LEU	15
16	ALA	ASN	SER	CMC	ASN	GLU	PRO	CMC	VAL	ARG	GLN	CMC	GLU	ALA	SER	30
31	ARG	VAL	VAL	ILE	GLN	PRO	SER	THR	VAL	GLN VAL	VAL	THR	LEU	PRO	GLY	45
46	PRO	ILE	LEU	SER THR	SER	PHE	PRO	GLN	SER	THR	ALA VAL	VAL	GLY	GLY	SER	60
60	ALA	SER	SER	SER	VAL	GLY	ASN	GLU	LEU	LEU	ALA	SER	GLN	GLY	VAL	75
76	PRO	TYR ILE	PHE	GLY SER	GLY	GLY TYR	PHE	GLY	LEU	GLY	GLY	LEU	GLY	CMC	PHE TYR	90
91	SER	GLY	ARG	ARG	GLY	CMC	TYR	PRO	CMC OOO							105

Note: ALA was also found at positions 56, 62 and 63.
Amino acid sequence of a feather keratin from silver gull (*Larus novae-hollandiae*) and comparison with one from emu (*Dromains novae-hollandiae*).
I. J. O'Donnell and A. S. Inglis.
Aust. J. Biol. Sci., **27**, 369–382 (1974).

COMPONENT 0.62 FROM WOOL KERATIN

		1			5					10					15		
1	SER	TYR	CMC	PHE	SER	SER	THR	VAL	PHE	PRO	GLY	CMC	TYR	TRP	GLY	15
16	SER	TYR	GLY	TYR	PRO	LEU	GLY	TYR	SER	VAL	GLY	CMC	GLY	TYR	GLY	30
31	SER	THR	TYR	SER	PRO	VAL	GLY	TYR	GLY	PHE	GLY	TYR	GLY	TYR	ASP	45
46	GLY	GLY	SER	ALA	PHE	GLY	CMC	ARG	ARG	PHE	TRP	PRO	PHE	ALA	LEU	60
61	TYR															75

The primary structure of a protein, component 0.62, rich in glycine and aromatic residues, obtained from wool keratin.
T. A. A. Dopheide.
Eur. J. Biochem., **34**, 120–124 (1973).

MUSCLE PROTEINS

ACTIN OF RABBIT MUSCLE

	1			5					10					15		
1	AC	ASP	GLU	THR	GLU	ASP	THR	ALA	LEU	VAL	CYS	ASP	ASP	GLY	SER	15
16	GLY	LEU	VAL	LYS	ALA	GLY	PHE	ALA	GLY	ASP	ASP	ALA	PRO	ARG	ALA	30
31	VAL	PHE	PRO	SER	ILE	VAL	GLY	ARG	PRO	ARG	HIS	GLN	GLY	VAL	MET	45
46	VAL	GLY	MET	GLY	GLN	LYS	ASP	SER	TYR	VAL	GLY	ASP	GLU	ALA	GLN	60
61	SER	LYS	ARG	GLY	ILE	LEU	THR	LEU	LYS	TYR	PRO	ILE	GLU	MMH	TRP	75
76	GLY	ILE	ILE	THR	ASN	ASP	ASP	MET	GLU	LYS	ILE	TRP	HIS	HIS	THR	90
91	PHE	TYR	ASN	GLU	LEU	ARG	VAL	ALA	PRO	GLU	GLU	HIS	PRO	THR	LEU	105
106	LEU	THR	GLU	ALA	PRO	LEU	ASN	PRO	LYS	ALA	ASN	ARG	GLU	LYS	MET	120
121	THR	GLN	ILE	MET	PHE	GLU	THR	PHE	ASN	VAL	PRO	ALA	MET	TYR	VAL	135
136	ALA	ILE	GLN	ALA	VAL	LEU	SER	LEU	TYR	ALA	SER	GLY	ARG	THR	THR	150
151	GLY	ILE	VAL	LEU	ASP	SER	GLY	ASP	GLY	VAL	THR	HIS	ASN	VAL	PRO	165
166	ILE	TYR	GLU	GLY	TYR	ALA	LEU	PRO	HIS	ALA	ILE	MET	ARG	LEU	ASP	180
181	LEU	ALA	GLY	ARG	ASP	LEU	THR	ASP	TYR	LEU	MET	LYS	ILE	LEU	THR	195
196	GLU	ARG	GLY	TYR	SER	PHE	VAL	THR	THR	ALA	GLU	ARG	GLU	ILE	VAL	210
211	ARG	ASP	ILE	LYS	GLU	LYS	LEU	CYS	TYR	VAL	ALA	LEU	ASP	PHE	GLU	225
226	ASN	GLU	MET	ALA	THR	ALA	ALA	SER	SER	SER	LEU	GLU	LYS	SER	TYR	240
241	GLU	LEU	PRO	ASP	GLY	GLN	VAL	ILE	THR	ILE	GLY	ASN	GLU	ARG	PHE	255
256	ARG	CYS	PRO	GLU	THR	LEU	PHE	GLN	PRO	SER	PHE	ILE	GLY	MET	GLU	270
271	SER	ALA	GLY	ILE	HIS	GLU	THR	THR	TYR	ASN	SER	ILE	MET	LYS	CYS	285
286	ASP	ILE	ASP	ILE	ARG	LYS	ASP	LEU	TYR	ALA	ASN	ASN	VAL	MET	SER	300
301	GLY	GLY	THR	THR	MET	TYR	PRO	GLY	THR	ALA	ASP	ARG	MET	GLN	LYS	315
316	GLU	ILE	THR	ALA	LEU	ALA	PRO	SER	THR	MET	LYS	ILE	LYS	ILE	ILE	330
331	ALA	PRO	PRO	GLU	ARG	LYS	TYR	SER	VAL	TRP	ILE	GLY	GLY	SER	ILE	345
346	LEU	ALA	SER	LEU	SER	THR	PHE	GLN	GLN	MET	TRP	ILE	THR	LYS	GLN	360
361	GLU	TYR	ASP	GLU	ALA	GLY	PRO	SER	ILE	VAL	HIS	ARG	LYS	CYS	PHE	375

Complete amino acid sequence of actin of rabbit skeletal muscle.
M. Elzinga, J. H. Collins, W. M. Kuehl, and R. S. Adelstein.
Proc. Natn. Acad. Sci., U.S.A., **70**, 2687–2691 (1973).
And
The primary structure of actin from rabbit skeletal muscle; Completion and analysis of the amino acid sequence.
J. H. Collins, M. Elzinga, and N. Jackman.
J. Biol. Chem., **250**, 5915–5920 (1975).

MUSCLE PROTEINS

ALKALI LIGHT CHAINS OF RABBIT MYOSIN

	1				5					10					15	
1	PRO	LYS	LYS	ASN	VAL	LYS	LYS	PRO	ALA	ALA	ALA	ALA	ALA	PRO	ALA	15
16	PRO	LYS	ALA	PRO	ALA	PRO	ALA	PRO	ALA	PRO	ALA	PRO	ALA	PRO	LYS	30
31	GLU	GLU	LYS	ILE	ASP	LEU	SER	ALA	ILE	LYS	ILE	GLU	PHE	SER	LYS	45
46	GLU	GLN	GLN	ASP	GLU	PHE	LYS	GLU	ALA	PHE	LEU	LEU	TYR	ASP	ARG	60
61	THR	GLY	ASP	SER	LYS	ILE	THR	LEU	SER	GLN	VAL	GLY	ASP	VAL	LEU	75
76	ARG	ALA	LEU	GLY	THR	ASN	PRO	THR	ASN	ALA	GLU	VAL	LYS	LYS	VAL	90
91	LEU	GLY	ASN	PRO	SER	ASP	GLU	GLN	MET	ASN	ALA	LYS	LYS	ILE	GLU	105
106	PHE	GLU	GLN	PHE	LEU	PRO	MET	LEU	GLN	ALA	ILE	SER	ASN	ASN	LYS	120
121	ASP	GLN	GLY	THR	TYR	GLU	ASP	PHE	VAL	GLU	GLY	LEU	ARG	VAL	PHE	135
136	ASP	LYS	GLU	ASP	GLY	THR	VAL	GLY	MET	GLY	ALA	GLU	LEU	ARG	HIS	150
151	VAL	LEU	ALA	THR	LEU	GLY	GLU	LYS	MET	LYS	GLU	GLU	GLU	VAL	GLU	165
166	ALA	LEU	MET	ALA	GLY	GLN	GLU	ASP	SER	ASN	GLY	CYS	ILE	ASN	TYR	180
181	GLU	ALA	PHE	VAL	LYS	HIS	ILE	MET	SER	ILE						195

Notes: (i) The N-terminus is blocked by an unknown group. (ii) The above sequence is the
A1 chain. The A2 chain lacks residues 1–41. The first eight residues of the A2 chain are AC
SER PHE SER ALA ASP GLN ILE ALA, and replace residues 42–49 in the above
sequence. The remainder of the A2 sequence is identical to the A1 sequence.
The amino acid sequence of the alkali light chains of rabbit skeletal muscle myosin.
G. Frank and A. G. Weeds.
Eur. J. Biochem., **44**, 317–334 (1974).

BOVINE CARDIAC TROPONIN C

	1				5					10					15	
1	AC	MET	ASP	ASP	ILE	TYR	LYS	ALA	ALA	VAL	GLU	GLN	LEU	THR	GLU	15
16	GLU	GLN	LYS	ASN	GLU	PHE	LYS	ALA	ALA	PHE	ASP	ILE	PHE	VAL	LEU	30
31	GLY	ALA	GLU	ASP	GLY	CYS	ILE	SER	THR	LYS	GLU	LEU	GLY	LYS	VAL	45
46	MET	ARG	MET	LEU	GLY	GLN	ASN	PRO	THR	PRO	GLU	GLU	LEU	GLN	GLU	60
61	MET	ILE	ASP	GLU	VAL	ASP	GLU	ASP	GLY	SER	GLY	THR	VAL	ASP	PHE	75
76	ASP	GLU	PHE	LEU	VAL	MET	MET	VAL	ARG	CYS	MET	LYS	ASP	ASP	SER	90
91	LYS	GLY	LYS	SER	GLU	GLU	GLU	LEU	SER	ASP	LEU	PHE	ARG	MET	PHE	105
106	ASP	LYS	ASN	ALA	ASP	GLY	TYR	ILE	ASP	LEU	GLU	GLU	LEU	LYS	ILE	120
121	MET	LEU	GLN	ALA	THR	GLY	GLU	THR	ILE	THR	GLU	ASP	ASP	ILE	GLU	135
136	GLU	LEU	MET	LYS	ASP	GLY	ASP	LYS	ASN	ASN	ASP	GLY	ARG	ILE	ASP	150
151	TYR	ASP	GLU	PHE	LEU	GLU	PHE	MET	LYS	GLY	VAL	GLU				165

Determination of the complete amino acid sequence of bovine cardiac troponin C.
J.-P. van Eerd and K. Takahashi.
Biochemistry, **15**, 1171–1180 (1976).
The amino acid sequence of bovine cardiac troponin C. Comparison with rabbit skeletal
troponin C.
J.-P. van Eerd and K. Takahashi.
Biochem. Biophys. Res. Commun., **64**, 122–127 (1975).

MUSCLE PROTEINS

CALCIUM-BINDING PROTEIN OF RABBIT—TROPONIN C

	1		5				10					15				
1	AC	(GLN,	ASP,	GLN,	THR)	ALA	GLU	ALA	ARG	SER	TYR	LEU	SER	GLU	GLU	15
16	MET	ILE	ALA	GLU	PHE	LYS	ALA	ALA	PHE	ASP	MET	PHE	ASP	ALA	ASP	30
31	GLY	GLY	GLY	ASP	ILE	SER	VAL	LYS	GLU	LEU	GLY	THR	VAL	MET	ARG	45
46	MET	LEU	GLY	GLN	THR	PRO	THR	LYS	GLU	GLU	LEU	ASP	ALA	ILE	ILE	60
61	GLU	GLU	(VAL,	ASP,	GLU,	ASP,	GLY,	SER,	GLY,	THR)	ILE	ASP	PHE	GLU	GLU	75
76	PHE	LEU	VAL	MET	VAL	ARG	GLN	MET	LYS	GLU	ASP	ALA	LYS	GLY	LYS	90
91	SER	GLU	GLU	GLU	LEU	ALA	GLU	CYS	PHE	ARG	ILE	PHE	ASP	ARG	ASN	105
106	ALA	ASP	GLY	TYR	ILE	ASP	ALA	GLU	GLU	LEU	ALA	GLU	ILE	PHE	ARG	120
121	ALA	SER	GLY	GLU	HIS	VAL	THR	ASP	GLU	GLU	ILE	GLU	SER	LEU	MET	135
136	LYS	ASP	GLY	ASP	LYS	ASP	ASN	ASP	GLY	ARG	ILE	ASP	PHE	ASP	GLU	150
151	PHE	LEU	LYS	MET	MET	GLU	GLY	VAL	GLN							165

The amino acid sequence of rabbit skeletal muscle troponin C: gene replication and homology with calcium binding proteins from carp and hake muscle.
J. H. Collins, J. D. Potter, M. J. Horn, G. Wiltshire, and N. Jackman.
FEBS Letters, **36**, 268–272 (1973).

TROPONIN C-LIKE PROTEIN—BOVINE UTERUS

	1		5				10					15				
1	(ALA,	ASP,	GLN)	LEU	THR	GLU	GLU	GLN	ILE	ALA	GLU	PHE	LYS	GLU	ALA	15
16	PHE	SER	LEU	PHE	ASP	LYS	ASP	GLY	ASP	GLY	THR	ILE	THR	THR	LYS	30
31	GLU	LEU	GLY	THR	VAL	MET	ARG	SER	LEU	GLY	GLN	ASN	PRO	THR	GLU	45
46	ALA	GLU	LEU	GLN	ASP	MET	ILE	ASN	GLU	VAL	ASP	ALA	ASP	GLY	ASN	60
61	GLY	THR	ILE	ASP	PHE	PRO	GLU	PHE	LEU	THR	MET	MET	ALA	ARG	LYS	75
76	MET	LYS	ASP	THR	ASP	SER	GLU	GLU	GLU	ILE	ARG	GLU	ALA	PHE	ARG	90
91	VAL	PHE	ASP	LYS	ASP	GLY	ASP	GLY	TYR	ILE	SER	ALA	ALA	GLU	LEU	105
106	ARG	HIS	VAL	MET	THR	ASN	LEU	GLY	GLU	TML	LEU	THR	ASP	GLU	GLU	120
121	VAL	ASP	GLU	MET	ILE	ARG	GLU	ALA	ASN	ILE	ASP	GLY	ASP	GLY	GLU	135
136	VAL	ASN	TYR	GLU	GLU	PHE	VAL	GLN	MET	MET	THR	ALA	LYS			150

Note: The N-terminus of this protein is blocked by an unknown group.
The amino acid sequence of the troponin C-like protein (Modulator protein) from bovine uterus.
R. J. A. Grand and S. V. Perry.
FEBS Letters, **92**, 137–142 (1978).

RABBIT SKELETAL TROPONIN-T

	1				5				10					15		
1	AC	SER	ASP	GLU	GLU	VAL	GLU	HIS	VAL	GLU	GLU	GLU	ALA	GLU	GLU	15
16	GLU	ALA	PRO	SER	PRO	ALA	GLU	VAL	HIS	GLU	PRO	ALA	PRO	GLU	HIS	30
31	VAL	VAL	PRO	GLU	GLU	VAL	HIS	GLU	GLU	GLU	LYS	PRO	ARG	LYS	LEU	45
46	THR	ALA	PRO	LYS	ILE	PRO	GLU	GLY	GLU	LYS	VAL	ASP	PHE	ASP	ASP	60
61	ILE	GLN	LYS	LYS	ARG	GLN	ASN	LYS	ASP	LEU	MET	GLU	LEU	GLN	ALA	75
76	LEU	ILE	ASP	SER	HIS	PHE	GLU	ALA	ARG	LYS	LYS	GLU	GLU	GLU	GLU	90
91	LEU	VAL	ALA	LEU	LYS	GLU	ARG	ILE	GLU	LYS	ARG	ARG	ALA	GLU	ARG	105
106	ALA	GLU	GLN	GLN	ARG	ILE	ARG	ALA	GLU	LYS	GLU	ARG	GLU	ARG	GLN	120
121	ASN	ARG	LEU	ALA	GLU	GLU	LYS	ALA	ARG	ARG	GLU	GLU	GLU	ASP	ALA	135
136	LYS	ARG	ARG	ALA	GLU	GLU	ASP	LEU	LYS	LYS	LYS	LYS	ALA	LEU	SER	150
151	SER	MET	GLY	ALA	ASN	TYR	SER	SER	TYR	LEU	ALA	LYS	ALA	ASP	GLN	165
166	LYS	ARG	GLY	LYS	LYS	GLN	THR	ALA	ARG	GLU	MET	LYS	LYS	LYS	ILE	180
181	LEU	ALA	GLU	ARG	ARG	LYS	PRO	LEU	ASN	ILE	ASP	HIS	LEU	SER	ASP	195
196	GLU	LYS	LEU	ARG	ASP	LYS	ALA	LYS	GLU	LEU	TRP	ASP	THR	LEU	TYR	210
211	GLN	LEU	GLU	THR	ASP	LYS	PHE	GLU	PHE	GLY	GLU	LYS	LEU	LYS	ARG	225
226	GLN	LYS	TYR	ASP	ILE	MET	ASN	VAL	ARG	ALA	ARG	VAL	GLU	MET	LEU	240
241	ALA	LYS	PHE	SER	LYS	LYS	ALA	GLY	THR	THR	ALA	LYS	GLY	LYS	VAL	255
256	GLY	GLY	ARG	TRP	LYS											270

Amino acid sequence of tropomyosin-binding component of rabbit skeletal muscle troponin.
J. R. Pearlstone, M. R. Carpenter, P. Johnson, and L. B. Smillie.
Proc. Natn. Acad. Sci., U.S.A., **73**, 1902–1906 (1976); *Proc. Natn. Acad. Sci., U.S.A.*, **73**, 4711 (1976).

RABBIT MUSCLE TROPONIN I

	1				5				10					15		
1	AC	GLY	ASP	GLU	GLU	LYS	ARG	ASN	ARG	ALA	ILE	THR	ALA	ARG	ARG	15
16	GLN	HIS	LEU	LYS	SER	VAL	MET	LEU	GLN	ILE	ALA	ALA	THR	GLU	LEU	30
31	GLU	LYS	GLU	GLU	GLY	ARG	ARG	GLU	ALA	GLU	LYS	GLN	ASN	TYR	LEU	45
46	ALA	GLU	HIS	CYS	PRO	PRO	LEU	SER	LEU	PRO	GLY	SER	MET	ALA	GLU	60
61	VAL	GLN	GLU	LEU	CYS	LYS	GLN	LEU	HIS	ALA	LYS	ILE	ASP	ALA	ALA	75
76	GLU	GLU	GLU	LYS	TYR	ASP	MET	GLU	ILE	LYS	VAL	GLN	LYS	SER	SER	90
91	LYS	GLU	LEU	GLU	ASP	MET	ASN	GLN	LYS	LEU	PHE	ASP	LEU	ARG	GLY	105
106	LYS	PHE	LYS	ARG	PRO	PRO	LEU	ARG	ARG	ARG	VAL	ARG	MET	SER	ALA	120
121	ASP	ALA	MET	LEU	LYS	ALA	LEU	LEU	GLY	SER	LYS	HIS	LYS	VAL	CYS	135
136	MET	ASP	LEU	ARG	ALA	ASN	LEU	LYS	GLN	VAL	LYS	LYS	GLU	ASP	THR	150
151	GLU	LYS	GLU	ARG	ASP	VAL	GLY	ASP	TRP	ARG	LYS	ASN	ILE	GLU	GLU	165
166	LYS	SER	GLY	MET	GLU	GLY	ARG	LYS	LYS	MET	PHE	GLU	SER	GLU	SER	180

The amino acid sequence of Troponin I from rabbit skeletal muscle.
J. M. Wilkinson and R. J. A. Grand.
Biochem. J., **149**, 493–496 (1975).

MUSCLE PROTEINS

TROPONIN I—CHICKEN

```
       1              5                    10                      15
  1  SER ASP GLU GLU LYS LYS ARG ARG ALA ALA THR ALA ARG ARG GLN   15
 16  HIS LEU LYS SER ALA MET LEU GLN LEU ALA VAL THR GLU ILE GLU    30
 31  LYS GLU ALA ALA ALA LYS GLU VAL GLU LYS GLN ASN TYR LEU ALA    45
 46  GLU HIS CYS PRO PRO LEU SER LEU PRO GLY SER MET GLN GLU LEU    60
 61  GLN GLU LEU CYS LYS LYS LEU HIS ALA LYS ILE ASP SER VAL ASP    75
 76  GLU GLU ARG TYR ASP THR GLU VAL LYS LEU GLN LYS THR ASN LYS    90
 91  GLU LEU GLU ASP LEU SER GLN LYS LEU PHE ASP LEU ARG GLY LYS   105
106  PHE LYS ARG PRO PRO LEU ARG ARG VAL ARG MET SER ALA ASP ALA   120
121  MET LEU ARG ALA LEU LEU GLY SER LYS HIS LYS VAL ASN MET ASP   135
136  LEU ARG ALA ASN LEU LYS GLN VAL LYS LYS GLU ASP THR GLU LYS   150
151  GLU LYS ASP LEU ARG ASP VAL GLY ASP TRP ARG LYS ASN ILE GLU   165
166  GLU LYS SER GLY MET GLU GLY ARG LYS LYS MET PHE GLU ALA GLY   180
181  GLU SER                                                       195
```

Note: The N-terminus of this protein is blocked by an unknown group.
The amino acid sequence of chicken fast-skeletal muscle Troponin I.
J. M. Wilkinson and R. J. A. Grand.
Eur. J. Biochem., **82**, 493–501 (1978).

RABBIT MUSCLE PARVALBUMIN

```
       1              5                    10                      15
  1  AC  ALA MET THR GLU LEU LEU ASN ALA GLU ASP ILE LYS LYS ALA    15
 16  ILE GLY ALA PHE ALA ALA ALA GLU SER PHE ASP HIS LYS LYS PHE    30
 31  PHE GLN MET VAL GLY LEU LYS LYS LYS SER THR GLU ASP VAL LYS    45
 46  LYS VAL PHE HIS ILE LEU ASP LYS ASP LYS SER GLY PHE ILE GLU    60
 61  GLU GLU GLU LEU GLY PHE ILE LEU LYS GLY PHE SER PRO ASP ALA    75
 76  ARG ASP LEU SER VAL LYS GLU THR LYS THR LEU MET ALA ALA GLY    90
 91  ASP LYS ASP GLY ASP GLY LYS ILE GLY ALA ASP GLU PHE SER THR   105
106  LEU VAL SER GLU SER                                           120
```

Amino acid sequence of parvalbumin from rabbit skeletal muscle.
D. L. Enfield, L. H. Ericsson, H. E. Blum, E. H. Fischer, and H. Neurath.
Proc. Natn. Acad. Sci., U.S.A., **72**, 1309–1313 (1975).
Confirmation,
Parvalbumin from rabbit muscle. Isolation and primary structure.
J.-P. Capony, C. Pina, and J.-F. Pechere.
Eur. J. Biochem., **70**, 123–135 (1976).

FROG MUSCLE PARVALBUMIN

	1				5					10					15	
1	AC	SER	ILE	THR	ASP	ILE	VAL	SER	GLU	LYS	ASP	ILE	ASP	ALA	ALA	15
16	LEU	GLU	SER	VAL	LYS	ALA	ALA	GLY	SER	PHE	ASN	TYR	LYS	ILE	PHE	30
31	PHE	GLN	LYS	VAL	GLY	LEU	ALA	GLY	LYS	SER	ALA	ALA	ASP	ALA	LYS	45
46	LYS	VAL	PHE	GLU	ILE	LEU	ASP	ARG	ASP	LYS	SER	GLY	PHE	ILE	GLU	60
61	GLN	ASP	GLU	LEU	GLY	LEU	PHE	LEU	GLN	ASN	PHE	ARG	ALA	SER	ALA	75
76	ARG	VAL	LEU	SER	ASP	ALA	GLU	THR	SER	ALA	PHE	LEU	LYS	ALA	GLY	90
91	ASP	SER	ASP	GLY	ASP	GLY	LYS	ILE	GLY	VAL	GLU	GLU	PHE	GLN	ALA	105
106	LEU	VAL	LYS	ALA												120

The amino acid sequence of the most acidic major parvalbumin from frog muscle.
J.-P. Capony, J. Demaille, C. Pina, and J.-F. Pechère.
Eur. J. Biochem., **56**, 215–227 (1975).

PARVALBUMIN II—PIKE

	1				5					10					15	
1	AC	SER	PHE	ALA	GLY	LEU	LYS	ASP	ALA	ASP	VAL	ALA	ALA	ALA	LEU	15
16	ALA	ALA	CYS	SER	ALA	ALA	ASP	SER	PHE	LYS	HIS	LYS	GLU	PHE	PHE	30
31	ALA	LYS	VAL	GLY	LEU	ALA	SER	LYS	SER	LEU	ASP	ASP	VAL	LYS	LYS	45
46	ALA	PHE	TYR	VAL	ILE	ASP	GLN	ASP	LYS	SER	GLY	PHE	ILE	GLU	GLU	60
61	ASP	GLU	LEU	LYS	LEU	PHE	LEU	GLN	ASN	PHE	SER	PRO	SER	ALA	ARG	75
76	ALA	LEU	THR	ASP	ALA	GLU	THR	LYS	ALA	PHE	LEU	ALA	ASP	GLY	ASP	90
91	LYS	ASP	GLY	ASP	GLY	MET	ILE	GLY	VAL	ASP	GLU	PHE	ALA	ALA	MET	105
106	ILE	LYS	ALA													120

The primary structure of the parvalbumin II of pike (*Esox lucius*).
C. Gerday.
Eur. J. Biochem., **70**, 305–318 (1976).

MUSCLE PROTEINS

PARVALBUMIN III—PIKE

```
       1              5                  10                    15
  1  AC  ALA LYS ASP LEU LEU LYS ALA ASP ASP ILE  LYS LEU LYS ALA   15
 16  LEU ASP ALA VAL LYS ALA GLU GLY SER PHE ASN HIS  LYS ALA PHE    30
 31  PHE ALA LYS VAL GLY LEU LYS ALA MET SER ALA ASN ASP VAL LYS     45
 46  LYS VAL PHE LYS ALA ILE  ASP ALA ASP ALA SER GLY PHE ILE  GLU   60
 61  GLU GLU GLU LEU LYS PHE VAL LEU LYS SER PHE ALA ALA ASP GLY     75
 76  ARG ASP LEU THR ASP ALA GLU THR LYS ALA PHE LEU LYS ALA ALA     90
 91  ASP LYS ASP GLY ASP GLY LYS ILE  GLY ILE  ASP GLU PHE GLU THR  105
106  LEU VAL HIS  GLU ALA                                           120
```

The amino acid sequence of the pike (*Esox lucius*) parvalbumin III.
F. Frankenne, L. Joassin, and C. Gerday.
FEBS Letters, **35**, 145–147 (1973).

PARVALBUMIN—THORNBACK RAY

```
       1              5                  10                    15
  1  AC  SER SER LYS ILE  THR SER ILE  LEU ASN PRO ALA ASP ILE  THR  15
 16  LYS ALA LEU GLU GLN CYS ALA ALA GLY PHE HIS HIS  THR ALA PHE    30
 31  PHE LYS ALA SER GLY LEU SER LYS LYS SER ASP ALA GLU LEU ALA     45
 46  GLU ILE  PHE ASN VAL LEU ASP GLY ASP GLN SER GLY TYR ILE  GLU   60
 61  VAL GLU GLU LEU LYS ASN PHE LEU LYS CYS PHE SER ASP GLY ALA     75
 76  ARG VAL LEU ASN ASP LYS GLU THR SER ASN PHE LEU ALA ALA GLY     90
 91  ASP SER ASP GLY ASP HIS LYS ILE  GLY VAL ASP GLU PHE LYS SER   105
106  MET ALA LYS MET THR                                            120
```

The amino acid sequence of the major parvalbumin from thornback-ray muscle.
D. R. Thatcher and J. Pechère.
Eur. J. Biochem., **75**, 121–132 (1977).

MUSCLE PROTEINS

PARVALBUMIN—WHITING

	1		5				10				15				
1	AC	ALA	PHE	ALA	GLY	ILE	LEU	ALA	ASP	ALA	ASP	ALA	CYS	ALA ALA	15
16	VAL	LYS	ALA	CYS	GLU	ALA	ALA	ASP	SER	PHE	SER	TYR	LYS	ALA PHE	30
31	PHE	ALA	LYS	CYS	GLY	LEU	SER	GLY	LYS	SER	ALA	ASP	ASP	ILE LYS	45
46	LYS	ALA	PHE	VAL	PHE	ILE	ASP	GLN	ASP	LYS	SER	GLY	PHE	ILE GLU	60
61	GLU	ASP	GLU	LEU	LYS	LEU	PHE	LEU	GLN	VAL	PHE	LYS	ALA	GLY ALA	75
76	ARG	ALA	LEU	THR	ASP	ALA	GLU	THR	LYS	ALA	PHE	LEU	LYS	ALA GLY	90
91	ASP	SER	ASP	GLY	ASP	GLY	ALA	ILE	GLY	VAL	GLU	GLU	TRP	VAL ALA	105
106	LEU	VAL	LYS	ALA											120

The amino acid sequence of the major parvalbumin of the Whiting (*Gadus merlangus*).
L. Joassin and C. Gerday.
Comp. Biochem. Physiol., **57B**, 159–161 (1977).

PARVALBUMIN—HAKE

	1		5				10				15				
1	AC	ALA	PHE	ALA	GLY	ILE	LEU	ALA	ASP	ALA	ASP	ILE	THR	ALA ALA	15
16	LEU	ALA	ALA	CYS	LYS	ALA	GLU	GLY	SER	PHE	LYS	HIS	GLY	GLU PHE	30
31	PHE	THR	LYS	ILE	GLY	LEU	LYS	GLY	LYS	SER	ALA	ALA	ASP	ILE LYS	45
46	LYS	VAL	PHE	GLY	ILE	ILE	ASP	GLN	ASP	LYS	SER	ASP	PHE	VAL GLU	60
61	GLU	ASP	GLU	LEU	LYS	LEU	PHE	LEU	GLN	ASN	PHE	SER	ALA	GLY ALA	75
76	ARG	ALA	LEU	THR	ASP	ALA	GLU	THR	ALA	THR	PHE	LEU	LYS	ALA GLY	90
91	ASP	SER	ASP	GLY	ASP	GLY	LYS	ILE	GLY	VAL	GLU	GLU	PHE	ALA ALA	105
106	MET	VAL	LYS	GLY											120

The Amino Acid Sequence of the Major Parvalbumin from hake muscle.
J.-F. Pechère, J. P. Capony, L. Rydèn, and J. Demaille.
Biochem. Biophys. Res. Commun., **43**, 1106–1111 (1971); *Eur. J. Biochem.*, **32**, 97–108 (1973).

MUSCLE PROTEINS

CARP MYOGEN

	1				5					10					15	
1	AC	ALA	PHE	ALA	GLY	VAL	LEU	ASN	ASP	ALA	ASP	ILE	ALA	ALA	ALA	15
16	LEU	GLU	ALA	CYS	LYS	ALA	ALA	ASP	SER	PHE	ASN	HIS	LYS	ALA	PHE	30
31	PHE	ALA	LYS	VAL	GLY	LEU	THR	SER	LYS	SER	ALA	ASP	ASP	VAL	LYS	45
46	LYS	ALA	PHE	ALA	ILE	ILE	ASP	GLN	ASP	LYS	SER	GLY	PHE	ILE	GLU	60
61	GLU	ASP	GLU	LEU	LYS	LEU	PHE	LEU	GLN	ASN	PHE	LYS	ALA	ASP	ALA	75
76	ARG	ALA	LEU	THR	ASP	GLY	GLU	THR	LYS	THR	PHE	LEU	LYS	ALA	GLY	90
91	ASP	SER	ASP	GLY	ASP	GLY	LYS	ILE	GLY	VAL	ASP	GLU	PHE	THR	ALA	105
106	LEU	VAL	LYS	ALA												120

Structure of a calcium-binding Carp Myogen.
C. E. Nockolds, R. K. Kretsinger, C. J. Coffee, and R. A. Bradshaw.
Proc. Natn. Acad. Sci., U.S.A., **69**, 581–584 (1972).
Carp muscle calcium binding protein. I. Characterization of the tryptic peptides and the complete amino acid sequence of component B.
C. J. Coffee and R. A. Bradshaw.
J. Biol. Chem., **248**, 3305–3312 (1973).

BOVINE γ-CRYSTALLIN

	1				5					10					15	
1	GLY	LYS	ILE	THR	PHE	TYR	GLU	ASP	ARG	GLY	PHE	GLN	GLY	HIS	CYS	15
16	TYR	GLN	CYS	SER	SER	ASN	ASN	CYS	LEU	GLN	PRO	PRO	TYR	PHE	SER	30
31	ARG	CYS	ASN	SER	ILE	ARG	VAL	ASP	VAL	HIS	SER	LEU	LEU	TYR	MET	45
46	LEU	GLN	ARG	PRO	ASP	TYR	GLY	HIS	TYR	GLN	ARG	GLY	ASN	TYR	PRO	60
61	GLN	TYR	GLN	TRP	MET	GLY	PHE	ASP	ASP	SER	ILE	ARG	SER	CYS	ARG	75
76	LEU	ILE	PRO	GLN	HIS	THR	GLY	THR	PHE	ARG	MET	ARG	ILE	TYR	GLU	90
91	ARG	ASP	ASP	PHE	ARG	GLY	GLN	MET	SER	GLU	ILE	THR	ASP	PRO	CYS	105
106	ASP	SER	LEU	GLN	ASP	ARG	PHE	HIS	LEU	THR	GLU	VAL	ASN	TYR	VAL	120
121	LEU	GLU	GLY	SER	TRP	GLU	MET	PRO	SER	TYR	ARG	GLY	ARG	GLN	TYR	135
136	LEU	LEU	ARG	PRO	GLY	GLU	TYR	ARG	ARG	TYR	LEU	ASP	TRP	GLY	ALA	150
151	MET	ASN	ALA	LYS	VAL	GLY	SER	LEU	ARG	ARG	VAL	MET	ASP	PHE	TYR	165

The Amino Acid Sequence of γ-Crystallin (Fraction II) from Calf Lens.
L. R. Croft.
Biochem. J., **128**, 961–970 (1972).

BOVINE α-CRYSTALLIN α A₂ CHAIN

	1				5					10					15	
1	AC	MET	ASP	ILE	ALA	ILE	GLN	HIS	PRO	TRP	PHE	LYS	ARG	THR	LEU	15
16	GLY	PRO	PHE	TYR	PRO	SER	ARG	LEU	PHE	ASP	GLN	PHE	PHE	GLY	GLU	30
31	GLY	LEU	PHE	GLU	TYR	ASP	LEU	LEU	PRO	PHE	LEU	SER	SER	THR	ILE	45
46	SER	PRO	TYR	TYR	ARG	GLN	SER	LEU	PHE	ARG	THR	VAL	LEU	ASP	SER	60
61	GLY	ILE	SER	GLU	VAL	ARG	SER	ASP	ARG	ASP	LYS	PHE	VAL	ILE	PHE	75
76	LEU	ASP	VAL	LYS	HIS	PHE	SER	PRO	GLU	ASP	LEU	THR	VAL	LYS	VAL	90
91	GLN	GLU	ASP	PHE	VAL	GLU	ILE	HIS	GLY	LYS	HIS	ASN	GLU	ARG	GLN	105
106	ASP	ASP	HIS	GLY	TYR	ILE	SER	ARG	GLU	PHE	HIS	ARG	ARG	TYR	ARG	120
121	LEU	PRO	SER	ASN	VAL	ASP	GLN	SER	ALA	LEU	SER	CYS	SER	LEU	SER	135
136	ALA	ASP	GLY	MET	LEU	THR	PHE	SER	GLY	PRO	LYS	ILE	PRO	SER	GLY	150
151	VAL	ASP	ALA	GLY	HIS	SER	GLU	ARG	ALA	ILE	PRO	VAL	SER	ARG	GLU	165
166	GLU	LYS	PRO	SER	SER	ALA	PRO	SER	SER							180

The amino acid sequence of the α A₂ chain of bovine α-Crystallin.
F. J. van der Ouderaa, W. W. de Jong, and H. Bloemendal.
Eur. J. Biochem., **39**, 207–222 (1973).

LENS PROTEINS

α-CRYSTALLIN A₂ CHAIN—HUMAN

	1				5					10					15	
1	AC	MET	ASP	VAL	THR	ILE	GLN	HIS	PRO	TRP	PHE	LYS	ARG	THR	LEU	15
16	GLY	PRO	PHE	TYR	PRO	SER	ARG	LEU	PHE	ASP	GLN	PHE	PHE	GLY	GLU	30
31	GLY	LEU	PHE	GLU	TYR	ASP	LEU	LEU	PRO	PHE	LEU	SER	SER	THR	ILE	45
46	SER	PRO	TYR	TYR	ARG	GLN	SER	LEU	PHE	ARG	THR	VAL	LEU	ASP	SER	60
61	GLY	ILE	SER	GLU	VAL	ARG	SER	ASP	ARG	ASP	LYS	PHE	VAL	ILE	PHE	75
76	LEU	ASP	VAL	LYS	HIS	PHE	SER	PRO	GLU	ASP	LEU	THR	VAL	LYS	VAL	90
91	GLN	ASP	ASP	PHE	VAL	GLU	ILE	HIS	GLY	LYS	HIS	ASN	GLU	ARG	GLN	105
106	ASP	ASP	HIS	GLY	TYR	ILE	SER	ARG	GLU	PHE	HIS	ARG	ARG	TYR	ARG	120
121	LEU	PRO	SER	ASN	VAL	ASP	GLN	SER	ALA	LEU	SER	CYS	SER	LEU	SER	135
136	ALA	ASN	GLY	MET	LEU	THR	PHE	GLY	PRO	LYS	ILE	GLN	THR	GLY	LEU	150
151	ASP	ALA	HIS	THR	GLU	ARG	ALA	ILE	PRO	VAL	SER	ARG	GLU	GLU	LYS	165
166	PRO	THR	SER	ALA	PRO	SER	SER									180

The amino acid sequence of the A chain of human α-crystallin.
W. W. de Jong, E. C. Terwindt, and H. Bloemendal.
FEBS Letters, **58**, 310–313 (1975).

α-CRYSTALLIN A₂ CHAIN—KANGAROO

	1				5					10					15	
1	AC	MET	ASP	ILE	THR	ILE	GLN	HIS	PRO	TRP	PHE	LYS	ARG	ALA	LEU	15
16	GLY	SER	LEU	TYR	PRO	SER	ARG	LEU	PHE	ASP	GLN	PHE	PHE	GLY	GLU	30
31	GLY	LEU	PHE	GLU	TYR	ASP	LEU	LEU	PRO	PHE	LEU	SER	SER	THR	ILE	45
46	SER	PRO	TYR	TYR	ARG	GLN	SER	LEU	PHE	ARG	THR	VAL	LEU	GLU	SER	60
61	GLY	ILE	SER	GLU	VAL	ARG	SER	ASP	ARG	ASP	LYS	PHE	VAL	ILE	PHE	75
76	LEU	ASP	VAL	LYS	HIS	PHE	SER	PRO	GLU	ASP	LEU	THR	VAL	LYS	VAL	90
91	LEU	ASP	ASP	PHE	VAL	GLU	ILE	HIS	GLY	LYS	HIS	SER	GLU	ARG	GLN	105
106	ASP	ASP	HIS	GLY	TYR	ILE	SER	ARG	GLU	PHE	HIS	ARG	ARG	TYR	ARG	120
121	LEU	PRO	SER	ASN	VAL	ASP	GLN	SER	ALA	ILE	SER	CYS	SER	LEU	SER	135
136	ALA	ASP	GLY	MET	LEU	THR	PHE	SER	GLY	PRO	LYS	ILE	HIS	SER	ASP	150
151	MET	ASP	ALA	SER	HIS	SER	ASP	ARG	SER	ILE	PRO	VAL	SER	ARG	GLU	165
166	GLU	LYS	PRO	THR	LEU	ALA	PRO	SER	SER							180

The amino acid sequences of the α-crystallin A chains of red kangaroo and virginia opossum.
W. W. de Jong and E. C. Terwindt.
Eur. J. Biochem., **67**, 503–510 (1976).

α-CRYSTALLIN A₂ CHAIN—PIG

	1				5					10					15	
1	AC	MET	ASP	ILE	ALA	ILE	GLN	HIS	PRO	TRP	PHE	LYS	ARG	ALA	LEU	15
16	GLY	PRO	PHE	TYR	PRO	SER	ARG	LEU	PHE	ASP	GLN	PHE	PHE	GLY	GLU	30
31	GLY	LEU	PHE	GLU	TYR	ASP	LEU	LEU	PRO	PHE	LEU	SER	SER	THR	ILE	45
46	SER	PRO	TYR	TYR	ARG	GLN	SER	LEU	PHE	ARG	THR	VAL	LEU	ASP	SER	60
61	GLY	VAL	SER	GLU	VAL	ARG	SER	ASP	ARG	ASP	LYS	PHE	VAL	ILE	PHE	75
76	LEU	ASP	VAL	LYS	HIS	PHE	SER	PRO	GLU	ASP	LEU	THR	VAL	LYS	VAL	90
91	GLN	GLU	ASP	PHE	VAL	GLU	ILE	HIS	GLY	LYS	HIS	ASN	GLU	ARG	GLN	105
106	ASP	ASP	HIS	GLY	TYR	ILE	SER	ARG	GLU	PHE	HIS	ARG	ARG	TYR	ARG	120
121	LEU	PRO	SER	ASN	VAL	ASP	GLN	SER	ALA	LEU	SER	CYS	SER	LEU	SER	135
136	ALA	ASP	GLY	MET	LEU	THR	PHE	SER	GLY	PRO	LYS	VAL	PRO	SER	GLY	150
151	VAL	ASP	ALA	GLY	HIS	SER	GLU	ARG	ALA	ILE	PRO	VAL	SER	ARG	GLU	165
166	GLU	LYS	PRO	SER	SER	ALA	PRO	THR	SER							180

α-CRYSTALLIN A₂ CHAIN—HORSE, DOG, CAT, RABBIT, RAT AND MONKEY

The sequences of the A₂ chain from the horse, dog, cat, rabbit, rat and monkey are the same as shown above for the pig, except for the following variations:

Residue no.	3	4	13	61	90	91	127	133	146	147	148	150
HORSE	ILE	ALA	ALA	ILE	GLN	GLU	THR	VAL	ILE	PRO	SER	MET
DOG	ILE	ALA	ALA	ILE	LEU	GLU	SER	LEU	VAL	PRO	SER	VAL
CAT	ILE	ALA	ALA	ILE	LEU	GLU	SER	LEU	VAL	PRO	SER	VAL
RABBIT	VAL	THR	THR	ILE	GLN	GLU	SER	LEU	VAL	GLN	SER	LEU
RAT	VAL	THR	ALA	ILE	LEU	GLU	SER	LEU	VAL	GLN	SER	LEU
MONKEY	VAL	THR	THR	ILE	GLN	ASP	SER	LEU	ILE	GLN	THR	LEU

Residue no.	153	155	162	168	172
HORSE	GLY	SER	SER	GLY	SER
DOG	GLY	SER	SER	SER	SER
CAT	GLY	SER	SER	SER	SER
RABBIT	GLY	SER	SER	SER	SER
RAT	GLY	SER	SER	SER	SER
MONKEY	OOO	THR	ALA	SER	SER

Primary structures of the α-crystallin A chains of seven mammalian species.
W. W. de Jong, F. J. van der Ouderaa, M. Versteeg, G. Groenewoud, J. M. van Amelsvoort, and H. Bloemendal.
Eur. J. Biochem., **53**, 237–242 (1975).

LENS PROTEINS

α-A^Ins-CRYSTALLIN—RAT

	1				5					10					15		
1	AC	MET	ASP	VAL	THR	ILE	GLN	HIS	PRO	TRP	PHE	LYS	ARG	ALA	LEU	15
16	GLY	PRO	PHE	TYR	PRO	SER	ARG	LEU	PHE	ASP	GLN	PHE	PHE	GLY	GLU	30
31	GLY	LEU	PHE	GLU	TYR	ASP	LEU	LEU	PRO	PHE	LEU	SER	SER	THR	ILE	45
46	SER	PRO	TYR	TYR	ARG	GLN	SER	LEU	PHE	ARG	THR	VAL	LEU	ASP	SER	60
61	GLY	ILE	SER	GLU	LEU	MET	THR	HIS	MET	PHE	VAL	HIS	MET	GLN	PRO	75
76	HIS	ALA	GLY	ASN	PRO	LYS	ASN	ASN	PRO	GLY	LYS	VAL	ARG	SER	ASP	90
91	ARG	ASP	LYS	PHE	VAL	ILE	PHE	LEU	ASP	VAL	LYS	HIS	PHE	SER	PRO	105
106	GLU	ASP	LEU	THR	VAL	LYS	VAL	LEU	GLU	ASP	PHE	VAL	GLU	ILE	HIS	120
121	GLY	LYS	HIS	ASN	GLU	ARG	GLN	ASP	ASP	HIS	GLY	TYR	ILE	SER	ARG	135
136	GLU	PHE	HIS	ARG	ARG	TYR	ARG	LEU	PRO	SER	ASN	VAL	ASP	GLN	SER	150
151	ALA	LEU	SER	CYS	SER	LEU	SER	ALA	ASP	GLY	MET	LEU	THR	PHE	SER	165
166	GLY	PRO	LYS	VAL	GLN	SER	GLY	LEU	ASP	ALA	GLY	HIS	SER	GLU	ARG	180
181	ALA	ILE	PRO	VAL	SER	ARG	GLU	GLU	LYS	PRO	SER	SER	ALA	PRO	SER	195
196	SER															210

Rat α-crystallin A-chain with an insertion of 22 residues.
L. H. Cohen, L. W. Westerhuis, W. W. de Jong, and H. Bloemendal.
Eur. J. Biochem., **89**, 259–266 (1978).

α-CRYSTALLIN B₂ CHAIN—BOVINE

	1				5					10					15		
1	AC	MET	ASP	ILE	ALA	ILE	HIS	HIS	PRO	TRP	ILE	ARG	ARG	PRO	PHE	15
16	PHE	PRO	PHE	HIS	SER	PRO	SER	ARG	LEU	PHE	ASP	GLN	PHE	PHE	GLY	30
31	GLU	HIS	LEU	LEU	GLU	SER	ASP	LEU	PHE	PRO	ALA	SER	THR	SER	LEU	45
46	SER	PRO	PHE	TYR	LEU	ARG	PRO	PRO	SER	PHE	LEU	ARG	ALA	PRO	SER	60
61	TRP	ILE	ASP	THR	GLY	LEU	SER	GLU	MET	ARG	LEU	GLU	LYS	ASP	ARG	75
76	PHE	SER	VAL	ASN	LEU	ASN	VAL	LYS	HIS	PHE	SER	PRO	GLU	GLU	LEU	90
91	LYS	VAL	LYS	VAL	LEU	GLY	ASP	VAL	ILE	GLU	VAL	HIS	GLY	LYS	HIS	105
106	GLU	GLU	ARG	GLN	ASP	GLU	HIS	GLY	PHE	ILE	SER	ARG	GLU	PHE	HIS	120
121	ARG	LYS	TYR	ARG	ILE	PRO	ALA	ASP	VAL	ASP	PRO	LEU	ALA	ILE	THR	135
136	SER	SER	LEU	SER	SER	ASP	GLY	VAL	LEU	THR	VAL	ASN	GLY	PRO	ARG	150
151	LYS	GLN	ALA	SER	GLY	PRO	GLU	ARG	THR	ILE	PRO	ILE	THR	ARG	GLU	165
166	GLU	LYS	PRO	ALA	VAL	THR	ALA	ALA	PRO	LYS	LYS					180

The amino acid sequence of the α B₂ chain of bovine α-crystallin.
F. J. van der Ouderaa, W. W. de Jong, A. Hilderink, and H. Bloemendal.
Eur. J. Biochem., **49**, 157–168 (1974).

α-CRYSTALLIN B₂ CHAIN—HUMAN

	1				5					10					15	
1	AC	MET	ASP	ILE	ALA	ILE	HIS	HIS	PRO	TRP	ILE	ARG	ARG	PRO	PHE	15
16	PHE	PRO	PHE	HIS	SER	PRO	SER	ARG	LEU	PHE	ASP	GLN	PHE	PHE	GLY	30
31	GLU	HIS	LEU	LEU	GLU	SER	ASP	LEU	PHE	PRO	THR	SER	THR	SER	LEU	45
46	SER	PRO	PHE	TYR	LEU	ARG	PRO	PRO	SER	PHE	LEU	ARG	ALA	PRO	SER	60
61	TRP	PHE	ASP	THR	GLY	LEU	SER	GLU	MET	ARG	LEU	GLU	LYS	ASP	ARG	75
76	PHE	SER	VAL	ASN	LEU	ASN	VAL	LYS	HIS	PHE	SER	PRO	GLU	GLU	LEU	90
91	LYS	VAL	LYS	VAL	LEU	GLY	ASP	VAL	ILE	GLU	VAL	HIS	GLY	LYS	HIS	105
106	GLU	GLU	ARG	GLN	ASP	GLU	HIS	GLY	PHE	ILE	SER	ARG	GLU	PHE	HIS	120
121	ARG	LYS	TYR	ARG	ILE	PRO	ALA	ASP	VAL	ASP	PRO	LEU	ALA	ILE	THR	135
136	SER	SER	LEU	SER	SER	ASP	GLY	VAL	LEU	THR	VAL	ASN	GLY	PRO	ARG	150
151	LYS	GLN	VAL	SER	GLY	PRO	GLU	ARG	THR	ILE	PRO	ILE	THR	ARG	GLU	165
166	GLU	LYS	PRO	ALA	VAL	THR	ALA	ALA	PRO	LYS	LYS					180

The primary structure of the B₂ chain of human α-crystallin.
J. A. Kramps, B. M. de Man, and W. W. de Jong.
FEBS Letters, **74**, 82–84 (1977).

MILK PROTEINS

BOVINE α s1 CASEIN

	1				5					10					15		
1	ARG	PRO	LYS	HIS	PRO	ILE	LYS	HIS	GLN	GLY	LEU	PRO	GLN	GLU	VAL	15
16	LEU	ASN	GLU	ASN	LEU	LEU	ARG	PHE	PHE	VAL	ALA	PRO	PHE	PRO	GLN	30
31	VAL	PHE	GLY	LYS	GLU	LYS	VAL	ASN	GLU	LEU	SER	LYS	ASP	ILE	GLY	45
46	PSE	GLU	PSE	THR	GLU	ASP	GLN	ALA	MET	GLU	ASP	ILE	LYS	GLN	MET	60
61	GLU	ALA	GLU	PSE	ILE	PSE	PSE	PSE	GLU	GLU	ILE	VAL	PRO	ASN	PSE	75
76	VAL	GLU	GLN	LYS	HIS	ILE	GLN	LYS	GLU	ASP	VAL	PRO	SER	GLU	ARG	90
91	TYR	LEU	GLY	TYR	LEU	GLU	GLN	LEU	LEU	ARG	LEU	LYS	LYS	TYR	LYS	105
106	VAL	PRO	GLN	LEU	GLU	ILE	VAL	PRO	ASN	PSE	ALA	GLU	GLU	ARG	LEU	120
121	HIS	SER	MET	LYS	GLU	GLY	ILE	HIS	ALA	GLN	GLN	LYS	GLU	PRO	MET	135
136	ILE	GLY	VAL	ASN	GLN	GLU	LEU	ALA	TYR	PHE	TYR	PRO	GLU	LEU	PHE	150
151	ARG	GLN	PHE	TYR	GLN	LEU	ASP	ALA	TYR	PRO	SER	GLY	ALA	TRP	TYR	165
166	TYR	VAL	PRO	LEU	GLY	THR	GLN	TYR	THR	ASP	ALA	PRO	SER	PHE	SER	180
181	ASP	ILE	PRO	ASN	PRO	ILE	GLY	SER	GLU	ASN	SER	GLU	LYS	THR	THR	195
196	MET	PRO	LEU	TRP												210

The primary structure of bovine α s1 casein.
J.-C. Mercier, F. Grosclaude, and B. Ribadeau-Dumas.
Eur. J. Biochem. **23**, 41–51 (1971).
Note: The above sequence is that of variant B. Variant A lacks residues 14–26; variant C residue 192 is GLY; and in variant D, residue 53 is O-phosphothreonine.
And correcting;
Structure of bovine α s1 casein and β casein.
F. Grosclaude, M.-F. Mahé, and B. Ribadeau-Dumas.
Eur. J. Biochem. **40**, 323–324 (1973).

MILK PROTEINS

BOVINE α s2 CASEIN

	1				5					10					15	
1	LYS	ASN	THR	MET	GLU	HIS	VAL	PSE	PSE	PSE	GLU	GLU	SER	ILE	ILE	15
16	PSE	GLN	GLU	THR	TYR	LYS	GLN	GLU	LYS	ASN	MET	ALA	ILE	ASN	PRO	30
31	SER	LYS	GLU	ASN	LEU	CYS	SER	THR	PHE	CYS	LYS	GLU	VAL	VAL	ARG	45
46	ASN	ALA	ASN	GLU	GLU	GLU	TYR	SER	ILE	GLY	PSE	PSE	PSE	GLU	GLU	60
61	PSE	ALA	GLU	VAL	ALA	THR	GLU	GLU	VAL	LYS	ILE	THR	VAL	ASP	ASP	75
76	LYS	HIS	TYR	GLN	LYS	ALA	LEU	ASN	GLU	ILE	ASN	GLU	PHE	TYR	GLN	90
91	LYS	PHE	PRO	GLN	TYR	LEU	GLN	TYR	LEU	TYR	GLN	GLY	PRO	ILE	VAL	105
106	LEU	ASN	PRO	TRP	ASP	GLN	VAL	LYS	ARG	ASN	ALA	VAL	PRO	ILE	THR	120
121	PRO	THR	LEU	ASN	ARG	GLU	GLN	LEU	PSE	THR	PSE	GLU	GLU	ASN	SER	135
136	LYS	LYS	THR	VAL	ASP	MET	GLU	PSE	THR	GLU	VAL	PHE	THR	LYS	LYS	150
151	THR	LYS	LEU	THR	GLU	GLU	GLU	LYS	ASN	ARG	LEU	ASN	PHE	LEU	LYS	165
166	LYS	ILE	SER	GLN	ARG	TYR	GLN	LYS	PHE	ALA	LEU	PRO	GLN	TYR	LEU	180
181	LYS	THR	VAL	TYR	GLN	HIS	GLN	LYS	ALA	MET	LYS	PRO	TRP	ILE	GLN	195
196	PRO	LYS	THR	LYS	VAL	ILE	PRO	TYR	VAL	ARG	TYR	LEU				210

Complete amino acid sequence of bovine α_{s2}-casein.
G. Brignon, B. Ribadeau Dumas, J. Mercier and J. Pelissier.
FEBS Letters **76**, 274–279 (1977).

BOVINE β-CASEIN (A²)

	1				5					10					15	
1	ARG	GLU	LEU	GLU	GLU	LEU	ASN	VAL	PRO	GLY	GLU	ILE	VAL	GLU	PSE	15
16	LEU	PSE	PSE	PSE	GLU	GLU	SER	ILE	THR	ARG	ILE	ASN	LYS	LYS	ILE	30
31	GLU	LYS	PHE	GLN	PSE	GLU	GLU	GLN	GLN	GLN	THR	GLU	ASP	GLU	LEU	45
46	GLN	ASP	LYS	ILE	HIS	PRO	PHE	ALA	GLN	THR	GLN	SER	LEU	VAL	TYR	60
61	PRO	PHE	PRO	GLY	PRO	ILE	PRO	ASN	SER	LEU	PRO	GLN	ASN	ILE	PRO	75
76	PRO	LEU	THR	GLN	THR	PRO	VAL	VAL	VAL	PRO	PRO	PHE	LEU	GLN	PRO	90
91	GLU	VAL	MET	GLY	VAL	SER	LYS	VAL	LYS	GLU	ALA	MET	ALA	PRO	LYS	105
106	HIS	LYS	GLU	MET	PRO	PHE	PRO	LYS	TYR	PRO	VAL	GLN	PRO	PHE	THR	120
121	GLU	SER	GLN	SER	LEU	THR	LEU	THR	ASP	VAL	GLU	ASN	LEU	HIS	LEU	135
136	PRO	PRO	LEU	LEU	LEU	GLN	SER	TRP	MET	HIS	GLN	PRO	HIS	GLN	PRO	150
151	LEU	PRO	PRO	THR	VAL	MET	PHE	PRO	PRO	GLN	SER	VAL	LEU	SER	LEU	165
166	SER	GLN	SER	LYS	VAL	LEU	PRO	VAL	PRO	GLU	LYS	ALA	VAL	PRO	TYR	180
181	PRO	GLN	ARG	ASP	MET	PRO	ILE	GLN	ALA	PHE	LEU	LEU	TYR	GLN	GLN	195
196	PRO	VAL	LEU	GLY	PRO	VAL	ARG	GLY	PRO	PHE	PRO	ILE	ILE	VAL		210

The complete primary structure of β-casein.
B. Ribadeau-Dumas, G. Brignon, F. Grosclaude and J.-C. Mercier.
Eur. J. Biochem. **25**, 505–514 (1972).
The variant βE casein, and the phosphorylation rule for caseins.
F. Grosclaude, M.-F. Mahe, and G.-F. Voglino.
FEBS Letters **45**, 3–5 (1974).
The E variant of bovine β-casein differs from the A² variant by the substitution 36 GLU(A²)–LYS(E).

MILK PROTEINS

BOVINE PARA κ-CASEIN

	1			5					10					15	
1	PYG	GLN	GLN	ASN	GLU	GLU	GLU	PRO	ILE	ARG	CYS	GLU	LYS	ASP	GLU	15
16	ARG	PHE	PHE	SER	ASP	LYS	ILE	ALA	LYS	TYR	ILE	PRO	ILE	GLN	TYR	30
31	VAL	LEU	SER	ARG	TYR	PRO	SER	TYR	GLY	LEU	ASN	TYR	TYR	GLN	GLN	45
46	LYS	PRO	VAL	ALA	LEU	ILE	ASN	ASN	GLN	PHE	LEU	PRO	TYR	PRO	TYR	60
61	TYR	ALA	LYS	PRO	ALA	ALA	VAL	ARG	SER	PRO	ALA	GLN	ILE	LEU	GLN	75
76	TRP	GLN	VAL	LEU	SER	ASN	THR	VAL	PRO	ALA	LYS	SER	CYS	GLN	ALA	90
91	GLN	PRO	THR	THR	MET	ALA	ARG	HIS	PRO	HIS	PRO	HIS	LEU	SER	PHE	105

The Primary Structure of bovine para κ-casein.
G. Brignon, J.-C. Mercier, B. Ribadeau-Dumas and B. C. Das.
FEBS Letters **27**, 301–305 (1972).
And Correction:
Studies on the primary structure of cow κ-casein: the primary sequence of cow para-κ-casein.
J. Jollès, F. Schoentgen, C. Alais, and P. Jollès.
Chimia, **26**, 645–646 (1972).

BOVINE κ B₁ CASEIN

	1			5					10					15	
1	PYG	GLU	GLN	ASN	GLN	GLU	GLN	PRO	ILE	ARG	CYS	GLU	LYS	ASP	GLU	15
16	ARG	PHE	PHE	SER	ASP	LYS	ILE	ALA	LYS	TYR	ILE	PRO	ILE	GLN	TYR	30
31	VAL	LEU	SER	ARG	TYR	PRO	SER	TYR	GLY	LEU	ASN	TYR	TYR	GLN	GLN	45
46	LYS	PRO	VAL	ALA	LEU	ILE	ASN	ASN	GLN	PHE	LEU	PRO	TYR	PRO	TYR	60
61	TYR	ALA	LYS	PRO	ALA	ALA	VAL	ARG	SER	PRO	ALA	GLN	ILE	LEU	GLN	75
76	TRP	GLN	VAL	LEU	SER	ASP	THR	VAL	PRO	ALA	LYS	SER	CYS	GLN	ALA	90
91	GLN	PRO	THR	THR	MET	ALA	ARG	HIS	PRO	HIS	PRO	HIS	LEU	SER	PHE	105
106	MET	ALA	ILE	PRO	PRO	LYS	LYS	ASN	GLN	ASP'	LYS	THR	GLU	ILE	PRO	120
121	THR	ILE	ASN	THR	ILE	ALA	SER	GLY	GLU	PRO	THR	SER	THR	PRO	THR	135
136	ILE	GLU	ALA	VAL	GLU	SER	THR	VAL	ALA	THR	LEU	GLU	ALA	PSE	PRO	151
151	GLU	VAL	ILE	GLU	SER	PRO	PRO	GLU	ILE	ASN	THR	VAL	GLN	VAL	THR	165
166	SER	THR	ALA	VAL												180

Note. Variant A has at position 136 THR, and at position 148 ASP.
Primary structure of bovine κ B casein.
J.-C. Mercier, G. Brignon, and B. Ribadeau-Dumas.
Eur. J. Biochem. **35**, 222–235 (1973).

MILK PROTEINS

SHEEP PARA-κ A-CASEIN

		1				5				10				15		
1	GLN	GLN	GLN	ASN	GLN	GLU	GLU	ARG	ILE	CYS	CYS	GLU	LYS	ASP	GLU	15
16	ARG	PHE	PHE	ASP	ASP	LYS	ILE	ALA	LYS	TYR	ILE	PRO	ILE	GLN	TYR	30
31	VAL	LEU	SER	ARG	TYR	PRO	SER	TYR	GLY	LEU	ASN	TYR	TYR	GLN	GLN	45
46	ARG	PRO	VAL	ALA	LEU	ILE	ASN	ASN	GLN	PHE	LEU	PRO	TYR	PRO	TYR	60
61	TYR	ALA	LYS	PRO	VAL	ALA	VAL	ARG	SER	PRO	ALA	GLN	THR	LEU	GLN	75
76	TRP	GLN	VAL	LEU	PRO	ASN	ALA	VAL	PRO	ALA	LYS	SER	CYS	GLN	ASP	90
91	GLN	PRO	THR	ALA	MET	ALA	ARG	HIS	PRO	HIS	PRO	HIS	LEU	SER	PHE	105

The sequence of sheep κ-casein: primary structure of para-κ A-casein.
J. Jollès, F. Schoentgen, J. Hermann, C. Alais, and P. Jollès.
Eur. J. Biochem. **46**, 127–132 (1974).

SHEEP κ A-CASEIN

		1				5				10				15		
1	GLN	GLN	GLN	ASN	GLN	GLU	GLU	ARG	ILE	CYS	CYS	GLU	LYS	ASP	GLU	15
16	ARG	PHE	PHE	ASP	ASP	LYS	ILE	ALA	LYS	TYR	ILE	PRO	ILE	GLN	TYR	30
31	VAL	LEU	SER	ARG	TYR	PRO	SER	TYR	GLY	LEU	ASN	TYR	TYR	GLN	GLN	45
46	ARG	PRO	VAL	ALA	LEU	ILE	ASN	ASN	GLN	PHE	LEU	PRO	TYR	PRO	TYR	60
61	TYR	ALA	LYS	PRO	VAL	ALA	VAL	ARG	SER	PRO	ALA	GLN	THR	LEU	GLN	75
76	TRP	GLN	VAL	LEU	PRO	ASN	ALA	VAL	PRO	ALA	LYS	SER	CYS	GLN	ASP	90
91	GLN	PRO	THR	ALA	MET	ALA	ARG	HIS	PRO	HIS	PRO	HIS	LEU	SER	PHE	105
106	MET	ALA	ILE	PRO	PRO	LYS	LYS	ASP	GLN	ASP	LYS	THR	GLU	ILE	PRO	120
121	ALA	ILE	ASN	THR	ILE	ALA	SER	ALA	GLU	PRO	THR	VAL	HIS	SER	THR	135
136	PRO	THR	THR	GLU	ALA	VAL	VAL	ASN	ALA	VAL	ASP	ASN	PRO	GLU	ALA	150
151	SER	SER	GLU	SER	ILE	ALA	SER	ALA	PRO	GLU	THR	ASN	THR	ALA	GLN	165
166	VAL	THR	SER	THR	GLU	VAL										180

The amino acid sequence of sheep κ A-casein. II. Sequence studies concerning the κ
A-caseinoglycopeptide and establishment of the complete primary structure of the protein.
J. Jollès, A.-M. Fiat, F. Schoentgen, C. Alais, and P. Jollès.
Biochim. Biophys. Acta, **365**, 335–343 (1974).

MISCELLANEOUS PROTEINS

α_1-ACID GLYCOPROTEIN FROM HUMAN PLASMA

	1				5					10					15	
1	PYG	ILE	PRO	LEU	CYS	ALA	ASN	LEU	VAL	PRO	VAL	PRO	ILE	THR	ASN	15
16	ALA	THR	LEU	ASP	ARG GLN	ILE	THR	GLY	LYS	TRP	PHE	TYR	ILE	ALA	SER	30
31	ALA	PHE ALA	ARG	ASN	GLU	GLU	TYR	ASN	LYS	SER	VAL	GLU	GLU	ILE	GLN	45
46	ALA	THR ALA	PHE	PHE	TYR	PHE	THR	PRO	ASN	LYS	THR	GLU	ASP	THR	ILE	60
61	PHE	LEU	ARG	GLU	TYR	GLN	THR	ARG	GLN	ASP	GLN	CYS	ILE PHE	TYR	ASN	75
76	THR SER	THR SER	TYR	LEU	ASN	VAL	GLN	ARG	GLU	ASN	GLY	THR	VAL ILE	SER	ARG	90
91	TYR	VAL GLU	GLY	GLY	GLN ARG	GLU	HIS	VAL PHE	ALA	HIS	LEU	LEU	ILE	LEU	ARG	105
106	ASP	THR	LYS	THR	LEU TYR	MET	PHE	GLY	SER	TYR	LEU	ASP	ASP	GLU	LYS	120
121	ASN	TRP	GLY	LEU	SER	PHE VAL	TYR	ALA	ASP	LYS	PRO	GLU	THR	THR	LYS	135
136	GLU	GLN	LEU	GLY	GLU	PHE	TYR	GLU	ALA	LEU	ASP	CYS	LEU	CYS ARG	ILE	150
151	PRO	ARG LYS	SER	ASP	VAL	MET VAL	TYR	THR	ASP	TRP	LYS	LYS	ASP	CYS	GLU	165
166	PRO	LEU	GLU	LYS	GLN	HIS	GLU	LYS	ARG	LYS	GLN	GLU	GLU	GLY	GLU	180
181	SER															195

Note: LEU may also be at position 112, ALA at 113, PHE at 114, ASP at 115, VAL at 116, and ASN at 117.
Structure of α_1-acid glycoprotein. The complete amino acid sequence, multiple amino acid substitutions, and homology with the immunoglobulins.
K. Schmid, H. Kaufmann, S. Isemura, F. Bauer, J. Emura, T. Motoyama, M. Ishiguro, and S. Nanno.
Biochemistry, **12**, 2711–2724 (1973).

HUMAN β_2-MICROGLOBULIN

	1				5					10					15	
1	ILE	GLN	ARG	THR	PRO	LYS	ILE	GLN	VAL	TYR	SER	ARG	HIS	PRO	ALA	15
16	GLU	ASN	GLY	LYS	SER	ASN	PHE	LEU	ASN	CYS	TYR	VAL	SER	GLY	PHE	30
31	HIS	PRO	SER	ASP	ILE	GLU	VAL	ASP	LEU	LEU	LYS	ASP	GLY	GLU	ARG	45
46	ILE	GLU	LYS	VAL	GLU	HIS	SER	ASP	LEU	SER	PHE	SER	LYS	ASP	TRP	60
61	SER	PHE	TYR	LEU	LEU	TYR	SER	TYR	THR	GLU	PHE	THR	PRO	THR	GLU	75
76	LYS	ASP	GLU	TYR	ALA	CYS	ARG	VAL	ASN	HIS	VAL	THR	LEU	SER	GLN	90
91	PRO	LYS	ILE	VAL	LYS	TRP	ASP	ARG	ASP	MET						105

Note: A disulphide bridge links residues CYS 25 and 81.
The complete amino acid sequence of β_2-microglobulin.
B. A. Cunningham, J. L. Wang, I. Berggård, and P. A. Peterson.
Biochemistry, **12**, 4811–4822 (1973).

MISCELLANEOUS PROTEINS

APOLIPOPROTEIN GLUTAMINE I

```
       1                    5                        10                      15
  1  ASP GLU PRO PRO GLN SER PRO TRP ASP ARG VAL LYS ASP LEU ALA   15
 16  THR VAL TYR VAL ASP VAL LEU LYS ASP SER GLY ARG ASP TYR VAL   30
 31  SER GLN PHE GLN GLY SER ALA LEU GLY LYS GLN LEU ASN LEU LYS   45
 46  LEU LEU TRP ASP ASP VAL THR SER THR PHE SER LYS LEU ARG GLN   60
 61  GLU LEU GLY PRO VAL THR GLU GLU TRP PHE ASN ASP LEU GLN GLU   75
 76  LYS LEU ASN LEU GLU LYS GLU THR GLY GLU LEU ARG GLN GLU MET   90
 91  SER LYS ASP LEU GLU GLU VAL LYS ALA LYS VAL GLN PRO TYR LEU  105
106  ASP ASP PHE GLN LYS LYS TRP GLN GLU MET GLU LEU TYR ARG GLN  120
121  LYS VAL GLU PRO LEU ARG ALA GLU LEU GLN GLU GLY ALA ARG GLN  135
136  LYS LEU HIS GLU LEU GLN GLU LYS LEU SER PRO LEU GLY GLU GLU  150
151  MET ARG ASP ARG ALA ARG ALA HIS VAL ASP ALA LEU ARG THR HIS  165
166  LEU ALA PRO TYR SER ASP GLU LEU ARG GLN ARG LEU ALA ALA ARG  180
181  LEU GLU ALA LEU LYS GLU ASN GLY ALA GLY ARG LEU ALA GLU TYR  195
196  HIS ALA LYS ALA THR GLU HIS LEU SER THR LEU SER GLU LYS ALA  210
211  LYS PRO ALA LEU GLU ASP LEU ARG GLN GLY LEU LEU PRO VAL LEU  225
226  GLU SER PHE LYS VAL SER PHE LEU SER ALA LEU GLU GLU TYR THR  240
241  LYS LEU ASN THR GLN                                          255
```

The primary structure of human plasma high density apolipoprotein glutamine I (ApoA-1). II.
The amino acid sequence and alignment of cyanogen bromide fragments IV, III, and I.
H. N. Baker, A. M. Gotto, Jr., and R. L. Jackson.
J. Biol. Chem. **250**, 2725–2738 (1975).

HUMAN APOLIPOPROTEIN APOLP–GLN

```
       1                    5                        10                      15
  1  PYG ALA LYS GLU PRO CYS VAL GLU SER LEU VAL SER GLN TYR PHE   15
 16  GLN THR VAL THR ASP TYR GLY LYS ASP LEU MET GLU LYS VAL LYS   30
 31  SER PRO GLU LEU GLN ALA GLN ALA LYS SER TYR PHE GLU LYS SER   45
 46  LYS GLU GLN LEU THR PRO LEU ILE LYS LYS ALA GLY THR GLU LEU   60
 61  VAL ASN PHE LEU SER TYR PHE VAL GLU LEU GLY THR GLN PRO ALA   75
 76  THR GLN                                                       90
```

Note: This protein is found as a dimer formed from two chains of identical sequence, joined
by a disulphide bridge at CYS 6.
Isolation and characterization of the tryptic and cyanogen bromide peptides of ApoLp–Gln-II
(ApoA-II), a plasma High density Apolipoprotein.
S. E. Lux, K. M. John, R. Ronan, and H. B. Brewer, Jr.
J. Biol. Chem., **247**, 7519–7527 (1972).

MISCELLANEOUS PROTEINS

APOLIPOPROTEIN A-II—RHESUS MONKEY

	1				5					10					15	
1	PYG	ALA	GLU	GLU	PRO	SER	VAL	GLU	SER	LEU	VAL	SER	GLN	TYR	PHE	15
16	GLN	THR	VAL	THR	ASP	TYR	GLY	LYS	ASP	LEU	MET	GLU	LYS	VAL	LYS	30
31	SER	PRO	GLU	LEU	GLN	ALA	GLN	ALA	LYS	ALA	TYR	PHE	GLU	LYS	SER	45
46	LYS	GLU	GLN	LEU	THR	PRO	LEU	VAL	LYS	LYS	ALA	GLY	THR	ASP	LEU	60
61	VAL	ASN	PHE	LEU	SER	TYR	PHE	VAL	GLU	LEU	ARG	THR	GLN	PRO	ALA	75
76	THR	GLN														90

Covalent structure of apolipoprotein A-II from *Macaca mulatta* serum high density lipoproteins.
C. Edelstein, C. Noyes, P. Keim, R. L. Heinrikson, R. E. Fellows, and A. M. Scanu.
Biochemistry, **15**, 1262–1270 (1976).

APOLIPOPROTEIN—SERINE

	1				5					10					15	
1	THR	PRO	ASP	VAL	SER	SER	ALA	LEU	ASP	LYS	LEU	LYS	GLU	PHE	GLY	15
16	ASN	THR	LEU	GLU	ASP	LYS	ALA	ARG	GLU	LEU	ILE	SER	ARG	ILE	LYS	30
31	GLN	SER	GLU	LEU	SER	ALA	LYS	MET	ARG	GLU	TRP	PHE	SER	GLU	THR	45
46	PHE	GLN	LYS	VAL	LYS	GLU	LYS	LEU	LYS	ILE	ASP	SER				60

The complete amino acid sequence of C-1 (ApoLp–Ser), an apolipoprotein from human very low density lipoproteins.
R. S. Shulman, P. N. Herbert, K. Wehrly, and D. S. Fredrickson.
J. Biol. Chem., **250**, 182–190 (1975).
The primary structure of apolipoprotein–serine.
R. L. Jackson, J. T. Sparrow, H. N. Baker, J. D. Morrisett, O. D. Taunton, and A. M. Gotto, Jr.
J. Biol. Chem., **249**, 5308–5313 (1974).

MISCELLANEOUS PROTEINS

HUMAN APOLIPOPROTEIN APOLP–ALA

	1				5					10					15	
1	SER	GLU	ALA	GLU	ASP	ALA	SER	LEU	LEU	SER	PHE	MET	GLN	GLY	TYR	15
16	MET	LYS	HIS	ALA	THR	LYS	THR	ALA	LYS	ASP	ALA	LEU	SER	SER	VAL	30
31	GLN	SER	GLN	GLN	VAL	ALA	ALA	GLN	GLN	ARG	GLY	TRP	VAL	THR	ASP	45
46	GLY	PHE	SER	SER	LEU	LYS	ASP	TYR	TRP	SER	THR	VAL	LYS	ASP	LYS	60
61	PHE	SER	GLU	PHE	TRP	ASP	LEU	ASP	PRO	GLU	VAL	ARG	PRO	THR	SER	75
76	ALA	VAL	ALA	ALA												90

Note: Carbohydrate is attached to residue 74.
The complete amino acid sequence of an apolipoprotein obtained from human very low density lipoprotein (VLDL).
H. B. Brewer, Jr, R. Shulman, P. Herbert, R. Ronan, and K. Wehrly.
Advances in Exp. Med. and Biol., **26**, 280 (1972).
The complete amino acid sequence of alanine apolipoprotein (apoC-III), an apolipoprotein from human plasma, very low density lipoproteins.
H. B. Brewer, Jr, R. Shulman, P. Herbert, R. Ronan, and K. Wehrly.
J. Biol. Chem., **249**, 4975–4984 (1974).

APOLIPOPROTEIN VLDL-II—HEN

	1				5					10					15	
1	LYS	SER	ILE	ILE	ASP	ARG	GLU	ARG	ARG	ASP	TRP	LEU	VAL	ILE	PRO	15
16	ASP	ALA	ALA	ALA	ALA	TYR	ILE	TYR	GLU	ALA	VAL	ASN	LYS	VAL	SER	30
31	PRO	ARG	ARG	ALA	GLY	GLU	PHE	LEU	LEU	ASP	THR	VAL	SER	GLN	THR	45
46	VAL	VAL	SER	GLY	ILE	ARG	ASN	PHE	LEU	ILE	ASN	THR	ALA	GLU	ARG	60
61	LEU	THR	LYS	LEU	ALA	GLU	GLN	LEU	MET	GLU	LYS	ILE	LYS	ASP	LEU	75
76	CYS	TYR	THR	LYS	VAL	LEU	GLY									90

Amino Acid Sequence of a Major Apoprotein from Hen Plasma very low density lipoproteins.
R. L. Jackson, H.-Y. Lin, L. Chan, and A. R. Means.
J. Biol. Chem., **252**, 250–253 (1977).

510

MISCELLANEOUS PROTEINS

HUMAN SERUM ALBUMIN

```
          1              5                    10                        15
   1  ASP ALA HIS LYS SER GLU VAL ALA HIS  ARG PHE LYS ASP LEU GLY   15
  16  GLU GLU ASN PHE LYS ALA LEU VAL LEU ILE  ALA PHE ALA GLN TYR   30
  31  LEU GLN GLN CYS PRO PHE GLU ASP HIS  VAL LYS LEU VAL ASN GLU   45
  46  VAL THR GLU PHE ALA LYS THR CYS VAL ALA ASP  GLU SER ALA GLU   60
  61  ASN CYS ASP LYS SER LEU HIS THR LEU PHE GLY ASP LYS LEU CYS    75
  76  THR VAL ALA THR LEU ARG GLU THR TYR GLY GLU MET ALA ASP CYS    90
  91  CYS ALA LYS GLU GLN PRO GLU ARG ASN GLU CYS PHE LEU GLN HIS   105
 106  LYS ASP ASP ASN PRO ASN LEU PRO ARG LEU VAL ARG PRO GLU VAL   120
 121  ASP VAL MET CYS THR ALA PHE HIS  ASP ASN GLN GLU THR PHE LEU  135
 136  LYS LYS TYR LEU TYR GLU ILE  ALA ARG ARG HIS  PRO TYR PHE TYR 150
 151  ALA PRO GLU LEU LEU PHE PHE ALA LYS  ARG TYR LYS ALA ALA PHE  165
 166  THR GLU CYS CYS GLU ALA ALA ASP LYS ALA ALA CYS LEU LEU PRO   180
 181  LYS LEU ASP GLU LEU ARG ASP GLU GLY LYS ALA SER SER ALA LYS   195
 196  GLN ARG LEU LYS CYS ALA SER LEU GLN LYS PHE GLY GLU ARG ALA   210
 211  PHE LYS ALA TRP ALA VAL ALA ARG LEU SER GLN ARG PHE PRO LYS   225
 226  ALA GLU PHE ALA GLU VAL SER LYS LEU VAL THR ASP LEU THR LYS   240
 241  VAL HIS  THR GLU CYS CYS HIS  GLY ASP LEU LEU GLU CYS ALA ASP 255
 256  ASP ARG ALA ASP LEU ALA LYS TYR ILE  CYS GLU ASN GLN ASP SER  270
 271  ILE  SER SER LYS LEU LYS GLU CYS CYS GLU LYS PRO LEU LEU GLU  285
 286  LYS SER HIS CYS ILE  ALA GLU VAL GLU ASN ASP GLU MET PRO ALA  300
 301  ASP LEU PRO SER LEU ALA ALA ASP PHE VAL GLU SER LYS ASP VAL   315
 316  CYS LYS ASN TYR ALA GLU ALA LYS ASP VAL PHE LEU GLY MET PHE   330
 331  LEU TYR GLU TYR ALA ARG ARG HIS  PRO ASP TYR SER VAL VAL LEU  345
 346  LEU LEU ARG LEU ALA LYS THR TYR GLU THR THR LEU GLU LYS CYS   360
 361  CYS ALA ALA HIS  ASP PRO TYR GLU CYS ALA ALA LYS VAL PHE ASP  375
 376  GLU PHE LYS PRO LEU VAL GLU GLU PRO GLN ASN LEU ILE  LYS GLN  390
 391  ASN CYS GLU LEU PHE GLU GLN LEU GLY GLU TYR LYS PHE GLN ASN   405
 406  ALA LEU LEU VAL ARG TYR THR LYS LYS VAL PRO GLN VAL SER THR   420
 421  PRO THR LEU VAL GLU VAL SER ARG ASN LEU GLY LYS VAL GLY SER   435
 436  LYS CYS CYS LYS HIS  PRO GLU ALA LYS ARG MET PRO CYS ALA GLU  450
 451  ASP TYR LEU SER VAL VAL LEU ASN GLN LEU CYS VAL LEU GLU HIS   465
 466  LYS THR PRO VAL SER ASP ARG VAL THR LYS CYS CYS THR GLU SER   480
 481  LEU VAL ASN ARG ARG PRO CYS PHE SER ALA LEU GLU VAL ASP GLU   495
 496  THR TYR VAL PRO LYS GLN PHE ASN ALA GLU THR PHE THR PHE HIS   510
 511  ALA ASP ILE  CYS THR LEU SER GLU LYS GLU ARG GLN ILE  LYS LYS 525
 526  GLN THR ALA LEU VAL GLU LEU VAL LYS HIS  LYS PRO LYS ALA THR  540
 541  LYS GLU GLN LEU LYS ALA VAL MET ASP ASP PHE ALA ALA PHE VAL   555
 556  GLU LYS CYS CYS LYS ALA ASP ASP LYS GLU THR CYS PHE ALA GLU   570
 571  GLU GLY LYS LYS LEU VAL ALA ALA SER GLN ALA ALA LEU GLY LEU   585
```

Complete amino acid sequence of human serum albumin.
B. Meloun, L. Morávek, and V. Kostka.
FEBS Letters, **58**, 134–137 (1975).

MISCELLANEOUS PROTEINS

HUMAN PLASMA PREALBUMIN

	1				5					10					15	
1	GLY	PRO	THR	GLY	THR	GLY	GLU	SER	LYS	CYS	PRO	LEU	MET	VAL	LYS	15
16	VAL	LEU	ASP	ALA	VAL	ARG	GLY	SER	PRO	ALA	ILE	ASN	VAL	ALA	VAL	30
31	HIS	VAL	PHE	ARG	LYS	ALA	ALA	ASP	ASP	THR	TRP	GLU	PRO	PHE	ALA	45
46	SER	GLY	LYS	THR	SER	GLU	SER	GLY	GLU	LEU	HIS	GLY	LEU	THR	THR	60
61	GLX	GLX	GLN	PHE	VAL	GLU	GLY	ILE	TYR	LYS	VAL	GLU	ILE	ASP	THR	75
76	LYS	SER	TYR	TRP	LYS	ALA	LEU	GLY	ILE	SER	PRO	PHE	HIS	GLU	HIS	90
91	ALA	GLU	VAL	VAL	PHE	THR	ALA	ASN	ASP	SER	GLY	PRO	ARG	ARG	TYR	105
106	THR	ILE	ALA	ALA	LEU	LEU	SER	PRO	TYR	SER	TYR	SER	THR	THR	ALA	120
121	VAL	VAL	THR	ASN	PRO	LYS	GLU									135

Primary structure of human prealbumin.
Y. Kanda, F. J. Morgan, R. E. Canfield, and D. S. Goodman.
Fed. Proc., **33**, 1563 (Abstract 1920) (1974).
The amino acid sequence of human plasma prealbumin.
Y. Kanda, D. S. Goodman, R. E. Canfield, and F. J. Morgan.
J. Biol. Chem., **249**, 6796–6805 (1974).

BOVINE FACTOR X1 (STUART FACTOR)—LIGHT CHAIN

	1				5					10					15	
1	ALA	ASN	SER	PHE	LEU	GLA	GLA	VAL	LYS	GLN	GLY	ASN	LEU	GLA	ARG	15
16	GLA	CYS	LEU	GLA	GLA	ALA	CYS	SER	LEU	GLA	GLA	ALA	ARG	GLA	VAL	30
31	PHE	GLA	ASP	ALA	GLA	GLN	THR	ASP	GLN	PHE	TRP	SER	LYS	TYR	LYS	45
46	ASP	GLY	ASP	GLN	CYS	GLU	GLY	HIS	PRO	CYS	LEU	ASN	GLN	GLY	HIS	60
61	CYS	LYS	ASN	GLY	ILE	GLY	ASP	TYR	THR	CYS	THR	CYS	ALA	GLU	GLY	75
76	PHE	GLU	GLY	LYS	ASN	CYS	GLU	PHE	SER	THR	ARG	GLU	ILE	CYS	SER	90
91	LEU	ASP	ASN	GLY	GLY	CYS	ASP	GLN	PHE	CYS	ARG	GLU	GLU	ARG	SER	105
106	GLU	VAL	ARG	CYS	SER	CYS	ALA	HIS	GLY	TYR	VAL	LEU	GLY	ASP	ASP	120
121	SER	LYS	SER	CYS	VAL	SER	THR	GLU	ARG	PHE	PRO	CYS	GLY	LYS	PHE	135
136	THR	GLN	GLY	ARG	SER											150

Notes: (i) Residues GLA are tentatively identified as gamma carboxyglutamic acid. (ii) The identity of residues 38 and 39 is only tentative.
Bovine factor X1 (Stuart Factor). Primary structure of the light chain.
D. L. Enfield, L. H. Ericsson, K. A. Walsh, H. Neurath, and K. Titani.
Proc. Natn. Acad. Sci., U.S.A., **72**, 16–19 (1975).

512

MISCELLANEOUS PROTEINS

β-THROMBOGLOBULIN—HUMAN

	1				5					10					15	
1	GLY	LYS	GLU	GLU	SER	LEU	ASP	SER	ASP	LEU	TYR	ALA	GLU	LEU	ARG	15
16	CYS	MET	CYS	ILE	LYS	THR	THR	SER	GLY	ILE	HIS	PRO	LYS	ASN	ILE	30
31	GLN	SER	LEU	GLU	VAL	ILE	GLY	LYS	GLY	THR	HIS	CYS	ASN	GLN	VAL	45
46	GLU	VAL	ILE	ALA	THR	LEU	LYS	ASP	GLY	ARG	LYS	ILE	CYS	LEU	ASP	60
61	PRO	ASP	ALA	PRO	ARG	ILE	LYS	LYS	ILE	VAL	GLN	LYS	LYS	LEU	ALA	75
76	GLY	ASP	GLU	SER	ALA	ASP										90

Complete Covalent structure of Human β-Thromboglobulin.
G. S. Begg, D. S. Pepper, C. N. Chesterman, and F. J. Morgan.
Biochemistry, **17**, 1739–1744 (1978).

HUMAN HAPTOGLOBIN α 1-CHAIN

	1				5					10					15	
1	VAL	ASN	ASP	SER	GLY	ASN	ASP	VAL	THR	ASP	ILE	ALA	ASP	ASP	GLY	15
16	GLN	PRO	PRO	PRO	LYS	CYS	ILE	ALA	HIS	GLY	TYR	VAL	GLU	HIS	SER	30
31	VAL	ARG	TYR	GLN	CYS	LYS	ASN	TYR	TYR	LYS	LEU	ARG	THR	GLN	GLY	45
46	ASP	GLY	VAL	TYR	THR	LEU	ASN	ASN	GLU/LYS	LYS	GLN	TRP	ILE	ASN	LYS	60
61	ALA	VAL	GLY	ASP	LYS	LEU	PRO	GLU	CYS	GLU	ALA	VAL	GLY	LYS	PRO	75
76	LYS	ASN	PRO	ALA	ASN	PRO	VAL	GLN								90

Amino acid Sequence of alpha Chains of Human Haptoglobins.
J. A. Black and G. H. Dixon.
Nature, **218**, 736–741 (1968).

MISCELLANEOUS PROTEINS

HUMAN HAPTOGLOBIN α 2-CHAIN

	1				5					10					15	
1	VAL	ASN	ASP	SER	GLY	ASN	ASP	VAL	THR	ASP	ILE	ALA	ASP	ASP	GLY	15
16	GLN	PRO	PRO	PRO	LYS	CYS	ILE	ALA	HIS	GLY	TYR	VAL	GLU	HIS	SER	30
31	VAL	ARG	TYR	GLN	CYS	LYS	ASN	TYR	TYR	LYS	LEU	ARG	THR	GLN	GLY	45
46	ASP	GLY	VAL	TYR	THR	LEU	ASN	ASN	LYS GLU	LYS	GLN	TRP	ILE	ASN	LYS	60
61	ALA	VAL	GLY	ASP	LYS	LEU	PRO	GLU	CYS	GLU	ALA	ASP	ASP	GLY	GLN	75
76	PRO	PRO	PRO	LYS	CYS	ILE	ALA	HIS	GLY	TYR	VAL	GLU	HIS	SER	VAL	90
91	ARG	TYR	GLN	CYS	LYS	ASN	TYR	TYR	LYS	LEU	ARG	THR	GLN	GLY	ASP	105
106	GLY	VAL	TYR	THR	LEU	ASN	ASN	LYS GLU	LYS	GLN	TRP	ILE	ASN	LYS	ALA	120
121	VAL	GLY	ASP	LYS	LEU	PRO	GLU	CYS	GLU	ALA	VAL	GLY	LYS	PRO	LYS	135
136	ASN	PRO	ALA	ASN	PRO	VAL	GLN									150

Gene Action in the Human Haptoglobin. IV. Amino Acid Sequence Studies on the Haptoglobin α chains.
J. A. Black and G. H. Dixon.
Can. J. Biochem., **48**, 133–146 (1970).

ANAPHYLATOXIN (C5a)—HUMAN

	1				5					10					15	
1	THR	LEU	GLN	LYS	LYS	ILE	GLU	GLU	ILE	ALA	ALA	LYS	TYR	LYS	HIS	15
16	SER	VAL	VAL	LYS	LYS	CYS	CYS	TYR	ASP	GLY	ALA	CYS	VAL	ASN	ASN	30
31	ASP	GLU	THR	CYS	GLU	GLN	ARG	ALA	ALA	ARG	ILE	SER	LEU	GLY	PRO	45
46	ARG	CYS	ILE	LYS	ALA	PHE	THR	GLU	CYS	CYS	VAL	VAL	ALA	SER	GLN	60
61	LEU	ARG	ALA	ASN	ILE	SER	HIS	LYS	ASP	MET	GLN	LEU	GLY	ARG		75

Primary structural analysis of the polypeptide portion of human C5a Anaphylatoxin.
H. N. Fernandez and T. E. Hugli.
J. Biol. Chem., **253**, 6955–6964 (1978).

ANAPHYLATOXIN (C3a)—HUMAN

	1				5					10					15	
1	SER	VAL	GLN	LEU	THR	GLU	LYS	ARG	MET	ASN	LYS	VAL	GLY	LYS	TYR	15
16	PRO	LYS	GLU	LEU	ARG	LYS	CYS	CYS	GLU	ASP	GLY	MET	ARG	GLN	ASN	30
31	PRO	MET	ARG	PHE	SER	CYS	GLN	ARG	ARG	THR	ARG	PHE	ILE	SER	LEU	45
46	GLY	GLU	ALA	CYS	LYS	LYS	VAL	PHE	LEU	ASP	CYS	CYS	ASN	TYR	ILE	60
61	THR	GLU	LEU	ARG	ARG	GLN	HIS	ALA	ARG	ALA	SER	HIS	LEU	GLY	LEU	75
76	ALA	ARG														90

Human anaphylatoxin (C3a) from the third component of complement.
T. E. Hugli.
J. Biol. Chem., **250**, 8293–8301 (1975).

MISCELLANEOUS PROTEINS

HUMAN UBIQUITIN

	1				5					10					15	
1	MET	GLN	ILE	PHE	VAL	LYS	THR	LEU	THR	GLY	LYS	THR	ILE	THR	LEU	15
16	GLU	VAL	GLU	PRO	SER	ASP	THR	ILE	GLU	ASN	VAL	LYS	ALA	LYS	ILE	30
31	GLN	ASP	LYS	GLU	GLY	ILE	PRO	PRO	ASP	GLN	GLN	ARG	LEU	ILE	PHE	45
46	ALA	GLY	LYS	GLN	LEU	GLU	ASP	GLY	ARG	THR	LEU	SER	ASP	TYR	ASN	60
61	ILE	GLN	LYS	GLU	SER	THR	LEU	HIS	LEU	VAL	LEU	ARG	LEU	ARG		75

Molecular conservation of 74 amino acid sequence of ubiquitin between cattle and man.
D. H. Schlesinger and G. Goldstein.
Nature, **255**, 423–424 (1975).

BOVINE UBIQUITIN

The amino acid sequence of bovine ubiquitin is identical to that of human ubiquitin, shown above.

The complete amino acid sequence of ubiquitin an adenylate cyclase stimulating polypeptide probably universal in living cells.
D. H. Schlesinger, G. Goldstein, and H. D. Niall.
Biochemistry, **14**, 2214–2218 (1975).

NON-HISTONE CHROMOSOMAL PROTEIN HMG-17

	1				5					10					15	
1	PRO	LYS	ARG	LYS	ALA	GLU	GLY	ASP	ALA	LYS	GLY	ASP	LYS	ALA	LYS	15
16	VAL	LYS	ASP	GLU	PRO	GLN	ARG	ARG	SER	ALA	ARG	LEU	SER	ALA	LYS	30
31	PRO	ALA	PRO	PRO	LYS	PRO	GLU	PRO	LYS	PRO	LYS	LYS	ALA	PRO	ALA	45
46	LYS	LYS	GLY	GLU	LYS	VAL	PRO	LYS	GLY	LYS	LYS	GLY	LYS	ALA	ASP	60
61	ALA	GLY	LYS	ASX	GLY	ASX	ASX	PRO	ALA	GLX	ASX	GLY	ASX	ALA	LYS	75
76	THR	ASX	GLX	ALA	GLX	LYS	ALA	GLU	GLY	ALA	GLY	ASP	ALA	LYS		90

The primary structure of a non-histone chromosomal protein.
J. M. Walker, J. R. B. Hastings, and E. W. Johns.
Eur. J. Biochem., **76**, 461–468 (1977).

BOVINE BONE PROTEIN

	1				5					10					15	
1	TYR	LEU	ASP	HIS	TRP	LEU	GLY	ALA	HYP	ALA	PRO	TYR	PRO	ASP	PRO	15
16	LEU	GLA	PRO	LYS	ARG	GLA	VAL	CYS	GLA	LEU	ASN	PRO	ASP	CYS	ASP	30
31	GLU	LEU	ALA	ASP	HIS	ILE	GLY	PHE	GLN	GLU	ALA	TYR	ARG	ARG	PHE	45
46	TYR	GLY	PRO	VAL												60

Primary structure of the γ-carboxyglutamic acid-containing protein from bovine bone.
P. A. Price, J. W. Poser, and N. Raman.
Proc. Natn. Acad. Sci., U.S.A., **73**, 3374–3375 (1976).

BOVINE β-LACTOGLOBULIN

	1				5					10					15	
1	LEU	ILE	VAL	THR	GLN	THR	MET	LYS	GLY	LEU	ASP	ILE	GLN	LYS	VAL	15
16	ALA	GLY	THR	TRP	TYR	SER	LEU	ALA	MET	ALA	ALA	SER	ASP	ILE	SER	30
31	LEU	LEU	ASP	ALA	GLN	SER	ALA	PRO	LEU	ARG	VAL	TYR	VAL	GLU	GLU	45
46	LEU	LYS	PRO	THR	PRO	GLU	GLY	ASP	LEU	GLU	ILE	LEU	LEU	GLN	LYS	60
61	TRP	GLU	ASN	ASP/GLY	GLU	CYS	ALA	GLN	LYS	LYS	ILE	ILE	ALA	GLU	LYS	75
76	THR	LYS	ILE	PRO	ALA	VAL	PHE	LYS	LEU	ASP	ALA	ILE	ASN	GLU	ASN	90
91	LYS	VAL	LEU	VAL	LEU	ASP	THR	ASP	TYR	LYS	LYS	TYR	LEU	LEU	PHE	105
106	CYS	MET	GLU	ASN	SER	ALA	GLU	PRO	GLU	GLN	SER	LEU	VAL/ALA	CYS	GLN	120
121	CYS	LEU	VAL	ARG	THR	PRO	GLU	VAL	ASP	ASP	GLU	ALA	LEU	GLU	LYS	135
136	PHE	ASP	LYS	ALA	LEU	LYS	ALA	LEU	PRO	MET	HIS	ILE	ARG	LEU	SER	150
151	PHE	ASN	PRO	THR	LEU	GLN	GLU	GLU	GLN	CYS	HIS	ILE				165

The sequence of β-lactoglobulin.
G. Braunitzer, R. Chen, B. Schrank, A. Stangl.
Hoppe-Seyler's Z. Physiol. Chem., **354**, 867–878 (1973).

MISCELLANEOUS PROTEINS

PROTEIN S-100—BOVINE BRAIN

	1				5					10					15	
1	PYG	SER	GLU	LEU	LYS	ALA	VAL	VAL	ALA	LEU	ILE	ASP	VAL	PHE	HIS	15
16	GLN	TYR	SER	GLY	ARG	GLU	GLY	ASP	LYS	HIS	LYS	LEU	LYS	LYS	SER	30
31	GLU	LEU	LYS	GLU	LEU	ILE	ASN	ASN	GLU	LEU	SER	HIS	PHE	LEU	GLU	45
46	GLU	ILE	LYS	GLU	GLN	GLU	VAL	VAL	ASP	LYS	VAL	MET	GLU	THR	LEU	60
61	ASP	SER	ASP	GLY	ASP	GLY	GLU	CYS	ASP	PHE	GLN	GLU	PHE	MET	ALA	75
76	PHE	VAL	ALA	MET	ILE	THR	THR	ALA	CYS	HIS	GLU	PHE	PHE	GLU	HIS	90
91	GLU															105

The Amino acid Sequence of S-100 Protein (PAP I-b protein) and its relation to the calcium-binding proteins.
T. Isobe and T. Okuyama.
Eur. J. Biochem., **89**, 379–388 (1978).

BASIC PROTEIN FROM HUMAN MYELIN

	1				5					10					15	
1	AC	ALA	SER	GLN	LYS	ARG	PRO	SER	GLN	ARG	HIS	GLY	SER	LYS	TYR	15
16	LEU	ALA	THR	ALA	SER	THR	MET	ASP	HIS	ALA	ARG	HIS	GLY	PHE	LEU	30
31	PRO	ARG	HIS	ARG	ASP	THR	GLY	ILE	LEU	ASP	SER	ILE	GLY	ARG	PHE	45
46	PHE	GLY	GLY	ASP	ARG	GLY	ALA	PRO	LYS	ARG	GLY	SER	GLY	LYS	ASP	60
61	SER	HIS	HIS	PRO	ALA	ARG	THR	ALA	HIS	TYR	GLY	SER	LEU	PRO	GLN	75
76	LYS	SER	HIS	GLY	ARG	THR	GLN	ASP	GLN	ASP	PRO	VAL	VAL	HIS	PHE	90
91	PHE	LYS	ASN	ILE	VAL	THR	PRO	ARG	THR	PRO	PRO	PRO	SER	GLN	GLY	105
106	LYS	GLY	MMA DMA	GLY	LEU	SER	LEU	SER	ARG	PHE	SER	TRP	GLY	ALA	GLU	120
121	GLY	GLN	ARG	PRO	GLY	PHE	GLY	TYR	GLY	GLY	ARG	ALA	SER	ASP	TYR	135
136	LYS	SER	ALA	HIS	LYS	GLY	PHE	LYS	GLY	VAL	ASP	ALA	GLN	GLY	THR	150
151	LEU	SER	LYS	ILE	PHE	LYS	LEU	GLY	GLY	ARG	ASP	SER	ARG	SER	GLY	165
166	SER	PRO	MET	ALA	ARG	ARG										180

Amino Acid Sequence of the Encephalitogenic Basic Protein from Human Myelin.
P. R. Carnegie.
Biochem. J., **123**, 57–67 (1971).

MISCELLANEOUS PROTEINS

BASIC A1 PROTEIN FROM BOVINE MYELIN

```
         1              5                  10                    15
  1  AC  ALA SER ALA GLN LYS ARG PRO SER GLN ARG SER LYS TYR LEU    15
 16  ALA SER ALA SER THR MET ASP HIS ALA ARG HIS GLY PHE LEU PRO    30
 31  ARG HIS ARG ASP THR GLY ILE LEU ASP SER LEU GLY ARG PHE PHE    45
 46  GLY SER ASP ARG GLY ALA PRO LYS ARG GLY SER GLY LYS ASP GLY    60
 61  HIS HIS ALA ALA ARG THR THR HIS TYR GLY SER LEU PRO GLN LYS    75
 76  ALA GLN GLY HIS ARG PRO GLN ASP GLU ASN PRO VAL VAL HIS PHE    90
 91  PHE LYS ASN ILE VAL THR PRO ARG THR PRO PRO PRO SER GLN GLY   105
106  LYS GLY ARG GLY LEU SER LEU SER ARG PHE SER TRP GLY ALA GLU   120
121  GLY GLN LYS PRO GLY PHE GLY TYR GLY GLY ARG ALA SER ASP TYR   135
136  LYS SER ALA HIS LYS GLY LEU LYS GLY HIS ASP ALA GLN GLY THR   150
151  LEU SER LYS ILE PHE LYS LEU GLY GLY ARG ASP SER ARG SER GLY   165
166  SER PRO MET ALA ARG ARG                                       180
```

Basic A1 Protein of the Myelin Membrane. The complete amino acid sequence.
E. H. Eylar, S. Brostoff, G. Hashim, J. Caccam, and P. Burnett.
J. Biol. Chem., **246**, 5770–5784 (1971).

BASIC PROTEIN FROM RAT BRAIN MYELIN

```
         1              5                  10                    15
  1  AC  ALA SER GLN LYS ARG PRO SER GLN ARG HIS GLY SER LYS TYR    15
 16  LEU ALA THR ALA SER THR MET ASP HIS ALA ARG HIS GLY PHE LEU    30
 31  PRO ARG HIS ARG ASP THR GLY ILE LEU ASP SER ILE GLY ARG PHE    45
 46  PHE SER GLY ASP ARG GLY ALA PRO LYS ARG GLY SER GLY LYS ASP    60
 61  SER HIS THR ARG THR THR HIS TYR GLY SER LEU PRO GLN LYS SER    75
 76  GLN ARG THR GLN ASP GLU ASN PRO VAL VAL HIS PHE PHE LYS ASN    90
 91  ILE VAL THR PRO ARG THR PRO PRO PRO SER GLN GLY LYS GLY  MMA  105
                                                              DMA
106  GLY LEU SER LEU SER ARG PHE SER TRP GLY GLY ARG ASP SER ARG   120
121  SER GLY SER PRO MET ALA ARG ARG                               135
```

Amino acid sequence of the smaller basic protein from rat brain myelin.
P. R. Dunkley and P. R. Carnegie.
Biochem. J., **141**, 243–255 (1974).

518

MISCELLANEOUS PROTEINS

TESTIS-SPECIFIC BASIC PROTEIN OF THE RAT

```
     1              5              10             15
 1   SER THR SER ARG LYS LEU LYS THR HIS  GLY MET ARG ARG GLY LYS   15
16   ASN ARG ALA PRO HIS LYS GLY VAL LYS  ARG GLY GLY SER LYS ARG   30
31   LYS TYR ARG LYS SER SER LEU LYS SER  ARG LYS ARG GLY ASP SER   45
46   ALA ASP ARG ASN TYR ARG SER HIS LEU                            60
```

The amino acid sequence of a testis-specific basic protein that is associated with spermatogenesis.
W. S. Kistler, C. Noyes, R. Hsu, and R. L. Heinrikson.
J. Biol. Chem., **250**, 1847–1853 (1975).

MONKEY AMYLOID PROTEIN A

```
     1              5              10             15
 1   ARG SER TRP PHE SER PHE LEU GLY GLU  ALA TYR ASP GLY ALA ARG   15
16   ASP MET TRP ARG ALA TYR SER ASP MET  LYS GLU ALA ASN TYR LYS   30
31   ASN SER ASP LYS TYR PHE HIS ALA ARG  GLY ASN TYR ASP ALA ALA   45
46   GLN ARG GLY PRO GLY GLY VAL TRP ALA  ALA GLU VAL ILE SER ASP   60
61   ALA ARG GLU ASN ILE GLN LYS LEU LEU  GLY HIS GLY ALA GLU ASP   75
76   THR                                                            90
```

Amino Acid Sequence of Monkey Amyloid Protein A.
M. A. Hermodson, R. W. Kuhn, K. A. Walsh, H. Neurath, N. Eriksen, and E. P. Benditt.
Biochemistry, **11**, 2934–2938 (1972).

AMYLOID PROTEIN AS

```
     1              5              10             15
 1   ARG SER PHE PHE SER PHE LEU GLY GLU  ALA PHE ASP GLY ALA ARG   15
16   ASP MET TRP ARG ALA TYR SER ASN MET  ARG GLU ALA ASN TYR ILE   30
31   GLY SER ASP LYS TYR PHE HIS ALA ARG  GLY ASN TYR ASP ALA ALA   45
46   LYS ARG GLY PRO GLY GLY VAL TRP ALA  ALA GLU ALA ILE SER ASP   60
61   ALA ARG GLU ASN ILE GLN ARG PHE PHE  GLY HIS GLY ALA GLU ASN   75
76   SER                                                            90
```

The complete amino acid sequence of non-immunoglobulin amyloid fibril protein AS in rheumatoid arthritis.
K. Sletten and G. Husby.
Eur. J. Biochem., **41**, 117–125 (1974).

MISCELLANEOUS PROTEINS

AMYLOID IV PROTEIN

```
    1              5                  10                 15
 1  ARG SER PHE PHE SER PHE LEU GLY GLU ALA PHE ASP GLY ALA ARG   15
16  ASP MET TRP ARG ALA TYR SER ASP MET ARG GLU ALA ASN TYR ILE   30
31  GLY SER ASP LYS TYR PHE HIS  ALA ARG GLY ASX (TYR, ASX, ALA) ALA   45
```

Amino acid sequence of an amyloid fibril protein of unknown origin.
D. Ein, S. Kimura, W. D. Terry, J. Magnotta, and G. G. Glenner.
J. Biol. Chem., **247**, 5653–5655 (1972).

AMYLOID PROTEIN ASF

```
    1              5                  10                 15
 1  ARG SER PHE PHE SER PHE LEU GLY GLU ALA PHE ASP GLY ALA ARG   15
16  ASP MET TRP ARG ALA TYR SER ASP MET ARG GLU ALA ASN TYR ILE   30
31  GLY SER ASP LYS TYR PHE HIS  ALA ARG GLY ASN TYR ASP ALA ALA   45
46  LYS ARG GLY PRO GLY GLY ALA TRP/ARG ALA ALA GLU VAL ILE SER ASN   60
61  ALA ARG GLU ASN ILE  GLN ARG LEU THR GLY ARG GLY ALA GLU ASP   75
76  SER                                                           90
```

The amino acid sequence of a major nonimmunoglobulin component of some amyloid fibrils.
M. Levin, E. C. Franklin, B. Frangione and M. Pras.
J. Clin. Invest., **51**, 2773–2776 (1972).

UTEROGLOBIN—RABBIT

```
    1              5                  10                 15
 1  GLY ILE CYS PRO ARG PHE ALA HIS VAL ILE GLU ASN LEU LEU LEU   15
16  GLY THR PRO SER SER TYR GLU THR SER LEU LYS GLU PHE GLU PRO   30
31  ASP ASP THR MET LYS ASP ALA GLY MET GLN MET LYS LYS VAL LEU   45
46  ASP SER LEU PRO GLN THR THR ARG GLU ASN ILE MET LYS LEU THR   60
61  GLN LYS ILE VAL LYS SER PRO LEU CYS MET                       75
```

Amino acid sequence of progesterone-induced rabbit uteroglobin.
H. Ponstingl, A. Nieto, and M. Beato.
Biochemistry, **17**, 3908–3912 (1978).

MISCELLANEOUS PROTEINS

GLYCOPROTEIN OF ANTARCTIC FISH BLOOD—FRACTION 8

	1		5			10			15			
1	ALA	ALA	THR	ALA	ALA	THR	PRO/ALA	ALA	THR	ALA/PRO	ALA	THR	PRO ALA	15

Antifreeze glycoproteins from the blood of an antarctic fish. The structure of the proline-containing glycopeptides.
H. R. Morris, M. R. Thompson, D. T. Osuga, A. I. Ahmed, S. M. Chan, J. R. Vandenheede, and R. E. Feeney.
J. Biol. Chem., **253**, 5155–5162 (1978).

GLYCOPHORIN A

	1	5								10					15	
1	SER/LEU	SER	THR	THR	GLY/GLU	VAL	ALA	MET	HIS	THR	THR	THR	SER	SER	SER	15
16	VAL	SER	LYS	SER	TYR	ILE	SER	SER	GLN	THR	ASN	ASP	THR	HIS	LYS	30
31	ARG	ASP	THR	TYR	ALA	ALA	THR	PRO	ARG	ALA	HIS	GLU	VAL	SER	GLU	45
46	ILE	SER	VAL	ARG	THR	VAL	TYR	PRO	PRO	GLU	GLU	GLU	THR	GLY	GLU	60
61	ARG	VAL	GLN	LEU	ALA	HIS	HIS	PHE	SER	GLU	PRO	GLU	ILE	THR	LEU	75
76	ILE	ILE	PHE	GLY	VAL	MET	ALA	GLY	VAL	ILE	GLY	THR	ILE	LEU	LEU	90
91	ILE	SER	TYR	GLY	ILE	ARG	ARG	LEU	ILE	LYS	LYS	SER	PRO	SER	ASP	105
106	VAL	LYS	PRO	LEU	PRO	SER	PRO	ASP	THR	ASP	VAL	PRO	LEU	SER	SER	120
121	VAL	GLU	ILE	GLU	ASN	PRO	GLU	THR	SER	ASP	GLN					135

Primary structure of human erythrocyte Glycophorin A. Isolation and characterization of peptides and complete amino acid sequence.
M. Tomita, H. Furthmayr, and V. T. Marchesi.
Biochemistry, **17**, 4756–4770 (1978).

MISCELLANEOUS PROTEINS

EGG WHITE AVIDIN

	1			5						10					15	
1	ALA	ARG	LYS	CYS	SER	LEU	THR	GLY	LYS	TRP	THR	ASN	ASP	LEU	GLY	15
16	SER	ASN	MET	THR	ILE	GLY	ALA	VAL	ASN	SER	ARG	GLY	GLU	PHE	THR	30
31	GLY	THR	TYR	THR ILE	THR	ALA	VAL	THR	ALA	THR	SER	ASN	GLU	ILE	LYS	45
46	GLU	SER	PRO	LEU	HIS	GLY	THR	GLU	ASN	THR	ILE	ASN	LYS	ARG	THR	60
61	GLN	PRO	THR	PHE	GLY	PHE	THR	VAL	ASN	TRP	LYS	PHE	SER	GLU	SER	75
76	THR	THR	VAL	PHE	THR	GLY	GLN	CYS	PHE	ILE	ASP	ARG	ASN	GLY	LYS	90
91	GLU	VAL	LEU	LYS	THR	MET	TRP	LEU	LEU	ARG	SER	SER	VAL	ASN	ASP	105
106	ILE	GLY	ASP	ASP	TRP	LYS	ALA	THR	ARG	VAL	GLY	ILE	ASN	ILE	PHE	120
121	THR	ARG	LEU	ARG	THR	GLN	LYS	GLU								135

Note: A disulphide bridge links residues CYS 4 and 83.
Egg white Avidin. III. Sequence of the 78 residue middle cyanogen bromide peptide.
Complete amino acid sequence of the protein subunit.
R. J. DeLange and T.-S. Huang.
J. Biol. Chem., **246**, 698–709 (1971).

APOVITELLENIN I—DUCK

	1			5						10					15	
1	LYS	SER	ILE	PHE	GLU	ARG	ASP	ARG	ARG	ASP	TRP	LEU	VAL	ILE	PRO	15
16	ASP	ALA	ILE	ALA	ALA	TYR	ILE	TYR	GLU	THR	VAL	ASN	LYS	MET	SER	30
31	PRO	ARG	VAL	GLY	GLN	PHE	LEU	ALA	ASP	ALA	ALA	GLN	THR	PRO	VAL	45
46	VAL	VAL	GLY	THR	ARG	THR	PHE	LEU	ILE	ARG	GLU	THR	SER	LYS	LEU	60
61	THR	LEU	LEU	ALA	GLU	GLN	LEU	MET	GLU	LYS	ILE	LYS	ASN	LEU	TRP	75
76	TYR	THR	LYS	VAL	LEU	GLY	TYR									90

Determination of the amino acid sequence of apovitellenin I from duck's egg yolk using an
improved sequenator procedure: a comparison with other avian species.
A. S. Inglis and R. W. Burley.
FEBS Letters, **73**, 33–37 (1977).

MISCELLANEOUS PROTEINS

CONCANAVALIN A

	1				5					10					15		
1	ALA	ASP	THR	ILE	VAL	ALA	VAL	GLU	LEU	ASP	THR	TYR	PRO	ASN	THR		15
16	ASP	ILE	GLY	ASP	PRO	SER	TYR	PRO	HIS	ILE	GLY	ILE	ASP	ILE	LYS		30
31	SER	VAL	ARG	SER	LYS	LYS	THR	ALA	LYS	TRP	ASN	MET	GLN	ASP	GLY		45
46	LYS	VAL	GLY	THR	ALA	HIS	ILE	ILE	TYR	ASN	SER	VAL	ASP	LYS	ARG		60
61	LEU	SER	ALA	VAL	VAL	SER	TYR	PRO	ASN	ALA	ASP	ALA	THR	SER	VAL		75
76	SER	TYR	ASP	VAL	ASP	LEU	ASN	ASP	VAL	LEU	PRO	GLU	TRP	VAL	ARG		90
91	VAL	GLY	LEU	SER	ALA	SER	THR	GLY	LEU	TYR	LYS	GLU	THR	ASN	THR		105
106	ILE	LEU	SER	TRP	SER	PHE	THR	SER	LYS	LEU	LYS	SER	ASN	SER	THR		120
121	HIS	GLN	THR	ASP	ALA	LEU	HIS	PHE	MET	PHE	ASN	GLN	PHE	SER	LYS		135
136	ASP	GLN	LYS	ASP	LEU	ILE	LEU	GLN	GLY	ASP	ALA	THR	THR	GLY	THR		150
151	ASP	GLY	ASN	LEU	GLU	LEU	THR	ARG	VAL	SER	SER	ASN	GLY	SER	PRO		165
166	GLU	GLY	SER	SER	VAL	GLY	ARG	ALA	LEU	PHE	TYR	ALA	PRO	VAL	HIS		180
181	ILE	TRP	GLU	SER	SER	ALA	THR	VAL	SER	ALA	PHE	GLU	ALA	THR	PHE		195
196	ALA	PHE	LEU	ILE	LYS	SER	PRO	ASP	SER	HIS	PRO	ALA	ASP	GLY	ILE		210
211	ALA	PHE	PHE	ILE	SER	ASN	ILE	ASP	SER	SER	ILE	PRO	SER	GLY	SER		225
226	THR	GLY	ARG	LEU	LEU	GLY	LEU	PHE	PRO	ASP	ALA	ASN					240

The covalent and three-dimensional structure of Concanavalin A. I. Amino acid sequence of cyanogen bromide fragments F1 and F2.
J. L. Wang, B. A. Cunningham, M. J. Waxdal, and G. M. Edelman.
J. Biol. Chem., **250**, 1490–1502 (1975).
And
II. Amino acid sequence of cyanogen bromide fragment F3.
B. A. Cunningham, J. L. Wang, M. J. Waxdal, and G. M. Edelman.
J. Biol. Chem., **250**, 1503–1512 (1975).

PEA LECTIN—α SUBUNIT

	1				5					10					15		
1	VAL	THR	SER	TYR	THR	LEU	SER	ASP	VAL	VAL	SER	LEU	LYS	ASP	VAL		15
16	VAL	PRO	GLU	TRP	VAL	ARG	ILE	GLY	PHE	SER	ALA	THR	THR	GLY	ALA		30
31	GLU	TYR	ALA	ALA	HIS	GLU	VAL	LEU	SER	TRP	SER	PHE	HIS	SER	GLU		45
46	LEU	SER	GLY	THR	SER	SER	LYS	GLN									60

The complete amino acid sequence of the α-subunit of pea lectin, *Pisum sativum*.
C. Richardson, W. D. Behnke, J. H. Freisheim, and K. M. Blumenthal.
Biochim. Biophys. Acta, **537**, 310–319 (1978).

MISCELLANEOUS PROTEINS

RAGWEED ALLERGEN Ra5

	1		5					10					15		
1	LEU	VAL/LEU	PRO	CYS	ALA	TRP	ALA	GLY	ASN	VAL	CYS	GLY	GLU	LYS	ARG	15
16	ALA	TYR	CYS	CYS	SER	ASP	PRO	GLY	ARG	TYR	CYS	PRO	TRP	GLN	VAL	30
31	VAL	CYS	TYR	GLU	SER	SER	GLU	ILE	CYS	SER	LYS	LYS	CYS	GLY	LYS	45

The amino acid sequence of ragweed pollen allergen Ra5.
L. E. Mole, L. Goodfriend, C. B. Lapkoff, J. M. Kehoe, and J. D. Capra.
Biochemistry, **14**, 1216–1220 (1975).

β-PUROTHIONIN—WHEAT

	1		5					10					15		
1	LYS	SER	CYS	CYS	LYS	SER	THR	LEU	GLY	ARG	ASN	CYS	TYR	ASN	LEU	15
16	CYS	ARG	ALA	ARG	GLY	ALA	GLN	LYS	LEU	CYS	ALA	ASN	VAL	CYS	ARG	30
31	CYS	LYS	LEU	THR	SER	GLY	LEU	SER	CYS	PRO	LYS	ASP	PHE	PRO	LYS	45

The amino acid sequence of wheat β-purothionin.
A. S. Mak and B. L. Jones.
Can. J. Biochem., **22**, 835–842 (1976).

TUBERCULIN—ACTIVE PROTEIN

	1		5					10					15		
1	ARG	LEU	LEU	ASP	ASP	THR	PRO	GLU	VAL	LYS	VAL	LEU	GLY	ALA	VAL	15
16	ALA	ASP	ALA	ILE	GLU	THR	PRO	LYS	ALA	GLU	PRO	CYS	ILE	ASP	LEU	30
31	ASP	VAL	ALA	GLY	GLU	ALA	THR	PHE	ALA	ARG	GLU	ASP	ASP	LEU	PRO	45
46	ASP	TYR	VAL	LEU	TYR	ALA	GLU	VAL	THR	PHE	HIS	GLU	ILE	CYS	ARG	60
61	ASP	GLY	GLY	SER	GLU	SER	GLU	GLY	LYS	ASN	GLY	SER	GLN	MET	ARG	75
76	LEU	ILE	ALA	ASP	VAL	GLY	PRO	GLU	SER	ALA	THR	VAL	ALA	LYS		90

Note: There is one disulphide bridge linking residues CYS 27 and 59.
Amino acid sequence of tuberculin-active protein from *Mycobacterium tuberculosis*.
S. Kuwabara.
J. Biol. Chem., **250**, 2563–2568 (1975).

MISCELLANEOUS PROTEINS

PUROTHIONIN A—WHEAT

AI-CHAIN

```
      1              5                    10                   15
 1  LYS SER CYS CYS LYS SER THR LEU GLY ARG ASN CYS TYR ASN LEU   15
16  CYS ARG ALA ARG GLY ALA GLN LYS LEU CYS ALA ASN VAL CYS ARG   30
31  CYS LYS LEU THR SER GLY LEU SER CYS PRO LYS ASP PHE PRO LYS   45
```

AII-CHAIN

```
      1              5                    10                   15
 1  LYS SER CYS CYS ARG SER THR LEU GLY ARG ASN CYS TYR ASN LEU   15
16  CYS ARG ALA ARG GLY ALA GLN LYS LEU CYS ALA GLY VAL CYS ARG   30
31  CYS LYS ILE SER SER GLY LEU SER CYS PRO LYS GLY PHE PRO LYS   45
```

Complete primary structures of two subunits of Purothionin A, a lethal protein for Brewer's yeast from wheat flour.
S. Ohtani, T. Okada, H. Yoshizumi, and H. Kagamiyama.
J. Biochem., **82**, 753–767 (1977).

NEOCARZINOSTATIN

```
       1              5                    10                   15
  1  ALA ALA PRO THR ALA THR VAL THR PRO SER SER GLY LEU SER ASP   15
 16  GLY THR VAL VAL LYS VAL ALA GLY ALA GLY LEU GLN ALA GLY THR   30
 31  ALA TYR ASP VAL GLY GLN CYS ALA SER VAL ASN THR GLY VAL LEU   45
 46  TRP ASN SER VAL THR ALA ALA GLY SER ALA CYS ASX PRO ALA ASN   60
 61  PHE SER LEU THR VAL ARG ARG SER PHE GLU GLY PHE LEU PHE ASP   75
 76  GLY THR ARG TRP GLY THR VAL ASX CYS THR THR ALA ALA CYS GLN   90
 91  VAL GLY LEU SER ASP ALA ALA GLY ASP GLY GLU PRO GLY VAL ALA  105
106  ILE SER PHE ASN                                              120
```

Structure of the antitumor protein neocarzinostatin, purification, amino acid composition, disulfide reduction and isolation and composition of tryptic peptides.
H. Maeda, C. B. Glaser, J. Czombos, and J. Meienhofer.
Arch. Biochem. Biophys., **164**, 369–378 (1974).
And
Structure of the antitumor protein neocarzinostatin, amino acid sequence.
H. Maeda, C. B. Glaser, K. Kuromizu, and J. Meienhofer.
Arch. Biochem. Biophys., **164**, 379–385 (1974).

MISCELLANEOUS PROTEINS

SUBSTANCE A FROM STREPTOMYCES CARZINOSTATICUS

	1				5					10					15	
1	ALA	ALA	GLY	ASN	PRO	SER	GLU	THR	GLY	GLY	ALA	VAL	ALA	THR	TYR	15
16	SER	THR	ALA	VAL	GLY	SER	PHE	LEU	ASX	GLY	THR	VAL	LYS	VAL	VAL	30
31	ALA	THR	GLY	GLY	ALA	SER	ARG	VAL	PRO	GLY	ASN	CYS	GLY	THR	ALA	45
46	ALA	VAL	LEU	GLU	CYS	ASP	ASN	PRO	GLU	SER	PHE	ASP	GLY	THR	ARG	60
61	ALA	TRP	GLY	ASP	LEU	SER	ALA	ASP	GLN	GLY	THR	GLY	GLU	ASP	ALA	75
76	PRO	PRO	GLU	THR	ALA	SER	LEU	ILE	PHE	ALA	VAL	ASN				90

Note: A disulphide bridge links CYS 42 and 50.
The total structure of Substance A produced by *Streptomyces carzinostaticus*.
H. Sato, T. Tanimura, T. Nakajima, and Z. Tamura.
Chem. Pharm. Bull. (*Japan*), **17**, 2188–2191 (1969).

BACTERIOPHAGE φ X174 GENE D PROTEIN

	1				5					10					15	
1	SER	GLN	VAL	THR	GLU	GLN	SER	VAL	ARG	PHE	GLN	THR	ALA	LEU	ALA	15
16	SER	ILE	LYS	LEU	ILE	GLN	ALA	SER	ALA	VAL	LEU	ASP	LEU	THR	GLU	30
31	ASP	ASP	PHE	ASP	PHE	LEU	THR	SER	ASN	LYS	VAL	TRP	ILE	ALA	THR	45
46	ASP	ARG	SER	ARG	ALA	ARG	ARG	CYS	VAL	GLU	ALA	CYS	VAL	TYR	GLY	60
61	THR	LEU	ASP	PHE	VAL	GLY	TYR	PRO	ARG	PHE	PRO	ALA	PRO	VAL	GLU	75
76	PHE	ILE	ALA	ALA	VAL	ILE	ALA	TYR	TYR	VAL	HIS	PRO	VAL	ASN	ILE	90
91	GLN	THR	ALA	CYS	LEU	ILE	MET	GLU	GLY	ALA	GLU	PHE	THR	GLU	ASN	105
106	ILE	ILE	ASN	GLY	VAL	GLU	ARG	PRO	VAL	LYS	ALA	ALA	GLU	LEU	PHE	120
121	ALA	PHE	THR	LEU	ARG	VAL	ARG	ALA	GLY	ASN	THR	ASP	VAL	LEU	THR	135
136	ASP	ALA	GLU	GLU	ASN	VAL	ARG	GLN	LYS	LEU	ARG	ALA	GLU	GLY	VAL	150
151	MET															165

Overlapping genes in bacteriophage φ X174.
B. G. Barrell, G. M. Air, and C. A. Hutchison.
Nature, **264**, 34–41 (1976).

MISCELLANEOUS PROTEINS

GENE 5 PROTEIN OF M13 BACTERIOPHAGE

```
     1               5                   10                  15
 1  MET ILE LYS VAL GLU ILE LYS PRO SER GLN ALA GLN PHE THR THR   15
16  ARG SER GLY VAL SER ARG GLN GLY LYS PRO TYR SER LEU ASN GLU   30
31  GLN LEU CYS TYR VAL ASP LEU GLY ASN GLU TYR PRO VAL LEU VAL   45
46  LYS ILE THR LEU ASP GLU GLY GLN PRO ALA TYR ALA PRO GLY LEU   60
61  TYR THR VAL HIS LEU SER SER PHE LYS VAL GLY GLN PHE GLY SER   75
76  LEU MET ILE ASP ARG LEU ARG LEU VAL PRO ALA LYS             90
```

The amino acid sequence of gene 5 protein of bacteriophage M13.
T. Cuypers, F. J. van der Ouderaa, and W. W. de Jong.
Biochem. Biophys. Res. Commun., **59**, 557–563 (1974).

GENE 5 PROTEIN OF fd BACTERIOPHAGE

The amino acid sequence of the gene 5 protein from fd bacteriophage is identical to that isolated from M13 bacteriophage.*

The amino acid sequence of a DNA binding protein, the gene 5 product of fd filamentous bacteriophage.
Y. Nakashima, A. K. Dunker, D. A. Marvin, and W. Konigsberg.
FEBS Letters, **40**, 290–292 (1974).
The sequence in the above paper was corrected:
Erratum
FEBS Letters, **43**, 125 (1974).
*I thank Dr. W. W. de Jong (University of Nijmegen) for informing me of the identity of these two proteins.

MISCELLANEOUS PROTEINS

lac REPRESSOR FROM ESCHERICHIA COLI

```
      1               5                  10                    15
  1  MET LYS PRO VAL THR LEU TYR ASP VAL ALA GLU TYR ALA GLY VAL    15
 16  SER TYR GLN THR VAL SER ARG VAL VAL ASN GLN ALA SER HIS VAL    30
 31  SER ALA LYS THR ARG GLU LYS VAL GLU ALA ALA MET ALA GLU LEU    45
 46  ASN TYR ILE PRO ASN ARG VAL ALA GLN GLN LEU ALA GLY LYS GLN    60
 61  SER LEU LEU ILE GLY VAL ALA THR SER SER LEU ALA LEU HIS ALA    75
 76  PRO SER GLN ILE VAL ALA ALA ILE LYS SER ARG ALA ASP GLN LEU    90
 91  GLY ALA SER VAL VAL VAL SER MET VAL GLU ARG SER GLY VAL GLU   105
106  ALA CYS LYS ALA ALA VAL HIS ASN LEU LEU ALA GLN ARG VAL SER   120
121  GLY LEU ILE ILE ASN TYR PRO LEU ASP ASP GLN ASP ALA ILE ALA   135
136  VAL GLU ALA ALA CYS THR ASN VAL PRO ALA LEU PHE ILE ILE PHE   150
151  SER HIS GLN ASP GLY THR ARG LEU GLY VAL GLU HIS LEU VAL ALA   165
166  LEU GLY HIS GLN GLN ILE ALA LEU LEU ALA GLY PRO LEU SER SER   180
181  VAL SER ALA ARG LEU ARG LEU ALA GLY TRP HIS LYS TYR LEU THR   195
196  ARG ASN GLN ILE GLN PRO ILE ALA GLU ARG GLU GLY ASP TRP SER   210
211  ALA MET SER GLY PHE GLN GLN THR MET LEU ASN GLU GLY ILE VAL   225
226  PRO THR ALA MET LEU VAL ALA ASN ASP GLN MET ALA LEU GLY ALA   240
241  MET ARG ALA ILE THR GLU SER GLY LEU ARG VAL GLY ALA ASP ILE   255
256  SER VAL VAL GLY TYR ASP ASP THR GLU ASP SER SER CYS TYR ILE   270
271  PRO PRO LEU THR THR ILE LYS GLN ASP PHE ARG LEU LEU GLY GLN   285
286  THR SER VAL ASP ARG LEU LEU GLN LEU SER GLN GLY GLN ALA VAL   300
301  LYS GLY ASN GLN LEU LEU PRO VAL SER LEU VAL LYS ARG LYS THR   315
316  THR LEU ALA PRO ASN THR GLN THR ALA SER PRO ARG ALA LEU ALA   330
331  ASP SER LEU MET GLN LEU ALA ARG GLN VAL SER ARG LEU GLU SER   345
346  GLY GLN                                                        360
```

Amino acid sequence of *lac* repressor from *Escherichia coli*.
K. Beyreuther, K. Adler, E. Fanning, C. Murray, A. Klemm, and N. Geisler.
Eur. J. Biochem., **59**, 491–509 (1975).

MISCELLANEOUS PROTEINS

INITIATION FACTOR IF-3 FROM ESCHERICHIA COLI

	1		5					10					15			
1	MET	LYS	GLY	GLY	LYS	ARG	VAL	GLN	THR	ALA	ARG	PRO	ASN	ARG	ILE	15
16	ASN	GLY	GLU	ILE	ARG	ALA	GLU	GLU	VAL	ARG	LEU	THR	GLY	LEU	GLU	30
31	GLY	GLU	GLN	ILE	GLY	MET	VAL	VAL	SER	LEU	ARG	GLU	ALA	LEU	GLU	45
46	LYS	ALA	GLN	GLU	ALA	GLY	VAL	ASN	LEU	VAL	GLU	ILE	SER	PRO	ASN	60
61	ALA	GLN	PRO	PRO	VAL	CYS	ARG	ILE	MET	ASP	TYR	GLY	LYS	PHE	LEU	75
76	TYR	GLU	LYS	SER	LYS	SER	SER	LYS	GLU	GLN	LYS	LYS	GLU	GLN	LYS	90
91	LYS	VAL	ILE	GLN	VAL	LYS	GLU	ILE	LYS	PHE	ARG	PRO	GLY	THR	ASN	105
106	GLU	GLY	ASN	TYR	GLN	VAL	LYS	LEU	ARG	SER	LEU	ILE	ARG	PHE	LEU	120
121	GLU	GLU	GLY	ASP	LYS	ALA	LYS	ILE	THR	LEU	ARG	PHE	ARG	GLY	ARG	135
136	GLU	MET	ALA	HIS	GLN	GLN	ILE	GLY	MET	GLU	VAL	LEU	ASN	ARG	VAL	150
151	LYS	ASP	ASP	LEU	GLN	GLU	LEU	ALA	VAL	VAL	GLU	SER	PHE	PRO	THR	165
166	LYS	ILE	GLU	GLY	ARG	GLN	MET	ILE	MET	VAL	LEU	ALA	PRO	LYS	GLN	180
181	LYS															195

Notes: (i) The N-terminal residue in the above protein is N-methylated. (ii) The above protein exists in several forms: the above sequence corresponds to the long form, IF-3l; an identical form also occurs but lacks the N-terminal residue. A short form is found lacking the first six amino acid residues: this is known as IF-3s.

The primary structure of the initiation factor IF-3 from *Escherichia coli*.

D. Braver and B. Wittmann-Liebold.

FEBS Letters, **79**, 269–275 (1977).

MISCELLANEOUS PROTEINS

LIV-BINDING PROTEIN FROM ESCHERICHIA COLI

	1				5					10					15	
1	GLU	ASP	ILE	LYS	VAL	ALA	VAL	VAL	GLY	ALA	MET	SER	GLY	PRO	VAL	15
16	ALA	GLN	TYR	GLY	ASP	GLN	GLU	PHE	THR	GLY	ALA	GLU	GLN	ALA	VAL	30
31	ALA	ASP	ILE	ASN	ALA	LYS	GLY	GLY	ILE	LYS	GLY	ASN	LYS	LEU	GLN	45
46	ILE	VAL	LYS	TYR	ASP	ASP	ALA	CYS	ASP	PRO	LYS	GLN	ALA	VAL	ALA	60
61	VAL	ALA	ASN	LYS	VAL	VAL	ASN	ASP	GLY	ILE	LYS	TYR	VAL	ILE	GLY	75
76	HIS	LEU	CYS	SER	SER	SER	THR	GLN	PRO	ALA	SER	ASP	ILE	TYR	GLU	90
91	ASP	GLU	GLY	ILE	LEU	MET	ILE	THR	PRO	ALA	ALA	THR	ALA	PRO	GLU	105
106	LEU	THR	ALA	ARG	GLY	TYR	GLN	LEU	ILE	LEU	ARG	THR	THR	GLY	LEU	120
121	ASP	SER	ASP	GLN	GLY	PRO	THR	ALA	ALA	LYS	TYR	ILE	LEU	GLU	LYS	135
136	VAL	LYS	PRO	GLN	ARG	ILE	ALA	ILE	VAL	HIS	ASP	LYS	GLN	GLN	TYR	150
151	GLY	GLU	GLY	LEU	ALA	ARG	ALA	VAL	GLN	ASP	GLY	LEU	LYS	LYS	GLY	165
166	ASN	ALA	ASN	VAL	VAL	PHE	PHE	ASP	GLY	ILE	THR	ALA	GLY	GLU	LYS	180
181	ASP	PHE	SER	THR	LEU	VAL	ALA	ARG	LEU	LYS	LYS	GLU	ASN	ILE	ASP	195
196	PHE	VAL	TYR	TYR	GLY	GLY	TYR	HIS	PRO	GLU	MET	GLY	GLN	ILE	LEU	210
211	ARG	GLN	ALA	ARG	ALA	ALA	GLY	LEU	LYS	THR	GLN	PHE	MET	GLY	PRO	225
226	GLU	GLY	VAL	ALA	ASN	VAL	SER	LEU	SER	ASN	ILE	ALA	GLY	GLU	SER	240
241	ALA	GLU	GLY	LEU	LEU	VAL	THR	LYS	PRO	LYS	ASN	TYR	ASP	GLN	VAL	255
256	PRO	ALA	ASN	LYS	PRO	ILE	VAL	ALA	ASP	ILE	LYS	ALA	LYS	LYS	GLN	270
271	ASP	PRO	SER	GLY	ALA	PHE	VAL	TRP	THR	THR	TYR	ALA	ALA	LEU	GLN	285
286	SER	LEU	GLN	ALA	GLY	LEU	ASN	GLN	SER	ASP	ASP	PRO	ALA	GLU	ILE	300
301	ALA	LYS	TYR	LEU	LYS	ALA	ASN	SER	VAL	ASP	THR	VAL	MET	GLY	PRO	315
316	LEU	THR	TRP	ASP	GLU	LYS	GLY	ASP	LEU	LYS	GLY	PHE	GLU	PHE	GLY	330
331	VAL	PHE	ASP	TRP	HIS	ALA	ASN	GLY	THR	ALA	THR	ALA	ASP	LYS		345

The primary structure of a LEU, ILE and VAL (LIV)-Binding protein from *Escherichia coli*. Y. A. Ovchinnikov, N. A. Aldanova, V. A. Grinkevich, N. M. Arzamazova, and I. N. Moroz. *FEBS Letters*, **78**, 313–316 (1977).

MISCELLANEOUS PROTEINS

L-ARABINOSE-BINDING PROTEIN FROM ESCHERICHIA COLI

	1				5					10					15	
1	GLU	ASN	LEU	LYS	LEU	GLY	PHE	LEU	VAL	LYS	GLN	PRO	GLU	GLU	PRO	15
16	TRP	PHE	GLN	THR	GLU	TRP	LYS	PHE	ALA	ASP	LYS	ALA	GLY	LYS	ASP	30
31	LEU	GLY	PHE	GLU	VAL	ILE	LYS	ILE	ALA	VAL	PRO	ASP	GLY	GLU	LYS	45
46	THR	LEU	ASN	ALA	ILE	ASP	SER	LEU	ALA	ALA	SER	GLY	ALA	LYS	GLY	60
61	PHE	VAL	ILE	CYS	THR	PRO	ASP	PRO	LYS	LEU	GLY	SER	ALA	ILE	VAL	75
76	ALA	LYS	ALA	ARG	GLY	TYR	ASP	MET	LYS	VAL	ILE	ALA	VAL	ASP	ASP	90
91	GLN	PHE	VAL	ASN	ALA	LYS	GLY	LYS	PRO	MET	ASP	THR	VAL	PRO	LEU	105
106	VAL	MET	MET	ALA	ALA	THR	LYS	ILE	GLY	GLU	ARG	GLN	GLY	GLN	GLU	120
121	LEU	TYR	LYS	GLU	MET	GLN	LYS	ARG	GLY	TRP	ASP	VAL	LYS	GLU	SER	135
136	ALA	VAL	MET	ALA	ILE	THR	ALA	ASN	GLU	LEU	ASP	THR	ALA	ARG	ARG	150
151	ARG	THR	THR	GLY	SER	MET	ASP	ALA	LEU	LYS	ALA	ALA	GLY	PHE	PRO	165
166	GLU	LYS	GLN	ILE	TYR	GLN	VAL	PRO	THR	LYS	SER	ASN	ASP	ILE	PRO	180
181	GLY	ALA	PHE	ASP	ALA	ALA	ASN	SER	MET	LEU	VAL	GLN	HIS	PRO	GLU	195
196	VAL	LYS	HIS	TRP	LEU	ILE	VAL	GLY	MET	ASN	ASP	SER	THR	VAL	LEU	210
211	GLY	GLY	VAL	ARG	ALA	THR	GLU	GLY	GLN	GLY	PHE	LYS	ALA	ALA	ASP	225
226	ILE	ILE	GLY	ILE	GLY	ILE	ASN	GLY	VAL	ASP	ALA	VAL	SER	GLU	LEU	240
241	SER	LYS	ALA	GLN	ALA	THR	GLY	PHE	TYR	GLY	SER	LEU	LEU	PRO	SER	255
256	PRO	ASP	VAL	HIS	GLY	TYR	LYS	SER	SER	GLU	MET	LEU	TYR	ASN	TRP	270
271	VAL	ALA	LYS	ASP	VAL	GLU	PRO	PRO	LYS	PHE	THR	GLU	VAL	THR	ASP	285
286	VAL	VAL	LEU	ILE	THR	ARG	ASP	ASN	PHE	LYS	GLU	GLU	LEU	GLU	LYS	300
301	LYS	GLY	LEU	GLY	GLY	LYS										315

Amino acid sequence of the L-Arabinose binding protein from *Escherichia coli* B/r.
R. W. Hogg and M. A. Hermodson.
J. Biol. Chem., **252**, 5135–5141 (1977).

FLAGELLIN—BACILLUS SUBTILIS 168

	1				5					10					15	
1	MET	ARG	ILE	ASN	HIS	ASN	ILE	ALA	ALA	LEU	ASN	THR	LEU	ASN	ARG	15
16	LEU	SER	SER	ASN	ASN	SER	ALA	SER	GLN	LYS	ASN	MET	GLU	LYS	LEU	30
31	SER	SER	GLY	LEU	ARG	ILE	ASN	ARG	ALA	GLY	ASP	ASP	ALA	ALA	GLY	45
46	LEU	ALA	ILE	SER	GLU	LYS	MET	ARG	GLY	GLN	ILE	ARG	GLY	LEU	GLU	60
61	MET	ALA	SER	LYS	ASN	SER	GLN	ASP	GLY	ILE	SER	LEU	ILE	GLN	THR	75
76	ALA	GLU	GLY	ALA	LEU	THR	GLU	THR	HIS	ALA	ILE	LEU	GLN	ARG	VAL	90
91	ARG	GLU	LEU	VAL	VAL	GLN	ALA	GLY	ASN	THR	THR	GLY	GLN	ASP	LYS	105
106	ALA	THR	ASP	LEU	GLN	SER	ILE	GLN	ASP	GLU	ILE	SER	ALA	LEU	THR	120
121	ASP	GLU	ILE	ASP	GLY	ILE	SER	ASN	ARG	THR	GLU	PHE	ASN	GLY	LYS	135
136	LYS	LEU	LEU	ASP	GLY	THR	TYR	LYS	VAL	ASP	THR	ALA	THR	PRO	ALA	150
151	ASN	GLN	LYS	ASN	LEU	VAL	PHE	GLN	ILE	GLY	ALA	ASN	ALA	THR	GLN	165
166	GLN	ILE	SER	VAL	ASN	ILE	GLU	ASP	MET	GLY	ALA	ASP	ALA	LEU	GLY	180
181	ILE	LYS	GLU	ALA	ASP	GLY	SER	ILE	ALA	ALA	LEU	HIS	SER	VAL	ASN	195
196	ASP	LEU	ASP	VAL	THR	LYS	PHE	ALA	ASP	ASN	ALA	ALA	ASP	THR	ALA	210
211	ASP	ILE	GLY	PHE	ASP	ALA	GLN	LEU	LYS	VAL	VAL	ASP	GLU	ALA	ILE	225
226	ASN	GLN	VAL	SER	SER	GLN	ARG	ALA	LYS	LEU	GLY	ALA	VAL	GLN	ASN	240
241	ARG	LEU	GLU	HIS	THR	ILE	ASN	ASN	LEU	SER	ALA	SER	GLY	GLU	ASN	255
256	LEU	THR	ALA	ALA	GLU	SER	ARG	ILE	ARG	ASP	VAL	ASP	MET	ALA	LYS	270
271	GLU	MET	SER	GLU	PHE	THR	LYS	ASN	ASN	ILE	LEU	SER	GLN	ALA	SER	285
286	GLN	ALA	MET	LEU	ALA	GLN	ALA	ASN	GLN	GLN	PRO	GLN	ASN	VAL	LEU	300
301	GLN	LEU	LEU	ARG												315

Amino acid sequence of flagellin of Bacillus subtilis 168. III. Tryptic peptides, N-bromosuccinimide peptides and the complete amino acid sequence.
R. J. DeLange, J. Y. Chang, J. H. Shaper, and A. N. Glazer.
J. Biol. Chem., **251**, 705–711 (1976).

MOUSE EPIDERMAL GROWTH FACTOR

	1				5					10					15	
1	ASN	SER	TYR	PRO	GLY	CYS	PRO	SER	SER	TYR	ASP	GLY	TYR	CYS	LEU	15
16	ASN	GLY	GLY	VAL	CYS	MET	HIS	ILE	GLU	SER	LEU	ASP	SER	TYR	THR	30
31	CYS	ASN	CYS	VAL	ILE	GLY	TYR	SER	GLY	ASP	ARG	CYS	GLN	THR	ARG	45
46	ASP	LEU	ARG	TRP	TRP	GLU	LEU	ARG								60

The Primary Structure of Epidermal Growth Factor.
C. R. Savage, Jr, T. Inagami, and S. Cohen.
J. Biol. Chem., **247**, 7612–7621 (1972).

MISCELLANEOUS PROTEINS

HUMAN GASTRIC JUICE PEPTIDE

	1	5				10			15		
1	LEU	ALA	ALA	GLY	LYS	VAL	GLU	ASP	SER	ASP	15

Peptides of Normal Human Gastric Juice.
J. G. Heathcote and R. J. Washington.
Int. J. Protein Res., **2**, 117–126 (1970).

SCOTOPHOBIN

	1	5				10			15		
1	SER	ASX	ASN	ASN	GLX	GLN	GLY	LYS	SER	ALA	GLX	GLN	GLY	GLY	TYR	15
16	NH₂															30

The Use of Mass Spectrometry in the Structural Elucidation of Scotophobin—A Specific Behaviour-inducing Brain Peptide.
D. M. Desiderio, G. Ungar, and P. A. White.
Chem. Commun., 432–433 (1971).

OVINE SOMATOSTATIN

	1	5				10			15		
1	ALA	GLY	CYS	LYS	ASN	PHE	PHE	TRP	LYS	THR	PHE	THR	SER	CYS	15

Primary structure of somatostatin, a hypothalamic peptide that inhibits the secretion of pituitary growth hormone.
R. Burgus, N. Ling, M. Butcher, and R. Guillemin.
Proc. Natn. Acad. Sci., U.S.A., **70**, 684–688 (1973).

CITRATE LYASE ACYL CARRIER PROTEIN

	1	5				10			15		
1	MET	GLU	MET	LYS	ILE	ASP	ALA	LEU	ALA	GLY	THR	LEU	GLU	SER	SER	15
16	ASP	VAL	MET	VAL	ARG	ILE	GLY	PRO	ALA	ALA	GLN	PRO	GLY	ILE	GLN	30
31	LEU	GLU	ILE	ASP	SER	ILE	VAL	LYS	GLN	GLU	PHE	GLY	ALA	ALA	ILE	45
46	GLN	GLN	VAL	VAL	ARG	GLU	THR	LEU	ALA	GLN	LEU	GLY	VAL	LYS	GLU	60
61	CYS	ASP	ASN	VAL	GLN	LEU	ALA	ARG	VAL	GLN	ALA	ALA	ALA	LEU	ARG	75
76	TRP	GLN	GLN													90

Amino acid sequence of citrate-lyase acyl-carrier protein from *Klebsiella aerogenes*.
K. Beyreuther, H. Böhmer, and P. Dimroth.
Eur. J. Biochem., **87**, 101–110 (1978).

MISCELLANEOUS PROTEINS

*MATING FACTOR—*SACCHAROMYCES CEREVISIAE

1				5					10					15
1	TRP	HIS	TRP	LEU	GLN	LEU	LYS	PRO	GLY	GLN	PRO	MET	TYR	15

Purification and amino acid sequence of mating factor from Saccharomyces cerevisiae.
T. Tanaka, H. Kita, T. Murakami, and K. Narita.
J. Biochem., **82**, 1681–1687 (1977).

APPENDIX I

Human Haemoglobins

Normal human haemoglobin consists of four polypeptide chains, usually two pairs of identical chains each attached to a haem moiety. During development from the embryonic to the adult state at least six different polypeptide chains are synthesised, α, β, γ, δ, ε and ζ, at varying rates. Thus at any one stage in development there are present several different haemoglobin molecules in varying amounts, as summarized in Table A.1.

Table A.1

Stage of development	Subunit structure	Name
Very young embryo	$\alpha_2 \varepsilon_2$	Gower II
	ε_4	Gower I
Gestational age greater than 3 months	$\alpha_2 \gamma_2$	Haemoglobin F_0 (major)
	γ_4	Haemoglobin Barts (minor)
	$\alpha_2 \beta_2$	Haemoglobin A (minor)
	$\alpha_2 \gamma_2$ (AC)	Haemoglobin F_1 (minor)
	$\zeta_2 \gamma_2$	Haemoglobin-Portland 1 (minor)
Infant, 6 months old	$\alpha_2 \beta_2$	Haemoglobin A (major)
	$\alpha_2 \gamma_2$	Haemoglobin F_0 (minor)
Adult	$\alpha_2 \beta_2$	Haemoglobin A (major)
	$\alpha_2 \delta_2$	Haemoglobin A_2 (2.5%)
	?	Haemoglobin A_{1a} (minor)
	?	Haemoglobin A_{1b} (minor)
	?	Haemoglobin A_{1d} (minor)

ABNORMAL HAEMOGLOBINS

Abnormal haemoglobins may arise because of genetic factors or from modifications of an originally normal haemoglobin. Examples of the latter are Haemoglobin A_3 (CYS (93) of the beta chain forms a mixed disulphide with glutathione), Haemoglobin A_{1c} (the N-terminus forms a Schiff's base with a sugar molecule), and haemoglobins modified at the C-terminus owing to reaction with plasma carboxypeptidase. The classical haemoglobin variants are those in which the variation presumably reflects a variation in DNA coding; many have been discovered and are given in Table A.2.

Table A.2. Abnormal human haemoglobins

Alpha-chain variants

Residue no.	From	To		Name of variant	Reference no.
5	ALA	ASP	J	Toronto	(1)
6	ASP	ALA		Sawara	(152)
11	LYS	GLU		Anantharaj	(197)
12	ALA	ASP	J	Paris	(2)
15	GLY	ASP	J	Oxford	(4)
15	GLY	ARG		Ottawa	(153)
15	GLY	ARG		Siam	(222)
15	GLY	ASP	I	Interlaken	(3)
16	LYS	GLU	I		(5)
19	ALA	ASP	J	Kurosh	(223)
21	ALA	ASP	J	Nyanza	(154)
22	GLY	ASP	J	Medellin	(6)
23	GLU	GLN		Memphis	(7)
23	GLU	VAL	G	Audhali	(8)
23	GLU	LYS		Chad	(9)
27	GLU	GLY	G	Fort Worth	(10)
27	GLU	VAL		Spanish Town	(224)
30	GLU	GLN	G	Chinese	(11)
43	PHE	VAL		Torino	(12)
43	PHE	LEU		Hirosaki	(198)
47	ASP	HIS		Sealy	(13)
47	ASP	GLY	L	Ferrara	(14)
47	ASP	ASN		Arya	(199)
47	ASP	HIS		Hasharon	(15)
48	LEU	ARG		Montgomery	(200)
50	HIS	ASP	J	Sardegna	(16)
51	GLY	ARG		Russ	(17)
53	ALA	ASP	J	Rovigo	(156)
54	GLN	ARG		Shimonoseki	(18), (19)
54	GLN	GLU		Mexico	(20)
57	GLY	ARG	L	Persian Gulf	(21)
57	GLY	ASP		Norfolk	(22)
58	HIS	TYR	M	Boston	(23)
58	HIS	TYR	M	Osaka	(24)
58	HIS	TYR	M	Kiskunhalas	(25)
60	LYS	ASN		Zambia	(26)
61	LYS	ASN	J	Buda	(157)
61	LYS	ASN		Budapest	(27)
64	ASP	TYR		Persepolis	(223)
64	ASP	ASN	G	Waimanalo	(158)
68	ASN	ASP		Ube 2	(28);
68	ASN	LYS	G	Philadelphia	(29)
68	ASN	LYS		Knoxville 1	(30)
68	ASN	LYS	G	ST 1	(31)
71	ALA	GLU	J	Habana	(159)
72	HIS	ARG		Daneshgah–Tehran	(160)
74	ASP	HIS	G	Taichung	(32)
74	ASP	HIS	Q	Thailand	(33)
74	ASP	ASN	G	Pest	(157)

536

Table A.2. (continued)

Table A.2. (*continued*)

Alpha-chain variants				
Residue no.	From	To	Name of variant	Reference no.
15	TRP	ARG	Belfast	(207)
16	GLY	ARG	D Bushman	(62)
16	GLY	ASP	J Baltimore	(63)
17	LYS	GLU	Nagasaki	(64)
19	ASN	LYS	D Ouled Rabah	(167)
20	VAL	ASP	Strasbourg	(229)
20	VAL	MET	Olympia	(168)
22	GLU	ALA	G Hsin-Chu	(65)
22	GLU	ALA	G Saskatoon	(66)
22	GLU	GLN	D Iran	(167)
22	GLU	LYS	E Saskatoon	(67)
22	GLU	GLY	G Taipei	(68)
22	GLU	ALA	G Coushatta	(69)
24	GLY	ARG	Riverdale–Bronx	(70)
24	GLY	ASP	Moscva	(169)
24	GLY	VAL	Savannah	(71)
25	GLY	ARG	G Taiwan-Ami	(72)
26	GLU	LYS	E	(73)
26	GLU	VAL	Mondor	(230)
27	ALA	ASP	Volga	(231), (232)
28	LEU	PRO	Genova	(74), (170)
28	LEU	GLN	Saint Louis	(171)
30	ARG	SER	Tacoma	(173)
32	LEU	ARG	Castilla	(233)
32	LEU	PRO	Abraham Lincoln	(174)
32	LEU	PRO	Perth	(175)
35	TYR	PHE	Philly	(75)
37	TRP	SER	Hirose	(76)
39	GLN	LYS	Alabama	(208)
40	ARG	LYS	Athens–Georgia	(234)
42	PHE	LEU	Bucuresti	(77)
42	PHE	SER	Hammersmith	(78)
43	GLU	ALA	G Galveston	(79)
46	GLY	GLU	K Ibadan	(80)
47	ASP	ASN	G Copenhagen	(81)
52	ASP	ASN	Osu-Christiansborg	(82)
56	GLY	ASP	J Manado	(83)
56	GLY	ASP	J Korat	(84)
56	GLY	ARG	Hamadan	(209)
56	GLY	ASP	J Meinung	(84)
56	GLY	ASP	J Bangkok	(43)
58	PRO	ARG	Dhofar	(85)
58	PRO	ARG	Ziguinchor*	(235)
61	LYS	ASN	Hikari	(86)
61	LYS	GLU	Seattle	(87)
62	ALA	PRO	Duarte	(176)
63	HIS	TYR	M Radom	(88)
63	HIS	TYR	M Saskatoon	(89)
63	HIS	ARG	Zurich	(90)

Table A.2. (*continued*)

Alpha-chain variants

Residue no.	From	To		Name of variant	Reference no.
63	HIS	TYR	M	Hamburg	(91)
65	LYS	GLN	J	Cairo	(236)
65	LYS	ASN	J	Sicilia	(177)
66	LYS	GLU	I	Toulouse	(92)
67	VAL	GLU	M	Milwaukee	(89)
67	VAL	ALA		Sydney	(93)
67	VAL	ASP		Bristol	(94)
69	GLY	ASP	J	Cambridge	(81)
70	ALA	ASP		Seattle	(178)
71	PHE	SER		Christchurch	(95)
73	ASP	ASN	C	Harlem*	(56)
73	ASP	ASN		Korle-Bu	(96)
74	GLY	ASP		Shepherds Bush	(97)
75	LEU	PRO		Atlanta	(210)
76	ALA	GLU		Seattle	(98)
77	HIS	ASP	J	Iran	(99)
79	ASP	ASN	G	Accra	(100)
79	ASP	GLY	G	Hsi-Tsou	(101)
80	ASN	LYS	G	Szuhu	(102)
83	GLY	CYS		Ta-Li	(179)
87	THR	LYS	D	Ibadan	(103)
88	LEU	ARG		Boras	(104)
88	LEU	PRO		Santa Ana	(105)
89	SER	ASN		Creteil	(180)
90	GLU	LYS		Agenogi	(106)
91	LEU	PRO		Sabine	(107)
92	HIS	TYR	M	Hyde Park	(108)
92	HIS	GLN		Saint Etienne	(109)
92	HIS	PRO		Newcastle	(237)
95	LYS	GLU		Hopkins 1	(110)
95	LYS	GLU		Jenkins	(111)
95	LYS	GLU	N	Baltimore	(112)
97	HIS	LEU		Wood	(211)
97	HIS	GLN		Malmo	(113)
98	VAL	ALA		Djelfa	(212)
98	VAL	MET		Koln	(114)
98	VAL	MET		Ube–1	(181)
99	ASP	HIS		Yakima	(115)
99	ASP	ASN		Kempsey	(116)
99	ASP	ALA		Radcliffe	(238)
100	PRO	LEU		Brigham	(182)
102	ASN	THR		Kansas	(117)
102	ASN	LYS		Richmond	(118)
103	PHE	LEU		Heathrow	(183)
104	ARG	SER		Camperdown	(239)
106	LEU	PRO		Southampton	(119)
106	LEU	GLN		Tubingen	(240)
108	ASN	ASP		Yoshizuka	(120)
109	VAL	MET		San Diego	(213)

Table A.2. (*continued*)

Alpha-chain variants

Residue no.	From	To		Name of variant	Reference no.
111	VAL	PHE		Peterborough	(184)
113	VAL	GLU		New York	(121)
117	HIS	ARG		P	(122)
119	GLY	ASP		Fannin–Lubbock	(241)
120	LYS	GLU		Hijiyama	(123)
121	GLU	GLN	D	Los Angeles	(124)
121	GLU	VAL		Beograd	(185)
121	GLU	GLN	D	Punjab	(125)
124	PRO	ARG		Khartoum	(52)
126	VAL	GLU		Hofu	(126)
127	GLN	GLU		Hacettepe	(242)
129	ALA	ASP	J	Taichung	(127)
130	TYR	ASP		Wien	(243)
131	GLN	GLU		Camden	(186)
132	LYS	GLN	K	Woolwich	(80)
135	ALA	PRO		Altdorf	(244)
136	GLY	ASP		Hope	(128)
141	LEU	ARG		Olmsted	(113)
143	HIS	GLN		Little Rock	(164)
143	HIS	ARG		Abruzzo	(129)
143	HIS	ASP		Hiroshima	(187)
144	LYS	ASN		Andrew–Minneapolis	(215)
145	TYR	CYS		Rainier	(130)
145	TYR	ASP		Fort Gordon	(216)
145	TYR	ASP		Nancy	(217)
145	TYR	HIS		Bethesda	(130)
146	HIS	PRO		York	(245)
146	HIS	ARG		Cochin–Port Royal	(218)

Gamma-chain variants

Residue no.	From	To		Name of variant	Reference no.
1	GLY	CYS	F	Malaysia	(247)
5	GLU	LYS	F	Texas I	(131)
6	GLU	LYS	F	Texas II	(132)
7	ASP	ASN	F	Auckland	(219)
12	THR	LYS	F	Alexandra	(133)
16	GLY	ARG	F	Melbourne	(248)
22	ASP	GLY	F	Kuala Lumpur	(189)
61	LYS	GLU	F	Jamaica	(134)
80	ASP	TYR	F	Victoria Jubilee	(246)
97	HIS	ARG	F	Dickinson	(220)
117	HIS	ARG	F	Malta	(135)
121	GLU	LYS	F	Hull	(136), (190)
121	GLU	LYS	F	Carlton	(248)
125	GLU	ALA	F	Port Royal	(191)

Delta-chain variants

Residue no.	From	To		Name of variant	Reference no.
2	HIS	ARG	A$_2$	Sphakia	(137)
12	ASN	LYS		Nyu	(138), (249)

Table A.2. (*continued*)

Alpha-chain variants

Residue no.	From	To	Name of variant	Reference no.
16	GLY	ARG	A$_2'$	(139)
22	ALA	GLU	A$_2$ Flatbush	(140)
43	GLU	LYS	A$_2$ Melbourne	(188)
69	GLY	ARG	A$_2$ Indonesia	(141)
136	GLY	ASP	Babinga	(142)

Note: *indicates two variations in the same chain.

Deletions of residues

Chain	Residue(s) deleted	Name of variant	Reference no.
Alpha	ARG (141)	Koelliker	(143)
Beta	GLU (6 or 7)	Leiden	(194)
Beta	LYS VAL (17–18)	Lyon	(193)
Beta	VAL (23)	Frieburg	(144)
Beta	GLY ASN PRO LYS (56–59)	Tochigi	(145)
Beta	GLY LEU (74–75)	St. Antoine	(192)
Beta	THR (87)	Tours	(192)
Beta	GLN (131)	Leslie	(250)
Beta	GLN (131)	Deaconess	(214)
Beta	LEU (141)	Coventry	(251)

Additions of residues

Chain	Addition	Name of variant	Reference no.
Alpha	31 residues	Constant Spring	(147)
Alpha	THR GLU PHE (between 115/116, or 118/119)	Dakar/Grady	(252), (221)
Beta	10 residues	Tak	(146)

Fusion of chains

Chains involved	Name of variant	Reference no.
Gamma/beta	Kenya	(195)
Beta/delta	P-Nilotic	(196)

Abnormal human myoglobins

Residue no.	From	To	Reference no.
54	GLU	LYS	(148)
133	LYS	ASN	(149)
139	ARG	TRP	(150)
139	ARG	GLN	(151)

Table A.3. Human haemoglobin alpha and beta chain sequences with variants. The reference no. is given in parentheses after the amino acid substitution

(a) Alpha chain and variants

No.	Residue	Variant (reference)	No.	Residue	Variant (reference)
1	VAL		29	LEU	
2	LEU		30	GLU	Gln(11)
3	SER		31	ARG	
4	PRO		32	MET	
5	ALA	Asp(1)	33	PHE	
6	ASP	Ala(152)	34	LEU	
7	LYS		35	SER	
8	THR		36	PHE	
9	ASN		37	PRO	
10	VAL		38	THR	
11	LYS	Glu(197)	39	THR	Val(12); Leu(198)
12	ALA	Asp(2)	40	LYS	
13	ALA		41	THR	
14	TRP		42	TYR	
15	GLY	Asp(4, 3); Arg(153, 222)	43	PHE	His(13, 15); Gly(14); Asn(199)
16	LYS	Glu(5)	44	PRO	Arg(200)
17	VAL		45	HIS	
18	GLY		46	PHE	
19	ALA	Asp(223)	47	ASP	Asp(16)
20	HIS		48	LEU	Arg(17)
21	ALA	Asp(154)	49	SER	
22	GLY	Asp(6)	50	HIS	Asp(156)
23	GLU	Gln(7);Val(8); Lys(9)	51	GLY	Arg(18); Glu(20)
24	TYR		52	SER	
25	GLY		53	ALA	
26	ALA		54	GLN	
27	GLU	Gly(10); Val(224)	55	VAL	
28	ALA		56	LYS	

Table A.3. (continued)

No.	Residue	Variant (reference)	No.	Residue	Variant (reference)
57	GLY	Arg(21); Asp(22)	86	LEU	Tyr(40, 41)
58	HIS	Tyr(23, 24, 25)	87	HIS	
59	GLY		88	ALA	
60	LYS	Asn(26)	89	HIS	
61	LYS	Asn(157)	90	LYS	Thr(42)
62	VAL		91	LEU	
63	ALA		92	ARG	Leu(43); Gln(44)
64	ASP	Asn(158); Tyr(223)	93	VAL	
65	ALA		94	ASP	Asn(203)
66	LEU		95	PRO	Leu(45); Ser(163); Ala(46)
67	THR		96	VAL	
68	ASN	Asp(28); Lys(30, 31)	97	ASN	
69	ALA		98	PHE	
70	VAL		99	LYS	
71	ALA	Glu(159)	100	LEU	
72	HIS	Arg(160)	101	LEU	
73	VAL		102	SER	Arg(47)
74	ASP	His(32, 33); Asn(157)	103	HIS	
75	ASP	His(33); Tyr(161)	104	CYS	
76	MET		105	LEU	
77	PRO		106	LEU	
78	ASN	Lys(35, 165); Asp(36)	107	VAL	
79	ALA	Gly(36)	108	THR	
80	LEU	Arg(37)	109	LEU	
81	SER		110	ALA	
82	ALA		111	ALA	
83	LEU		112	HIS	Asp(48); Arg(204, 205)
84	SER	Arg(38)	113	LEU	
85	ASP	Val(162); Tyr(39); Asn (201, 202)	114	PRO	Arg(20)
			115	ALA	Asp(49)

No.	Residue	Variant (reference)
116	GLU	Lys(50)
117	PHE	
118	THR	
119	PRO	
120	ALA	Glu(155, 225)
121	VAL	
122	HIS	
123	ALA	
124	SER	
125	LEU	
126	ASP	Asn(226)
127	LYS	Thr(206)
128	PHE	
129	LEU	
130	ALA	
131	SER	
132	VAL	
133	SER	
134	THR	
135	VAL	
136	LEU	Pro(51)
137	THR	
138	SER	
139	SER	
140	LYS	
141	TYR	
	ARG	Pro(52)

(b) Beta chain and variants

No.	Residue	Variant (reference)
1	VAL	
2	HIS	Arg(227)
3	LEU	
4	THR	
5	PRO	
6	GLU	Ala(53); Lys(54); Val(55, 56, 165, 235)
7	GLU	Gly(57); Lys(58, 59)
8	LYS	
9	SER	Cys(60)
10	ALA	Asp(166)
11	VAL	
12	THR	
13	ALA	
14	LEU	Arg(61); Pro(228)
15	TRP	Arg(207)
16	GLY	Arg(62); Asp(63)
17	LYS	Glu(64)
18	VAL	
19	ASN	Lys(167)
20	VAL	Met(168); Asp(229)
21	ASP	
22	GLU	Ala(65, 66, 69); Gln(167); Gly(68); Lys(67)
23	VAL	
24	GLY	Arg(70); Asp(169); Val(71)
25	GLY	Arg(72)
26	GLU	Lys(73); Val(230)
27	ALA	Asp(231, 232)
28	LEU	Gln(171); Pro(74, 170)
29	GLY	
30	ARG	Ser(172, 173)
31	LEU	
32	LEU	Pro(174, 175); Arg(233)
33	VAL	

Table A.3. (*continued*)

No.	Residue	Variant (reference)	No.	Residue	Variant (reference)
34	VAL		64	GLY	Asn(177); Gln(236)
35	TYR	Phe(75)	65	LYS	Glu(92)
36	PRO	Ser(76)	66	LYS	Glu(89); Asp(94); Ala(93)
37	TRP		67	VAL	
38	THR		68	LEU	
39	GLN	Lys(208)	69	GLY	Asp(81)
40	ARG	Lys(234)	70	ALA	Asp(178)
41	PHE		71	PHE	Ser(95)
42	PHE	Leu(77); Ser(78)	72	SER	
43	GLU	Ala(79)	73	ASP	Asn(56, 96)
44	SER		74	GLY	Asp(97)
45	PHE		75	LEU	Pro(210)
46	GLY	Glu(80)	76	ALA	
47	ASP	Asn(81)	77	HIS	Asp(99)
48	LEU		78	LEU	
49	SER		79	ASP	Asn(100); Gly(101)
50	THR		80	ASN	Lys(102)
51	PRO		81	LEU	
52	ASP	Asn(82)	82	LYS	
53	ALA		83	GLY	
54	VAL		84	THR	Cys(179)
55	MET		85	PHE	
56	GLY	Asp(43, 83, 84); Arg(209)	86	ALA	
57	ASN		87	THR	
58	PRO	Arg(85, 235)	88	LEU	Lys(103)
59	LYS		89	SER	Arg(104); Pro(105)
60	VAL		90	GLU	Asn(180)
61	LYS	Asn(86); Glu(87)	91	LEU	Lys(106)
62	ALA	Pro(176)	92	HIS	Pro(107)
63	HIS	Tyr(88, 89, 91); Arg(90)	93	CYS	Tyr(108); Gln(109); Pro(237)

94	ASP	
95	LYS	Glu(110, 111, 112)
96	LEU	
97	HIS	Gln(113); Leu(211)
98	VAL	Met(114, 181); Ala(212)
99	ASP	His(115); Asn(116); Ala(238)
100	PRO	Leu(182)
101	GLU	
102	ASN	Thr(117); Lys(118)
103	PHE	Leu(183)
104	ARG	Ser(239)
105	LEU	
106	LEU	Pro(119); Gln(240)
107	GLY	
108	ASN	Asp(120)
109	VAL	Met(213)
110	LEU	
111	VAL	Phe(184)
112	CYS	
113	VAL	Glu(121)
114	LEU	
115	ALA	
116	HIS	Arg(122)
117	HIS	
118	PHE	
119	GLY	Asp(241)
120	LYS	Glu(123)
121	GLU	Gln(124, 125); Val(185)
122	PHE	
123	THR	
124	PRO	Arg(52)
125	PRO	
126	VAL	Glu(126)
127	GLN	Glu(242)
128	ALA	
129	ALA	Asp(127)
130	TYR	Asp(243)
131	GLN	Glu(186)
132	LYS	Gln(80)
133	VAL	
134	VAL	
135	ALA	Pro(244)
136	GLY	Asp(128)
137	VAL	
138	ALA	
139	ASN	
140	ALA	
141	LEU	Arg(113)
142	ALA	
143	HIS	Asp(187); Arg(129); Gln(164)
144	LYS	Asn(215)
145	TYR	Cys(130); His(130); Asp(216, 217)
146	HIS	Arg(218); Pro(245)

546

(1) New Haemoglobin, J. Toronto (α-5-Alanine–Aspartic Acid).
   J. H. Crookston, D. Beale, D. Irvine, and H. Lehmann.
   Nature, **208**, 1059–1061 (1965).
(2) A New Abnormal Haemoglobin, J α Paris, 12 ALA–ASP.
   J. Rosa, N. Maleknia, D. Vergoz, and R. Dunet.
   Nouv. Revue Franc Hemat., **6**, 423–426 (1966).
(3) A New Haemoglobin Variant, Hb I Interlaken.
   H. R. Marti, C. Pik, and P. Mosimann.
   Acta Haemat., **32**, 9–16 (1964).
(4) A New Haemoglobin J α Oxford, Found During a Survey of an English Population.
   J. Liddell, D. Brown, D. Beale, H. Lehmann, and R. G. Huntsman.
   Nature, **204**, 269–270 (1964).
(5) Hemoglobin I in an American Negro Family: Structural and Hematologic Studies.
   R. G. Schneider, J. B. Alperin, D. Beale, and H. Lehmann.
   J. Lab. Clin. Med., **68**, 940–946 (1966).
(6) Hb J. Medellin: Chemical and Genetic Study.
   A. J. Gottlieb, A. Restrepo, and H. A. Itano.
   Fed. Proc., **23**, 172 (1964).
(7) A New Variety of Sickle Cell Anemia with Clinically mild symptoms due to an α-Chain Variant of Hemoglobin (α-23-Glu-NH_2).
   A. P. Kraus, T. Miyaji, I. Iuchi, and L. M. Kraus.
   J. Lab. Clin. Med., **66**, 886–887 (1965).
(8) New Haemoglobin Variant from Southern Arabia: G. Audhali (α-23(B4) Glutamic acid–Valine) and the Variability of B4 in Human Haemoglobin.
   A. J. Marengo-Rowe, D. Beale, and H. Lehmann.
   Nature, **219**, 1164–1166 (1968).
(9) A Survey of Hemoglobins in the Republic of Chad and Characterization of Hemoglobin Chad: $\alpha^{23}{}_2{}^{Glu-Lys} \beta_2$.
   S. H. Boyer, E. F. Crosby, G. F. Fuller, L. Ulenurn, and A. A. Buch.
   Amer. J. Hum. Genetics, **20**, 570–578 (1968).
(10) Hb. Ft. Worth α-27 Glu–Gly (B8). A Variant Present in Unusually Low Concentration.
   R. G. Schneider, B. Brimhall, R. T. Jones, R. Bryant, C. B. Mitchell and A. I. Goldberg.
   Biochim. Biophys. Acta, **243**, 164–169 (1971).
(11) A Chemical Abnormality in Hemoglobin G from Chinese Individuals.
   R. T. Swenson, R. L. Hill, H. Lehmann, and R. T. S. Jim.
   J. Biol. Chem., **237**, 1517–1520 (1962).
(12) Haemoglobin Torino-α-43(CD1) Phenylalanine–valine.
   A. Beretta, V. Prato, E. Gallo, and H. Lehmann.
   Nature, **217**, 1016–1018 (1968).
(13) Hemoglobin Sealy ($\alpha_2{}^{47\,His} \beta_2$): A New Variant in a Jewish Family.
   R. G. Schneider, S. Ueda, J. B. Alperin, B. Brimhall, and R. T. Jones.
   Amer. J. Hum. Genetics, **20**, 151–156 (1968).
(14) Alteration in the α-Chain of Haemoglobin.
   L. Ferrara. I. Bianco, G. Modiano, E. Bottini, and R. Lucci.
   Nature, **198**, 395–396 (1963).
(15) Hemoglobin Hasharon. (α-47 Aspartic Acid–Histidine).
   I. Halbrecht, W. A. Isaacs, H. Lehmann, and F. Ben-Porat.
   Israel J. Med. Sci., **3**, 827–831 (1967).
(16) Haemoglobin J. Sardegna: α-50 (CD8) Histidine–Aspartic Acid.
   W. Tangheroni, G. Zorcolo, E. Gallo, and H. Lehmann.
   Nature, **218**, 470–471 (1968).

(17) Haemoglobin Russ, or, $\alpha_2^{51\ \text{Arg}}\beta_2$.
C. A. Reynolds and T. H. J. Huisman.
Biochim. Biophys. Acta, **130**, 541–543 (1966).

(18) The Characterization of Hemoglobin Shimonoseki.
M. Hanada and D. L. Rucknagel.
Blood, **24**, 624–635 (1964).

(19) Hemoglobin Shimonoseki ($\alpha_2^{54\ \text{Arg}}\beta_2^A$), a slow-moving Hemoglobin found in a Japanese Family, with Special Reference to its Chemistry.
T. Miyaji, I. Iuchi, I. Takeda, and S. Shibata.
Acta Haem. Jap., **26**, 531–537 (1963).

(20) Chemical characterization of Hemoglobin Mexico and Hemoglobin Chiapas.
R. T. Jones, B. Brimhall, and R. Lisker.
Biochem. Biophys. Acta, **154**, 488–495 (1968).

(21) Haemoglobin L Persian Gulf: α-57 (E6) Glycine–Arginine.
S. Rahbar, J. L. Kinderlerer, and H. Lehmann.
Acta. Haemat., **42**, 169–175 (1969).

(22) A Chemical Study of Hemoglobin Norfolk.
C. Baglioni.
J. Biol. Chem., **237**, 69–74 (1962).

(23) Chemical Studies on Several Varieties of Hb M.
P. S. Gerald and M. L. Efron.
Proc. Natn. Acad. Sci., U.S.A., **47**, 1758–1767 (1961).

(24) Structural Studies on a New Hemoglobin Variant, Hb M_{Osaka}.
A. Shimizu, A. Hayashi, Y. Yamamura, A. Tsugita, and K. Kitayama.
Biochim. Biophys. Acta, **97**, 472–482 (1965).

(25) A Boston Type Haemoglobin M in Hungary: Haemoglobin M Kiskunhalas.
S. R. Hollán, J. G. Szelényi, H. Lehmann, and D. Beale.
Haematologia, **1**, 11–18 (1967).

(26) Abnormal Haemoglobins in Zambia. A New Haemoglobin Zambia α-60(E9), Lysine–Asparagine.
G. P. T. Barclay, D. Charlesworth, and H. Lehmann.
Brit. Med. J., **4**, 595–596 (1969).

(27) Multiple Alpha-Chain Loci For Human Hemoglobin.
B. Brimhall, S. Hollán, R. T. Jones, R. D. Koler, Z. Stocklen, and J. G. Szelényi.
Clin. Res., **18**, 184 (1970).

(28) Amino Acid Substitution of Hemoglobin UBE 2 ($\alpha_2^{68\ \text{Asp}}\beta_2$): An Example of successful application of partial hydrolysis of peptide with 5% Acetic Acid.
T. Miyaji, I. Iuchi, K. Yamamoto, Y. Ohba and S. Shibata.
Clin. Chem. Acta, **16**, 347–352 (1967).

(29) Abnormal Human Haemoglobins V. Chemical Investigation of Haemoglobins A, G, C and X from one Individual.
C. Baglioni and V. M. Ingram.
Biochim. Biophys. Acta, **48**, 253–265 (1961).

(30) The Amino Acid Composition of Hemoglobin VI. Separation of the Tryptic Peptides of Hemoglobin Knoxville No 1, on Dowex 1 and Sephadex.
A. I. Chernoff and N. Pettit, Jr.
Biochim. Biophys. Acta, **97**, 47–60 (1965).

(31) Chemical Characterization of Haemoglobin $G_{\text{ST-1}}$.
B. H. Bowman, D. R. Barnett, K. T. Hodgkinson, and R. G. Schneider.
Nature, **211**, 1305–1306 (1966).

(32) Hemoglobin G. Taichung: α-74 Asp–His.
R. Q. Blackwell and C.-S. Liu.
Biochim. Biophys. Acta, **200**, 70–75 (1970).

(33) Two Haemoglobins Q, α-74 (EF_3) and α-75 (EF_4) Aspartic acid–Histidine.

548

P. A. Lorkin, D. Charlesworth, H. Lehmann, S. Rahbar, S. Tuchinda, and L. I. L. Eng.
Brit. J. Haemat., **19**, 117–125 (1970).

(34) Hemoglobin Mahidol: A New Hemoglobin α-Chain Variant.
S. Pootrakul and G. H. Dixon.
Can. J. Biochem., **48**, 1066–1078 (1970).

(35) Haemoglobin Stanleyville II (α-78 Asparagine–Lysine).
G. van Ros, D. Beale, and H. Lehmann.
Brit. Med. J., **4**, 92–93 (1968).

(36) Hemoglobin J. Singapore: α-78 Asn–Asp; α-79 Ala–Gly.
R. Q. Blackwell, W. H. Boon, C.-S. Liu, and M.-I. Weng.
Biochim. Biophys. Acta, **278**, 482–490 (1972).

(37) The Biosynthesis of Hemoglobin Ann Arbor.
J. G. Adams, W. P. Winter, D. L. Rucknagel, and H. H. Spencer.
Blood, **36**, 851 (1970).

(38) Hemoglobin Etobicoke: α-84(F5) Serine replaced by Arginine.
J. H. Crookston, H. A. Farquharson, D. Beale, and H. Lehmann.
Can. J. Biochem., **47**, 143–146 (1969).

(39) Hemoglobin Atago ($\alpha_2^{85\ \text{Tyr}}\beta_2$). A New Abnormal Hemoglobin Found in Nagasaki.
N. Fujiwara, T. Maekawa, and G. Matsuda.
Int. J. Protein Res., **3**, 35–39 (1971).

(40) The Structural Abnormality of Hemoglobin M. Kankakee.
R. T. Jones, R. D. Coleman, and P. Heller.
J. Biol. Chem., **241**, 2137–2143 (1966).

(41) Possible Amino Acid Substitution in the α-Chain ($\alpha^{87\ \text{Tyr}}$) of Hb M. Iwate.
T. Miyaji, I. Iuchi, S. Shibata, I. Takeda, and A. Tamura.
Acta Haem. Jap., **26**, 538–543 (1963).

(42) Haemoglobin J. Rajappen; α-90 (FG2) Lys–Thr.
R. D. Hyde, J. L. Kinderlerer, H. Lehmann, and M. D. Hall.
Biochim. Biophys. Acta, **243**, 515–519 (1971).

(43) Abnormal Human Haemoglobins. Separation and Characterization of the α and β chains by Chromatography and the Determination of two New Variants Hb Chesapeake and Hb J Bangkok.
J. B. Clegg, M. A. Naughton, and D. J. Weatherall.
J. Mol. Biol., **19**, 91–108 (1966).

(44) Haemoglobin J Cape Town $\alpha_2$92 Arg–Gln β_2.
M. C. Botha, D. Beale, W. A. Isaacs, and H. Lehmann.
Nature, **212**, 792–795 (1966).

(45) Hemoglobin G Georgia or $\alpha_2^{95\ \text{Leu (G2)}}\beta_2$.
T. H. J. Huisman, H. R. Adams, J. B. Wilson, G. D. Efremov, C. A. Reynolds, and R. N. Wrightstone.
Biochim. Biophys. Acta, **200**, 578–580 (1970).

(46) Haemoglobin Denmark Hill α-95 (G2) Pro–Ala, a Variant with Unusual Electrophoretic and Oxygen Binding properties.
B. G. Wiltshire, K. G. A. Clark, P. A. Lorkin and H. Lehmann.
Biochim, Biophys. Acta, **278**, 459–464 (1972).

(47) Hemoglobin Manitoba: α-102(G9) Serine replaced by Arginine.
J. H. Crookston, H. A. Farquharson, J. L. Kinderlerer, and H. Lehmann.
Can. J. Biochem., **48**, 911–914 (1970).

(48) Haemoglobin Hopkins 2 (α-112 Asp)$_2$ β_2: 'Low Output' protects from Potentially Harmful Effects.
S. Charache and W. Ostertag.
Blood, **36**, 852 (1970).

(49) Haemoglobin J. Tongariki (α-115 Alanine–Aspartic acid): The First New Haemoglobin Variant Found in a Pacific (Melanesian) Population.
D. C. Gajdusek, J. Guiart, R. L. Kirk, R. W. Carrell, D. Irvine, P. A. M. Kynoch, and H. Lehmann.
J. Med. Genetics, **4**, 1–6 (1967).

(50) Chemical Heterogeneity of Haemoglobin O.
C. Baglioni and H. Lehmann.
Nature, **196**, 229–232 (1962).

(51) Hemoglobin Bibba or $\alpha_2^{136\ Pro}\beta_2$, an Unstable α-Chain Abnormal Haemoglobin.
E. F. Kleihauer, C. A. Reynolds, A. M. Dozy, J. B. Wilson, R. R. Moores, M. P. Berenson, C. S. Wright, and T. H. J. Huisman.
Biochim. Biophys. Acta, **154**, 220–222 (1968).

(52) Two New Haemoglobin Variants involving Proline Substitutions.
J. B. Clegg, D. J. Weatherall, W. H. Boon, and D. Mustafa.
Nature, **222**, 379–380 (1969).

(53) Hemoglobin G. Makasser: β-6 Glu–Ala.
R. Q. Blackwell, S. Oemijati, W. Pribadi, M.-I. Weng, and C.-S. Liu.
Biochim. Biophys, Acta, **214**, 396–401 (1970).

(54) Abnormal Human Haemoglobins IV. The Chemical Difference Between Normal Human Haemoglobin and Haemoglobin C.
J. A. Hunt and V. M. Ingram.
Biochim. Biophys. Acta, **42**, 409–421 (1960).

(55) Abnormal Human Haemoglobins III. The Chemical Difference between Normal and Sickle Cell Haemoglobins.
V. M. Ingram.
Biochim, Biophys. Acta, **36**, 402–411 (1959).

(56) Hemoglobin C. Harlem: A Sickling Variant Containing Amino Acid Substitutions in Two Residues of the β-Polypeptide Chain.
R. M. Bookchin, R. L. Nagel, H. M. Ranney, and A. S. Jacobs.
Biochem. Biophys. Res. Commun., **23**, 122–127 (1966).

(57) Characterization of a Chemical Abnormality in Hemoglobin G.
R. L. Hill, R. T. Swenson, and H. C. Schwartz.
J. Biol. Chem., **235**, 3182–3187 (1960).

(58) A New Haemoglobin in a Thai Family, A Case of Haemoglobin Siriraj–β Thalassaemia.
S. Tuchinda, D. Beale, and H. Lehmann.
Brit. Med. J., **1**, 1583–1585 (1965).

(59) New Hemoglobin Variant with Sickling Properties.
L. E. Pierce, C. E. Rath, and K. McCoy.
New Eng. J. Med., **268**, 862–866 (1963).

(60) Hemoglobin Pôrto Alegre, Polymerization of Hemoglobins of Mouse and Man: Structural Basis.
J. Bonaventura and A. Riggs.
Science, **158**, 800–802 (1967).

(61) Haemoglobin Sogn (β-14 Arginine). A New Haemoglobin Variant.
E. Monn, P. J. Gaffney, Jr, and H. Lehmann.
Scand. J. Haemat., **5**, 353–360 (1968).

(62) Haemoglobin Variant in a Bushman: Haemoglobin D β-Bushman.
P. T. Wade, T. Jenkins, and E. R. Huehns.
Nature, **216**, 688–690 (1967).

(63) Abnormal Hemoglobins IX. Chemisty of Hemoglobin J Baltimore.
C. Baglioni and D. J. Weatherall.
Biochim. Biophys. Acta, **78**, 637–643 (1963).

550

(64) Hemoglobin Nagasaki ($\alpha_2^A \beta_2^{17 \text{ Glu}}$). A New Abnormal Human Hemoglobin Found in One Family in Nagasaki.
M. Maekawa, T. Maekawa, N. Fujiwara, K. Tabara, and G. Matsuda.
Int. J. Protein Res., **2**, 147–156 (1970).

(65) Hemoglobin Variant Common to Chinese and North American Indians.
R. Q. Blackwell, C.-S. Liu, H.-J. Yang, C. C. Wang, and J. T.-H. Huang.
Science, **161**, 381–382 (1968).

(66) Hemoglobin G. Saskatoon: β-22 Glu–Ala.
F. Vella, W. A. Isaacs, and H. Lehmann.
Can. J. Biochem., **45**, 351–353 (1967).

(67) A New Hemoglobin Variant Resembling Hemoglobin E. Hemoglobin E Saskatoon $\beta^{22 \text{ Glu–Lys}}$.
F. Vella, P. A. Lorkin, R. W. Carrell, and H. Lehmann.
Can. J. Biochem., **45**, 1385–1391 (1967).

(68) Hemoglobin G. Taipei: $\alpha_2 \beta_2^{22 \text{ Glu–Gly}}$.
R. Q. Blackwell, H. J. Yang, and C. C. Wang.
Biochim. Biophys. Acta, **175**, 237–241 (1969).

(69) Hemoglobin G. Coushatta: A Beta Variant with a Delta-like Substitution.
B. H. Bowman, D. R. Barnett, and R. Hite.
Biochem. Biophys. Res. Commun., **26**, 466–470 (1967).

(70) Hemoglobin Riverdale–Bronx, and Unstable Hemoglobin Resulting from the Substitution of Arginine For Glycine at Helical Residue B6 of the β Polypeptide Chain.
H. M. Ranney, A. S. Jacobs, L. Udem, and R. Zalusky.
Biochem. Biophys. Res. Commun., **33**, 1004–1011 (1968).

(71) Hemoglobin Savannah (B6(24) β-Glycine-Valine): An Unstable Variant Causing Anemia with Inclusion Bodies.
T. H. J. Huisman, A. K. Brown, G. D. Efremov, J. B. Wilson, C. A. Reynolds, R. Uy, and L. L. Smith.
J. Clin. Invest., **50**, 650–659 (1971).

(72) Hemoglobin G. Taiwan-Ami: $\alpha_2 \beta_2^{25 \text{ Gly–Arg}}$.
R. Q. Blackwell and C.-S. Liu.
Biochem. Biophys. Res. Commun., **30**, 690–696 (1968).

(73) Abnormal Human Haemoglobins VI. The Difference Between Haemoglobins A and E.
J. A. Hunt and V. M. Ingram.
Biochim. Biophys. Acta, **49**, 520–536 (1961).

(74) Haemoglobin Genova: β-28(B10) Leu–Pro.
G. Sansone, R. W. Carrell, and H. Lehmann.
Nature, **214**, 877–879 (1967).

(75) Hemoglobin Philly (β-35 Tyrosine–Phenylalanine): Studies in the Molecular Pathology of Hemoglobin.
R. F. Rieder, F. A. Oski, and J. B. Clegg.
J. Clin. Invest., **48**, 1627–1642 (1969).

(76) Hemoglobin Hirose: $\alpha_2 \beta_2$ 37(C3) Tryptophan yielding Serine.
K. Yamaoka.
Blood, **38**, 730–738 (1971).

(77) Haemoglobin Bucureşti β-42(CD1) Phe–Leu, A Cause of Unstable Haemoglobin Haemolytic Anaemia.
V. Bratu, P. A. Lorkin, H. Lehmann, and C. Predescu.
Biochim. Biophys. Acta, **251**, 1–6 (1971).

(78) Haemoglobin Hammersmith (β-42(CD1) Phe–Ser).
J. V. Dacie, N. K. Shinton, P. J. Gaffney, Jr, R. W. Carrell, and H. Lehmann.
Nature, **216**, 663–665 (1967).

(79) Chemical Characterization of Three Hemoglobins G.
B. H. Bowman, C. P. Oliver, D. R. Barnett, J. E. Cunningham, and R. G. Schneider.
Blood, **23**, 193–199 (1964).

(80) Three Haemoglobins K: Woolwich, an Abnormal Cameroon and Ibadan,
N. Allan, D. Beale, D. Irvine, and H. Lehmann.
Nature, **208**, 658–661 (1965).

(81) Haemoglobin G. Copenhagen and Haemoglobin J. Cambridge. Two New β-Chain Variants of Haemoglobin A.
K. Sick, D. Beale, D. Irvine, H. Lehmann, P. T. Goodall, and S. MacDougall.
Biochim. Biophys. Acta, **140**, 231–242 (1967).

(82) Haemoglobin Osu-Christiansborg: A New β-Chain Variant of Haemoglobin A (β-52(D3) Aspartic acid–Asparagine).
F. I. D. Konotey-Ahulu, J. L. Kinderlerer, H. Lehmann, and B. Ringelhann.
J. Med. Genetics, **8**, 302–305 (1971).

(83) A Fast Haemoglobin Variant in Minahassan People of Sulawesi, Chinese and Thais: $\alpha_2 \beta_2^{56 \text{ Gly-Asp}}$.
R. Q. Blackwell, C.-S. Liu, L. E. Lie-Injo, and W. Pribadi.
Amer. J. Phys. Anthrop., **32**, 147–150 (1970).

(84) The Identical Structural Anomalies of Hemoglobins J. Meinung and J. Korat.
R. Q. Blackwell and C.-S. Liu.
Biochem. Biophys. Res. Commun., **24**, 732–738 (1966).

(85) Haemoglobin Dhofar — A New Variant From Southern Arabia.
A. J. Marengo-Rowe, P. A. Lorkin, E. Gallo, and H. Lehmann.
Biochim. Biophys. Acta, **168**, 58–63 (1968).

(86) Hemoglobin Hikari ($\alpha_2^A \beta_2^{61 \text{ AspNH2}}$): A Fast-Moving Hemoglobin in two Unrelated Japanese Families.
S. Shibata, T. Miyaji, I. Iuchi, S. Ueda, and I. Takeda.
Clin. Chem. Acta, **10**, 101–105 (1964).

(87) Structural Characterization of Hemoglobin N Seattle $\alpha_2^A\beta_2^{61 \text{ Glu}}$.
R. T. Jones, B. Brimhall, E. R. Huehns, and A. G. Motulsky.
Biochim. Biophys. Acta, **154**, 278–283 (1968).

(88) Observations on the Behaviour of Haemoglobin M. Radom.
K. Murawski, S. Carta, M. Sorcini, L. Tentori, G. Vivaldi, E. Antonini, M. Brunori, J. Wyman, E. Bucci, and A. Rossi-Fanelli.
Arch. Biochem. Biophys., **111**, 197–201 (1965).

(89) Chemical Studies on Several Varieties of Hb M.
P. S. Gerald and M. L. Efron.
Proc. Natn. Acad. Sci., U.S.A., **47**, 1758–1767 (1961).

(90) Haemoglobin Zürich: $\alpha_2^A \beta_2^{63 \text{ Arg}}$.
C. J. Müller and S. Kingma.
Biochim. Biophys. Acta, **50**, 595 (1961).

(91) Haemoglobin M. Hamburg.
R. Gehring-Müller, E. Kleihauer, G. Braunitzer, and K. Betke.
Hoppe-Seyler's Z. Physiol. Chem., **345**, 181–186 (1966).

(92) Haemoglobin I Toulouse: β-66(E10) Lys–Glu; A New Abnormal Haemoglobin with a Mutation Localized on the E 10 Porphyrin Surrounding Zone.
J. Rosa, D. Labie, H. Wajcman, J. M. Boigne, R. Cabannes, R. Bierme, and J. Ruffie.
Nature, **223**, 190–191 (1969).

(93) Haemoglobin Sydney, β-67 (E11) Valine–Alanine; An Emerging Pattern of Unstable Haemoglobins.

552

R. W. Carrell, H. Lehmann, P. A. Lorkin, E. Raik, and E. Hunter.
Nature, **215**, 626–628 (1967).

(94) Idiopathic Heinz Body Anaemia: Hb Bristol (β-67(E11) Val–Asp).
J. H. Steadman, A. Yates, and E. R. Huehns.
Brit. J. Haemat., **18**, 435–446 (1970).

(95) A New Approach to Haemoglobin Variant Identification. Haemoglobin Christchurch β-71 (E15) Phenylalanine–Serine.
R. W. Carrell and M. C. Owen.
Biochim. Biophys. Acta, **236**, 507–511 (1971).

(96) Haemoglobin Korle-Bu, (β-73 Aspartic Acid–Asparagine). Showing One of the Two Amino Acid Substitutions of Haemoglobin C. Harlem.
F. I. D. Konotey-Ahulu, E. Gallo, H. Lehmann, and B. Ringelhann.
J. Med. Genetics, **5**, 107–111 (1968).

(97) Mild 'Unstable Haemoglobin Haemolytic Anaemia' Caused by Haemoglobin Shepherds Bush (β-74(E18) Gly–Asp).
J. M. White, M. C. Brain, P. A. Lorkin, H. Lehmann, and M. Smith.
Nature, **225**, 939–941 (1970).

(98) Hemoglobin Seattle ($\alpha_2^A \beta_2^{76 \text{ Glu}}$): An Unstable Hemoglobin Causing Chronic Hemolytic Anemia.
E. R. Huehns, F. Hecht, A. Yoshida, G. Stamatoyannopoulos, J. Hartman, and A. G. Motulsky.
Blood, **36**, 209–218 (1970).

(99) Abnormal Haemoglobins in Iran. Observations of a New Variant — Haemoglobin J. Iran ($\alpha_2 \beta_2$ 77 His–Asp).
S. Rahbar, D. Beale, W. A. Isaacs and H. Lehmann.
Brit. Med. J., **1**, 674–677 (1967).

(100) Haemoglobin G. Accra.
H. Lehmann, D. Beale, and F. S. Boi-Doku.
Nature, **203**, 363–365 (1964).

(101) Hemoglobin G. Hsi–Tsou: β-79 Asp–Gly.
R. Q. Blackwell, T.-B. Shih, C.-L. Wang, and C.-S. Liu.
Biochim. Biophys. Acta, **257**, 49–53 (1972).

(102) Hemoglobin G. Szuhu: β-80 Asn–Lys.
R. Q. Blackwell, H.-J. Yang, and C. C. Wang.
Biochim. Biophys. Acta, **188**, 59–64 (1969).

(103) A New Haemoglobin D. Ibadan (β-87 Threonine–Lysine), Producing no Sickle-Cell Haemoglobin D Disease with Haemoglobin S.
E. J. Watson-Williams, D. Irvine, D. Beale, and H. Lehmann.
Nature, **205**, 1273–1276 (1965).

(104) New Unstable Haemoglobin Boras; β-88(F4), Leucine–Arginine.
A. Hollender, P. A. Lorkin, H. Lehmann, and B. Svensson.
Nature, **222**, 953–955 (1969).

(105) Hereditary Non-Spherocytic Haemolytic Anaemia with Post-Splenectomy Inclusion Bodies and Pigmenturia Caused by an Unstable Haemoglobin Santa Ana — β-88 (F4) Leucine–Proline.
R. W. Opfell, P. A. Lorkin, and H. Lehmann.
J. Med. Genetics, **5**, 292–297 (1968).

(106) Hemoglobin Agenogi ($\alpha_2 \beta_2^{90 \text{ Lys}}$), A slow moving Hemoglobin of a Japanese Family resembling Hb.E.
T. Miyaji, H. Susuki, Y. Ohba, and S. Shibata.
Clin. Chem. Acta, **14**, 624–629 (1966).

7) Hemoglobin Sabine β-91 (F7) Leu–Pro. An Unstable Variant Causing Severe Anemia with Inclusion Bodies.
R. G. Schneider, S. Ueda, J. B. Alperin, B. Brimhall, and R. T. Jones.
New Eng. J. Med., **280**, 739–745 (1969).

(108) Hemoglobin M. Hyde Park: A New Variant of Abnormal Methemoglobin.
P. Heller, R. D. Coleman, and V. Yakulis.
J. Clin. Invest., **45**, 1021 (1966).

(109) Structural Studies of Hemoglobin Saint Etienne β-92 (F8) His–Gln; a New Abnormal Hemoglobin with loss of β proximal Histidine and Absence of Heme on the β chains.
Y. Beuzard, J. Cl. Cournulin, M. C. Solal, M. C. Garel, J. Rosa, C. P. Brizard, and A. Gibaud.
FEBS Letters, **27**, 76–80 (1972).

(110) Primary Structure of Hopkins -1 Haemoglobin.
A. J. Gottlieb, E. A. Robinson, and H. A. Itano.
Nature, **214**, 189–190 (1967).

(111) Hemoglobin Jenkins or Hemoglobin Baltimore, $\alpha_2 \beta_2^{95 \text{ Glu}}$.
N. B. Dobbs, Jr., J. W. Simmons, J. B. Wilson, and T. H. J. Huisman.
Biochim. Biophys. Acta, **117**, 492–494 (1966).

(112) An Improved Method for the Characterization of Human Haemoglobin Mutants: Identification of $\alpha_2 \beta_2^{95 \text{ Glu}}$, Haemoglobin N. Baltimore.
J. B. Clegg, M. A. Naughton, D. J. Weatherall.
Nature, **207**, 945–947 (1965).

(113) Two New Pathological Haemoglobins Olmsted β-141 (H19) Leu–Arg and Malmö β-97 (FG4) His–Gln.
P. A. Lorkin and H. Lehmann.
Biochem. J., **119**, 68P (1970).

(114) Haemoglobin Köln (β-98 Valine–Methionine): An Unstable Protein Causing Inclusion-Body Anaemia.
R. W. Carrell, H. Lehmann, and H. E. Hutchinson.
Nature, **210**, 915–916 (1966).

(115) Hemoglobin Yakima: Clinical and Biochemical Studies.
R. T. Jones, E. E. Osgood, B. Brimhall, and R. D. Koler.
J. Clin. Invest., **46**, 1840–1847 (1967).

(116) Erythrocytosis Secondary to Increased Oxygen Affinity of a Mutant Hemoglobin, Hemoglobin Kempsey.
C. S. Reed, R. Hampson, S. Gordon, R. T. Jones, M. J. Novy, B. Brimhall, M. J. Edwards, and R. D. Koler.
Blood, **31**, 623–632 (1968).

(117) Hemoglobin Kansas, A Human Hemoglobin with a Neutral Amino Acid Substitution and an Abnormal Oxygen Equilibrium.
J. Bonaventura and A. Riggs.
J. Biol. Chem., **243**, 980–991 (1968).

(118) Hemoglobin Richmond, A Human Hemoglobin which forms Asymmetric Hybrids with other Hemoglobins.
G. D. Efremov, T. H. J. Huisman, L. L. Smith, J. B. Wilson, J. L. Kitchens, R. N. Wrightstone, and H. R. Adams.
J. Biol. Chem., **244**, 6105–6116 (1969).

(119) Haemoglobin Southampton, β-106 (G8) Leu–Pro: An Unstable Variant Producing Severe Haemolysis.
R. D. Hyde, M. D. Hall, B. G. Wiltshire, and H. Lehmann.
Lancet, **2**, 1170–1172 (1972).

(120) Hemoglobin Yoshizuka (G10 108 β Asparagine–Aspartic Acid): A New Variant with a Reduced Oxygen Affinity From a Japanese Family.
T. Imamura, S. Fujita, Y. Ohita, M. Hanada, and T. Yanase.
J. Clin. Invest., **48**, 2341–2348 (1969).

(121) Haemoglobin New York.
H. M. Ranney, A. S. Jacobs, and R. L. Nagel.
Nature, **213**, 876–878 (1967).

554

(122) Hemoglobin P. ($\alpha_2 \beta_2^{117 \, \text{Arg}}$): Structure and Properties.
R. G. Schneider, J. B. Alperin, B. Brimhall, and R. T. Jones.
J. Lab. Clin. Med., **73**, 616–622 (1969).

(123) Hemoglobin Hijiyama: A New Fast-Moving Hemoglobin in a Japanese Family.
T. Miyaji, Y. Ohba, K. Yamamoto, S. Shibata, I. Iuchi, and H. B. Hamilton.
Science, **159**, 204–206 (1968).

(124) Hemoglobin D. Los Angeles: $\alpha_2^A \beta_2^{121 \, \text{GluNH2}}$.
D. R. Babin, R. T. Jones, and W. A. Schroeder.
Biochim. Biophys. Acta, **86**, 136–143 (1964).

(125) Abnormal Human Haemoglobins VIII. Chemical Studies on Haemoglobin D.
C. Baglioni.
Biochim. Biophys. Acta, **59**, 437–449 (1962).

(126) Japanese Haemoglobin Variant.
T. Miyaji, Y. Ohba, K. Yamamoto, S. Shibata, I. Iuchi, and M. Takenaka.
Nature, **217**, 89–90 (1968).

(127) Hemoglobin J. Taichung: β 129 Ala–Asp.
R. Q. Blackwell, H.-J. Yang, and C.-C. Wang.
Biochim. Biophys. Acta, **194**, 1–5 (1969).

(128) Hemoglobin Hope: A Beta Chain Variant.
V. Minnich, R. J. Hill, P. D. Khuri, and M. E. Anderson.
Blood, **25**, 830–838 (1965).

(129) Hemoglobin Abruzzo: Beta 143 (H21) His–Arg.
L. Tentori, M. C. Sorcini, and C. Buccella.
Clin. Chem. Acta, **38**, 258–262 (1972).

(130) Haemoglobin Rainier: β 145 (HC2) Tyrosine–Cysteine and Haemoglobin Bethesda: β 145 (HC2) Tyrosine–Histidine.
A. Hayashi, G. Stamatoyannopoulos, A. Yoshida, and J. Adamson.
Nature, (New Biol.), **230**, 264–267 (1971).

(131) Haemoglobin F. Texas I ($\alpha_2 \gamma_2^{5 \, \text{Glu–Lys}}$). A Variant of Haemoglobin F.
G. C. Jenkins, D. Beale, A. J. Black, R. G. Huntsman, and H. Lehmann.
Brit. J. Haemat., **13**, 252–255 (1967).

(132) Haemoglobin F. Texas II ($\alpha_2 \gamma_2^{6 \, \text{Glu–Lys}}$). The Second of The Haemoglobin F. Texas Variants.
I. L. M. Larkin, T. Baker, P. A. Lorkin, H. Lehmann, A. J. Black, and R. G. Huntsman.
Brit. J. Haemat., **14**, 233–238 (1968).

(133) On the Chemical Abnormality of Hb Alexandra, a Fetal Hemoglobin Variant.
D. Loukopoulos, A. Kaltsoya, and P. Fessas.
Blood, **33**, 114–118 (1969).

(134) Haemoglobin F. Jamaica ($\alpha_2 \gamma_2^{61 \, \text{Lys–Glu: 136 Ala}}$).
E. J. Ahern, R. T. Jones, B. Brimhall, and R. H. Gray.
Brit. J. Haemat., **18**, 369–375 (1970).

(135) Haemoglobin F (Malta): A New Foetal Haemoglobin Variant with High Incidence in Maltese Infants.
M. N. Cauchi, J. B. Clegg, and D. J. Weatherall.
Nature, **223**, 311–313 (1969).

(136) Haemoglobin F. Hull (γ 121 Glutamic acid–Lysine), Homologous with Haemoglobins O. Arab and O. Indonesia.
L. S. Sacker, D. Beale, A. J. Black, R. G. Huntsman, H. Lehmann, and P. A. Lorkin.
Brit. Med. J., **3**, 531–533 (1967).

(137) Haemoglobin Sphakiá: A Delta-Chain Variant of Hemoglobin A_2 from Crete.
R. T. Jones, B. Brimhall, E. R. Huehns, and N. A. Barnicot.
Science, **151**, 1406–1408 (1966).

(138) Hemoglobin NYU, A Delta Chain Variant, $\alpha_2 \delta_2^{12\ \text{Lys}}$.
H. M. Ranney, A. S. Jacobs, B. Ramot, and T. B. Bradley, jr.
J. Clin. Invest., **48**, 2057–2062 (1969).

(139) Haemoglobin A_2': $\alpha_2 \delta_2^{16\ \text{Gly–Arg}}$.
E. W. Ball, M. J. Meynell, D. Beale, H. Lehmann, A. O. W. Stretton, and P. A. M. Kynoch.
Nature, **209**, 1217–1218 (1966).

(140) Structural Characterization of Two δ Chain Variants.
R. T. Jones, B. Brimhall, and T. H. J. Huisman.
J. Biol. Chem., **242**, 5141–5145 (1967).

(141) Hemoglobin A_2 Indonesia or $\alpha_2 \delta_2^{69\ (\text{E13})\ \text{Gly–Arg}}$.
L. I. L. Eng, W. Pribadi, F. W. Boerma, G. D. Efremov, J. B. Wilson, C. A. Reynolds, and T. H. J. Huisman.
Biochim. Biophys. Acta, **229**, 335–342 (1971).

(142) Haemoglobin Babinga (δ 136 Glycine–Aspartic Acid): A New Delta Chain Variant.
W. W. W. de Jong and L. F. Bernini.
Nature, **219**, 1360–1362 (1968).

(143) Haemoglobin Koelliker: A New Acquired Haemoglobin Appearing After Severe Haemolysis: α_2 minus 141 β_2.
H. R. Marti, D. Beale, and H. Lehmann.
Acta Haemat., **37**, 174–180 (1967).

(144) Hemoglobin Freiburg: Abnormal Hemoglobin Due to a Single Amino Acid Deletion.
R. T. Jones, B. Brimhall, T. H. J. Huisman, E. Kleihauer, and K. Betke.
Science, **154**, 1024–1027 (1966).

(145) Hemoglobin Tochigi (β 56–59 Deleted). A New Unstable Hemoglobin Discovered in a Japanese Family.
S. Shibata, T. Miyaji, S. Ueda, M. Matsuoka, I. Iuchi, K. Yamada, and N. Shinkai.
Proc. Japan Acad., **46**, 440–445 (1970).

(146) Haemoglobin Tak: A Variant with Additional Residues At the End of The β Chains.
G. Flatz, J. L. Kinderlerer, J. V. Kilmartin, and H. Lehmann.
Lancet, **1**, 732–733 (1971).

(147) Haemoglobin H Disease Due to a Unique Haemoglobin Variant with an Elongated α-Chain.
P. F. Milner, J. B. Clegg, and D. J. Weatherall.
Lancet, **1**, 729–732 (1971).

(148) Abnormal Human Myoglobin: 53(D4) Glutamic Acid–Lysine.
F. E. Boulton, R. G. Huntsman, P. A. Lorkin, and H. Lehmann.
Nature, **223**, 832–833 (1969).

(149) A Human Myoglobin Variant 133 (H10) Lysine–Asparagine.
F. E. Boulton, R. G. Huntsman, A. E. R. Herrera, P. A. Lorkin, and H. Lehmann.
Biochim. Biophys. Acta, **229**, 871–876 (1971).

(150) The Third Variant of Human Myoglobin, Showing Unusual Substitution.
F. E. Boulton, R. G. Huntsman, A. E. R. Herrera, P. A. Lorkin, and H. Lehmann.
Biochim. Biophys. Acta, **229**, 716–719 (1971).

556

(151) The Second Variant of Human Myoglobin, 138 (H16) Arg–Gln.
F. E. Boulton, R. G. Huntsman, G. I. Yawson, A. E. R. Herrera, P. A. Lorkin, and H. Lehmann.
Brit. J. Haemat., **20**, 69–74 (1971).

(152) Haemoglobin Sawara: α-6(A4) Aspartic acid–Alanine.
I. Sumida, Y. Ohta, T. Imamura, and T. Yanase.
Biochim. Biophys. Acta, **322**, 23–26 (1973).

(153) Haemoglobin Ottawa: α_2-15(A13) GLY–ARG, β_2.
F. Vella, R. Casey, H. Lehmann, A. Labossiere, and T. G. Jones.
Biochim. Biophys. Acta, **336**, 25–29 (1974).

(154) Haemoglobin J. Nyanza: α-21(B2) ALA–ASP.
A. G. Kendall, R. D. Barr, A. Land, and H. Lehmann.
Biochim. Biophys. Acta, **310**, 357–359 (1973).

(155) Haemoglobin J. Meerut: α-120 ALA–GLU.
R. Q. Blackwell, W. H. Boon, C.-L. Wang, M.-I. Weng, and C.-S. Liu.
Biochim. Biophys. Acta, **351**, 7–12 (1974).

(156) A new haemoglobin variant: J-Rovigo alpha-53 (E-2) ALA–ASP.
R. Alberti, G. M. Mariuzzi, L. Artibani E. Bruni, and L. Tentori.
Biochim. Biophys. Acta, **342**, 1–4 (1974).

(157) Structural characterizations of hemoglobins J-Buda (α-61(E10) LYS–ASN) and G-Pest (α-74(EF$_3$) ASP–ASN).
B. Brimhall, M. Duerst, S. R. Hollán, P. Stenzel, J. Szelényi, and R. T. Jones.
Biochim. Biophys. Acta, **336**, 344–360 (1974).

(158) Hemoglobin G Waimanalo: α-64 ASP–ASN.
R. Q. Blackwell, R. T. S. Jim, T. G. H. Tan, M.-I. Weng, C.-S. Liu, and C.-L. Wang.
Biochim. Biophys. Acta, **322**, 27–33 (1973).

(159) A new haemoglobin J-Habana, α-71(E20) Alanine–Glutamic acid.
B. Colombo, H. Vidal, H. Kamuzora, and H. Lehmann.
Biochim. Biophys. Acta, **351**, 1–6 (1974).

(160) Haemoglobin Daneshgah-Tehran, α_2-72(EF$_1$) HIS–ARG, $\beta_2{}^A$.
S. Rahbar, G. Nowzari, and P. Danèshmand.
Nature (New Biol.) **245**, 268–269 (1973).

(161) Hemoglobin Winnipeg: α_2-75 ASP–TYR, β_2.
F. Vella, B. Wiltshire, H. Lehmann, and P. Galbraith.
Clin. Biochem., **6**, 66–70 (1973).

(162) Haemoglobin Inkster (α_2-85 aspartic acid–valine, β_2) Coexisting with β-Thalassaemia in a Caucasian family.
R. E. Reed, W. P. Winter, and D. L. Rucknagel.
Brit. J. Haem., **20**, 475–484 (1974).

(163) Haemoglobin Rampa: α-95 PRO–SER.
W. W. De Jong, L. F. Bernini, and P. M. Khan.
Biochim. Biophys. Acta, **236**, 197–200 (1971).

(164) Hemoglobin Little Rock (β-143(H21) HIS–GLN). Effects of an amino acid substitution at the 2,3 diphosphoglycerate binding site.
G. H. Bare, J. O. Alben, P. A. Bromberg, R. T. Jones, B. Brimhall, and F. Padilla.
J. Biol. Chem., **249**, 773–779 (1974).

(165) Interaction between haemoglobin Stanleyville II and haemoglobin S in a family of Zaire. Study of the hybrid Stanleyville II/S (α_2 78LYS, β_2 6VAL).
G. van Ros, B. Wiltshire, A. M. Renoirte-Monjoie, T. Vervoort, and H. Lehmann.
Biochimie, **55**, 1107–1120 (1973).

(166) A new Haemoglobin J from Turkey—Hb Ankara (β 10(A) ALA–ASP).
A. Arcasoy, R. Casey, H. Lehmann, A. O. Cavdar, and A. Berki.
FEBS Letters, **42**, 121–123 (1974).

(167) Two variants of hemoglobin D in the Algerian population: Hemoglobin D Ouled Rabah β_{19}(B1) ASN–LYS and hemoglobin D Iran β_{22}(B4) GLU–GLN.
J. Elion, O. Belkhodja, H. Wajcman, and D. Labie.
Biochim. Biophys. Acta, **310**, 360–364 (1973).

(168) Hemoglobin Olympia (β-20 Valine–Methionine): An electrophoretically silent variant associated with high oxygen affinity and erythrocytosis.
G. Stamatoyannopoulos, P. E. Nute, J. W. Adamson, A. J. Bellingham, D. Funk, and S. Hornung.
J. Clin. Invest., **52**, 342–349 (1973).

(169) New unstable haemoglobin (Hb Moscva, β-24(B4) GLY–ASP) found in the USSR.
L. I. Idelson, N. A. Didkowsky, R. Casey, P. A. Lorkin, and H. Lehmann.
Nature, **249**, 768–770 (1974).

(170) A new case of hemoglobin Genova α_2 β_2 28(B10) LEU–PRO. Further studies on the mechanism of instability and defective synthesis.
M. C. Solal and D. Labie.
Biochim. Biophys. Acta, **295**, 67–76 (1973).

(171) Haemoglobin Saint Louis β-28(B10) Leucine–glutamine. A new unstable haemoglobin only present in a ferri form.
M. Cohen–Solal, M. Seligmann, J. Thillet, and J. Rosa.
FEBS Letters, **33**, 37–41 (1973).

(172) Structural characterization of Hemoglobin Tacoma.
B. Brimhall, R. T. Jones, E. W. Baur, and A. G. Motulsky.
Biochemistry **8**, 2125–2129 (1969).

(173) Electrophoretic and functional abnormalities of haemoglobin Tacoma β-30(B12) ARG–SER.
A. Hayashi, T. Suzuki, and G. Stamatoyannopoulos.
Biochim. Biophys. Acta, **351**, 453–456 (1974).

(174) Synthesis of hemoglobin Abraham Lincoln (β-32 LEU–PRO).
G. R. Honig, R. G. Mason, L. N. Vida, and M. Shamsuddin.
Blood, **43**, 657–664 (1974).

(175) Haemoglobin Perth: β-32(B14) LEU–PRO An unstable haemoglobin causing haemolysis.
J. M. Jackson, A. Yates, and E. R. Huehns.
Brit. J. Haem., **25**, 607–610 (1973).

(176) Hemoglobin Duarte (α_2 β_2 62(E6) ALA–PRO): A new unstable hemoglobin with increased oxygen affinity.
E. Beutler, A. Lang, and H. Lehmann.
Blood, **43**, 527–536 (1974).

(177) Hb. J. Sicilia: β-65(E9) LYS–ASN, a beta homologue of Hb. Zambia. G. Ricco, G. Rossi, and E. Gallo.
FEBS Letters, **39**, 200–204 (1974).

(178) Structure of haemoglobin Seattle.
S. Kurachi, M. Hermodson, S. Hornung, and G. Stamatoyannopoulos.
Nature (New Biol.), **243**, 275–276 (1973).

(179) Hemoglobin Ta-Li: β-83 GLY–CYS.
R. Q. Blackwell, C.-S. Liu, and C.-L. Wang.
Biochim. Biophys. Acta, **243**, 467–474 (1971).

(180) A method for isolation of abnormal haemoglobin with high oxygen affinity due to a frozen quaternary R-structure, application to Hb Creteil α_2^A β_2 (F5) 89 ASN.

558

M. C. Garel, M. Cohen-Solal, Y. Blouquit, and J. Rosa.
FEBS Letters, **43**, 93–96 (1974).

(181) Identical substitution in Hb Ube-1 and Hb Koln.
Y. Ohba, T. Miyaji, and S. Shibata.
Nature (New Biol.), **243**, 205–207 (1973).

(182) Hemoglobin Brigham ($\alpha_2{}^A$, β_2 100 PRO–LEU) Hemoglobin variant associated with familial erythrocytosis.
J. J. Lokich, W. C. Moloney, H. F. Bunn, S. M. Brunkheimer, and H. M. Ranney.
J. Clin. Invest., **52**, 2060–2067 (1973).

(183) Hb. Heathrow: β G5 103 phenylalanine–leucine: a new high affinity haemoglobin.
J. M. White, L. Szur, P. Roberts, P. A. Lorkin, and H. Lehmann.
Brit. J. Haem., **25**, 284 (1973).

(184) An unstable haemoglobin with reduced oxygen affinity: haemoglobin Peterborough, β-111(G13) Valine–Phenylalanine, its interaction with normal haemoglobin and with haemoglobin Lepore.
M. A. R. King, B. G. Wiltshire, H. Lehmann, and H. Morimoto.
Brit. J. Haem., **22**, 125–134 (1972).

(185) Hemoglobin Beograd, or, $\alpha_2 \beta_2$ 121 GLU–VAL (GH4).
G. D. Efremov, H. Duma, R. Ruvidic, Z. Rolovic, J. B. Wilson, and T. H. J. Huisman.
Biochim. Biophys. Acta, **328** 81–83 (1973).

(186) Amino acid substitution in the $\alpha^1 \beta^1$ intersubunit contact of haemoglobin–Camden β 131 (H9) GLN–GLU.
P. T. W. Cohen, A. Yates, A. J. Bellingham, and E. R. Huehns.
Nature, **243**, 467–468 (1973).

(187) Hemoglobin Hiroshima (β-^{143}Histidine–Aspartic acid): a newly identified fast moving beta chain variant, associated with increased oxygen affinity and compensatory erythremia.
H. B. Hamilton, I. Iuchi, T. Miyaji, and S. Shibata.
J. Clin. Invest., **48**, 525–535 (1969).

(188) A new δ chain variant, Haemoglobin -A_2-Melbourne, or $\alpha_2 \delta_2$ 43 GLU–LYS (CD2).
R. S. Sharma, D. L. Harding, S. C. Wong, J. B. Wilson, M. E. Gravely, and T. H. J. Huisman.
Biochim. Biophys. Acta, **359**, 233–235 (1974).

(189) Structural identification of haemoglobin F Kuala Lumpur: $\alpha_2 \gamma_2$ 22(B4) ASP–GLY; 136 ALA.
L.-I. L. Eng, B. G. Wiltshire, and H. Lehmann.
Biochim. Biophys. Acta, **322**, 224–230 (1973).

(190) Further characterization of haemoglobin F Hull γ-121 glutamic acid–lysine; γ-136 Alanine.
E. J. Ahern, V. Ahern, B. G. W.ltshire, and H. Lehmann.
Biochim. Biophys. Acta, **303**, 242–245 (1973).

(191) Haemoglobin F Port Royal ($\alpha_2{}^G \gamma_2$ 125 GLU–ALA)
B. Brimhall, T. S. Vedvick, R. T. Jones, E. Ahern, E. Palomino, and V. Ahern.
Brit. J. Haem., **27**, 313–318 (1974).

(192) Two new hemoglobin variants with deletion. Hemoglobin Tours: THR β-87(F3) deleted and hemoglobin St. Antoine: GLY LEU β-74, 75 (E 18–19) deleted. Consequences for oxygen affinity and protein stability.
H. Wajcman, D. Labie, G. Schapira, O. Belkhodja, and R. Kernemp.
Biochem. Biophys. Acta, **295**, 495–504 (1973).

(193) Haemoglobin LYON (β 17–18 (A14–15) LYS VAL – –O). Determination by sequenator analysis.
M. Cohen-Solal, Y. Blouquit, M. C. Garel, J. Thillet, L. Gaillard, R. Creyssel, A. Giband, and J. Rosa.
Biochim. Biophys. Acta, **351**, 306–316 (1974).

(194) Functional properties of hemoglobin Leiden, ($\alpha_2{}^A \beta_2$ 6 or 7, GLU deleted).
J. Bonaventura, C. Bonaventura, G. Amiconi, E. Antonini, and M. Brunori.
Arch. Biochem. Biophys., **161**, 328 (1974).

(195) Hemoglobin Kenya, the product of fusion of γ and β polypeptides.
T. H. J. Huisman, R. N. Wrightstone, J. B. Wilson, W. A. Schroeder, and A. G. Kendall.
Arch. Biochem. Biophys., **153**, 850–853 (1972).

(196) Haemoglobin P-Nilotic containing a β–δ chain.
F. M. Badr, P. A. Lorkin, and H. Lehmann.
Nature (New Biol.), **242**, 107–110 (1973).

(197) A new haemoglobin variant: Haemoglobin Anantharaj alpha 11 (A9) Lysine–Glutamic acid.
S. Pootrakul, B. Kematorn, S. Na-Nakorn, and S. Suanpan.
Biochim. Biophys. Acta, **405**, 161–166 (1975).

(198) Hemoglobin Hirosaki. (α-43(CE1) PHE–LEU), A new unstable variant. Y. Ohba, T. Miyaji, M. Matsuoka, M. Yokoyama, H. Numakura, K. Nagata, Y. Takebe, Y. Izumi, and S. Shibata.
Biochim. Biophys. Acta, **405**, 155–160 (1975).

(199) Haemoglobin ARYA: α_2 47(CD5) Aspartic acid–Asparagine.
S. Rahbar, N. Mahdavi, G. Nowzari, and I. Mostafavi.
Biochem. Biophys. Acta, **386**, 525–529 (1975).

(200) Two new hemoglobins, Hemoglobin Alabama (β-39 (C5) GLN–LYS) and Hemoglobin Montgomery (α-48 (CD6) LEU–ARG).
B. Brimhall, R. T. Jones, R. G. Schneider, T. S. Hosty, G. Tomlin, and R. Atkins.
Biochim. Biophys. Acta, **379**, 28–32 (1975).

(201) Haemoglobin G. Norfolk: α-85 (F6) ASP–ASN.
P. A. Lorkin, R. G. Huntsman, J. A. M. Ager, H. Lehmann, F. Vella, and P. D. Darbre.
Biochim. Biophys. Acta, **379**, 22–27 (1975).

(202) Haemoglobin G. Norfolk α-85 (F6) ASP–ASN. Structural characterization by sequenator analysis and functional properties of a new variant with high oxygen affinity.
M. Cohen-Solal, B. Manesse, J. Thillet, and J. Rosa.
FEBS Letters, **50**, 163–167 (1975).

(203) Haemoglobin Titusville α-94 ASP–ASN. A new haemoglobin with a lowered affinity for oxygen.
R. G. Schneider, R. J. Atkins, T. S. Hosty, G. Tomlin, R. Casey, H. Lehmann, P. A. Lorkin, and K. Nagai.
Biochim. Biophys. Acta, **400**, 365–373 (1975).

(204) Hb. Serbia (α-112 (G19) HIS–ARG), A new haemoglobin variant from Yugoslavia.
D. Beksedic, T. Rajevska, P. A. Lorkin, and H. Lehmann.
FEBS Letters, **58**, 226–229 (1975).

(205) Hemoglobin Strumica or α_2 112 (G19) HIS–ARG β_2. (With an addendum: Hemoglobin J Paris I, α_2 12 (A10) ALA–ASP β_2, in the same population.)
G. A. Niazi, G. D. Efremov, N. Nikolov, E. Hunter, Jr, and T. H. J. Huisman.
Biochim. Biophys. Acta, **412**, 181–186 (1975).

560

(206) Hemoglobin St. Claude or α_2 127 (H10) LYS–THR β_2.
F. Vella, P. Galbraith, J. B. Wilson, S. C. Wong, G. C. Folger, and T. J. H. Huisman.
Biochim. Biophys. Acta, **365**, 318–322 (1974).

(207) Haemoglobin Belfast 15 (A12) Tryptophan–Arginine: A new unstable haemoglobin variant.
C. C. Kennedy, G. Blundell, P. A. Lorkin, A. Lang, and H. Lehmann.
Brit. Med. J., **4**, 324–326 (1974).

(208) Two new hemoglobins. Hemoglobin Alabama (β-39 (C5) GLN–LYS) and Hemoglobin Montgomery (α-48 (CD6) LEU–ARG).
B. Brimhall, R. T. Jones, R. G. Schneider, T. S. Hosty, G. Tomlin, and R. Atkins.
Biochim. Biophys. Acta, **379**, 28–32 (1975).

(209) Haemoglobin Hamadan: α_2A β_2 56 (D7) Glycine–Arginine.
S. Rahbar, G. Nowzari, H. Haydari and P. Daneshmand.
Biochim. Biophys. Acta, **379**, 645–648 (1975).

(210) Haemoglobin Atlanta or α_2 β_2 75 LEU–PRO (E19) : An unstable variant found in several members of a Caucasian family.
M. Hubbard, E. F. Winton, J. G. Lindeman, P. L. Dessauer, J. B. Wilson, R. N. Wrightstone, and T. H. J. Huisman.
Biochim. Biophys. Acta, **386**, 538–541 (1975).

(211) Hemoglobin Wood β-97 (FG4) HIS–LEU. A new high oxygen affinity hemoglobin associated with familial erythrocytosis.
F. Taketa, Y. P. Huang, J. A. Libnoch, and B. H. Dessel.
Biochim. Biophys. Acta, **400**, 348–353 (1975).

(212) A new unstable hemoglobin mutated in β-98 (FG5) VAL–ALA: Hb DJELFA.
G. Gacon, H. Wajcman, D. Labie, and A. Cosson.
FEBS Letters, **58**, 238–240 (1975).

(213) Hemoglobinopathic erythrocytosis due to a new electrophoretically silent variant, Haemoglobin San Diego (β-109 (G11) VAL–MET).
P. E. Nute, G. Stamatoyannopoulos, M. A. Hermodson, and D. Roth.
J. Clin. Invest., **53**, 320 (1974).
And
Erythraemia due to Haemoglobin San Diego.
I. Chanarin, D. Samson, A. Lang, R. Casey, P. A. Lorkin, and H. Lehmann.
Brit. J. Haem., **30**, 167–175 (1975).

(214) Hemoglobin Deaconess. A new deletion mutant: β-131 (H9) glutamine deleted.
W. F. Moo-Penn, D. L. Jue, K. C. Bechtel, M. H. Johnson, E. Bemis, E. Brosious, and R. M. Schmidt.
Biochem. Biophys. Res. Commun., **65**, 8–15 (1975).

(215) Hb. Andrew-Minneapolis. Hemoglobin Andrew-Minneapolis α_2 β_2 144 LYS–ASN. A new high oxygen affinity mutant human haemoglobin.
S. J. Zak, B. Brimhall, R. T. Jones, and M. E. Kaplan.
Blood, **44**, 543–550 (1974).

(216) Hemoglobin Fort Gordon or α_2 β_2 145 TYR–ASP, a new high oxygen affinity hemoglobin variant.
H. B. Kleckner, J. B. Wilson, J. G. Lindeman, P. D. Stevens, G. Niazi, E. Hunter, C. J. Chen, and T. H. J. Huisman.
Biochim. Biophys. Acta, **400**, 343–347 (1975).

(217) Structural and functional study of Hb Nancy β-145 (Hc2) TYR–ASP. A high oxygen affinity hemoglobin.
G. Gacon, H. Wajcman, D. Labie, and C. Vigneron.
FEBS Letters, **56**, 39–42 (1975).

(218) Hemoglobin Cochin-Port-Royal: consequences of the replacement of the β-chain C-terminal by an arginine.
H. Wajcman, J. V. Kilmartin, A. Najman, and D. Labie.
Biochim Biophys. Acta, **400**, 354–364 (1975).

(219) Haemoglobin F Auckland G γ-7 ASP–ASN; further evidence for multiple genes for the gamma chain.
R. W. Carrell, M. C. Owen, R. Anderson, and E. Berry.
Biochim. Biophys. Acta, **365**, 323–327 (1974).

(220) Genetic haemoglobin abnormalities in about 9000 black and 7000 white newborns; haemoglobin F. Dickinson (A γ-97 HIS–ARG), a new variant.
R. G. Schneider, M. E. Haggard, L. P. Gustavson, B. Brimhall, and R. T. Jones.
Brit. J. Haem., **28**, 515–525 (1974).

(221) Hemoglobin Grady: The first example of a variant with elongated chains due to an insertion of residues.
T. H. J. Huisman, J. B. Wilson, M. Gravely, and M. Hubbard.
Proc. Natn. Acad. Sci., U.S.A., **71**, 3270–3273 (1974).

(222) Hemoglobin Siam (α_2 15 arg β_2): A new α-chain variant.
S. Pootrakul, S. Srichiyanont, P. Wasi, and S. Suanpan.
Humangenetik, **23**, 199–204 (1974).

(223) Two new haemoglobins: Haemoglobin Perspolis (α-64 (E13) Asp–Tyr) and Haemoglobin J-Kurosh (α-19 (AB) Ala–Asp).
S. Rahbar, F. Ala, E. Akhauan, G. Nowzari, I. Shoa'i, and M. H. Zamanianpoor.
Biochim. Biophys. Acta, **427**, 119–125 (1976).

(224) Haemoglobin Spanish Town α-27 GLU–VAL (B8).
E. Ahern, V. Ahern, W. Holder, E. Palomino, G. R. Serjeant, B. E. Sergeant, M. Forbes, B. Brimhall, and R. T. Jones.
Biochim. Biophys. Acta, **427**, 530–538 (1976).

(225) A new haemoglobin variant Haemoglobin J Birmingham α-120 (H3) Ala–Glu.
H. Kamuzora, H. Lehmann, K. D. Griffiths, J. R. Mann, and D. N. Raine.
Ann. clin. biochem., **11**, 53 (1974).

(226) Hemoglobin Tarrant: α-126 (H9) Asp–Asn. A new hemoglobin variant in the $\alpha_1 \beta_1$ contact region showing high oxygen affinity and reduced cooperativity.
W. F. Moo-Penn, D. L. Jue, M. H. Johnson, S. M. Wilson, B. Therrell, Jr, and R. M. Schmidt.
Biochim. Biophys. Acta, **490**, 443–451 (1977).

(227) Hemoglobin Deer Lodge (β_2 His–Arg). Consequences of altering the 2,3 diphosphoglycerate binding site.
J. Bonaventura, C. Bonaventura, B. Sullivan, G. Godette.
J. Biol. Chem., **250**, 9250–9255 (1975).

(228) Haemoglobin Saki $\alpha_2 \beta_2$ 14 Leu–Pro (A11) Structure and Function.
Y. Beuzard, P. Basset, F. Braconnier, H. El Gammal, L. Martin, J. L. Oudard, J. Thillet, and J. Caburi.
Biochim. Biophys. Acta, **393**, 182–187 (1975).

(229) Hb Strasbourg $\alpha_2 \beta_2$ 20 (B2) Val–Asp: A variant at the same locus as Hb Olympia β-20 Val–Met.
M. C. Garel, Y. Blouquit, N. Arous, J. Rosa, and M. L. North.
FEBS Letters, **72**, 1–4 (1976).

(230) Hb Henri Mondor: β-26 (B8) Glu–Val: a variant with a substitution localized at the same position as that of the HbE β-26 Glu–Lys.
Y. Blouquit, N. Arous, P. E. A. Machado, M. C. Garel, and F. Perrone.
FEBS Letters, **72**, 5–7 (1976).

(231) Haemoglobin Volga, β-27, (B9) Ala–Asp, A new highly unstable

562

haemoglobin with a suppressed charge.
L. I. Idelson, N. A. Didkovsky, A. V. Filippova, R. Casey, P. A. M. Kynoch, and H. Lehmann.
FEBS Letters, **58**, 122–125 (1975).
(232) Hb-Volga or $\alpha_2 \beta_2$ 27 (B9) Ala–Asp. An unstable hemoglobin variant in three generations of a Dutch family.
J. D. Kuis-Reerink, J. H. P. Jonxis, G. A. Niazi, J. B. Wilson, K. C. Bolch, M. Gravely, and T. H. J. Huisman.
Biochim. Biophys. Acta, **439**, 63–69 (1976).
(233) Hemoglobin Castilla β-32 (B14) Leu–Arg; A new unstable variant producing severe hemolytic disease.
M. C. Garel, Y. Blouquit, J. Rosa, N. Arous, and C. Romero Garcia.
FEBS Letters, **58**, 145–148 (1975).
(234) Hemoglobin Athens–Georgia, or $\alpha_2 \beta_2$ 40 (C6) Arg–Lys, A hemoglobin variant with an increased oxygen affinity.
W. J. Brown, G. A. Niazi, M. Jayalakshmi, E. C. Abraham, and T. H. J. Huisman.
Biochim. Biophys. Acta, **439**, 70–76 (1976).
(235) Hemoglobin C. Ziguinchor $\alpha_2^A \beta_2^6$ (A3) Glu–Val, β-58 (E2) Pro–Arg; The second sickling variant with amino acid substitutions in 2 residues of the β polypeptide chain.
M. Goossens, M. C. Garel, J. Auvinet, P. Basset, P. Ferreira Gomes, J. Rosa, and N. Arous.
FEBS Letters, **58**, 149–154 (1975).
(236) Hemoglobin J. Cairo: β-65 (E9) Lys–Gln, A new hemoglobin variant discovered in an Egyptian family.
M. C. Garel, W. Hassan, M. T. Coquelet, M. Goossens, J. Rosa, and N. Arous.
Biochim. Biophys. Acta, **420**, 97–104 (1976).
(237) Hb Newcastle: β-92 (F8) His–Pro.
R. Finney, R. Casey, H. Lehmann, and W. Walker.
FEBS Letters, **60**, 435–438 (1975).
(238) Haemoglobin Radcliffe ($\alpha_2 \beta_2$ 99 (G1) Ala): A high oxygen-affinity variant causing familial polycythaemia.
D. J. Weatherall, J. B. Clegg, S. T. Callender, R. M. G. Wells, R. E. Gale, E. R. Huehns, M. F. Perutz, G. Viggiano, and C. Ho.
Brit. J. Haem., **35**, 177–191 (1977).
(239) Haemoglobin Camperdown β-104 (G6) Arginine–serine.
T. Wilkinson, C. G. Chua, R. W. Carrell, H. Robin, T. Exner, K. M. Lee, and H. Kronenberg.
Biochim. Biophys. Acta, **393**, 195–200 (1975).
(240) Structural and Functional characteristics of Hb Tubingen: β-106 (G8) Leu–Gln.
E. Kohne, H. P. Kley, E. Kleihauer, H. Versmold, H. Ch. Benohr, and G. Braunitzer.
FEBS Letters, **64**, 443–447 (1976).
(241) Hemoglobin Fannin-Lubbock ($\alpha_2 \beta_2$ 119 (GH2) Gly–Asp) A new hemoglobin variant at the $\alpha_1 \beta_1$ contact.
W. F. Moo-Penn, K. C. Bechtel, M. H. Johnson, D. L. Jue, B. L. Therrell, B. Y. Morrison, and R. M. Schmidt.
Biochim. Biophys. Acta, **453**, 472–477 (1976).
(242) Hemoglobin Hacettepe or $\alpha_2 \beta_2$ 127 (H5) Gln–Glu.
C. Altay, N. Altinoz, J. B. Wilson, K. C. Bolch, and T. H. J. Huisman.
Biochim. Biophys. Acta, **434**, 1–3 (1976).

(243) Structure of Haemoglobin Wien β-130 (H8) Tyrosine–Aspartic acid; an unstable haemoglobin variant.
P. A. Lorkin, H. Pietschmann, H. Braunsteiner, and H. Lehmann.
Acta Haem., **51**, 351–361 (1974).

(244) Hb ALTDORF $\alpha_2 \beta_2$ 135 (H13) Ala–Pro: A new electrophoretically silent unstable haemoglobin variant from Switzerland.
H. R. Marti, K. H. Winterhalter, E. E. Di Iorio, P. A. Lorkin, and H. Lehmann.
FEBS Letters, **63**, 193–196 (1976).

(245) Altered C-terminal salt bridges in haemoglobin York cause high oxygen affinity.
G. H. Bare, P. A. Bromberg, J. O. Alben, B. Brimhall, R. T. Jones, S. Mintz, and I. Rother.
Nature, **259**, 155–156 (1976).

(246) Haemoglobin F Victoria Jubilee ($\alpha_2{}^A \gamma_2$ 80 Asp–Tyr).
E. Ahern, W. Holder, V. Ahern, G. R. Serjeant, B. E. Serjeant, M. Forbes, B. Brimhall, and R. T. Jones.
Biochim. Biophys. Acta, **393**, 188–194 (1975).

(247) Haemoglobin F. Malaysia: $\alpha_2 \gamma_2$ 1 (NA1) Glycine–Cysteine; 136 Glycine.
L.-I. L. Eng, H. Kamuzora, and H. Lehmann.
J. Med. Genetics, **11**, 25–30 (1974).

(248) Haemoglobin F Melbourne $^G\gamma$-16 Gly–Arg and Haemoglobin F Carlton $^G\gamma$-121 Glu–Lys; Further evidence for varied activity of γ-chain genes.
S. O. Brennan, M. B. Smith, and R. W. Carrell.
Biochim. Biophys. Acta, **490**, 452–455 (1977).

(249) Haemoglobin A_2-NYU in the Netherlands incidence of δ-chain variants in human populations.
W. W. de Jong and L. N. Went.
Human Heredity, **24**, 32–39 (1974).

(250) Hb Leslie, an unstable Hemoglobin due to deletion of glutaminyl residue β-131 (H9) occurring in association with $\beta°$-thalassemia, HbC, and HbS.
C. L. Lutcher, J. B. Wilson, M. E. Gravely, P. D. Stevens, C. J. Chen, J. G. Lindeman, S. C. Wong, A. Miller, M. Gottleib, and T. H. J. Huisman.
Blood, **47**, 99–112 (1976).

(251) Double Heterozygosity for two unstable haemoglobins: Hb Sydney (β-67 (E11) Val–Ala) and Hb Coventry (β-141 (H19) Leu deleted).
R. Casey, A. Lang, H. Lehmann, and N. K. Shinton.
Brit. J. Haem., **33**, 143–144 (1976).

(252) Hemoglobin DAKAR = Hb GRADY: Demonstration by a new approach to the analysis of the tryptic core region of the α-chain and the oxygen equilibrium properties.
M. C. Garel, M. Goossens, J. L. Oudart, Y. Blouquit, J. Thillet, J. Rosa, and N. Arous.
Biochim. Biophys. Acta, **453**, 459–471 (1976).

APPENDIX II

Amino Acid Replacements that May Occur as a Result of Single Base Changes in the Genetic Code

Amino acid	Replacement
TRP	ARG, GLY, SER, LEU, CYS
GLN	ARG, PRO, LEU, LYS, GLU, HIS
PHE	LEU, ILE, VAL, SER, TYR, CYS
ASN	SER, THR, ILE, TYR, HIS, ASP, LYS
PRO	HIS, ARG, LEU, GLN, THR, ALA, SER
ASP	GLY, ALA, VAL, ASN, HIS, TYR, GLU
MET	THR, VAL, LYS, LEU, ARG, ILE
LYS	ARG, THR, ILE, MET, GLN, GLU, ASN
CYS	TYR, SER, PHE, ARG, GLY, TRP
HIS	TYR, GLN, ASN, ASP, ARG, PRO, LEU
ALA	VAL, ASP, GLY, GLU, THR, PRO, SER
GLU	GLY, ALA, VAL, ASP, LYS, GLN
VAL	ALA, MET, ILE, LEU, GLY, GLU, ASP, PHE
TYR	CYS, SER, PHE, HIS, ASN, ASP
THR	ILE, ASN, MET, LYS, ARG, SER, ALA, PRO
GLY	ARG, SER, TRP, CYS, VAL, ALA, ASP, GLU
ILE	LEU, PHE, VAL, THR, ASN, LYS, SER, ARG, MET
LEU	ILE, VAL, MET, SER, TRP, PHE, PRO, HIS, GLN, ARG
SER	PHE, TYR, CYS, LEU, TRP, PRO, THR, ALA, ASN, ILE, GLY, ARG
ARG	HIS, LYS, CYS, TRP, SER, GLY, LEU, PRO, GLN, THR, MET

APPENDIX III

Notes

ACID GLYCOPROTEIN (ALPHA-1)
Alpha-1 acid glycoprotein is isolated from Cohn Fraction VI of pooled normal human plasma. Although the protein appears to be homogeneous by several criteria of purity analysis, sequence analysis indicates that of the 181 amino acid residues, 21 have multiple amino acid substitutions. The substitutions (except 2) can be explained as being due to point mutations. The protein shows remarkable homology to human IgG, which might suggest that it is related to an ancestral immunoglobulin.

ACTIN
Actin constitutes about 15% of the total protein of muscle, and is the major force-producing protein. It is located in the isotropic regions of the myofibril. Actin is a globular protein and in the absence of NaCl it exists as a double-stranded polymer (F-actin). The polypeptide chain of actin contains one molecule of ATP (or ADP) and a divalent cation, either Mn^{2+}, or Ca^{2+}.

ACYL CARRIER PROTEIN
Acyl Carrier Protein is involved in the biosynthesis of long chain fatty acids; the amino acid sequence of the protein from *Escherichia coli* has been determined.

ADRENOCORTICOTROPIC HORMONE (ACTH)
This polypeptide hormone, containing 39 amino acid residues, is produced in the anterior pituitary gland. Its main function is to stimulate the synthesis and release of corticosteriods from the adrenal gland. The secretion of hormone is governed by the levels of corticosteriods present. It has been found that only residues 1–23 are essential for biological activity.

ADRENODOXIN
Adrenodoxin is a non-haem iron containing protein found in the mitochondria of the mammalian adrenal cortex, and is a component of the steroid 11-β-hydroxylase complex.

ALCOHOL DEHYDROGENASE
Alcohol dehydrogenase catalyses the conversion of alcohols to aldehydes or ketones.

AMELETIN
Ameletin is a 'learning' peptide. This peptide is found only in the brains of animals trained to respond to a specific sound stimulus. The name 'ameletin' is derived from the Greek 'ameleteos', meaning indifferent.

AMYLOID FIBRIL PROTEIN
Amyloid fibril protein is the non-immunoglobulin protein found in patients with amyloidosis, secondary to chronic inflammatory diseases. The protein was originally

565

described by Benditt *et al.* (p. 518) as protein A, but this was modified by Sletten and Husby to protein AS (i.e. amyloid subunit). Protein AS is approximately 50% of the total protein of amyloid fibril suspension. It is thought that protein AS is possibly a degraded fragment or subunit of a unique serum protein. Alternatively it has been suggested that it might arise from the accumulation of exogenous material, for example from micro-organisms.

ANAPHLATOXIN (C3a)

Complement is the heat-labile substance present in serum necessary for full antibody activity. In the classical definition it is described as that factor, which of itself has no antibody activity, that is destroyed on heating fresh serum at 56°C for 30 minutes. Complement has been found to consist of eleven serum proteins, namely, C_{1q}, C_{1r}, C_{1s}, C_2, C_3, C_4, C_5, C_6, C_7, C_8, C_9, that act in sequence and result in a cascade effect, in many ways similar to the blood clotting process. The main component of complement is C_3, and during activation this is converted into C_{3a} and C_{3b}. C_{3a} is known as anaphylatoxin and represents about 5% of the C_3 molecule. Approximately 1g of C_{3a} may be isolated from 240 litres of human serum. C_{3a} is thought to be derived from the N-terminal region of the α-chain of C_3. The various *in vitro* activities of C_{3a}, viz. muscle contraction and histamine release from mast cells, suggest that *in vivo* it acts as a mediator of local inflammatory processes. It is also known to cause the directed migration of polymorphonuclear leukocytes (chemotaxis). An interesting feature of the structure of C_{3a} is the presence of several (CYS CYS) repetitions, as these are also found in several snake toxins, the viscotoxins, and the hormones insulin and neurophysin.

ANGIOTENSIN

Angiotensin is produced by the action of renin on plasma angiotensinogen. A 'converting' enzyme acts on angiotensin I, to give the dipeptide HIS–LEU and angiotensin II, which is the form having high pressor activity.

APAMIN

Apamin is a peptide isolated from bee venom and has excitatory effects on the central nervous system.

APOLIPOPROTEIN

The high density lipoproteins isolated from normal human plasma (HDL) and the protein moeity alone (apo HDL) are classified by their C-terminal amino acids. HDL contains two major (apoLp–GLN I and apoLp–GLN II) and at least three minor (apoLp–SER, apoLp–GLU, and apoLp–ALA) protein components. Their function is to bind and solubilize lipids.

L-ASPARAGINASE

This enzyme converts asparagine into aspartic acid, and is particularly interesting as it has the ability to suppress certain tumours. It is at present useful as an anti-leukaemic drug, in certain cases of human acute leukaemia. The enzyme has been isolated from guinea pig serum, though commercial preparations are extracted from *E. coli*.

ASPARTATE AMINOTRANSFERASE

Aspartate aminotransferase is an enzyme involved with transamination reactions and is thus the link between the metabolic pathways of amino acids and dicarboxylic acids.

ASPARTATE TRANSCARBAMYLASE
Aspartate transcarbamylase is involved in the first stages of pyrimidine biosynthesis. The enzyme is a complex consisting of a regulatory (R) chain and a catalytic (C) chain. The regulatory (R) chain of the enzyme from *Escherichia coli* has been isolated and its amino acid sequence determined.

AVIDIN
Avidin is a basic glycoprotein found in egg-white. It binds to biotin by non-covalent interaction and apparently functions as part of an antibacterial system.

AZURIN
Azurin is a blue, copper-containing protein, found in bacteria.

BENCE JONES PROTEINS
Bence Jones Proteins are proteins produced in certain pathological conditions and excreted in the urine. They are immunoglobulin light chains (i.e. kappa or lambda chains), and are normally named by the first three letters of the patient's surname.

BETA-2-MICROGLOBULIN
Beta-2-microglobulin is found in the serum of normal individuals and in elevated amounts in the urine of patients with Wilson's disease. The protein consists of a single polypeptide chain having a molecular weight of 11 600 Daltons. Its function is unknown. It is homologous to the 'homology regions' of human gamma G1 immunoglobulin. The protein has been found on the surface of human lymphocytes and is synthesized by these cells. Its synthesis is increased by stimulation with mitogenic lectins. Recently, it has been reported that beta-2-microglobulin constitutes one of the two polypeptide chains of high purified papain-solubilized human transplantation antigens.

BLANCHING HORMONE
The sinus gland of crustaceans is a neuroendocrine organ, whose function is to control various physiological processes, such as changes in body colour, adaptation to light etc. As in vertebrates the control of this gland is mediated by hormones secreted by nerve cells, and one of the crustacean neurohormones is the red-pigment concentrating hormone the 'blanching hormone', which adapts the animal to light backgrounds by stimulating concentration of the pigment in its red body-chromatophores. The amino acid sequence of the hormone isolated from the sinus gland of the shrimp, *Pandalus borealis*, has been determined.

BONE PROTEIN
This protein has been isolated from calf bones and tooth dentine, after demineralization in EDTA, and accounts for 1–2% of the total protein. A similar protein has been found in human and chicken tibia, and swordfish vertebrae. The protein has been found to behave physically like a random coil, rather than a globular protein, since it emerges from a Sephadex column at a position expected for a globular protein of molecular weight 11 500 Daltons, whereas its true molecular weight is 5700. The distribution and abundance of this protein suggests that it has an important function in calcified tissue; also, it has been found to bind strongly to hydroxyapatite crystals, and it appears that this binding is due to the co-ordination of Ca^{2+} ions at the crystal surface with the carboxyl groups of GLA. This bone protein is thought to be synthesised by the same cells as make bone collagen, and it has been suggested that it could be a fragment of procollagen released during collagen biosynthesis.

BPN'

BPN' is a protease isolated from the culture filtrates of Bacillus protease, strain N'.

BRADYKININ (KALLIDIN I)

Bradydinin (Kallidin I) is the hypotensive and smooth-muscle stimulating peptide (Kinin) obtained by the *in vitro* action of trypsin, or snake venom on plasma.

CAERULIN

Caerulin is a biologically active peptide isolated from the skin of the Australian amphibian *Hyla caerulea*.

CALCITONIN

Calcitonin is a hormone produced by the thyroid gland; its function is to regulate blood calcium levels.

CARBONIC ANHYDRASE

Carbonic anhydrase is the enzyme present in erythrocytes that catalyses the reversible hydration of carbon dioxide. Two distinct forms of the enzyme, called B, and C, have been found in the human red blood cell. Both of these enzymes contain zinc and have molecular weights of about 30 000. Enzyme B is more abundant (about 5 times) than enzyme C, the latter having the greater specific activity. The two forms of the enzyme have different sequences.

CARBOXYPEPTIDASE A

Carboxypeptidase A is a zinc-containing exopeptidase which removes amino acids sequentially from the C-terminus of polypeptides. It is secreted in zymogen form by the pancreas as procarboxypeptidase A and the formation of active carboxypeptidase A involves enzymic cleavage of a peptide bond that releases the N-terminal activation fragment. The exact location of the bond cleaved appears to be relatively unimportant, as evidenced by the fact that three different forms occur, Aα, Aβ, and Aγ, all with similar activity. The α- and β- contain seven and five additional amino acids at the N-terminus, than the γ-form.

CARBOXYPEPTIDASE B

This enzyme is an exopeptidase that removes amino acids sequentially from the C-terminus of polypeptides and resembles carboxypeptidase A in molecular weight, amino acid composition, metal content and mechanism of action. It differs from carboxypeptidase A in its substrate specificity which is toward basic, rather than hydrophobic amino acid residues. Both enzymes are secreted by the pancreas in zymogen form and they have amino acid sequences that are homologous (49% identity), with similar three-dimensional structures.

CASEIN

Casein is defined as the protein precipitated from skim milk at pH 4.6 and at 20°C, casein so defined can be subdivided into three classes of milk protein: alpha$_s$1, beta, and kappa caseins, each of which contain further allelic variants. There are at least four variants of the alpha$_s$1 casein, three of which B, C, D differ from each other in one amino acid position, whereas the A variant contains a deletion of 13 consecutive amino acid residues. Six variants have been discovered in beta-casein, namely, A^1, A^2, A^3, B, C, and E. Kappa-casein is the principal casein upon which renin acts, to yield an insoluble part, para kappa-casein, and a soluble fraction, kappa$_A$-caseinoglycopeptide. Para kappa$_A$-casein constitutes the N-terminal portion and the glycopeptide the C-terminal part of the kappa-casein molecule.

CHORIONIC SOMATOMAMMOTROPHIN

Chorionic somatomammotropin is another name for lactogen.

CHYMOTRYPSIN

Chymotrypsin is a protease secreted as an inactive zymogen (chymotrypsinogen), by the pancreas. Two forms exist, chymotrypsinogen A and B: they are isoenzymes, with an overall sequence homology of 78%. Activation requires both trypsin and α-chymotrypsin to form α-chymotrypsin. Two dipeptides, residues (14–15) and (147–148), are split out resulting in the active enzyme, which is composed of three polypeptide chains, linked together by disulphide bonds. Chymotrypsins A and B hydrolyse the peptide bonds at the carboxyl side especially of aromatic amino acid residues.

CLUPEINE

Clupeine is the protamine found in herring sperm.

COLIPASE

Colipase is a small protein isolated from porcine pancreas. Two forms exist, I and II, which differ in size by 10 amino acid residues. The function of the protein is to neutralise the inhibitory effect exerted by bile salts on the lipase-catalysed intraduodenal hydrolysis of dietary long-chain triglycerides.

CONCANAVALIN A

Concanavalin A is one of a group of plant proteins known as lectins, that have the ability to agglutinate certain animal cells. This lectin is isolated from the jack bean *Canavalia ensiformis*. Recently interest has been focussed on this protein because of its mitogenic action on human lymphocytes. It is thought that this protein interacts with specific glycoprotein receptors on the lymphocyte membrane and initiates mitosis. Concanavalin A (Con A) consists of a number of identical subunits, of molecular weight 26 000. Below pH 6, Con A consists largely of dimers of these subunits and above this pH the predominant form is the tetramer. Each subunit contains one Mn^{2+} ion and one Ca^{2+} ion, and has a single carbohydrate binding site. It is thought that the mitogenic action of Con A is initiated directly at the cell surface, as covalently bond Con A to solid particles retains its ability to stimulate lymphocytes. It has been found that purified Con A consists not only of intact subunits, but also two smaller fragments, A1 and A2. Analysis of these fragments has shown that A2 is derived from the C-terminal portion of the molecule, extending from SER (119) to the C-terminal ASN (237); and fragment A1 to be derived from the N-terminal region, from ALA (1) through to residue ASN (118). It has therefore been concluded that there is a natural point of cleavage between residues 118 and 119, (ASN–SER) and that this break in the peptide chain is due to the reaction of a specific enzyme; moreover, studies on the three-dimensional structure have indicated that this cleavage would have little effect on the folding of the Con A polypeptide chain.

α-CRYSTALLIN

α-Crystallin comprises about one-third of the soluble proteins of the vertebrate lens. It was first isolated by Mörner in 1894. The molecular weight of α-crystallin can vary up to about 10^6 Daltons. It is an aggregate of two different types of subunits, A and B, each with molecular weights of about 20 000. Each of these subunits occurs in electrophoretically distinct forms A1, A2 and B1, B2, which are thought to arise by deamidation *in vivo*. α-Crystallin is a structural protein and apparently has no other biological activity.

γ-CRYSTALLIN

γ-Crystallin is a protein isolated from the vertebrate lens. It behaves as a cryoprotein and is responsible for the phenomenon of cold-cataract.

CYTOCHROME b_5

Cytochrome b_5 is an haem-containing enzyme that is involved in electron transport; it is located in the microsomes of mammalian and avian liver. Although its sequence has some similarity to that of haemoglobin, cytochrome b_5 does not bind molecular oxygen.

CYTOCHROME c

Cytochrome c is an enzyme which is present in the cells of all aerobic organisms, being located in the mitochrondira. An iron-containing porphyrin (the same as occurs in haemoglobin) is attached to the two cysteine residues near the N-terminus. This enzyme, which is widely distributed, functions as an electron-transporter and plays an essential role in cellular oxidation reactions.

CYTOCHROME c_2

Cytochrome c_2 is present in the photoanaerobe *Rhodospirillum rubrum* and is the major cytochrome c-like enzyme present in the chromatophores of cells cultured photosynthetically. Its exact biological function is not known, but it is thought to be involved in the photosynthetic electron transfer chain, donating electrons to light-activated chlorophyll. It exhibits activities different from those of mammalian cytochromes and fails to react with mammalian cytochrome oxidase.

CYTOCHROME c_3

Cytochrome c_3 is found in *Desulfovibrio vulgaris* as well as other species of sulphate-reducing bacteria. It is similar to mammalian cytochrome c, but differs from the latter by having two haem groups per molecule, and a relatively low redox potential.

CYTOCHROME c 551

Cytochrome c 551 is isolated from the denitrifying cultures of *Pseudomonas aeruginosa* and related Ps. species. It has a lower molecular weight and isoelectric point than mammalian cytochrome c, yet resembles the latter in the haem attachment site, and by having methionine as the sixth iron ligand.

CYTOCHROME f

Cytochrome f is an electron carrier in the photosynthetic system of eukaryotic plants and blue-green algae. In higher plants it is membrane-bound and may be isolated in an aggregated form, whereas that isolated from algae is a soluble monomer. It has a cytochrome c-type spectrum and a high redox potential.

DEOXYRIBONUCLEASE

Pancreatic deoxyribonuclease is the enzyme that hydrolyses DNA (in the presence of divalent cations) to give 5'-mononucleotides and larger fragments. Chromatography of the enzyme on phosphocellulose indicates the presence of three active components, deoxyribonuclease A (a glycoprotein), deoxyribonuclease B (a sialoglycoprotein), and deoxyribonuclease C (identical to A but having a PRO residue substituted for HIS at position 118). The carbohydrate side chain in enzymes A and C is attached to residue 18 (ASN) and contains two residues of N-acetyl glucosamine, and between two and six residues of mannose.

DNA–BINDING PROTEIN (gene 5 product of Fd bacteriophage)
Certain bacterial viruses, e.g. Fd, M13, synthesize single-stranded circular DNA. The gene 5 product is essential for this synthesis. The product is a protein with a molecular weight of about 10 000 Daltons. It forms a complex with intracellular single-stranded DNA, so preventing its conversion into double-stranded DNA. During development and maturation of the bacteriophage the 5p protein is completely displaced from the DNA.

ELASTASE
Elastase is a protease secreted by the pancreas as an inactive zymogen and activated by proteolytic removal of an N-terminal fragment. It can hydrolyse a variety of substrates and is uniquely effective in hydrolysing elastin, the elastic protein of ligaments.

ELEDOISIN
Eledoisin is a peptide with hypotensive and vasodilator properties isolated from the posterior salivary glands of the small octopus *Eledone moschata*.

ENCEPHALITOGENIC PROTEIN
This protein is isolated from the myelin of the central nervous system of several mammals, and when injected into other species may induce autoimmune encephalomyelitis.

ENKEPHALIN AND ENDORPHIN
These endogenous peptides have opiate activity. Enkephain I, isolated from porcine brain, is derived from lipotropin (previously thought only to be the prohormone of beta-MSH) residues 61–65, and was found to have morphine-like activity in peripheral pharmacological assays; however, in more direct tests it was found to produce only weak and transient analgesia. Further studies showed that the C-terminal fragment of lipotropin, (residues 61–91) had far stronger analgesic properties, and in fact was more active than morphine. It is thought that Enkephalin (residues 1–5 of the active C-terminal fragment of lipotropin) is readily destroyed in the brain by enzymes and that this accounts for its transient activity. Alpha-Endorphin and gamma-endorphin account for residues 1–16 and 1–17 of the C-terminal fragment of lipotropin, and were first isolated from the hypothalamus. These peptides do not produce significant analgesia in the brain and one suggestion is that they possess other neuroactivity, possibly of a behavioural nature.

ENTEROTOXINS
Enterotoxins are toxic proteins produced by staphylococci and are a common cause of food poisoning. They are classified, according to their reaction with certain specific antibodies as enterotoxin A, B etc.

EPIDERMAL GROWTH FACTOR
This protein is isolated from the submaxillary glands of the male mouse and shows growth stimulating activity on various epidermal and epithelial tissues both in vivo and in vitro.

ERABUTOXINS
These are neurotoxic proteins isolated from the venom of the sea-snake (*Laticauda semifasciata*)

FERREDOXINS
Ferredoxins are a group of proteins isolated from various anaerobic bacteria and all

photosynthetic organisms: their function is electron transport. They have been classified into three types: (i) those from green plants e.g. spinach, (ii) those isolated from photosynthetic bacteria e.g. Chromatium and (iii) those isolated from nonphotosynthetic anaerobic bacteria e.g. Clostridium.

FIBRINOGEN

Fibrinogen is a plasma glycoprotein of molecular weight about 340 000 and contains three different kinds of polypeptide chain, α, β and γ. During the process of blood clotting, the enzyme thrombin cleaves off fibrinopeptides A (18 residues) and B (20 residues) from the N-terminus of the α- and β- chains respectively and polymerisation of the fibrin follows.

FOLLICLE STIMULATING HORMONE (FSH)

This hormone in the female promotes follicle growth, whereas in the male it stimulates testicular growth and spermatogenesis. In the female, plasma levels of FSH show a marked cycling, a peak being reached slightly before ovulation.

FRUCTOSE -1,6-BIS-PHOSPHATE ALDOLASE

Fructose -1,6-bis-phosphate alolase is the enzyme that catalyses a key reaction in glycolysis, that of reversible cleavage of fructose 1,6-bis-phosphate to form glyceraldehyde-3-phosphate and dihydroxyacetone phosphate. The enzyme constitutes about 3% of the soluble protein in rabbit muscle. It has a molecular weight of about 160 000 Daltons, and is made up of four subunits. The subunits are not identical and may be separated into two distinct types (alpha, beta) each having a different susceptibility to carboxypeptidase A digestion. It has been shown that the subunits differ only at position 358: the alpha subunit has ASP, and the beta subunit has ASN.

GASTRIC JUICE PEPTIDE

This peptide has been shown to be present in normal human gastric juice and absent in samples from pernicious anaemia patients. Its function is unknown.

GASTRIN

Gastrin is a peptide isolated from the pyloric gland area of the gastric mucosa, the non-acid secreting part of the stomach. It has effects on all major gastrointestinal activities including secretion, motility and absorption.

GLUCAGON

Glucagon is an important hormone that originates in the alpha cells of the pancreas and is involved in the rapid mobilization of hepatic glucose. Glucagon directly stimulates insulin release, and in cases of severe diabetes the plasma levels of glucagon are elevated. It has been found that the amino acid sequence of glucagon is very similar to that of another intestinal hormone, secretin.

GLUTAMATE DEHYDROGENASE

This enzyme catalyses the oxidative deamination of glutamate to α-ketoglutarate.

GLYCERALDEHYDE-3-PHOSPHATE DEHYDROGENASE

This enzyme catalyses the oxidative phosphorylation of glyceraldehyde-3-phosphate during carbohydrate metabolism.

HAPTOGLOBIN

Is a serum protein that specifically combines with oxyhaemoglobin. It is composed of α- and β- chains; the α^1-chain is a mixture of two polypeptide chains differing in one position (F≡LYS : S≡GLU). The α^2 -chain represents the fusion of the C-terminal portion of the α^1 -chain, at residue A 70 or 71, with the N-terminal portion of a second α^1 -chain (B) at B 12 or 13. The α^2 -chain, it is suggested is formed as a result of an unequal crossover in the structural gene for the α-chain. Following haemolysis, haptoglobin binds with plasma haemoglobin, causing it to undergo a conformational change and making the haem group accessible to liver haem α-methenyl-oxygenase (an enzyme converting haem to a precursor of biliverdin).

HEMERYTHRIN
Hemerythrin is a red, non-haem oxygen transporting pigment present in sipunculid worms.

HIGH-POTENTIAL IRON-SULPHUR PROTEIN
This is a non-haem iron-containing protein found in purple photosynthetic bacteria. It differs from ferredoxin in that it has a high redox potential.

HISTONES
Histones are basic proteins found in the chromosomes of all eukaryotic organisms. Most cells contain essentially the same types of histone, which are classified as follows:

New nomenclature	Old nomenclature
H 1	Lysine-rich, or Fraction 1 (f1)
H 2A	Arginine-Lysine rich histone, ALK-Histone, Fraction IIb1, (f2a2)
H 2B	Slightly lysine rich histone, fraction F2B, (f2b2)
H 3	Glutamic acid-arginine rich histone, fraction III, (f3)
H 4	Glycine-arginine rich histone, GAR-histone, Fraction IV, (f2al)

Each of the above histone fractions may contain several further subfractions.

HUMAN CHORIONIC GONADOTROPIN
Human chorionic gonadotropin is a glycoprotein hormone produced by the placenta during pregnancy. In the early stages of pregnancy it prolongs the life of the corpus luteum. Several pregnancy tests are based on its estimation in urine and blood. It has a molecular weight of about 37 900 and is composed of two subunits, the alpha subunit molecular weight 14 900 (10 200 for the protein and 4 700 for the carbohydrate part), and the beta subunit molecular weight 23 000 (16 000 for the protein and 7000 for the carbohydrate part). The beta subunit is hormone specific while the alpha subunit is common to other glycoprotein hormones.

HUMAN PLASMA PREALBUMIN
Plasma prealbumin has a molecular weight of 54 980 and is made up of four identical subunits. It has a secondary structure composed of mainly beta-structure with little alpha-helix. It forms a stable complex with retinol-binding protein and is important in vitamin A transport. It also binds thyroxine and is involved with its transport.

IMMUNOGLOBULINS
These are present in the plasma of vertebrates and are produced by lymphocytes and plasma cells as a protective measure against infection. They are termed antibodies and react with antigens to form inactive complexes. The basic structure is two light chains and two heavy chains linked together by disulphide bridges. The chains are

classed according to their C-terminal amino acid sequences. There are five classes IgG, IgM, IgA, IgD and IgE, depending on the class of heavy chain they contain. There are five heavy chain classes, gamma, mu, alpha, delta, and epsilon, and two light chain types, kappa chain and lamda chain. IgG, IgD and IgE usually exist in monomeric form, whereas IgA and IgM exist as a dimer and a pentamer respectively, of the basic structure, connected by disulphide bonds and connecting peptide (the J-chain). In mammalian sera the main immunoglobulins are IgG, IgA and IgM.

IMMUNOGLOBULIN IgM (Protein Ou)

IgM is the first antibody made during the primary immune response, and in the newborn animal, and it plays an important role in certain auto-immune diseases. It is a pentamer of the basic immunoglobulin structure, with a molecular weight of 950 000. The monomer has a molecular weight of 190 000 and is composed of a pair of light chains joined by disulphide bridges to a pair of heavy chains. The subunits are held together by disulphide bridges between the heavy chains. Protein Ou has been isolated from a patient with macroglobulinemia.

INSULIN

Insulin is a hormone synthesised in the pancreatic beta cells, the function of which is to control the concentration of glucose in the blood.

IRIDINE

This is the protamine isolated from trout sperm.

ISOTOCIN

This is the oxytocin-like hormone isolated from bony fishes.

KALLIDINS

Kallidins are hypotensive peptides (kinins) released by the action of endogenous enzymes (Kallikreins) on plasma.

KERATINS

Keratins are the structural proteins of hair, hoofs, feathers etc., and are characterized by their high cysteine content and their generally insoluble nature. Wool keratin has been extensively studied and found to contain a heterogeneous mixture of proteins, the polypeptide chains of which have a molecular weight range of between 10 000 and 50 000.

LAC REPRESSOR

The *lac* repressor from *E. coli* is the protein that binds to operator DNA and represses the *in vitro* transcription and translation of the *lac* operon. Using genetic analysis it has been shown that the N-terminal region (residues 1–50) is the part involved in operator-DNA binding. The sequence shows little similarity with the sequences of histones.

α-LACTALBUMIN

This is found in milk whey and is one of the two protein components of lactose synthetase (the other is galactosyl transferase). Although no direct enzymic activity for α-lactalbumin has been shown it acts as a regulatory subunit, controlling the acceptor specificity of the galactosyl transferase. During lactation α-lactalbumin is synthesized in large amounts and regulates the biosynthesis of milk sugar (lactose). There is considerable structural homology between α-lactalbumin and lysozyme.

LACTOGEN (PROLACTIN)
This hormone is isolated from the placenta. Its main function is to stimulate lactation. It has many similarities to growth hormone.

LUTEINIZING HORMONE (ICSH)
This hormone in the female stimulates maturation of the follicle, ovulation and development of the corpus luteum; also oestrogen and progesterone secretion is stimulated. In the male, luteinizing hormone stimulates the production of testosterone by the testis, thus maintaining spermatogenesis.

LYSOZYME
Lysozyme is an enzyme that catalyses the hydrolysis of the mucopolysaccharides present in bacterial cell walls. In vertebrates the enzyme occurs in tears, nasal mucus, saliva, blood serum, milk and in egg white.

MELANOCYTE-STIMULATING HORMONES (MSH)
These are present in the intermediate lobe of the pituitary and the two forms, α- and β-MSH, stimulate melanocyte cells to produce the black pigment melanin.

MELITTIN
Melittin is a basic peptide isolated from bee venom.

MESOTOCIN
Mesotocin is the oxytocin-like hormone produced by birds and amphibians.

MYOSIN
Myosin amounts to about 40% of the protein of muscle and is the main protein in the A-band when the muscle is relaxed. Rabbit muscle myosin contains two heavy chains with molecular weight of 200 000, and four light chains with molecular weight of 20 000. Two distinct types of light chain have been identified, 'Nbs$_2$ light chain', and 'alkali light chain'. SDS–gel electrophoresis of myosin shows three light chain components with molecular weights of 25 000, 18 000, and 16 000. The 18 000 component is the Nbs$_2$ chain, whereas the alkali chains are A1 (25 000 component) and A2 (16 000 component). It has been suggested that the A2 chain is a degraded fragment of the A1.

NEOCARZINOSTATIN
Neocarzinostatin is an antitumour antibiotic isolated from the culture filtrates of *Streptomyces carzinostaticus*. It is an acidic protein, having a single polypeptide chain. It exhibits antibiotic activity against Gram-positive bacteria, and is highly effective against experimental tumours in mice. Its action is to stop DNA synthesis and hence prevent mitosis. It has been used in the treatment of some human tumours, and experiments are in progress to modify it so as to reduce its toxicity. The protein contains several disulphide bridges, that are extremely difficult to reduce using conventional means, although use of sodium in liquid ammonia was successful. The structure of neocarzinostatin bears no resemblance to Substance A from *S. carzinostaticus*.

NEUROPHYSINS
The polypeptide hormones oxytocin and vasopressin are stored in association with neurophysins in neurosecretory granules of the neurohypophysis. These proteins are thought to act as carriers for the hormones of the hypothalmo-neurohypophysial system.

576

OXYTOCIN
Oxytocin is the main uterus-contracting and lactation-stimulating hormone of the posterior pituitary gland.

PAPAIN
Papain is a proteolytic enzyme isolated from the papaya latex which is obtained from the green fruit of the tropical papaw or melon tree.

PARATHYROID HORMONE
This is produced by the parathyroid gland and regulates serum calcium levels.

PARVALBUMIN
The parvalbumins are low-molecular-weight, acidic water-soluble, calcium-binding proteins, long believed to occur only in the white muscle of lower vertebrates. Amino acid sequence studies have shown these proteins to be homologous to other muscle calcium-binding proteins, such as troponin C, and one of the light chains of myosin. Recently, parvalbumins have been isolated from the skeletal muscle of higher vertebrates including man. The retention of these proteins throughout vertebrate evolution suggests that they must serve some essential physiological function, possibly related to the contractile process.

PENICILLINASES
These are enzymes that are able to hydrolyse the β-lactam ring structure of penicillin and thus render it inactive. The enzyme confers penicillin resistance on populations of bacilli or staphylococci.

PHOSPHOLIPASE A
This occurs in many animal tissues; the richest sources are the snake venoms. Its function is to hydrolyse specific ester linkages of phospholipids.

PHYSALAEMIN
Physalaemin is a peptide isolated from the skin of the South American amphibian *Physalaemus fuscumaculatus*. It is a powerful vasodilator and hypotensive agent.

PROINSULIN
Proinsulin is the single-chain precursor of insulin. The proinsulin from pig has a molecular weight of 9082, about 50% greater than insulin itself. The A-chain is joined to the B-chain by a connecting peptide, the so-called C-peptide, which is of constant size when isolated from different species. The C-peptide is important in providing the alignment of the molecule for correct disulphide synthesis and this mode of biosynthesis accounts for the early difficulties experienced in the chemical synthesis of insulin. Proinsulin is converted to insulin by proteolysis, in many ways analogous to the zymogen activation of proteolytic enzymes. This conversion takes place in the granule package, and not in the endoplasmic reticulum of the β-cells where the proinsulin is synthesised.

PROMELITTIN
Promelittin is the precursor of melittin, the main toxin of bee venom. It has been isolated from the venom glands of both the queen and the worker bees, and is heterogeneous. The main component has eight amino acids more than melittin.

PROTAMINES
These are a family of chromosomal proteins of small molecular weight and marked basic properties, found in the sperm of some birds and fish.

β-PUROTHIONIN

The purothionins are a group of low-molecular-weight proteins isolated from wheat flour. They have the unusual property of being soluble, as lipoprotein complexes, in organic solvents. The *in vivo* function of the purothionins is not clear, but they are known to be toxic to animals, to certain bacteria and yeasts.

β-Purothionin has a structure similar to that of the viscotoxins isolated from the European mistletoe, which are also toxic to animals. It is thought that both types of protein perform a vital function in these plants, possibly having some role in the protection of the plant from attack by pathogenic microbes.

RIBONUCLEASE

This is the enzyme that catalyses the cleavage of the phosphodiester bond between 3′ and 5′ positions of the ribose moieties of the RNA chain, with the formation of oligonucleotides terminating in 2′, 3′-cyclic phosphate derivatives. In subsequent steps these are split off as free mononucleotide cyclic phosphates and then hydrolysed to the corresponding nucleoside 3′-phosphate. The enzyme from pancreas hydrolyses the bond adjacent to pyrimidine nucleotides.

RIBONUCLEASE T 1

This is an enzyme produced by the fungus *Aspergillus oryzae*. It hydrolyses the phosphate on the 3′ position of the sugar attached to guanine in RNA.

RIBONUCLEASE U2

This enzyme preferentially catalyses the cleavage of the phosphodiester bond between 3′ and 5′ positions of the ribose moieties of the RNA chain, adjacent to purine nucleotides. The mechanism consists of two reactions, the transfer of the phosphate group to the 2′-hydroxyl group of the purine nucleotide and then hydrolysis to give the 3′ phosphate of the purine nucleoside.

RIBOSOMAL PROTEINS

The *E. coli* ribosome is a complex structure with a sedimentation coefficient of 70S, and of molecular weight in the region of 2.5×10^6 Daltons. The ribosome may be dissociated into two subunits, a large subunit (50S) and a small subunit (30S). These subunits have been found to consist of combinations of RNA and protein. The 30S subunit is built up of one RNA molecule (16S) and 21 unique proteins, S1–S21. The large subunit can be dissociated to give two RNA molecules (of sedimentation coefficients 23S and 5S) and 34 unique proteins, L1–L35 (L7 and L12 have been found to be identical, except for the presence of an acetyl group on the N-terminal residue of L7). The properties of some of the ribosomal proteins, the sequences of which have been deduced, are summarized below.

PROTEIN S4

This protein forms a complex with the 16S RNA and binds with the 5′ terminal region. It plays an important role in protein synthesis and is involved in the selection of the correct tRNA at the ribosomal acceptor site.

PROTEIN S6

This is the most acidic of the 30S subunit proteins. It has an important role in the initiation of protein synthesis. Also, together with proteins S18, S8, and S15 it protects the 16S RNA molecule from nuclease digestion.

PROTEIN S8

This protein binds specifically to the 16S RNA molecule. Because of this, it has been studied, with the hope that it could shed light on the mechanism of protein–RNA interaction.

PROTEIN S9
This protein plays an important role in the assembly of the 30S subunit. It occurs at the interface of the two ribosomal subunits, and plays a role in their association. It is also necessary for the GTPase activity of elongation factor EF-G.

PROTEIN S12
This is a very basic protein of the 30S subunit, and is thought to play an important role in the fidelity and initiation of translation. Mutation of the S12 protein confers resistance to the antibiotic streptomycin, and investigations on the amino acid sequences of this protein from these mutants indicates that the amino acid replacements are restricted to two regions of the protein LYS 42 and a short region from 85 to 91.

PROTEIN S15
This very basic protein is isolated from the 30S ribosomal subunit, and is one of the proteins to bind to the 16S rRNA.

PROTEIN S16
This protein in the presence of proteins S4 and S20 binds to the 16S rRNA molecule of the small ribosomal subunit. Extensive homology has been found between protein S16 and S20.

PROTEIN S18
This very basic protein plays an important role in the binding of aminoacyl t-RNA to the ribosome.

PROTEIN S20
Protein S20 is a very basic protein of the 30S ribosomal subunit, located near the surface interface, and specifically binds to the 16S RNA. This binding of the protein to the RNA involves the C-terminal amino acid. Protein S20 has a high α-helix content.

PROTEIN L16
This protein, isolated from the large ribosomal subunit, directly binds to the 23S rRNA molecule. It is thought to be located at the A-site of the peptidyltransferase centre and possibly it may itself exert peptidyltransferase activity.

PROTEIN L25
This protein, from the 50S ribosomal subunit, forms a stable, functionally active, complex with 5S RNA.

PROTEIN L27
This protein is thought to be situated near the interface of the two ribosomal subunits. Studies have also indicated that it is situated close to the peptidyl-tRNA binding site of the ribosome.

PROTEIN L30
Protein L30 is isolated from the 50S ribosomal subunit and is located near the GTPase centre.

PROTEIN L32
This is one of the smallest proteins in the *E. coli* 50S ribosomal subunit.

PROTEIN L33
This very basic protein is also one of the smallest proteins in the *E. coli* ribosome and is involved in polypeptide chain elongation.

RUBREDOXIN
This is a non-haem iron-containing protein found in anaerobic bacteria. It can replace ferredoxin as an electron-carrier, but its role in anaerobes is not clear.

SALMINE
Salmine is the protamine from salmon.

SCOTOPHOBIN
Scotophobin is a polypeptide that has been shown to be responsible for the transfer of a learned behaviour from one animal to another.

SECRETIN
The presence of acid chyme activates the duodenum to produce the hormone secretin, which in turn, stimulates the flow of pancreatic juice. This peptide hormone of 27 amino acid residues has recently been synthesised. There is an interesting homology between secretin and the hormone glucagon.

SOMATOSTATIN
This peptide was originally named for its ability to inhibit growth hormone (somatotropin) and was isolated from hypothalamus. Subsequent work indicated that it could inhibit a far greater variety of peptides, including insulin, glucagon, and gastrin. Using the technique of radioimmunoassay it has been located in the stomach and pancreas. Also, immunocytochemical methods have demonstrated its presence in nerve fibres of the intestine wall.

STAPHYLOCOCCAL NUCLEASE
This is an enzyme produced by *Staphylococcus aureus* and is able to hydrolyse specific phosphodiester bonds of both RNA and DNA to produce $3'$-phosphomononucleosides and -dinucleotides.

STUART FACTOR (BOVINE FACTOR X$_1$)
Bovine factor X, or Stuart Factor, is the zymogen of a protease involved in blood coagulation. Zymogen activation is initiated by activated factor IX (Christmas Factor), in the presence of factor VIII (anti-haemophilic factor). Factor X catalyses the conversion of prothrombin to thrombin. Factor X itself consists of two components X_1 and X_2, each having similar chemical and biological properties. It is a glycoprotein of molecular weight 54 000 Daltons, and containing about 10% carbohydrate, and consists of two polypeptide chains, a heavy chain and a light chain, linked together by disulphide bridges. The molecular weight of the light chain is 16 000 and that of the heavy chain 38 000. The carbohydrate is attached to the heavy chain. The amino acid sequence of the heavy chain of factor X is homologous with trypsin, thrombin, and other serine proteases. Both Factor X and prothrombin bind Ca^{2+} ions, and both of these proteins contain the unusual amino acid gamma-carboxyglutamic acid (GLA), two adjacent residues of which would be expected to make effective centres for chelation of calcium ions.

SUBSTANCE A
This is a protein, with antibacterial properties, produced by *Streptomyces carzinostaticus*.

SUBSTANCE P

von Euler and Gaddum in 1931 observed that powdered (hence 'P') preparations of horse brain and intestine contained a substance that stimulated the contraction of isolated rabbit jejunum and caused transient hypotension when injected into rabbits. Subsequent work showed that it could be isolated in pure form from bovine hypothalamus. Substance P is found throughout the nervous system and it has been suggested that it might be a hormone. A further hypothesis is that it serves a neurotransmitter role in the nervous system. Its amino acid sequence has been confirmed by synthesis.

SUBSTANCE PS1

Substance PS1 is produced in the paragonial gland of the adult male *Drosophila funebris* and influences the mating behaviour of virgin female flies after injection. This is the first substance identified in flies that causes a biological response in the opposite sex after mating.

SUBTILISIN

This is a protease isolated from the culture filtrates of Bacillus subtilis.

SUPEROXIDE DISMUTASE

The metalloprotein erythrocuprein was only recently (1969) found to have the unusual enzymic property of converting superoxide radicals into oxygen and hydrogen peroxide, for this reason its name was revised to superoxide dismutase. This enzyme has a molecular weight of about 33 500 Daltons and is composed of two identical subunits. It is a metalloprotein and contains approximately 2 moles of copper and zinc per mole of protein. It is an unusually stable enzyme and retains activity in solutions of 10 M urea. There is one intrasubunit disulphide bond that joins CYS 55 and CYS 144.

TESTIS-SPECIFIC PROTEIN

The testis of a number of mammalian species, including man, contains a small basic protein that is readily obtained by extraction with dilute sulphuric acid. This protein appears to be specific for testis as it cannot be isolated from other organs. This small basic protein is rich in the amino acids arginine, lysine, glycine and serine. It is thought to play a role in the development of spermatids in the seminiferous tubules, as it is absent in epididymal spermatozoa, and is therefore different from other basic proteins associated with spermatogenesis.

THERMOLYSIN

This is a protease isolated from cultures of the thermophilic bacterium *Bacillus thermoproteolyticus* Rokko. Normally it will hydrolyse the peptide bonds on the N-terminal side of hydrophobic residues.

THIOREDOXIN

Thioredoxin is a protein from *Escherichia coli* which functions as an hydrogen carrier in the enzymic reduction of ribonucleotides, through the reversible oxidation–reduction of its single disulphide bridge.

THYROTROPIN

The main function of this hormone is to stimulate the thyroid gland. Injection of thyrotropin, also known as Thyroid Stimulating Hormone or TSH, brings about all the symptoms of hyperthyroidism. It is thought that TSH activates the thyroid via the enzyme adenyl cyclase.

TRIOSE PHOSPHATE ISOMERASE
This is the glycolytic enzyme that interconverts D-glyceraldehyde-3-phosphate and dihydroxyacetone phosphate. The enzyme is widely distributed and highly active.

TROPONIN
Troponin is a protein found associated with tropomyosin in the thin filaments of vertebrate striated muscle. Troponin has a molecular weight of about 80 000 Daltons and is composed of three subunits, namely Troponin I, Troponin T and Troponin C, with molecular weights of 24 000; 37 000; and 18 000 Daltons respectively. Troponin is a slightly elongated molecule, that is located at intervals of 385 Å in the thin filament—a period dictated by the length of the tropomyosin molecule. Troponin, together with tropomyosin ATPase in vertebrate striated muscle, and hence for the control of muscular contraction. Troponin I is able, on its own, to inhibit the actomyosin ATPase, and has been found to be a basic protein, with an isoelectric point of 9.3, and a blocked N-terminal residue.

TRYPSIN
This is secreted by the pancreas as an inactive zymogen (trypsinogen) and activated, by proteolytic removal of a short N-terminal peptide, in the duodenum. The enzyme hydrolyses peptide bonds on the carboxyl of arginine and lysine.

TRYPTOPHAN SYNTHETASE
This is an enzyme which is involved in the final stages of tryptophan biosynthesis.

TUFTSIN
Tuftsin is the phagocytosis-stimulating peptide that is isolated from leucokinin after digestion with leucokininase.

UBIQUITIN
Ubiquitin, or as originally named UBIP (Ubiquitous immunopoietic polypeptide), was discovered by chance during an investigation of thymic hormones. This protein was first purified from bovine thymus gland, and subsequently it has been found in many other tissues, and is now thought to be of widespread occurrence, probably present in all living cells. Ubiquitin, unlike the thymic hormone thymopoietin, is capable of inducing the differentiation of both T-, and B-lymphocyte precursors, possibly by combining with a receptor on the cell membrane and triggering the enzyme adenylate cyclase. Ubiquitin is a single-chain polypeptide of molecular weight 8451 Daltons, and containing 74 amino acid residues. The amino acid sequences of ubiquitin from several sources shows a high degree of evolutionary conservation.

UPEROLEIN
Uperolein is isolated by methanol extraction of the skins of Australian leptodactylid frogs *Uperoleia rugosa* and *Uperoleia marmorata*. Its biological activity is similar to that of the peptide physalaemin.

UROGASTRONE
This is a potent inhibitor of gastric acid secretion, isolated from normal human urine, in yields of less than 1 mg per 1000 litres. It is probable that it is identical to epidermal growth factor, which can also be isolated from human urine. It is hoped that urogastrone might be a useful therapeutic agent in the treatment of duodenal ulceration.

582

VASOTOCIN

Vasotocin is a pressor hormone, present only in birds, reptiles and fishes that is involved with the regulation of water and mineral balance.

VISCOTOXIN

Viscotoxin is a mixture of pharmacologically active basic peptides isolated from the European mistletoe *Viscum album* L. Three main components have been isolated, viscotoxin A2, viscotoxin A3 and viscotoxin B.

Author Index

583

584

594

Index of Protein Sources

Index of Protein Names

618

General Index to the Methodology Section